D1480507

The Lichen Flora
of the United States

by BRUCE FINK

Completed for publication by Joyce Hedrick

With a new Foreword by Alexander H. Smith

Ann Arbor

The University of Michigan Press

FOREWORD

The Lichen Flora of the United States has for years filled a very great need for the naturalists of North America as well as for those living abroad. With the increased emphasis which has been given the study of lichens in the last twenty years because of their importance to investigators in the fields of phytogeography and ecology, it is evident to all students of the plant sciences that this manual, published in 1935, is out of date in many respects. However, since the more recent work has not been brought together in manual form, *The Lichen Flora of the United States* is still a foundation stone for the study of lichens in this country. It is, therefore, gratifying to have this basic work again made available.

ALEXANDER H. SMITH

PREFACE

Following the publication of *The Lichens of Minnesota* in the "Contributions from the United States National Herbarium," Volume 14, 1910, Professor Fink started work looking forward to a larger and more complete manual, at first intending to include all species known for North America. In 1922 he limited the scope to the species of the United States. While on sabbatical leave from his duties as Professor of Botany at Miami University, Oxford, Ohio, during the first semester of 1924-25, Professor Fink studied the lichen collections at various eastern herbaria. Until his death in 1927, he encouraged collectors throughout the United States to send their material to him for study. He corresponded and exchanged material with some of the leading contemporary European lichenologists, especially E. A. Vainio, A. Zahlbruckner, and H. Sandstede.

Through financial aid granted by the Trustees and the Research Committee of Miami University, it was possible for him to have the services of student assistants. From 1925 to 1927, the writer assisted Professor Fink in the study of material and the writing of descriptions. This assistantship was financed by combining fellowship grants from the Society of Sigma Xi, grants from the American Association for the Advancement of Science, and grants from Miami University. Grants were received by the writer from the Society of Sigma Xi in 1928, 1929, and 1930, and from the American Association for the Advancement of Science in 1923. After the death of Professor Fink in 1927, the writer became an instructor in the Botany Department of Miami University and continued work on the manuscript.

In 1929, through the efforts of the late Professor C. H. Kauffman, the Fink Herbarium and Library were acquired by the University of Michigan. The writer at that time became a member of the staff of the University Herbarium, and was encouraged by Professor Kauffman and his successor, Professor E. B. Mains, to use a greater part of her time for the purpose of carrying the manual to completion.

Dr. Howard A. Kelly has taken a very active interest in the completion of this project, expressed through his contribution toward the purchase of the Fink Herbarium and Library, the gift of specimens and publications, and especially the encouragement given through his correspondence.

At the time of the death of Professor Fink the descriptions of species and subspecies had been nearly completed, and preliminary notes had been made for the descriptions of families and for keys and arrangement, as well as some notes for the introduction to the manual. The descriptions which have been added and revised follow the outline adopted by Professor Fink, and the making of keys and the final arrangement have been guided by his preliminary notes. The original plans have been followed as carefully as possible. An attempt has been made to see authentic specimens of all species reported for the United States. In a few instances this has not been possible. Such species have been listed but not described. Also, if specimens have been insufficient to justify definite conclusions in regard to their status, the species to which they have been ascribed are only listed. In so far as possible all literature cited has been seen. Many difficulties have been encountered and much more time than anticipated has been required to prepare the manuscript for publication.

The preliminary notes made by Professor Fink for the introduction were found to be insufficient, and it therefore has been thought wise to reprint a large part of the introductory material from *The Lichens of Minnesota*. Changes have been made in order to bring the introduction into conformity with Fink's later ideas and to incorporate his preliminary notes. Since the earlier monograph is out of print it has also seemed advisable to use a number of the plates from it for this manual. These have been made available through the kindness of Dr. Alexander Wetmore of the Smithsonian Institution.

The descriptions have been made as short as possible with the omission of all but the diagnostic characters. Generic characters have not been repeated under the specific descriptions. Only the synonyms used by Tuckerman, Hasse, Herre, Willey, Fink, and occasionally others have been given. For complete synonymy the student is referred to Zahlbruckner's *Catalogus Lichenum Universalis*, which has been followed for synonymy in this manual.

The system of classification is based on that of A. Zahlbruckner.* Modifications have been made following the treatment proposed by Professor Fink.† The Ascolichenes are presented first, beginning with the pyrenomycetous forms, which are followed by the discomycetous ones. Within the larger groups the structure of the thallus is used as the chief basis of classification. The Hymenolichenes follow the Ascolichenes and the Lichenes Imperfecti are placed at the end.

Much has been written concerning the position of lichens among the families of plants. Several theories have been advanced concerning the origin and composition of the lichens and especially concerning the relationship of the two components, the fungus and the alga. It seems desirable here to use the term "lichen" as defined by Fink‡—"The lichen is a fungus which lives during all or part of its life in parasitic relation with the algal host and also sustains a relation with an organic or an inorganic substratum." While this manual treats lichens as a group, the underlying idea is that they could be distributed among the other fungi. In some groups the relationship seems very close, in others more remote. The descriptions are based on the fungus, and the alga is mentioned only as the host-plant.

The following is quoted from the preliminary notes made by Professor Fink for the manual: "I wish to acknowledge my obligations to many amateur and professional lichenologists whose aid and encouragement have made the difficult task of preparing this manual possible. The work of the pioneer American lichenologist, Edward Tuckerman, was the starting point for me and many others. W. G. Farlow, Clara E. Cummings, A. B. Seymour, T. A. Williams, L. R. Riddle, W. W. Calkins, J. W Eckfeldt, H. E. Hasse, Henry Willey, W. C. T. Herre, S. H. Burnham, Annie Morrill Smith, H. A. Green, John Macoun, C. Audrey Richards, Freda M. Bachman, G. K. Merrill, R. S. Williams, and A. Schneider are some of the American workers who by their publications or distribution of specimens have aided in the present work.

"Among Europeans who have aided in way of determinations and publications are E. A. Vainio, A. Zahlbruckner, F. Arnold, T. Hedlund, G. Lindau, O. V. Darbishire, W. Nylander, J. Müller Arg., A. Massalongo, A. M. Hue, J. Harmand, H. Oliver, A. von Krempelhuber, J. M. Crombie, Annie L. Smith, G. W. Koerber, W. A. Leighton, E. Acharius, E. Fries, T. M. Fries, L. E. Schaerer, E. Stizenberger, L. Scriba, H. Sandstede, M. B. de Lesdain, and others.

*Engler and Prantl, *Die Natürlichen Pflanzenfamilien* (2d Ed.), 8. 1926.

†Bruce Fink, "The Ascomycetes of Ohio," *Ohio Biological Survey Bulletin*, 5. 1915.

‡Bruce Fink, "The Nature and Classification of Lichens. II," *Mycologia*, 5. 1913.

"Very much to my regret, space is lacking to mention at various points in the manual the specific aid rendered by some of these workers and others. Finally, it is impossible to enumerate the names of American botanists and other persons who have encouraged me to go forward with what would have been otherwise an impossible task."

Thanks are also due to Professor E. B. Mains and Professor H. H. Bartlett for helpful suggestions and criticisms, to Mr. J. L. Lowe for help in preparing the keys and arrangement of the species, to the several collectors of material, to those who so kindly lent herbarium material for study, to the Smithsonian Institution for the loan of plates, to the Field Museum, and to Mr. G. D. Smith of Richmond, Kentucky, for several of the photographs. It is impossible to list all those who have contributed to the completing of this manual.

In completing the manual and preparing the manuscript for publication, it has been the earnest wish of the writer that the lifelong efforts of Professor Fink might be preserved and made available to students in the field of lichenology.

JOYCE HEDRICK

(MRS. VOLNEY H. JONES)

CONTENTS

INTRODUCTION 1

   Hymenolichenes 2

   Lichenes Imperfecti 2

   Ascolichenes 2

      Gross Morphology 2

      Minute Morphology 6

      Reproduction 17

      Habitat and Distribution 18

GLOSSARY 20

OUTLINE OF CLASSIFICATION 23

KEY TO ORDERS AND FAMILIES 26

SYSTEMATIC TREATMENT OF FAMILIES, GENERA, AND SPECIES . . . 29

   Verrucariaceae 29

   Dermatocarpaceae 37

   Pyrenothamniaceae 43

   Pyrenulaceae 44

   Trypetheliaceae 60

   Astrotheliaceae 63

   Strigulaceae 64

   Pyrenidiaceae 65

   Pyrenotrichaceae 65

   Mycoporaceae 66

   Caliciaceae 67

   Cypheliaceae 75

   Sphaerophoraceae 78

   Arthoniaceae 78

   Graphidaceae 95

   Chiodectonaceae 119

   Dirinaceae 123

Roccellaceae 125

Lecanactidaceae 127

Thelotremaceae 130

Diploschistaceae 135

Ectolechiaceae 137

Gyalectaceae 137

Coenogoniaceae 140

Ephebaceae 142

Pyrenopsidaceae 145

Lichinaceae 151

Collemaceae 152

Heppiaceae 168

Pannariaceae 170

Stictaceae 178

Peltigeraceae 183

Lecideaceae 189

Cladoniaceae 241

Gyrophoraceae 271

Acarosporaceae 277

Pertusariaceae 289

Lecanoraceae 293

Parmeliaceae 318

Usneaceae 339

Caloplacaceae 351

Teloschistaceae 363

Buelliaceae 365

Physciaceae 382

Thelephoraceae 391

Leprariaceae 392

INDEX TO SYSTEMATIC NAMES 393

PLATES 1 TO 47

ILLUSTRATIONS

PLATES

PLATE

Verrucaria viridula (Schrad.) Ach. and Staurothele clopima (Wahl.)
T. Fries 1
Pyrenula farrea (Ach.) Branth & Rostr. and Coniocybe pallida (Pers.)
E. Fries 2
Arthonia radiata (Pers.) Ach. and Graphis scripta (L.) Ach. . . . 3
Conotrema urceolatum (Ach.) Tuck. 4
Ephebe lanata (L.) Vainio 5
Ephebe lanata (L.) Vainio and Synechoblastus nigrescens (Huds.) Trev. 6
Collema pulposum (Bernh.) Ach. 7
Leptogium tremelloides (L.) S. F. Gray 8
Pannaria leucosticta Tuck. 9
Sticta pulmonaria (L.) Bir. 10
Sticta verrucosa (Huds.) Fink 11
Solorina saccata (L.) Ach. and Peltigera venosa (L.) Baumg. . . . 12
Peltigera aphthosa (L.) Willd. 13
Lecidea melancheima Tuck. 14
Lecidea pantherina (Hoffm.) Ach. and Lecidea granulosa (Hoffm.) Ach. 15
Lecidea speirea Ach. and Lecidea albocaerulescens (Wulf.) Ach. . . 16
Psora Russellii (Tuck.) Schneid. 17
Mycoblastus sanguinarius (L.) Norm. 18
Rhizocarpon concentricum (Davies) Beltr. and Rhizocarpon geographi-
cum (L.) Lam. & DC. 19
Baeomyces rufus (Huds.) Rebent. and Cladonia fimbriata coniocraea
(Floerke) Vainio 20
Cladonia pyxidata chlorophaea (Spreng.) Floerke 21
Cladonia bellidiflora (Ach.) Schaer. and Cladonia deformis (L.) Hoffm. 22
Cladonia verticillata Hoffm. 23
Stereocaulon coralloides E. Fries 24
Gyrophora hyperborea Ach. 25
Gyrophora dillenii (Tuck.) Müll. Arg. 26
Umbilicaria pustulata (L.) Hoffm. and Pertusaria velata (Turn.) Nyl. 27
An Acarospora 28
Lecanora varia (Hoffm.) Ach. and Lecanora frustulosa (Dicks.) Ach. 29
Lecanora versicolor (Pers.) Ach. 30

PLATE

Ochrolechia pallescens (L.) Mass. 31
Icmadophila ericetorum (L.) Zahlbr. 32
Parmeliopsis aleurites (Ach.) Nyl. 33
Parmelia pertusa (Schrank.) Schaer. . . . . •. 34
Parmelia caperata (L.) Ach. 35
Cetraria juniperina pinastri (Scop.) Ach. and Cetraria lacunosa Ach. . 36
Evernia prunastri (L.) Ach. 37
Alectoria jubata (L.) Ach. 38
Ramalina calicaris (L.) Röhling 39
Ramalina reticulata (Noedh.) Kremph. 40
Teloschistes polycarpus (Ehrh.) Tuck. and Ramalina dilacerata
  (Hoffm.) Vainio 41
Ramalina subamplicata (Nyl.) Fink and Usnea florida (L.) Web. . . 42
Caloplaca cerina (Ehrh.) T. Fries and Caloplaca elegans (Link) T. Fries 43
Teloschistes chrysophthalmus (L.) Beltr. 44
Buellia parasema (Ach.) De Not. 45
Pyxine sorediata (Ach.) E. Fries 46
Physcia stellaris (L.) Nyl. and Anaptychia ciliaris (L.) Koerb. . . . 47

TEXT FIGURES

PAGE
Fig. 1. Algal types with associated fungal hyphae 1
Fig. 2. Algal types with associated fungal hyphae 2
Fig. 3. Cephalodia of *Peltigera aphthosa* 9
Fig. 4. Cyphellae 10

INTRODUCTION

Most of the lichens of the temperate regions of the United States belong with the Ascomycetes. They have become so modified, in many instances, since entering into relationship with the alga that there is little resemblance between them and the ancestral forms. There is sufficient likeness, however, to lead to a general conviction that part of them have evolved from the Discomycetes and part from the Pyrenomycetes. Of these two groups such genera as Peziza, Patellaria, Hysterographium, Phacidium, Chaetomium, and Sordaria are among those which may be closely related to the ancestors of the lichens. In the subtropical regions of southern United States are found two genera which belong to the Hymenolichenes. Their relationship apparently is with the fungi of the family Thelephoraceae. The imperfect lichens are represented by one genus in which no spore form has been discovered. This has been retained in the imperfects although many workers have placed it among the Ascolichenes.

The algal hosts are much better understood than the fungi. Indeed, in the description of genera, statements are made regarding the algae to be found in each genus, and some use is made of these algal types in classification into families and genera. The algae most commonly found in the lichen thalli belong to the genus Cystococcus (Fig. 1 a), and this genus is closely related to Pleurococcus (Fig. 2 d), which is supposed to be the algal host of a few common lichens.

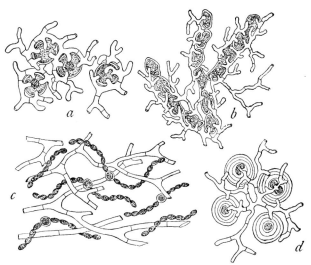

FIGURE 1

Algal types with associated fungal hyphae. a, Cystococcus, each cell surrounded by haustoria. b, Trentepohlia, showing a branching chain of cells, surrounded by haustorial hyphae. c, Nostoc, showing the algal filaments and the intermingled fungal hyphae. d, Gloeocapsa, showing the haustoria and the fungal hyphae surrounding the algal cells. a, enlarged 750 diameters; b, 325 diameters; c, 500 diameters; d, 650 diameters. From Schneider.

1

In the genera Collema, Synechoblastus, Leptogium, and some others the algal host is Nostoc (Fig. 1 *c*). Trentepohlia (Fig. 1 *b*) is found associated with a considerable number of crustose lichens. Other algae which occur only rarely are Gloeocapsa (Fig. 1 *d*), Rivularia (Fig. 2 *a*), Polycoccus (Fig. 2 *b*), Dactylococcus (Fig. 2 *c*), and Sirosiphon (Fig. 2 *e*).

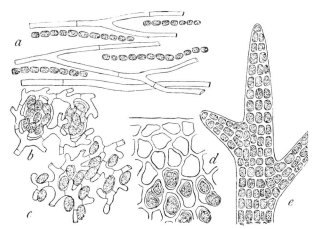

FIGURE 2

Algal types with associated fungal hyphae. *a*, Rivularia with the fungal hyphae intermingled. *b*, Polycoccus: colonies of cells surrounded by hyphae and haustoria. *c*, Dactylococcus: elliptical algal cells and fungal hyphae. *d*, Pleurococcus, the irregular algal cells inclosed in fungal hyphae. *e*, Sirosiphon, a terminal branch not showing the fungal hyphae. *a*, much enlarged; *b*, *c*, enlarged 325 diameters; *d*, 450 diameters; *e*, 250 diameters. From Schneider.

HYMENOLICHENES

The Hymenolichenes are those which produce their spores on basidia. The thallus or vegetative tissue spreads irregularly over the substratum or becomes pileate. It is composed of interwoven hyphae and shows little or no differentiation into layers. On the under surface of the thallus is produced the hymenium, which is composed of basidia and paraphyses. Each basidium produces 4 sterigmata on the tips of which are borne hyaline or brownish spores.

LICHENES IMPERFECTI

Lichens in which no spore form has been discovered have been placed in this group. The thallus is composed of a more or less densely woven mass of hyphae often giving a powdery appearance to the substratum.

ASCOLICHENES

The Ascolichenes are those which produce their spores in sacs or asci. To this group belong most of the lichens of the United States. They are discussed in detail in the following pages.

GROSS MORPHOLOGY

THE THALLUS. The fundamental part of the lichen is the vegetative tissue or thallus. This thallus may be erect, rising from the substratum; pendulous, hanging downward from it; conspicuous or inconspicuous and flat, closely or loosely attached to the substratum; or inconspicuous and largely or even wholly imbedded in the substratum. Erect and pendulous forms are commonly called fruticose thalli, and the flat or horizontal ones may be either foliose or crustose: foliose when somewhat leaflike and crustose when forming a closely attached crust resting on or within the substratum. Various intermediate conditions between crustose and foliose and between foliose and fruticose forms may be expected.

GENERAL FORMS OF THALLI. Of the foliose forms, many are variously lobed, and some are almost entire at the margin. In instances where the lobing is evident, the lobes may be variously imbricated. In both lobed and unlobed forms the margin may be wavy or crenate instead of entire, and it may be either ciliate or devoid of cilia. The most obtrusive differences among the fruticose thalli consist in their being branched or unbranched, and, when branched, in the manner of their branching. Secondary differences are found in the character of the surface, particularly in various small outgrowths other than the branches, known as phyllocladia. The crustose thalli appear usually as a more or less conspicuous layer spread over the substratum or sometimes really lying wholly or partly in it and indicated at the surface often only by a change in color. These crustose thalli will be found to be irregular in outline or more or less plainly orbicular and to form a continuous or a variously broken and scattered stratum. In some species the tendency is toward orbicular forms and in others toward irregularity in form, but in any case the peculiarities of the surface of bark, old wood, or rock forming the substratum will determine the form of the particular thallus to a large extent.

SIZES OF THALLI. In the northern and northwestern states the fruticose thalli of *Usnea longissima,* which grow in tangled masses hanging over the branches of trees, frequently reach 1.5 meters in length, while the foliose thalli of *Gyrophora Dillenii* sometimes reach 35 cm. or more in their largest diameter. Both fruticose and foliose thalli may vary from these large forms to minute ones not more than 0.2 mm. in height or diameter. In the crustose thalli the spread over and within the substratum may vary greatly, but is seldom more than 10 cm. In these and the foliose forms the thickness is to be taken into account. In the descriptions, however, actual measurements are very seldom given, though comparative statements are often employed.

SURFACES OF THALLI. In the foliose thalli the upper surface is comparatively smooth, wrinkled, corrugated, or pustulate, and it may bear cilia, soredia, or the minute growths known as isidioid or coralloid branchlets. The margin of the thallus may be closely attached to the substratum, or more or less ascending. The lower surface is variously covered with the attaching organs known as rhizoids. These may be large or small, numerous or few, and evenly scattered or collected into rows or into groups of different forms. The lower surface is sometimes quite smooth except for these rhizoids, but may be variously wrinkled or pitted, or, in one species of Gyrophora, provided with vertical plates which give strength.
In the fruticose thalli the surface is either smooth or variously pitted, and in some instances it is somewhat tomentose. The species of Cladonia put forth as superficial outgrowths the flat expansions known as squamules. The species of Stereocaulon bear the peculiar structures more irregular in form called phyllocladia. The form, size, frequency of occurrence, and distribution of these organs must be noted carefully. In species of Cladonia, especially, it is necessary to observe whether the cortex of the podetium is entire or somewhat broken, so that it becomes areolate or even disappears over some portion of the organ.
Finally, turning to the crustose thalli, they are also smooth or variously roughened. Those that are hypophloeodal or hypolithic simply take the contour of the surface of the substratum, as do also some thin and smooth forms that

are in part or wholly epiphloeodal or epilithic. Others are scurfy or granular, and these are usually rather poorly developed and thin. In thicker forms is found the warty or verrucose condition; sometimes there occur here and there minute chinks, so that the thallus is said to be rimose or chinky; or finally the chinks may become numerous and divide the thallus into minute or small, several-sided areas, known as areoles, in which case the thallus is said to be areolate.

COLORS OF THALLI. As compared with size and form, color is usually regarded as a rather more variable and therefore less reliable taxonomic character. Yet the colors of thalli play an important part in identifying lichens and, though often quite variable, they must be carefully noted. Colors in lichen thalli vary all the way from. a white to a black, but the most common is a greenish gray. Some other colors which occur are ashy, olivaceous, brown, and straw-color, as ,well as yellow and various intermediate shades, such as brownish black, olive-brown, etc. The thallus, furthermore, is often variegated and the lower surface is frequently of a different color from the upper. Also, in the fruticose forms the basal portion is frequently of a different color from the distal portions, usually darker. The tendency of thalli, as of other lichen structures, is to darken with age, and the variations of color in a species may usually be traced to peculiar conditions of growth.

THE ASCOCARP. In the fruit, or ascocarp, the main features of gross morphology are size, form, and color. The ascocarps are usually superficial and large enough to be seen easily with the unaided eye. In some lichens, however, they are so small that they can be made out only with difficulty with the hand lens; or they may be immersed in the thallus and indicated at the surface by a slight elevation or depression as a disk or an ostiole; or, when immersed, they may be scarcely discernible in any way except in sections of the thallus. From 0.1 to 5 mm. is well within the usual range for diameters of the ascocarps, though larger ones will be found.

The ascocarp may be an open or disk-shaped body called an apothecium. The apothecia are most commonly saucer-shaped, or some slight modification of this form, as when the disk is flat or somewhat convex instead of concave. In some instances the disk becomes very concave, the apothecium at last becoming cup-shaped, or it may be strongly convex, sometimes becoming at maturity spheroidal. In all of these forms the outline of a transverse section of the apothecium when young would usually be very nearly a perfect circle; but the form may become irregular as growth proceeds, so that at maturity this outline is quite irregular. In other lichens the apothecia are non-circular from the beginning. Thus, there are the elongated and often-branched forms, such as are found in the Graphidaceae, and the difform or variously irregular forms, as in the Arthoniaceae.

The ascocarp may be closed, with only a small opening at the top for the escape of spores. It is then called a perithecium and usually approximates a spherical form, inclosed by a more or less well-developed perithecial wall.

THE DISK. In those lichens in which the exciple is not produced into a perithecial wall the upper surface of the ascocarp is naked, except for a very thin film of thallus which may persist as an epithecium, a structure not mentioned in the descriptions of species. This upper and essentially naked surface, whether flat or more or less strongly concave or convex, forms the disk. The outline of the disk, then, may be circular or variously elongated or irregular, varying in this respect with the form of the ascocarp as a whole. In color the disk varies considerably even in the same species. It is usually light colored in its early development and commonly becomes darker as it reaches maturity. The final color may be a light or darker flesh color or a light or darker shade of yellow, orange, red, brown, chestnut, olive, or even black. Whatever the color, it is very seldom the same as that of the thallus. The surface of the disk, further, may be pruinose, concealing the essential color.

THE EXCIPLE. Below the disk is the hymenium, which, in sections, may easily be seen with the hand lens. This structure is usually lighter in color than the disk and is composed of paraphyses and asci. Below the hymenium is the hypothecium, often darker in color than the hymenium above it, so that the line of demarcation between the two structures may easily be made out with a hand lens. The hymenium and hypothecium are mentioned here mainly that another structure, the exciple, may be located with reference to them. The exciple is a saucer-shaped or cup-shaped rim around the hymenium, consisting primarily of a continuation of the hypothecium upward on all sides. Such is the proper exciple; but there is sometimes outside of this, or more often replacing it, what is known as a thalloid exciple. This is similar to the thallus in structure, and usually of the same color, which is never true of the proper exciple, the latter usually approaching the disk in color. Either of the exciples may be entirely absent, and either or both may be quite evanescent and seen only in young ascocarps; but usually one of them is present and either permanent or only tardily disappearing. It may be seen readily with the unaided eye or by the aid of the lens, and its nature and degree of development and permanence are points of considerable value in the classification of lichens, even in the determination of species. In the perithecium, the proper exciple has grown completely around the upper part of the hymenium except for a small opening or ostiole at the summit. The exciple thus forms the perithecial wall. The margin of the proper exciple is usually about the level of the outer margin of the disk, or it may be somewhat raised above the disk. This margin is almost always entire, while the margin of a thalloid exciple is frequently crenulate or crenate, or variously branched, ciliate, or irregular.

POSITION OF THE ASCOCARP. Sometimes the ascocarp is raised on a slender, upward extension of the thallus, a short stalk or pedicel, quite different in form from the stipe and podetia soon to be described. A stalk is most frequently met in the larger foliose lichens. It may be absent and the ascocarp attached to the thallus at the center of its lower side, in which case the ascocarp is said to be sessile. Again, the ascocarp may be more closely attached to the thallus by the whole of its lower side, when it is said to be adnate. Finally, the ascocarp may be more or less immersed in the thallus, sometimes deeply, so that when the disk is more or less overgrown by the thallus or by a perithecial wall, the structures are often quite obscured. The development of the ascocarp begins below the surface of the thallus, and the tendency in general is for it to become more and more superficial as maturity is reached. Sometimes, however, it remains permanently more or less immersed, and somewhat varying positions with reference to the thallus may be expected in many species.

STIPES AND PODETIA. These are structures which serve to raise the ascocarp into the air, and are both to be regarded as primarily important for this purpose. In the genera of Caliciaceae and Cypheliaceae, they have no other function, and are called stipes. In Cladonia and Stereocaulon, however, the stipe takes up, in addition, the structure of the primary thallus with a more or less definite algal layer, and is called a podetium, the proper stipe being devoid of algal cells. The stipe, therefore, belongs to the sporogenous tissue, whereas the podetium has the essential character of the thallus and more properly belongs to the vegetative tissue.

RHIZOIDS AND CILIA. The rhizoids are found on the ventral side of most foliose thalli and serve as attaching organs. They appear to the eye as rootlike bodies, varying in color from white to black.

The cilia are like rhizoids in structure, but are found on the upper surface of the thallus and along the margin. The hyphal rhizoids of the crustose lichens are quite different morphologically. The functions of cilia are doubtless to retain drops of water and gradually absorb them. Closely related to rhizoids is the single attaching organ known as the umbilicus on the ventral sides of the thalli of species of Gyrophora, Umbilicaria, and some species of Dermatocarpon.

OTHER STRUCTURES. Spermagonia, soredia, cephalodia, and cyphellae are structures which occur on or near the surface of thalli. The spermagonia are supposedly the male reproductive organs, sometimes quite conspicuous as dark-colored spots on the upper surface of the thallus, as in some species of Parmelia and other large foliose lichens; but these structures are more often minute and of the color of the thallus so that they appear only in sections. They were formerly thought to be of considerable value in the determination of species. Their structure and function will be further considered in the section on reproduction. The soredia are small, powdery masses, usually whitish in color, and scattered over the surface of the thallus as in *Pyxine sorediata,* and many other lichens. They will be considered in succeeding sections. Cephalodia are wartlike bodies found on the upper surface of the thallus as in *Peltigera aphthosa,* or within the thallus, as in some other lichens. Cyphellae are small pits or depressions in the lower surface of some foliose thalli as in some species of Sticta. Cephalodia and cyphellae will be further considered under minute morphology, as their structure can be made out only with the microscope.

Finally, in some lichens the hypothallus is conspicuous to the unaided eye or seen with the hand lens. This is true of some members of the family Pannariaceae. For instance, in *Placynthium nigrum* this structure appears as a bluish black ring all around the thallus. Some of the older workers considered the rhizoids a portion of the hypothallus.

MINUTE MORPHOLOGY

FOLIOSE THALLI. In the foliose type of thallus there are the following layers: an upper dermis, an upper plectenchymatous cortex, an algal layer, a medullary layer, and a lower plectenchymatous cortex. The dermis, however, is scarcely distinguishable in many foliose lichens, and there are several other variations from the structure just outlined. For instance, in Collema there is no cortex, and the algae are not arranged in a definite layer; in one genus of the Physciaceae the plectenchymatous cortex is replaced by layers of densely interwoven hyphae; in species of Peltigera the upper plectenchymatous cortex is present, but there is none below; a few small foliose thalli, as in some species of Acaropsora, are plectenchymatous throughout. Other instances of similar modifications in structure will be met in the descriptions of the genera.

CRUSTOSE THALLI. In those crustose forms that are hypophloeodal or hypolithic, there is simply a tangled layer of interwoven algal cells and fungal hyphae, without any differentiation into layers. In the epiphloeodal and epilithic species the structure may be quite as rudimentary, or there may be a more or less evident upper pseudocortex of interwoven hyphae. In instances of the latter there is frequently also a more or less distinct algal layer below the pseudocortex and some representation of a medulla below the algal layer. Whether these superficial forms are thus differentiated or not, the modified hyphae known as hyphal rhizoids may always be looked for, penetrating the substratum. It is, however, very difficult to observe them in sections of these thalli. With each description of the crustose genera will be found a statement regarding the amount of differentiation.

FRUTICOSE THALLI. The fruticose type of lichen thallus is peculiar, and is for this reason treated after the crustose type. Fruticose thalli are usually, though as noted below not always, more or less cylindrical in form. The outer layer of the cylinder or other form is a pseudocortex of densely interwoven hyphae, extending either in the direction of the axis or at right angles to it. Within this outer layer is the algal layer, which, like the outer layer of hyphae, is commonly more or less nearly circular in transverse section. Sometimes, as in species of Alectoria, there is within the algal layer a well-developed medullary layer filling the remainder of the space and making the cylinder a solid one. In other instances the medulla is poorly or scarcely at all developed. Within it, when only partially developed or within the algal layer when the medulla is wanting, is frequently found a solid or a hollow cylinder of hyphae extending in a longitudinal direction. If this cylinder of hyphae is hollow there are usually strengthening bundles of hyphae to be found traversing the hollow central portion of the thallus in transverse direction.

The outer pseudocortex is usually composed of hyphae that are more or less gelatinized, so that the structure is very difficult to make out. This gelatinization no doubt increases the protective function of the pseudocortex. The inner cylinder of hyphae functions principally for conduction like a stele, and the walls of the hyphae show much less gelatinization. The algal layer is seldom a complete cylinder, the algae more often appearing in clusters incompletely filling the space. The pseudocortex is seldom even approximately of the same thickness throughout and is sometimes scarcely at all developed except over the algal clusters. This arrangement brings the algal layer into closer contact with the atmosphere without completely exposing the algae. The hyphae are much less frequently branched in fruticose thalli than in foliose and crustose forms. In connection with this fact it is to be noted that fruticose thalli are not always even approximately cylindrical in form. *Ramalina calicaris fraxinea* departs most widely from the cylindrical form and appears much more like a foliose thallus growing away from the substratum, to which it is attached at a single point. However, when this thallus is sectioned, the structure is seen to be essentially that of the fruticose type. Indeed, in outward form, there is every gradation between the fruticose and the foliose thallus, and in a few so-called fruticose thalli there is found plectenchymatous cortex characteristic of a foliose thallus.

THE DERMIS. This structure consists of a few layers of flattened plectenchyma, lying upon the cortex and derived from it. The dermis aids in protection against excessive evaporation of moisture, and from its surface there sometimes arises a dense covering of short hyphae which also function in the same way. These are the trichomatic hyphae of certain species of Peltigera, and they serve in *Peltigera aphthosa* to help in retaining the soredia which develop into cephalodia. The dermis is rudimentary or wanting in most lichens except species of Peltigera and Sticta. The inner layers of plectenchyma are less flattened and gradually pass into those of the cortex from which they are developed.

THE UPPER CORTEX. This structure is plectenchymatous, consisting usually of several layers. The cells of these layers may be as distinct as those of any ordinary parenchyma or the walls may be gelatinized and swollen to such an extent that the cellular nature is not made out. This layer may appear quite hyaline in section or it may contain some coloring matter. In the majority of the foliose lichens, such a structure is developed both above and below, and the lower cortex is more frequently of a dark color. However, as already stated, there are a number of foliose genera in which part or all of the species lack such a cortex on one or both sides. And it may be added here that in species of Leptogium the cortex usually consists of a single layer of plectenchyma.

The cortex is constantly being built up from the hyphae of the algal layer below and is gradually transformed above into a dermis. By this gradual upward passage of tissues dead entangled, algal cells are at length carried off by the abrasion of the upper surface. The lower cortex is usually thinner and is more often absent than the upper; but in thalli in which this lower cortex is especially needed for mechanical support it is often better developed and thicker than the upper cortex.

THE ALGAL LAYER. In some lichens, as in species of Collema, the fungal hyphae are simply in contact with the algae and in others they are attached to them by haustoria. In some cases the haustoria penetrate the walls of the algal cells and are then said to be intracellular. These naturally secure the closest union. Every gradation between intracellular and extracellular haustoria may be looked for in certain species, but it is rarely that the haustorium attains a full development, i.e., is divided into a network of hyphae, within the algal cells. Indeed, intracellular haustoria are either very rare or not often distinguished as such. The extracellular haustoria usually consist of a network of short, thin-walled hyphae growing over a large portion of the outer surface of the wall of each algal cell. Where these are present the food must pass through the wall of the haustorium and also through that of the alga, but in instances where the haustoria become intracellular the passage is through the wall of the haustorium only. The algal cells of the algal layer are numerous in vigorous thalli, but in old and dying thalli few of them remain alive. The hyphae of this layer give rise to the outer or upper cortex, whether a true cortex or a pseudocortex, and are also continuous with the hyphae of the medullary layer. The food assimilated by the living algae, together with that which the hyphae may be able to take from the substratum through the rhizoids, the umbilicus, or the hyphal rhizoids, serves both for the production of new algal cells by division and for the growth of various portions of the thallus. As the algal cells die and pass outward new ones are constantly being formed toward the lower and inner portions of the algal layer, so that the thallus is always possessed of an abundance of assimilative tissue. The growth and division of the algal cells is of course most active in young and vigorous thalli and in the younger and more active portions of older thalli.

THE MEDULLARY LAYER. The medullary layer lies below the algal layer in horizontal thalli and within it in fruticose thalli. This layer consists of loosely interwoven hyphae and is especially adapted to give strength by connecting the layers above with those below, or those without with those within. It serves also as a medium for the free passage of gases much after the manner of the spongy parenchyma of a leaf. The differentiation into algal layer and medullary layer is not always perfect even in the best-developed thalli, and algal cells may occur in small numbers in the latter layer. The medulla is commonly the thickest of all the layers of the thallus, and the section in this portion of the thallus is more constantly transparent or hyaline than in either of the cortical layers. As the hyphae of this layer serve for giving strength, the walls are scarcely ever percep-

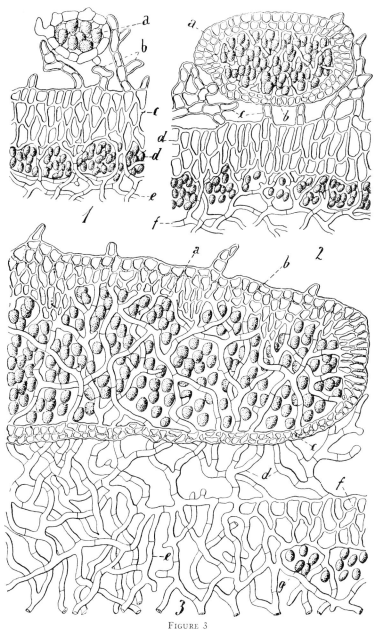

FIGURE 3

Cephalodia of *Peltigera aphthosa:* Diagram 1, *a,* a young cephalodium; *b,* the trichomatic hyphae holding the céphalodium. Diagram 2, an older cephalodium; *a,* the internal hypae and algal cells; *b,* the well-developed cortex; *c,* the supporting trichomatic hyphae. Diagram 3, a mature cephalodium; *a,* the internal hyphae and algal cells; *b,* the upper cortex; *c,* the lower cortex; *d,* the supporting hyphae; *e,* the thallus below the cephalodium, where the algal cells have disappeared and the cortex is transformed into hyphal tissue; *f,* the cortex; *g,* the algal layer of the supporting thallus. Diagram 1, enlarged about 100 diameters; diagram 2, enlarged 400 diameters; diagram 3, enlarged 200 diameters. From Schneider.

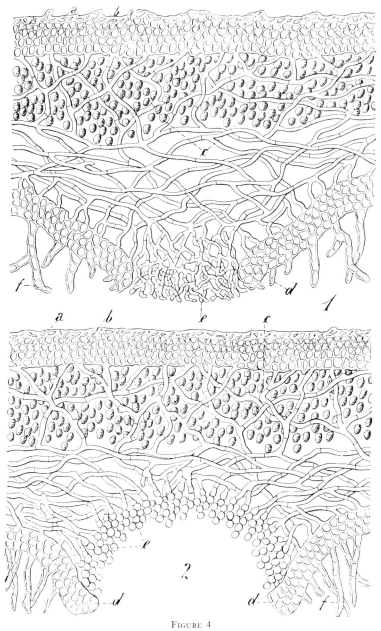

FIGURE 4

Cyphellae: Diagram 1, a section of the thallus of a Sticta; *e*, a cyphella composed of a network of hyphae and protruding from an opening in the lower cortex of the thallus. Diagram 2, the form of cyphella found in *Sticta damaecornis*, consisting of a depression in the lower side of the thallus and surrounded by hyphae composed of almost spherical cells. In diagrams 1 and 2 the usual layers of the thallus are shown; *a*, the dermis; *b*, the upper cortex; *c*, the algal layer; *d*, the lower cortex; between *c* and *d*, the medullary layer; *f*, the rhizoids. Diagrams 1 and 2 enlarged 400 diameters. From Schneider.

tibly gelatinized. Aside from the functions already named, the hyphae of the medulla must carry up to the algae any materials taken in a crude state from the substratum by the attaching organs. Also the foods assimilated by the algae must in part pass downward or inward by means of these hyphae for the nourishment of certain portions of the thalli. It is also supposed that fats and other food materials are often stored in the hyphae of the medulla.

THE LOWER CORTEX. In most respects the lower cortex is very similar to the upper, but, as already stated, it is neither so constantly present nor is it as a rule so thick. When the lower cortex is present the rhizoids extend from it into the substratum, but when it is absent rhizoids are usually present as continuations of certain hyphae of the medullary layer. Plainly, such a plectenchymatous tissue on the lower side of the thallus must serve for support, and it becomes very thick in those large foliose thalli which are attached by an umbilicus, such as species of Gyrophora, Umbilicaria, and Dermatocarpon. But, since it lies between the rhizoids and the tissue above, this cortical tissue must permit the passage of any crude or elaborated materials taken from the·substratum by the rhizoids, for which reason it remains thinner than might otherwise be expected. Also, the lower cortex is usually a looser tissue than the upper cortex and is usually darker colored. Peltigera is a genus of large foliose lichens in which there is a well-developed upper cortex and no lower cortex.

SOREDIA AND SPERMAGONIA. A soredium consists of a tangled mass of algal cells and hyphae which has pushed upward from the algal layer and appears at the surface in a small spot where the upper cortex is broken. The soredia function for reproduction. The spermagonia appear as little spherical or cup-shaped bodies, sunken in the surface of the thallus. Within each spermagonium are borne the spermatia on stalks called sterigmata. The spermatium is a small, slender body, commonly colorless, and straight or slightly curved. The spermatia are usually regarded as male reproductive bodies.

CEPHALODIA. These bodies (Fig. 3) sometimes appear upon the surface of the thallus and in other instances within it. Those situated on the upper or lower surface are called ectotrophic, and those that are found within the thallus endotrophic cephalodia. There is much difference of opinion as to the frequency of the appearance of cephalodia, due partly to lack of careful observation and partly also to difference of view as to their nature. A cephalodium is an abnormal development upon or within the lichen thallus, containing some other alga than the one found in other portions of the thallus. The cephalodia of *Peltigera aphthosa* are ectotrophic and plainly visible. The foreign algae found in the cephalodia of this lichen are of the genus Rivularia, and they are supposed to be brought to the thallus in some way, and, being held by the trichomatic hyphae, to multiply and become surrounded by a true cortex. Ectotrophic cephalodia also occur in species of Stereocaulon, and the algae contained are not always the same. But these are minute structures and seldom noticed. Endotrophic cephalodia are said to occur sometimes in *Sticta amplissima*.

CYPHELLAE. These structures (Fig. 4) are small pits found on the lower side of certain thalli. They are common in the majority of species of Sticta, and appear at points on the lower surface of the lichen thallus corresponding to the position of breathing pores. In their development a circular break first appears in the lower cortex. As the opening in the cortex increases in size, the adjacent hyphae of the medullary layer give off numerous short branches, which fill the bottom of the opening so that the cyphella appears as a minute cup-shaped or saucer-shaped depression, whose bottom and sides are covered with a dense coating of short hyphal branches. The position of the cyphellae over the breathing pores would seem to indicate that they serve to admit air to the interior of the thallus.

BREATHING PORES. In lichens having a thallus well developed on both sides, it is evident that some provision for the admission of air to the interior will be advantageous. This is especially true where the plectenchymatous cortex is quite thick. The breathing pores of the lower cortex in species of Sticta have just been mentioned. Such structures are found in the lower cortex of many other lichens, but are even more common in the upper plectenchymatous cortex. They consist of more or less branched pores extending from the surface of the algal layer upward through the cortex in a somewhat irregular course and having no proper wall of their own but forming simply intracellular canals. They resemble stomata in that they can be closed, and, also, as is true of stomata, it is doubtful whether they are really of greater use for the exchange of gases than for some other purposes. They are found closed when the thallus becomes dry, and the closing doubtless helps to prevent the transpiration of moisture. Similar openings between the hyphae of pseudocortices may sometimes be made out, especially when these cortices are thick. However, whether the cortex is plectenchymatous or not, these pores are to be looked for, for the most part, in the thinnest portions of the cortex, especially over areas where the algal cells are numerous.

GROWTH OF THALLI. In crustose and foliose lichens the growth is for the most part horizontal and mainly at or just behind the margin of the thallus. The hyphae in all portions of the thallus, however, may increase in length, either by formation of new cells or by the elongation of old ones. In some instances the initial cells are equally active along the whole margin and the thallus is not lobed. But in some of the higher crustose forms and the majority of the foliose forms there are certain marginal areas where the initial cells are especially active, so that the horizontal growth is more active here than elsewhere. This uneven growth along the margin gives rise to the lobing so common in foliose lichens. Doubtless in the lower crustose forms, where lobing is so uniformly absent, the frequent irregularity in form is caused partly by the irregularities in the surface of the substratum which impede growth more at certain points than elsewhere, and partly also by the loss of portions of the epiphloeodal or epilithic thallus by abrasion. In all instances of lobing the form of the lobes is determined by the size and activity of the areas of initial cells whose division forms the lobes. The thallus reaches its full thickness a short distance back of the growing margin. There is no further increase owing to the fact that, while new cells, both algal and fungal, are formed internally, abrasion of the general surface disposes of dead superficial cells to the same amount.

In most fruticose thalli the growth is mainly vertical instead of horizontal. There may be a single apical region, consisting of a continuous area of initial cells, and in such instances the thallus or the podetium will be unbranched, but generally there are areas of special activity, one corresponding to each branch of the thallus, whether horizontal, vertical, or lying at some intermediate angle. Here, as in all thalli, the manner of branching and the number of branches will depend upon the number and disposition of these areas of special activity.

Sometimes the growth of the algal colony determines the size and form of the so-called thallus. This is so in *Ephebe pubescens,* in which the dichotomously branched alga appears to be the thallus, but the real thallus consists of hyphae within the sheath of the alga. In the species of the Collemaceae, the hyphae have penetrated more or less throughout the algal colony, thus giving the appearance of a somewhat foliose thallus. In the great majority of lichens, however, as already stated, the algal cells simply increase in number as the thallus increases in size. Thus the algae always sustain a physiological relation to the growth of the thallus and perform the function of assimilation.

THE ASCOCARP IN GENERAL. The fruit of an ascolichen is commonly called an ascocarp, and consists of an epithecium, a hymenium, a hypothecium, and a thalloid or a proper exciple or both. Either or both of the exciples, however, may disappear, or the proper exciple may be produced into a structure known as a perithecial wall. Also, when a perithecial wall is present, it sometimes incloses an additional structure known as an amphithecium. These structures may now be explained in order.

THE EPITHECIUM. This structure is supposed to be a film of the thallus extending over the upper surface of the ascocarp, and its presence is explained by the fact that the development of the ascocarp begins within the thallus and that the overlying part of this is carried up with the ascocarp as it finally bursts through the upper cortex of the thallus. The epithecium is of the same color as the upper portion of the hymenium and is usually, when present, not distinguishable from it. Indeed, many of the older lichenologists considered this portion of the hymenium a part of the epithecium and spoke of the epithecium as having certain colors, when the color was in the upper portion of the hymenium. In the descriptions to follow the epithecium has been ignored as something too rudimentary to be distinguished in an ordinary examination of a fruit, or, as probably in the large majority of lichens, entirely absent in mature ascocarps. Special statements are made, however, of the color of the upper portion of the hymenium when differing from that of the lower portion.

THE HYMENIUM. The hymenium is composed of the asci or spore-containing sacs, and the protective filaments called paraphyses. In position this structure lies below the epithecium and above the hypothecium. The asci are always thicker and usually shorter than the paraphyses, and the mature spores may usually be distinguished in them more or less plainly. It need be further stated here only that the asci and paraphyses are usually erect or suberect and constitute a densely packed mass composed of the two structures.

THE THALLOID EXCIPLE. This structure is commonly found in lichens having a well-developed thallus, whether fruticose or foliose, and is found, therefore, most commonly in the foliose forms and least commonly in the crustose ones. In structure the thalloid exciple resembles the thallus, with which it is always continuous. The outer layer of such an exciple is directly continuous with the upper layer of the thallus, whether a true plectenchymatous cortex or a pseudocortex. This cortex of the exciple is often thicker than that of the thallus, to serve both for protection and support to the structures within and to aid in the dispersal of the spores. Within the cortex of the thalloid exciple there may be an algal layer and within this a medullary layer, but these two layers are by no means always clearly differentiated. There is no layer in any thalloid exciple that corresponds to the lower cortex found in so many foliose lichens. Occasionally the algae may disappear from the thalloid exciple with age, but such a structure is still a thalloid exciple. The structure of the thalloid exciple is perfectly plain if the ascocarps are adnate, sessile, or pedicellate, but if they are immersed it is by no means so easy to determine whether the portion of thallus surrounding should be regarded as a thalloid exciple. Also, if the thallus itself is of a rudimentary character and devoid of distinct differentiation into layers, the thalloid exciple may be present in a similarly rudimentary condition, often as a thin veil, which may be evanescent.

THE PROPER EXCIPLE. As the name indicates, the proper exciple is in reality a portion of the ascocarp, being merely an upward extension of the hypothecium and, like it, either plectenchymatous in structure or composed of closely interwoven hyphae. Both hyphal and plectenchymatous areas are found in a thalloid exciple, so that it is not always easy to distinguish between the two kinds of exciples by microscopic structure alone. The fundamental distinction is that if an exciple can be traced to the hypothecium it is to be regarded as a proper exciple, and if it can be traced to the thallus it is thalloid. But an evanescent thallus may disappear and a thalloid exciple still be present. In such instances the algal cells are usually present and the structure, further, does not appear to be continuous with the hypothecium. The hypothecium is always present, and the proper exciple may always be traced back to it in vertical sections through the center of the ascocarp. Some authors seem to consider any exciple that does not contain algal cells a proper exciple, but such a disposition disregards morphological relationships and leads to confusion in the study of species. The proper exciple may be pale in section or varying to a black color. It may be permanent or evanescent, and thin to very thick and conspicuous. In stating that certain exciples become covered by the growing hymenium, it is by no means certain that some of these exciples do not disappear instead of becoming covered. Again, they seem sometimes to become covered and then to disappear. The exciple is a protective covering about the hymenium and is often produced into a perithecial wall, which completely surrounds the hymenium, except for the ostiole at the summit. The proper exciple also aids in the dispersion of spores.

THE HYPOTHECIUM. This area lies immediately below the hymenium and varies considerably both in thickness and structure. Sometimes it exceeds the hymenium in thickness, but in most instances it is considerably thinner in vertical section. In structure it may be composed entirely of interwoven hyphae or entirely of plectenchyma similar to that of a plectenchymatous cortex, or it may be partly plectenchymatous and partly hyphal. In some of the higher lichens, even when the structure is hyphal throughout, the hypothecium is more or less plainly differentiated into two layers, with the hyphae extending in a generally vertical direction in the upper layer and more nearly horizontally in the lower layer. The cells and hyphae of the hypothecium are smaller than the similar structures of the thallus, and the walls are more inclined to become gelatinized so that the structure is obscured; and the same statement applies to the proper exciple and the perithecial wall, which, when present, are continuations of the hypothecium. The color of the hypothecium, like that of the exciple, varies from the palest shades to black, and likewise the sections may appear perfectly hyaline. Both exciple and hypothecium often become darker with age, so that there may be a considerable amount of variation in color in the same species. The hypothecium has not been carefully studied in the pyrenomycetous lichens. Sometimes the perithecial wall is open below, and sometimes it is entire. Data on this point would have been valuable, and yet it seems that it has been possible to distinguish the species in most instances without taking this feature into account.

THE AMPHITHECIUM. In those lichens in which the proper exciple is produced into a perithecial wall, there is sometimes a dark layer outside and a lighter and often hyaline layer within between the dark outer covering and the hymenium. This inner layer is known as the amphithecium. In some pyrenocarpic lichens, in which the fruits are immersed in the thallus, as in Dermatocarpon, the dark outer protective layer is not needed, and the whole of the tissue surrounding the hymenium is hyaline or colorless, but it is also known as an amphithecium.

THE PARAPHYSES. These structures are specialized hyphae which arise from the tissues of the hypothecium. They are commonly cylindrical in form and divided by transverse septa into a number of cells. They appear on hasty examination to be uniformly simple in most lichen species, but more thorough observation usually brings to light some that are branched in nearly every hymenium. The branching may be very limited, or it may be extensive, as in most of the species of Arthoniaceae. Statements as to the branching are included in the description of each genus. The paraphyses are usually distinct, but sometimes their walls are more or less gelatinized, forming a structure in some degree coherent and indistinct. They are usually longer than the asci, but are shorter in the species of Verrucaria, in which they also become imperfectly or often wholly gelatinized. The tips, or apices, are usually thickened and darker in color than the remaining part. Other portions of the paraphysis may be somewhat colored; but usually the single organ appears quite hyaline, though the section of the hymenium often shows color. The paraphyses serve to protect the asci and the contained spores against too rapid transpiration and aid in the dispersion of the spores. The thickening and coloration of the apices are protective in function.

THE ASCI. The asci arise, as do the paraphyses, from the tissue of the hypothecium. They are usually shorter and wider than the paraphyses which surround them. In form they are most commonly clavate, but they may be cylindrical, pyriform, subglobose, or variously ventricose, or otherwise irregular. The walls are usually more or less thickened toward the apex, probably by an accumulation of epiplasm. The thickening may be very slight or it may occupy the upper third or more of the ascus, as in some of the Arthoniaceae. There is a succession of asci produced in each ascocarp, and one may rarely find asci of two generations together, those of one generation containing mature or perhaps old and shriveled spores, and those of the other younger, larger, and unshriveled ones, perhaps immature, as shown by color or condition of septation. In species of Calicium and other closely related genera the upper portion of the wall of the ascus becomes gelatinized and dissolved before the spores are mature, and the spores escape and ripen in the hymenium outside the asci. In other ascomycetous lichens the spores mature within the asci, which then open at the apex for their escape. The apical wall may rupture irregularly, the end may become torn across in some regular way, or probably in many instances an apical plug is pushed out, as in some other ascomycetous fungi.

THE SPORES. These bodies are usually eight in each ascus and rather small in size, but the number may vary from one to many and the size is inversely proportional to number, varying from $3\,\mu$ to $200\,\mu$ or more in length. The most common forms are oblong or ellipsoid, but the spores vary from acicular to spherical. Usually the size and form are quite constant in a given species, but there are instances of considerable variation even in the same hymenium.

The spores as arranged in the ascus may be seriate, oblique, parallel, or more or less irregularly placed. They are likely to be parallel when acicular in form, uniseriate when spherical or oblong in a cylindrical ascus, and obliquely or irregularly arranged when the ascus is pyriform, thickly clavate, or ventricose-clavate.

The spores may be non-septate, 1-septate, 3-septate, or several-septate, the cells being, in most of the compound conditions, arranged in a single series, separated by transverse walls. Besides the transverse divisions, others may be formed in the direction of the long axis of the spore, giving what is known as a muriform spore. In the development of the muriform spores the transverse septations always appear first, and in some species only a portion of the spores are ever found in the muriform condition, though the others are probably to be regarded as immature. In the genera of Teloschistaceae and Caloplacaceae the spores are usually 1-septate, but with a very thick septum through which a narrow canal joins the small cells placed one at each end of the spore. It might be argued that this spore is not truly septate, as a dividing wall across the connecting canal is very rarely seen.

In color the spores vary from hyaline to a blackish brown. Simple spores are usually hyaline, but there are exceptions to the rule. Compound spores are very frequently more or less colored. It is sometimes very difficult to decide the color of spores. Some spores become brown or tinged brown very tardily, sometimes not until shriveled out of recognition and probably dead. These are sometimes seen in the same hymenium with normal spores which are hyaline. In such instances, the spores should be called hyaline. Finally, aside from these exceptions there are instances in which the beginning student will not be able to decide whether spores which show a slight tinge of color should be called hyaline, nor does the experienced worker decide correctly in all instances.

THECIAL ALGAE. In some lichens there are found in the hymenium certain algal cells, commonly known as thecial or hymenial algae. These algae are usually smaller than those of the thallus, and are perhaps of the same species, varying in size because of a difference in nutrition; but it is by no means certain that the thecial algae are derived from those of the thallus of the lichen in which they occur. They may be looked for especially in mature plants of Dermatocarpon and Endocarpon, though they may occur in some other closely related genera. The algal cells are usually smaller than those of the thallus, and are often found clinging to the asci or to the paraphyses. By some workers it is supposed that they are dispersed with the spores and are at hand when the spore germinates, so that the parasitic relation may be established at once and a thallus readily built up, provided other conditions are favorable. However, it may well be doubted whether reproduction often takes place in this way in nature, and it is much more probable that the main function of these algal cells is to nourish the tissues within the ascocarp. The fact that thecial algae are more common in immature than in mature ascocarps would favor this view. They are found in many ascocarps of other lichen genera, but seldom persist. Doubtless these non-persisting thecial algae at least are foreign organisms which, having gained access to the young ascocarps, endure for a time under more or less unfavorable conditions.

DEVELOPMENT OF THE ASCOCARP. The origin and development seem to be very similar to that in the Ascomycetes in general. The first thing to be observed in the development of an ascocarp is a mass of closely interwoven hyphae below the algal zone, in the medullary area—this, of course, in those lichens in which there is a distinct differentiation into layers. In species of Collema and some related types, this differentiation is wanting, but the development here also begins within the thalloid body. Even in the crustose thalli which show very little differentiation, the first evidence of the ascocarp appears as more closely interwoven hyphae than those of the surrounding thallus.

This mass of hyphae constitutes the beginning of the hypothecium, and the structure increases rapidly in size, spreading out laterally and also increasing in thickness. From the hyphae of this young hypothecium arise vertical hyphae, which soon become differentiated into paraphyses and asci, appearing first over the central portions of the hyphal mass and extending laterally in all directions as the hypothecium spreads out by lateral growth. The paraphyses and the asci are very similar in their early development, but the hyphae which produce the asci very soon begin to enlarge so that they may be distinguished from those producing the paraphyses while still very small. Also these ascus-producing hyphae always remain non-septate and are much richer in protoplasm than the others. Some observers have thought that the asci and paraphyses arise from different systems of hyphae, and have called the supposed ascus-producing elements ascogenous hyphae, regarding them as arising from the ascogonia, but Sturgis arrived at the conclusion that both asci and paraphyses arise from the same system of hyphae. As the development proceeds, the hypothecium is produced into the exciple or the perithecial wall, as the case may be.

Beginning its development within the thallus, the ascocarp may remain immersed or it may become more or less superficial, being supported in ways already described. As the ascocarp pushes upward the surrounding thallus may or may not grow up about it to form the thalloid exciple, and now, if at all, is formed the epithecium.

REPRODUCTION

SOREDIA. Among the means of reproduction in lichens soredia play an important part. These masses of hyphae and algae may in proper environment produce a lichen thallus. They occur on many foliose and fruticose lichens and on some crustose species. A whole soredium or a portion of one is easily carried by the wind, and resting on a favorable substratum may develop into a lichen thallus having the same structure and bearing the same kind of ascocarps, soredia, spermagonia, etc., as that on which the soredium developed.

There is no differentiation into layers in the soredium, nor is dorsiventrality established until after it begins to grow on the substratum. As growth begins, the hyphal rhizoids penetrate the substratum to secure nourishment and to anchor the minute mass of tissue. As growth proceeds, the hyphae usually become differentiated into cortex and medulla, and the algae come to occupy their proper place in the thallus.

Soredia may develop on the thallus on which they are produced into isidioid or coralloid branchlets. These are frequently found on the thalli of some of the foliose forms. Doubtless the reproduction by soredia is the most important method in many lichens. Indeed, a considerable number of the foliose lichens and a few fruticose and crustose ones seldom produce apothecia and spores.

FRAGMENTATION. Another method of vegetative reproduction among lichens is by fragments of thalli becoming detached and blowing away and growing upon a suitable substratum. It does not matter how small the fragment provided it contains both the algae and the hyphae. There may or may not be all the layers of the thallus represented in the fragment. Sometimes the fragment is an isidioid or coralloid branchlet and in other instances it is a large and conspicuous portion of the thallus. The latter condition is well illustrated in *Usnea longissima,* long masses of which are often seen in the northern states hanging over branches, without any attachment whatever. In foliose and crustose lichens also the fragments may be large, and even whole thalli may be torn loose by the wind and transported to a new substratum and there grow.

REJUVENESCENCE. In a considerable number of lichens the older portions of the thallus die while the younger portions continue to grow. This condition is quite common among species of Cladonia, where the basal portions of the podetia die and the branching above continues. The branches thus become separated and a number of individuals arise from one. Usually such an assemblage forms a dense cluster, but the central and more raised portion of the cluster frequently dies or is blown away, leaving a continuous or more or less broken ring of plants.

In foliose and crustose lichens the central portion of the thallus often dies and the outer portions form a "fairy ring." The ring often becomes discontinuous, and thus a number of individuals arise from one. The dying at the center may be due to age or to the exhaustion of food substances from the substratum. *Lecanora muralis* and *Lecidea speirea* are crustose species in which this method of reproduction is often seen.

Spores. The spores of lichens have repeatedly been proved to be capable of germination in culture and of producing the usual thalli of their species, both when sown with the algae and when sown without them in favorable nutrient media. But the question still remains whether lichens are often produced from spores in nature. Evidently, except in the instances of germination in certain culture media, the spores of lichens must happen to come into contact with the alga of the same species as the one that forms the algal host in the species of lichen by which the spore was produced. And, in addition, the conditions in the substratum, and otherwise, must be sufficiently favorable for germination and the production of a new lichen individual. Though it has been proved that the fungus can exist for some time without the alga, it may be doubted whether the above combination is likely to come about often enough so that, among lichens, spores may be regarded as important agents in reproduction. The chances of reproduction by spores were plainly decreased greatly when the relationship with the alga was taken on, and the result has in all probability been a considerable physiological degeneration of the spores in the course of phylogenetic development.

Sexual Reproduction. The sexual processes have been studied in many of the fungi most closely related to lichens, and discoveries indicate that sexuality is common among them and in the ascomycetous lichens as well. In species of Collema, Stahl and others have found that the ascocarp is preceded by an archicarp and a trichogyne, which are supposed to be reproductive organs. The research of Baur, Darbishire, Lindau, and Vainio has proved the existence of similar organ in lichens of several genera, and although there is yet much need of research regarding nuclear behavior, the general presence of sexual organs in some of the lichens can scarcely be questioned longer.

The spermagonia have been supposed to constitute the male reproductive organs, and Stahl thinks that he has established beyond reasonable doubt that fertilization actually takes place, the spermatia from the spermagonia becoming attached to the apex of the trichogyne, where a transfer of protoplasm occurs. Strangely enough, Möller, experimenting on lichens not closely related to Collema has produced, from the spermatia, thalli in all respects similar to those which he obtained from the spores. This would seem to indicate that the spermatia, if they are sexual cells, have become so degenerate in certain lichens as to lose their sexual function, becoming capable at the same time of reproducing vegetatively. It seems necessary to add that some botanists regard the spermagonia as bodies belonging to fungi parasitic on the lichen thallus. Some reject the view that these are sexual organs and regard them as similar to pycnidia in related fungi.

HABITAT AND DISTRIBUTION

Lichens on trees usually grow on the trunks and lower branches, and much more commonly on the former. Some especially foliose and fruticose species are more common on old trees with rough bark. Crustose species are more commonly found on trunks or branches with smooth bark. Definite statements regarding these points would be desirable, but they are not usually available.

It would be helpful if definite statements could be made about the kinds of rocky substrata. However, some lichens grow on several different kinds of rocks, and collectors often do not state the kind of rock on which a lichen is found.

It would also be helpful if more could be given about the habitat, but statements are usually fragmentary, and the facts desired could be obtained only by extensive studies in many localities.

Lichens are not commonly confined to a particular species of tree, and the statements regarding their occurrence on certain trees may indicate that there has been little observation rather than that the lichen in question is not found on other trees.

For many crustose lichens a very limited distribution is given. It is highly probable that careful and critical collecting in many regions would greatly extend the known range of what now appear to be rather rare forms.

GLOSSARY

ACICULAR. Slender or needle-shaped, as the spores in species of Bacidia.

ADNATE. As applied to the ascocarp, attached to the thallus or substratum by the whole lower side.

ALGOID. Alga-like, applied to the exciple in species of the Collemaceae, consisting of hyphae and algae.

AMPHITHECIUM. A layer of tissue continuing upward from the hypothecium in some angiocarpic lichens and nearly surrounding the hymenium.

ANGIOCARPIC. Having the hymenium inclosed by a perithecial wall, by an amphithecium, or by both structures.

APOTHECIUM. An open or disk-shaped ascocarp.

AREOLE. A small area of a lichen thallus, separated from other similar areas by minute chinks.

ASCOCARP. The spore-bearing organ, consisting of the hymenium, the epithecium, the hypothecium, and the exciple or exciples.

ASCOGENOUS. Ascus-producing.

ASCUS. A specialized hyphal cell in which the spores are produced.

BIATOROID. Resembling the species of Lecidea in the section Biatora; used specially of apothecial structure.

CEPHALODIUM. A small, regular or irregular outgrowth appearing on the surface of a few lichen thalli, containing algal cells and hyphae, usually inclosed finally in plectenchymatous cortex.

CILIUM. A slender filament, composed of a bundle of hyphae, occurring on the upper surface or at the margin of the thallus.

CORALLOID. Coral-like; as applied to the outgrowths on the thalli in foliose and fruticose forms.

CORTEX. Plectenchyma forming the upper and lower protective layers in many lichen thalli.

CRUSTOSE. As applied to some lichen thalli, crustlike, or closely attached to the substratum and usually without distinct cortex.

CYPHELLA. A minute depression in the undersurface of certain lichen thalli.

DERMIS. A distinctly marked layer above the upper cortex, consisting of flattened cells.

DIFFORM. Irregular in form, as in certain apothecia.

DIMIDIATE. Applied to the perithecial wall when the outer wall covers only the upper portion.

ECTOTROPHIC. Lying on the surface of the thallus.

ELLIPSOID. In the form of an ellipse, or oblong with round ends.

ENDOTROPHIC. Within the thallus.

EPILITHIC. Upon rocks.

EPIPHLOEDAL. Upon bark.

EPITHECIUM. A structureless thalloid remnant lying upon the hymenium.

EXCIPLE. A layer surrounding the hymenium laterally and sometimes developed into a perithecial wall.

EXOSPORIUM. The outer coat of the spore wall.

FARINOSE. Covered with a mealiness.

FLEXUOUS. Bent alternately in and out and thus irregular in outline; used in describing the exciples of certain apothecia.

FOLIOSE. Flat and more or less leaflike; applied to thalli.

FRUTICOSE. Shrublike in form; applied to thalli.

GELATINIZED. Transformed into a jellylike mass.

GRANULOSE. Composed of small or minute granules; applied to certain thalli.

GYMNOCARPIC. Having an open disk, the exciple not being produced so as to cover the disk.

HAUSTORIUM. An expanded or a branched area of a hypha, entering or closely applied to an algal cell from which it secures nourishment.

HYALINE. Colorless or transparent.

HYMENIUM. The portion of the ascocarp composed of the asci and the paraphyses.

HYPHA. One of the septate, cylindrical, and branched filaments of the fungus.

HYPHAL RHIZOID. A hypha which penetrates the substratum and performs the function of a rhizoid.

HYPOLITHIC. Below the surface of rocks.

HYPOPHLOEODAL. Below the surface of bark.

HYPOTHALLUS. The first growth of the hyphae, before any differentiation has taken place, often persisting as a colored layer below or surrounding a few lichen thalli.

HYPOTHECIUM. The dense hyphal or plectenchymatous tissue below the hymenium.

IMMERSED. Sunken into the thallus or the substratum.

ISIDIOID. See coralloid.

LECIDEOID. Resembling the species of Lecidea of the section Eulecidea; used with special reference to the apothecial structure.

LEPROSE. Scurfy; said of certain thalli.

MAZAEDIUM. Powdery mass of spores as in Caliciales.

MEDULLA. The network of hyphae in the interior of well-developed thalli.

MURIFORM. Resembling bricks in a wall; applied to spores which are both transversely and longitudinally septate.

NUTANT. Nodding.

OSTIOLE. The aperture at the summit of a perithecium, through which the spores escape.

PARAPHYSIS. One of the specialized, simple, or more commonly branched hyphae, occurring in the hymenium.

PERITHECIAL WALL. Exciple of the angiocarpic lichens, inclosing the hymenium, except for the apical ostiole.

PERITHECIUM. A closed ascocarp, opening only at the apex.

PHYLLOCLADIUM. A small, specialized, and highly assimilative branch of a fruticose thallus.

PILEATE. Referring to the pileus-like thallus of certain Hymenolichenes.

PLECTENCHYMA. Pseudoparenchyma of fungi.

PLECTENCHYMATOUS. Referring to structures composed of plectenchyma.

PODETIUM. An alga-bearing branched or unbranched stalk, rising from the primary or horizontal thallus in certain lichens and bearing the ascocarp.

POLAR. As applied to cells of 1-septate spores which are widely separated, situated at the opposite ends of the spore.

PROLIFERATION. Used in describing species of Cladonia with reference to the production of podetia from the side or top of other podetia.

PROPER EXCIPLE. The exciple which is an upward continuation of the hypothecium and devoid of algal cells.

PRUINOSE. Covered with a bloom or powdery secretion.

PSEUDOCORTEX. A cortex devoid of cellular structure and commonly showing well-defined or more or less gelatinized hyphae.

PUSTULE. A pimple-like or blister-like elevation.

PYRENOCARPIC. See angiocarpic.

RHIZOID. A slender filament, consisting of a bundle of hyphae, extending downward from the lower side of the thallus and usually penetrating the substratum.

RIMOSE. Having chinks and cracks.

SCYPHIFORM. Cuplike, or forming a cup; said of some podetia.

SESSILE. As applied to an ascocarp, meaning attached to the substratum by the central portion of the lower side.

SOREDIUM. A tangled mass of algal cells and hyphae which is able to grow into a new thallus under favorable circumstances of environment.

SPERMAGONIUM. A minute cavity more or less imbedded in the thallus and containing the spermatia borne on sterigmata.

SPERMATIUM. One of the sporelike bodies contained in the spermagonia and supposed by some lichenologists to be male reproductive bodies.

SQUAMULE. A small scale.

SQUAMULOSE. Composed of or bearing squamules.

STIPE. A stalk of an ascocarp, devoid of algal cells.

THALLOID. Thallus-like, having the structure of the thallus.

THALLUS. The vegetative portion of any lichen, on which are borne the reproductive areas or organs.

THECIAL. Occurring within the thecium (hymenium).

TRICHOMATIC. Pertaining to or like a hair.

TURBINATE. Top-shaped.

UMBILICUS. The single strong attaching organ of some lichen thalli, composed of a large number of closely united hyphae.

UNISERIATE. Placed in a single row; applied to spore arrangement in the ascus.

URCEOLATE. Pitcher-shaped, or cup-shaped.

VERRUCA. A wartlike elevation of a lichen thallus.

VERRUCOSE. Covered with verrucae.

OUTLINE OF CLASSIFICATION

CLASS ASCOLICHENES
SUBCLASS PYRENOCARPEAE
ORDER PYRENULALES
Family 1. Verrucariaceae

1. Verrucaria	4. Thelidiella	7. Thrombium
2. Trimmatothele	5. Polyblastia	8. Microglaena
3. Thelidium	6. Staurothele	

Family 2. Dermatocarpaceae

9. Normandina	11. Heterocarpon	12. Endocarpon
10. Dermatocarpon		

Family 3. Pyrenothamniaceae

13. Pyrenothamnia

Family 4. Pyrenulaceae

14. Microthelia	18. Pseudopyrenula	22. Thelopsis
15. Arthopyrenia	19. Porina	23. Pyrenula
16. Leptorhaphis	20. Clathroporina	24. Pyrenulella
17. Polyblastiopsis	21. Belonia	25. Anthracothecium

Family 5. Trypetheliaceae

26. Melanotheca	27. Trypethelium	28. Laurera

Family 6. Astrotheliaceae

29. Pyrenastrum	30. Parmentaria	

Family 7. Strigulaceae

31. Strigula

Family 8. Pyrenidiaceae

32. Hassea

Family 9. Pyrenotrichaceae

33. Pyrenothrix

Family 10. Mycoporaceae

34. Mycoporellum	35. Mycoporum

SUBCLASS GYMNOCARPEAE
ORDER CALICIALES
Family 11. Caliciaceae

36. Chaenotheca	39. Caliciella	42. Sphinctrina
37. Calicium	40. Coniocybe	
38. Mycocalicium	41. Stenocybe	

Family 12. Cypheliaceae

43. Cyphelium	44. Cypheliopsis	45. Pyrgillus

Family 13. Sphaerophoraceae

46. Sphaerophorus

23

ORDER HYSTERIALES

Family 14. Arthoniaceae

47. Arthonia   48. Arthothelium

Family 15. Graphidaceae

49. Xylographa   52. Melaspilea   55. Graphina
50. Opegrapha   53. Graphis   56. Phaeographina
51. Opegraphoidea   54. Phaeographis   57. Helminthocarpon

Family 16. Chiodectonaceae

58. Glyphis   60. Medusulina   62. Sclerophyton
59. Sarcographa   61. Chiodecton   63. Enterostigma

Family 17. Dirinaceae
64. Dirina

Family 18. Roccellaceae

65. Dendrographa   66. Roccella   67. Schizopelte

ORDER LECANORALES

Family 19. Lecanactidaceae

68. Lecanactis   69. Schismatomma   70. Platygraphopsis

Family 20. Thelotremaceae

71. Ocellularia   73. Thelotrema   75. Gyrostomum
72. Phaeotrema   74. Leptotrema

Family 21. Diploschistaceae

76. Conotrema   77. Urceolaria

Family 22. Ectolechiaceae
78. Lopadiopsis

Family 23. Gyalectaceae

79. Microphiale   81. Secoliga   83. Pachyphiale
80. Gyalecta   82. Ramonia

Family 24. Coenogoniaceae

84. Coenogonium   85. Racodium

Family 25. Ephebaceae

86. Thermutis   89. Ephebe   92. Porocyphus
87. Zahlbrucknerella   90. Leptogidium
88. Spilonema   91. Polychidium

Family 26. Pyrenopsidaceae

93. Pyrenopsis   95. Psorotichia   97. Thyrea
94. Synalissa   96. Forssellia   98. Peccania

Family 27. Lichinaceae

99. Pterygium   100. Lichina

Family 28. Collemaceae

101. Lempholemma   103. Collema   105. Leptogium
102. Synechoblastus   104. Collemodes

Family 29. Heppiaceae

106. Heppia   107. Solorinaria

Family 30. Pannariaceae

108. Hydrothyria   111. Parmeliella   114. Coccocarpia
109. Massalongia   112. Pannaria
110. Placynthium   113. Psoroma

Family 31. Stictaceae
115. Sticta

Family 32. Peltigeraceae

116. Solorina	117. Nephroma	118. Peltigera

Family 33. Lecideaceae

119. Lecidea	123. Catillaria	127. Toninia
120. Psora	124. Megalospora	128. Lopadium
121. Nesolechia	125. Bilimbia	129. Rhizocarpon
122. Mycoblastus	126. Bacidia	

Family 34. Cladoniaceae

130. Baeomyces	132. Cladonia	133. Stereocaulon
131. Pilophorus		

Family 35. Gyrophoraceae

134. Gyrophora	135. Umbilicaria	136. Dermatiscum

Family 36. Acarosporaceae

137. Thelocarpon	139. Maronea	140. Acarospora
138. Biatorella		

Family 37. Pertusariaceae
141. Pertusaria

Family 38. Lecanoraceae

142. Lecanora	146. Solenopsora	150. Phlyctidia
143. Ochrolechia	147. Haematomma	151. Candelariella
144. Icmadophila	148. Phlyctis	
145. Lecania	149. Phlyctella	

Family 39. Parmeliaceae

152. Candelaria	154. Parmelia	155. Cetraria
153. Parmeliopsis		

Family 40. Usneaceae

156. Evernia	159. Ramalina	161. Thamnolia
157. Dufourea	160. Usnea	162. Siphula
158. Alectoria		

Family 41. Caloplacaceae

163. Protoblastenia	165. Bombyliospora	166. Caloplaca
164. Blastenia		

Family 42. Teloschistaceae
167. Teloschistes

Family 43. Buelliaceae

168. Buellia	170. Leciographa	172. Rinodina
169. Buelliella	171. Buelliopsis	

Family 44. Physciaceae

173. Pyxine	174. Physcia	175. Anaptychia

CLASS HYMENOLICHENES

Family 45. Thelephoraceae

176. Cora	177. Dictyonema

CLASS LICHENES IMPERFECTI

Family 46. Leprariaceae
178. Amphiloma

KEY TO ORDERS AND FAMILIES

A. Thallus of more or less definite form, usually bearing fruits
   B. Spores borne in asci . . . . ASCOLICHENES
   B. Spores borne on basidia . . . . HYMENOLICHENES
                                       (45. THELEPHORACEAE)
A. Thallus of entangled hyphae, without fruits . . LICHENES IMPERFECTI
                                       (46. LEPRARIACEAE)

ASCOLICHENES

A. Hymenium produced in a closed structure opening
   by a minute pore, for the escape of spores . . . . PYRENULALES
A. Hymenium produced in an open disklike structure
   B. Asci disintegrating and the spores forming a mazaedium . . . CALICIALES
   B. Asci persistent, no mazaedium formed
      C. Thallus rudimentary to rarely well developed;
         apothecia irregular, linear, or oblong . . . . HYSTERIALES
      C. Thallus commonly well developed; apothecia
        more or less round or cuplike . . . . LECANORALES

PYRENULALES

A. Perithecia opening through irregular pores, crowded
   together, divided by more or less complete walls . . . . . 10. MYCOPORACEAE
A. Perithecia opening through round pores, separate
   B. On leaves . . . . 7. STRIGULACEAE
   B. On rocks, trees, old wood, and soil
      C. With Nostoc as the algal host . . . . 8. PYRENIDIACEAE
      C. With Scytonema as the algal host . . . . 9. PYRENOTRICHACEAE
      C. With Pleurococcus as the algal host (or Palmella)
         D. Thallus crustose . . . . 1. VERRUCARIACEAE
         D. Thallus foliose or squamulose . . . . 2. DERMATOCARPACEAE
         D. Thallus shrubby or fruticose . . . . 3. PYRENOTHAMNIACEAE
      C. With Trentepohlia as the algal host
         D. Perithecia not seated in a stroma . . . . 4. PYRENULACEAE
         D. Perithecia seated in a stroma
            E. Perithecia upright, separate, each with single mouth 5. TRYPETHELIACEAE
            E. Perithecia crooked or bent, more or less united,
               mouths joined into a central canal . . . . . 6. ASTROTHELIACEAE

CALICIALES

A. Thallus crustose, without cortex
   B. Apothecia borne on stipes . . . . 11. CALICIACEAE
   B. Apothecia not borne on stipes . . . . 12. CYPHELIACEAE
A. Thallus foliose or bushy, with cortex . . . . 13. SPHAEROPHORACEAE

HYSTERIALES

A. Apothecia without the exciple . . . . 14. ARTHONIACEAE
A. Apothecia with the exciple
   B. Thallus crustose
      C. Thallus rudimentary, often inconspicuous
         D. Apothecia not seated in a stroma . . . . 15. GRAPHIDACEAE
         D. Apothecia seated in a stroma . . . . 16. CHIODECTONACEAE
      C. Thallus well developed . . . . 17. DIRINACEAE
   B. Thallus fruticose . . . . 18. ROCCELLACEAE

LECANORALES

A. Host usually a species of Myxophyceae
  B. Thallus taking its form from that of the algal host
    C. Thallus appearing to be squamulose to foliose,
      algal host Nostoc . . . . 28. COLLEMACEAE
    C. Thallus appearing to be crustose or more commonly dwarf-
      like fruticose, algal host Scytonema or Stigenoma . . . . 25. EPHEBACEAE
  B. Thallus rarely taking its form from that of the algal host
    C. Thallus large, plainly foliose
      D. Apothecia without exciple, sometimes borne on the
        under surface of the thallus . . . . 32. PELTIGERACEAE
      D. Apothecia with exciple, sessile; thallus commonly with
        cyphellae below . . . . 31. STICTACEAE
    C. Thallus small, crustose to somewhat foliose or dwarflike
      fruticose
      D. Thallus crustose to scaly or more or less fruticose
        E. Thallus rarely differentiated into layers
          F. Algal host usually Gloeocapsa or Xanthocapsa 26. PYRENOPSIDACEAE
          F. Algal host usually Rivularia . . . . 27. LICHINACEAE
        E. Thallus differentiated into more or less definite layers 29. HEPPIACEAE
      D. Thallus somewhat foliose, commonly forming an irregu-
        lar granulose crust . . . . 30. PANNARIACEAE
A. Host a species of Chlorophyceae
  B. Apothecia without exciple or with rudimentary one, more
    or less immersed in the thallus
    C. Thallus foliose, rather large; apothecia commonly large . 32. PELTIGERACEAE
    C. Thallus crustose; apothecia small
      D. Spores non-septate to several-septate . . . . . 19. LECANACTIDACEAE
      D. Spores commonly transversely and longitudinally
        septate . . . . 22. ECTOLECHIACEAE
  B. Apothecia with well-developed exciple
    C. Apothecia with both thalloid and proper exciples, the
      thalloid one sometimes disappearing
      D. Apothecia more or less deeply immersed in the sub-
        stratum . . . . 20. THELOTREMACEAE
      D. Apothecia somewhat immersed to more commonly
        superficial
        E. Proper exciple dark . . . . 21. DIPLOSCHISTACEAE
        E. Proper exciple hyaline . . . . 23. GYALECTACEAE
    C. Apothecia with either proper or thalloid exciple, but very
      rarely with both
      D. Apothecia with proper exciple
        E. Thallus taking its form from that of the algal host 24. COENOGONIACEAE
        E. Thallus not taking its form from that of the algal
          host
          F. Thallus foliose or 2-fold
            G. Thallus plainly foliose . . . . 35. GYROPHORACEAE
            G. Thallus 2-fold . . . . 34. CLADONIACEAE
          F. Thallus crustose to squamulose
            G. Spores brown . . . . 43. BUELLIACEAE
            G. Spores hyaline
               H. Apothecia usually yellowish; spores non-
                septate or septate with lenticular cells . 41. CALOPLACACEAE
               H. Apothecia rarely yellowish; spores non-
                septate to septate with rectangular or
                cubical cells . . . . 33. LECIDEACEAE
      D. Apothecia with thalloid exciple
        E. Thallus foliose or fruticose
          F. Thallus plainly foliose or rarely somewhat fruticose
            G. Thallus small to middle-sized, foliose to
              somewhat fruticose
               H. Thallus more or less yellow in color;
                spores hyaline . . . . 42. TELOSCHISTACEAE

H. Thallus greenish gray to ashy or darker;
    spores brown . . . . 44. PHYSCIACEAE
  G. Thallus small to middle-sized or larger, plainly
    foliose
    H. Spores non-septate . . . . 39. PARMELIACEAE
    H. Spores septate . . . . 31. STICTACEAE
  F. Thallus plainly fruticose . . . . 40. USNEACEAE
E. Thallus crustose to squamulose
  F. Spores minute, many in each ascus . . . . 36. ACAROSPORACEAE
  F. Spores usually 1–8 in each ascus, rarely more
    G. Spores usually septate, with lenticular cells
      H. Spores hyaline . . . . 41. CALOPLACACEAE
      H. Spores brown . . . . 43. BUELLIACEAE
    G. Spores non-septate to septate with cubical or
    rectangular cells
      H. Spores large, with thick wall . . . . 37. PERTUSARIACEAE
      H. Spores small to middle-sized or large, with
      thin wall . . . . 38. LECANORACEAE

SYSTEMATIC TREATMENT OF FAMILIES, GENERA, AND SPECIES

1. VERRUCARIACEAE

Thallus crustose, partly within the substratum, or rarely imbedded in the lichen host, devoid of differentiation into layers; perithecia more or less immersed, single, upright, the ostiole terminal; paraphyses very soon gelatinizing and becoming indistinct or rarely persistent and distinct.
The algal hosts are Protococcus and Pleurococcus.

A. Paraphyses persistent, but indistinct
  B. Spores non-septate . . . . 7. THROMBIUM
  B. Spores transversely and longitudinally septate . . . . 8. MICROGLAENA
A. Paraphyses becoming slimy, disappearing or wanting
  B. Spores non-septate
    C. Spores 1–8 in each ascus . . . . 1. VERRUCARIA
    C. Spores many in each ascus . . . . 2. TRIMMATOTHELE
  B. Spores septate
    C. Spores transversely 1–3-septate
      D. Thallus imbedded in that of the host; spores 1-septate . 4. THELIDIELLA
      D. Thallus superficial, crustose; spores 1–3-septate . . . . 3. THELIDIUM
    C. Spores transversely and longitudinally septate
      D. Apothecia more or less immersed; ostiole rarely visible . 5. POLYBLASTIA
      D. Apothecia immersed in raised areas; ostiole protruding . 6. STAUROTHELE

1. **Verrucaria** Scop., Intr. Hist. Nat. 61. 1777.

Thallus crustose, partly or wholly within the substratum, the superficial portion warty or areolate, thin to thick, seated upon a well-developed hypothallus, the imbedded portion usually indicated at the surface by a discoloration of the substratum, devoid of differentiation into layers; perithecia minute to small, more or less immersed, 1–several in each thalloid wart or areole, or later protruding, the wall dimidiate or complete, the superficial portion flat to more commonly hemispherical or convex, the ostiole minute, commonly inconspicuous; hypothecium hyaline to brown; hymenium hyaline or brownish above; paraphyses soon gelatinized and indistinct; asci clavate; spores 8, hyaline to rarely brownish, non-septate.
The algal host is Pleurococcus.

A. Thallus on rocks along seacoast or inland streams
  B. Spores rarely more than 10 μ in length
    C. Thallus more or less uniform
      D. Thallus smooth to slightly rough, areolate . . . . . 2. V. ceuthocarpa
      D. Thallus marked by many minute spots or lines . . . . . 1. V. striatula
    C. Thallus interspersed with very thin areas . . . . . . 3. V. subsuperficialis
  B. Spores rarely less than 10 μ in length
    C. Perithecia rarely more than 0.15 mm. across
      D. Spores 7–15 × 4–8 μ . . . . 5. V. mucosa
      D. Spores 16–22 × 6–10 μ . . . . 8. V. papillosa
    C. Perithecia rarely less than 0.15 mm. across
      D. Spores rarely more than 20 μ in length
        E. Perithecia rarely more than 0.3 mm. across
          F. Spores 14–20 × 5–8 μ . . . . 6. V. aethiobola

F. Spores 18–22 × 8–9 µ . . . . 7. V. silicicola
E. Perithecia 0.3–0.6 mm. across . . . . 4. V. maura
D. Spores rarely less than 20 µ in length
  E. Thallus smooth to sometimes chinky, olive-green to
    brownish . . . . 9. V. hydrela
  E. Thallus chinky, olive to grayish brown . . . . . 10. V. margacea
A. Thallus on rocks in dry places
  B. Spores rarely more than 15 µ in length
    C. Spores hyaline
      D. Perithecia rarely more than 0.15 mm. across . . . . . 15. V. fuscella
      D. Perithecia rarely less than 0.15 mm. across
        E. Thallus grayish to ashy brown . . . . 12. V. pinguicula
        E. Thallus grayish brown to dull black . . . . 17. V. nigrescentoidea
    C. Spores becoming dark brown . . . . 21. V. calciseda fuscospora
  B. Spores rarely less than 15 µ in length
    C. Thallus smooth to chinky or powdery
      D. Thallus grayish white to rose-red or pink
        E. Thallus grayish white; perithecia 0.1–0.2 mm. across . 21. V. calciseda
        E. Thallus rose-red to pink; perithecia 0.2–0.4 mm. across 23. V. marmorea
      D. Thallus gray to brownish- or greenish-black
        E. Thallus smooth to minutely chinky . . . . . . 20. V. dacryodes
        E. Thallus smooth to becoming scurfy and slightly
          granulose or powdery . . . . 22. V. rupestris
    C. Thallus more or less chinky or areolate
      D. Spores rarely more than 20 µ in length
        E. Thallus areolate to granulose, reddish brown . . . 18. V. aquilella
        E. Thallus chinky, areolate, ashy to greenish or sordid
          F. Thallus indistinctly chinky-areolate, sordid . . . 13. V. sordida
          F. Thallus areolate, areoles warty, ashy to dusky green . 14. V. virens
      D. Spores rarely less than 20 µ in length
        E. Thallus brownish or greenish to black
          F. Spores 15–26 × 7–11 µ . . . . 16. V. nigrescens
          F. Spores 21–32 × 10–15 µ . . . . 19. V. viridula
        E. Thallus grayish to whitish . . . . 11. V. submuralis

1. **Verrucaria striatula** Wahl., in Ach., Meth. Lich. Suppl. 21. 1803.
Superficial thallus somewhat thickened, greenish black, marked by many minute spots or lines; perithecia minute to small, 0.1–0.3 mm. across, the superficial portion subhemispherical, with a depressed ostiole, shining black; spores ellipsoid, 8–10 × 4–5 µ.
On stones near tidewater, Maine and Massachusetts.

2. **Verrucaria ceuthocarpa** Wahl., in Ach., Meth. Lich. Suppl. 22. 1803.
Thallus thin to somewhat thick, smooth to slightly rough, areolate, greenish gray to grayish black; perithecia minute to small, 0.2–0.3 mm. across, immersed, the superficial portion convex, black, with a minute papillate ostiole; spores ellipsoid to somewhat spherical, 6–10 × 4–8 µ.
On rocks, Maine and Massachusetts. Zahlbruckner gives no American distribution.

3. **Verrucaria subsuperficialis** Fink; Hedrick, Mycologia 25:304. 1933.
Thallus thin to somewhat thick, smooth or slightly rough, olivaceous, occurring fully developed with perithecia in small areas, these areas interspersed in about equally extensive very thin areas (hypothallus) showing the lichen hyphae and the algal host cells, both the thick and thin areas remaining firm when wet; perithecia minute, 0.17–0.2 mm. across, olivaceous black, spheroidal or subconical above and flattened below, scattered to closely placed, entirely above the substratum and readily removed with the thallus, the basal third immersed in the latter, complete with perithecial wall thin below, or sometimes dimidiate and centrally open below; spores ovoid-oblong, 7–9 × 4–5 µ.
On a littoral quartz pebble, Long Island, New York.

4. **Verrucaria maura** Wahl., in Ach., Meth. Lich. Suppl. 19. 1803.

V. maura var. *aractina* (Wahl.) Torss.

Superficial thallus thin or somewhat thickened, smooth, minutely chinky-areolate to rough-verrucose, grayish- or brownish-black to black; perithecia small to middle-sized, 0.3–0.6 mm. across, immersed, except the black apex, in sub-hemispherical to hemispherico-conoid raised areas; spores oblong to ellipsoid, 9–17 × 5–9 μ.

On rocks along the seashore, Maine, Massachusetts, Rhode Island, Washington, and California.

5. **Verrucaria mucosa** Wahl., in Ach., Meth. Lich. Suppl. 23. 1803.

V. ceuthocarpa var. *mucosa* (Wahl.) Tuck.

Superficial thallus thin or sometimes rather thick, smooth, sometimes chinky, olive-green to greenish black or lead-colored; perithecia minute, 0.08–0.15 mm. across, appearing as black spots in the thallus, sometimes protruding; spores ellipsoid, 7–15 × 4–8 μ.

On wet or submerged rocks, Maine, Massachusetts, and New York, usually along the seashore.

6. **Verrucaria aethiobola** Wahl., in Ach., Meth. Lich. Suppl. 17. 1803.

Superficial thallus thin, in small areas or rather widespread, sometimes some-what chinky, olive-green to tan or ashy; perithecia minute to small, 0.1–0.4 mm. across, at first largely immersed in raised areas, later more or less exposed, the superficial portion subhemispherical, somewhat shining, black; spores oblong to ellipsoid or rarely subovoid, 14–20 × 5–8 μ.

On argillaceous rocks, Massachusetts, Illinois, and southern California.

7. **Verrucaria silicicola** Fink*; Hedrick, Mycologia 25:305. 1933.

Thallus thin to moderately thick, smooth to rough, becoming chinky, sometimes appearing minutely granulose, dark greenish gray to black; perithecia minute to small, 0.15–0.4 mm. across, scattered or more or less clustered, immersed to partly superficial, the wall dimidiate and centrally open below, the superficial portion subhemispherical or subconical, dull black, the ostiole minute, often scarcely visible; spores oblong-ellipsoid, 18–22 × 8–9 μ, irregularly arranged.

On a littoral quartz pebble, Long Island, New York.

8. **Verrucaria papillosa** Ach., Lich. Univ. 286. 1810.

V. margacea var. *papillosa* (Ach.) Leight.

Superficial thallus thin, widespread, becoming chinky and somewhat wrinkled, greenish brown or darker; perithecia minute, 0.1–0.16 mm. across, immersed in warts, the upper portion protruding, black; spores ovoid-ellipsoid, 16–22 × 6–10 μ.

On argillaceous rocks, southern California.

9. **Verrucaria hydrela** Ach., Syn. Meth. Lich. 94. 1814.

V. margacea var. *hydrela* Torss.

Superficial thallus thin or becoming thicker, usually widespread, smooth, some-times chinky, olive-green to brownish; perithecia small to middle-sized, 0.2–0.5 mm. across, immersed in the thallus except the dark apex; spores ellipsoid, 19–34 × 9–17 μ.

On rocks, Washington.

10. **Verrucaria margacea** Wahl., Fl. Lapp. 465. 1812.

Thelotrema margaceum Wahl., in Ach., Meth. Lich. Suppl. 30. 1803. *V. margacea* subsp. *terrestris* Nyl.

Superficial thallus rather thick or sometimes thinner or disappearing, chinky, usually widespread, olive- to grayish-brown; perithecia small to middle-sized, 0.3–0.5 mm. across, at first immersed in raised areas, the black apex later more or

---

* Misspelled *V. silicola* in earlier publication.

less exposed, the superficial portion subhemispherical, black; spores oblong to ellipsoid, 24–33 × 10–16 μ.
On often-submerged rocks, New Hampshire, Massachusetts, and California.

11. **Verrucaria submuralis** Nyl., Flora 58:14. 1875.
V. integrella Nyl. *V. rupestris* var. *submuralis* (Nyl.) Zahlbr.
Superficial thallus very thin, scurfy, indistinctly chinky-areolate, grayish to whitish; perithecia small, 0.2–0.3 mm. across, immersed in pits in the substratum, the black apex protruding beyond the thallus; spores oblong-ellipsoid to ovoid, 17–25 × 10–14 μ.
On rocks, Tennessee, Illinois (?), and California.

12. **Verrucaria pinguicula** Mass., Lotos 6:80. 1856.
Thallus very thin to thin, smooth to slightly rough, becoming areolate, grayish to ashy brown; perithecia minute, 0.15–0.25 mm. across, immersed 1 or more in an areole, the superficial portion subhemispherical, black; spores ellipsoid, 13–16 × 6–8 μ.
On limestone, New York. Zahlbruckner gives no American distribution, but Tuckerman gives it in Lich. Gen. 268. 1872.

13. **Verrucaria sordida** Fink, Proc. Ind. Acad. Sci. 273. 1918.
Superficial thallus thin, roughened, minutely and indistinctly chinky-areolate, sordid; perithecia minute to small, 0.15–0.25 mm. across, numerous, the superficial portion subconical, of the same color as the thallus or darker; spores oblong-ellipsoid, 16–22 × 9–12 μ.
On calcareous rocks, Montgomery County, Indiana.

14. **Verrucaria virens** Nyl., Bot. Notis. 180. 1853.
Superficial thallus thick, sometimes thinner, chinky to areolate, the areoles wart-like, ashy to dusky green; perithecia minute to small, 0.15–0.3 mm. across, at first largely immersed in the thallus, later protruding, the superficial portion convex, black; spores ovoid to oblong-ellipsoid, 15–21 × 7–9 μ.
On rocks, Vermont and Massachusetts.

15. **Verrucaria fuscella** (Turn.) Ach., Lich. Univ. 289. 1810.
Lichen fuscellus Turn., Trans. Linn. Soc. Lond. 7:90. pl. 8, f. 2. 1806.
Superficial thallus rather thick, in small patches or becoming more widespread, chinky to minutely areolate, ashy gray to olive-green or blackish; perithecia minute, 0.08–0.15 mm. across, usually completely immersed in the thallus, often more than 1 in an areole; spores ellipsoid, 9–14 × 4–7 μ.
On rocks, from Illinois and Wisconsin westward to California and southward to Alabama.

16. **Verrucaria nigrescens** Pers., Ann. Bot. Usteri 14:36. 1795.
V. elaeochroa Tuck.
Superficial thallus somewhat thickened, widespread, chinky or rarely becoming areolate, brownish to dull black; perithecia minute to small, 0.15–0.4 mm. across, the superficial portion subhemispherical, black; spores ellipsoid, 15–26 × 7–11 μ.
On rocks, widely distributed, northern United States and southward to Louisiana.

17. **Verrucaria nigrescentoidea** Fink; Hedrick, Mycologia 25:303. 1933.
Thallus very thin to thin, widespread, smooth to slightly rough, becoming areolate, grayish brown to dull black; perithecia minute to small, 0.1–0.3 mm. across, dimidiate, numerous, more or less immersed, the superficial portion subhemispherical, dull black; spores ellipsoid, 12–15 × 5–6 μ, irregularly arranged.
On rocks, Minnesota.

18. **Verrucaria aquilella** Nyl., Flora 59:237. 1876.
Superficial thallus thin, rather widespread, areolate to granulose, reddish brown; perithecia small, 0.2–0.4 mm. across, the superficial portion subhemispherical, black; spores long-oblong to ellipsoid, 12–19 × 3–5.8 μ.
On micaceous rocks, southern California.

19. **Verrucaria viridula** (Schrad.) Ach., Meth. Lich. Suppl. 16. 1803.
Endocarpum viridulum Schrad., Spic. Fl. Germ. 192. pl. 2, f. 4. 1794. *V. nigrescens* var. *viridula* Nyl.
Superficial thallus rather thick, chinky-areolate, dark olive-green to greenish brown; perithecia small, 0.2–0.45 mm. across, at first largely immersed in raised places, later becoming exposed, the superficial portion subconoid, black; spores ovoid-ellipsoid, 21–32 × 10–15 μ. (PLATE 1 a.)
On rocks, Vermont, Ohio, Illinois, Minnesota, and California.

20. **Verrucaria dacryodes** Nyl.; Hasse, Bull. South. Calif. Acad. 2:73. 1903.
Thallus thin, widespread, smooth, minutely chinky, greenish black to dark olive-green; perithecia minute to small, 0.2–0.3 mm. across, immersed except the black ostiole, the wall dimidiate; spores ovoid to ovoid-oblong, 15–20 × 6.5–11 μ.
On argillaceous rocks, southern California.

21. **Verrucaria calciseda** Lam. & DC., Fl. Fr. ed. 3. 2:317. 1805.
Superficial thallus thin, widespread, sometimes disappearing, powdery, grayish white; perithecia minute to small, 0.1–0.2 mm. across, partly immersed in pits in the substratum, the superficial portion commonly convex, brownish black to black; spores ovoid-ellipsoid, 20–24 × 8–11 μ.
On calcareous rocks, southern California.

f. **fuscospora** Herre, Proc. Wash. Acad. Sci. 12:42. 1910.
Superficial thallus very thin, whitish, and powdery, widespread or disappearing; perithecia small, 0.15–0.4 mm. across, numerous, immersed to slightly protruding, the superficial portion flat to subhemispherical, black; spores ovoid, hyaline to dark brown, 9–15 × 18–28 μ.
On limestone, Santa Cruz Peninsula, California.

22. **Verrucaria rupestris** Schrad., Spic. Fl. Germ. 1:109. 1794.
V. muralis Ach.
Superficial thallus thin, sometimes disappearing, smooth, chinky or becoming scurfy and slightly granulose or powdery, widespread, whitish to gray or brownish; perithecia minute to small, 0.15–0.35 mm. across, the superficial portion convex to hemispherical, black; spores oblong-ellipsoid, 16–30 × 6–12 μ.
On rocks, from New England and New York westward to California.

23. **Verrucaria marmorea** (Scop.) Arnold, Flora 68:73. 1885.
Lichen marmoreus Scop., Fl. Carn. 2:367. 1772. *V. rupestris* var. *purpurascens* (Hoffm.) Schaer. *V. purpurascens* Hoffm.
Superficial thallus thin, widespread, slightly powdery, purplish to rose-red or pink; perithecia small to middle-sized, 0.2–0.4 mm. across, immersed in pits in the substratum, the superficial portion flat or sometimes protruding slightly, black; spores oblong-ovoid, 16–23 × 7–12 μ.
On rocks, the Carolinas, Alabama, and Tennessee.

OTHER SPECIES REPORTED

Verrucaria caerulea (Ram.) Lam. & DC.—Eastern United States.
Verrucaria fusconigricans Nyl.—Texas.
Verrucaria glaucina subsp. canella A. L. Smith—California.
Verrucaria melas Herre—California.
Verrucaria perpusilla Russell—North America.
Verrucaria ruderella Nyl.—Tennessee.
Verrucaria Sprucei Bab.—North America.
Verrucaria Stanfordi Herre—California.
Verrucaria terebrata (Mudd.) Leight.—California.
Verrucaria umbrinula Nyl.—Illinois.

2. **Trimmatothele** Norm., in Blombg. et Forss. Enum. Plat.
Scand. 160. 1880.

Thallus crustose, partly or wholly without the substratum, the superficial portion warty or areolate, thin, the imbedded portion usually indicated at the surface by a discoloration of the substratum, devoid of differentiation into layers; perithecia minute to small, more or less immersed, the wall dimidiate, the superficial portion hemispherical to convex or conical, the ostiole minute, commonly inconspicuous; hypothecium hyaline to brown; paraphyses wanting; asci not plainly evident; spores many, very small, ovoid or ellipsoid.
The algal host is Pleurococcus.

1. **Trimmatothele Umbellulariae** Herre, Bryologist 15:82. 1912.
Superficial thallus very thin, widespread, dusky gray; perithecia minute to small, 0.1–0.3 mm. across, partly immersed, the superficial portion black, hemispherical to conical, the ostiole obscure; hypothecium hyaline; spores ovoid to short-ellipsoid, 2.5–3 $\times$ 2–2.5 μ.
On trees, near Berkeley, California.

3. **Thelidium** Mass., Framm. Lich. 15. 1855.

Thallus crustose, smooth to chinky, minutely granulose or areolate, seated upon a poorly developed hypothallus, devoid of differentiation into layers; apothecia minute to small or larger, more or less immersed, the wall dimidiate or rarely complete, the superficial portion depressed to subhemispherical, the ostiole rarely visible; hypothecium and hymenium hyaline; paraphyses soon becoming gelatinized and indistinct; asci broadly clavate; spores 8, hyaline, 1–3-septate.
The algal host is Pleurococcus.

A. Thallus minutely granulose to areolate; perithecia
  0.1–0.3 mm. across . . . . 2. T. microbolum
A. Thallus rough to wrinkled and chinky; perithecia
  0.4–0.8 mm. across . . . . 1. T. pyrenophorum

1. **Thelidium pyrenophorum** (Ach.) Mudd, Man. Brit. Lich. 294, 295. 1861.
Verrucaria pyrenophora Ach., Lich. Univ. 285. 1810.
Superficial thallus thin, widespread, rough, becoming wrinkled and chinky, whitish to grayish; perithecia middle-sized to large, 0.4–0.8 mm. across, the superficial portion depressed, subhemispherical-conoid, black, the wall dimidiate; spores 1–3-septate, oblong-ellipsoid, 22–41 $\times$ 9–16 μ.
On rocks, Vermont, New York, Florida, Tennessee, Illinois, and Iowa.

2. **Thelidium microbolum** (Tuck.) Hasse, Cont. U. S. Nat. Herb. 17:6. 1913.
Verrucaria microbola Tuck., Gen. Lich. 269. 1872.
Superficial thallus thin, minutely granulose to areolate, olivaceous to grayish or whitish; perithecia minute to small, 0.1–0.3 mm. across, the superficial portion depressed-subhemispherical, black; spores 3-septate, ovoid-ellipsoid, 23–30 $\times$ 10–15 μ.
On rocks, Ohio and southern California.

OTHER SPECIES REPORTED
Thelidium viride (Deak.) Zahlbr.—New York.

4. **Thelidiella** Fink; Hedrick, Mycologia 25:305. 1933.

Thallus immersed in that of the lichen host and invisible; perithecia minute, more or less immersed, the wall dimidiate, the superficial portion hemispherical to conical, the ostiole rarely visible; hypothecium and hymenium hyaline; paraphyses soon becoming gelatinized and disappearing; asci broadly clavate, the wall not much thickened in the apical region; spores 8, hyaline, 1-septate, the cells unequal.
The algal host is Pleurococcus.

1. **Thelidiella blastenicola** Fink; Hedrick, Mycologia 25:305. 1933.
Thallus immersed and invisible; perithecia very minute, 0.06–0.09 mm. across, dimidiate and partly immersed, black, seated 1–several on single squamules or apothecia, the superficial portion hemispherical to obscurely subconical, the ostiole only very rarely and tardily visible; spores ellipsoid-dactyloid, the upper cell larger, becoming slightly constricted, 9–11 × 3–4 μ, irregularly arranged.
On the thallus and the apothecia of *Blastenia novomexicana*, near Los Vegas, New Mexico.

5. **Polyblastia** Lönnr., Flora 41:630. 1858.

Thallus crustose, smooth to chinky, powdery or minutely granulose, sometimes seated upon a well-developed hypothallus, partly within the substratum, devoid of differentiation into layers; perithecia minute to small, more or less immersed, the wall dimidiate or complete, the superficial portion convex to hemispherical or conical, the ostiole minute, rarely visible; hypothecium hyaline; hymenium hyaline or brownish above; paraphyses soon becoming gelatinized; asci broadly clavate; spores 1–8, hyaline to faintly brownish, ovoid to ovoid-ellipsoid or oblong-ellipsoid, transversely and longitudinally septate.
The algal host is Protococcus.

A. On rocks; thallus greenish gray to brownish
  B. Spores 26–34 × 13–17 μ . . . . 1. P. intercedens
  B. Spores smaller, 18–24 × 8–12 μ . . . . . 1. P. intercedens aethioboloides
A. On moss; thallus whitish . . . . 2. P. bryophila

1. **Polyblastia intercedens** (Nyl.) Lönnr., Flora 41:631. 1858.
Verrucaria intercedens Nyl., Mém. Soc. Acad. Maine et Loire 4:33. 1858.
Thallus thin, smooth to faintly chinky, greenish gray to brownish; perithecia minute to small, 0.25–0.5 mm. across, the wall dimidiate, the superficial portion subhemispherical to conical, black, the ostiole minute, deeply depressed, and rarely visible; spores 2, hyaline to pale brownish, ovoid-ellipsoid, 5–8-septate transversely and 3–5-septate longitudinally, 26–34 × 13–17 μ, irregularly arranged.
On rocks, California.

var. **aethioboloides** (Nyl.) Hasse, Cont. U. S. Nat. Herb. 17:6. 1913.
Verrucaria intercedens var. *aethioboloides* Nyl., Not. Sällsk. Faun. Flor. Fenn. 1:235. 1859.
Thallus very thin, subdeterminate; spores smaller, 18–24 × 8–12 μ.
On rocks, southern California. Doubtfully included as the only specimen seen did not show the smaller spores.

2. **Polyblastia bryophila** Lönnr., Flora 41:631. 1858.
Verrucaria bryophila (Lönnr.) Nyl.
Thallus thin, whitish, minutely granulose or crumbling and disappearing; perithecia minute, 0.1–0.3 mm. across, partly immersed, the superficial portion strongly convex, black, the ostiole scarcely visible; spores 8, hyaline, ovoid, 5–7-septate transversely and 3–5-septate longitudinally, 18–36 × 12–18 μ, finally irregularly arranged.
On mosses, Maine.

OTHER SPECIES REPORTED

Polyblastia gelatinosa (Ach.) T. Fries—New Hampshire.
Polyblastia Henscheliana (Koerb.) Lönnr.—North America.

6. **Staurothele** Norm., Nyt. Mag. Nat. 7:240. 1853.

Thallus crustose, smooth to granulose, warty, or chinky-areolate, sometimes seated upon an indistinct hypothallus, partly within the substratum, devoid of differentiation into layers; perithecia minute to small or middle-sized, more or less immersed in raised areas, indicated by the protruding apex or the minute ostiole, the wall complete; hypothecium hyaline to brownish; hymenium hyaline; paraph-

yses soon becoming gelatinized; asci broadly clavate; spores 1–8, hyaline to
brown, oblong to ellipsoid, transversely and longitudinally septate.
The algal host is Protococcus.

A. Spores commonly more than 30 μ in length
  B. Perithecia minute to small, 0.1–0.3 mm. across . . . . 1. S. clopima
  B. Perithecia small to middle-sized, more than 0.3 mm. across
    C. Thallus zonate at the margin . . . . 4. S. circinata
    C. Thallus not zonate at the margin . . . . 2. S. umbrina
A. Spores 15–22 × 9–12 μ . . . . 3. S. diffractella

1. **Staurothele clopima** (Wahl.) T. Fries, Nov. Act. Soc. Sci. Ups. III. 3:363.
1861.
Verrucaria clopima Wahl.; Ach. Vet. Akad. Nya Handl. 152. 1809. *S. umbrina*
var. *clopima* (Wahl.) Tuck.
Thallus thick, rough, warty or becoming areolate, widespread or broken up
into smaller irregular areas, brown to dull black; perithecia minute to small,
0.1–0.3 mm. across, immersed in the thallus, except the depressed ostiole; spores
2, brown, oblong, 7–13-septate transversely and 3–5-septate longitudinally, 30–48 ×
12–20 μ. (PLATE 1 b.)
On rocks, New Hampshire and Minnesota.

2. **Staurothele umbrina** (Ach.) Tuck., Gen. Lich. 258. 1872.
Lichen umbrinus Ach., Lich. Suec. 14. 1798. *S. lithina* (Ach.) Zahlbr.
Thallus rather thin, smooth, becoming granulose or areolate, widespread or
often broken up into smaller irregular areas, olive-gray to dusky-brown; perithecia
small to middle-sized, 0.3–0.6 mm. across, immersed in raised areas, the black
apex finally protruding; spores 2, brown, oblong, 7–11-septate transversely and
3–5-septate longitudinally, 30–48 × 12–20 μ.
On rocks, from New England to Florida and westward to the Rocky Mountains.

3. **Staurothele diffractella** (Nyl.) Tuck., Gen. Lich. 258. 1872.
Verrucaria diffractella Nyl., Mém. Soc. Acad. Maine et Loire 4:33. 1858.
Phalostauris diffractella (Nyl.) Clements. *S. petersii* Tuck. nomen nudum.
Thallus moderately thick, chinky-areolate, widespread or broken up into
smaller irregular areas, ashy or yellowish to olive-brown; perithecia minute to
small, 0.1–0.3 mm. across, immersed in raised areas, or more or less of the black
apex finally protruding; spores 8, hyaline, ellipsoid, 5–7-septate transversely and
1–2-septate longitudinally, 15–22 × 9–12 μ.
On rocks, from New England to the Gulf of Mexico and westward to Missouri
and Minnesota.

4. **Staurothele circinata** Tuck., Gen. Lich. 257. 1872.
Thallus round to somewhat irregular, zonate at the circumference, becoming
chinky, hypothallus darkening, fimbriate, olive-brown; perithecia middle-sized,
0.4–0.7 mm. across, located toward the center of the thallus, immersed in subhemispherical raised areas, or the upper portion finally protruding, black; spores 1–2,
brown, oblong to ellipsoid, often narrower toward one end, 9–15-septate transversely and 3–5-septate longitudinally, 34–50 × 16–20 μ.
On calcareous rocks, Trenton Falls, New York.

7. **Thrombium** Wallr., Fl. Crypt. Germ. 3:287. 1831.

Thallus crustose, smooth or minutely granulose, partly or wholly within the
substratum, devoid of differentiation into layers; apothecia minute to small, more
or less immersed, the wall complete, the ostiole minute; hypothecium hyaline to
brown; hymenium hyaline; paraphyses delicate, commonly persistent; asci clavate
or cylindrical; spores 8, hyaline, ellipsoid or oblong-ellipsoid, non-septate.
The algal host is Protococcus.

1. **Thrombium epigaeum** (Pers.) Wallr., Fl. Crypt. Germ. 3:294, 295. 1831. *Sphaeria epigaea* Pers., Syn. Meth. Fung. Add. XXVII. 1801. *Verrucaria epigaea* (Pers.) Ach.

Superficial thallus thin, widespread, sometimes disappearing, often finely granulose, greenish to brown or ashy; perithecia minute, 0.1–0.15 mm. across, appearing as black spots in the thallus; spores oblong-ellipsoid, 16–28 × 7–10 μ.

On soil, from New England to Virginia and westward to Iowa and Minnesota, and in California.

OTHER SPECIES REPORTED

Thrombium discordans (Nyl.) Zahlbr.—Southern California.

8. **Microglaena** Koerb., Syst. Lich. 388, 389. 1855.

Thallus crustose, smooth to minutely warty, granulose, chinky, areolate or squamulose, partly within the substratum, devoid of differentiation into layers; perithecia minute to small, more or less immersed in the thalloid areoles or squamules, the wall complete or rarely dimidiate, the superficial portion depressed to convex, the ostiole minute, rarely visible; hypothecium hyaline to brown; hymenium hyaline; paraphyses delicate, persistent; asci oblong-cylindrical; spores 2–8, hyaline to brownish, ovoid-ellipsoid to ellipsoid, transversely and longitudinally septate.

The algal host is Protococcus.

A. Thallus thin, chinky to areolate, greenish to olive gray . . . . . . 1. M. Hassei
A. Thallus warty to minutely squamulose, greenish gray to whitish or ashy
   B. Spores 4 in each ascus . . . . 3. M. sychnogonoides
   B. Spores 8 in each ascus . . . . 2. M. subcorallina

1. **Microglaena Hassei** Zahlbr., Beih. Bot. Centralb. 13:152. 1902.

Thallus thin, widespread, minutely warty, becoming chinky or areolate, greenish-to olive-gray; perithecia minute, 0.2–0.3 mm. across, dimidiate, immersed, usually 1 in each raised areole; spores 8, hyaline or becoming brown, ovoid-ellipsoid to ellipsoid, 7–9-septate transversely and 2–3-septate longitudinally, 20–30 × 9–13 μ.

On trees, southern California.

2. **Microglaena subcorallina** Hasse, Cont. U. S. Nat. Herb. 17:7. 1913.

Thallus moderately thick, warty to minutely squamulose, whitish to dull greenish gray; perithecia minute, 0.1–0.3 mm. across, the wall complete, partly immersed, 1 or rarely 2 in each squamule, the superficial portion depressed to convex, dark brown to black; spores 8, ellipsoid, hyaline to pale brownish, 5–8-septate transversely and 1–3-septate longitudinally, 34–40 × 12–18 μ.

On trees, San Gabriel Mountains, southern California.

3. **Microglaena sychnogonoides** Zahlbr., Beih. Bot. Centralb. 13:151, 152. 1902.

Thallus thin, smooth to becoming minutely warty, composed of minute squamules, greenish gray to ashy; perithecia minute to small, 0.15–0.4 mm. across, immersed, usually 1 in each squamule, the wall complete, the superficial portion convex or depressed, brownish gray to brown; spores 4, hyaline to brownish, ellipsoid, 7–11-septate transversely and 3–5-septate longitudinally, 20–34 × 9–11 μ.

On trees, southern California.

2. DERMATOCARPACEAE

Thallus crustose to squamulose and distinctly foliose, differentiated into more or less developed upper and lower cortices, algal and medullary layers, attached to the substratum by rhizoids or an umbilicus; perithecia immersed, single, upright, the ostiole terminal, punctiform; paraphyses soon gelatinizing, indistinct or wanting.

The algal host is Pleurococcus.

A. Thallus with poorly developed cortex . . . . 9. NORMANDINA
A. Thallus with well-developed, plectenchymatous cortex
   B. Spores non-septate, hyaline . . . . .10. DERMATOCARPON
   B. Spores septate
      C. Spores transversely septate . . . . 11. HETEROCARPON
      C. Spores transversely and longitudinally septate . . . . . 12. ENDOCARPON

9. Normandina Nyl., Mém. Soc. Sci. Nat. Cherb. 3:191. 1855.

Thallus scaly or squamulose, the scales or squamules round, more or less lobed, adnate or ascending, showing a poorly developed upper cortex, attached to the substratum by rhizoids; perithecia minute to small, immersed, indicated by the small ostiole, the wall complete; hypothecium hyaline to brown; hymenium hyaline or brownish above; paraphyses wanting; asci clavate; spores 6–8, hyaline to brownish, oblong to cylindrical, 5–7- or more-septate.

The algal host is Pleurococcus.

1. **Normandina pulchella** (Borr.) Nyl., Ann. Sci. Bot. IV. 15:382. 1861.
Verrucaria pulchella Borr., in Sowerby, Engl. Bot. Suppl. 1:2602. 1831. *N. Jungermanniae* Nyl. *N. lactevirens* (Borr.) Nyl.

Thallus adnate, composed of round or round-lobulate, concave, imbricated, often concentrically wrinkled, marginally ascending and slightly recurved, often sorediate, greenish to greenish gray squamules; whitish to pale brownish below and bearing short rhizoids; perithecia rare. immersed in raised areas, indicated by a small, black ostiole; spores 8, cylindrical, 6–7-septate, hyaline to brownish, 28–40 × 6–10 μ.

On trees, from New England to South Carolina.

10. Dermatocarpon E. Fries, Syst. Orb. Veg. 259. 1825.

Thallus foliose, small and closely adnate to larger and attached by an umbilicus, upper cortex thin, lower cortex better developed, with algal and medullary layers between, squamulose, the squamules thin to thick, smooth to rough, irregularly lobed; perithecia minute to small, immersed 1–several in each areole or squamule, the superficial portion subconical, black, or only the minute ostiole visible, the wall dimidiate; paraphyses gelatinizing and becoming coherent; asci cylindrico-clavate to ventricose; spores 8, rarely 16, hyaline, non-septate, subglobose to oblong-ellipsoid.

The algal host is Pleurococcus.

A. Thallus umbilicate
   B. Thallus large, lobes wrinkled
      C. Thallus grayish to brownish
         D. Lower surface densely covered with villous rhizoids . . 7. D. Moulinsii
         D. Lower surface minutely papillose . . . 7. D. Moulinsii subpapillosum
      C. Thallus ashy or bluish gray to dusky brown
         D. Olive to blackish brown below
            E. Thallus deeply divided . . . . 1. D. miniatum complicatum
            E. Thallus not deeply divided . . . . 1. D. miniatum
         D. Reticulated and often yellowish
            brown below . . . . 1. D. miniatum fulvofuscum
   B. Thallus small to middle-sized, lobes smooth . . . . 2. D. aquaticum
A. Thallus more or less closely adnate
   B. Thallus areolate to squamulose
      C. Becoming plainly squamulose toward the margin . . . . 6. D. cinereum
      C. Not squamulose toward the margin
         D. Perithecia 0.1–0.2 mm. across . . . . 13. D. lecideoides
         D. Perithecia 0.8–1.5 mm. across . . . . 10. D. Zahlbruckneri
   B. Thallus distinctly squamulose
      C. Spores not more than 18 μ in length
         D. Spores spherical . . . . 5. D. acarosporoides
         D. Spores ellipsoid
            E. Thallus bearing rhizoids below
               F. Pale with blackening rhizoids . . . . . . 11. D. arboreum
               F. Black and densely covered with rhizoids . . . 4. D. hepaticum

E. Thallus without rhizoids below
  F. Thallus reddish brown . . . . 8. D. rufescens
  F. Thallus gray to bluish or grayish pruinose . . 3. D. polyphyllum
C. Spores 16–24 μ in length
  D. Thallus dull greenish . . . . 9. D. squamellum
  D. Thallus hoary gray to brownish . . . . 12. D. Heppioides

1. **Dermatocarpon miniatum** (L.) Mann, Lich. Bohem. 66. 1825.
    Lichen miniatus L., Sp. Pl. 1149. 1753. *Endocarpon miniatum* var. *Mühlenbergii* (Ach.) Calkins. *D. Mühlenbergii* (Ach.) Müll. Arg.
    Thallus loosely adnate, large, rather thick, spreading, umbilicate, more or less round, wrinkled or undulating, the margin entire or irregularly lobed, often recurved downward, ashy or bluish gray varying toward dusky brown; pale olive to blackish brown below; perithecia minute, 0.08–0.3 mm. across, immersed in the thallus, only the dark ostiole visible; spores ellipsoid, 9–16 × 5–8 μ.
    On rocks, throughout the United States.

    var. **complicatum** (Light.) T. Fries, Nov. Act. Soc. Sci. Ups. III. 3:353. 1861.
    Lichen miniatus var. *complicatus* Light., Fl. Scot. ed. 2. 858. 1777.
    Thallus deeply divided, the divisions often extending almost to the umbilicus, the lobes becoming much imbricated and sometimes severed from the plant.
    On rocks, especially calcareous, widely distributed in the United States.

    var. **fulvofuscum** (Tuck.) Zahlbr. Cat. Lich. Univ. 1:229. 1921.
    Endocarpon fluviatile var. *fulvofuscum* Tuck. Proc. Am. Acad. 1:275. 1848.
    Endocarpon miniatum fulvofuscum Tuck.
    Reticulated and often yellowish brown below.
    On rocks, from Maryland to Florida and westward to Colorado and Montana.

2. **Dermatocarpon aquaticum** (Weis.) Zahlbr., Ann. Naturh. Hofmus. Vein 16:81. 1901.
    Lichen aquaticus Weis., Pl. Crypt. Gott. 77. 1770. (not L. 1753.) *D. fluviatile* (Web.) T. Fries. *D. manitense* (Tuck.) Zahlbr.
    Thallus small to middle-sized, thick, umbilicate, but many-lobed, becoming tufted, lobes crowded, imbricated, margins round, entire or somewhat cut-lobulate, ascending and recurved downward, ashy to olive- or dusky-brown; light brown to blackish below; perithecia minute, 0.1–0.25 mm. across, immersed in the thallus, only the minute dark ostiole visible; spores ellipsoid, 9–16 × 6–9 μ.
    On rocks, most commonly on those inundated or often wet, from New England to Florida and westward to the Rocky Mountains, and in Nevada and California.

3. **Dermatocarpon polyphyllum** (Wulf.) Dalla Torre & Sarnth., Fl. Grafs. Tirol 4:504. 1902.
    Lichen polyphyllus Wulf., Ges. Naturf. Freund. Mag. 8:142. 1787. *D. intestiniforme* (Koerb.) Hasse.
    Thallus thick, tufted, middle-sized, squamulose, creamy gray to tinged bluish or grayish pruinose, the squamules smooth to rough, small to middle-sized, crowded into small, irregular areoles toward the center, expanded and imbricated toward the circumference, with downward curved margins; brownish black and smooth below; perithecia minute, 0.05–0.1 mm. across, immersed several in each areole or squamule, the superficial portion depressed-convex, dull black, the ostiole minute, brownish black; spores ellipsoid, 10–18 × 5–8.5 μ, uniseriately to irregularly arranged.
    On rocks, Arizona and California.

4. **Dermatocarpon hepaticum** (Ach.) T. Fries, Nov. Act. Soc. Sci. Ups. III. 3:355. 1861.
    Endocarpon hepaticum Ach., Vet. Akad. Nya Handl. 156. 1809. *D. Tuckermani* (Rav.) Zahlbr. *D. lachneum* (Ach.) A. L. Smith.
    Thallus closely adnate, squamulose, the squamules round to irregular, entire to crenate, usually appressed, sometimes ascending and somewhat imbricated, red-

dish brown to dusky; black below, densely covered with rhizoids; perithecia minute, 0.05–0.25 mm. across, immersed in the thallus, only the dark ostiole visible; spores ellipsoid, 10–14 × 5–9 μ.

On soil, throughout the United States.

5. **Dermatocarpon acarosporoides** Zahlbr., Beih. Bot. Centralb. 13:153, 154. 1902.

Thallus thick, rather small, reddish brown, squamulose, the squamules often fissured and obscurely warty, closely grouped or scattered; perithecia minute, 0.1–0.2 mm. across, subconical, pale, immersed 1 or more in each squamule, the apex becoming black, the ostiole punctiform but sometimes sunken in the thallus; asci ventricose; spores globose or subglobose, 10–12 μ in diameter.

On granite, San Jacinto Mountains, California.

6. **Dermatocarpon cinereum** (Pers.) T. Fries, Nov. Act. Soc. Sci. Ups. III. 3:356. 1861.

Endocarpon cinereum Pers., Ann. Bot. Usteri 7:28. 1794. *Endocarpon tephroides* Ach.

Thallus rather small, closely adnate, chinky-areolate toward the center, or breaking into squamiform areoles, lobed and sometimes plainly squamulose toward the margins, the lobes wavy, short to linear; blackish below; perithecia minute, 0.08–0.2 mm. across, numerous, largely immersed, indicated by the prominent protruding, blackish ostiole; spores oblong-ellipsoid, sometimes appearing pseudoseptate because of vacuoles, 17–24 × 7–10.5 μ.

On soil, Vermont, Illinois, South Dakota, and California.

7. **Dermatocarpon Moulinsii** (Mont.) Zahlbr., in E. & P., Nat. Pfl. 1:60. 1907. *Endocarpon Moulinsii* Mont., Ann. Sci. Nat. Bot. II. 20:51. 1843.

Thallus loosely adnate, large, spreading, thick and stout, attached by an umbilicus, round to irregularly lobed, the lobes sometimes imbricated, undulating to wrinkled, grayish to brownish; blackish below and densely covered with villous rhizoids; perithecia minute, 0.2–0.35 mm. across, imbedded in the thallus, only the dark ostiole visible; spores ovoid-ellipsoid, 10–14 × 6–7 μ.

On rocks, Texas.

var. **subpapillosum** Fink; Hedrick, Mycologia 25:306. 1933.
The lower surface minutely papillose.
On rocks, Idaho and Washington.

8. **Dermatocarpon rufescens** (Ach.) T. Fries, Nov. Act. Soc. Sci. Ups. III. 3:354. 1861.

Endocarpon rufescens Ach., Lich. Univ. 304. 1810.

Thallus closely adnate, squamulose, the squamules cut-lobulate, often angular or irregular, contiguous, the margins recurved downward, forming a crust, or sometimes somewhat scattered, with the margins ascending, becoming imbricated, reddish brown; blackish below; perithecia minute, 0.1–0.25 mm. across, immersed, often several in a squamule, only the dark ostiole visible; spores ovoid-ellipsoid to ellipsoid, 13–18 × 5–8 μ.

On soil, New England, Illinois, Nebraska, Arizona, and southern California.

9. **Dermatocarpon squamellum** (Nyl.) Herre, Proc. Wash. Acad. Sci. 12:44. 1910.

Verrucaria squamella Nyl.; Hasse, Bull. Torr. Club 24:449. 1897.

Thallus thin to moderately thick, small, dull greenish, squamulose, the squamules crenate, lobulate, and imbricate; perithecia minute, 0.1–0.25 mm. across, immersed, 1–several in each squamule, indicated by dark punctiform spots; asci clavate to ventricose; spores oblong to ellipsoid, 15–24 × 5.5–8 μ.

On shaded soil, among moss, southern California. Material is doubtful. It is omitted by Hasse from his *Lichen Flora of Southern California*.

10. **Dermatocarpon Zahlbruckneri** Hasse, Bryologist 16:2. 1913.
Thallus areolate-squamulose, greenish gray, the squamules small, clustered, convex, round or angular; perithecia large, 0.8–1.5 mm. across, 1–6 in each squamule, the superficial portion dark brown to black, conical or flattened; asci becoming saccate or ventricose; spores narrowly oblong-ellipsoid, 16–25 × 4–7.5 μ.
On trap rock, Santa Monica Range, California.

11. **Dermatocarpon arboreum** (Schwein.) Fink, Cont. U. S. Nat. Herb. 14:244. 1910.
Endocarpon arboreum Schwein., in E. Fries, Lich. Eur. 407. 1831.
Thallus closely adnate or the margins slightly raised, squamulose-foliose, the squamules small, clustered and more or less imbricated, or sometimes scattered, the margins round, entire or lobed, pale olive-green to brownish; pale below with darkening rhizoids; perithecia minute, 0.05–0.15 mm. across, numerous, immersed in the thallus, only the brownish ostiole visible; spores ellipsoid, 10–15 × 4–6 μ.
On trees, from Massachusetts to Florida and westward to Texas and Minnesota.

12. **Dermatocarpon Heppioides** Zahlbr., Ann. Mycolog. 10:359. 1912.
Thallus thick, closely adnate, small to middle-sized, squamulose, hoary gray to brownish, the squamules irregular, running into convex, irregular warts toward the center, flattened and imbricated toward the circumference, with sparingly lobed and toothed margins; black and smooth below; perithecia minute, 0.08–0.2 mm. across, immersed several in each squamule, only the minute ostiole visible; asci clavate; spores oblong to oblong-ellipsoid, containing 1–3 oil globules, 16–24 × 6–10 μ, biseriately arranged.
On sandstone, southern California.

13. **Dermatocarpon lecideoides** (Mass.) Hasse, Bryologist 18:92. 1915.
Thrombium lecideoides Mass., Ric. Lich. 157. f. 305. 1852.
Thallus thin, finely wrinkled, composed of small, flat, dark gray to blackening areoles; perithecia minute, 0.1–0.2 mm. across, immersed, the apex black; spores oblong-ellipsoid, 16–24 × 8–9.5 μ.
On quartz, southern California. Doubtfully admitted, description adapted from Hasse.

OTHER SPECIES REPORTED

Dermatocarpon peltatum (Tayl.) Zahlbr.—Arizona.

11. **Heterocarpon** Müll. Arg., Flora 68:515. 1885.

Thallus areolate, scaly, the areoles or scales often lobed, more or less densely arranged, the upper cortex plectenchymatous, the lower cortex thin or wanting, the algal and medullary layers more or less distinct; perithecia minute to small, immersed, indicated by the small ostiole surrounded by the black exciple; hypothecium brown; hymenium hyaline or brownish above; paraphyses becoming indistinct; asci clavate; spores 6–8, brown or blackish, boat-shaped, ellipsoid or fusiform, 1–3-septate.
The algal host is Pleurococcus.

1. **Heterocarpon ochroleucum** (Tuck.) Müll. Arg., Flora 68:515. 1885.
Endocarpon ochroleucum Tuck., Gen. Lich. 250. 1872.
Thallus thick, smooth, yellowish green, areolate, the areoles small and densely arranged, usually convex, the central ones substipitate, those of the margin often lobed; perithecia minute, 0.15–0.35 mm. across, immersed, 1–several in each areole, the exposed portion and the whole exciple black; hypothecium brownish black; spores boat-shaped, blackish, 18–25 × 3.5–5 μ.
On rocks, California.

12. **Endocarpon** Hedw., Descr. Musc. Frond. 2:56. pl. 20, f. *a*. 1789.

Thallus crustose, with algal, medullary, and upper cortical layers well developed, minutely squamulose, squamules round to more or less irregular, scattered or clustered, closely attached by rhizoids; perithecia minute to small, immersed, 1 to several or many in a squamule, only the minute, dark ostiole visible, the wall dimidiate; paraphyses soon gelatinizing; asci clavate; spores 2–4 or rarely 6, hyaline to brown, oblong to ovoid-ellipsoid, transversely and longitudinally septate, uniseriately to irregularly arranged.

The algal host is Pleurococcus.

A. Thallus areolate or the squamules passing into an areolate crust
   B. Thallus dusky olive-green to blackish . . . . 4. E. Wilmsoides
   B. Thallus olive-gray to ashy or dusky gray . . . . 5. E. Monicae
A. Thallus more or less persistently squamulose
   B. Spores not more than 13-septate transversely
      C. Thallus of small, more or less lobed squamules
         D. Thallus pale reddish brown or lighter colored . . . . 6. E. pallidum
         D. Thallus light brown to olive- or dusky-brown . . . . 1. E. pusillum
      C. Thallus of small, twisted and knotted, often-
         stalked squamulose . . . . 7. E. tortuosum
   B. Spores commonly more than 13-septate transversely
      C. Spores 46–70 μ in length . . . . 2. E. subnitescens
      C. Spores 28–40 μ in length . . . . 3. E. lepidallum

1. **Endocarpon pusillum** Hedw., Descr. Musc. Frond. 2:56. pl. 20, f. *a*. 1789.
E. pusillum var. *Garovaglii* (Mont.) Willey. *E. Schaereri* (Koerb.) Fink.

Thallus rather thick, squamulose, closely adnate, the squamules minute, scattered, or clustered and forming an areolate surface, or becoming more or less lobed and imbricated, the smaller ones round, the larger irregular, light brown to olive- or dusky-brown; perithecia minute, 0.08–0.2 mm. across, immersed, often several in a squamule, the dark ostiole protruding slightly, the wall dimidiate; spores usually 2, hyaline to brownish, oblong, 7–13-septate transversely and 2–3-septate longitudinally, 23–45 × 12–18 μ, uniseriately arranged.

On soil and rocks, throughout the United States east of the Rocky Mountains, and in Nevada and California.

2. **Endocarpon subnitescens** Nyl., in Hue, Rev. Bot. 6:103. 1888.
Verrucaria subnitescens Nyl., Flora 68:299. 1885.

Thallus thin, composed of small, lobulate, reddish brown squamules; perithecia minute, 0.14–0.2 mm. across, immersed, often several in each squamule, indicated by a minute darker depression, the wall dimidiate; spores 2, hyaline to pale brown, oblong, 17–23-septate transversely and 3–7-septate longitudinally, 46–70 × 18–24 μ, uniseriately arranged.

On soil, southern California.

3. **Endocarpon lepidallum** Nyl., in Hasse, Lich. South. Calif. ed. 2. 17. 1898.

Thallus thin, composed of small, round to wavy and lobulate, whitish to smoky gray squamules, the margin often ascending or recurved and blackening; perithecia minute, 0.08–0.1 mm. across, immersed, 1–12 or more in a squamule, indicated by the minute, protruding gray apices, the wall dimidiate; spores 2, hyaline to brown, oblong to ovoid-ellipsoid, 11–17-septate transversely and 5–7-septate longitudinally, 28–40 × 14–18 μ, irregularly arranged.

On soil, southern California.

4. **Endocarpon Wilmsoides** Zahlbr., Beih. Bot. Centralb. 13:152, 153. 1902.

Thallus in small, round areas, scattered or confluent, minutely chinky to chinky-areolate, dusky olive-green to blackish; perithecia minute to small, 0.2–0.4 mm. across, immersed, except the minute ostiole, 1 or 2 in each small, sub-hemispherical raised area, the wall dimidiate; spores 2, hyaline to brown, ovoid to oblong-ovoid, 7–11-septate transversely and 2–4-septate longitudinally, 33–48 × 13–20 μ, uniseriately arranged.

On argillaceous schist, southern California.

5. **Endocarpon Monicae** Zahlbr., Beih. Bot. Centralb. 13:153. 1902.

Thallus thin, widespread, squamulose, the squamules minute, forming an areolate crust, becoming swollen when moist, olive-gray or ashy to dusky gray; perithecia minute, 0.1–0.25 mm. across, immersed, 1 or 2 in each squamule, indicated by the protruding black apices, the wall dimidiate; spores 2–3, ovate to oblong, 8–15-septate transversely and 2–4-septate longitudinally, 25–50 × 11–19 μ, irregularly arranged.

On argillaceous schist, southern California.

6. **Endocarpon pallidum** Ach., Lich. Univ. 301. 1810.

Thallus thin, composed of small, lobed and sometimes imbricate, often scattered, pale reddish brown or lighter colored squamules; perithecia minute to small, 0.1–0.3 mm. across, immersed, 1–10 or rarely more in a squamule, indicated by the protruding brownish black apices, the wall dimidiate; spores 2, brown, oblong, 7–13-septate transversely and 3–7-septate longitudinally, 36–52 × 14–18 μ, uniseriately arranged.

On soil, New England and California.

7. **Endocarpon tortuosum** Herre, Bot. Gaz. 51:288. 1911.

Thallus thin, composed of small, irregular, twisted and knotted, often stalked and erect, lobulate, ashy brown to darker, imbricate-foliose, scattered or clustered squamules; perithecia minute, 0.05–0.1 mm. across, immersed, the ostiole not plainly visible, the wall dimidiate; spores 2, hyaline to brown, ellipsoid to oblong-ellipsoid, 7–11-septate transversely and 1–3-septate longitudinally, 45–60 × 18–26 μ.

On rocks, Nevada and Montana.

OTHER SPECIES REPORTED

Endocarpon petrolepideum (Nyl.) Hasse—California.
Endocarpon pulvinatum T. Fries—California.

3. PYRENOTHAMNIACEAE

Thallus fruticose, more or less branched, differentiated into a well-developed cortex surrounding a loosely interwoven medulla; perithecia immersed, single, upright, the ostiole terminal.

The algal host is Pleurococcus.

13. **Pyrenothamnia** Tuck., Bull. Torr. Club 10:22. 1883.

Thallus fruticose, caespitose, dilated or dichotomously branched above, the plectenchymatous cortex surrounding a loosely interwoven medulla; perithecia minute, immersed in warts on the upper side of the branches, the wall complete; hypothecium hyaline to brownish; paraphyses soon coherent, gelatinized and disappearing; asci clavate to inflated-clavate; spores 1–4, ellipsoid, brown to blackish brown, transversely and longitudinally septate.

The algal host is Pleurococcus and occurs in the medulla and in the hymenium.

A. On rocks; thallus crowded into an irregular crust . . . . . . 2. P. Brandegei
A. On soil; thallus not crowded into a crust . . . . 1. P. Spraguei

1. **Pyrenothamnia Spraguei** Tuck., Bull. Torr. Club 10:22, 23. 1883.

Thallus composed of short, erect, slender, crowded, ashy brown to blackish, dichotomously much-branched stalks, the branches dilated above, the tips becoming crenate; perithecia minute, 0.15–0.3 mm. across, immersed, the ostiole closed, surrounded by a depressed, sometimes lighter colored area, the wall complete, hyaline to slightly tinged with brown; asci inflated-clavate; spores 1–4, brown, broadly ellipsoid, 7–11-septate transversely and 2–5-septate longitudinally, 28–52 × 18–24 μ.

On moss, Washington.

2. **Pyrenothamnia Brandegei** (Tuck.) Zahlbr., Cat. Lich. Univ. 1:251. 1921.
Staurothele Brandegei Tuck., Bull. Torr. Club 11:26. 1884.
Thallus composed of very short, erect, round, finger-shaped stalks, soon crowded
and dilated into a warty, brown to blackish, more or less irregular crust; perithecia minute, 0.15–0.25 mm. across, immersed, the ostiole closed, surrounded by
a depressed, sometimes lighter colored area, the wall complete, hyaline to slightly
tinged with brown; spores 1, brown to blackish, broadly ellipsoid, 7–11-septate
transversely and 2–4-septate longitudinally, 26–50 × 20–24 μ.
On rocks, Washington.

4. PYRENULACEAE

Thallus crustose, partly or wholly within the substratum or rarely immersed
in the lichen host, devoid of differentiation into layers; perithecia more or less
immersed, spherical to subspherical, single or clustered, the ostiole terminal;
paraphyses distinct, unbranched and free or branched and more or less interwoven.
The algal host is Trentepohlia.

A. Paraphyses branched and netlike interwoven
  B. Spores transversely several-septate
    C. Spores with lenticular cells . . . . 18. Pseudopyrenula
    C. Spores with cylindrical cells
      D. Spores brown . . . . 14. Microthelia
      D. Spores hyaline
        E. Spores ovoid to oblong, 1–5-septate . . . . . 15. Arthopyrenia
        E. Spores acicular to threadlike, 1–several-septate . . 16. Leptorhaphis
  B. Spores transversely and longitudinally septate . . . . . 17. Polyblastiopsis
A. Paraphyses unbranched, free
  B. Spores with cylindrical cells
    C. Asci soon disappearing . . . . 21. Belonia
    C. Asci remaining
      D. Spores many in each ascus . . . . 22. Thelopsis
      D. Spores 1–8 in each ascus
        E. Spores transversely several-septate, hyaline . . . . . 19. Porina
        E. Spores transversely and longitudinally septate . . 20. Clathroporina
  B. Spores with lenticular cells
    C. Spores transversely 1–5-septate, brown
      D. Thallus imbedded in that of lichen host . . . . . 24. Pyrenulella
      D. Thallus not imbedded . . . . 23. Pyrenula
    C. Spores transversely and longitudinally septate, brown   25. Anthracothecium

14. Microthelia Koerb., Syst. Lich. 372. 1855.

Thallus forming a thin, smooth to minutely granulose crust over the substratum,
partly or wholly within the substratum, devoid of differentiation into layers;
perithecia minute to small, more or less immersed, the superficial portion flat to
convex or hemispherical, the ostiole minute to small, often depressed, the wall
dimidiate or complete; hypothecium brownish to dark brown; hymenium hyaline
or brownish above; paraphyses branched and interwoven; asci clavate to cylindrico-
clavate; spores commonly 8, brown, oblong-ellipsoid, ellipsoid or slipper-shaped,
1–3- or rarely 5-septate, the cells cylindrical.
The algal host is Trentepohlia.

A. On trees
  B. Apothecia round, not more than 0.5 mm. across
    C. Spores reaching 20–30 μ in length
      D. Thallus more or less bordered and intersected
        by black lines . . . . 5. M. Willeyana
      D. Thallus more or less bordered but not intersected
        by black lines . . . . 2. M. thelena
    C. Spores not more than 18 μ in length
      D. Spores 1-septate . . . . 1. M. micula
      D. Spores becoming 2–3-septate . . . . . . 1. M. micula quadriloculata

B. Apothecia oblong, reaching 1 × 0.8 mm. . . . . 4. M. oblongata
A. On rocks . . . . 3. M. aterrima

1. **Microthelia micula** Koerb., Syst. Lich. 373. 1855.
Pyrenula cinerella (Nyl.) Branth. et Rostr.
Thallus rudimentary or absent or imbedded in the substratum and indicated by a whitish area; perithecia minute to small, 0.1–0.4 mm. across, dimidiate, semi- or more deeply immersed, round, or becoming oblong on birch, the superficial portion strongly convex, often depressed, black; spores 1-septate, oblong-ellipsoid, 10–18 × 5–9 μ.
On trees, from New England to Florida and westward to Missouri and Minnesota.

var. **quadriloculata** (Fink) Zahlbr., Cat. Lich. Univ. 1:263. 1922.
Pyrenula cinerella var. *quadriloculata* Fink, Cont. U. S. Nat. Herb. 14:239. 1910.
Spores becoming 2–3-septate, perhaps smaller than above.
On trees, Minnesota and Florida.

2. **Microthelia thelena** (Ach.) Trevis., Cons. Verr. 10. 1860.
Verrucaria thelena Ach., Syn. Lich. 92. 1814. *Pyrenula thelena* (Ach.) Trevis.
Thallus very thin, ashy to greenish gray, disappearing, or imbedded in the substratum and indicated by a whitish or yellowish area and surrounded by a black line; perithecia minute to small, 0.1–0.4 mm. across, dimidiate, the superficial portion convex, dilated below, black; spores 1-septate, constricted at the septum, oblong-ellipsoid, 16–30 × 7–10 μ.
On trees, Florida.

3. **Microthelia aterrima** (Anzi) Zahlbr., Cat. Lich. Univ. 1:255. 1921.
Rinodina aterrima Anzi, Comm. Soc. Critt. Ital. 2:11. 1864. *M. Metzleri* Lahm.
Superficial thallus widespread, thin, granulose or scurfy, greenish black to dull black; perithecia minute to small, 0.1–0.4 mm. across, superficial portion convex, the ostiole depressed, becoming much dilated, black; spores 1– rarely 3-septate, slipper-shaped, 14–19 × 5–8 μ.
On rocks, Nevada and California.

4. **Microthelia oblongata** Müll. Arg., Flora 68:332, 333. 1885.
Pyrenula oblongata Willey.
Superficial thallus very thin, smooth, widespread, white to yellowish; perithecia middle-sized to large, oblong, 0.6–0.8 × 0.9–1.1 mm. or narrower and trident-shaped, the superficial portion concave to flat, dilated below, black; spores becoming 1-septate, oblong-ellipsoid, 14–18 × 7–8 μ.
On trees, Massachusetts.

5. **Microthelia Willeyana** Müll. Arg., Flora 68:332. 1885.
Pyrenula Willeyana (Müll. Arg.) Willey.
Thallus thin, ashy to brownish, intersected and bordered by black lines, some-times disappearing; perithecia minute to small, 0.2–0.4 mm. across, dimidiate, the superficial portion black, hemispherical, dilated below; spores brownish to brown, 1-septate, one cell larger, oblong-ellipsoid, 22–24 × 8–9 μ.
On trees, Massachusetts and Illinois.

15. **Arthopyrenia** Mass., Ric. Lich. 165. f. 326–41. 1852.

Thallus crustose, more or less within the substratum, the superficial portion thin, smooth, irregularly widespread, whitish or ashy; perithecia minute to small or middle-sized, more or less immersed, the superficial portion black, subconical to hemispherical, the ostiole minute and often inconspicuous, the wall dimidiate or rarely complete; paraphyses branched and interwoven, becoming somewhat gelatinized; spores 8, hyaline, ellipsoid-oblong to linear-oblong, 1–3-septate, unseriate, obliquely uniseriate, or irregularly arranged, the cells cylindrical or almost cubical, sometimes unequal. The algal host is Trentepohlia.

A. On rocks
  B. Spores constantly 1-septate
    C. Perithecia less than 0.3 mm. across
      D. Thallus smooth, grayish; spores 13–20 × 5–8 μ . . . . . 4. A. litoralis
      D. Thallus smooth to chinky or areolate, greenish brown
        or blackish; spores 12–15 × 4.5–7 μ . . . . 5. A. halodytes
    C. Perithecia 0.3–0.7 mm. across . . . . 12. A. conoidea
  B. Spores becoming 2- and 3-septate
    C. Thallus grayish to ashy
      D. Spores 10–14 × 5–6 μ . . . . 17. A. dimidiata
      D. Spores 14–21 × 5–7 μ . . . . 16. A. distans
    C. Thallus tinged rose-colored . . . . 14. A. prospersella
A. On trees
  B. Spores constantly 1-septate
    C. Perithecia less than 0.3 mm. across
      D. Thallus usually indicated by a coloration of the substratum
        E. Thallus whitish; spores 11–16 × 3–5.5 μ . . . . . .3. A. subprostans
        E. Thallus light gray; spores 12–16 × 5–7 μ . . . . . . 1. A. biformis
      D. Thallus usually in small, ashy gray patches . . . . . .2. A. parvula
    C. Perithecia usually more than 0.3 mm. across
      D. Thallus usually indicated by a coloration of the substratum
        E. Spores 32–60 μ in length . . . . 8. A. Finkii
        E. Spores less than 30 μ in length
          F. Thallus somewhat powdery, whitish to ashy gray;
            spores 12–22 × 7–13 μ . . . . 9. A. alba
          F. Thallus smooth, grayish or brownish gray;
            spores 16–25 × 5–7.5 μ . . . . 6. A. epidermidis
      D. Thallus very thin, usually persistent
        E. Perithecia apparently pruinose . . . . . . 7. A. cinereopruinosa
        E. Perithecia not pruinose
          F. Spores 14–21 × 5–7 μ . . . . 11. A. leucochlora
          F. Spores 16–25 × 6–8 μ . . . . .10. A. analepta
  B. Spores 1–3- or more-septate
    C. Spores 1–3-septate
      D. Spores more than 16 μ in length
        E. Perithecia 0.25–0.3 mm. across . . . . 13. A. rhyponta
        E. Perithecia larger, reaching 0.5–0.8 mm. across
          F. Thallus whitish . . . . 19. A. Cinchonae
          F. Thallus ashy gray to brownish
            G. Ostiole punctiform . . . . 18. A. punctiformis
            G. Ostiole round . . . . 20. A. Cerasi
      D. Spores 9–16 × 3.5–5.5 μ . . . . 15. A. conformis
    C. Spores more than 3-septate
      D. Spores 3–5-septate . . . . 21. A. hyalospora
      D. Spores 5–7-septate . . . . 22. A. quinqueseptata

1. **Arthopyrenia biformis** (Borr.) Mass., Framm. Lich. 26. 1855.

Verrucaria biformis Borr., in Sowerby, Engl. Bot. Suppl. 1: pl. 2617. 1831.

Thallus thin, smooth, light gray or disappearing superficially and indicated by a widespread, light gray area; perithecia minute, 0.1–0.2 mm. across, the superficial portion convex, black, the wall dimidiate, the ostiole indicated by a whitish area; spores obliquely uniseriate, 1-septate, ellipsoid, 12–16 × 5–7 μ.

On trees, Maine, Florida, and California.

2. **Arthopyrenia parvula** Zahlbr., Beih. Bot. Centralb. 13:149, 150. 1902.

Superficial thallus usually in small patches, thin, smooth, ashy gray; perithecia minute, 0.08–0.12 mm. across, superficial portion hemispherical, black, the wall thin, complete, black, the apex becoming depressed, the ostiole punctiform; spores 1-septate, ellipsoid, 15–17 × 5–7 μ, uniseriately arranged.

On trees, Santa Monica Range, California.

3. **Arthopyrenia subprostans** (Nyl.) Müll. Arg., Flora 66:317. 1883.
Verrucaria subprostans Nyl., Mém. Soc. Acad. Maine et Loire 4:56. 1858.
Pyrenula subprostans (Nyl.) Tuck.
Thallus rudimentary, the imbedded portion indicated by a widespread, whitish, sometimes disappearing area; perithecia minute to small, 0.1–0.3 mm. across, the wall dimidiate, superficial portion depressed, subhemispherical, black, the ostiole minute, sometimes indicated by a whitish area; spores 1-septate, ellipsoid, 11–16 × 3–5.5 μ, irregularly arranged.
On trees, South Carolina, Florida, and Texas.

4. **Arthopyrenia litoralis** (Leight.) Arn., Berecht. Bayr. Bot. Gesell. 1:120. 1891.
Verrucaria litoralis Leight., Brit. Spec. Angioc. Lich. 46. pl. 20, f. 2. 1851.
Verrucaria consequens Nyl. *Verrucaria consequella* Nyl. *A. consequella* (Nyl.) Zahlbr.
Thallus very thin, smooth, grayish, sometimes disappearing; perithecia minute, 0.1–0.15 mm. across, partly immersed, the wall dimidiate, the superficial portion subhemispherical, black; paraphyses scanty, sometimes distinct; asci clavate, swollen; spores 8, hyaline, ovoid to ovoid-ellipsoid, 1-septate, one cell sometimes larger, 13–20 × 5–8 μ, irregularly arranged.
On siliceous rocks and on barnacles, Massachusetts.

5. **Arthopyrenia halodytes** (Nyl.) Arn., Bericht. Bayr. Bot. Gesell. 1:121. 1891.
Verrucaria halodytes Nyl., Mém. Soc. Sci. Nat. Cherb. 5:142. 1857.
Thallus thin, smooth to chinky and areolate, somewhat gelatinous, greenish brown or blackish; perithecia minute, 0.1–0.25 mm. across, slightly immersed, very numerous and somewhat crowded, the superficial portion hemispherical, black, the ostiole rarely visible, indicated by a whitish area, the wall dimidiate; asci inflated clavate; spores 8, hyaline, oblong, 1-septate, one cell slightly larger, 12–15 × 4.5–7 μ, irregularly arranged.
On rocks along the coast, southern California.

6. **Arthopyrenia epidermidis** (DC.) Mass., Ric. Lich. 167. f. 331. 1852.
Verrucaria epidermidis DC., in DC. & Lam., Fl. Fr. ed. 3. 2:313. 1815.
Thallus rudimentary, the superficial portion disappearing or absent, and the imbedded portion indicated at the surface by smooth, grayish or brownish gray areas; perithecia minute to small, 0.2–0.5 mm. across, partly immersed, the superficial portion hemispherical, black, the wall dimidiate, the ostiole minute, sometimes indicated by a whitish area; asci broadly clavate; spores 8, hyaline, 1-septate, oblong or oblong-ellipsoid, sometimes slightly constricted, one cell larger, 16–25 × 5–7.5 μ, irregularly arranged.
On trees, Louisiana and Ohio.
There are specimens in herbarium under this name from California and Illinois, but these specimens have 3-septate spores and much different-looking asci.

7. **Arthopyrenia cinereopruinosa** (Schaer.) Koerb., Syst. Lich. 368. 1855.
Verrucaria cinereopruinosa Schaer., Lich. Helv. Spic. 6:343. 1833.
Thallus thin, smooth, greenish gray to olivaceous; apothecia minute to small, 0.2–0.4 mm. across, wholly or partly immersed, when apparently pruinose from the thalloid covering, black, dimidiate, the superficial portion hemispherical, the ostiole umbilicate; spores 1-septate, narrowly ellipsoid, 12–17 × 3.5–5 μ, irregularly arranged.
On trees, Santa Cruz Peninsula, California.

8. **Arthopyrenia Finkii** Zahlbr., Cat. Lich. Univ. 1:306. 1921.
A. macrospora Fink, Cont. U. S. Nat. Herb. 14:237. 1910, preoccupied by *A. macrospora* Stiz., Ann. Natur. Hist. Hofmus. Wien. 23:109. 1909.
Thallus widespread, very thin and disappearing, smooth, ashy white; perithecia small to middle-sized, 0.4–0.75 mm. across, the wall dimidiate, superficial portion

hemispherical with papillate ostiole, brownish black to black; spores 1-septate, oblong-ellipsoid, somewhat constricted at the septum, $32–60 \times 14–21 \mu$, uniseriately or obliquely uniseriately arranged. On trees, Minnesota.

9. **Arthopyrenia alba** (Schrad.) Zahlbr., Cat. Lich. Univ. 1:315. 1922.
Verrucaria alba Schrad., Spic. Fl. Germ. 1:109. 1794. *Pyrenula gemmata* (Ach.) Naeg. *A. gemmata* (Ach.) Mass.
Thallus usually imbedded, indicated at the surface by a moderately widespread whitish to ashy gray area, superficial portion very thin when present, smooth or somewhat powdery; perithecia small to middle-sized, 0.3–0.65 mm. across, the wall dimidiate, superficial portion depressed-hemispherical, black, the ostiole minute, not always visible; spores 1-septate, ellipsoid, $12–22 \times 7–13 \mu$, uniseriately arranged.
On trees, from New England to Florida and westward to Illinois, Minnesota, and Washington.

10. **Arthopyrenia analepta** (Ach.) Mass., Ric. Lich. 165. 1852.
Lichen analeptus Ach., Lich. Suec. 15. 1798.
Thallus thin, smooth to obscurely scurfy, greenish gray to olivaceous, sometimes disappearing; apothecia minute to small, 0.2–0.5 mm. across, partly immersed, black, dimidiate, the superficial portion subconical; the ostiole indicated by a whitish area; asci cylindrical; spores ellipsoid, 1-septate, constricted, one cell larger, $16–25 \times 6–8 \mu$, irregularly arranged.
On trees, Santa Cruz Peninsula, California.

11. **Arthopyrenia leucochlora** Müll. Arg., Flora 66:287. 1883.
Thallus greenish to ashy white, thin, smooth, or becoming chinky; apothecia minute, 0.2–0.5 mm. across, hemispherical, black and shining, the apex finally pertuse, the ostiole minute, sometimes indicated by a whitish area, dimidiate, the basal portion immersed in a thallus; asci broadly clavate; spores ovoid-ellipsoid, 1-septate, $14–21 \times 5–7 \mu$, irregularly arranged or roughly biseriate.
On trees, Massachusetts and Ohio.

12. **Arthopyrenia conoidea** (E. Fries) Zahlbr., in E. & P., Nat. Pfl. 1:65. 1907.
Verrucaria conoidea E. Fries, Lich. Eur. 432. 1831.
Thallus a whitish or minutely powdery crust, or absent and indicated only by an ashy or pinkish coloration of the substratum; perithecia small to middle-sized, 0.3–0.7 mm. across, partly immersed, superficial portion convex, black, the wall dimidiate, the ostiole minute, rarely visible; spores 1-septate, oblong-ellipsoid, $13–20 \times 8–10 \mu$, uniseriately arranged.
On calcareous rocks, Minnesota.

13. **Arthopyrenia rhyponta** (Ach.) Mass., Ric. Lich. 166. 1852.
Verrucaria rhyponta Ach., Vet. Akad. Nya Handl. 150. 1809. *Pyrenula rhyponta* (Ach.) Trevis.
Thallus rudimentary, the imbedded portion indicated by a moderately widespread, brownish black coloration; perithecia small, 0.25–0.3 mm. across, superficial portion subhemispherical, black; spores 3-septate, oblong-ellipsoid, $18–24 \times 6–8 \mu$.
On trees, Massachusetts. (Not certainly algicolous.)

14. **Arthopyrenia prospersella** (Nyl.) Zahlbr., Cat. Lich. Univ. 1:288. 1921.
Verrucaria prospersella Nyl., Lich. Jap. 108, 109. 1890.
Thallus very thin, dull, smooth, greenish gray to whitish, usually tinged rose-colored; apothecia minute, 0.1–0.2 mm. across, semi-immersed, black and conical, dimidiate, the ostiole minute, rarely visible; hyaline within; spores oblong-ellipsoid, 1–2-septate, one cell slightly larger, $12–18 \times 5–5.5 \mu$, irregularly arranged.
On rocks, northern Illinois.

15. **Arthopyrenia conformis** (Nyl.) Herre, Proc. Wash. Acad. Sci. 12:52. 1910.
Verrucaria conformis Nyl., Flora 47:357. 1864.
Thallus thin, smooth, finally chinky, ashy; perithecia numerous, minute to small, 0.1–0.4 mm. across, semi-immersed, the superficial portion hemispherical, black, dimidiate, the ostiole minute, very rarely visible; asci cylindrical, hyaline internally; spores narrowly ellipsoid, 1-septate, constricted strongly at the septum and at the middle of each cell, giving the appearance of being 3-septate, or finally 3-septate, 9–16 × 3.5–5.5 μ, commonly uniseriately arranged.
On trees, Santa Cruz Peninsula, California.

16. **Arthopyrenia distans** (Willey) Zahlbr., Cat. Lich. Univ. 1:276. 1921.
Verrucaria distans Willey, Enum. Lich. New Bedford, Mass. 38. 1892. *Thelidium distans* (Willey) Zahlbr.
Thallus very thin to thin, smooth to rough, grayish to ashy, sometimes disappearing; perithecia minute, 0.1–0.25 mm. across, partly immersed, the wall dimidiate, the superficial portion subhemispherical, black; spores 8, hyaline, ellipsoid, 1–2 or rarely 3-septate, 14–21 × 5–7 μ, irregularly arranged.
On shaded rocks, near New Bedford, Massachusetts.

17. **Arthopyrenia dimidiata** Fink; Hedrick, Mycologia 25:306. 1933.
Thallus very thin to thin, smooth to somewhat rough, continuous to chinky and sometimes areolate, grayish to ashy; perithecia minute, 0.1–0.25 mm. across, the superficial portion subhemispherical, dull black, the wall dimidiate; spores reaching 8, ellipsoid, 1– rarely 2-septate, the upper cell larger, 10–14 × 5–6 μ, irregularly arranged.
On rocks, Connecticut.

18. **Arthopyrenia punctiformis** (Schrank) Mass., Ric. Lich. 168. f. 335. 1852.
Lichen punctiformis Schrank, Bayer. Flora 2:513. 1789. *Pyrenula punctiformis* (Schrank) Trevis. *Pyrenula subpunctiformis* Nyl. *A. floridana* Zahlbr. *Verrucaria punctiformis* (Schrank) Pers.
Thallus rudimentary, the imbedded portion indicated by a lighter coloration of the substratum, more or less pronounced, frequently disappearing; perithecia minute to small, 0.1–0.5 mm. across, the latter the long dimension in oblong forms, round to oblong, the wall dimidiate, superficial portion depressed, convex, black, the ostiole punctiform, usually indicated by a whitish area; spores 1–3-septate, oblong-ellipsoid, 18–24 × 5–9 μ, uniseriately to irregularly arranged.
On trees, throughout the eastern states and westward to Missouri and Minnesota, reappearing in California.

19. **Arthopyrenia Cinchonae** (Ach.) Müll. Arg., Flora 66:287. 1883.
Verrucaria Cinchonae Ach., Syn. Meth. Lich. 90. 1814. *Pyrenula Cinchonae* (Ach.) Tuck. *Verrucaria prostans* Mont.
Thallus whitish, superficial portion very thin and disappearing; perithecia small to middle-sized, 0.2–0.5 mm. across, superficial portion convex, black, the ostiole minute, indicated by a whitish area, the wall dimidiate; spores 1–3-septate, oblong-ellipsoid, 17–25 × 6–9 μ, for most part obliquely uniseriate.
On trees, South Carolina, Florida, Alabama, Louisiana, and Texas. Nylander describes under same name a plant having spores 25–30 × 7–8 μ.

20. **Arthopyrenia Cerasi** (Schrad.) Mass., Ric. Lich. 167. f. 332. 1852.
Verrucaria Cerasi Schrad., Crypt. Exsicc. No. 174. 1797.
Superficial thallus rudimentary or absent, imbedded thallus indicated by a sometimes widespread, thin, shining, ashy gray or lead-colored to brownish area; perithecia small to middle-sized, 0.3–0.8 mm. across, elliptical, the superficial portion slightly convex, black, shining, the perithecial wall dimidiate; spores 3-septate, ellipsoid, rounded at the ends, 15–25 × 4–8 μ.
On young oaks, Maryland, Iowa, and California.

21. **Arthopyrenia hyalospora** (Nyl.) Fink n. comb.
Verrucaria hyalospora Nyl., Mém. Soc. Imp. Sci. Nat. Cherb. 5:337. 1857
Pyrenula hyalospora (Nyl.) Tuck.
Superficial thallus widespread, very thin and disappearing, ashy white; perithecia rather large, 0.4–0.8 mm. across, superficial portion hemispherical with papillate ostiole, black, the wall dimidiate; spores 3- and rarely 4–5-septate, ellipsoid, 20–25 × 9–11 μ, irregularly arranged.
On trees, New England to Florida and westward to Iowa.

22. **Arthopyrenia quinqueseptata** (Nyl.) Müll. Arg., Flora 68:326. 1885.
Verrucaria quinqueseptata Nyl., Mém. Soc. Acad. Maine et Loire 4:58. 1858.
Pyrenula quinqueseptata (Nyl.) Tuck.
Thallus widespread, thin, sometimes disappearing, ashy white; perithecia rather large, 0.4–0.8 mm. across, the wall dimidiate, superficial portion hemispherical, black, the ostiole minute, sometimes visible; spores 5–7-septate, linear-oblong, 16–27 × 5–8 μ, irregularly arranged.
On trees, from Pennsylvania to Florida and westward to Iowa and Minnesota.

OTHER SPECIES REPORTED
Arthopyrenia analeptella (Nyl.) Arn.—California.
Arthopyrenia macrocarpa (Koerb.) Zahlbr.—Massachusetts and Louisiana.
Arthopyrenia sphaeroides (Wallr.) Zahlbr.—California.

16. **Leptorhaphis** Koerb., Syst. Lich. 371. 1855.
Thallus forming a thin, smooth to rough crust over the substratum, partly or wholly within the substratum, devoid of differentiation into layers; perithecia minute to small, more or less immersed, the superficial portion subhemispherical, the ostiole minute, the wall dimidiate or complete; hypothecium hyaline to dark brown; hymenium hyaline; paraphyses branched and interwoven or rarely unbranched; asci clavate to cylindrico-clavate; spores 4–8, hyaline, acicular, straight or curved, 3–7-septate, the cells cylindrical.
The algal host is Trentepohlia.

1. **Leptorhaphis epidermidis** (Ach.) T. Fries, Nov. Act. Soc. Sci. Ups. III. 3:373. 1861.
Lichen epidermidis Ach., Lich. Suec. 16. 1798. *Sagedia oxyspora* (Nyl.) Tuck.
L. oxyspora (Nyl.) Koerb.
Thallus very thin, slightly scurfy, ashy, often disappearing, or imbedded in the substratum and invisible; perithecia minute, 0.08–0.2 mm. across, partly immersed in the substratum, the superficial portion subhemispherical, black, the ostiole minute, the perithecial wall brownish black and dimidiate; paraphyses slender, distinct, commonly unbranched; asci long-clavate; spores 8, acicular, more or less curved, 3–7-septate, 20–34 × 2–4 μ.
On trees, from New England to Florida and westward to Illinois and Minnesota.

17. **Polyblastiopsis** Zahlbr., in E. & P., Nat. Pfl. 1¹:65. 1907.
Thallus forming a thin, smooth crust over the substratum, partly or wholly within the substratum, devoid of differentiation into layers; perithecia minute to small, more or less immersed, the superficial portion commonly hemispherical or convex, the ostiole minute, the wall dimidiate or complete; hypothecium hyaline to brown; hymenium hyaline or brownish above; paraphyses branched and netlike interwoven; asci clavate to cylindrico-clavate; spores 1–8, hyaline, ovoid-ellipsoid to oblong-ellipsoid, transversely and longitudinally septate, the cells cubical.
The algal host is Trentepohlia.

A. Spores less than 50 μ in length
  B. Spores less than 25 μ in length
    C. Spores 3–5-septate transversely . . . . 7. P. fallax
    C. Spores 5–7-septate transversely . . . . 6. P. fallaciosa

B. Spores commonly more than 25 μ in length
   C. Thallus thin, smooth to chinky or powdery, ashy to grayish
      D. Thallus sometimes becoming powdery; spores
         30–38 × 15–16 μ . . . . 5. P. dealbens
      D. Thallus becoming chinky and subareolate; spores
         20–34 × 8–14 μ . . . . 4. P. lactea
   C. Thallus rather thick, chinky-areolate, dull brownish . . . . 3. P. inductula
A. Spores more than 50 μ in length
   B. Spores large, 50–68 × 13–16 μ . . . . 1. P. floridana
   B. Spores larger, 118–160 × 28–40 μ . . . . 2. P. intrusa

1. **Polyblastiopsis floridana** Fink; Hedrick, Mycologia 25:307. 1933.
Thallus thin to moderately thick, becoming rough and warty, yellowish ashy, varying toward brownish; perithecia minute to small, 0.15–0.4 mm. across, imbedded in thalloid warts, the wall dimidiate, the apex visible and black, with the ostiole sometimes showing; asci long-clavate; spores 4– rarely 6 or 8, ellipsoid, 7–9-septate transversely and 1–2-septate longitudinally, 50–68 × 13–16 μ, irregularly arranged.
   On trees, Florida.

2. **Polyblastiopsis intrusa** (Nyl.) Zahlbr., Cat. Lich. Univ. 1:349. 1922.
Verrucaria intrusa Nyl., Mém. Soc. Acad. Maine et Loire 4:43. 1858.
Thallus very thin, smooth to slightly rough, ashy to grayish brown, or imbedded and indicated by a grayish area; apothecia minute to small, 0.1–0.25 mm. across, immersed, the ostiole minute, rarely visible, the wall dimidiate; spores 1 or rarely 2, brownish to brown, oblong, 23–31-septate transversely and 6–9-septate longitudinally, 118–160 × 28–40 μ.
   On trees, North Carolina, South Carolina, and Florida.

3. **Polyblastiopsis inductula** (Nyl.) Fink n. comb.
Verrucaria inductula Nyl., in Hasse, Bull. Torr. Club 24:448. 1897. *Polyblastia* (?) *inductula* (Nyl.) Zahlbr.
Superficial thallus rather thick, widespread, chinky-areolate, dull brownish; perithecia small to middle-sized, 0.2–0.5 mm. across, largely immersed in the thallus except dark at the apex, the ostiole minute; spores 6–10-septate transversely and 1–2-septate longitudinally, 26–32 × 10–14 μ, uniseriately to irregularly arranged.
   On shale, Santa Monica Range, California. Omitted by Hasse in his *Lichens of Southern California,* but recognized by Zahlbruckner in *Catalogus Lichenum Universalis* as a distinct species.

4. **Polyblastiopsis lactea** (Mass.) Zahlbr., in E. & P., Nat. Pfl. 1¹:65. 1907.
Blastodesmia lactea Mass., Ric. Lich. 181. f. 369. 1852. *Pyrenula lactea* (Mass.) Tuck.
Thallus very thin to thin, smooth to slightly rough, ashy gray to whitish, becoming chinky and subareolate; perithecia minute, 0.1–0.25 mm. across, round, the superficial portion strongly convex and black, the ostiole minute and scarcely visible; spores 4–8, hyaline or tinged brownish, oblong-ellipsoid, 5–7- or rarely 9-septate transversely and 1–3- or rarely 5-septate longitudinally, 20–34 × 8–14 μ, irregularly arranged.
   On trees, New England to South Carolina, and westward to Tennessee, and in Illinois.

5. **Polyblastiopsis dealbens** Fink; Hedrick, Mycologia 25:307. 1933.
Thallus thin and ashy, smooth to slightly rough, chinky, sometimes becoming powdery; perithecia minute to small, 0.15–0.4 mm. across, round to irregular, the superficial portion depressed-convex, black or more commonly whitish pruinose, the ostiole rarely visible; hypothecium dark brown; spores 4–8, oblong-ellipsoid, 8–9-septate transversely and 1–2-septate longitudinally, 30–38 × 15–16 μ, irregularly arranged.
   On trees, South Carolina and Tennessee.

6. **Polyblastiopsis fallaciosa** (Stizenb.) Zahlbr., in E. & P., Nat. Pfl. 1¹:65. 1907.
Sporodictyon fallaciosum Stizenb.; Arn., Flora 46:604. 1863. *Pyrenula fallaciosa* (Stizenb.) Willey.

Thallus thin, ashy gray, slightly rough, or the superficial portion sometimes
absent and the imbedded portion indicated by a grayish coloration; perithecia
minute, 0.15–0.25 mm. across, the superficial portion hemispherical, black, the ostiole minute, rarely visible, sometimes indicated by a whitish area, the wall
dimidiate; hypothecium hyaline; spores 8, ellipsoid, 5–7-septate transversely and
1–2-septate longitudinally, 14–21 × 6–8 μ, irregularly arranged.

On trees, New Hampshire, Massachusetts, and Illinois.

7. **Polyblastiopsis fallax** (Nyl.) Fink n. comb.
Verrucaria epidermidis var. *fallax* Nyl., Bot. Not. 178. pl. 1, f. 12*b*. 1852. *Arthopyrenia punctiformis* var. *fallax* (Nyl.) Anzi. *Pyrenula punctiformis* var.
fallax (Nyl.) Willey. *Didymella fallax* (Nyl.) Vainio. *Arthopyrenia fallax*
. (Nyl.) Arn.

Thallus very thin or more commonly imbedded and indicated by greenish-gray
to ashy coloration of the substratum; perithecia minute to small, 0.1–0.5 mm.
across, round to oblong, the superficial portion depressed-convex, black, the wall
dimidiate, the ostiole minute and not often visible; spores 8, oblong-ellipsoid,
3–5-septate transversely and becoming 1-septate longitudinally, 16–24 × 5–8 μ,
irregularly arranged.

On trees, Massachusetts, New York, Missouri, Iowa, and Minnesota.

OTHER SPECIES REPORTED

Polyblastiopsis dispora (Müll. Arg.) Zahlbr.—Texas.

18. **Pseudopyrenula** Müll. Arg., Flora 66:247, 248. 1883.

Thallus forming a thin, smooth crust over the substratum, partly or wholly
within the substratum, devoid of differentiation into layers; perithecia small to
middle-sized, more or less immersed, often surrounded by a thin, thalloid veil,
the superficial portion a flat, black apex, the ostiole minute, the wall dimidiate or
complete; paraphyses branched and netlike interwoven; asci clavate to cylindrico-
clavate; spores 8, hyaline, oblong to oblong-ellipsoid, 3-septate (rarely more),
the cells lenticular or almost spherical.

The algal host is Trentepohlia.

1. **Pseudopyrenula Pupula** (Ach.) Müll. Arg., Flora 68:331, 332. 1885.
Pyrenula Pupula Ach., Meth. Lich. 123. 1814. *Pyrenula discolor* Fée.

Thallus thin, rudimentary, the superficial portion sometimes absent and the
imbedded portion indicated by a smooth, olive-green to yellowish or whitish area;
perithecia small to middle-sized, 0.4–0.8 mm. across, the wall thin, complete, imbedded in conical elevations, the flat, black apex showing, surrounded by a whitish
area of the thalloid covering, and sometimes showing the minute ostiole at the
center; spores 3-septate, oblong-ellipsoid, 28–36 × 10–13 μ, biseriately to irregularly
arranged.

On trees, Florida.

19. **Porina** Müll. Arg., Flora 66:320. 1883.

Thallus forming a very thin to thin, smooth to minutely rough crust over the
substratum, partly or wholly within the substratum, devoid of differentiation into
layers; perithecia minute to small, more or less immersed, the superficial portion
hemispherical or somewhat convex, the ostiole minute, punctiform, the wall dimidiate or rarely complete; paraphyses unbranched, rarely forked at the apices;
asci clavate or cylindrico-clavate; spores commonly 8, hyaline, ellipsoid, fusiform
or acicular, 3- rarely 1–7- or more-septate, the cells cylindrical.

The algal host is Trentepohlia.

A. Spores 1–3-septate
  B. Thallus usually appearing as a coloration of the substratum
    C. Spores 1-septate . . . . 1. P. plumbaria
    C. Spores becoming 3-septate
      D. Thallus surrounded by a black hypothallus;
        spores 16–20 $\times$ 3.5–6 μ . . . . 3. P. subcinerea
      D. Thallus not surrounded by a black hypothallus;
        spores 12–16 $\times$ 4.5–6 μ . . . . 2. P. cinerea
  B. Thallus very thin, but persistent
    C. Thallus thin to granulose or scurfy
      D. Thallus granulose; spores 18–30 $\times$ 4.5–7 μ . . . . . 8. P. lectissima
      D. Thallus becoming scurfy; spores 15–23 $\times$ 3.5–4.5 μ . . 7. P. chlorotica
    C. Thallus smooth to minutely wrinkled
      D. Spores rarely more than 16 μ in length
        E. Spores 9–10 $\times$ 3–4 μ . . . . 5. P. viridiseda
        E. Spores 13–16 $\times$ 4.5–5 μ . . . . 6. P. salicina
      D. Spores rarely less than 16 μ in length
        E. Thallus dark olive-brown; spores
          15–22 $\times$ 4–4.5 μ . . . . 9. P. olivacea microspora
        E. Thallus greenish gray to ashy or brownish;
          spores 18–24 $\times$ 5–7.5 μ . . . . 4. P. Carpinea
A. Spores 5- or more- septate
  B. Perithecia 0.3–0.7 mm. across
    C. Spores 40–70 $\times$ 8–11 μ . . . . 10. P. nucula
    C. Spores 65–92 $\times$ 10–12 μ . . . . 10. P. nucula heterospora
  B. Perithecia not more than 0.45 mm. across
    C. Spores 5–8-septate
      D. Thallus blackish green
        E. Spores 30–115 $\times$ 2.5–5 μ . . . . 12. P. cestrensis
        E. Spores 36–50 $\times$ 5–9 μ . . . . 12. P. cestrensis platyspora
      D. Thallus greenish gray to ashy or darker . . . . . 11. P. mastoidea
    C. Spores 7–11-septate . . . . 13. P. rhaphidosperma

1. **Porina plumbaria** (Stizenb.) Hasse, Cont. U. S. Nat. Herb. 17:12. 1913.
Verrucaria plumbaria Stizenb.; Hasse, Erythea 3:44. 1893. *Verrucaria carpinea, plumbaria* (Stizenb.) Nyl.
Thallus grayish, rudimentary, the superficial portion sometimes absent, and the imbedded portion indicated at the surface by a light or darker gray coloration; perithecia minute to small, 0.15–0.4 mm. across, the superficial portion hemispherical, shiny black, the ostiole minute, sometimes invisible, the wall dimidiate; spores fusiform, larger toward one end, 1-septate, 12–22 $\times$ 4–6 μ, uniseriately to irregularly arranged.
On trees, especially *Quercus agrifolia*, southern California.

2. **Porina cinerea** (Pers.) Zahlbr., Cat. Lich. Univ. 1:376. 1921.
Verrucaria cinerea Pers., Ann. Bot. Usteri 7:28. pl. 3, f. 6. 1794.
Thallus ashy gray, rudimentary, the superficial portion very thin and disappearing, the imbedded portion indicated at the surface as a grayish coloration; perithecia minute to small, 0.15–0.35 mm. across, often clustered, the superficial portion hemispherical, black, the ostiole minute and rarely visible, the wall dimidiate; spores hyaline or tinged brownish, spindle-shaped to ellipsoid, finally 3-septate, 12–16 $\times$ 4.5–6 μ, irregularly arranged.
On trees, California.

3. **Porina subcinerea** (Nyl.) Zahlbr., Cat. Lich. Univ. 1:405. 1922.
Verrucaria subcinerea Nyl., Mém. Soc. Acad. Maine et Loire 4:37. 1858.
Pyrenula subcinerea (Nyl.) Tuck.
Thallus ashy, rudimentary, surrounded by a black hypothallus, the superficial portion indicated at the surface as an ashy coloration; perithecia minute, 0.1–0.3 mm. across, commonly clustered, the superficial portion depressed-convex, black, the ostiole minute, indicated by a whitish coloration and rarely visible, the wall

dimidiate; spores fusiform, larger toward one end, 3-septate, 16–20 × 3.5–6 μ, biseriately to irregularly arranged.
On trees, Florida, Texas, and Illinois.

4. **Porina Carpinea** (Pers.) Zahlbr., in E. & P., Nat. Pfl. 1:66. 1907.
Verrucaria Carpinea Pers., in Ach., Meth. Lich. 120. 1803.
Thallus thin, smooth to slightly wrinkled, greenish gray to ashy or brownish; perithecia minute to small, 0.15–0.3 mm. across, the superficial portion hemispherical, black, shining, the ostiole minute, indicated by a whitish coloration and often becoming visible, the wall dimidiate; spores fusiform, 3-septate, 18–24 × 5–7.5 μ, uniseriately to irregularly arranged.
On trees, California.

5. **Porina viridiseda** (Nyl.) Zahlbr., Cat. Lich. Univ. 1:409. 1922.
Verrucaria viridiseda Nyl., Mém. Soc. Acad. Maine et Loire 4:55. 1858.
P. viridiseda f. *albiseda* (Nyl.) Zahlbr.
Thallus thin, smooth, greenish gray to ashy or whitish; perithecia minute, 0.1–0.25 mm. across, the superficial portion hemispherical to subconical, black, the ostiole minute, rarely visible, the wall dimidiate; spores ovoid to ovoid-ellipsoid, 1-septate, 9–10 × 3–4 μ, uniseriately to irregularly arranged.
On trees, Florida.

6. **Porina salicina** Müll. Arg., Hedwigia 34:34. 1895.
Thallus thin, ashy white, smooth to slightly rough; perithecia minute to small, 0.15–0.35 mm. across, the superficial portion hemispherical, dull black or whitish pruinose, the ostiole minute and rarely visible, the wall dimidiate; spores ovoid-ellipsoid, 1-septate and constricted at the septum or rarely 3-septate, 13–16 × 4.5–5 μ, uniseriately arranged.
On trees, Louisiana.

7. **Porina chlorotica** (Ach.) Müll. Arg., Rev. Mycol. 6:20. 1884.
Verrucaria chlorotica Ach., Lich. Univ. 283. 1810. *Sagedia chlorotica* (Ach.) Mass.
Thallus thin, smooth, gelatinous, becoming scurfy, widespread, olive-green to ashy gray; perithecia minute to small, 0.1–0.4 mm. across, partly immersed in a thalloid veil, the superficial portion convex, black, the ostiole minute, rarely visible, the wall dimidiate; spores 3-septate, fusiform-dactyloid, 15–23 × 3.5–4.5 μ, irregularly arranged.
On rocks and trees, Massachusetts and North Carolina.
Tuckerman described a form having spores 5–7-septate and 25–40 × 4.5–7 μ.

8. **Porina lectissima** (E. Fries) Zahlbr., in E. & P., Nat. Pfl. 1:66. 1907.
Segestria lectissima E. Fries, Syst. Orb. Veg. 287. 1825.
Thallus thin, smooth, becoming granulose, pale olive-green to reddish yellow; perithecia minute to small, 0.15–0.3 mm. across, the superficial portion convex, reddish to dull black, the ostiole becoming large, the wall dimidiate; spores fusiform, 3-septate, 18–30 × 4.5–7 μ, irregularly arranged.
On rocks, New Hampshire.

9. **Porina olivacea** (Pers.) A. L. Smith var. **microspora** Fink; Hedrick, Mycologia 25:308. 1933.
Thallus superficial, thin, smooth or somewhat wrinkled or chinky, dark olive-brown; perithecia minute, 0.15–0.25 mm. across, hemispherical, the wall dimidiate, the ostiole invisible, slightly immersed, the superficial portion black; hypothecium and hymenium hyaline; spores long-ellipsoid, 3-septate, 15–22 × 4–4.5 μ, arranged irregularly.
On trees, New Hampshire. (The typical form of the species is European.)

10. **Porina nucula** Ach., Syn. Meth. Lich. 112. 1814.
Porophora nucula (Ach.) Spreng.
Thallus thin, becoming warty-granulose, ashy green to gray; perithecia small to middle-sized, 0.3–0.7 mm. across, imbedded in hemispherical or conical thalloid warts, 1 in each, with a small or larger ostiole, the wall dimidiate; spores fusiform-acicular, 7–11-septate, 40–70 × 8–11 μ, parallel to irregularly arranged.
On trees, South Carolina, Florida, Alabama, and Louisiana.

var. **heterospora** Fink; Hedrick, Mycologia 25:308. 1933.
Spores becoming larger than in species, 5–13-septate, 65–92 × 10–12 μ.
On trees, Florida.

11. **Porina mastoidea** (Ach.) Müll. Arg.; Engler, Bot. Jahr. 6:399. 1885.
Pyrenula mastoidea Ach., Ges. Nat. Fr. Berl. Mag. 6:16. pl. 2, f. 16. 1814.
Thallus thin to moderately thick, smooth to somewhat rough, greenish gray to ashy or sometimes blackening; perithecia minute to small, 0.15–0.45 mm. across, imbedded in thalloid warts, the superficial portion slightly convex, dull black, the ostiole minute, very rarely visible, the wall dimidiate; spores fusiform, sometimes curved, 5– more commonly 7-septate, 32–50 × 5–7 μ, parallel to more commonly irregularly arranged.
On trees, Florida.

12. **Porina cestrensis** (Tuck.) Müll. Arg., Flora 66:338. 1883.
Sagedia cestrensis Tuck., Gen. Lich. 265. 1872. *Sagedia cestrensis* f. *olivacea* Tuck.
Thallus thin, smooth to chinky, blackish green, a conspicuous dark hypothallus sometimes present; perithecia minute, 0.1–0.25 mm. across, the superficial portion hemispherical, black, the ostiole invisible, the wall dimidiate; spores fusiform-acicular, larger toward one end, 5–8-septate, 30–115 × 2.5–5 μ, parallel to irregularly arranged.
On trees and rarely on rocks, from New England to Georgia and westward to Alabama and Tennessee.

var. **platyspora** Fink; Hedrick, Mycologia 25:308. 1933.
Spores 36–50 × 5–9 μ, thus reaching twice the width usually found in the species.
On beech trunks, near Scipio, Indiana.

13. **Porina rhaphidosperma** Müll. Arg., Hedwigia 34:35. 1895.
Thallus thin, ashy white to grayish, smooth to slightly rough, sometimes becoming chinky; perithecia minute to small, 0.1–0.35 mm. across, sometimes clustered, the superficial portion hemispherical, dull black, the ostiole minute, rarely visible, the wall dimidiate; spores acicular, 7–11-septate, 60–70 × 1.5–2.5 μ, parallel to irregularly arranged.
On trees, southeastern United States.

OTHER SPECIES REPORTED

Porina faginea (Schaer.) Arnold.—Massachusetts and Illinois.

20. **Clathroporina** Müll. Arg., Flora 65:517. 1882.

Thallus forming a very thin to thin, smooth crust over the substratum, partly or wholly within the substratum, devoid of differentiation into layers; perithecia minute to small, more or less immersed, the superficial portion convex or subconical, the wall dimidiate, the ostiole minute, punctiform; paraphyses unbranched; asci clavate; spores 8, hyaline, ellipsoid to oblong or fusiform, transversely and longitudinally septate, the cells cylindrical.
The algal host is Trentepohlia.

1. **Clathroporina amygdalina** (Müll. Arg.) Fink n. comb.
Porina amygdalina Müll. Arg., Hedwigia 34:34. 1895.
Superficial thallus thin, in small or larger areas, smooth, somewhat shining, greenish gray, varying toward ashy or yellowish; perithecia small, oblong, 0.15–0.3 × 0.25–0.5 mm. across, superficial portion convex, black; spores oblong-ovoid, 8–12-septate transversely and 2–3-septate longitudinally, 22–37×11–18μ.
On trees, Louisiana.

21. **Belonia** Koerb., in T. Fries, Gener. Heterol. 105. 1861.

Thallus forming a very thin to thin, smooth crust over the substratum, partly or wholly within the substratum, devoid of differentiation into layers; perithecia minute to small or middle-sized, more or less immersed in thalloid warts, the superficial portion a black apex, the ostiole minute to rarely larger, the wall complete, thick above and thin below; paraphyses threadlike, unbranched, sometimes indistinct; asci cylindrico-clavate, soon breaking down; spores 4– commonly 8, hyaline, acicular, many-septate, the cells cylindrical.
The algal host is Trentepohlia.

1. **Belonia americana** Fink; Hedrick, Mycologia 25:309. 1933.
Thallus very thin to thin, smooth, ashy gray to whitish; perithecia small to middle-sized, 0.3–0.8 mm. across, partly immersed, covered by a thin, whitish thalloid veil, the apex visible, black, sometimes surrounded by a white border, the ostiole minute, usually invisible, and sometimes covered by a white layer, the wall complete, thick above and thin below; hypothecium tinged brownish; hymenium hyaline; spores 8, long-acicular, reaching 39–44-septate, 170–250×2–3μ, parallelly arranged.
On trees, Texas.

22. **Thelopsis** Nyl., Mém. Soc. Sci. Nat. Cherb. 3:194. 1855.

Thallus forming a thin, smooth to more or less rough crust upon the substratum, partly or wholly within the substratum, devoid of differentiation into layers; perithecia minute, more or less immersed in thalloid warts, the wall thin, brownish to black, complete, the superficial portion a black apex, the ostiole minute, punctiform; paraphyses slender, unbranched; asci cylindrico-clavate; spores many, hyaline, ellipsoid to oblong-ellipsoid, 1–3-septate, rarely non-septate, the cells cylindrical.
The algal host is Trentepohlia.

1. **Thelopsis subporinella** Nyl.; Hasse, Bull. Torr. Club 25:632. 1898.
Dithelopsis subporinella (Nyl.) Clements.
Thallus composed of small, irregular warts, scattered or crowded together into an uneven, chinky, reddish yellow or buff-colored crust; perithecia minute, 0.1–0.25 mm. across, immersed 1–several in the thalloid warts, the ostiole scarcely visible, indicated by a minute light brown area; hyaline within; spores oblong-ellipsoid, 1-septate, 8–15×4–8μ.
On trees, southern California.

23. **Pyrenula** Mass., Ric. Lich. 162. 1852.

Thallus forming a thin, smooth to rough crust upon the substratum, partly or wholly within the substratum, devoid of differentiation into layers; perithecia minute to small or middle-sized, more or less immersed to adnate, the superficial portion hemispherical to conical, the ostiole minute, often rarely visible, the wall thin and complete or dimidiate; paraphyses unbranched; asci clavate; spores 8, brown, ellipsoid, oblong or pointed-ellipsoid, 3– rarely 5–7-septate, the cells lenticular.
The algal host is Trentepohlia.

A. Spores 3-septate
  B. Perithecia minute, not more than 0.4 mm. across
    C. Thallus commonly indicated by a coloration of the substratum
      D. Thallus a whitish or yellowish coloration . . . . 1. P. aspistea

D. Thallus an ashy coloration . . . . 2. P. farrea
C. Thallus very thin but distinct
    D. Thallus dull to bright orange . . . . 6. P. cerina
    D. Thallus ashy or greenish brown to brown . . . . . . 7. P. Herrei
B. Perithecia larger, rarely less than 0.4 mm. across
    C. Thallus commonly indicated by a coloration of the substratum
        D. Thallus a greenish or grayish brown coloration . . . 4. P. mamillana
        D. Thallus a grayish or yellowish white coloration . . . . 3. P. laevigata
    C. Thallus very thin, but distinct, greenish gray to grayish brown . 5. P. nitida
A. Spores 4–7-septate . . . . 2. P. farrea pluriloculata

1. **Pyrenula aspistea** (Afz.) Ach., Ges. Naturf. Freund. Mag. 6:17. pl. 2, f. 18. 1814.
   Verrucaria aspistea Afz., in Ach., Meth. Lich. 121. 1803.
   Thallus rudimentary, the superficial portion thin, sometimes absent, the imbedded portion indicated at the surface by a whitish or yellowish area; perithecia minute to small, 0.2–0.35 mm. across, ·partly immersed, sometimes clustered or conglomerate, the superficial portion subhemispherical, becoming black, the ostiole minute, rarely visible, the wall very thin, complete; spores 3-septate, ellipsoid, 20–28 × 8–12 μ.
   On trees, Massachusetts, Delaware, and Florida.

2. **Pyrenula farrea** (Ach.) Branth. & Rostr., Bot. Tidss. 3:260. 1869.
   Verrucaria farrea Ach., Meth. Lich. 115. 1803. *P. leucoplaca* (Wallr.) Koerb.
   Thallus ashy or whitish, rudimentary, the superficial portion smooth, very thin, often disappearing, the imbedded portion indicated at the surface by an ashy coloration; perithecia minute to small, 0.15–0.35 mm. across, the superficial portion hemispherical, becoming depressed, black, the ostiole rarely visible, the wall very thin, complete; spores ellipsoid or pointed-ellipsoid, 3-septate, 14–25 × 5–9 μ. (PLATE 2 a.)
   On trees, New England, New York, and westward to Iowa and Minnesota.

   var. **pluriloculata** (Fink) Zahlbr., Cat. Lich. Univ. 1:430. 1922.
   P. leucoplaca var. *pluriloculata* Fink, Minn. Bot. Stud. 2:709. 1902.
   Perithecia somewhat larger than in the species, 0.2–0.45 mm. across; spores 4–7-septate.
   On trees, Minnesota.

3. **Pyrenula laevigata** (Pers.) Arn., Flora 68:158. 1885.
   Verrucaria laevigata Pers., Ann. Wet. Ges. 2:11. 1811. *P. glabrata* (Ach.) Mass.
   Thallus rudimentary, the superficial portion sometimes absent and the imbedded portion indicated at the surface as a dull grayish or yellowish white coloration; perithecia middle-sized to large, 0.4–0.8 mm. across, the superficial portion hemispherical to conical, black, the ostiole minute, visible, usually indicated by a whitish area, the wall very thin, complete; spores ellipsoid, 3-septate, 18–25 × 6–9 μ.
   On trees, from New England to Florida and westward to Louisiana and Iowa, recurring in Washington.

4. **Pyrenula mamillana** (Ach.) Trev., Conspect. Verruc. 13. 1860.
   Verrucaria mamillana Ach., Meth. Lich. 120. pl. 3, f. 2. 1803. *P. mamillana* var. *santensis* (Nyl.) Trev. *P. santensis* (Nyl.) Müll. Arg.
   Thallus rudimentary, often bordered by a black hypothallus, the superficial portion sometimes absent and the imbedded portion indicated at the surface as a greenish or grayish brown coloration; perithecia middle-sized to large, 0.35–1 mm. across, the superficial portion subhemispherical, becoming depressed, black, the ostiole papillate, the wall dimidiate; spores ellipsoid to ovoid, 3-septate, 12–20 × 7–8.5 μ.
   On trees, from South Carolina to Florida and westward to Texas.

5. **Pyrenula nitida** (Weig.) Ach., Ges. Naturf. Freund. Mag. 6:21. 1814.
Sphaeria nitida Weig., Obs. Bot. 45. pl. 2, f. 14. 1772. *Verrucaria nitida* (Weig.)
Schrad. *P. nitida* var. *nitidella* Floerke. *P. nitidella* (Floerke) Müll. Arg.

Thallus rudimentary, the superficial portion limited or sometimes rather wide-spread, very thin, somewhat shining, greenish gray to grayish brown; perithecia middle-sized to large, 0.3–0.9 mm. across, often clustered and becoming conglomerate, the wall complete, the superficial portion convex to subhemispherical, black, the ostiole often papillate; spores ellipsoid, 3-septate, $15–28 \times 7–12 \mu$.

On trees, throughout the United States.

6. **Pyrenula cerina** Eschw., Syst. Lich. 25. f. 14. 1824.
P. aurantiaca Fée.

Thallus very thin, the superficial portion smooth to somewhat wrinkled, sometimes becoming areolate and intersected by dark lines, dull to bright orange, whitish within; perithecia minute, 0.1–0.2 mm. across, partly immersed, the superficial portion convex, black, the ostiole minute, rarely visible, indicated by a whitish area, the wall very thin, complete; spores oblong-ellipsoid, 3-septate, $20–35 \times 8–13 \mu$.

On trees, Florida.

7. **Pyrenula Herrei** Fink; Hedrick, Mycologia 25:309. 1933.

Thallus rudimentary, the superficial portion thin, smooth or obscurely scurfy, ashy or greenish brown to brown; perithecia minute to small, 0.2–0.35 mm. across, partly immersed to adnate, black, often shiny, hemispherical or sometimes subglobose, the ostiole rarely visible, the wall dimidiate; spores fusiform to ellipsoid, 3-septate, $16–20 \times 6–8 \mu$.

On trees, Santa Cruz Peninsula, California.

OTHER SPECIES REPORTED

Pyrenula claudestina Ach.—North America.
Pyrenula pinguis (Sprengl.) Fée—Tennessee.
Pyrenula pulicina Nyl.—Florida and North Carolina.

24. **Pyrenulella** Fink*

Thallus imbedded in that of the lichen host and therefore invisible; perithecia minute to small, more or less immersed, the superficial portion hemispherical to convex, the ostiole minute, rarely visible, the wall complete; paraphyses unbranched; asci clavate; spores 8, hyaline, ellipsoid to oblong-ellipsoid, 3-septate, the cells lenticular.

The algal host is Protococcus.

1. **Pyrenulella endococcoidea** (Nyl.) Fink n. comb.
Verrucaria endococcoidea Nyl., Flora 48:356. 1865.

Thallus imbedded in the lichen host and therefore invisible; perithecia minute, globular, the superficial portion convex, black; spores 3-septate, oblong-ellipsoid, $14–18 \times 5–7 \mu$.

On *Buellia petraea*, Massachusetts.

25. **Anthracothecium** Hampe, in Mass., Atti Ist.
Veneto III. 5:330. 1860.

Thallus forming a thin, smooth to slightly rough crust upon the substratum, partly or wholly within the substratum, devoid of differentiation into layers; perithecia minute to small or rarely middle-sized or larger, more or less immersed in thalloid warts, the wall complete or dimidiate, the superficial portion convex to conical, the ostiole minute to small, more or less visible; paraphyses unbranched, free; asci clavate to cylindrico-clavate; spores commonly 8, brownish to brown, oblong-ellipsoid to ellipsoid to fusiform, transversely and longitudinally septate, the cells lenticular.

The algal host is Trentepohlia.

* Pyrenulella Fink gen. nov. A Pyrenula Mass. thallo parasitico et inconspicuo, in hospitis thallo immerso differens.

A. Thallus very thin, inconspicuous or sometimes absent
  B. Spores more than 30 μ in length . . . . 3. A. pyrenuloides
  B. Spores less than 30 μ in length
    C. Spores 5–7-septate transversely . . . . 2. A. staurosporum
    C. Spores 7–9-septate transversely . . . . 5. A. thelomorphum
A. Thallus thin to thicker, plainly visible
  B. Spores more than 35 μ in length
    C. Thallus thin, smooth, greenish gray to ashy . . . . . . 4. A. libricola
    C. Thallus rather thick, smooth, whitish to olive-green, partly
      bordered by a blackish hypothalus . . . . 6. A. mucosum
  B. Spores less than 35 μ in length . . . . 1. A. ochraceoflavum

1. **Anthracothecium ochraceoflavum** (Nyl.) Müll. Arg., Linnaea 63:44. 1880.
Verrucaria ochraceoflava Nyl., Mém. Soc. Acad. Maine et Loire 4:50. 1858.
Thallus thin, smooth to slightly rough, yellowish orange to yellow; perithecia small to middle-sized, 0.3–0.7 mm. across, immersed in subhemispherical thalloid warts, the superficial portion convex, black, the wall very thin, complete, the ostiole minute, depressed, sometimes indicated by a whitish area; spores 8, brown, oblong-ellipsoid to ellipsoid, 5–7-septate transversely and 1–3-septate longitudinally, 18–32 × 9–12 μ, arrangement obliquely uniseriate.
On trees, Florida.

2. **Anthracothecium staurosporum** (Tuck.) Zahlbr., Cat. Lich. Univ. 1:468. 1922.
Pyrenula staurospora Tuck., in Willey, Enum. Lich. New Bedford, Mass. 38. 1892.
Thallus thin, brownish yellow, smooth; perithecia minute to small. 0.1–0.4 mm. across, largely immersed in convex thalloid warts, the wall very thin, complete, the superficial portion convex with an inconspicuous ostiole, black; tinged brownish within; spores 8, ellipsoid, tinged brown, 5–7-septate transversely and partly 1-septate longitudinally, 16–24 × 7–9 μ, arrangement obliquely uniseriate.
On trees, Massachusetts.

3. **Anthracothecium pyrenuloides** (Mont.) Müll. Arg., Linnaea 63:44. 1880.
Trypethelium pyrenuloides Mont., Ann. Sci. Nat. Bot. II. 19:69. 1843. *Pyrenula pachycheila* Tuck. *A. pachycheilum* (Tuck.) Zahlbr.
Thallus rudimentary, the superficial portion very thin, smooth, sometimes absent, and the imbedded portion indicated at the surface by an ashy or yellowish gray coloration; perithecia middle-sized to large, 0.6–1 mm. across, immersed 1 or more in thalloid warts, the superficial portion convex, black, the wall thin, complete, the ostiole small, slightly depressed; spores 8, brown, oblong-ellipsoid to ellipsoid, 5–9-septate transversely, and 1–2- or rarely 3-septate longitudinally, 30–65 × 12–23 μ, arrangement obliquely uniseriate to irregular.
On trees, from Massachusetts to Florida and westward to Tennessee and Texas.

4. **Anthracothecium libricola** (Fée) Müll. Arg., Linnaea 63:43, 44. 1880.
Pyrenula libricola Fée, Essai Crypt. Suppl. 82. 1837.
Thallus thin, smooth, pale greenish gray to pale cream-colored or ashy; perithecia minute to small, 0.1–0.6 mm. across, wholly or partly immersed, dimidiate; superficial portion convex to hemispherical, black, the ostiole rarely visible, minute; spores light brown, oblong-ellipsoid, 7–9-septate transversely and 1–2-septate longitudinally, 35–45 × 15–18 μ, obliquely uniseriately arranged.
On trees, Florida.

5. **Anthracothecium thelomorphum** (Tuck.) Zahlbr., Cat. Lich. Univ. 1:469. 1922.
Pyrenula thelomorpha Tuck., Gen. Lich. 275. 1872.
Thallus inconspicuous, pale greenish gray, tinged with yellow, sometimes scarcely visible; perithecia middle-sized or larger, 0.4–0.7 mm. across, solitary or grouped in thalloid warts, largely immersed, the exposed portions subconical, black,

the wall thin, complete, the ostiole minute, slightly depressed; spores oblong-ellipsoid, 7–9-septate transversely and 1–2-septate longitudinally, 18–28 × 7–9 μ, arrangement obliquely uniseriate.
On trees, southern states.

6. **Anthracothecium mucosum** (Vainio) Zahlbr., Cat. Lich. Univ. 1:464. 1922.
Bottaria mucosa Vainio, Hedwigia 38:257. 1899.
Thallus of medium thickness, whitish to pale olive-green, smooth and shining, partly bordered by a blackish hypothallus; apothecia middle-sized, 0.5–0.7 mm. across, immersed to emergent, convex, dark brown to blackish, the wall complete, black, thin, the ostiole inconspicuous but opening finally; asci cylindrical; spores 8, light brown, oblong-fusiform, 7–9-septate transversely and 1–3-septate longitudinally, 35–50 × 12–20 μ, arrangement obliquely uniseriate.
On trees, Florida.

5. TRYPETHELIACEAE

Thallus crustose, rudimentary, partly or wholly within the substratum, devoid of differentiation into layers, or rarely showing some differentiation; perithecia more or less immersed, usually several in each stroma, the ostiole terminal; paraphyses unbranched and free, or branched and more or less interwoven.
The algal host is Trentepohlia.
A. Spores with lenticular cells
  B. Spores hyaline . . . . 27. TRYPETHELIUM
  B. Spores brown . . . . 26. MELANOTHECA
A. Spores with cylindrical cells . . . . 28. LAURERA

26. **Melanotheca** Fée, Suppl. Essai Crypt. 70. 1837.

Thallus crustose, rudimentary, partly or wholly within the substratum, the superficial portion thin, smooth to rough, devoid of differentiation into layers; stroma round to irregular; perithecia minute to small, several to many immersed in each stroma or rarely solitary in stromatic elevations, the wall complete, the superficial portion convex or depressed, the ostiole minute, rarely visible; hypothecium hyaline to brown; hymenium hyaline or brownish above; paraphyses unbranched and free or branched and netlike interwoven; asci cylindrico-clavate; spores 8, brown, ellipsoid to oblong-ellipsoid or fusiform, obliquely uniseriately to irregularly arranged, 3–several-septate, the cells lenticular.
The algal host is Trentepohlia.
A. Spores more than 18 μ in length
  B. Thallus ashy to dull yellowish . . . . 4. M. concatervans
  B. Thallus more or less reddish brown
    C. Perithecia minute, not more than 0.2 mm. across . . . 2. M. subincruenta
    C. Perithecia small, more than 0.2 mm. across . . . . . . 1. M. cruenta
A. Spores not more than 18 μ in length . . . . 3. M. aggregata

1. **Melanotheca cruenta** (Mont.) Müll. Arg., Engl. Bot. Jahr. 6:397. 1885.
Trypethelium cruentum Mont., Ann. Sci. Nat. Bot. II. 8:537. 1837.
Thallus very thin to thin, smooth to slightly rough, greenish to reddish brown; perithecia minute to small, 0.3–0.8 mm. across, heaped together in a stroma, or rarely solitary in stromatic elevations, the superficial portion convex, reddish brown to black, the wall thin, black, complete, the ostiole minute, rarely visible; spores 3-septate, oblong-ellipsoid, 22–30 × 9–14 μ.
On trees, from New Jersey to Florida and westward to Texas.

2. **Melanotheca subincruenta** (Nyl.) Zahlbr., Cat. Lich. Univ. 1:483. 1922.
Trypethelium subincruentum Nyl., Lich. Jap. 109. 1890.
Thallus very thin, smooth to slightly rough, ashy to reddish brown; perithecia minute, 0.06–0.2 mm. across, heaped together in irregular, reddish stromata, the

superficial portion convex, reddish brown to black, the ostiole minute, rarely visible, the wall complete; spores ellipsoid, 3-septate, 18–23 × 8–11 μ.

On trees, Florida.

3. **Melanotheca aggregata** (Fée) Müll. Arg., Mém. Soc. Phys. Hist. Nat. Genève 30:18. 1888.

Verrucaria aggregata Fée, Essai Crypt. 91. 1824.

Thallus very thin, smooth, dull yellowish; perithecia minute, 0.06–0.2 mm. across, heaped together in a stroma or rarely solitary in stromatic elevations, the superficial portion convex, black, the ostiole minute, rarely visible, the wall thin, black, complete; spores oblong-ellipsoid, 3-septate, 12–18 × 5–7 μ.

On trees, Florida, Louisiana, and Texas.

4. **Melanotheca concatervans** (Nyl.) Zahlbr., Cat. Lich. Univ. 1:479. 1922.

Verrucaria concatervans Nyl., Lich. Jap. 109. 1890.

Thallus very thin, smooth, ashy to dull yellowish; perithecia minute to small, 0.2–0.6 mm. across, several immersed in a stroma, or solitary in stromatic elevations, the superficial portion convex, black, the ostiole minute, sometimes indicated by a whitish area, the wall complete; spores oblong-ellipsoid, 5-septate, 25–30 × 8–12 μ.

On trees, Florida.

27. **Trypethelium** Spreng., Anleit. Kenn. Gewachse 3:309. 1805.

Thallus crustose, rudimentary, partly or wholly within the substratum, the superficial portion thin, smooth to rough, devoid of differentiation into layers, or showing very thin, poorly developed upper and lower cortices of entangled hyphae; stroma round to irregular, hemispherical, convex or rarely flat; perithecia minute to small, several to many immersed in each stroma or rarely solitary in stromatic elevations, the wall complete, the superficial portion convex to depressed, the ostiole minute, often scarcely visible; hypothecium hyaline to brown; hymenium hyaline; paraphyses branched and netlike interwoven; asci cylindrico-clavate; spores 8, hyaline, oblong-ellipsoid to ellipsoid or fusiform, 3–several-septate, the cells lenticular.

The algal host is Trentepohlia.

A. Spores not more than 3-septate
  B. Thallus yellowish to orange . . . . 1. T. aeneum
  B. Thallus yellowish or greenish gray to ashy
    C. Stromata blackish brown
      D. Thallus usually disappearing, indicated by
        yellowish or ashy coloration . . . . 2. T. mastoideum
      D. Thallus thin, greenish gray to yellowish . . . . . 3. T. tropicum
    C. Stromata ashy to yellowish
      D. Spores 20–28 μ in length . . . . 8. T. pallescens
      D. Spores 14–22 μ in length . . . . 5. T. catervarium
A. Spores more than 3-septate
  B. Spores not more than 9-septate
    C. Thallus ashy to brownish gray . . . . 6. T. scorites
    C. Thallus greenish yellow to brown
      D. Thallus indicated by a greenish brown coloration . . 7. T. exocanthum
      D. Thallus very thin, greenish yellow to brown . . . . . 4. T. virens
  B. Spores 9–13-septate . . . . 9. T. eluteriae

1. **Trypethelium aeneum** (Eschw.) Zahlbr., in E. & P., Nat. Pfl. 1:70. 1907.

Verrucaria aenea Eschw., in Mart., Icon. Pl. Crypt. 2:15. pl. 8, f. 3. 1828–34.

T. Kunzei Fée. *Verrucaria heterochroa* Mont.

Thallus very thin, smooth to slightly rough, yellowish to deep orange; perithecia minute, 0.08–0.15 mm. across, several to many immersed in irregular, yellowish orange stromata, or solitary in stromatic elevations, the superficial portion convex, black; spores oblong-ellipsoid, 3-septate, 19–27 × 7–9 μ.

On trees, Florida.

2. **Trypethelium mastoideum** Ach., Lich. Univ. 307. pl. 4, f. 9. 1810.
Bathelium mastoideum Ach., Meth. Lich. 111. pl. 8, f. 3. 1803. *T. scoria* Nyl.
T. carolinianum Tuck.
Thallus very thin to thin, smooth, greenish gray to yellowish or ashy, bordered
by a black hypothallus, the superficial portion sometimes disappearing and the imbedded portion indicated at the surface as a yellowish or ashy coloration; perithecia
minute, 0.05–0.15 mm. across, heaped together in irregular, convex, blackish brown
stromata, or rarely solitary in stromatic elevations, the superficial portion black,
the ostiole minute, black; spores oblong-ellipsoid, 3-septate, 18–24 × 6.5–9 μ.
On trees, from New Jersey to Florida and in Alabama and Texas.

3. **Trypethelium tropicum** (Ach.) Müll. Arg.; Engler, Bot. Jahr. 6:393. 1885.
Verrucaria tropica Ach., Lich. Univ. 278. 1810. *Pyrenula tropica* (Ach.) Trev.
Thallus very thin to thin, smooth to rough, greenish gray to yellowish; perithecia
minute to small, 0.08–0.3 mm. across, heaped together in irregular, brownish black
stromata, or solitary in globose, clustered, stromatic elevations, the superficial
portion depressed, black or whitish pruinose, the ostiole small, black; spores oblong,
3-septate, 18–24 × 6–8 μ.
On trees, South Carolina, Florida, Alabama, Texas, and Mississippi.

4. **Trypethelium virens** Tuck., in Darl., Fl. Cestr. ed. 3. 453. 1853.
Thallus very thin to thin, smooth, greenish yellow to brownish; perithecia
minute, 0.05–0.15 mm. across, several to many immersed in slightly convex, round
or irregular, scattered or clustered, greenish yellow or brownish stromata, the ostiole
minute, black; spores oblong-ellipsoid, 3–9-septate, 30–50 × 10–15 μ.
On trees, from New England to Florida and westward to Louisiana and Ohio.

5. **Trypethelium catervarium** (Fée) Tuck., Gen. Lich. 260. 1872.
Verrucaria catervaria Fée, Essai Crypt. 90. pl. 22, f. 1. 1824.
Thallus very thin, rudimentary, smooth to rough, ashy gray to yellowish, the
superficial portion sometimes disappearing, and the imbedded portion indicated at
the surface as a yellowish gray coloration; perithecia minute, 0.08–0.15 mm. across,
immersed 1–several in ashy, irregular stromata, the ostiole minute, black; spores
ellipsoid, 3-septate, 14–22 × 6–8.5 μ.
On trees, Florida and Alabama.

6. **Trypethelium scorites** Tuck.; Nyl., Ann. Sci. Nat. Bot. IV. 20:259. 1863.
Thallus very thin, smooth, the superficial portion sometimes absent, and the
imbedded portion indicated at the surface by an ashy or brownish gray coloration;
perithecia minute, 0.05–0.15 mm. across, heaped together in very irregular, convex,
blackish brown stromata, or rarely solitary in stromatic elevations, the ostiole
minute, black, scarcely visible; spores oblong to oblong-ellipsoid, 5–7-septate,
42–52 × 12–17 μ.
On trees, North Carolina, Florida, Alabama, and Mississippi.

7. **Trypethelium exocanthum** Tuck.; Nyl., Ann. Sci. Nat. Bot. IV. 20:258. 1863.
Thallus very thin, rudimentary, smooth, the superficial portion usually absent,
and the imbedded portion indicated at the surface by a greenish brown coloration;
perithecia minute, 0.05–0.2 mm. across, 1–several immersed in subglobose, irregular
stromata, the ostiole rarely visible; spores oblong-ellipsoid, 5–9-septate, 40–46 ×
9–12 μ.
On trees, North Carolina, South Carolina, Florida, Alabama, Louisiana, Tennessee, and West Virginia.

8. **Trypethelium pallescens** Fée, Ann. Sci. Nat. 23:440. pl. 8, f. 3 *a-c*. 1831.
Trypethelium ochroleucum var. *pallescens* (Fée) Müll. Arg.
Thallus very thin, smooth, yellowish gray or ashy; perithecia minute, 0.05–0.25
mm. across, heaped together in irregular, ashy or yellowish stromata, the ostiole
minute, black; spores ellipsoid, 3-septate, 20–28 × 8–9.5 μ.
On trees, Louisiana, Florida, and Texas.

9. **Trypethelium eluteriae** Spreng., Einl. Stud. Krypt. Gewach. 351. 1804.
Trypethelium Sprengelii Ach.

Thallus very thin, rudimentary, smooth to rough, yellowish gray to brownish, the superficial portion sometimes absent, and the imbedded portion indicated at the surface as a yellowish gray coloration; perithecia minute, 0.05–0.2 mm. across, heaped together in strongly convex, somewhat irregular, brownish to brown stromata, or rarely solitary in stromatic elevations, the ostiole minute, black; spores fusiform, 9–13-septate, 40–54 × 10–13 μ.

On trees, Florida.

OTHER SPECIES REPORTED

Trypethelium favulosum Ach.—Florida.
Trypethelium porosum Ach.—Maryland.
Trypethelium variatum Nyl.—Florida.

28. **Laurera** Reich., Der Deutsch. Bot. 15. 1841.

Thallus crustose, rudimentary, partly or wholly within the substratum, the superficial portion thin, smooth to rough, devoid of differentiation into layers; stroma round to irregular, hemispherical to flat or more or less indistinct; perithecia minute to small or middle-sized, 1–several immersed in each stroma, the wall complete, the superficial portion convex, flat or depressed, the ostiole scarcely visible; hypothecium hyaline to brown; hymenium hyaline; paraphyses branched and netlike interwoven; asci cylindrico-clavate; spores 2–8, hyaline, oblong to oblong-ellipsoid or ellipsoid, transversely and longitudinally septate, the cells cubical or cylindrical.

The algal host is Trentepohlia.

A. Spores more than 100 μ in length   .   .   .   . 2. L. megasperma
A. Spores rarely more than 50 μ in length   .   .   .   . 1. L. madreporiformis

1. **Laurera madreporiformis** (Eschw.) Riddle; Howe, Torreya 16:50. 1916.
Trypethelium madreporiforme Eschw., Syst. Lich. 26. f. 24 *a–c*. 1824.

Thallus very thin, smooth, greenish gray to brownish; perithecia minute to small, 0.2–0.5 mm. across, several immersed in irregular stromata, the superficial portion flat, the ostiole minute and slightly depressed; spores 8, oblong, 9–13-septate transversely and 2–3-septate longitudinally, the cells cubical, 40–50 × 12–16 μ.

On trees, Florida.

2. **Laurera megasperma** (Mont.) Riddle, Bull. Torr. Club 44:323. 1917.
Trypethelium megaspermum Mont., Ann. Sci. Nat. Bot. II. 19:68. 1843.

Thallus very thin, smooth to rough, ashy to pale yellow; perithecia small to middle-sized, 0.4–1 mm. across, 1–several immersed in wartlike stromata, the superficial portion flat, black; spores 2–4, oblong-ellipsoid, 33–43-septate transversely and 3–5-septate longitudinally, the cells almost cubical, 150–240 × 24–36 μ.

On trees, Florida.

6. ASTROTHELIACEAE

Thallus crustose, partly within the substratum, devoid of differentiation into layers or showing a poorly developed upper cortex of coherent hyphae; perithecia immersed, more or less radiately arranged, simple or united, the ostioles usually converging, rarely terminal; paraphyses unbranched or branched and more or less interwoven.

The algal host is Trentepohlia.

A. Spores brown, transversely several-septate   .   .   .   . 29. PYRENASTRUM
A. Spores brown, transversely and longitudinally septate   .   .   .   . 30. PARMENTARIA

29. Pyrenastrum Eschw., Syst. Lich. 16. 1824.

Thallus crustose, thin, smooth to rough, partly within the substratum, devoid of differentiation into layers or showing a poorly developed upper cortex of coherent hyphae; perithecia minute to small, immersed, clustered and more or less united, the wall complete, the superficial portion more or less convex, the ostiole minute; hypothecium brownish; hymenium hyaline or brownish above; paraphyses branched and interwoven; asci clavate; spores 4–8, brownish to brown, ellipsoid to oblong-ellipsoid, 3–7-septate, the cells lenticular.

The algal host is Trentepohlia.

1. **Pyrenastrum pyrenastraeum** (Nyl.) Zahlbr., Cat. Lich. Univ. 1:520. 1922.
Astrothelium pyrenastrum Nyl., Lich. Jap. 109, 110. 1890.

Superficial thallus thin, yellowish brown, smooth to becoming slightly rough and cracked; perithecia minute to small, 0.2–0.6 mm. across, partly immersed, the whitish ostiole protruding, the superficial portion convex, black; tinged brownish within; asci cylindrico-clavate; spores 8, ellipsoid, tinged brown, 3-septate, 16–18 × 5–6.5 μ.

On trees, near Jacksonville, Florida.

30. Parmentaria Fée, Essai Crypt. 70. 1824.

Thallus crustose, thin, smooth to rough, partly within the substratum, devoid of differentiation into làyers, or rarely showing a poorly developed upper cortex of coherent hyphae; perithecia minute to small, 1–several immersed in each thalloid elevation, radially arranged, the wall complete, black, the ostiole minute, converging, canal-like; hypothecium brownish; hymenium hyaline or brownish above; paraphyses branched and netlike interwoven; asci clavate; spores 1–8, brown, ovoid to ovoid-ellipsoid or oblong, transversely and longitudinally septate.

The algal host is Trentepohlia.

A. Spores 30–36 μ in length　.　.　.　.　.　.　.　.　.　.　.　.　.　. 1. P. astroidea
A. Spores 38–76 μ in length　.　.　.　.　.　.　.　.　.　.　.　.　.　. 2. P. Ravenelii

1. **Parmentaria astroidea** Fée, Essai Crypt. 70. pl. 1, f. 14. 1824.
Pyrenastrum gemmeum Tuck. *Pyrenastrum americanum* Spreng.

Thallus thin, smooth to wrinkled and slightly warty, greenish gray to straw-colored; perithecia small, 0.3–0.7 mm. across, black, 1–3 or 4 borne in elevated warts of thallus, in groups of 4–6, radially arranged, converging but not meeting, the proper exciple black, the ostioles minute, canal-like; spores 8, ovoid to ovoid-ellipsoid, 5–9-septate transversely and 1–3-septate longitudinally, 30–36 × 8–12 μ. (Nyl. says 34–45 × 14–18 μ.)

On trees, South Carolina and Texas.

2. **Parmentaria Ravenelii** (Tuck.) Müll. Arg., Flora 68:249, 250. 1885.
Pyrenastrum Ravenelii Tuck., Am. Journ. Sci. II. 25:429. 1858.

Thallus thin, smooth to somewhat wrinkled, waxy, greenish to yellowish brown; perithecia small, 0.3–0.6 mm. across, black, flask-shaped, borne in slightly elevated warts of thallus, radially arranged, the proper exciple black, the ostioles minute, canal-like, convergent, brownish black with pale mouth; spores 8, ellipsoid, 7–9-septate transversely and 4–5-septate longitudinally, 38–76 × 16–27 μ.

On trees, Florida and Texas.

7. STRIGULACEAE

Thallus crustose, devoid of differentiation into layers, attached to the substratum by hyphal rhizoids; perithecia more or less immersed, single or rarely clustered, the ostiole terminal.

The algal hosts are Cephaleurus, Heterothallus, Phycopeltis, and Phyllactidium. The family is limited to the tropics and subtropics and confined to leaves.

31. **Strigula** E. Fries, Vet. Akad. Handl. 323. 1821.

Thallus crustose, forming small areas with minutely lobed margins, often partly within the substratum, rudimentary, devoid of differentiation into layers, attached to the substratum by hyphal rhizoids; perithecia minute, more or less immersed, the wall dimidiate, the superficial portion subhemispherical to convex or depressed, the ostiole minute to small; hypothecium hyaline to brownish; hymenium hyaline or brownish above; paraphyses unbranched and free; asci cylindrical; spores 8, hyaline, ellipsoid to fusiform, 1–3-septate, the cells cylindrical.

The algal host is Phyllactidium, Heterothallus, or Cephaleurus.

1. **Strigula complanata** Mont., in Sagra, Hist. Nat. Cub. 140. pl. 7, f. 3. 1842. *S. elegans* (Fée) Müll. Arg. *S. elegans* f. *hirtella* Müll. Arg. *S. Féei* Mont.

Thallus thin to thick, in small, round or irregular areas, frequently lobed at the margin, wholly or mainly superficial, smooth or sometimes minutely ridged, greenish to yellow or ashy gray; perithecia minute, 0.08–0.2 mm. across, numerous, finally protruding, the superficial portion depressed-subhemispherical, black, the wall dimidiate; spores ellipsoid-fusiform, 1–3-septate, 12–24 × 3–7 μ, uniseriately arranged.

On leaves of trees, from South Carolina to Florida and westward to Mississippi and Texas.

8. PYRENIDIACEAE

Thallus crustose, membranous, scaly to squamulose and rarely distinctly foliose, showing little or no differentiation into layers; perithecia more or less immersed, single, the ostiole terminal.

The algal hosts are Nostoc and Polycoccus.

32. **Hassea** Zahlbr., Beih. Bot. Centralb. 13:150. 1902.

Thallus crustose, smooth, without cortex, attached to the substratum by hyphal rhizoids; perithecia minute to small, immersed, blackish, the wall dimidiate; hypothecium hyaline; paraphyses branched and loosely arranged; asci cylindrico-clavate; spores 8, hyaline, cylindrical, non-septate.

The algal host is Nostoc, scattered throughout the thallus, but absent from the hymenium.

1. **Hassea bacillosa** (Nyl.) Zahlbr., Beih. Bot. Centralb. 13:150. 1902. *Verrucaria bacillosa* Nyl., in Hasse, Lich. South. Calif. 20. 1898.

Thallus thin to moderately thick, olive-brownish, somewhat smooth to chinky and subareolate, sometimes becoming scurfy or powdery; perithecia minute, 0.2–0.3 mm. across, partly immersed, scattered, the superficial portion more or less subhemispherical, black; spores long-cylindrical, straight or nearly so, 30–40 × 1.5–2 μ.

On sandstone, Santa Monica Range, California.

9. PYRENOTRICHACEAE

Thallus taking its form from the algal host, the hyphae forming a layer about the filamentous alga; perithecia more or less immersed, often with a rather long neck and terminal ostiole.

The algal host is Scytonema.

33. **Pyrenothrix** Riddle, Bot. Gaz. 64:513. 1917.

Thallus of hyaline, septate, branched hyphae, forming a layer about the filamentous algal host; perithecia minute, pear-shaped, with terminal, inconspicuous ostiole; paraphyses slender, hyaline, interwoven, and rarely branched; asci clavate;

spores 8, dark brown, ellipsoid, transversely and longitudinally septate, irregularly arranged.
The algal host is Scytonema.

1. **Pyrenothrix nigra** Riddle, Bot. Gaz. 64:513–15. 1917.

Thallus composed of hyaline, septate, flexuous, branched hyphae, 3–4 μ thick and closely applied to the surface of the brownish black, branched algal host; perithecia minute, 0.15–0.25 mm. across, blackish, immersed to closely adnate, the neck short and thick, the ostiole minute and indistinct, the wall thin but complete, plectenchymatous; spores blackish brown, oblong to broadly ellipsoid, 4–5-septate transversely and becoming 1-septate longitudinally, 17–20 $\times$ 6–9 μ.
Growing over *Scytonema* sp., Florida.

10. MYCOPORACEAE

Thallus crustose, partly within the substratum, devoid of differentiation into layers; perithecia more or less immersed, united by complete or incomplete walls to form a more or less compound perithecium, each hymenium with a terminal ostiole.
The algal hosts are Palmella and Trentepohlia.

A. Spores transversely several-septate . . . . 34. MYCOPORELLUM
A. Spores transversely and longitudinally septate . . . . 35. MYCOPORUM

34. **Mycoporellum** Müll. Arg., Revue Mycol. 6:14. 1884.

Thallus crustose, smooth to slightly rough, rudimentary, partly or wholly within the substratum, devoid of differentiation into layers; perithecia minute to small, more or less immersed to adnate, the wall dimidiate or rarely complete, the superficial portion round to oblong or irregular, convex to flat or depressed, the ostioles several to many, round to more or less irregular; hypothecium hyaline to brown; hymenium hyaline or brownish above; paraphyses wanting or poorly developed and branched and interwoven; asci ovoid-clavate, enlarged toward the apices and the apical wall somewhat thickened; spores 8, hyaline to rarely brown, ovoid-ellipsoid to oblong or ellipsoid, 1–3 or rarely 5-septate, the cells cylindrical, often unequal.
The algal host is Trentepohlia.

A. Perithecia reaching 1 mm. or more across; ostioles many
   B. Spores 1–3-septate, 16–21 μ in length . . . . 3. M. californicum
   B. Spores 1-septate, 18–28 μ in length . . . . 2. M. Hassei
A. Perithecia not more than 0.6 mm. across; ostioles several
   B. Spores 1–3-septate . . . . 4. M. difforme
   B. Spores 1-septate . . . . 1. M. sparsellum

1. **Mycoporellum sparsellum** (Nyl.) Müll. Arg., Revue Mycol. 6:14. 1884.
Mycoporum sparsellum Nyl., Ann. Sci. Nat. Bot. V. 7:343. 1867.

Thallus very thin, ashy, smooth to slightly rough, or disappearing; perithecia minute to small, 0.3–0.6 mm. across, adnate, often irregular, dull black, ostioles 2 or 3 to several; spores 1-septate, slightly constricted, ovoid-ellipsoid, sometimes slightly curved, 16–24 $\times$ 6–9 μ.
On trees, Florida and southern California.

2. **Mycoporellum Hassei** Zahlbr., in Hasse, Cont. U. S. Nat. Herb. 17:13, 14. 1913.

Thallus very thin, becoming squamulose, whitish to ashy white; perithecia small to middle-sized, 0.4–1 mm. across, slightly immersed to adnate, flat to slightly convex, often irregular or elongated, dull black, ostioles 14–18; spores 1-septate, oblong, 18–28 $\times$ 7.5–10 μ, one cell narrower and more pointed.
On trees, Catalina Island, California.

3. **Mycoporellum californicum** Zahlbr., Ann. Mycol. 10:363, 364. 1912.

Thallus very thin, smooth to slightly rough, ashy white, often disappearing and the imbedded portion indicated at the surface by an ashy white coloration; perithecia small to middle-sized, 0.5–1.2 mm. across, partly immersed, the superficial portion slightly convex, dull black, becoming irregular, the ostioles numerous, 20 or more, round to slightly irregular; spores oblong-ellipsoid, 1–3-septate, 16–21 ✕ 5–6 μ.

On trees, southern California.

4. **Mycoporellum difforme** (Minks) Fink n. comb.

Mycoporum difforme Minks, in Willey, Enum. Lich. New Bedford, Mass. 32. 1892. *Dermatina difformis* (Minks) Zahlbr.

Thallus very thin, greenish gray to ashy, smooth, or imbedded and indicated by a whitish area; perithecia small, 0.3–0.5 mm. across, partly immersed, the superficial portion round to oblong or irregular, strongly convex, becoming obscurely papillate; spores 1–3-septate, ellipsoid, 16–27 × 5–9 μ.

On trees, near New Bedford, Massachusetts.

35. **Mycoporum** Mey., Nebenstud. 327. 1825.

Thallus crustose, smooth to rough, rudimentary, partly or wholly within the substratum, devoid of differentiation into layers; perithecia minute to small, more or less immersed, the wall dimidiate or complete, the superficial portion convex to subhemispherical or depressed, the ostioles several, papillate; hypothecium hyaline; hymenium hyaline or brownish above; paraphyses disappearing or persistent and branched and interwoven; asci cylindrico-clavate, the apical wall somewhat thickened; spores 6–8, hyaline to brownish, oblong-ellipsoid to ellipsoid, transversely and longitudinally septate.

The algal host is Palmella.

A. Spores very large, reaching 100 μ or more in length . . . . 2. M. ohiense
A. Spores not so large, not more than 50 μ in length . . . . 1. M. pyrenocarpum

1. **Mycoporum pyrenocarpum** Nyl., Flora 41:381. 1858.

M. pycnocarpum Nyl. *Dermatina pyrenocarpa* (Nyl.) Zahlbr.

Thallus thin, smooth to rarely scurfy or warty, sometimes disappearing, ashy gray; perithecia small, 0.4–0.5 mm. across, oblong to irregular, the superficial portion convex to subhemispherical or often depressed, more or less distinctly papillate, black; hypothecium hyaline; spores 8, hyaline to brownish, oblong-ellipsoid, 7–9-septate transversely and 1–3-septate longitudinally, 33–46 × 13–19 μ.

On trees, from Massachusetts to Florida and westward to Nebraska and California.

2. **Mycoporum ohiense** (Nyl.) Fink n. comb.

M. pycnocarpum ohiense Nyl., Mém. Soc. Sci. Nat. Cherb. 5:135. 1857.

Thallus thin, smooth to slightly rough, ashy gray, sometimes disappearing; perithecia small, 0.3–0.5 mm. across, irregular, the superficial portion convex or sometimes depressed, more or less distinctly papillate, black; hypothecium hyaline; spores 8, hyaline, oblong-ellipsoid, 7–11-septate transversely and 1–3-septate longitudinally, 94–120 × 23–30 μ.

On trees, North Carolina, Ohio, and California.

OTHER SPECIES REPORTED

Mycoporum Eschweileri Müll. Arg.—Florida.

11. CALICIACEAE

Thallus crustose, partly within the substratum, rudimentary, inconspicuous and sometimes disappearing to well developed, showing little or no differentiation; stipes rudimentary to well developed, rarely wanting, rarely branched or forked;

apothecia borne on the tip of the stipe, cup-shaped to top-shaped, usually with a proper exciple.

The algal hosts are Protococcus, Pleurococcus, and Stichococcus.

A. Spores septate
  B. Spores 1-septate
    C. Parasitic on other lichens . . . . 39. Caliciella
    C. Not parasitic on other lichens . . . . 37. Calicium
  B. Spores 3– rarely 7-septate . . . . 41. Stenocybe
A. Spores non-septate
  B. Parasitic on other lichens . . . . 42. Sphinctrina
  B. Not parasitic on other lichens
    C. Spores brown
      D. Thallus inconspicuous; spores ovoid to ellipsoid . . 38. Mycocalicium
      D. Thallus thin to thick, minutely granulose; spores
        spherical or subspherical . . . . 36. Chaenotheca
    C. Spores hyaline . . . . 40. Coniocybe

36. Chaenotheca T. Fries, Gen. Het. Eur. 102. 1861.

Thallus rudimentary, with definite layers, thin to moderately thick, minutely granulose, or warty, stipes short to long, brown to black; apothecia minute, globose to top-shaped, the disk convex to flat, brown to black, or rarely lighter, the exciple thin, usually colored like the disk; hypothecium dark brown; paraphyses unbranched or branched, more or less coherent and indistinct; asci cylindrical; spores 8, brown, non-septate, spherical or subspherical.

The algal host is Cystococcus, Stichococcus, or Pleurococcus.

A. Thallus very thin, minutely granulose, soon disappearing
  B. Thallus ashy to greenish, the exciple ashy pruinose below . . 4. C. brunneola
  B. Thallus whitish to yellowish, the exciple brownish black . . 3. C. melanophaea
A. Thallus thin to moderately thick, more or less granulose,
  rarely disappearing
  B. Thallus ashy to yellowish or greenish; stipes rarely pruinose
    and exciple sometimes pruinose below
    C. Thallus moderately thick, subgranulose; stipes paler
      below . . . . 2. C. phaeocephala
    C. Thallus thinner, scurfy to almost squamulose; stipes brown
      to black . . . . 5. C. trichialis
  B. Thallus yellowish green to lemon-yellow; stipes and exciple
    more or less greenish pruinose . . . . 1. C. chrysocephala

1. **Chaenotheca chrysocephala** (Turn.) T. Fries, Gen. Het. Eur. 102. 1861.
    Lichen chrysocephalus Turn., Trans. Linn. Soc. Lond. 7:88. pl. 8, f. 1. 1804.
    Calicium chrysocephalum (Turn.) Ach. *C. chrysocephala* f. *filaris* (Ach.)
    Blombg. & Forss.

Thallus granulose-verrucose, yellowish green to lemon-yellow, conglomerate to scattered; stipes becoming elongated, dark brown to black, sometimes obscurely greenish pruinose; apothecia minute, 0.1–0.25 mm. across, spheroidal to top-shaped, the disk convex to finally flat, dark brown, the exciple brownish black, or yellowish green pruinose, the disk being also pruinose in young conditions; hypothecium dark brown; asci cylindrical; spores 3–6 μ in diameter.

On bark and wood of conifers, Massachusetts and Minnesota.

2. **Chaenotheca phaeocephala** (Turn.) T. Fries, Nov. Act. Soc. Sci. Ups. III.
    3:351. 1861.
    Lichen phaeocephalus Turn., Trans. Linn. Soc. Lond. 8:260. pl. 6, f. 1. 1807.
    Calicium phaeocephalum (Turn.) E. Fries. *C. phaeocephala* var. *trabinella*
    (J. Smith) Fink.

Thallus moderately thick, subgranulose, ashy to dusty yellow, sometimes becoming scattered and finally disappearing; stipes becoming long, brownish black, or paler toward the base, sometimes thinly yellowish green pruinose, especially toward the top; apothecia minute, 0.15–0.3 mm. across, spherical to top-shaped, the disk finally convex and dark brown, the exciple of the same color or yellowish green pruinose; hypothecium dark brown; spores spherical, brown, 3–6 μ in diameter.

On decorticate trees or wood, especially on conifers, New England and Minnesota.

3. **Chaenotheca melanophaea** (Ach.) Zwackh., Flora 45:535. 1862.
   Calicium melanophaeum Ach., Vet. Akad. Handl. 1816:276. pl. 8, f. 8. 1816.
   Thallus verrucose, whitish to yellowish, disappearing; stipes of moderate size and length, black; apothecia minute, 0.15–0.4 mm. across, top-shaped, the disk flat to convex, dark brown to black, the exciple brownish black, usually indistinct; spores pale brown, varying much in size, 2.5–8 μ in diameter.
   On pine bark, Michigan.

4. **Chaenotheca brunneola** (Ach.) Müll. Arg., Mém. Soc. Phys. Hist. Nat.
   Genève 16³:360. 1862.
   Calicium brunneolum Ach., Vet. Akad. Handl. 1816:297. 1816.
   Thallus minutely granulose, ashy to greenish, very thin and evanescent; stipes black, very long and slender; apothecia minute, 0.1–0.25 mm. across, globose-lenticular, the disk and the exciple dark brown, or the latter ashy pruinose below; hypothecium dark brown; asci cylindrical; spores 2.5–5 μ in diameter.
   On old wood, New England and Minnesota. Possibly too near *C. trichialis* (Ach.) T. Fries.

5. **Chaenotheca trichialis** (Ach.) T. Fries, Nov. Act. Soc. Sci. Ups. III. 3:351.
   1861.
   Calicium trichiale Ach., Kgl. Vet. Akad. Nya Handl. 283. 1808.
   Thallus of minute, ashy, yellowish, or greenish, clustered, or more often scattered, squamiform granules, or reduced to a scurfy condition; stipes brown to black, of medium length; apothecia minute, 0.1–0.25 mm. across, globose-lenticular, the disk and the exciple dark brown, or ashy pruinose below; hypothecium dark brown; asci cylindrical; spores spheroidal, 2.5–5 μ in diameter.
   On decorticate trees, Massachusetts and Minnesota. *C. trichialis* var. *cinerea* (Pers.) Blomb. & Forss. and *C. trichialis* var. *stemonea* (Ach.) Blomb. & Forss. are scarcely distinct.

37. **Calicium** Pers., Ann. Bot. Usteri 1:20. 1794.

Thallus usually smooth, inconspicuous and sometimes evanescent, but occasionally reaching granulose or verrucose conditions, rarely with the margins lobed; apothecia blackish, black, or more or less lighter pruinose, a proper exciple present, but no thalloid exciple; stipes well developed; asci cylindrical or cylindrico-clavate; spores 8, paler or darker brown, plainly or obscurely 1-septate, often constricted, usually uniseriate.
   The algal host is Cystococcus.

A. Thallus yellowish
   B. Thallus more or less intersected by the black hypothallus . 2. C. leucochlorum
   B. Thallus not intersected by the black hypothallus . . . . . 1. C. hyperellum
A. Thallus whitish, grayish, or greenish gray
   B. Exciple brownish black to black or rarely somewhat pruinose
      C. Disk more or less pruinose
         D. Spores 7–12 $\times$ 4–6 μ . . . . 4. C. abietinum
         D. Spores 5–9 $\times$ 3–5 μ . . . . 3. C. lenticulare
      C. Disk not pruinose
         D. Stipes very short to short
            E. Thallus black; stipes white to reddish or black . . . 6. C. Curtisii
            E. Thallus grayish white; stipes blackish . . . . . 7. C. populnéum
         D. Stipes of medium length or elongated
            E. Apothecia 0.1–0.2 mm. across . . . . 8. C. pusillum
            E. Apothecia 0.2–0.5 mm. across . . . . 5. C. trachelinum

B. Exciple yellowish- or bluish-green to darker
    C. Spores 8–12 × 2.5–4.5 μ . . . . 9. C. roscidum   trabinellum
    C. Spores 9–18 × 4–8 μ . . . . 9. C. roscidum

1. **Calicium hyperellum** Ach., Meth. Lich. 93. 1803.
    Lichen hyperellus Ach., Lich. Suec. 85. 1798.
    Thallus greenish yellow to yellowish gray, scurfy-granulose, well developed and continuous to thinner and more or less scattered; stipes of medium length, brownish black to black; apothecia minute to small, 0.15–0.3 mm. across, subspherical to top-shaped, the disk convex to flat, black, the exciple brownish black; hypothecium brown; spores dark brown, oblong-ellipsoid, 10–15 × 5–8 μ.
    On trees, California, Oregon, Idaho, and Washington.

2. **Calicium leucochlorum** Tuck., Proc. Am. Acad. 5:389. 1862.
    Thallus granulose, the yellow to yellowish gray granules subcontiguous and forming a thin, uneven crust, intersected more or less by the black hypothallus; stipes middle-length, stout and black; apothecia clavate-top-shaped, minute to small, 0.15–0.4 mm. across, the disk convex to flat, dark brown to blackish, the exciple dark rust-colored; spores brown, oblong, 10–14 × 7.5–8 μ.
    On old wood, Florida.

3. **Calicium lenticulare** (Hoffm.) E. Fries, Corp. Fl. Suec. 1:283. 1835.
    Trichia lenticularis Hoffm., Veg. Crypt. 2:16. pl. 4, f. 3. 1790. *C. subcinereum* Nyl. *C. viride* Tuck. *C. quercinum* Pers.
    Thallus ashy to white, smooth to scurfy-granulose, sometimes disappearing; stipes of moderate length, brownish black to black; apothecia small, 0.2–0.4 mm. across, subspherical to top-shaped or lenticular, the disk flat to strongly convex, blackish brown, or more or less white-pruinose, the exciple of same colors; hypothecium dark brown; spores ellipsoid, 5–9 × 3–5 μ.
    On trees and old wood, New England, New York, Ohio, Illinois, and Minnesota.

4. **Calicium abietinum** Pers., Tent. Disp. Meth. Fung. 59. 1797.
    C. curtum Borr. & Turn.
    Thallus ashy, thin, granulose, sometimes disappearing; stipes thin to stout, short to middle-length, black; apothecia minute to small, 0.2–0.4 mm. across, the disk convex to flat, dark brown to black, sometimes pruinose, the exciple of the same colors and likewise sometimes pruinose; spores blackish brown, 1-septate, ellipsoid, 7–12 × 4–6 μ.
    On trees and old wood, New England, Illinois, Minnesota, and California.

5. **Calicium trachelinum** Ach., Lich. Univ. 237. 1810.
    C. claviculare var. *trachelinum* Ach., Meth. Lich. 91. 1803. *C. salicinum* Pers.
    Thallus ashy, thin, granulose, commonly disappearing; stipes of medium size, becoming somewhat elongated, brownish black to black; apothecia small, 0.2–0.5 mm. across, subspherical to top-shaped, the disk convex to flat, brown to brownish black, the exciple brown; hypothecium dark brown; spores brown to blackish brown, ellipsoid, constricted, 7–12 × 3–5 μ.
    On decorticate trees, from New England to Florida, and westward to Missouri, Minnesota, and Oregon.

6. **Calicium Curtisii** Tuck., Am. Journ. Sci. II. 28:201. 1859.
    C. Curtisii var. *splendidula* Merrill.
    Thallus black, cottony, or rudimentary and disappearing; stipes short, white to reddish or black; apothecia minute, 0.05–0.1 mm. across, top-shaped, the disk and the exciple black and shining; spores finally 1-septate, oblong, 11–17 × 4–7 μ.
    On trees, New England, New York, Florida, and probably in Virginia, Montana, and California.

7. **Calicium populneum** De Brond., in Duby., Bot. Gall. 2:638. 1830.
Thallus grayish white, very thin, smooth, or obscurely scaly, often disappearing; stipe very short and slender, blackish; apothecia minute, 0.1–0.2 mm. across, subcylindrical to top-shaped, the disk convex to flat, black, the exciple black; spores 11–14 × 5–7 μ, showing a very obscure septum at maturity.
On trees, Illinois and California.

8. **Calicium pusillum** (Ach.) Floerke, Deutsch. Lich. part 10. 6. 1821.
Thallus evanescent, often showing as a whitish coloration on the substratum; stipes slender, of medium length, black; apothecia minute, 0.1–0.2 mm. across, subspherical to top-shaped, the disk convex, brownish black, the exciple usually darker; hypothecium brown; asci cylindrical; spores ellipsoid, 6–10 × 3–5 μ.
On decorticate trees, New York, Minnesota, and California. The algal host is rarely seen, and in this respect the plant resembles species of Mycocalicium.

9. **Calicium roscidum** Floerke, Deutsch. Lich. part 3. 3. 1821.
Thallus greenish gray, very thin, often scarcely visible; stipes rather short, black; apothecia small to middle-sized, 0.2–0.4 mm. across, lens-shaped, the disk convex, black, the exciple powdery and yellowish green above or throughout; spores brown to blackish, 9–18 × 4–8 μ.
On old wood, Massachusetts, New Hampshire, and Illinois.

var. **trabinellum** (Ach.) Schaer., Nat. Anz. All. Sch. Gesell. Nat. 5:36. 1821.
C. xylonellum var. *trabinellum* Ach., Meth. Lich. 91. 1803. *C. trabinellum* Ach.
Thallus ashy, whitish, thin, smooth to granulose, often disappearing; stipes of medium length and stoutness, brownish black, or at first partly bluish green pruinose; apothecia minute to small, 0.2–0.4 mm. across, globose to top-shaped, the disk flat to convex, brown or obscurely whitish pruinose, the exciple at first bluish green, becoming dark brown; hypothecium dark brown; asci cylindrical; spores oblong-ellipsoid, 8–12 × 2.5–4.5 μ, uniseriate.
On old wood, Massachusetts and Minnesota. The synonymy of this lichen is uncertain.

38. **Mycocalicium** Vainio, Etud. Lich. Brés. 2:182. 1890.

Thallus usually inconspicuous and often within the substratum; stipes well developed; apothecia borne on stipes, the disk commonly blackish, the exciple colored like the disk; paraphyses disappearing; asci cylindrical; spores 8, nonseptate, ovoid to ellipsoid, uniseriate.
The algal host is Cystococcus, rarely seen.
Calicium polyporeum Nyl., Flora 58:7. 1875, is closely related but without algal host; hence not a lichen.

A. Spores 6–8 × 2.5–3.5 μ . . . . 2. M. albonigrum
A. Spores rarely less than 8 μ in length
  B. Spores oblong or oblong-ellipsoid to ellipsoid
    C. Thallus greenish to greenish gray
      D. Apothecia 0.15–0.25 mm. across . . . . 6. M. disseminatum
      D. Apothecia 0.3–0.5 mm. across . . . . 4. M. Ravenelii
    C. Thallus whitish or inconspicuous
      D. Spores 6–11 × 3–6 μ . . . . 1. M. parietinum
      D. Spores 9–15 × 4–7 μ . . . . 3. M. fuscipes
  B. Spores subspherical to ovoid-ellipsoid . . . . 5. M. microcephalum

1. **Mycocalicium parietinum** (Ach.) Vainio, Etud. Lich. Brés. 2:182. 1890.
Calicium parietinum Ach., Vet. Akad. Handl. 260. pl. 8, f. 1, *a-b.* 1816. *Calicium subtile* Pers.
Thallus very thin, indicated by whitish patches of substratum, usually evanescent; stipes rather short and slender, brownish black; apothecia minute to small, 0.1–0.35 mm. across, top-shaped to lenticular, the disk convex, blackish brown, the exciple usually darker; spores oblong-ellipsoid, 6–11 × 3–6 μ.
On wood, throughout the United States, rarely parasitic on other lichens.

2. **Mycocalicium albonigrum** (Nyl.) Fink n. comb.
  Calicium albonigrum Nyl., Syn. Meth. Lich. 1:159. 1858. *Calicium subtile* var.
    albonigrum (Nyl.) Willey.
  Thallus very thin, whitish, becoming scurfy; stipes of medium length; apothecia small, 0.2–0.4 mm. across, subspherical to top-shaped, the disk convex, brownish black, the exciple darker; hypothecium brown; spores blackish brown, oblong-ellipsoid, 6–8 × 2.5–3.5 μ.
  On trees, New England, New York, Alabama, Texas, and California.

3. **Mycocalicium fuscipes** (Tuck.) Fink n. comb.
  Calicium fuscipes Tuck., Gen. Lich. 240. 1872.
  Thallus poorly developed and evanescent; stipes slender, dark brown, shading into white above; apothecia minute to small, 0.15–0.25 mm. across, lens-shaped to top-shaped, the disk convex, black, the exciple white below to black above; spores oblong-ellipsoid, 9–15 × 4–7 μ.
  On old wood, New Jersey.

4. **Mycocalicium Ravenelii** (Tuck.) Fink n. comb.
  Calicium Ravenelii Tuck.; Nyl., Not. Sällsk. Faun. Fl. Fenn. 5:42. 1861.
  Thallus granulose, greenish gray; stipes short, stout, brownish black; apothecia middle-sized, 0.3–0.5 mm. across, spherical to top-shaped, the exciple dark, incurved, radiate-striate; spores ellipsoid to fusiform-ellipsoid, brownish, 7–12 × 3–5 μ.
  On old wood, South Carolina.

5. **Mycocalicium microcephalum** (J. E. Smith) Fink n. comb.
  Lichen microcephalus J. E. Smith, Engl. Bot. 26:1865. 1808 pro parte. *Calicium
    microcephalum* (J. E. Smith) Ach.
  Thallus thin, obscurely granulose, greenish gray to olive-brown, often disappearing; stipe very short, dark-colored; apothecia minute to small, 0.2–0.5 mm. across, spherical varying toward top-shaped, the disk and the exciple black; spores subspherical to ovoid-ellipsoid, 8–13 × 6–9 μ.
  On old wood, New England.

6. **Mycocalicium disseminatum** (Ach.) Fink n. comb.
  Cyphelium disseminatum Ach., Vet. Akad. Handl. III. 5:227. pl. 1, f. 4. 1817.
    Chaenotheca disseminata (Ach.) Lettau.
  Thallus thin, scurfy, greenish to greenish gray, often scarcely visible; stipes very short; apothecia minute, 0.15–0.25 mm. across, hemispherical, the disk concave to flat, black or tinged green, the exciple black; spores blackish, oblong, 10–14 × 4–6 μ, said to be rarely spheroidal.
  On old wood, White Mountains, New Hampshire, and California. Seems near Caliciella.

39. **Caliciella** Vainio, Acta Soc. Faun. Flor. Fenn. 57:52. 1927.

  Thallus imbedded in that of the lichen host and therefore invisible; stipes short to moderately long; apothecia minute to small, subspherical to lenticular, convex to becoming flat, the exciple thin, colored like the disk; hypothecium hyaline to brownish; hymenium hyaline or brownish above; paraphyses short, threadlike; asci cylindrico-clavate; spores 8, brown, oblong to ellipsoid, 1-septate.
  The algal host is Protococcus.

A. Stipes very short to short; apothecia minute, reaching
    0.1 mm. across . . . . 2. C. pallidella
A. Stipes longer; apothecia larger, reaching 0.6 mm. across . . . . . 1. C. arenaria

1. **Caliciella arenaria** (Hampe) Fink n. comb.
  Cyphelium arenarium Hampe, in Mass., Misc. Lich. 20. 1856. *Calicium citri-
    num* (Leight.) Nyl.
  Thallus imbedded in the host and therefore invisible; stipe moderately long, stout, rusty brown; apothecia small to middle-sized, 0.4–0.6 mm. across, subspheri-

cal to lens-shaped, the disk convex to flat, and this and the exciple dark brown to dull black; spores brown to blackish brown, oblong, 6–11 × 2.5–3.5 μ.
On the thallus of *Lecidea lucida*, White Mountains, New Hampshire.

2. **Caliciella pallidella** (Willey) Fink n. comb.
Calicium pallidellum Willey, Enum. Lich. New Bedford, Mass. 35. 1892.
Thallus imbedded in that of the host and therefore invisible; stipes very short to short, brownish to black; apothecia minute, 0.05–0.1 mm. across, subspherical, the disk convex to flat, dull black; spores 6–10 × 3–5 μ.
On thallus of *Pertusaria velata*, Massachusetts.
Available material very scanty, the description adapted from Willey.

40. **Coniocybe** Ach., Vet. Akad. Handl. 1816:283. pl. 8, f. 16. 1816.
Thallus rudimentary, without cellular cortex, crustose, smooth to more or less scurfy, persistent and well developed or disappearing; stipes slender, rather long; apothecia minute to middle-sized, spherical to top-shaped, the disk convex, yellowish or white to light brown, the exciple of the same color, sometimes disappearing; hypothecium hyaline to brownish; hymenium hyaline below to usually brownish above; paraphyses usually branched; asci cylindrical; spores 8, hyaline, spherical to oblong, non-septate.
The algal hosts are Protococcus and Stichococcus.

A. Spores oblong . . . . 3. C. gracilescens
A. Spores spherical
  B. Thallus ashy gray; stipes whitish to yellowish or brownish above . 2. C. pallida
  B. Thallus greenish yellow; stipes ashy yellow to sulphur-colored . 1. C. furfuracea

1. **Coniocybe furfuracea** (L.) Ach., Vet. Akad. Handl. 1816:288. 1816.
Mucor furfuraceus L., Sp. Pl. 1185. 1753.
Thallus well developed, scurfy-powdery, greenish yellow, sometimes becoming thin or disappearing; stipes slender, rather long, powdered, ashy yellow to sulphur-colored; apothecia small to middle-sized, 0.2–0.45 mm. across, spherical, the disk convex, yellow to light brown, the exciple ashy yellow to sulphur-colored; spores 2.5–3 μ in diameter.
On roots of decayed trees, dead twigs, decayed mosses, and rarely on rocks, New England, New York, Ohio, Wisconsin, California, and Washington.

2. **Coniocybe pallida** (Pers.) E. Fries, Sched. Crit. Lich. Exsicc. Suec. fasc. 1.
   3. 1824.
Calicium pallidum Pers., Ann. Bot. Usteri 7:20. pl. 3, f. 1, 2. 1794.
Thallus thin, ashy gray, often widespread, sometimes disappearing; stipes slender, rather long, whitish to yellowish, often brownish toward the top; apothecia minute to small, 0.15–0.3 mm. across, spherical top-shaped, the disk usually convex, whitish to light brown; the exciple of the same colors; spores spherical, 3–7 μ in diameter. (PLATE 2 *b*.)
In depressions of rough-barked trees, New England, New York, Illinois, Iowa, Minnesota, and Washington.

3. **Coniocybe gracilescens** Willey, Enum. Lich. New Bedford, Mass. 35. 1892.
Thallus very thin and mainly inconspicuous, sometimes showing as minute, scattered, yellowish green granules; stipes yellow, short to longer, slender to somewhat enlarged toward the tip; apothecia minute, 0.05–0.15 mm. across, spherical to top-shaped, the disk convex, yellow, the exciple of the same color; spores oblong, 5.5 × 2 μ.
On old wood, Massachusetts.

41. **Stenocybe** Nyl., Bot. Notis. 84. 1854.

Thallus poorly developed, almost wanting, or the apothecia seated on a strange thallus; stipes well developed; apothecia minute to small, at first closed, later with punctiform disk; paraphyses slender, distinct; asci long, cylindrical; spores 8, brown, ellipsoid to oblong-ellipsoid, uniseriately arranged, commonly 3– rarely 7-septate, the cells cylindrical.

The algal hosts are Protococcus and Stichococcus.

A. Spores 18–36 μ in length . . . . 1. S. major
A. Spores not more than 20 μ in length
   B. Apothecia not more than 0.2 mm. across . . . . 3. S. tremulicola
   B. Apothecia reaching 0.6 mm. across . . . . 2. S. pullatula

1. **Stenocybe major** Nyl., Bot. Notis. 84. 1854.
S. euspora (Nyl.) Anzi.
Thallus poorly developed, mainly or wholly imbedded in the substratum; stipes short, slender, black; apothecia minute to small, 0.1–0.4 mm. across, globose to clavate, the disk flat, black, the exciple black; spores 8, brown, oblong-ellipsoid, 3-septate, 18–36 × 7–11 μ.
On trees, New York and Washington.

2. **Stenocybe pullatula** (Ach.) Stein; Cohn, Krypt. Flora von Schleisen, 2:298. 1879.
Calicium pullatulum Ach., Vet. Akad. Handl. 121. pl. 5, f. 5. 1816. *S. byssacea* (E. Fries) Koerb.
Thallus poorly developed, mainly or wholly imbedded in the substratum; stipes short, slender, black; apothecia minute to small, 0.25–0.6 mm. across, subspherical to somewhat clavate, the disk flat to convex, black, the exciple thin, black; spores 8, brown, oblong-ellipsoid, 3-septate, 13–22 × 5–7 μ.
On trees, Massachusetts and New Jersey.

3. **Stenocybe tremulicola** Norrl.; Lojka, Flora 66:531. 1883.
S. pullatula f. *tremulicola* (Norrl.) Zahlbr.
Thallus poorly developed, mainly or wholly imbedded in the substratum; stipes very short, slender, black; apothecia minute, 0.05–0.2 mm. across, globose, the disk concave to flat, black, the exciple black; spores 8, brown, oblong-ellipsoid, 3-septate, 12–18 × 4–5 μ.
On trees, southern California.

42. **Sphinctrina** E. Fries, Syst. Orb. Veg. 120. 1825.

Parasitic on other lichens and thallus invisible, but probably parasitic on algae within the lichen host; apothecia solitary, pear-shaped to spherical, closed or showing a small disk, black and shining, the proper exciple thick and stout, hypothecium brown; asci cylindrical; spores 8, non-septate, subspherical to oblong-ellipsoid, becoming dark brown, uniseriate; the mazaedium forming tardily.

The algal host is Protococcus.

A. Spores spherical to subspherical, 3–7 μ across . . . . 1. S. gelasinata
A. Spores ellipsoid, 9–14 μ in length . . . . 2. S. microcephala

1. **Sphinctrina gelasinata** (With.) Zahlbr., Cat. Lich. Univ. 1:654. 1922.
Lichen gelasinatus With., Arr. Brit. Pl. ed. 3. 4:6. pl. 31, f. 1. 1796. *Calicium turbinatum* Pers. *S. turbinata* (Pers.) De Not.
Mycelium imbedded in the lichen host and therefore invisible; stipes very short, stout, and scarcely visible; apothecia small, 0.2–0.4 mm. across, spherical to top-shaped, the disk flat and dull black at maturity, the exciple dull black, often lighter externally; spores dark brown, spherical to subspherical, 3–7 μ across.
Commonly on *Pertusaria communis* and rarely on *Cyphelium bolanderi*. On the former host, Massachusetts, New York, Illinois, and Minnesota; on the latter, California.

2. **Sphinctrina microcephala** (J. E. Smith) Nyl., Mém. Imp. Soc. Sci. Nat. Cherb. 3:168. 1855.
Lichen microcephalus J. E. Smith, Engl. Bot. 26: pl. 1865. 1808. *S. tubaeformis* Mass.

Mycelium imbedded in the lichen host and therefore invisible; stipes very short and scarcely visible; apothecia minute to small, 0.1–0.3 mm. across, spherical to top-shaped, dull black; spores ellipsoid, 9–14 × 6–8.5 μ.

On *Pertusaria lecanina* and *Pertusaria pustulata*, Florida and California.

OTHER SPECIES REPORTED

Sphinctrina leucopoda Nyl.—Virginia.

12. CYPHELIACEAE

Thallus crustose, partly within the substratum, rudimentary to more or less developed, showing little or no differentiation; apothecia sessile to adnate, with proper and thalloid exciples or with only a thalloid one.

The algal hosts are Pleurococcus, Protococcus, and Trentepohlia.

A. Spores non-septate . . . . 44. Cypheliopsis
A. Spores septate
  B. Spores 1-septate . . . . 43. Cyphelium
  B. Spores 3-septate . . . . 45. Pyrgillus

43. **Cyphelium** Ach., Vet. Akad. Handl. 263. 1815.

Thallus smooth to roughened, granulose, verrucose, or areolate, with margins lobed in some species; stipes very short or wanting; apothecia immersed in the thallus or wholly or partly superficial, a thalloid exciple present, and sometimes a proper one within; paraphyses unbranched or but little branched; hypothecium brown; asci cylindrical; spores brown, 1-septate, usually constricted, 8, uniseriate.

The algal hosts are Protococcus and Pleurococcus.

A. Parasitic on lichens . . . . 10. C. sessile
A. On rocks, soil, or wood
  B. Thallus yellow or yellowish green
    C. Spores 6–9 × 3–4 μ . . . . 2. C. lucidum
    C. Spores 14–24 × 7–11 μ . . . . 1. C. tigillare
  B. Thallus greenish gray to ashy or whitish, rarely yellowish
    C. Spores not over 14 μ in length
      D. Thallus whitish; apothecia sessile; spores 7–9 μ wide . 3. C. ventricosulum
      D. Thallus greenish gray to ashy; apothecia immersed to
        adnate; spores 5–6 μ wide . . . . 4. C. chloroconium
    C. Spores usually 14 μ or more in length
      D. Spores 10–18 μ or more wide
        E. Apothecia 0.6–1 mm. across; spores
          20–40 × 16–30 μ . . . . 8. C. Sancti Jacobi
        E. Apothecia 2–3 mm. across; spores 18–25 × 10–18 μ;
          margin plainly lobed . . . . 9. C. californicum
      D. Spores not over 12 μ wide
        E. Thallus continuous, becoming rough and
          finally areolate . . . . 5. C. carolinianum
        E. Thallus granulose or verrucose to areolate, or scattered
          F. Disk flat to convex; spores 14–22 × 8–12 μ . . . 6. C. Farlowii
          F. Disk flat; spores 12–20 × 7–12 μ . . . . . . 7. C. inquinans

1. **Cyphelium tigillare** Ach., Vet. Akad. Handl. 1815:266. 1815.
Lichen tigillaris Ach., Lich. Suec. 67. 1798. *Acolium tigillare* (Ach.) S. F. Gray.

Thallus well developed, yellowish green, or greenish yellow, chinky to areolate, or rarely granulose; apothecia minute to small, 0.3–0.5 mm. across, immersed often in raised areas, or becoming superficial, the disk dull black, flat to concave, the proper exciple black; asci cylindrical; spores constricted toward the septum, 14–24 × 7–11 μ.

On boards, posts, and other old wood, throughout eastern United States, and westward to Wyoming, and in California.

2. **Cyphelium lucidum** T. Fries, Gen. Heter. 101. 1861.
    Trachylia lucida T. Fries, Ofv. Vet. Akad. Forh. 12:18. pl. 1, f. 4. 1855. *Acolium lucidum* (T. Fries) Rabh. *Calicium viridulum* Schaer.

Thallus well developed, lemon-yellow, verrucose, and usually subareolate, continuous or scattered, the margins sometimes lobed; apothecia minute to small, 0.3–0.5 mm. across, extending above the thallus, the disk flat, bluish green pruinose to black, the exciple black, becoming raised; spores oblong, 6–9 × 3–4 μ.

On bark and old wood of conifers, northern Minnesota.

3. **Cyphelium ventricosulum** (Müll. Arg.) Zahlbr., in E. & P., Nat. Pfl. 1¹:84. 1907.
    Acolium ventricosulum Müll. Arg., Flora 74:108. 1891.

Thallus thin, closely adhering to the substratum, minutely granulose, scattered or continuous, white, often seated upon a concolorate, soon disappearing hypothallus; apothecia minute to small, sessile, round to irregular, the disk punctiform to flat, brownish black, the exciple thin, colored like the disk, subcrenulate; spores 8, brown, broadly ellipsoid, with both ends round or obtuse, 1-septate, slightly constricted at the septum, 12–14 × 7–9 μ.

On trees, Oregon.

Have seen no specimens; description adapted from one by Zahlbruckner based on original specimen. Zahlbruckner puts this under Pyrgillus in his description.

4. **Cyphelium chloroconium** (Tuck.) Zahlbr., Cat. Lich. Univ. 1:664. 1922.
    Acolium chloroconium Tuck., Lich. Calif. 28. 1866.

Thallus thin, greenish gray to ashy, wrinkled to chinky and areolate, continuous to more rarely scattered; apothecia minute to small, 0.3–0.6 mm. across, partly immersed to adnate, the disk flat, black, or somewhat grayish pruinose, the thalloid exciple thin, prominent, finally disappearing; spores short-ellipsoid, constricted, 7–12 × 5–6 μ.

On trees, southern California.

5. **Cyphelium carolinianum** (Tuck.) Zahlbr., in E. & P., Nat. Pfl. 1¹:84. 1907.
    Acolium carolinianum Tuck., Gen. Lich. 237. 1872.

Thallus well developed, gray to yellowish, continuous, becoming rough, chinky, and finally areolate; apothecia small, 0.5–1.5 mm. across, immersed in slightly raised areas, the disk flat to convex, black, the proper exciple indistinct; spores ellipsoid, 12–18 × 7–9 μ.

On logs and rails, the Carolinas and Florida.

6. **Cyphelium Farlowii** (Tuck.) Herre, Proc. Wash. Acad. Sci. 12:61, 62. 1910.
    Acolium Farlowii Tuck.; Herre, Proc. Wash. Acad. Sci. 12:61, 62. 1910.

Thallus greenish gray to ashy, chinky to areolate, becoming warty, well developed, and continuous to thinner and scattered; apothecia small to middle-sized, 0.5–1.5 mm. across, elevated, the disk flat to slightly convex, dull black, sometimes obscurely whitish pruinose, the proper exciple rudimentary and indistinct; spores oblong, constricted, 14–22 × 8–12 μ.

On old wood, California and Oregon.

7. **Cyphelium inquinans** (J. E. Smith) Trevis., Flora 45:4. 1862.
    Lichen inquinans J. E. Smith, in Sowerby, Engl. Bot. 12: pl. 810. 1801. *Acolium tympanellum* (Ach.) S. F. Gray.

Thallus granulose, or verrucose and chinky to subareolate, ashy to greenish gray, well developed and continuous to thinner and scattered; apothecia small, 0.5–1 mm. across, usually elevated, the disk flat, dull black or obscurely gray-pruinose, a thin pruinose or darkening thalloid exciple surrounding the thin, brown, proper one; spores oblong, constricted, 12–20 × 7–12 μ.

On trees and old wood, California, Montana, and Washington.

8. **Cyphelium Sancti Jacobi** (Tuck.) Zahlbr., Cat. Lich. Univ. 1:670. 1922.
Acolium Sancti Jacobi Tuck., Bull. Torr. Club 10:22. 1883.

Thallus well developed, whitish, granulose, finally forming a chinky crust; apothecia middle-sized, 0.6–1 mm. across, more or less nearly top-shaped, the disk elevated, convex to flat, yellowish green pruinose to black, the thalloid exciple prominent, becoming crenate; spores spherical to short-ellipsoid, 20–40 × 16–30 μ.

On soil, California.

9. **Cyphelium californicum** (Tuck.) Zahlbr., in E. & P., Nat. Pfl. 1¹:84. 1907.
Trachylia californica Tuck., Proc. Am. Acad. 6:263. 1866. *Acolium californicum* Tuck.

Thallus well developed, ashy to yellowish, chinky to areolate and verrucose, continuous with plainly lobed margin; apothecia large, 2–3 mm. across, immersed, the disk flat to slightly convex, black, the thalloid exciple thin, becoming crenate; spores 18–25 × 10–18 μ.

On rocks and old wood, California and Florida.

10. **Cyphelium sessile** (Pers.) Trev., Flora 45:4. 1862.
Calicium sessile Pers., Tent. Disp. Meth. Fung. 59. 1797. *Trachylia stigonella* (Ach.) E. Fries.

Thallus within the host and invisible; apothecia minute to small, 0.25–0.5 mm. across, adnate, the disk flat, black, the exciple thin, black or sometimes whitish pruinose, at last disappearing; spores ellipsoid with round ends, slightly constricted, 9–17 × 7–10 μ.

On thalli of *Pertusaria* sp., New England. Only one specimen studied and that from England.

OTHER SPECIES REPORTED

Cyphelium Andersoni Herre—California.

44. **Cypheliopsis** Vainio, Acta Soc. Faun. Flor. Fenn. 57:16. 1927.

Thallus smooth to granulose, warty or areolate, sometimes lobed at the margins, devoid of differentiation into layers; stipes very short, usually wanting; apothecia immersed, the disk flat to convex, the exciple colored like the thallus, often indistinct and sometimes surrounded by a thin thalloid one; hypothecium brownish to brown; hymenium hyaline or brownish above; paraphyses rarely branched; asci cylindrical; spores 8, brown, non-septate, spherical.

The algal host is Protococcus or Pleurococcus.

1. **Cypheliopsis Bolanderi** (Tuck.) Vainio, Acta Soc. Faun. Flor. Fenn. 57:16. 1927.
Acolium Bolanderi Tuck., Lich. Calif. 27. 1866.

Thallus well developed, yellowish ashy, verrucose, chinky to areolate, continuous or scattered, sometimes obscurely lobed, often bordered more or less by a blackening base; apothecia small, 0.5–1 mm. across, immersed in conspicuously raised areas, the disk flat to convex, black, the proper exciple indistinct; hypothecium light brown; spores 9–17 μ in diameter.

On rocks, California.

45. **Pyrgillus** Nyl., Flora 42:44. 1859.

Thallus thin, devoid of differentiation; apothecia immersed, conico-cylindrical, broad at the base and tapering slightly upward, the disk flat, brown to black; hypothecium brown; asci cylindrical; spores 8, dark brown, 3-septate, the cells lenticular and the septa thick.

The algal host is Trentepohlia.

A. Thallus greenish gray; thalloid exciple pruinose . . . . 1. P. javanicus
A. Thallus whitish; thalloid exciple not pruinose . . . . . . 2. P. americanus

1. **Pyrgillus javanicus** Nyl., Mém. Soc. Sci. Nat. Cherb. 5:334. 1857.
Calicium javanicum (Nyl.) Mont. & Bosch.
Thallus thin, greenish gray, smooth or becoming rough, sometimes granulose, continuous; apothecia small, 0.4–0.6 mm. across, the disk flat, black, the proper exciple thick, surrounded by a thin, pruinose, thalloid one; hypothecium thick and dark brown; spores ovoid-oblong, 9–15 × 7–8.5 μ.
On trees, South Carolina, Florida, and Louisiana.

2. **Pyrgillus americanus** Nyl., Syn. Meth. Lich. 1:168. pl. 5, f. 36. 1860.
Thallus thin, whitish, granulose, continuous or scattered; apothecia small, 0.4–0.6 mm. across, the disk flat, black, the proper exciple thick, surrounded by a thin thalloid one; spores oblong-ellipsoid, 11–18 × 6–8 μ.
On trees, Louisiana.

13. SPHAEROPHORACEAE

Thallus foliose to fruticose, showing more or less differentiation into cortical, algal, and medullary layers; apothecia adnate to sessile, laterally or terminally on the lobes or branches of the thallus, or borne within a thalloid receptacle at the tips of the branches, disklike, with a thalloid exciple or more or less inclosed. The algal host is Protococcus.

46. **Sphaerophorus** Pers., Ann. Bot. Usteri 7:23. 1794.

Thallus fruticose, more or less erect, branched, the branches smooth to rough, the cortex more or less cartilaginous, the medullary tissue forming a solid central cylinder surrounded by the algal layer; apothecia middle-sized to large, borne within thalloid receptacles on the tips of the branches, the receptacle opening more or less irregularly above, the disk more or less concave to flat; hypothecium hyaline; hymenium hyaline or brownish above; paraphyses fragile; asci clavate; spores 8, hyaline, with thin, black, dustlike covering, spherical, non-septate.
The algal host is Protococcus.

A. Thallus loosely branched, the branches bearing coralloid branchlets . 2. S. globosus
A. Thallus dichotomously branched, the branches smooth . . . . . . 1. S. fragilis

1. **Sphaerophorus fragilis** (L.) Pers., Ann. Bot. Usteri 7:23. 1794.
Lichen fragilis L., Sp. Pl. 1154. 1753.
Thallus nearly erect, dichotomously branched, grayish white to brownish or brown, the branches densely crowded, round, short, smooth; apothecia middlesized to large, 0.8–2.5 mm. across, borne within thalloid receptacles on the apices of the branches, the receptacle irregularly opening above, the disk concave to flat, black; asci clavate; spores spherical, 7–16 μ across.
On soil and rocks, Maine and New Hampshire.

2. **Sphaerophorus globosus** (Huds.) Vainio, Result. Voy. S. Y. Belgica Bot. 35. 1903.
Lichen globosus Huds., Flora Ang. 1:460. 1762. *S. coralloides* Pers. *S. globiferus* (L.) Lam. & DC.
Thallus erect, loosely branched, ashy gray to brownish or reddish brown, the branches numerous, round, rather short, bearing many lateral, coralloid branchlets; apothecia middle-sized to large, 0.5–2 mm. across, borne within thalloid receptacles on the apices of the branches, the receptacle irregularly opening above, the disk concave to almost flat, black; asci clavate; spores spherical, 8–15 μ across.
On soil, rocks, and trees, Maine, New Hampshire, Washington, Oregon, and California.

14. ARTHONIACEAE

Thallus crustose, partly within the substratum, devoid of differentiation into layers, attached to the substratum by hyphal rhizoids; apothecia round, linear, or irregular, sometimes branched, single or united in a stroma, the exciple absent or very poorly developed; paraphyses branched and interwoven. The algal hosts are Palmella, Trentepohlia, and Phyllactidium.

A. Spores transversely 1–several-septate . . . . 47. Arthonia
A. Spores transversely and longitudinally septate . . . . . . 48. Arthothelium

47. Arthonia Ach., Neu. Journ. Schrad. 1³:3. pl. 4. 1806.

Thallus rudimentary, without cortical tissues, partly or wholly within the substratum, appearing as a grayish coloration of the bark, becoming crustose to rarely areolate; apothecia minute to small, round to irregular, linear or star-shaped, more or less immersed to adnate, the disk flat to slightly convex, brownish black to black or rarely reddish brown or grayish pruinose; hypothecium rarely hyaline to more commonly brownish to dark brown; hymenium hyaline to brown; paraphyses usually branched; asci pyriform; spores 8, hyaline to rarely brownish, oblong-ovoid or ovoid-ellipsoid, 1–3 or rarely more septate, the cells cylindrical, often unequal. The algal hosts are Trentepohlia and Palmella.

A. Apothecia colored, but not black
  B. Spores 1- or rarely 2-septate
    C. Disk reddish brown to darker
      D. Spores 1-septate, cells equal . . . . 1. A. carneorufa
      D. Spores 1–2-septate, one cell larger . . . . 2. A. incarnata
    C. Disk dark brown or brownish gray to black or rarely yellowish
      D. Disk dark brown or brownish gray to black
        E. Thallus thin, smooth, greenish gray or ashy
          F. Spores 1-septate, 10–15 × 4–5 μ . . . . 3. A. lurida
          F. Spores 1-septate, 16–20 × 5.5–7.5 μ . . . . . 4. A. floridana
        E. Thallus thicker, rough, creamy to ashy white . . 6. A. lecanactidea
      D. Disk yellowish . . . . 5. A. ochrodiscodes
  B. Spores 1–3 or more septate
    C. Disk yellow, red, flesh-colored to reddish brown
      D. Disk yellow, flesh-colored, or light brown
        E. Spores 1–3-septate
          F. Apothecia linear and more or less branched . . . 7. A. impallens
          F. Apothecia irregular and often elongated . . . 8. A. ochrolutea
        E. Spores more than 3-septate
          F. Spores 4–5-septate . . . . 9. A. gyalectoides
          F. Spores 7–11-septate . . . . 10. A. fissurina
      D. Disk red or reddish brown or darker
        E. Spores 5–7-septate . . . . 11. A. pyrrhula
        E. Spores 3–5-septate
          F. Disk with an ochre-red margin . . . . . . 13. A. ochrocincta
          F. Disk without a margin
            G. Disk reddish brown to black or pruinose . . 12. A. gregaria
            G. Disk violet-brown . . . . 12. A. gregaria adspersa
    C. Disk reddish brown to black
      D. Spores 3–7-septate
        E. Spores large, 44–50 μ in length . . . . . . 18. A. subrubella
        E. Spores less than 30 μ in length
          F. Thallus whitish or ashy white
            G. Apothecia irregular and often elongated . . 24. A. platyspilea
            G. Apothecia elongated, curved and
              rarely branched . . . . 14. A. Ravenelii
          F. Thallus pale yellow . . . . 22. A. perminuta
      D. Spores 3–5-septate
        E. Spores 3–5-septate
          F. Spores 25–35 μ in length
            G. Thallus becoming granular or chinky . . . . 17. A. rubella
            G. Thallus slightly rough, surrounded
              by a black line . . . . 16. A. caribaea
          F. Spores less than 25 μ in length
            G. Apothecia irregular to oblong
              H. Spores 12–15 μ in length . . . . . . 23. A. pyrrhuliza

H. Spores 16–22 µ in length . . . . . 19. A. polygramma
G. Apothecia round to irregular
H. Spore cells equal
I. Apothecia 0.1–0.3 mm. across . . . 28. A. chiodectella
I. Apothecia 0.2–0.9 mm. across . . . . 29. A. impolita
H. Spore cells unequal
I. Apothecia often elongated . . . . . 30. A. byssacea
I. Apothecia not elongated . . . 33. A. Tuckermaniana
E. Spores constantly 3-septate
F. Disk not pruinose
G. Apothecia round to irregular or elongated
H. Thallus often intersected by black lines . 15. A. viridicans
H. Thallus not intersected by black lines
I. Spores 12–17 × 4.5–6 µ . . . . 20. A. varia
I. Spores 9–13 × 3–5 µ . . . . . 27. A. albofuscescens
G. Apothecia round to irregular or elongated
H. Thallus smooth, greenish gray . . . . 21. A. erubescens
H. Thallus smooth to powdery, ashy white
I. Apothecia 0.09–0.3 mm. across . . 32. A. cinereopruinosa
I. Apothecia 0.3–0.6 mm. across . . . . 34. A. Eckfeldtii
F. Disk more or less pruinose
G. Spores more than 16 µ in length
H. Thallus becoming chinky and subareolate . 25. A. lecideella
H. Thallus often bearing mealy soredia . . 31. A. glaucescens
G. Spores less than 16 µ in length
H. Apothecia round to slightly irregular . . 26. A. cupressina
H. Apothecia oblong to elongated . . . . 35. A. leucastraea
A. Apothecia black
B. Spores 1- or rarely 2-septate
C. On rocks and soil
D. Thallus squamulose . . . . 36. A. glebosa
D. Thallus crustose
E. Spores with cells equal
F. Apothecia 0.1–0.3 mm. across . . . . 37. A. lapidicola
F. Apothecia 0.06–0.08 mm. across . . . . . 38. A. terrigena
E. Spores with one cell larger . . . . 39. A. rupicola
C. On trees and old wood
D. Apothecia round to irregular but rarely elongated
E. Disk commonly pruinose
F. Apothecia 0.15–0.5 mm. across . . . 40. A. patellulata caesiocarpa
F. Apothecia 0.1–0.15 mm. across . . . . . 44. A. pruinosella
E. Disk not pruinose
F. Spores with cells equal
G. Disk flat to convex, smooth . . . . . 40. A. patellulata
G. Disk strongly convex and irregular or rough
H. Thallus smooth to powdery . . . . . 45. A. aleuromela
H. Thallus smooth to chinky . . . . . 42. A. convexella
F. Spores with one cell larger
G. Thallus dark gray, inconspicuous . . . . . . 43. A. exilis
G. Thallus dull white or ashy white
H. Spores 1-septate, 8–11 × 3–4.5 µ . . . . 50. A. dispersula
H. Spores 1- or 2-septate, 10–13 × 3–4 µ . . . 48. A. Willey
D. Apothecia round to irregular and more or less elongated
E. Spores 1-septate
F. Spores with one cell larger
G. Spores 9–12 × 4–5 µ . . . . 41. A. subdispuncta
G. Spores 7–9 × 2.5–3 µ . . . . . . 52. A. subminutissim
F. Spores with cells equal
G. Spores 19–26 × 7.5–9 µ . . . . . . 51. A. taedescen
G. Spores 11–16 × 4–5 µ . . . . 47. A. dispersa
E. Spores 1–2-septate
F. Apothecia more or less branched . . . . 53. A. microspermella
F. Apothecia not branched . . . . 46. A. Rhoidi

B. Spores 3–many-septate
  C. Spores 3-septate, rarely less
    D. Apothecia round to irregular
      E. Spores with cells unequal
        F. Spores 8–12 $\times$ 3–4.5 μ . . . . 55. A. diffusa
        F. Spores 12–15 $\times$ 3.5–4 μ . . . . 56. A. diffusella
      E. Spores with cells equal
        F. Thallus ashy white . . . . 57. A. subdiffusa
        F. Thallus yellowish or whitish . . . . 61. A. pruinosula
    D. Apothecia irregular and elongated
      E. Apothecia not branched
        F. Thallus smooth
          G. Apothecia 0.6–1 mm. long . . . . 54. A. luridoalba
          G. Apothecia 0.3 mm. long . . . . 67. A. radiata epipastoides
        F. Thallus smooth to becoming warty
          G. Spores 16–24 $\times$ 5–7 μ . . . . 66. A. epipastoides
          G. Spores 14–20 $\times$ 5–7.5 μ . . . . 74. A. galactitella
      E. Apothecia more or less branched
        F. Spores 16–25 μ in length . . . . 49. A. Cytisi
        F. Spores not more than 20 μ in length
          G. Apothecia stellately branched
            H. Thallus very thin, ashy, often
              disappearing . . . . 68. A. subastroidella
            H. Thallus thin, greenish gray to whitish
              or brownish . . . . 67. A. radiata
          G. Apothecia not stellately branched
            H. Thallus very thin or disappearing
              I. Apothecia often curved . . . . . 70. A. xylographica
              I. Apothecia not curved . . . . . 71. A. Hamamelidis
            H. Thallus thin, greenish gray to whitish
              or brownish . . . . 67. A. radiata angustata
  C. Spores 3–5- or more septate
    D. Spores more than 5-septate
      E. Spores 52–70 μ in length . . . . 76. A. platygraphidea
      E. Spores 18–25 μ in length . . . . 69. A. quintaria
    D. Spores not more than 5-septate
      E. Spores usually more than 25 μ in length
        F. Apothecia irregular and more or less branched . 64. A. excedens
        F. Apothecia elongated . . . . 63. A. complanata
      E. Spores usually less than 25 μ in length
        F. Spores usually less than 17 μ in length
          G. Thallus ashy white . . . . 73. A. asteriscus
          G. Thallus greenish gray to whitish or olive-green
            H. Apothecia 0.3–1 mm. across . . . . 62. A. polymorpha
            H. Apothecia 0.05–0.2 mm. across . . . . . 72. A. torulosa
        F. Spores rarely less than 17 μ in length
          G. Apothecia elongated
            H. Spores hyaline . . . . 75. A. stictella
            H. Spores dark brown . . . . 58. A. melaspora
          G. Apothecia round to irregular
            H. Thallus ashy white and often disappearing
              I. Disk grayish pruinose . . . . 59. A. pinastri
              I. Disk black . . . . 65. A. punctiformis
            H. Thallus whitish to olive-green or greenish
              gray to brownish
              I. On trees . . . . 60. A. reniformis
              I. On rocks; spores rarely becoming
              muriform . . . . 77. A. phaeobaea

4. Arthonia carneorufa Willey, Int. Stud. Lich. Suppl. 52. 1887.
Superficial thallus thin, white, smooth; apothecia minute to small, 0.1–0.3 mm. across, adnate, round, the disk convex, reddish brown; tinged yellowish brown within; spores ovoid-ellipsoid, 1-septate, 8–11 $\times$ 3.5–5 μ.
On wood, Washington.

2. **Arthonia incarnata** Kullh. Almq., Kgl. Svensk. Vet. Akad. Handl. 17:18. 1880.
Superficial thallus thin, greenish gray to ashy white, smooth to slightly rough;
apothecia minute to small, 0.1–0.3 mm. across, adnate, round to slightly irregular,
the disk convex, reddish brown and darker; tinged pale brownish within; asci
narrowly pyriform; spores hyaline, ovoid-ellipsoid, 2-septate, one end cell larger,
11–16 × 4.5–6.5 μ.
On trees, White Mountains, New Hampshire.

3. **Arthonia lurida** Ach., Lich. Univ. 143. 1810.
Superficial thallus smooth, greenish gray to whitish, thin and disappearing;
apothecia minute to small, 0.1–0.4 mm. across, adnate, round to somewhat irregular, the disk flat to convex, brownish black; hypothecium reddish; hymenium
lighter; spores hyaline, ovoid-ellipsoid, 1-septate, one end cell larger, 10–15 ×
4–5 μ.
On trees, New England, New York, and California.

4. **Arthonia floridana** Willey, Int. Stud. Lich. Suppl. 52. 1887.
Thallus ashy, very thin, smooth, surrounded by a thin dark line; apothecia
minute, 0.1–0.2 mm. across, immersed more or less in the substratum, round to
oblong or irregular, the disk flat to slightly convex, dark brown to black; hypothecium brown; hymenium hyaline; asci pyriform; spores hyaline, fusiform-ovoid,
1-septate, 16–20 × 5.5–7.5 μ.
On trees, Florida.

5. **Arthonia ochrodiscodes** Nyl., Lich. Jap. 107. 1890.
Thallus thin, ashy white, smooth; apothecia minute to small, 0.1–0.6 mm.
across, adnate, round, the disk flat to convex, ochre-yellow to blackish; tinged
brownish within; spores 1-septate, oblong-ovoid, constricted at the septum, hyaline,
14–17 × 6–8 μ.
On trees, Florida. Very similar to *A. floridana.*

6. **Arthonia lecanactidea** Zahlbr., Beih. Bot. Centralb. 13:155. 1902.
Superficial thallus thin to moderately thick, creamy to ashy white, rough,
obscurely chinky; apothecia minute to small, 0.2–0.5 mm. across, adnate, round
to slightly irregular, the disk flat to convex, brownish gray to black; tinged pale
brownish within; asci pyriform; spores hyaline, ovoid-ellipsoid, 1-septate, one cell
slightly larger, 10–15 × 3.5–4.5 μ.
On trees, southern California.

7. **Arthonia impallens** Nyl., Flora 68:448. 1885.
Superficial thallus thin, whitish, smooth; apothecia minute to small, 0.08–0.2
mm. across, often elongated to 0.7 mm., partly immersed to adnate, linear, or more
or less branched, the disk flat, pale yellowish to slightly brown; hyaline within;
asci pyriform; spores hyaline, ovoid-ellipsoid, 1–3-septate, one end cell larger,
11–14 × 3–4 μ.
On holly, New Jersey.

8. **Arthonia ochrolutea** Nyl., in Willey, Syn. Arth. 4. 1890.
Superficial thallus thin, dull white to pale yellowish, smooth; apothecia numerous, sometimes coalescing, small, 0.1–0.4 mm. across, adnate, irregular and often
elongated, reaching 1 mm. or more in length, often surrounded by a thalloid veil,
the disk flat, pale yellow; tinged pale yellowish within; spores hyaline, ovoid-
ellipsoid, 3-septate, 10–15.5 × 3–4 μ.
On trees, Florida.

9. **Arthonia gyalectoides** Müll. Arg., Flora 69:128. 1886.
Superficial thallus thin, ashy white, becoming powdery, smooth to rough and
chinky; apothecia small to middle-sized, 0.4–0.9 mm. across, adnate, round-flexuous
to irregular, or finally lobed, the disk concave to flat, flesh-colored to brownish

black, or white-pruinose; hyaline or tinged faintly brownish within; asci pyriform; spores hyaline, ovoid-ellipsoid, 4–5-septate, one end cell larger, 16–22 × 6–8 μ.
On trees, southern California.

10. **Arthonia fissurina** Nyl., Flora 68:447. 1885.
Superficial thallus thin, dull white, smooth; apothecia small to middle-sized, 0.2–0.8 × 0.1–0.2 mm., immersed, elongated and somewhat irregular, the disk slightly concave, brownish, sometimes showing a thalloid veil; hyaline or tinged pale brownish within; asci pyriform; spores ovoid-ellipsoid, 7–11-septate, 24–32 × 8–11 μ.
On trees, Florida.

11. **Arthonia pyrrhula** Nyl., Flora 68:447. 1885.
Superficial thallus thin, ashy whitish, smooth to slightly rough; apothecia minute to small, 0.2–0.4 mm. across, immersed, irregular to elongated and reaching 1 mm. long, sometimes clustered, the disk flat, reddish; tinged pale reddish within; spores hyaline, ovoid-ellipsoid, 5–7-septate, 30–50 × 14–18 μ.
On trees, from New England to Florida.

12. **Arthonia gregaria** (Weig.) Koerb., Syst. Lich. Germ. 291. 1855.
Sphaeria gregaria Weig., Obs. Bot. 43. 1772. *A. gregaria* var. *obscura* Koerb. *A. cinnabarina* (DC.) Wallr.
Superficial thallus thin, gray to whitish, smooth; apothecia minute to small, 0.1–0.3 mm. across, sometimes elongating to 1 mm., partly immersed, irregular to oblong, or even stellate, often clustered, the disk slightly concave to convex, reddish brown to blackish and often whitish or crimson-pruinose; hyaline within; asci pyriform; spores hyaline to light brownish, ovoid-ellipsoid, 3–5-septate, one end cell larger, 12–22 × 5–8 μ.
On trees, generally distributed throughout the United States.

var. **adspersa** (Mont.) Müll. Arg., Flora 71: 524. 1888.
Ustalia adspersa Mont., Ann. Sci. Nat. Bot. 18:278. 1842.
Apothecia violet-brown; spores 4-septate, 15–24 × 7–9 μ.
On trees, Louisiana.

13. **Arthonia ochrocincta** Willey, Syn. Arth. 8. 1890.
A. ochrocincta Nyl., Flora 69:104. 1886. (nomen nudum).
Thallus thin, gray to whitish, smooth or slightly rough; apothecium minute to small, 0.15–0.25 × 0.3–1 mm., adnate, subrotund to irregular, or elongated and curved, sometimes clustered, the disk flat to somewhat convex, dull black or obscurely whitish pruinose, bordered by an ochre-red margin; tinged pale yellowish within; asci pyriform; spores hyaline, ovoid-ellipsoid, 3–5-septate, one and rarely both end cells larger, 18–23 × 4–6 μ.
On trees, Florida.
Our specimens were determined by Merrill. Nylander gave no description, but merely cited Tuckerman's exsiccatus No. 134.

14. **Arthonia Ravenelii** Tuck., in Willey, Int. Stud. Lich. Suppl. 53. 1887.
Superficial thallus thin, whitish, smooth to obscurely rough; apothecia minute to small, 0.5–1.5 × 0.1–0.2 mm., immersed, elongated, usually curved and rarely branched, the disk flat, reddish brown to black; tinged faintly reddish within; spores hyaline, ovoid-ellipsoid, 3–7-septate, one end cell larger, 20–28 × 7–10 μ.
On trees, Louisiana and Texas. Differs slightly from material from Mexico.

15. **Arthonia viridicans** Willey, Syn. Arth. 10. 1890.
Superficial thallus thin, grayish green, often intersected by black lines; apothecia small, 0.2–0.4 mm. across, adnate, round to irregular or oblong, the disk slightly convex, brown to dull black; hyaline within; spores hyaline, ovoid-ellipsoid, 3-septate, 12–15 × 4–6 μ.
On trees, Texas.

16. **Arthonia caribaea** (Ach.) Mass., Mem. Lich. 114. f. 149. 1853.
   Graphis caribaea Ach., Lich. Univ. 272. 1810.
   Superficial thallus thin, ashy white, slightly rough, surrounded by a black line;
apothecia minute to small, 0.5 × 0.05–0.15 mm., immersed, dendroid-branched and
reaching 1 or 2 mm. long, the disk pale brown to brownish black; hyaline or tinged
pale yellowish within; asci broadly pyriform; spores hyaline, oblong-ovoid, 5-
septate, end cells larger, 25–35 × 13–16 μ.
   On trees, Texas.
   Spore measurements of Nylander and Müller Arg. are 42–50 × 16–22 μ, and
our material is doubtfully included.

17. **Arthonia rubella** (Fée) Nyl., Mém. Soc. Sci. Nat. Cherb. 4:89. 1856.
   Graphis rubella Fée, Essai Crypt. 43, 44. pl. 11, f. 5. 1824.
   Superficial thallus thin, greenish gray to ashy white, rough, becoming granular
or chinky; apothecia minute to small, 0.1–0.2 × 0.5–1.5 mm., immersed, elongated
and branched, the disk flat, reddish brown; tinged faintly brownish within; asci
pyriform; spores hyaline, ovoid-ellipsoid, 3–5-septate, end cells larger, 25–34 ×
10–14 μ.
   On trees, from South Carolina to Florida, and westward to Alabama, Louisiana,
and Texas. Spores large and like those of Arthothelium.

18. **Arthonia subrubella** Nyl., Act. Soc. Sci. Fenn. 7:479, 480. 1863.
   Superficial thallus grayish white, of moderate thickness, becoming rough and
chinky; apothecia minute, 0.07–0.15 mm. across, adnate, irregular, elongated and
often much-branched, the disk flat, light and darker brown; hypothecium tinged
brown; hymenium hyaline; asci ovoid; spores hyaline, ellipsoid to slightly ovoid-
ellipsoid, sometimes curved, 5–7-septate, one or both end cells larger, 44–50 ×
16–18 μ.
   On trees, Florida. Thallus scarcely visible according to Nylander, and our
plant may have to be referred elsewhere.

19. **Arthonia polygramma** Nyl., Act. Soc. Sci. Fenn. 7:480. 1863.
   Superficial thallus thin, ashy white, rough, becoming powdery; apothecia minute
to small, 0.1–0.3 mm. across, often elongated to 0.8 mm., somewhat immersed, irregular to oblong, sometimes stellate, scattered or clustered, the disk flat, brownish
black and thinly white-pruinose; tinged pale yellowish within; asci pyriform; spores
hyaline, ovoid-ellipsoid, 3–5-septate, 16–22 × 5–7.5 μ.
   On trees, Florida and southern California.

20. **Arthonia varia** (Ach.) Nyl., Mém. Soc. Sci. Nat. Cherb. 5:132. 1857.
   Opegrapha abnormis var. *varia* Ach., Lich. Univ. 259. 1810.
   Superficial thallus thin, ashy, often absent; apothecia minute, 0.09–0.13 mm.
across, often elongated to 0.5 mm., round to irregular or oblong, the disk flat, dark
brown to black; asci globose-ovoid; spores hyaline, ovoid-ellipsoid,
3-septate, one end cell larger, 12–17 × 4.5–6 μ.
   On trees, Florida.

21. **Arthonia erubescens** Willey, Int. Stud. Lich. Suppl. 53. 1887.
   Superficial thallus thin, greenish gray, smooth; apothecia minute, 0.05–0.15 mm.
across, immersed to subadnate, round to irregular, or lobed, the disk flat, reddish
brown; hyaline or tinged pale yellowish within; spores hyaline, oblong-ovoid, 3-
septate, 13–18 × 5–7.5 μ.
   On trees, Texas.

22. **Arthonia perminuta** Willey, Syn. Arth. 14. 1890.
   Thallus very thin to thin, widespread, pale yellow; apothecia minute, 0.08–0.15
mm. across, adnate, round to irregular or rarely becoming oblong, the disk flat,
dark brown to black, lighter when wet; hypothecium hyaline; spores oblong-fusiform, 5–6-septate, 18–23 × 4–5.5 μ.
   On trees, Florida.

23. **Arthonia pyrrhuliza** Nyl., Flora 68:447. 1885.

Thallus thin, smooth to slightly rough, whitish, bordered more or less by a narrow, inconspicuous dark line; apothecia minute to small, 0.1–0.2 × 0.4–0.8 mm., irregular and variously elongated, curved and branched, immersed, the disk flat, reddish brown and finally darker; hyaline within; spores oblong-ellipsoid, hyaline to pale brownish, 3– rarely 4-septate, 12–15 × 4–5 μ.

On trees, New England, and doubtfully New York and Illinois.

24. **Arthonia platyspilea** Nyl., Act. Soc. Sci. Fenn. 7:480. 1863.

Superficial thallus thin, ashy white, often surrounded by a brownish black line; apothecia middle-sized, 0.5–1 mm. across and often 3 mm. long, immersed, irregular and often elongated, sometimes clustered, the disk flat, light or darker reddish brown, or whitish pruinose; tinged brownish within; spores hyaline, ovoid-ellipsoid, 7-septate, 21–27 × 8–11 μ.

On trees, Florida.

25. **Arthonia lecideella** Nyl., Mém. Soc. Sci. Nat. Cherb. Suppl. 5:337. 1857.

Superficial thallus rather thick, greenish to greenish gray, rough, becoming chinky and subareolate; apothecia minute to small, 0.2–0.6 mm., immersed to adnate, round, the disk flat to convex, brown to black, or grayish pruinose; hypothecium dark brown; hymenium lighter; asci clavate; spores hyaline, slipper-shaped, 3-septate, one end cell larger, 16–22 × 5–7 μ.

On trees, from New England to Maryland, and westward to Iowa and Minnesota.

26. **Arthonia cupressina** Tuck., Gen. Lich. 221. 1872.

Superficial thallus thin, whitish, smooth to slightly rough, becoming powdery; apothecia minute, 0.2–0.5 mm. across, partly immersed to adnate, round to slightly irregular, the disk convex, pale brown to blackish, at first greenish pruinose; hyaline within; spores hyaline to slightly colored, narrowly ovoid-ellipsoid, con- stricted at the middle septum, 3-septate, two cells at one end larger, 11–15 × 3–5 μ.

On trees, Massachusetts.

27. **Arthonia albofuscescens** Tuck., in Willey, Syn. Arth. 17. 1890.

Superficial thallus thin to moderately thick, ashy white, becoming rough; apothecia minute to small, 0.1–0.4 mm. across, immersed to semi-superficial, round to irregular or oblong, often reaching 0.6 mm. in length, sometimes clustered, the disk flat, brown to blackish; hyaline or tinged pale brownish within; spores hyaline, ovoid-ellipsoid, 3-septate, 9–13 × 3–5 μ.

On trees, Massachusetts.

28. **Arthonia chiodectella** Nyl., Flora 52:125. 1869.

Superficial thallus thin to moderately thick, greenish gray to ashy white, smooth to slightly rough, and finally chinky; apothecia minute to small, 0.1–0.3 mm. across, clustered, round or more commonly somewhat irregular, adnate to semi-immersed, the disk flat, dirty blackish, or obscurely whitish pruinose, at least toward the mar- gin; hymenium hyaline; hypothecium reddish brown; spores oblong-ovoid, 3–5- septate, 17–21 × 6–8 μ.

On trees, Louisiana and Texas.

29. **Arthonia impolita** (Ehrh.) Borr., in Hook. & Sowerby, Eng. Bot. 1:2692. f. 1. 1831.

Lichen impolitus Ehrh., Plant. Crypt. 274. 1793. *A. pruinosa* Ach. *A. impolita* var. *chiodectonoides* Tuck.

Superficial thallus thick, ashy white, chinky, rough and crumbling; apothecia minute to small, 0.2–0.9 mm. across, partly immersed to adnate, often clustered, nearly round to irregular, the disk flat, brown to blackish, and whitish pruinose; tinged pale yellowish within; asci pyriform; spores hyaline, oblong-ovoid, 3–5- septate, 12–18 × 5–7 μ.

On trees, Washington and California.

30. **Arthonia byssacea** (Weig.) Almq., Kgl. Svensk. Vet. Akad. Handl. 17:25.
1880.
Sphaeria byssacea Weig., Obser. Bot. 42. pl. 2, f. 9. 1772. *A. biformis* (Floerke)
Schaer. *A. biformis* f. *develata* (Nyl.) Willey.
Superficial thallus thin, whitish, smooth, becoming powdery; apothecia minute
to small, 0.2–0.3 mm. across, adnate, round to irregular, often elongating, reaching
0.5–0.7 mm. long, the disk flat to convex, dark brown to blackish, sometimes pruinose; tinged faintly red within; hypothecium darker; asci ovoid-ventricose; spores
oblong-ovoid, 3–5-septate, one end cell larger, 12–24 × 6–9 μ.
On trees, Massachusetts and New Hampshire.

31. **Arthonia glaucescens** Nyl., Mém. Soc. Nat. Cherb. 5:337. 1857.
Superficial thallus dull grayish white to greenish gray, often bearing small, white,
mealy soredia, sometimes disappearing; apothecia middle-sized, 0.75–1.25 mm.
across, immersed, round to somewhat irregular, the disk flat, obscurely whitish
pruinose to brown or blackish; hyaline or tinged pale yellow within; spores hyaline, ovoid-ellipsoid, 3-septate, 18–30 × 5.5–8.5 μ.
On trees, Massachusetts and North Carolina.

32. **Arthonia cinereopruinosa** Schaer., Enum. Lich. Eur. 243. 1850.
Superficial thallus thin, ashy white, smooth to slightly rough, becoming powdery; apothecia minute to small, 0.09–0.3 mm. across, partly immersed to adnate,
round to slightly irregular, the disk flat to convex, dusky to black; hyaline within;
asci pyriform; spores hyaline, ovoid-ellipsoid, 3- or rarely 1–4-septate, one end
cell larger, 15–18 × 4–6 μ.
On trees, White Mountains, New Hampshire.

33. **Arthonia Tuckermaniana** Willey, Syn. Arth. 20, 21. 1890.
Thallus thin, smooth, white to ashy; apothecia numerous, minute, 0.1–0.2 mm.
across, the disk flat to slightly convex, reddish brown to black, sometimes pruinose;
hyaline to brownish within; spores oblong-ovoid, 3–5-septate, the cell at one end
larger, hyaline to brown, 16–23 × 5–6 μ.
On trees, Florida.

34. **Arthonia Eckfeldtii** Müll. Arg., Bull. Herb. Boiss. 3:48. 1895.
Thallus thin, continuous, smooth to sometimes slightly powdery, white and
shining or grayish, sometimes bordered by a thin, obscure line; apothecia small,
0.3–0.6 mm. across, closely adnate, round to irregular, the disk flat to convex,
reddish brown to brownish black; brownish within; asci broadly ellipsoid; spores
8, hyaline, oblong-ellipsoid, 3-septate, 13–16 × 4.5–6 μ.
On trees, Florida and Louisiana.

35. **Arthonia leucastraea** Tuck., Gen. Lich. 220. 1872.
Superficial thallus thin to moderately thick, dull white, smooth, becoming powdery; apothecia minute to small, 0.15–0.2 × 0.4–0.6 mm., partly immersed, oblong
to elongated, the disk flat, reddish brown, more or less pruinose; hypothecium dark
brown; hymenium tinged pale yellowish; spores oblong-ovoid, hyaline, 3-septate,
end cells larger, middle cells sometimes divided longitudinally, 12–16 × 5.5–7.5 μ.
On trees, Texas. Transitional between Arthonia and Arthothelium.

36. **Arthonia glebosa** Tuck., Gen. Lich. 221. 1872.
Superficial thallus thick and rough, composed of round, elevated, dusky squamules; apothecia small, 0.3–0.5 mm. across, partly immersed to adnate, often clustered, round, the disk convex, black; tinged pale brownish within, hypothecium
darker; asci pyriform; spores hyaline, oblong-ovoid, 1-septate, constricted, one cell
slightly larger, 11–16 × 4.5–6 μ.
On rocks and soil among mosses, Colorado, California, and Washington.

37. **Arthonia lapidicola** (Tayl.) Branth & Rostr., Bot. Tidssk. 3:245. 1869.
Lecidea lapidicola Tayl., in Mack., Fl. Hib. 2:124. 1836.
Superficial thallus thin and disappearing, ashy white to olive-brown; apothecia minute to small, 0.1–0.3 mm. across, adnate, round, the disk flat to convex, black; tinged pale brownish within; asci pyriform; spores oblong-ovoid, hyaline or tinged brown, 1-septate, 12–17 × 5–7 μ.
On sandstone, New York, Indiana, Illinois, and Nebraska. The algal host is Palmelloid, and some workers recognize the genus Allarthonia based on difference in host.

38. **Arthonia terrigena** Nyl., Flora 68:448. 1885.
Thallus grayish brown, thin and inconspicuous, widespread; apothecia very minute, 0.06–0.08 mm. across, round, the disk brownish black; flat to slightly convex; hymenium tinged brown; hypothecium light brown; spores hyaline to pale brown, oblong-ovoid, 1-septate, 11–12.5 × 3–4 μ.
On soil, near New Bedford, Massachusetts.

39. **Arthonia rupicola** Fink; Hedrick, Mycologia 25:310. 1933.
Thallus very thin, smooth, widespread, pale greenish gray to ashy, finally disappearing; apothecia minute, 0.1–0.25 mm. across, adnate, round to irregular, the disk convex, black; hypothecium tinged brownish; hymenium hyaline; paraphyses indistinct, appearing interwoven and branched; asci broadly clavate to sub-ovoid; spores hyaline, oblong, 1-septate, constricted at the septum, the upper cell larger, 10–15 × 4.5–6 μ, irregularly arranged.
On limestone rock, near Oxford, Ohio.

40. **Arthonia patellulata** Nyl., Nya Bot. Notis. 1853:95. 1853.
A. patellulata var. *pallidiuscula* Willey. *Allarthonia patellulata* (Nyl.) Zahlbr.
Superficial thallus thin, whitish, rough, often mealy, becoming chinky, sometimes disappearing; apothecia minute to small, 0.15–0.5 mm. across, adnate, round, the disk flat to convex, black; hypothecium pale brown; hymenium hyaline; asci subpyriform; spores hyaline, oblong-ovoid, 1-septate, 10–14 × 3.5–5 μ.
On trees, Massachusetts, Illinois, Iowa, Minnesota, and California.
var. **caesiocarpa** Zahlbr., Bull. Torr. Club 27:646. 1900.
Allarthonia patellulata var. *caesiocarpa* (Zahlbr.) Hasse.
Apothecia from grayish white pruinose to naked and black; spores 12–17 × 5–6 μ.
On trees, southern California.

41. **Arthonia subdispuncta** Nyl.; Hasse, Bull. Torr. Club 24:448. 1897.
Superficial thallus thin, dirty white, smooth; apothecia minute, 0.08–0.12 mm. across, slightly immersed to adnate, round, angular or oblong, reaching 0.3 mm. long, the disk flat, bluish black to black; brown within; asci pyriform; spores tinged brownish, oblong-ovoid, 1-septate, one cell larger, 9–12 × 4–5 μ.
On *Leptosyne gigantea*, Santa Monica Range, California.

42. **Arthonia convexella** Nyl., Act. Soc. Linn. Bord. 21:415. 1856.
Thallus thin, smooth, becoming chinky, pale greenish gray to whitish, often disappearing; apothecia minute to small, 0.2–0.4 mm. across, adnate, round or varying toward oblong, convex and often obscurely rough, black; hypothecium dark brown; hymenium lighter brown; asci subpyriform; spores oblong-ellipsoid, hyaline to light brown, 1-septate, 11–14 × 4–6 μ.
On trees, northern Minnesota.

43. **Arthonia exilis** (Floerke) Anzi, Cat. Lich. Sondr. 94. 1860.
Lecidea synotheca var. *exilis* Floerke, Deutsche. Lich. 187. 1821. *Allarthonia exilis* (Floerke) Sandst.
Superficial thallus thin, dark gray, inconspicuous, and disappearing, on trees thicker and becoming slightly rough and chinky; apothecia minute, 0.1–0.3 mm. across, adnate, round to slightly irregular, sometimes clustered, the disk convex

to subglobose, black; hymenium hyaline; hypothecium pale brown; asci pyriform; spores hyaline, oblong-ovoid, 1-septate, one cell larger, 10–14 × 4.5–5.5 μ.
On trees and old wood, New Bedford, Massachusetts.

44. **Arthonia pruinosella** Nyl., in Hasse, Lich. South. Calif. 16. 1898.
Thallus thin to rather thick, uneven and sometimes becoming scurfy, forming small, round to irregular, dirty white or cream-colored patches; apothecia minute, 0.1–0.15 mm. across, round to rarely somewhat irregular, immersed to adnate, the disk flat, black or more commonly grayish pruinose; hypothecium hyaline; spores hyaline, oblong-ellipsoid, 1-septate, 13–16 × 4–5 μ.
On trees, southern California.

45. **Arthonia aleuromela** Nyl., Bot. Gaz. 22:334. 1896.
Superficial thallus dull white, thin to moderately thick, smooth, becoming powdery; apothecia minute to small, 0.2–0.6 mm. across, partly immersed to adnate, round to somewhat irregular, the disk flat to irregular or strongly convex, black; tinged brownish within; spores ovoid-ellipsoid, 1-septate, 10–13 × 1.5–3.5 μ.
On trees, West Virginia.

46. **Arthonia Rhoidis** Zahlbr., Beih. Bot. Centralb. 13:156. 1902.
Superficial thallus thin, pale pinkish to grayish, smooth to slightly rough; apothecia minute to small, 0.1–0.25 mm. across, immersed, round to irregular and sometimes oblong, the disk flat, black; hyaline within; asci pyriform; spores hyaline, ovoid-ellipsoid, 2-septate, 12–14 × 4.5–6 μ.
On trees, southern California.

47. **Arthonia dispersa** (Schrad.) Nyl., Not. Sällsk. Faun. Flor. Fenn. 5:261. 1861.
   Opegrapha dispersa Schrad., Usteri, Ann. der Bot. 22:86. 1797. *A. astroidea* var. *epipasta* (Schrad.) Nyl.
Superficial thallus thin, ashy white, smooth to slightly rough; apothecia minute to small, 0.09–0.4 mm. across, partly immersed, round to irregular, or sometimes elongated, rarely branched, the disk flat to convex, dark brown to black, rarely grayish pruinose; hyaline or tinged pale brownish within; asci pyriform; spores hyaline, oblong-ovoid, 1-septate, 11–16 × 4–5 μ.
On trees, generally distributed throughout the United States.

48. **Arthonia Willeyi** Tuck.; Hedrick, Mycologia 25:311. 1933.
Superficial thallus dull white, of moderate thickness, smooth to slightly rough; apothecia minute to small, 0.1–0.35 mm. across, round to slightly irregular, partly immersed to adnate, the disk flat to convex, black; tinged pale yellowish within; asci pyriform; spores hyaline, ovoid-ellipsoid, 1-septate or rarely 2-septate, one cell larger, 10–13 × 3–4 μ.
On trees, near Athens, Illinois.

49. **Arthonia Cytisi** Mass., Nouv. Ann. Sci. Nat. Bologna 7:216. 1853.
   A. excipienda Nyl. *A. hibernica* Nyl.
Superficial thallus ashy white, thin, smooth, sometimes disappearing; apothecia minute to small, 0.1–0.4 mm. across, immersed or partly immersed, irregular and often more or less branched, the disk flat, black; tinged pale brownish within; spores ovoid-ellipsoid, hyaline, 3-septate, one end cell larger, 16–25 × 5.5–9 μ.
On trees, Massachusetts, Ohio, and California.

50. **Arthonia dispersula** Nyl., Flora 59:285. 1876.
   A. Austini Willey.
Superficial thallus thin, ashy white, smooth to slightly rough; apothecia minute to small, 0.1–0.4 mm. across, partly immersed to adnate, round to irregular, the disk flat to convex, black; tinged brownish within; spores hyaline, ovoid-ellipsoid, 1-septate, one cell larger, 8–11 × 3–4.5 μ.
On trees, Florida. Scarcely distinct from *A. dispersa,* spores slightly smaller.

51. **Arthonia taedescens** Nyl., in Willey, Syn. Arth. 30. 1890.

Superficial thallus thin, greenish gray, smooth, inconspicuous; apothecia minute, 0.1–0.2 mm. across, irregular to elongated, sometimes branched, partly immersed to adnate, the disk flat to convex, black; tinged light brown within; spores fusiform-ovoid, 1-septate, 19–26 × 7.5–9 μ.

On bark, Virginia, Louisiana, Florida, and Alabama.

52. **Arthonia subminutissima** Nyl., Flora 68:448. 1885.

Superficial thallus thin, ashy white, smooth; apothecia very minute, 0.06–0.13 mm. across, or reaching 0.3 mm. long, adnate, round to oblong, the disk flat, black; hyaline within; asci pyriform; spores hyaline, oblong-ovoid, 1-septate, one cell larger, 7–9 × 2.5–3 μ.

On trees, Massachusetts.

53. **Arthonia microspermella** Willey, Syn. Arth. 31, 32. 1890.

Thallus very thin to thin, widespread, dirty white; apothecia minute, 0.1–0.2 mm. across or reaching 0.4 mm. in length, irregular to somewhat elongated, sometimes more or less branched, the disk flat, brownish black to black, lighter when wet; hypothecium hyaline; spores hyaline, ovoid, 1–2-septate, 10–14 × 3.5–5 μ.

On trees, Texas and California.

54. **Arthonia luridoalba** Nyl., in Willey, Syn. Arth. 36. 1890.

Superficial thallus thin, ashy white, smooth to slightly rough; apothecia small, 0.2–0.6 mm. across, partly immersed to adnate, round to angular, or oblong and reaching 1 mm. long, the disk flat·to convex, lurid blackish; hypothecium darker; hymenium pale brownish; spores hyaline, oblong-ovoid, 3-septate, 12–15 × 5–6 μ.

On trees, New Hampshire.

55. **Arthonia diffusa** Nyl., Flora 68:448. 1885.

Superficial thallus thin, ashy white, rough, becoming scurfy and sometimes disappearing; apothecia minute to small, 0.2–0.8 mm. across, basally immersed to adnate, round to slightly irregular, the disk flat to convex, black to whitish pruinose; hyaline within; spores hyaline, oblong-ovoid, 3-septate, one end cell often larger, 8–12 × 3–4.5 μ.

On trees, northern United States east of the Mississippi River.

56. **Arthonia diffusella** Fink; Hedrick, Mycologia 25:310. 1933.

Thallus thin, smooth to slightly rough, dull white to ashy; apothecia minute to small, 0.1–0.3 mm. across, round to more frequently irregular, solitary or rarely clustered, partly immersed to adnate, the disk flat to slightly convex, black; hypothecium brownish; asci subpyriform; spores 8, hyaline, 1–3- usually 2-septate, constricted at the septa with one or two upper cells commonly larger, 12–15 × 3.5–4 μ, irregularly arranged.

On old wood, Minnesota and Michigan.

57. **Arthonia subdiffusa** Willey, Syn. Arth. 36. 1890.

Superficial thallus thin, ashy white, smooth, becoming obscurely powdery; apothecia minute, 0.07–0.15 mm. across, adnate, round to slightly irregular or oblong, the disk flat to convex, black; hyaline within; asci pyriform; spores hyaline, ovoid-ellipsoid, 3-septate, 13–17 × 4–5 μ.

On trees, Florida and southern California.

58. **Arthonia melaspora** Tuck., in Willey, Int. Stud. Lich. Suppl. 54. 1887.

Superficial thallus thin, white-powdery; apothecia minute to small, 0.05–0.2 mm. across, immersed, round to irregular or oblong, becoming 0.6 mm. long, the disk flat, whitish pruinose to blackish; tinged light brownish within; spores dark brown, oblong-ovoid, 3–5-septate, one end cell larger and darker in color, 23–26 × 10–12 μ.

On old wood, Florida.

59. **Arthonia pinastri** Anzi, Comm. Soc. Critt. Ital. 1862³:159. 1862.
Superficial thallus ashy white, thin, smooth, and disappearing; apothecia minute
to small, 0.1–0.3 mm. across, adnate, more or less irregular, scattered or clustered,
the disk flat to convex, black; hypothecium tinged light brownish; hymenium hyaline; spores hyaline, ovoid-ellipsoid, 3–4-septate, 16–22 × 6–9 μ.
On trees, near New Bedford, Massachusetts.

60. **Arthonia reniformis** (Pers.) Ach., in Schrad., Journ. Bot. 1:16. 1799.
Opegrapha reniformis Pers., Ann. Bot. Usteri 7:31. pl. 2. f. C. 1794.
Superficial thallus thin, smooth, whitish to olive-green; apothecia minute to
small, 0.01–0.3 mm. across, adnate, round to oblong, the disk flat, black; tinged
light brownish within; spores ovoid-ellipsoid, 5-septate, 18–23 × 5–8 μ.
On trees, Pennsylvania and Florida.

61. **Arthonia pruinosula** Nyl., Ann. Sci. Nat. Bot. V. 7:341. 1867.
Superficial thallus thin, whitish to yellowish white, smooth; apothecia minute,
0.1–0.25 mm. across, immersed, round to obscurely angular or oblong, the disk flat,
black, usually thinly whitish pruinose; hyaline within; asci pyriform; spores hyaline to brown, ovoid-ellipsoid, 3-septate, 12–16 × 3.5–4.5 μ.
On trees, Florida.

62. **Arthonia polymorpha** Ach., Syn. Meth. Lich. 7. 1814.
Superficial thallus thin, smooth to slightly rough, grayish green to whitish,
sometimes bounded by a black line; apothecia small to middle-sized, 0.3–1 mm.
across, adnate, round to irregular, rarely elongated or branched, often clustered, the
disk flat to convex, black; tinged brown within; asci pyriform; spores hyaline or
tinged brownish, ovoid-ellipsoid, 3–5-septate, one end cell sometimes larger, 14–19
× 4.5–7.5 μ.
On trees, Maryland, Florida, Louisiana, Illinois, Iowa, and California.

63. **Arthonia complanata** Fée, Essai Crypt. 54. 1824.
Superficial thallus thin, greenish gray to whitish, smooth to rough and chinky;
apothecia small to middle-sized, 0.3–0.7 mm. across, slightly immersed to adnate,
round, sometimes elongated to 1.2 mm., the disk flat to convex, black; tinged yellowish brown within; asci pyriform; spores hyaline, ovoid-ellipsoid, one or both
end cells larger, sometimes curved, 4–6- usually 5-septate, 23–32 × 6–12 μ.
On trees, Friday Harbor, Washington (far from its usual range).

64. **Arthonia excedens** Nyl., Act. Soc. Sci. Fenn. 7:484. 1863.
Superficial thallus thin, ashy white, smooth to slightly rough, becoming obscurely
chinky; apothecia middle-sized, 0.4–0.7 mm. across, or elongating to 1.5 mm., partly
immersed to adnate, irregular and rarely more or less branched, the disk flat to
convex, dark brown to black; tinged reddish brown within; spores hyaline or tinged
brown, ovoid-ellipsoid, 5-septate, 27–34 × 9–12 μ.
On trees, Oregon and New York.

65. **Arthonia punctiformis** Ach., Lich. Univ. 141. 1810.
Superficial thallus thin, ashy white, usually smooth, sometimes disappearing;
apothecia minute, 0.1–0.2 mm. across, partly immersed to adnate, round to slightly
irregular, sometimes becoming oblong, the disk flat to convex, black; hypothecium
tinged very pale brownish; hymenium hyaline; spores hyaline, ovoid-ellipsoid,
3–5-septate, one end cell larger, 16–22 × 5–7 μ.
On trees, throughout the United States.

66. **Arthonia epipastoides** Nyl., Flora 56. 206. 1873.
Superficial thallus gray to whitish, thin, smooth, becoming powdery; apothecia
minute, 0.05–0.1 mm. across, adnate, round to irregular or reaching 0.3 mm. long,
the disk flat, black; hyaline within; spores lanceolate, 1–3-septate, 16–24 × 5–7 μ.
On trees, from New England to Florida, and westward to the Mississippi River,
and in California.

67. **Arthonia radiata** (Pers.) Ach., Vet. Akad. Nya Handl. 131. 1808.
  Opegrapha radiata Pers., Ann. Bot. Usteri 7:29. pl. 2, f. 33. 1794. *A. astroidea*
  Ach. *Opegrapha atra* var. *macularis* E. Fries. *A. radiata* var. *Swartziana*
  (Ach.) Almq. *A. astroidea* var. *Swartziana* (Ach.) Nyl.
  Superficial thallus thin, greenish gray to whitish or brownish, smooth to
slightly rough, rarely bordered by a dark line; apothecia small to middle-sized or
larger, 0.3–1.5 mm. across, irregular to elongated, stellately branched, partly
immersed to subadnate, often clustered, the disk flat to slightly convex, black;
brownish within; hypothecium darker; asci pyriform; spores hyaline, ovoid-
ellipsoid, 3-septate, $12–19 \times 4–6 \mu$. (PLATE 3 *a*.)
  On trees, throughout the United States.

  f. **angustata** Vainio, Med. Soc. Faun. Fl. Fenn. 10:157. 1883.
  Apothecia linear, sometimes elongated to 1 mm., commonly curved, sometimes
branched.
  On trees, southern California.

  var. **epipastoides** (Nyl.) A. L. Smith, Brit. Lich. 2:216. 1911.
  A. astroidea var. *epipastoides* Nyl., Not. Sällsk. Faun. Flor. Fenn. 5:259. 1881.
  Superficial thallus ashy white, thin, smooth; apothecia minute to small, 0.1–
0.3 mm. across, partly immersed to adnate, slightly irregular, sometimes clustered,
the disk flat to convex, black; tinged pale yellowish within; asci narrowly pyriform; spores ovoid-ellipsoid, 3-septate, $13–16 \times 3–5 \mu$.
  On trees, Sanford, Florida.

68. **Arthonia subastroidella** Nyl., Flora 68:312. 1885.
  Superficial thallus thin, smooth, ashy, often disappearing; apothecia minute
to small, 0.2–0.8 mm. across, immersed to subadnate, round to irregular and obscurely stellate, or long, reaching 1 mm., often in clusters, the disk flat, dull
black; hyaline within; spores hyaline, ovoid-ellipsoid, 3-septate, $12–18 \times 4–5 \mu$.
  On trees, New Bedford, Massachusetts.

69. **Arthonia quintaria** Nyl., Flora 68:312. 1885.
  Superficial thallus thin, smooth, grayish to ashy white; apothecia minute to
small, 0.1–0.3 mm. across, immersed, sometimes clustered, irregular to substellate,
the disk flat to convex, black; tinged pale yellowish within; spores hyaline, ovoid-
ellipsoid, 3–7-septate, $18–25 \times 6–10 \mu$.
  On trees, from Massachusetts to Florida.

70. **Arthonia xylographica** Nyl., Flora 68:312. 1885.
  Superficial thallus thin, ashy white, smooth; apothecia minute to small, 0.2–
0.5 mm. across or reaching 1.3 mm. in length, adnate, round, irregular, or elongated
and often curved or branched, sometimes surrounded by a thalloid veil, the disk
slightly convex, blackish; hyaline to pale brownish within; asci pyriform; spores
ovoid-ellipsoid, 3-septate, $12–15 \times 4–5 \mu$.
  On trees, New Bedford, Massachusetts.

71. **Arthonia Hamamelidis** Nyl., Flora 68:447. 1885.
  Thallus very thin, indicated by a greenish gray to whitish coloration, often
entirely absent above the substratum; apothecia small to middle-sized, 0.3–0.5 mm.
or elongated to 1.5 mm. in one direction, irregular, and usually more or less
branched, slightly immersed to adnate, the disk flat and black; brownish within
with a dark hypothecium; spores hyaline, oblong-ellipsoid, 3-septate, $10–14 \times$
$3.5–4.5 \mu$.
  On *Hamamelis virginica*, near New Bedford, Massachusetts. Possibly too near
A. astroidea Ach.

72. **Arthonia torulosa** Fée, Essai Crypt. 55. pl. 24, f. 1. 1824.
  Superficial thallus thin, smooth, greenish gray to pale olive-green, surrounded
by a dark line; apothecia minute, 0.05–0.2 mm. across, immersed, irregular and

finally stellate, the disk flat to slightly convex, brownish black; hypothecium dark brown; hymenium light brown; asci globose-ovoid; spores hyaline, oblong-ovoid, 5-septate, one or rarely both end cells larger, 13–16 × 5–6 μ.
On trees, Louisiana.

73. **Arthonia asteriscus** Müll. Arg., Bull. Herb. Boiss. 3:49. 1895.
Superficial thallus thin, ashy white, smooth, and finally disappearing; apothecia minute to small, 0.2–0.5 mm. across, sometimes elongated to 0.6 mm., partly immersed to adnate, irregular to obscurely stellate, the disk flat to convex, black; hyaline or blackening within; asci pyriform; spores hyaline, oblong-ovoid, 4–5-septate, 14–17 × 4.5–6.5 μ.
On trees, Louisiana.

74. **Arthonia galactitella** Nyl., in Hasse, Cont. U. S. Nat. Herb. 17¹:18. 1913.
Superficial thallus thin, ashy white to cream-colored, smooth, becoming finely powdered; apothecia minute, 0.1–0.2 mm. across, partly immersed to adnate, round to irregular, or oblong, reaching 0.3 mm. long, the disk flat, black, more or less whitish pruinose; hyaline within; spores hyaline, ovoid-ellipsoid, 3-septate, 14–20 × 5–7.5 μ.
On trees, southern California.

75. **Arthonia stictella** Stizenb., in Hasse, Cont. U. S. Nat. Herb. 17¹:20. 1913.
Superficial thallus thin, dull white, becoming obscurely scurfy; apothecia minute, elongated, and parallel, 0.1–0.2 × 0.4–1 mm., immersed to subadnate, the disk flat to convex, black; hyaline within; asci pyriform; spores hyaline, ovoid-ellipsoid, 5-septate, 18–25 × 6–7 μ.
On trees, Catalina Island, California.

76. **Arthonia platygraphidea** Nyl., Act. Soc. Sci. Fenn. 7:483. 1863.
Superficial thallus thin, whitish to ashy, smooth to rough, surrounded by a brownish black line; apothecia small to middle-sized, 0.3–0.9 mm. across, often elongated to 1.5 mm., immersed in a thalloid veil or adnate, round to slightly irregular, the disk flat to convex, brownish black to black; tinged faintly reddish within; spores fusiform, hyaline or tinged brown, 11–13-septate, 52–70 × 15–21 μ.
On trees, Florida.

77. **Arthonia phaeobaea** Norm., Flora 52:525. 1869.
Segestrella phaeobaea Norm., Scrip. Soc. Reg. Sci. Norv. 5:367. 1868. *A. paralia* Nyl. *A. atlantica* Willey in Herb.
Superficial thallus thin to moderately thick, slightly rough, greenish gray to brownish; apothecia minute, 0.15–0.25 mm. across, adnate, round to somewhat irregular, numerous but seldom clustered, the disk convex, brownish black; hyaline within; spores hyaline, ovoid-ellipsoid, 3–5-septate, 17–25 × 6–8.5 μ, possibly becoming submuriform.
On rocks, near Eastport, Maine.

OTHER SPECIES REPORTED

Arthonia atrata (Fée) Müll. Arg.—Florida.
Arthonia caudata Willey—Massachusetts.
Arthonia didyma Koerb.—New Hampshire.
Arthonia erupta Nyl.—Florida and Texas.
Arthonia oxytera Nyl.—Florida and Texas.
Arthonia septiseptella Nyl.—Alabama.
Arthonia subminutula Nyl.—Massachusetts.
Arthonia tetramera (Stizenb.) Hasse—California.
Arthonia varians (Dav.) Nyl.—Massachusetts and New York.
Arthonia vernans Willey—Florida.
Celidium stictarum (De Not.) Tul. (Not a lichen, although treated as an Arthonia by some workers.)—New Hampshire.

48. **Arthothelium** Mass., Ric. Lich. 54. f. 101. 1852.

Thallus rudimentary, without cortical tissues, partly within the substratum and forming a thin to thicker, uneven, areolate crust; apothecia small to large, round to irregular, more or less immersed to adnate, the disk brownish black to black; hypothecium brownish to dark brown; hymenium hyaline to brown; paraphyses usually branched; asci pyriform; spores usually 8, hyaline to brownish, large, transversely and longitudinally septate.

The algal hosts are Trentepohlia and Palmella.

A. Apothecia not black . . . . 1. A. sanguineum
A. Apothecia black
 B. Spores rarely less than 9-septate transversely
  C. Spores more than 40 μ in length
   D. Thallus ashy white to grayish; apothecia
    0.4–1 mm. across . . . . 2. A. distendens
   D. Thallus yellowish ashy to whitish; apothecia
    0.6–3 mm. across . . . . 11. A. macrothecum
  C. Spores less than 40 μ in length . . . . 10. A. albovirescens
 B. Spores rarely more than 7-septate transversely
  C. Spores rarely more than 22 μ in length
   D. Disk more or less whitish pruinose
    E. Apothecia 0.15–0.35 mm. across . . . . 5. A. pruinascens
    E. Apothecia 0.2–1.2 mm. across . . . . 7. A. anastomosans
   D. Disk black . . . . 8. A. abnorme
  C. Spores rarely less than 22 μ in length
   D. Disk more or less whitish pruinose
    E. Apothecia 0.1–0.25 mm. across . . . . 9. A. taediosum
    E. Apothecia 0.3–1.5 mm. across . . . . 4. A. spectabile
   D. Disk brownish black to black
    E. Apothecia 0.4–0.8 mm. across . . . . 12. A. interveniens
    E. Apothecia not more than 0.5 mm. across
     F. Thallus whitish to lead-gray or ashy white
      G. Thallus bordered wholly or in part by
       a black line . . . . 13. A. Hallii
      G. Thallus not bordered by a black line . . . 6. A. orbilliferum
     F. Thallus light greenish gray . . . . 3. A. subcyrtodes

1. **Arthothelium sanguineum** (Willey) Zahlbr., in E. & P., Nat. Pfl. 1¹:91. 1907. *Arthonia sanguinea* Willey, Syn. Arth. 22. 1890.

Thallus very thin, white to pale yellowish white; apothecia small to middle-sized, 0.35–1 mm. across, immersed to semi-superficial, round to oblong or slightly irregular, the disk white-pruinose to dark reddish brown or finally blackening; hyaline within; asci pyriform; spores hyaline or tinged brown, oblong-ovoid, 7–11-septate transversely and 3–5-septate longitudinally, 20–32 × 12–18 μ.

On trees, Santa Monica Range, California.

2. **Arthothelium distendens** (Nyl.) Müll. Arg., Bull. Herb. Boiss. 2:736. 1894. *Arthonia distendens* Nyl., Ann. Sci. Nat. Bot. IV. 19:351. 1863.

Superficial thallus thin, ashy white to grayish, smooth to rough and becoming chinky; apothecia small to middle-sized, 0.4–1 mm. across, partly immersed to adnate, round to more or less irregular, the disk flat, black; tinged pale yellowish within; asci subglobose; spores hyaline, oblong–ellipsoid, sometimes slightly curved, 9–11-septate transversely and 1–4-septate longitudinally, 40–62 × 14–20 μ.

On trees, Florida.

3. **Arthothelium subcyrtodes** (Willey) Hasse, Bryologist 18:92. 1915. *Arthonia subcyrtodes* Willey, Int. Stud. Lich. Suppl. 54. 1887.

Thallus thin, smooth, light greenish gray; apothecia minute to small, 0.1–0.5 mm. across, immersed, round to commonly somewhat irregular, the disk flat to convex, black; tinged brownish within; spores oblong-ellipsoid, hyaline to finally brown, 5–7-septate transversely and 2–3-septate longitudinally, 20–25 × 7.5–10 μ.

On trees, Santa Monica Range, California.

4. **Arthothelium spectabile** Mass., Ric. Lich. 54. f. 101. 1852.
Arthonia spectabilis (Mass.) Flot., in E. Fries, Lich. Eur. 371. 1831.

Superficial thallus moderately thick, whitish or grayish, smooth to rough, rarely subareolate, occurring in small, round areas, or more commonly widespread and irregular, bordered and more or less dissected by black lines; apothecia small to middle-sized or larger, 0.3–1.5 mm. across, variously irregular, immersed to adnate, the disk flat to convex, obscurely white-pruinose, or more commonly black, tinged brown within; asci pyriform; spores oblong-ellipsoid, hyaline to pale brown, 5–9-septate transversely and 2–5-septate longitudinally, 26–38 × 12–20 μ.

On trees, throughout the United States.

5. **Arthothelium pruinascens** Zahlbr., Bull. Torr. Club 27:646, 647. 1900.

Superficial thallus thin, dirty white to greenish or yellowish gray, smooth to rough, round to widespread and irregular; apothecia small, 0.15–0.35 mm. across, immersed to adnate, round to irregular, the disk flat, white-pruinose; hyaline within; spores oblong-ellipsoid, 5–7-septate transversely and 1–3-septate longitudinally, 17–22 × 8–12 μ.

On trees, Santa Monica Range, California.
Near *A. spectabile* according to Zahlbruckner.

6. **Arthothelium orbilliferum** (Almq.) Hasse, Cont. U. S. Nat. Herb. 17:22. 1913.
Arthonia orbillifera Almq., Kgl. Svensk. Vet. Akad. Handl. 17:41. 1880.

Superficial thallus thin, whitish to lead-gray, smooth to slightly rough; apothecia minute to small, 0.2–0.5 mm. across, immersed to adnate, sometimes clustered, the disk round to more or less irregular, convex, black; hyaline within; asci pyriform; spores oblong-ovoid, hyaline, 5–7-septate transversely and 1–3-septate longitudinally, 20–28 × 10–17 μ.

On trees, Santa Monica Range and Catalina Island, California.

7. **Arthothelium anastomosans** (Ach.) Arn., in Rehm, Rabh. Krypt.–Fl.
Deutsch. ed. 2. 1:442. 1891.
Arthonia radiata var. *anastomosans* Ach., Lich. Univ. 146. 1810.

Superficial thallus thin, whitish, smooth to slightly rough, in small round patches, to irregular and covering larger areas; apothecia small to middle-sized or larger, 0.2–1.2 mm. across, irregular to branched and often distinctly radiate, often in clusters, the disk black throughout or white-pruinose toward the margins; asci ovoid-pyriform; spores hyaline, ovoid-ellipsoid, 5–9-septate transversely and 3–5-septate longitudinally, 17–23 × 7–8.5 μ.

On trees, southern California.

8. **Arthothelium abnorme** (Ach.) Müll. Arg., Flora 63:287. 1880.
Opegrapha abnormis Ach., Lich. Univ. 259. 1810. *Arthonia abnormis* (Ach.) Nyl.

Thallus thin, white to whitish, in small, round to irregular patches; apothecia small to middle-sized, round to irregularly angular or sometimes stellate, the disk black; asci pyriform to almost spherical; spores 4–8, hyaline, ovoid-ellipsoid, 4–8-septate transversely and 1–3-septate longitudinally, 14–20 × 7.5–10 μ.

On trees, California.
No specimen has been seen, the description adapted from Herre, Bryologist 15:83, 84. 1912.

9. **Arthothelium taediosum** (Nyl.) Müll. Arg., Flora 63:287. 1880.
Arthonia taediosa Nyl., Ann. Sci. Nat. IV. 3:171. 1855.

Thallus rather thin, smooth to slightly rough, whitish, limited more or less by a black line; apothecia minute to small, 0.1–0.25 mm. across, or elongated to more than 1 mm. in one direction, immersed, irregularly linear and becoming branched, often clustered, the disk dirty black or thinly white-pruinose; asci pyriform; spores hyaline to finally brown, ovoid-oblong, 5–9-septate transversely and 2–5-septate longitudinally, 27–35 × 11–15 μ.

On trees, from New England to Florida, and westward to Illinois, reappearing in California.

10. **Arthothelium albovirescens** (Nyl.) Fink n. comb.
Arthonia albovirescens Nyl., Bull. Torr. Club 16:105. 1889. *Allarthothelium albovirescens* (Nyl.) Zahlbr.
Superficial thallus thin, greenish white, obscurely scurfy; apothecia minute, 0.06–0.1 mm. across, partly immersed to adnate, round and often clustered, the disk convex, brownish black to black; hyaline within; asci ovoid-pyriform; spores hyaline, oblong-ellipsoid, 8–13-septate transversely and 2–3-septate longitudinally, 15–35 × 10–16 μ.
On trees, Florida, and doubtfully reported from Alabama and Louisiana.
The smaller, scarcely muriform spores of the original description were immature. In material examined, spores were partly the same.

11. **Arthothelium macrothecum** (Fée) Mass., Ric. Lich. 55. 1852.
Arthonia macrotheca Fée, Essai Crypt. Suppl. 42. 1837.
Superficial thallus thin, smooth to rough, yellowish ashy to whitish, becoming powdery and disappearing; apothecia middle-sized to large, 0.6–3 mm. across, round to irregular, usually subsuperficial, the disk white-pruinose to brownish black or black; asci ovoid-pyriform; spores hyaline, ellipsoid, 9–17-septate transversely and 3–7-septate longitudinally, 46–68 × 17–28 μ.
On trees, Texas.

12. **Arthothelium interveniens** (Nyl.) Zahlbr., Cat. Lich. Univ. 2:127. 1922.
Arthonia interveniens Nyl., Act. Soc. Sci. Fenn. 7:482, 483. 1863.
Superficial thallus thin, smooth to slightly rough, greenish gray to ashy; apothecia small to middle-sized, 0.4–0.8 mm. across, partly immersed to adnate, oblong to slightly irregular, scattered or 2 or 3 in a group, the disk flat, brownish black to black; dark-colored within; spores hyaline to brown, oblong-ellipsoid, 4–7-septate transversely and 1–2-septate longitudinally, 21–30 × 8–10 μ.
On trees, Florida, Louisiana, and Texas.

13. **Arthothelium Hallii** (Tuck.) Zahlbr., Cat. Lich. Univ. 2:126. 1924.
Arthonia Hallii Tuck., in Willey, Syn. Arth. Suppl. 55. 1890.
Superficial thallus thin, smooth, ashy white, bordered wholly or in part by a black line; apothecia minute to small, 0.15–0.5 mm. across, wholly or partly immersed, round to more often irregular, often clustered, the disk flat, brownish black to black; hyaline within; asci ovoid-pyriform; spores hyaline, oblong-ovoid to oblong-fusiform, 5–6-septate transversely and 1-septate longitudinally, 20–32 × 7–10 μ.
On trees, Illinois.

OTHER SPECIES REPORTED

Arthothelium adveniens Nyl.—California.
Arthothelium violascens var. subcinerascens (Nyl.) Zahlbr.—Ohio.

15. GRAPHIDACEAE

Thallus crustose, partly within the substratum, showing little or no differentiation, attached to the substratum by hyphal rhizoids; apothecia usually elongated, often curved, more or less branched, rarely round, single or clustered but not in a stroma, the proper exciple usually well developed, sometimes covered by a thin, thalloid layer; paraphyses unbranched or branched and interwoven, usually persistent.
The algal hosts are Palmella and Trentepohlia.

A. Spores hyaline or rarely brownish
  B. Spores non-septate .   .   .   .   49. Xylographa

B. Spores septate
  C. Paraphyses unbranched and not interwoven
    D. Spores with cylindrical or cubical cells . . . . . . 52. MELASPILEA
    D. Spores with lenticular cells
      E. Spores transversely several-septate . . . . 53. GRAPHIS
      E. Spores transversely and longitudinally septate . . . 55. GRAPHINA
  C. Paraphyses branched and interwoven
    D. Spores with cylindrical or cubical cells
      E. Parasitic on lichens . . . . 51. OPEGRAPHOIDEA
      E. Not parasitic on lichens . . . . 50. OPEGRAPHA
    D. Spores with lenticular cells . . . . 57. HELMINTHOCARPON
A. Spores brown
  B. Spores transversely several-septate . . . . 54. PHAEOGRAPHIS
  B. Spores transversely and longitudinally septate . . . . 56. PHAEOGRAPHINA

49. Xylographa E. Fries, Sum. Veg. Scand. 372. 1846.

Thallus wholly within the substratum, or appearing above as minute warts or as soredia or soralia; apothecia erumpent, round, elongated, or irregular, usually straight and unbranched, the proper exciple usually dark-colored, the disk closed or more or less open; hypothecium hyaline to brown; asci clavate; paraphyses seldom branched, several-celled, with thin transverse walls; hymenium hyaline; spores 8, non-septate, hyaline, usually ellipsoid; commonly on old wood.

The algal host is Palmella.

A. Spores 14–25 μ in length . . . . 3. X. disseminata
A. Spores not more than 16 μ in length
  B. Apothecia reaching 1–1.5 mm. in length . . . . 1. X. abietina
  B. Apothecia not more than 0.5 mm. in length
    C. Apothecia round to oblong . . . . 2. X. hians
    C. Apothecia round to irregular and sometimes branched . . 4. X. opegraphella

1. **Xylographa abietina** (Pers.) Zahlbr., Cat. Lich. Univ. 2:151–153. 1924.
Hysterium abietinum Pers., Obs. Mycol. 1:31. 1796. *X. parallela* (Ach.) Behlen & Desberg.

Thallus within the substratum and showing at the surface as a whitish coloration, or appearing above the surface as minute and uncertain whitish spots; apothecia minute to becoming long and narrow, 0.4–1.5 × 0.15–0.2 mm., straight, pointed at the ends, immersed, lying parallel in the substratum, the disk closed to open and concave to flat, black, the exciple thin, colored like the disk, rarely disappearing; spores ellipsoid, 9.5–15 × 5–6.5 μ.

On old wood, from New England westward to Washington.

2. **Xylographa hians** Tuck., Syn. N. A. Lich. 2:113. 1888.

Thallus usually within the substratum, indicated at the surface by a grayish white coloration, but rarely showing minute, superficial granules; apothecia minute, 0.3–0.5 × 0.15–0.2 mm., adnate, scattered or clustered, circular to oblong or broadly ellipsoid, the disk closed to open and concave to flat, brown to black, the exciple becoming thin, colored like the disk or slightly darker; spores oblong-ovoid, 9–14 × 5–7 μ.

On old wood, Washington and Oregon.

3. **Xylographa disseminata** Willey, in Tuck., Syn. N. A. Lich. 2:112, 113. 1888.

Thallus thin, continuous or scattered, greenish gray to ashy, composed of minute, spheroidal granules; apothecia minute, 0.2–0.4 × 0.2–0.25 mm., adnate, circular to irregular, ellipsoid or oblong, the disk closed to open and concave to flat, dark brown to black, the exciple black, becoming thin; spores oblong, sometimes reported 1–3-septate, 14–25 × 4–6 μ.

On old wood, New England.

4. **Xylographa opegraphella** Nyl., Mém. Soc. Sci. Nat. Cherb. 5:128. 1857.

Thallus becoming thick, rough and warty, greenish gray to pale brownish, rarely disappearing; apothecia minute, 0.2–0.3 × 0.1–0.2 mm., partly immersed to

adnate, 1–several on each wart, round to irregular or elongated, sometimes 1–3 times short-branched, the disk closed to open and concave, pale to darker brown, the exciple thin, colored like the disk; spores oblong-ellipsoid, 11–16 × 3–5 μ.
On old wood, along the coast of New England.

50. **Opegrapha** Humb., Fl. Friberg. 57. 1793.

Thallus forming a crust upon the substratum, and partly or rarely wholly within the substratum, devoid of differentiation into layers; apothecia linear, fusiform, ellipsoid, oblong, or rarely circular or irregular in outline, rarely branched, superficial or more or less immersed, usually black, the disk commonly closed and indicated by a black or blackish depressed line, but sometimes becoming open and black, the exciple usually black; hypothecium commonly brownish black in section; paraphyses interwoven and branched; asci commonly clavate with thin wall; spores usually 8, commonly hyaline but becoming brownish in some species, several- to many-septate with cylindrical cells, from oblong or ovate to ellipsoid, fusiform, or finger-shaped.
The algal host is Trentepohlia.

A. Spores constantly 3-septate
  B. On trees
    C. Hypothecium hyaline . . . . 5. O. Umbellulariae
    C. Hypothecium brownish to brown or black
      D. Spores less than 20 μ in length
        E. Thallus white or whitish
          F. Spores 11–13 × 4–5 μ . . . . 8. O. candida
          F. Spores 15–21 × 4–5 μ . . . . 1. O. atra
        E. Thallus greenish gray to ashy or brownish gray
          F. Thallus smooth to slightly rough
            G. Apothecia short and wide,
              0.4–1 × 0.3–0.6 mm. . . . . 4. O. diaphoroides
            G. Apothecia longer and narrower,
              0.5–2.5 × 0.2–0.3 mm. . . . . 2. O. agelaea
          F. Thallus minutely granulose . . . . 7. O. microcyclia
      D. Spores more than 20 μ in length
        E. Apothecia 1 or 2 times branched . . . . . 6. O. herpetica subocellata
        E. Apothecia very rarely branched . . . . 3. O. betulina
  B. On rocks
    C. Spores 12–16 × 3.5–5 μ . . . . 10. O. calcarea
    C. Spores 18–28 × 5–7 μ . . . . 9. O. saxicola
A. Spores 3–5- or more septate
  B. Spores 3–5- or 7-septate
    C. On trees and old wood
      D. Hypothecium hyaline
        E. Apothecia closely aggregate, usually straight . . . 20. O. longissima
        E. Apothecia scattered, frequently curved . . . . . . 11. O. filicina
      D. Hypothecium brownish black
        E. Thallus smooth
          F. Apothecia not branched or rarely so
            G. Apothecia short and wide,
              0.5–1 × 0.15–0.35 mm. . . . . 15. O. lichenoides
            G. Apothecia longer and narrower,
              0.4–2 × 0.15–0.25 mm. . . . . 14. O. cinerea
          F. Apothecia often branched . . . . 13. O. astraea
        E. Thallus becoming chinky, scurfy, scaly, or powdery
          F. Disk closed
            G. Thallus white, with plainly marked margins . 17. O. leucoplaca
            G. Thallus light greenish gray to ashy white
              or brownish . . . . 19. O. vulgata minor
          F. Disk more or less widely open
            G. Apothecia not more than 2 mm. long

H. Apothecia 0.3–1 × 0.1–0.25 mm.,
  usually scattered . . . . 16. O. diaphora
H. Apothecia 0.4–2 × 0.16–0.4 mm.,
  scattered or clustered . . . . 18. O. varia
    G. Apothecia 0.4–5 mm. long . . . . 19. O. vulgata
C. On rocks
  D. Thallus thin, smooth . . . . 12. O. lithyrga
  D. Thallus thicker, becoming chinky to subareolate,
    crumbling or powdery . . . . 21. O. Hassei
B. Spores 7–15-septate
  C. Spores not more than 45 μ in length
    D. Thallus very thin; spores 20–42 × 3.5–7.5 μ . . . . . 23. O. Bonplandi
    D. Thallus somewhat thicker; spores 24–32 × 6–11 μ . . . 22. O. prosodea
  C. Spores 35–70 × 4.5–7.5 μ . . . . 24. O. viridis

1. **Opegrapha atra** Pers., Ann. Bot. Usteri 7:30. pl. 1, f. 28. 1794.
O. atra var. *hapalea* (Ach.) Nyl.
Thallus thin, smooth, whitish, infrequently tending to disappear, rarely limited by a blackish line; apothecia moderately long and wide, 0.5–2.5 × 0.2–0.3
mm., oblong-ellipsoid, adnate, usually numerous, straight to curved or flexuous,
very rarely branched, the disk closed to narrowly open and black, the exciple
black; hypothecium brownish black; spores finger-shaped, 3-septate, 15–21 × 4–5 μ.
On trees, throughout the United States.

2. **Opegrapha agelaea** Fée, Mém. Mus. Hist. Nat. Strasb. 2¹⁰:23. 1835.
Thallus thin, smooth, pale greenish gray, varying toward ashy or olivaceous;
apothecia of moderate length and width, 0.5–2.5 × 0.2-0.3 mm. with ends rather
obtuse, slightly immersed to adnate, scattered to clustered, straight to curved or
rarely and obscurely flexuous, very rarely branched, the disk closed to narrowly
open and black, the exciple dull black; hypothecium black; spores 3-septate,
14–18 × 5–7 μ.
On trees, Florida.

3. **Opegrapha betulina** J. E. Smith, in Sowerby, Engl. Bot. 32: pl. 2281. 1811.
O. atrorimalis Nyl.
Thallus thin, smooth, ashy, varying toward yellowish or brownish, often margined by a blackish line; apothecia rather short and wide, 0.5–2 × 0.25–0.45 mm.,
ellipsoid, adnate, numerous, scattered or clustered, straight to curved, very rarely
branched, the disk soon open and black, the exciple black; hypothecium brownish
black; spores ovoid-ellipsoid, 3-septate, 19–25 × 6–8.5 μ.
On trees, Orange County, California.

4. **Opegrapha diaphoroides** Nyl., Flora 61:453. 1878.
O. varia var. *diaphora* f. *diaphoroides* Boist.
Thallus thin, smooth to slightly rough, greenish gray to ashy or brownish;
apothecia short and wide in proportion, or even subrotund, 0.4–1.4 × 0.3–0.6 mm.,
adnate, usually scattered, straight to rarely and obscurely curved, the disk soon
widely open and black, the exciple black; hypothecium thick and brownish black;
spores finger-shaped, 3-septate, 12–17 × 3–4 μ.
On trees, Florida.

5. **Opegrapha Umbellulariae** Zahlbr., Beih. Bot. Cent. 13:154. 1902.
Thallus thin, smooth, finally and obscurely chinky, pale greenish gray to whitish,
occurring in small roundish to irregular areas; apothecia rather short and narrow,
0.4–0.8 × 0.15–0.25 mm., narrowly oblong, subsessile, commonly scattered, straight
to curved or obscurely flexuous, sometimes branched, the disk closed to open,
concave to flat, dull black, the exciple black and of medium thickness; hypothecium hyaline; spores oblong-dactyloid, 3-septate, 12–15 × 3.5–4 μ, obscurely constricted, especially at the middle septum, sub-biseriately arranged.
On *Umbellularia californica*, Santa Monica Range, California.

6. **Opegrapha herpetica** Ach. var. **subocellata** Ach., Syn. Meth. Lich. 73. 1814.
Thallus thin, smooth to slightly rough, becoming chinky, greenish gray to ashy
or brownish, limited and sometimes dissected by blackish lines, becoming powdery
and sometimes disappearing; apothecia rather short, but of average width, $0.5–1.5 \times$
$0.2–0.25$ mm., oblong to slightly irregular, immersed in a white, thalloid exciple,
scattered or clustered, straight to curved, sometimes 1 or 2 times branched, the
disk closed to open, flat, and brownish black, the exciple rather thin; hypothecium
medium to dark brown; spores hyaline to finally brownish, ellipsoid-fusiform,
3-septate, $20–26 \times 4–5 \mu$.
On trees, near Sanford, Florida. (The species is reported from temperate regions.)

7. **Opegrapha microcyclia** Tuck., Proc. Am. Acad. 5:285. 1866.
O. myriocarpa Tuck. (non Fée).
Thallus rather thin, brownish gray, minutely granulose, the granules often
heaped, forming a somewhat rough crust; apothecia minute, round to slightly
elongated, $0.15–0.25$ mm. across, or reaching 0.4 mm. in one direction, adnate,
usually numerous, and scattered or clustered, the disk open, concave to flat, brownish black, the exciple well developed and of the same color; hypothecium light to
darker brown; spores ovoid-dactyloid, 3-septate, $13–15 \times 5–6 \mu$.
On trees, New Hampshire and Massachusetts.

8. **Opegrapha candida** Müll. Arg., Bull. Herb. Boiss. 3:42. 1895.
Thallus thin, smooth, and white, becoming powdery; apothecia rather short
and narrow, $0.3–2.5 \times 0.12–0.17$ mm., the ends obtuse, slightly immersed to adnate, scattered, straight to curved, infrequently and sparingly branched, the
disk closed, the exciple black and moderately thick; hypothecium brownish black;
spores ovoid-finger-shaped, 3-septate, $11–13 \times 4–5 \mu$,
On bark of Liriodendron, Florida.

9. **Opegrapha saxicola** Ach., Syn. Meth. Lich. 71. 1814.
Thallus thin, smooth to scurfy or granulose, rarely tending to disappear; apothecia rather short and wide, sometimes irregular, $0.3–2 \times 0.3–0.5$ mm., oblong-
ellipsoid, adnate, scattered or clustered, straight to infrequently curved, often and
variously branched, the disk closed to open and concave to flat, dull or brownish
black, the exciple black; hypothecium brownish black; spores hyaline to brownish,
ellipsoid to ovoid, 3-septate, $18–28 \times 5–7 \mu$.
On rocks, California.

10. **Opegrapha calcarea** Turn., in Sowerby, Engl. Bot. 25:1790. 1807.
O. chevallieri Leight. pr. p.
Thallus thin to moderately thick, smooth to slightly rough, scurfy or chinky,
pale greenish gray to whitish or yellow, sometimes breaking into powdery conditions and finally disappearing; apothecia of moderate length and width, $0.5–2 \times$
$0.2–0.3$ mm., oblong-ellipsoid, adnate, scattered to radiately clustered, soon curved
or flexuous, infrequently branched, the disk closed to open, flat, black, the exciple
moderately thick and black; hypothecium brownish black; spores hyaline to
brownish, ellipsoid, 3-septate, $12–16 \times 3.5–5 \mu$.
On rocks, southern California.

11. **Opegrapha filicina** Mont., in Sagra, Hist. Nat. Cub. Bot. 184. pl. 9, f. 1.
1835–42.
Opegraphella filicina (Mont.) Müll. Arg. *Fouragea filicina* (Mont.) Trev.
Thallus within the substratum and indicated at the surface by a greenish, greenish gray, or finally brownish coloration; apothecia becoming somewhat long, but
remaining very narrow, $0.2–1.5 \times 0.1–0.2$ mm., the ends usually obtuse, adnate,
scattered to sometimes rather loosely grouped, straight to curved or infrequently
flexuous, rarely 1–2 or 3 times branched, the disk closed and finally indicated by

a very obscure, depressed, black line, the exciple black and rather thin; hypothecium hyaline; spores cylindrical-ellipsoid to variously curved and rarely thicker in some regions between the two ends, 3–5-septate, 14–24 × 2–4 μ.
On trees, Louisiana.

12. **Opegrapha lithyrga** Ach., Lich. Univ. 247. 1810.
O. vulgata var. *lithyrga* (Ach.) Nyl.
Thallus thin, smooth, greenish gray, varying toward whitish or brownish, sometimes disappearing; apothecia rather short and of medium width, 0.4–2 × 0.2–0.3 mm., round to oblong-ellipsoid, adnate, scattered to rarely clustered, rarely stellately so, straight to curved, rarely branched, the disk narrowly open, flat and dull black, the exciple black; spores narrowly fusiform, 4–5-septate, 19–27 × 3–4 μ.
On rocks and adjacent trees, near Weymouth, Massachusetts.

13. **Opegrapha astraea** Tuck., Lich. Calif. 33. 1866.
Thallus thin, smooth to slightly rough, pale greenish gray to ashy, often limited more or less by a blackish line, rarely disappearing; apothecia of moderate length and width or rarely subcircular, 0.5–3 × 0.2–0.4 mm., the ends obtuse; partly immersed to adnate, scattered to clustered, usually curved or flexuous, often branched and becoming radiately so, the disk closed to narrowly open, black or more commonly whitish pruinose, the exciple black or likewise whitish pruinose; hypothecium brownish black; spores hyaline or finally brownish, finger-shaped, 3–5-septate, 16–26 × 5–7.5 μ.
On trees, South Carolina, Florida, and Louisiana.

14. **Opegrapha cinerea** Chev., Journ. Phys. Chem. Hist. Nat. 94:41. 1822.
Thallus thin, smooth, pale greenish gray to whitish or brownish; apothecia somewhat elongated but narrow, 0.4–2 × 0.15–0.25 mm., oblong-ellipsoid, slightly immersed to adnate, scattered to more closely placed, usually curved or flexuous, infrequently branched, the disk closed, the exciple black; hypothecium rather thin, brownish black; spores spindle-shaped to narrow-ellipsoid, 3–6-septate, 20–30 × 2.5–3 μ.
On trees, Florida.

15. **Opegrapha lichenoides** Pers., Ann. Bot. Usteri 7:30. pl. 1, f. 4*b*. 1794.
O. atra, lichenoides (Pers.) Hasse. *O. varia* var. *notha* (Ach.) E. Fries.
Thallus smooth, thin to moderately thick, pale greenish gray, varying toward ashy; apothecia rather short but of medium width, 0.5–1 × 0.15–0.35 mm., oblong-ellipsoid, subsessile, commonly scattered, straight to curved, the disk wide open, flat, dull black or obscurely greenish pruinose, the exciple of the same color; hypothecium brownish black; spores fusiform, 3–5-septate, 23–28 × 6–8 μ.
On trees, throughout the United States.

16. **Opegrapha diaphora** Ach., Meth. Lich. 19. 1803.
Lichen diaphorus Ach., Lich. Suec. 20. 1798.
Thallus thin, smooth, pale greenish gray to ashy, becoming obscurely chinky and sometimes scurfy; apothecia short and narrow, 0.3–1 × 0.1–0.25 mm., ellipsoid-fusiform, slightly immersed to adnate, usually scattered, straight to infrequently and obscurely curved or flexuous, the disk closed to slightly or more widely open and black, the exciple black, often dull; hypothecium brownish black; spores ellipsoid-dactyloid, 3–7-septate, 16–28 × 4.5–7 μ.
On trees, Massachusetts, California, and Washington.

17. **Opegrapha leucoplaca** Müll. Arg., Bull. Herb. Boiss. 3:42. 1895.
Thallus rather thick, with plainly marked margins, smooth, white, becoming obscurely powdery; apothecia of moderate length and width, 0.4–1.7 × 0.17–0.25 mm., oblong- to linear-ellipsoid, partly immersed to adnate, scattered or rarely clustered, straight to curved or obscurely flexuous, rarely 1 or more times branched,

the disk closed, the exciple black; hypothecium brownish black; spores fusiform, 3–7-septate, 16–23 × 3.5–4.5 μ.

On trees, Florida and Louisiana.

18. **Opegrapha varia** Pers., Ann. Bot. Usteri 7:30. 1794.

O. pulicaris (Hoffm.) Schrad. *O. varia* var. *pulicaris* (Hoffm.) E. Fries.

Thallus thin, smooth, or becoming thicker and obscurely chinky or powdery, pale greenish gray to whitish, rarely disappearing; apothecia rather short and wide, 0.4–2 × 0.16–0.4 mm., the ends often more or less pointed, partly immersed to adnate, scattered or clustered, straight to infrequently and obscurely curved or even rarely flexuous, the disk closed to soon open, slightly concave to convex, dull black, the exciple black, at first thick, prominent and inflexed, finally tending to disappear; hypothecium moderately thick, brownish black; spores hyaline to finally brownish, fusiform, varying toward oblong-ellipsoid, 3–5- or rarely 7-septate, 18–30 × 5–8 μ.

On trees, throughout the United States.

19. **Opegrapha vulgata** Ach., Lich. Suec. 21, 22. 1798.

O. vulgata var. *subsiderella* Nyl.

Thallus thin, smooth, becoming chinky, scaly, powdery, light greenish gray, varying toward ashy white or brownish; apothecia short to elongated but remaining narrow, 0.4–5 × 0.15–0.25 mm., the ends usually obtuse, slightly immersed to adnate, scattered or clustered, straight to curved or flexuous, rarely branched, the disk closed to rarely and narrowly open, slightly concave to flat and dull black, the exciple rather thin and black; hypothecium brownish black; spores narrowly fusiform, 4–7-septate, 16–28 × 3–4 μ.

On trees, distributed throughout the United States, but not common in most areas.

var. **minor** Müll. Arg., Bull. Herb. Boiss. 3:42. 1895.

Apothecia on the whole shorter and narrower, the disk tightly closed and obscurely visible.

On trees, Louisiana and Florida.

20. **Opegrapha longissima** Müll. Arg., Bull. Herb. Boiss. 3:43. 1895.

Thallus thin, smooth, continuous to sparingly and obscurely chinky or rarely becoming irregularly areolate, pale greenish gray to whitish, rarely tending to disappear; apothecia becoming very long but only moderately wide, 1.5–6 × 0.25–0.35 mm., with obtuse ends, immersed in the thallus and the substratum or becoming partly superficial, numerous, straight to infrequently curved, usually approximating parallel position and closely aggregated, the disk soon open and flat, dull brownish black or often obscurely whitish pruinose, becoming several to many times transversely fissured, the exciple black or obscurely whitish pruinose laterally, and often covered toward the base by a thalloid one; hypothecium hyaline; spores fusiform, usually 5-septate, 16–20 × 4–5 μ.

On decorticated wood, near St. Martinsville, Louisiana.

21. **Opegrapha Hassei** Zahlbr., Ann. Myc. 10:365. 1912.

Thallus thin to moderately thick, smooth, becoming chinky to subareolate, rough and crumbling, or finally powdery, dull dirty whitish, resting on a very thin, grayish, lead-colored hypothallus, the margin becoming obscurely lobulate; apothecia of moderate length but rather wide, 1.5–4 × 0.4–0.8 mm., more or less irregular with obtuse ends, adnate to subsessile, scattered or clustered, curved more or less strongly, becoming 1 or 2 times branched furcately, the disk open, flat, brown to brownish black, more or less grayish pruinose, the exciple thick, dark brown to blackish, thick, more or less irregularly covered toward the base by a thalloid one; hypothecium hyaline or tinged more or less with brown; spores oblong-dactyloid, usually 7-septate, 15–24 × 3.5–5.5 μ.

On rocks, Santa Catalina Island, California.

22. **Opegrapha prosodea** Ach., Meth. Lich. 22. 1803.

Thallus thin and smooth to thicker and sometimes obscurely rough, pale or darker greenish gray or tinged with brown, usually limited by a blackish line; apothecium often somewhat elongated but remaining narrow or of moderate width, 0.8–5 × 0.2–0.5 mm., with obtuse or somewhat pointed ends, partly immersed to adnate, commonly scattered, straight to more commonly curved or obscurely flexuous, infrequently branched, and rarely stellately so, the disk closed to rarely open, flat and dull black, the exciple black and moderately thick; hypothecium brownish black; spores oblong-fusiform, 5–15-septate, 24–32 × 6–11 μ.

On trees, Florida, Louisiana, Minnesota, and Texas.

23. **Opegrapha Bonplandi** Fée, Essai Crypt. 25. pl. 5, f. 4. 1824.

Thallus very thin to thin, smooth to slightly rough, pale greenish gray to ashy or brownish, often limited by a dark brown to black line, frequently disappearing; apothecia of medium length and width, 0.5–4 × 0.2–0.4 mm., oblong to linear-oblong or more nearly ellipsoid, adnate, usually scattered, straight to curved or rarely and obscurely flexuous, very rarely branched, the disk closed to more or less open, flat to concave, dull black, the exciple black; hypothecium brownish black; spores narrowly fusiform, 5–11-septate, 20–42 × 3.5–7.5 μ.

On trees, Florida, Louisiana, and Texas.

24. **Opegrapha viridis** Pers., in Ach., Meth. Lich. 22. 1803.

Thallus thin, smooth to scurfy, dark grayish green to yellowish or brownish; apothecia short to somewhat elongated but rather narrow, sometimes tending toward round or irregular forms, 0.3–1.5 × 0.13–0.2 mm., the ends obtuse, slightly immersed to adnate, scattered or clustered, straight to curved, rarely branched, the disk closed to rarely and narrowly open, flat, and black; hypothecium brownish black; spores fusiform-acicular, 7–15-septate, 35–70 × 4.5–7.5 μ.

On trees, Massachusetts, Illinois, Florida, and Missouri, the northern specimens doubtful.

OTHER SPECIES REPORTED

Opegrapha levidensis Willey—Massachusetts.
Opegrapha mesophlaebia Nyl.—Louisiana.
Opegrapha oulocheila Tuck.—North Carolina.
Opegrapha scaphella var. gemella (Eschw.) Eckf.—North Carolina.

51. **Opegraphoidea** Fink; Hedrick, Mycologia 25:311. 1933.

Thallus immersed in that of the lichen host and therefore invisible; apothecia round to more commonly oblong, partly immersed to adnate, scattered to clustered, the disk closed to rarely open, the exciple usually black; hypothecium commonly brownish black; paraphyses branched and interwoven; asci clavate to broadly clavate; spores 4, usually 8, hyaline to brownish or rarely brown, oblong to oblong-ellipsoid or ellipsoid-pointed, 3-septate, the cells cylindrical.

The algal host is usually Protococcus or that of the lichen host.

A. Apothecia conglomerate
   B. Spores 4, hyaline to brownish . . . . 1. O. quaternella
   B. Spores reaching 8, brown . . . . 2. O. pulvinata
A. Apothecia scattered or clustered . . . . 3. O. staurothelicola

1. **Opegraphoidea quaternella** (Nyl.) Fink n. comb.

Opegrapha quaternella Nyl., Flora 68:449. 1885.

Thallus within the substratum and invisible; apothecia minute, irregular to oblong and straight, 0.25–0.6 × 0.18–0.3, partly immersed to adnate, conglomerate in areas 2–3 mm. across with several to many in each area, the disk closed, the exciple black and moderately thick; hypothecium brownish black; spores 4, hyaline to brownish, oblong, 15–19 × 5–7 μ.

On *Pertusaria velata, Endocarpon pusillum,* and *Peltigera aphthosa,* Massachusetts, Ohio, and Minnesota.

2. **Opegraphoidea pulvinata** (Rehm.) Fink n. comb.
Opegrapha pulvinata Rehm., Verh. Zool. Bot. Ver. Wein. 1869:500. 1869.

Thallus immersed in the substratum and invisible; apothecia minute, round to irregular or oblong and straight, 0.5–0.6 × 0.18–0.3 mm., partly immersed to adnate, conglomerate in areas, 1.5–5 mm. across, with many in each area, the disk closed, the exciple black and moderately thick; hypothecium brownish black; spores brown, oblong-ellipsoid, 15–18 × 3.5–7 μ.

On *Endocarpon miniatum,* near Fayette, Iowa.

3. **Opegraphoidea staurothelicola** Fink; Hedrick, Mycologia 25:311. 1933.

Thallus immersed in that of the lichen host and therefore invisible; apothecia short and very narrow, 1.5–2.5 × 0.08–0.1 mm., partly immersed to superficial, scattered and straight to clustered and variously irregular, the disk closed and indicated by an obscure, depressed black line, to rarely open, black, concave to flat, the exciple black; hypothecium thick and dark brown; hymenium pale yellowish brown; spores reaching 8, ellipsoid with one end often more pointed, hyaline to finally brownish, 13–15 × 4.5–5 μ.

On *Staurothele umbrina,* Ohio.

52. **Melaspilea** Nyl., Act. Soc. Linn. Bord. 21:416. 1856.

Thallus forming a thin, usually smooth crust, partly or wholly within the substratum, devoid of differentiation into layers; apothecia round to irregular, more or less immersed to adnate or sessile, the disk closed to more or less open, concave to flat or slightly convex, commonly black, the exciple colored like the disk, often irregular; hypothecium hyaline to brownish or brown; hymenium hyaline to brownish above; paraphyses unbranched or rarely somewhat branched; asci clavate to subpyriform, the apical wall sometimes thickened; spores 4 or 6, more commonly 8, hyaline to brownish, oblong, ellipsoid or slipper-shaped, commonly 1-septate, and constricted at the septum, but rarely 3–7-septate, the cells cylindrical, often unequal.

The algal host is Trentepohlia.

A. On trees and old wood, not parasitic on lichens
  B. Apothecia more or less elongated
    C. Spores 1-septate
      D. Apothecia reaching 0.8–1.5 mm. in length
        E. Apothecia 1–1.5 mm. in length . . . . 1. M. maculosa
        E. Apothecia not more than 0.8 mm. in length
          F. Thallus greenish gray to ashy . . . . . . 5. M. cinerascens
          F. Thallus whitish . . . . 2. M. constrictella
      D. Apothecia not more than 0.6 mm. in length
        E. Apothecia 0.2–0.4 × 0.1–0.2 mm. . . . . 3. M. demissa
        E. Apothecia 0.4–0.6 × 0.2–0.4 mm. . . . . 4. M. deformis
    C. Spores 5–7-septate . . . . 6. M. octomera
  B. Apothecia irregular, but not elongated
    C. Apothecia reaching 0.8–1 mm. across
      D. Spores 12–17 × 6–8.5 μ . . . . 10. M. arthonioides
      D. Spores 16–22 × 7–10 μ . . . . 9. M. amota
    C. Apothecia not more than 0.4 mm. across
      D. Disk open, flat, and somewhat wrinkled . . . . . 8. M. proximella
      D. Disk closed to narrowly open . . . . 7. M. lentiginosula
A. Parasitic on lichens
  B. Apothecia 0.2–0.4 mm. across . . . . 12. M. cupularis
  B. Apothecia 0.3–0.9 × 0.12–0.2 mm. . . . . 11. M. tribuloides

1. **Melaspilea maculosa** (E. Fries) Müll. Arg., Mém. Soc. Phys. Hist. Nat. Genève 19:21. 1887.

Glyphis maculosa E. Fries, Vet. Akad. Handl. III. 8:44. 1820. *M. angulosa* Hue.

Thallus thin, smooth, greenish gray to ashy white, or disappearing and the imbedded portion indicated at the surface by an ashy coloration; apothecia small to middle-sized, 0.4–1 mm. across, and sometimes elongated to 1.5 mm., irregular, slightly immersed to adnate, the disk flat, black, the exciple thin, black, usually prominent; hypothecium hyaline to brownish; paraphyses conglutinate; asci subpyriform; spores hyaline to brownish, oblong, 18–24 × 8–11 μ.

On trees, Florida, Louisiana, and Texas.

2. **Melaspilea constrictella** (Stirt.) A. L. Smith, Brit. Lich. 2:228. 1911.

Opegrapha constrictella Stirt., Scott. Nat. 4:29. 1877.

Thallus very thin to thin, smooth, whitish, sometimes disappearing; apothecia short to somewhat elongated and narrow, 0.3–0.8 × 0.1–0.2 mm., sometimes crowded, the disk closed to more or less open, concave to flat, black, the exciple thin, black, prominent; hypothecium hyaline; paraphyses indistinct; asci clavate; spores hyaline to brownish, obovoid, one cell larger, 12–17 × 4.5–7 μ.

On trees, Louisiana and California.

3. **Melaspilea demissa** (Tuck.) Zahlbr., Cat. Lich. Univ. 2:273. 1924.

Opegrapha demissa Tuck., Syn. N. A. Lich. 2:134. 1888. *Hazslinszkya demissa* (Tuck.) Schneid.

Thallus very thin, whitish, or disappearing, and the imbedded portion indicated at the surface by an ashy white coloration; apothecia very short and narrow, 0.2–0.4 × 0.1–0.2 mm., irregularly oblong or elliptical, sessile, the disk closed to more or less open, flat, black, the exciple thin, black, prominent; hypothecium hyaline; paraphyses unbranched; asci clavate to subpyriform; spores hyaline to brown, ovoid, one cell larger, 15–21 × 6–9 μ.

On trees, Massachusetts, Maryland, Pennsylvania, Illinois, and Iowa.

4. **Melaspilea deformis** (Schaer.) Nyl., Act. Soc. Linn. Bord. 21:416. 1856.

Opegrapha cymbiformis var. *deformis* Schaer., Lich. Helv. Spic. sec. 7. 331. 1836.

Thallus very thin, smooth, whitish; apothecia small, 0.2–0.4 mm. across or elongated to 0.6 mm., round to variously irregular, sessile, the disk flat, black, the exciple thin, black, rarely disappearing; hypothecium hyaline; paraphyses indistinct; asci broadly clavate to subpyriform; spores hyaline, ovoid, one cell larger, 12–17 × 5–6.5 μ.

On trees, New Hampshire.

5. **Melaspilea cinerascens** (Willey) Fink n. comb.

Opegrapha cinerascens Willey, Enum. Lich. New Bedford, Mass. 30. 1892.

Thallus very thin, smooth, greenish gray to ashy, sometimes disappearing, and the imbedded portion indicated at the surface by a grayish coloration; apothecia short to elongated and narrow, 0.4–0.8 × 0.1–0.25 mm., sessile, the disk closed to more or less open, flat, black, the exciple thin, black, prominent; hypothecium hyaline; paraphyses unbranched; asci cylindrico-clavate; spores 4–8, hyaline, oblong-ovoid, one cell larger, 12–17 × 4–6.5 μ.

On old wood, Massachusetts.

6. **Melaspilea octomera** Müll. Arg., Bull. Herb. Boiss. 3:43. 1895.

Thallus very thin, smooth, greenish gray to whitish; apothecia short to middle-sized and narrow, 0.5–1 × 0.25–0.3 mm., irregularly oblong, sessile, the disk closed to more or less open, flat, black, the exciple black, prominent, becoming longitudinally furrowed; hypothecium brownish; spores hyaline to brownish, ellipsoid to fusiform, 5–7-septate, 18–25 × 5–7 μ.

On trees, Florida and Louisiana.

7. **Melaspilea lentiginosula** (Nyl.) A. L. Smith, Brit. Lich. 2:226. 1911..
Opegrapha lentiginosula Nyl., Flora 48:355. 1865.
Thallus very thin, smooth, ashy white, sometimes disappearing, and the imbedded portion indicated at the surface by an ashy white coloration; apothecia minute to small, 0.1–0.35 mm. across, round to irregular, rarely branched, the disk closed or narrowly open, black, the exciple thick, incurved; hypothecium hyaline; paraphyses conglutinate; spores hyaline, obovoid to ellipsoid, one cell larger, 13–18 × 5–7 μ.
On trees, Massachusetts. Material is doubtful.

8. **Melaspilea proximella** Nyl.; Norrl., Not. Sällsk. Faun. Flor. Fenn. 13:342. 1871–74.
Arthonia proximella Nyl., Not. Sällsk. Faun. Flor. Fenn. 5:262. 1861.
Thallus very thin, whitish, the superficial portion often scarcely visible and the imbedded portion indicated at the surface by an ashy white coloration; apothecia minute, 0.15–0.25 mm. across, round to somewhat irregular, sessile, the disk flat, black, somewhat wrinkled, the exciple thin, black; hypothecium hyaline; asci subpyriform; spores hyaline to brownish, ovoid, one cell larger, 17–19 × 7–8 μ.
On trees, Vermont.

9. **Melaspilea amota** Nyl., Flora 50:178, 179. 1867.
Thallus very thin, smooth, whitish, sometimes disappearing; apothecia small to middle-sized, 0.3–0.8 mm. across, partly immersed to adnate, round to irregular, the disk flat, black, the exciple thin, black, somewhat irregular; hypothecium brownish to brown; paraphyses few, slender; asci clavate to subpyriform, the apical wall somewhat thickened; spores 4–8, hyaline to brownish, ovoid-ellipsoid, 16–22 × 7–10 μ.
On trees, Louisiana.

10. **Melaspilea arthonioides** (Fée) Nyl., Act. Soc. Linn. Bord. 21:416. 1856.
Lecidea arthonioides Fée, Essai Crypt. 107. pl. 26, f. 3. 1824.
Thallus thin, smooth to somewhat powdery, whitish, often disappearing and the imbedded portion indicated at the surface by a grayish coloration; apothecia small to middle-sized, 0.4–1 mm. across, more or less immersed to adnate, round to irregularly oblong, the disk flat to slightly convex, black, the exciple thin, black, prominent or rarely disappearing; hypothecium brownish to dark brown; paraphyses rarely branched, enlarged toward the apices; asci clavate; spores hyaline to brownish, oblong, 12–17 × 6–8.5 μ.
On trees, New England, Florida, Louisiana, Iowa, Nebraska, and Minnesota.

11. **Melaspilea tribuloides** (Tuck.) Müll. Arg., Mém. Soc. Phys. Hist. Nat. Genève 29:20. 1887.
Opegrapha tribuloides Tuck., Gen. Lich. 199. 1872.
Thallus imbedded in the host and invisible; apothecia short and narrow, 0.3–0.9 × 0.12–0.2 mm., adnate, scattered to clustered, straight or rarely and obscurely curved, very rarely branched, the disk closed and usually indicated by an obscure, depressed, black line to narrowly open, concave to flat, black, the exciple rather thin and black; hypothecium hyaline; asci becoming saccate; spores brown, oblong-ellipsoid, 15–21 × 6–9 μ.
On species of Trypethelium, Conotrema, and Thelotrema, from North Carolina to Florida, and westward to Louisiana.

12. **Melaspilea cupularis** Müll. Arg., Bull. Herb. Boiss. 3:44. 1895.
Thallus imbedded in the host and invisible; apothecia minute to small, 0.2–0.4 mm. across, round to irregular, sessile, the disk flat, black, the exciple thin, black, becoming irregular; hypothecium hyaline; paraphyses indistinct; asci subpyriform, the apical wall somewhat thickened; spores 6– more commonly 8, hyaline to brownish, obovoid, one cell larger, 16–23 × 6–9 μ.
On the thallus of *Pyrenula* spp., Louisiana and Florida.

53. Graphis Adans., Fam. Pl. 2:11. 1763.

Thallus forming a thin, usually smooth crust upon the substratum, partly or wholly within the substratum, devoid of differentiation into layers; apothecia linear, curved, often branched, more or less immersed, the disk closed to open, commonly black, the exciple colored like the disk, often surrounded by a thin to thicker, thalloid one; hypothecium hyaline to brownish black; hymenium hyaline; paraphyses unbranched, commonly distinct; asci clavate to cylindrico-clavate; spores 4, more commonly 8, hyaline, oblong-ellipsoid, ellipsoid, or long-ellipsoid, 3–many-septate, the cells lenticular.

The algal host is Trentepohlia.

A. Spores 1–3-septate
  B. Spores 1-septate . . . . 1. G. turbulenta
  B. Spores 3-septate
    C. Apothecia rarely more than 4 mm. in length
      D. Thallus olive-green to lighter
        E. Apothecia not branched
          F. Apothecia straight or curved . . . . 2. G. botryosa
          F. Apothecia 2–3-angled . . . . 4. G. Dumastii
        E. Apothecia furcately branched . . . . 3. G. nitida
      D. Thallus greenish gray . . . . 5. G. Beaumontii
    C. Apothecia rarely less than 4 mm. in length
      D. Apothecia rarely branched
        E. Thallus indicated by a brownish to ashy gray area . . 6. G. Afzelii
        E. Thallus greenish gray to olive-green
          F. Apothecia straight to curved and flexuous . . . . 7. G. rufula
          F. Apothecia curved, flexuous, and abruptly bent
            or recurved . . . . 8. G. subparilis
      D. Apothecia 1 or 2 times branched . . . . 9. G. floridana
A. Spores 5- or more septate
  B. Apothecia not more than 3 mm. in length
    C. Spores rarely less than 25 μ in length
      D. Apothecia rarely or never branched
        E. Thallus greenish gray to olive-green . . . . . 20. G. leucopepla
        E. Thallus brownish yellow . . . . 19. G. intertexta
      D. Apothecia 1 or 2 times branched . . . . 17. G. lineola
    C. Spores 16–25 × 5–8 μ . . . . 10. G. mosquitensis
  B. Apothecia usually more than 3 mm. in length
    C. Apothecia rarely more than 6 mm. in length
      D. Spores more than 35 μ in length
        E. Exciple striate
          F. Apothecia rarely branched
            G. Thallus smooth to wrinkled or granulose . . 22. G. elegans
            G. Thallus smooth to minutely rough . . . . 24. G. rimulosa
          F. Apothecia much branched . . . . 23. G. striatula
        E. Exciple not striate . . . . 21. G. Poitaeoides
      D. Spores rarely more than 40 μ in length
        E. Apothecia rarely branched
          F. Apothecia narrow, not more than 0.2 mm. across
            G. Spores 5–9-septate . . . . 13. G. tenella
            G. Spores 7–11-septate . . . . 18. G. Celtidis
          F. Apothecia wider, not less than 0.2 mm. across
            G. Spores 18–28 × 5–7 μ . . . . 12. G. atrorubens
            G. Spores 25–38 × 6–9 μ . . . . 15. G. eulectra
        E. Apothecia more or less branched
          F. Thallus not limited by a black line
            G. Thallus thick, powdery . . . . 16. G. scripta pulverulenta
            G. Thallus thinner, rough to wrinkled . . . . 16. G. scripta
          F. Thallus limited by a black line . . . . 16. G. scripta limitata
    C. Apothecia reaching 8–10 mm. in length
      D. Apothecia straight and parallel . . . . . 16. G. scripta topographica
      D. Apothecia more or less branched
        E. Thallus smooth . . . . 14. G. intricata
        E. Thallus wrinkled or granulose . . . . 11. G. Pavoniana

1. **Graphis turbulenta** Nyl., Lich. Ins. Guin. 50. 1889.
Thallus thin, smooth to somewhat rough, pale greenish gray to whitish; apothecia short and of medium width, 0.5–2 × 0.25–0.4 mm., immersed, straight to curved, rarely short-branched, grouped into rough groups, the disk closed or narrowly open and dark-colored, the proper exciple thin and light to darker brown, surrounded laterally by a thalloid one; hypothecium hyaline; spores oblong-ellipsoid, 1-septate, 8–11 × 3.5–4.5 μ.
On trees, near Jacksonville, Florida.

2. **Graphis botryosa** Tuck., Syn. N. A. Lich. 2:122. 1888.
Thallus thin, smooth, pale olive-green and fading; apothecia short and very narrow, 0.5–2 × 0.15–0.2 mm., immersed and breaking through, straight or curved, often more or less clustered, the disk closed to open and white, the exciple brownish, covered by the thalloid one; hypothecium hyaline; spores oblong-ellipsoid, 3-septate, 14–20 × 3–4.5 μ.
On trees, Florida.

3. **Graphis nitida** (Eschw.) Tuck., Syn. N. A. Lich. 2:121. 1888.
Diorygna nitidum Eschw., in Mart., Fl. Bras. 68. 1829.
Thallus thin, smooth, shining, pale olive-green and fading to yellowish; apothecia from short to elongated, of medium width, 1–5 × 0.4–0.9 mm., immersed, straight to curved and flexuous, becoming clustered and furcately branched, the disk closed, the proper exciple pale and rudimentary, covered by a thalloid one; hypothecium hyaline; spores usually 8, oblong-ellipsoid, 3-septate, 12–16 × 8–10 μ.
On trees, South Carolina and Alabama. Spores are lacking in our material, and determinations are consequently doubtful. Have seen no material from Florida or Louisiana, where the species is reported, which could be placed here.

4. **Graphis Dumastii** (Fée) Spreng., Syst. Veg. 4:254. 1827.
Fissurina Dumastii Fée, Essai Crypt. 59. pl. 1, f. 7. 1824.
Thallus thin, smooth and shining, pale olive-green and fading; apothecia short, oblong-ellipsoid, 2- or 3-angled, and irregular, 1–3 × 0.5–2 mm., immersed, the disk soon open and whitish, the exciple thin, distinguishable above as a pale brownish zone, covered by a thalloid one; hypothecium hyaline; spores uniseriate, oblong-ellipsoid, 3-septate, 16–20 × 7–9.5 μ.
On trees, doubtfully determined, Florida.

5. **Graphis Beaumontii** Tuck., Syn. N. A. Lich. 2:124. 1888.
Thallus rather thick, shining, becoming rough, greenish gray; apothecia short and rather narrow, 1–3 × 0.3–0.6 mm., immersed to semisuperficial, straight or curved, the disk closed to open and yellowish gray, the exciple pale brown, covered by a thickish thalloid one; hypothecium hyaline; spores oblong-ellipsoid, 3-septate, 13–21 × 8–13 μ.
On trees, from South Carolina to Florida and Texas.

6. **Graphis Afzelii** Ach., Syn. Meth. Lich. 85. 1814.
Thallus thin, rudimentary, or disappearing and indicated by a light brownish to ashy gray area; apothecia oblong to much elongated, and of moderate width, 1–9 × 0.3–1 mm., adnate, straight, curved, or flexuous; rarely branched monopodially or bifurcately, the disk closed, the exciple white, superficially lending its color to the whole perithecium, but black within, the superficial white portion rarely disappearing more or less, leaving the perithecial surface partly or wholly black; hypothecium hyaline; spores oblong-ellipsoid, 3-septate, 15–20 × 6–8 μ, irregularly or uniseriately arranged.
On trees, from North Carolina to Florida, and westward to Texas.

7. **Graphis rufula** (Trev.) Mont., Ann. Sci. Nat. Bot. III. 16:57. 1851.
Opegrapha rufula Trev., Spig. Pagl. 12. 1853.
Thallus thin, smooth, olive-green to greenish gray, surrounded wholly or in part by a black hypothallus; apothecia long and wide, 5–12 × 0.5–1 mm., im-

mersed to partly immersed, straight to curved and flexuous, rarely branched, the disk closed, the proper exciple reddish to dark brown, thick and finally striated, covered more or less by an obscure thalloid one; hypothecium hyaline or tinged brownish; spores oblong-ellipsoid, 3-septate, 14–20 × 7–10 μ, uniseriately arranged. On trees, Florida. Spores finally brownish and perhaps nearer Phaeographis.

8. **Graphis subparilis** Nyl., Lich. Ins. Guin. 48. 1889.
Thallus very thin, smooth and shining, pale greenish gray to yellowish olive-green; apothecia long and wide, 4–18 × 0.6–0.8 mm., slightly immersed to super-ficial and much raised, curved, flexuous, abruptly bent or recurved, rarely branched, the disk closed or rarely open and yellow or whitish, the proper exciple reddish brown, becoming 1–3 times striate and wide above, covered above and laterally by a thalloid one; hypothecium hyaline or brownish; spores oblong-ellipsoid, 3-septate, 14–20 × 5.5–8 μ.
On trees, Florida.

9. **Graphis floridana** Tuck., Syn. N. A. Lich. 2:126. 1888.
Thallus thin, smooth, greenish gray to ashy; apothecia much elongated and narrow, 3–10 or more × 0.25–0.35 mm., immersed to partly immersed, crowded, straight to curved or flexuous, infrequently 1 or 2 times branched, the disk closed or open and blackish, the exciple and hypothecium hyaline, the former whitish powdery above and covered laterally by a swollen thalloid one; spores oblong-ellipsoid to ellipsoid, 3-septate, 10–15 × 6.5–9 μ.
On trees, Florida.

10. **Graphis mosquitensis** Tuck., Syn. N. A. Lich. 2:126. 1888.
Thallus thin, becoming slightly rough and scurfy, greenish gray varying to-ward whitish, bounded and intersected more or less by black lines; apothecia short and narrow, 0.5–2 × 0.15–0.2 mm., immersed to partly immersed, straight to curved or obscurely flexuous, the disk closed to finally open and black, the proper exciple black above and pale and inconspicuous below, covered at first wholly, then laterally by a finally disappearing thalloid one; hypothecium hyaline; spores ellipsoid, 5–9-septate, 16–25 × 5–8 μ.
On trees, Florida. Tuckerman's diagnosis does not agree with the type material.

11. **Graphis Pavoniana** Fée, Essai Crypt. 40. 1824.
Thallus moderately thick, becoming wrinkled, or granulose, pale greenish gray to whitish; apothecia very long, but narrow, 3–10 or more × 0.16–0.3 mm., more or less immersed, curved and flexuous, often running roughly parallel, sometimes more or less branched, the disk closed, the exciple black, pruinose above and cov-ered laterally by a thalloid one when not wholly immersed; hypothecium hyaline; spores oblong-ellipsoid, 5–9-septate, 18–37 × 6–9 μ.
On trees, Texas.

12. **Graphis atrorubens** Tuck.; Hedrick, Mycologia 25:312. 1933.
Thallus moderately thick, smooth to somewhat rough and chinky, greenish gray; apothecia moderately long and narrow, 0.1–4 × 0.2–0.4 mm., partly im-mersed to subsuperficial, usually curved to flexuous, seldom branched, the disk closed to open and reddish black, the exciple and the hypothecium reddish brown, the former covered laterally by a finally disappearing thalloid one; spores hyaline, or brownish when old, oblong-ellipsoid, 5–7-septate, 18–28 × 5–7 μ, resembling Opegraphae.
On trees, South Carolina, Florida, and Georgia.

13. **Graphis tenella** Ach., Syn. Meth. Lich. 81. 1914.
G. scripta var. *tenella* (Ach.) Tuck.
Thallus thin to moderately thick, smooth, greenish gray to whitish or rarely yellowish; apothecia becoming long and narrow, 1–5 × 0.17–0.22 mm., partly immersed, straight to curved or flexuous, seldom branched, the disk closed, the

proper exciple black, covered laterally by a thin, rarely disappearing, thalloid one; hypothecium hyaline; spores ellipsoid, 5–9-septate, 18–40 × 6–9 μ.

On trees, Florida, Alabama, and Louisiana.

14. **Graphis intricata** Fée, Essai Crypt. 42. pl. 9, f. 3. 1824.
   G. assimilis Nyl.
   Thallus thin, smooth, pale greenish gray to ashy; apothecia short to much elongated but narrow, 1–8 × 0.15–0.25 mm., partly immersed to adnate, straight, curved, or flexuous, infrequently 1 to several times branched, the disk closed or slightly open and black, the proper exciple black, covered more or less by a finally disappearing thalloid one; hypothecium brownish black; spores ellipsoid, 5–13-septate, 20–46 × 6–8 μ.

   On trees, New Jersey, Florida, Alabama, and Louisiana.

15. **Graphis eulectra** Tuck., Lich. Calif. 34. 1866.
   Phaeographis eulectra (Tuck.) Zahlbr.
   Thallus thin to moderately thick, smooth to obscurely rough, pale greenish gray to ashy; apothecia short to somewhat long, becoming rather wide, 0.6–4 or 5 × 0.2–0.5 mm., immersed more or less, straight to curved or flexuous, the disk closed to narrowly open and black, the proper exciple black, or sometimes whitish pruinose, inflexed, bordered laterally by a thalloid one; hypothecium hyaline; asci becoming saccate-inflated; spores 4–8, oblong-ellipsoid, 5–13-septate, 25–38 × 6–9 μ, often placed parallel, finally becoming brownish or pale brown, shriveled, and strongly coherent.

   On trees, Vermont and Illinois.

16. **Graphis scripta** (L.) Ach., Vet. Akad. Nya Handl. 145. 1809.
   Lichen scriptus L., Sp. Pl. 1140. 1753. *G. scripta* var. *serpentina* (Ach.) Meyer.
   Thallus thin, smooth to obscurely rough or wrinkled, greenish gray to whitish, yellowish, or olive-green; apothecia long and narrow, 1–5 or more × 0.12–0.25 mm., immersed to partly immersed, straight to curved and flexuous, infrequently 1 or 2 times branched, the disk closed to open and sordid black or grayish pruinose, the exciple black and covered laterally by a thin, rarely disappearing, thalloid one; hypothecium hyaline; spores long-ellipsoid, 5–11-septate, 20–50 × 6.5–12 μ. (PLATE 3 *b*.)

   On trees, throughout the United States.

   var. **pulverulenta** (Pers.) Ach., Syn. Meth. Lich. 82. 1814.
   Opegrapha pulverulenta Pers., Ann. Bot. Usteri 7:29. pl. 1, f. 2. 1794.
   Thallus thicker, paler, crumbling, and becoming finely powdery above; apothecia completely immersed or only slightly emergent.

   On trees, West Virginia, Louisiana, Missouri, Iowa, Minnesota, and Washington.

   var. **topographica** (Willd.) Zahlbr., Cat. Lich. Univ. 2:350–52. 1924.
   Verrucaria topographica Willd., Berol. Prod. 370. pl. 7, f. 14. 1787. *G. scripta* var. *recta* (Schaer.) Rabenh.
   Thallus poorly developed; apothecia long, straight, and parallel, or nearly so, 4–10 mm. in length.

   On trees, especially birches, throughout northern United States.

   var. **limitata** (Pers.) Ach., Vet. Akad. Nya Handl. 1809:146. 1809.
   Opegrapha limitata Pers., Ann. Bot. Usteri 7:30. 1794.
   The thallus surrounded wholly or in part by a black, hypothallic line.

   On trees, Massachusetts, Louisiana, Ohio, Minnesota, and Nebraska.

17. **Graphis lineola** Ach., Lich. Univ. 264. 1810.
   G. comma (Ach.) Spreng.
   Thallus thin and smooth to minutely pulverulent or granulose, light greenish gray to whitish; apothecia short to moderately long, but narrow, 0.5–2 or 3 × 0.1–0.35 mm., slightly immersed to adnate, straight to curved or obscurely flexuous, very rarely 1 or 2 times branched, the disk closed to very narrowly open and

black, the proper exciple black, covered laterally by a more or less disappearing thalloid one; hypothecium hyaline; spores ellipsoid, 6–12-septate, 16–50 × 7–9.5 μ. On trees, Florida.

18. **Graphis Celtidis** Müll. Arg., Bull. Herb. Boiss. 3:45. 1895.
Thallus very thin, smooth to slightly and obscurely rough, finally chinky, greenish gray; apothecia short to longer, and very narrow, 1–4 × 0.15–0.2 mm., immersed to subsuperficial, straight to curved or flexuous, infrequently and sparingly branched, the disk closed to slightly open and brownish black or slightly grayish pruinose, the exciple brownish black, covered laterally by a thalloid one; spores ellipsoid, 7–11-septate, 24–38 × 8–10 μ.
On trees, Louisiana and Florida.

19. **Graphis intertexta** Müll. Arg., Bull. Herb. Boiss. 3:45. 1895.
Thallus very thin, becoming minutely rough and chinky, said to be sometimes granulose, brownish yellow, fading to lighter shades; apothecia short and narrow, 0.5–2 × 0.25–0.4 mm., immersed often in groups, straight to curved or slightly flexuous, seldom branched, the disk sunken, closed or slightly open and grayish white, the exciple and the hypothecium hyaline, the former poorly developed and covered by a raised thalloid one; spores 6–8, oblong-ellipsoid, 9–16-septate, 18–44 × 6.5–8.5 μ.
On trees, Louisiana and Florida.

20. **Graphis leucopepla** Tuck., Syn. N. A. Lich. 2:126. 1888.
Thallus thin, becoming slightly rough and scurfy, greenish gray, varying toward olive-green; apothecia short, oblong, and narrow, 0.5–1 × 0.2–0.3 mm., partly immersed, straight to slightly curved, the disk closed to open and whitish powdery, the exciple and hypothecium pale, the former rudimentary but sometimes blackish above, covered by a thalloid one; spores 4–8, oblong-ellipsoid and slightly constricted at the septa, 13–20-septate, 28–47 × 6–8 μ.
On trees, Florida.

21. **Graphis Poitaeoides** Nyl., in Tuck., Syn. N. A. Lich. 2:126. 1888.
Thallus thin, smooth to slightly granulose, pale greenish gray; apothecia short to elongated, but narrow, 1–4 × 0.15–0.25 mm., immersed to partly immersed, curved to flexuous, rarely becoming somewhat branched, finally radiately grouped, the disk closed or rarely opening narrowly and pale, the proper exciple pale to brownish, covered laterally and often above by a strong thalloid one; hypothecium hyaline; spores 4–8, long-ellipsoid, 11–21-septate, 36–90 × 8–13 μ.
On trees, Florida, Georgia, and Texas.

22. **Graphis elegans** (J. E. Smith) Ach., Syn. Meth. Lich. 85. 1814.
Opegrapha elegans J. E. Smith, in Sowerby, Engl. Bot. 26: pl. 1812. 1807.
Thallus thin, smooth to wrinkled and sometimes granular, pale greenish gray to whitish or yellowish; apothecia short to elongated, becoming wide, 0.3–5 × 0.35–0.9 mm., subadnate, straight to curved or rarely flexuous, very rarely branched, the disk closed, the exciple black, thick and strongly 1–4 or more times striate, covered laterally by a finally obscure or disappearing thalloid one; hypothecium hyaline; spores usually 8, long-ellipsoid, 7–15-septate, 35–90 × 8–14 μ.
On trees, from New Jersey to Florida, and westward to Texas.

23. **Graphis striatula** (Ach.) Spreng., Syst. Veg. 4:250. 1827.
Opegrapha striatula Ach., Syn. Meth. Lich. 74. 1814. *G. duplicata* Eschw.
Thallus thin, smooth, pale greenish gray to whitish; apothecia becoming long and rather narrow, 1–5 × 0.2–0.4 mm., partly immersed; usually curved or flexuous, sometimes 1–3 or 4 times branched, the disk closed, the proper exciple black, 1–3 times obscurely striate, covered laterally by a thalloid one; hypothecium hyaline; spores 6–8, 7–15-septate, ellipsoid, 35–52 × 7–10 μ.
On trees, South Carolina, Louisiana, and Florida.

24. **Graphis rimulosa** (Mont.) Trev., Spighe e Paglie 11. 1853.
Opegrapha rimulosa Mont., Ann. Sci. Nat. Bot. II. 18:271. 1842.
Thallus thin to rather thin, smooth to minutely rough, pale greenish gray to ashy; apothecia becoming long and narrow, 1.5–6 × 0.2–0.35 mm., partly immersed to subadnate, straight to curved or flexuous, the disk closed or narrowly open, the exciple black, thick, 1–4 or more times deeply striate, covered laterally by a thin, disappearing, thalloid one; hypothecium hyaline; spores usually 8, long-ellipsoid, 9–13-septate, 40–70 × 8–10 μ.
On trees, Louisiana. Very similar to *G. elegans*. Herbarium sheet marked that *G. rimulosa* has complete but very thin basal apothecial wall.

OTHER SPECIES REPORTED

Graphis amicta Nyl.—Louisiana.
Graphis anguilliformis Tayl.—Louisiana.
Graphis balbisina Nyl.—Florida.
Graphis cinerea Fée—Florida.
Graphis diversa Nyl.—Texas.
Graphis lactea (Fée) Sprengl.—North America.
Graphis radiata (Mont.) Nyl.—Texas.
Graphis ramificans Nyl.—Maryland.
Graphis scripta var. varia Ach.—Louisiana.
Graphis subdiversa Nyl.—Florida.

54. **Phaeographis** Müll. Arg., Flora 65:336. 1882.

Thallus forming a thin, usually smooth crust upon the substratum, partly or wholly within the substratum, devoid of differentiation into layers; apothecia linear, curved, often branched, more or less immersed, the disk closed to open, commonly black, the exciple colored like the disk, often surrounded by a thin to thicker thalloid one; hypothecium hyaline to brownish black; hymenium hyaline; paraphyses unbranched, commonly distinct; asci clavate to cylindrico-clavate; spores 4– more commonly 8, brown, oblong-ellipsoid, ellipsoid, or long-ellipsoid, 3–many-septate, the cells lenticular.
The algal host is Trentepohlia.

A. Spores 3–5-septate
  B. Spores constantly 3-septate
    C. Apothecia rarely branched . . . . 2. P. subfulgurata
    C. Apothecia much branched
      D. Thallus somewhat rough and minutely warty . . . . 1. P. tortuosa
      D. Thallus smooth . . . . 3. P. dendriticella
  B. Spores 3–5-septate . . . . 4. P. dendritica
A. Spores 5–7- or 9-septate
  B. Apothecia round to irregular . . . . 5. P. punctiformis
  B. Apothecia more or less elongated
    C. Apothecia not more than 2 mm. in length
      D. Apothecia unbranched and straight . . . . 10. P. lobata
      D. Apothecia curved and more or less branched
        E. Apothecia much branched . . . . 6. P. intricans
        E. Apothecia infrequently branched . . . . 7. P. erumpens
    C. Apothecia 1–5 mm. in length
      D. Thallus greenish gray to whitish or pale olivaceous . . . 9. P. inusta
      D. Thallus greenish gray to olive-brown . . . . . . 8. P. haematites

1. **Phaeographis tortuosa** (Ach.) Müll. Arg., Mém. Soc. Phys. Hist. Nat. Genève 29:26. 1887.
Graphis tortuosa Ach., Syn. Lich. 85. 1814.
Thallus thin, smooth to somewhat rough and minutely warty, yellowish gray; apothecia elongated, 0.5–2 × 0.1–0.2 mm., immersed, branched, much curved,

clustered and sometimes radiately arranged, the disk open, concave to flat, black, the exciple thin, colored like the disk, sometimes rudimentary and scarcely visible, surrounded by a very thin, often obscure, thalloid one; hypothecium hyaline; spores 8, oblong-ellipsoid, 3-septate, 15–18 × 6–7 μ.
On trees, Florida.

2. **Phaeographis subfulgurata** (Nyl.) Zahlbr., Cat. Lich. Univ. 2:387. 1924
Graphis subfulgurata Nyl., Lich. Ins. Guin. 48, 49. 1889.
Thallus thin, smooth, pale greenish gray to whitish; apothecia short and narrow, 0.5–1.5 × 0.15–0.25 mm., immersed, straight to curved or obscurely flexuous rarely branched, the disk covered entirely by the thallus or becoming narrowly open and light-colored, the exciple thin, light or darker brown, covered laterally by a thalloid one; hypothecium hyaline; spores 8, oblong, 3-septate, 17–22 × 6–8 μ.
On trees, Florida.

3. **Phaeographis dendriticella** Müll. Arg., Engl. Bot. Jahrb. 5:139. 1884.
Thallus thin, smooth, whitish, somewhat shining; apothecia becoming moderately long and wide, 1–2.5 × 0.12–0.27 mm., immersed to partly immersed, variously curved and flexuous, becoming much branched, often radiately, the disk soon open and brownish black, the exciple thin and brownish black, surrounded laterally by a thin, finally disappearing, thalloid one; hypothecium thin, brownish black; spores 8, oblong-ellipsoid, 3-septate, 15–20 × 4.5–7.5 μ.
On trees, near Jacksonville, Florida.

4. **Phaeographis dendritica** (Ach.) Müll. Arg., Flora 65:382. 1882.
Opegrapha dendritica Ach., Meth. Lich. 31. pl. 1, f. 10. 1803. *P. dendritica* var. *medusula* (Pers.) Hue.
Thallus thin to somewhat thick, pale greenish gray to whitish, smooth to slightly rough and wrinkled; apothecia becoming long and wide, 1–5 × 0.2–0.4 mm., immersed to partly immersed, straight to commonly curved or flexuous, usually branched, often much and radiately, the disk soon open and dull black, often obscurely or plainly grayish pruinose, the exciple thin and dull black, surrounded laterally by a thin, disappearing, thalloid one; hypothecium thin, brownish black; spores 8, oblong to oblong-ellipsoid, 3–5-septate, becoming brown, 15–30 × 5–9 μ.
On trees, from southern New England to Florida, and westward to Texas and Nebraska.

5. **Phaeographis punctiformis** (Eschw.) Müll. Arg., Flora 65:383. 1882.
Leiogramma punctiforme Eschw., in Mart., Fl. Bras. 1:101. 1833.
Thallus moderately thick, smooth to slightly rough, pale greenish gray to whitish, bordered more or less by a narrow black border; apothecia small, 0.3–0.7 mm. across, immersed, rarely round to oblong or variously irregular and angular, the disk open, concave to flat, black, the exciple thin, brownish black; hypothecium hyaline; spores 8, oblong-ellipsoid, 5–7-septate, 22–28 × 6–8 μ.
On young trees, Louisiana.

6. **Phaeographis intricans** (Nyl.) Vainio, Act. Soc. Faun. Flor. Fenn. 7²:116. 1890.
Graphis intricans Nyl., Ann. Sci. Nat. Bot. IV. 19:372. 1863.
Thallus very thin, smooth, greenish gray to ashy, or white about the apothecia or their branches; apothecia short and wide, 0.5–2 × 0.2–0.5 μ, immersed, radiately much-curved and flexuously branched, often clustered into confused groups, the disk soon open, flat, grayish pruinose to finally black, the exciple thin and brownish to brown, surrounded laterally by a very thin, disappearing, thalloid one; hypothecium hyaline; spores 8, oblong-ellipsoid, 5–7-septate, 16–26 × 6–9 μ.
On trees, Florida.

7. **Phaeographis erumpens** (Nyl.) Müll. Arg., Bull. Herb. Boiss. 3:48. 1895.
Graphis erumpens Nyl., in Hue, Lich. Exot. 240. 1892.

Thallus thin, smooth, pale olivaceous to whitish, somewhat shining; apothecia short and moderately wide, 0.5–2 × 0.2–0.3 mm., straight to curved and infrequently branched, immersed and wholly covered by the thin thallus or partly immersed, and the disk finally open, concave to flat, whitish pruinose to dull black, the exciple thin, black, covered laterally by a thin thalloid one; hypothecium thin, brownish black; spores 8, oblong, 5–7-septate, 23–30 × 6–9 μ.

On trees, from North Carolina to Florida, and in Louisiana.

8. **Phaeographis haematites** (Fée) Müll. Arg., Flora 65:384. 1882.
Graphis haematites Fée, Essai Crypt. 45. pl. 12, f. 1. 1824.

Thallus very thin, smooth, greenish gray to olive-brown, more or less shining; apothecia becoming long and wide, 2–5 × 0.3–0.5 mm., immersed to partly immersed, straight, curved, or flexuous, often closely grouped, but rarely branched, the disk soon open, concave to flat, red varying toward blackish, the exciple thin, reddish brown to brown; hypothecium hyaline or tinged brownish; spores 8, oblong-ellipsoid, becoming brown, 5–9-septate, 20–35 × 8–10 μ.

On trees, southwestern Florida.

9. **Phaeographis inusta** (Ach.) Müll. Arg., Flora 65:383. 1882.
Graphis inusta Ach., Syn. Meth. Lich. 85. 1814. *Opegrapha inusta* (Ach.) Tuck. *Graphis dendritica* var. *inusta* (Ach.) Tuck.

Thallus thin, smooth, pale greenish gray, varying toward whitish or pale olivaceous; apothecia moderately long and wide, 1–5 × 0.25–0.45 mm., obtuse at the ends, immersed to partly immersed, straight to curved or slightly flexuous, rarely branched, the disk open, flat, brownish black to black, the exciple thin, dark brown to black, surrounded by a thin, disappearing, thalloid one; hypothecium hyaline; spores 8, oblong-ellipsoid, 5–7-septate, 20–36 × 6–9 μ.

On trees, from Massachusetts to Florida, Louisiana, and California.

10. **Phaeographis lobata** (Eschw.) Müll. Arg., Flora 65:383. 1882.
Leiogramma lobatum Eschw., in Mart., Fl. Bras. 100. 1829.

Thallus very thin or wholly within the substratum, greenish gray, varying toward whitish or olivaceous; apothecia small, 0.5–1.3 × 0.4–0.8 mm., immersed to partly immersed, circular to shortly oblong, the disk open, flat, brownish black to black or obscurely grayish pruinose, the exciple thin, raised, and blackish; hypothecium hyaline; spores 8, finally brown, oblong-ellipsoid, 5–9-septate, 25–38 × 7–9.5 μ.

On wood, Florida and Louisiana.

OTHER SPECIES REPORTED

Phaeographis patellula (Fée) Müll. Arg.—Florida and Louisiana.

55. Graphina Müll. Arg., Flora 63:22. 1880.

Thallus forming a thin, usually smooth crust, partly or wholly within the substratum, devoid of differentiation into layers; apothecia linear, curved, often branched, more or less immersed, the disk closed to open, commonly black, the exciple colored like the disk, often surrounded by a thin to thicker thalloid one; hypothecium hyaline to brownish black; hymenium hyaline; paraphyses unbranched, commonly distinct; asci clavate to cylindrico-clavate; spores 1–8, hyaline, oblong-ellipsoid, ellipsoid, or long-ellipsoid, transversely and longitudinally septate, the cells almost cubical.

The algal host is Trentepohlia.

A. Spores 8 or rarely 6 in each ascus
  B. Spores rarely less than 30 μ in length
    C. Spores large, reaching 60–75 μ in length
      D. Spores 5–11-septate transversely . . . . 10. G. platycarpa
      D. Spores 13–23-septate transversely . . . . 18. G. virginea

C. Spores not so large, reaching 30–45 μ in length
  D. Spores 7–13-septate transversely . . . . 13. G. acrophaea
  D. Spores 5–7- or rarely 9-septate transversely
    E. The disk whitish . . . . 8. G. subnitida
    E. The disk pale flesh-colored to brownish . . . . . 5. G. virginalis
B. Spores not more than 30 μ in length
  C. Spores 3–5- or rarely 7-septate transversely
    D. Spores 3-septate transversely . . . . 4. G. sophisticascens
    D. Spores 3–more-septate transversely
      E. Thallus mealy, scaly, or
        roughly granulose . . . . 2. G. glaucoderma Cypressi
      E. Thallus smooth
        F. Apothecia 2–6 mm. in length . . . . 7. G. Scolecitis
        F. Apothecia not more than 3 mm. in length
          G. The disk whitish . . . . 3. G. leuconephela
          G. The disk whitish to brownish yellow . . 2. G. glaucoderma
  C. Spores 7–9-septate transversely
    D. Apothecia 3–8 × 0.4–0.9 mm. . . . . 6. G. adscribens
    D. Apothecia 2–5 × 0.15–0.25 mm. . . . . 9. G. subnitidula
A. Spores 1, 2, 4 or rarely 6–8 in each ascus
  B. Spores 1 or 2 in each ascus
    C. The disk whitish pruinose . . . . 17. G. mendax
    C. The disk reddish brown . . . . 16. G. subvirginalis fulvescens
  B. Spores 2–4 or rarely 6–8 in an ascus, very rarely only 1
    C. Spores reaching 75–140 μ in length
      D. Spores 9–13-septate transversely . . . . 12. G. leprocarpa
      D. Spores 19–31-septate transversely
        E. The exciple 2–3 times striate . . . . 15. G. Acharii
        E. The exciple obscurely striate . . . . 14. G. abaphoides
    C. Spores not more than 75 μ in length
      D. Spores not more than 13-septate transversely
        E. Spores 15-22 × 4–8 μ . . . . 1. G. incrustans
        E. Spores more than 20 μ in length . . . . . 11. G. substriatula
      D. Spores 13–27-septate transversely . . . . . . 16. G. subvirginalis

1. **Graphina incrustans** (Fée) Müll. Arg., Mém. Soc. Phys. Hist. Nat. Genève
   29:47. 1887.
   Fissurina incrustans Fée, Essai Crypt. 60. pl. 13, f. 2. 1824. *Graphis nitidescens*
   Nyl.
   Thallus thin, smooth and shining, yellow to olive-green or brown; apothecia
   short or somewhat elongated, but narrow, 1–3 × 0.15–0.25 mm., immersed or breaking through and somewhat raised, unbranched, the disk closed to open and pale
   brown, the proper exciple pale brown, covered laterally and at first above by a
   whitish thalloid one; hypothecium hyaline; spores 4–8, oblong-ovoid, 3–5-septate
   transversely and 1–3-septate longitudinally, 15–22 × 4–8 μ.
   On trees, Florida.

2. **Graphina glaucoderma** (Nyl.) Müll. Arg., Bull. Herb. Boiss. 3:47, 48. 1895.
   Graphis glaucoderma Nyl., Flora 69:103. 1886.
   Thallus thin to moderately thick, smooth and shining, greenish gray or tinged
   with olive; apothecia colored like the thallus or lighter, short and somewhat
   elongated, and of moderate width, 0.8–3 × 0.25–0.5 mm., immersed-erumpent,
   straight to variously curved or flexuous, confluently more or less branched, the
   disk closed to finally opened widely, whitish to brownish yellow, the proper exciple
   thin, brown; hypothecium hyaline to light brown; spores 8, ellipsoid, 3–5-septate
   transversely and 1-septate longitudinally, 14–20 × 6–9 μ.
   On trees, Louisiana, Florida, Georgia, and Alabama.

   var. **Cypressi** (Müll. Arg.) Fink n. comb.
   G. Cypressi Müll. Arg., Bull. Herb. Boiss. 2:47. 1895.
   Thallus dull white, mealy, scaly, or roughly granulose; exciple thicker.
   On bald cypress, near St. Martinsville, Louisiana.

3. **Graphina leuconephela** (Nyl.) Zahlbr., Cat. Lich. Univ. 2:413. 1924.
   Fissurina leuconephela Nyl., Flora 52:73. 1869. *Graphis leuconephela* (Nyl.)
   Kremphl.
   Thallus mainly or wholly within the substratum, indicated at the surface by a greenish gray to olive-green coloration; apothecia seated in whitish areas of the thallus, short and of medium width, 0.5–2 × 0.2–0.5 mm., immersed and straight to curved or flexuous, sometimes branched or confluent, the disk closed or narrowly open, whitish, the proper exciple and hypothecium hyaline, the former covered by a thalloid or substratic layer, not forming an exciple; spores 8, long-ellipsoid, 3–5-septate transversely and 1–2-septate longitudinally, 15–26 × 8–12 μ.
   On trees, Louisiana.

4. **Graphina sophisticascens** (Nyl.) Zahlbr., Cat. Lich. Univ. 2:425. 1924.
   Graphis sophisticascens Nyl., Lich. Jap. 108. 1890.
   Thallus thin, smooth, greenish gray to ashy; apothecia rather short and narrow, 0.5–2.5 × 0.15–0.35 mm., slightly immersed, straight to curved or obscurely flexuous, very rarely and sparingly branched, the disk closed to widely open and brownish black or whitish pruinose, the proper exciple black, covered laterally by a thin, disappearing, thalloid one; hypothecium hyaline; spores 8, oblong, 3-septate transversely and 1-septate longitudinally, 18–23 × 9–14 μ.
   On trees, Missouri.

5. **Graphina virginalis** (Tuck.) Müll. Arg., Bull. Herb. Boiss. 3:47. 1895.
   Graphis virginalis Tuck.; Eckf., Bull. Torr. Club 17:256. 1890.
   Thallus thin, smooth, somewhat shining, dark greenish gray to olive-green; apothecia short and narrow, 1–3 × 0.15–0.25 mm., immersed to semisuperficial, covered by the thallus or breaking through, straight to curved or flexuous, usually occurring in whitish groups but seldom branched, the disk at first covered by the thalloid exciple, but finally opening and pale flesh-colored to brownish, the proper exciple pale or darker brownish covered laterally by a thalloid one; hypothecium hyaline; spores 8, ellipsoid, 5–9-septate transversely and 1–3-septate longitudinally, 24–35 × 12–18 μ.
   On trees, Florida.

6. **Graphina adscribens** (Nyl.) Müll. Arg., Bull. Herb. Boiss. 3:46. 1895.
   Graphis adscribens Nyl., Bull. Soc. Linn. Norm. II. 2:117, 118. 1868.
   Thallus thin, greenish gray to white or whitish, smooth to slightly rough; apothecia long and rather wide, 3–8 × 0.4–0.9 mm., partly immersed, curved and flexuous, rarely branched, the disk closed or slightly open and yellowish brown, the proper exciple brown, obscurely striate, mostly covered by a thalloid one; hypothecium hyaline; spores 8, ellipsoid, 6–7-septate transversely and 2-septate longitudinally, 21–28 × 8–10 μ.
   On trees, Florida.

7. **Graphina Scolecitis** (Tuck.) Fink n. comb.
   Graphis Scolecitis Tuck., Gen. Lich. 210. 1872.
   Thallus smooth, very thin and indistinct, greenish gray to olive-green, often bordered and intersected by black lines; apothecia long and narrow, 2–6 × 0.2–0.35 mm., partly immersed, curved or flexuous, infrequently once to radiately branched, the disk closed, the proper exciple brown, covered wholly or laterally by a very thin thalloid one; hypothecium hyaline; asci cylindrico-clavate to saccate; spores 8, oblong-ellipsoid, 3–7-septate transversely and 2–3-septate longitudinally, 14–25 × 6–9 μ.
   On trees, Florida and Alabama.

8. **Graphina subnitida** (Nyl.) Zahlbr., Cat. Lich. Univ. 2:427. 1924.
   Graphis subnitida Nyl.; Leight., Trans. Linn. Soc. Lond. 25:453. pl. 56, f. 14. 1866. *Fissurina subnitida* Nyl.
   Thallus thin, smooth, somewhat shining, pale yellowish to olive-green; apothecia short to longer, but narrow, 1–3 × 0.15–0.25 mm., immersed, straight to curved or flexuous, sometimes branched, often clustered, the disk becoming open and whitish, the proper exciple pale brown, covered by a thin thalloid one; hypothecium hyaline; spores 8, oblong-ellipsoid, 5–7-septate transversely and 1–3-septate longitudinally, 25–40 × 12–18 μ.
   On trees, near Covington, Louisiana.

9. **Graphina subnitidula** (Nyl.) Zahlbr., Cat. Lich. Univ. 2:427. 1924.
   Graphis subnitidula Nyl., in Tuck., Syn. N. A. Lich. 2:123. 1888.
   Thallus thin, smooth, shining, greenish gray to olive-green or yellowish; apothecia short to somewhat elongated, but narrow, 2–5 × 0.15–0.25 mm., immersed, curved, and flexuous, becoming sparingly branched and often occurring in radiating groups, the disk becoming open and whitish, the proper exciple brownish, covered by a raised thalloid one; hypothecium hyaline; spores 8, oblong-ellipsoid, 7–9-septate transversely and 1-septate longitudinally, 20–30 × 6–9 μ.
   On trees, Florida and Louisiana.

10. **Graphina platycarpa** (Eschw.) Zahlbr., Sitz. Akad. Wein. Math. Nat. Classe III:385. pl. 2, f. 14–17. 1902.
    Graphis platycarpa Eschw., in Mart., Fl. Bras. 1:74. 1833. *G. sophistica* (Tuck.) Müll. Arg. *Graphis scripta* var. *sophistica* Tuck. *Graphis sophistica* (Tuck.) Nyl.
    Thallus smooth, thin to moderately thick, greenish gray to ashy; apothecia becoming much elongated, but rather narrow, 3–8 or 10 × 0.2–0.4 mm., partly immersed to adnate, straight to curved or flexuous, frequently and sometimes much radiately branched, the disk closed or narrowly open and black, the proper exciple black and finally striate, covered laterally by a disappearing thalloid one; hypothecium hyaline; spores 6–8, oblong-ellipsoid, 5–11-septate transversely and 1–7-septate longitudinally, 30–64 × 8–30 μ.
    On trees, Florida.

11. **Graphina substriatula** (Nyl.) Zahlbr., Cat. Lich. Univ. 2:427. 1924.
    Graphis substriatula Nyl., Act. Soc. Sci. Fenn. 7:467. 1863. *Graphis elegans* var. *substriatula* (Nyl.) Tuck.
    Thallus thin, smooth, greenish gray to dull whitish; apothecia becoming long, but narrow, 1–5 × 0.2–0.35 mm., partly immersed, curved and flexuous, rarely branched, the disk closed, the proper exciple black or whitish pruinose, sometimes obscurely striate, covered more or less laterally by a thalloid one; hypothecium hyaline; spores 4–8, ellipsoid, 9–13-septate transversely and 1–5-septate longitudinally, 30–40 × 10–15 μ.
    On trees, Florida.

12. **Graphina leprocarpa** (Nyl.) Zahlbr., Cat. Lich. Univ. 2:412. 1924.
    Graphis leprocarpa Nyl., Act. Soc. Sci. Fenn. 7:472. 1863. *Thelotrema leprocarpum* (Nyl.) Tuck.
    Thallus very thin, smooth to slightly rough, pale greenish gray to whitish; apothecia round, irregular to oblong, 3–6 × 3–4 mm., immersed, the disk sunken but flat to convex, pale, the proper exciple pale and rudimentary, covered by the thallus or by an irregular and often torn thalloid exciple; hypothecium hyaline; spores 1, 2, 4, or rarely 6 or even 8, oblong, 9–13-septate transversely and 3–5-septate longitudinally, 25–100 × 8–20 μ.
    On trees, Louisiana.

13. **Graphina acrophaea** Müll. Arg., Bull. Herb. Boiss. 3:46. 1895.
    Thallus thin, smooth to slightly granulose and uneven, greenish gray to ashy, usually bordered by a dark line; apothecia short to somewhat elongated, but

rather narrow, 1–4 × 0.2–0.4 mm., partly immersed, curved or flexuous, the ends pointed, rarely 1 or 2 times branched, the disk closed or slightly open and black, the proper exciple black and obscurely striate, mostly covered by a thalloid one; hypothecium hyaline; spores 8, ellipsoid, 7–13-septate transversely and 1–3-septate longitudinally, 35–42 × 13–16 μ.
On trees, near St. Martinsville, Louisiana.

14. **Graphina abaphoides** (Nyl.) Müll. Arg., Bull. Herb. Boiss. 3:46. 1895.
Graphis abaphoides Nyl.; Eckf., Bull. Torr. Club 16:105. 1889.
Thallus usually thin, ashy gray, smooth or finally rough and chinky, sometimes subgranulose; apothecia short to somewhat elongated, and rather wide, 1–3 × 0.4–0.8 mm., partly immersed, becoming obscurely striate, straight, curved, or obscurely flexuous, rarely branched bifurcately, the disk closed, the proper exciple and hypothecium hyaline or tinged brown, the former covered by a prominent thalloid one; spores 2–4, long-ellipsoid, 19–31-septate transversely and 3–5-septate longitudinally, 58–130 × 10–32 μ.
On trees, Florida.

15. **Graphina Acharii** (Fée) Müll. Arg., Mém. Soc. Phys. Hist. Nat. Genève 29:38. 1887.
Graphis Acharii Fée, Essai Crypt. 39. pl. 10, f. 4. 1824. *Graphis rigida* (Fée) Spreng.
Thallus thin, smooth to wrinkled and obscurely warty, greenish gray to whitish; apothecia short to long, and of medium width, 1–8 × 0.2–0.5 mm., adnate, straight to curved or flexuous, 1 or more times branched, the disk closed or narrowly open and black, the thick proper exciple black, 2–3 times striate, covered wholly or laterally by a thalloid one; hypothecium brownish black; spores 2–8, oblong-ellipsoid, 19–31-septate transversely and 2–5-septate longitudinally, 50–140 × 15–27 μ.
On trees, Florida and Texas.

16. **Graphina subvirginalis** (Nyl.) Müll. Arg., Bull. Herb. Boiss. 3:47. 1895.
Graphis subvirginalis Nyl.; Eckf., Bull. Torr. Club 16:106. 1889.
Thallus thin, smooth to rough and chinky-areolate, greenish gray to whitish; apothecia short to longer, but narrow, 1–4 × 0.12–0.3 mm., immersed to semi-superficial, becoming variously curved and flexuous, and 1–several times branched, the disk closed to open and brownish black, the proper exciple brownish, covered wholly or laterally by a well-developed thalloid one; hypothecium hyaline; spores 4–8, ellipsoid, 13–27-septate transversely and 3–7-septate longitudinally, 36–64 × 9–15 μ.
On trees, Florida.

var. **fulvescens** (Nyl.) Müll. Arg., Bull. Herb. Boiss. 3:47. 1895.
Graphis virginea var. *fulvescens* Nyl., Lich. Ins. Guin. 49. 1889.
The disk reddish brown when open and reaching 0.6–0.7 mm. across, the exciple rudimentary and pale brownish; spores 1 or 2, 11–31-septate transversely, and 3–11-septate longitudinally, 35–92 × 16–30 μ.
On trees, Florida.

17. **Graphina mendax** (Nyl.) Müll. Arg., Rev. Mycol. 10:177. 1888.
Graphis mendax Nyl., Ann. Sci. Nat. Bot. IV. 11:283. 1859.
Thallus thin, dull white, smooth to minutely warty or granulose, finally crumbling; apothecia somewhat elongated and of medium width, 2–4 × 0.3–0.5 mm., immersed, curved to flexuous, usually branched and often dendroid, the disk soon open and pale to light brown, more or less whitish pruinose; the proper exciple and hypothecium hyaline, the former surrounded by a thalloid one; spores 1, oblong-ellipsoid, 19–29-septate transversely and 5–7-septate longitudinally, 65–120 × 21–38 μ.
On trees, Louisiana.

18. **Graphina virginea** (Eschw.) Müll. Arg., Flora 63:41. 1880.
Leiogramma virgineum Eschw., in Mart., Fl. Bras. 1:98. 1833. *Graphis cometia* Fée.

Thallus thin, smooth, greenish gray to whitish; apothecia short to elongated, but narrow, 1–5 × 0.15–0.2 mm., immersed or slightly emergent, straight to curved or obscurely flexuous, frequently 1 to several times branched, sometimes radiately, the disk opening and brown but covered by the thalloid exciple, the likewise covered proper exciple brown above and pale below; hypothecium hyaline; spores 8, oblong-ellipsoid to ellipsoid, 13–23-septate transversely and 1–7-septate longitudinally, 38–75 × 10–18 μ.

On trees, Florida.

56. **Phaeographina** Müll. Arg., Flora 65:398. 1882.

Thallus forming a thin, usually smooth crust, partly or wholly within the substratum, devoid of differentiation into layers; apothecia linear, curved, often branched, more or less immersed, the disk closed to open, commonly black, the exciple colored like the disk, often surrounded by a thin to thicker thalloid one; hypothecium hyaline to brownish black; hymenium hyaline; paraphyses unbranched; asci clavate to cylindrico-clavate; spores 1–8, brown, oblong-ellipsoid, ellipsoid, or long-ellipsoid, transversely and longitudinally septate, the cells almost cubical.

The algal host is Trentepohlia.

A. Spores less than 50 μ in length
  B. Apothecia closely grouped and often branched . . . . . . 4. P. columbiana
  B. Apothecia radiately clustered and rarely branched . . . . . 5. P. explicans
A. Spores more than 50 μ in length
  B. Spores 1 in an ascus . . . . 1. P. scalpturata
  B. Spores 4–8 in an ascus
    C. Spores large, 50–85 μ in length . . . . 3. P. caesiopruinosa
    C. Spores very large, 75–160 μ in length . . . . 2. P. plurifera

1. **Phaeographina scalpturata** (Ach.) Müll. Arg., Flora 69:314, 315. 1886.
Graphis scalpturata Ach., Syn. Meth. Lich. 86. 1814.

Thallus rather thin, smooth, greenish gray to yellowish or pale olive-green; apothecia moderately long and wide, 1–4 × 0.3–0.7 mm., immersed to partly immersed, straight to slightly curved or flexuous, very rarely branched, the disk open, flat, more or less grayish pruinose to brown or blackish brown, the proper exciple thin, pale to darker brown, surrounded by a disappearing thalloid one; hypothecium wholly hyaline or becoming brownish black below; spores 1, oblong-ellipsoid, becoming brown, 19–31-septate transversely and 3–8-septate longitudinally, 90–155 × 20–25 μ.

On trees, from New Jersey to Florida, and westward to Alabama and Louisiana.

2. **Phaeographina plurifera** (Nyl.) Fink n. comb.
Graphis scalpturata var. *plurifera* Nyl., Ann. Sci. Nat. Bot. V. 7:332. 1887.

Thallus thin and smooth, yellowish to olivaceous; apothecia long and wide, 3–10 × 0.6–1.4 mm., immersed to partly immersed, slightly curved to obscurely flexuous, the disk open, flat, more or less grayish pruinose, the proper exciple well developed, brownish black, surrounded by a disappearing thalloid one; hypothecium hyaline; spores 4–8, cylindrico-ellipsoid, 13–15-septate transversely and 3–5-septate longitudinally, 75–160 × 22–30 μ.

On trees, Florida.

3. **Phaeographina caesiopruinosa** (Fée) Müll. Arg., Mém. Soc. Phys. Hist. Nat. Genève 29⁸:48. 1887.
Arthonia caesiopruinosa Fée, Essai Crypt. Suppl. 36. pl. 40, f. 4. 1837.

Thallus thin to moderately thick, smooth, greenish gray to pale olive-green; apothecia becoming long and wide, 6.5–7 × 0.3–0.9 mm., partly immersed, straight to curved or flexuous, infrequently branched, the disk open, flat, more or less grayish pruinose, or finally black, the proper exciple brown, surrounded laterally by a rarely disappearing thalloid one; hypothecium hyaline; spores 8, or rarely 4, oblong-ellipsoid, 11–17-septate transversely and 2–5-septate longitudinally, 50–85 × 14–25 μ.

On trees, Florida and Louisiana.

4. **Phaeographina columbiana** (Tuck.) Zahlbr., Cat. Lich. Univ. 2:436. 1924.

Graphis columbiana Tuck., Syn. N. A. Lich. 2:123. 1888.

Thallus thin, smooth, pale greenish gray to ashy; apothecia short and narrow, 0.5–3.5 × 0.2–0.25 mm., immersed, straight to curved or obscurely flexuous, closely grouped and often branched, the disk closed to finally open and brown, the proper exciple thin, brown to reddish brown, surrounded laterally by a thalloid one; hypothecium hyaline; spores 8, oblong-ellipsoid, 3–7-septate transversely and 1–3-septate longitudinally, 14–30 × 8–12 μ.

On trees, Florida and southern Alabama.

5. **Phaeographina explicans** Fink; Hedrick, Mycologia 25:313. 1933.

Graphis dendritica var. *explicans* Tuck. in litt.

Thallus thin, smooth, greenish yellow to olive-green; apothecia moderately long and wide, 1–3 × 0.2–0.4 mm., partly immersed to adnate, straight to much more commonly curved or flexuous, rarely branched, but more often clustered, sometimes radiately, the disk open and flat, blackish brown or obscurely grayish pruinose, the proper exciple dark brown; hypothecium brown; spores 8, oblong-ellipsoid, 3–7-septate transversely and 1-septate longitudinally, 21–35 × 8–12 μ.

On trees, Alabama.

57. **Helminthocarpon** Fée, Essai Crypt. Suppl. 156. 1837.

Thallus crustose, whitish, usually smooth; apothecia becoming adnate, covered partly or wholly by the thalloid exciple, round to elongated, exciple thin and dark-colored; hypothecium hyaline; paraphyses much branched and interwoven, the apex not thickened; asci oblong or clavate; spores 4–8, hyaline, transversely and longitudinally septate.

The algal host is Trentepohlia.

1. **Helminthocarpon Leeprevostii** Fée, Essai Crypt. Suppl. 156. pl. 35, f. 11. 1837.

Thallus moderately thick, smooth to minutely warty, pale greenish gray to whitish; apothecia middle-sized, 0.5–1 mm. across, or reaching 3 mm. in one direction, adnate, round to irregular or elongated, straight to rarely curved or flexuous, rarely branched, the disk flat, white, the exciple thin and dark brown, covered laterally and sometimes above by a thick thalloid one; spores 4–8, oblong-ellipsoid, 13–35-septate transversely and 4–7-septate longitudinally, 110–165 × 22–50 μ.

On trees, Louisiana.

16. **CHIODECTONACEAE**

Thallus crustose, partly within the substratum, showing little or no differentiation into layers, attached to the substratum by hyphal rhizoids; apothecia more or less immersed in a stroma, round to elongated, sometimes branched, the proper exciple usually well developed; paraphyses unbranched and free or branched and more or less interwoven.

The algal hosts are Trentepohlia and Phycopeltis.

A. Paraphyses unbranched and free
B. Spores transversely septate
C. Spores hyaline . . . . 58. GLYPHIS
C. Spores brown . . . . 59. SARCOGRAPHA
B. Spores transversely and longitudinally septate . . . . . 60. MEDUSULINA

A. Paraphyses branched and netlike interwoven
  B. Spores transversely septate
    C. Spores hyaline . . . . 61. CHIODECTON
    C. Spores brown . . . . 62. SCLEROPHYTON
  B. Spores transversely and longitudinally septate . . . . . 63. ENTEROSTIGMA

58. Glyphis Ach., Syn. Meth. Lich. 106. 1814.

Thallus crustose, superficial, rudimentary, commonly devoid of differentiation into layers, attached to the substratum by hyphal rhizoids; apothecia clustered into a more or less raised stroma, immersed, round to elongated, often branched, the disk flat, the exciple colored like the disk, well developed, smooth or furrowed; hypothecium and hymenium hyaline; paraphyses unbranched, free; asci oblong to clavate, with the apical wall somewhat thickened; spores 4–8, hyaline, oblong-ellipsoid to ellipsoid or fusiform, 3–11-septate, the cells lenticular. The algal host is Trentepohlia.

A. Apothecia much branched, often confluent . . . . 2. G. confluens
A. Apothecia rarely branched, not confluent . . . . 1. G. cicatricosa

1. **Glyphis cicatricosa** Ach., Syn. Meth. Lich. 107. 1814.
  G. Achariana Tuck. *G. favulosa* Ach.
  Thallus mainly and wholly within the substratum, indicated at the surface by a whitish, greenish gray, olive-green, or brownish coloration; stromata raised, circular to irregular or elongated, 1–5 mm. across in various directions, whitish at the surface, thick, blackish within; apothecia small, 0.15–0.8 mm. across, immersed usually many in each stroma, circular to irregular or elongated, rarely branched, the disk slightly concave to flat, dark brown; spores 8, ellipsoid, 5–11-septate, 22–46 × 7–11 μ.
  On trees, from North Carolina to Florida, and westward to Louisiana and Texas.

2. **Glyphis confluens** Zenk., in Goeb. & Kunze, Pharmazent. Waarenk. 1:163. pl. 21, f. 6. 1827.
  G. favulosa var. *confluens* (Zenk.) Müll. Arg. *G. cicatricosa* var. *confluens* (Zenk.) Zahlbr.
  Thallus mainly or wholly within the substratum, indicated at the surface by an olive-green to brownish coloration; stromata raised, circular to irregular, 2–5 mm. across, whitish to brownish above, thick, blackish within; apothecia small to middle-sized, 0.2–0.35 × 0.2–2 mm., immersed usually many in each stroma, round to elongated and much branched, often confluent laterally or terminally, the disk slightly concave to flat, dark brown; spores 8, ellipsoid, 5–9-septate, 20–45 × 8–14 μ.
  On trees, Florida. Regarded by some as a subspecies of *G. cicatricosa* Ach., which may be a better disposition than ours.

59. Sarcographa Fée, Essai Crypt. 58. 1824.

Thallus crustose, superficial, rudimentary, commonly devoid of differentiation into layers, attached to the substratum by hyphal rhizoids; apothecia clustered in flattened stromata, immersed, round to elongated, often branched, the disk flat, the exciple colored like the disk, well developed, smooth or furrowed; hypothecium hyaline to dark brown; hymenium hyaline or brownish above; paraphyses unbranched, free; asci oblong to clavate, with the apical wall somewhat thickened; spores 4–8, brown, oblong-ellipsoid to ellipsoid or fusiform, 3–11-septate, the cells lenticular. The algal host is Trentepohlia.

A. Spores more than 16 μ in length
  B. Thallus an ashy green to brownish coloration . . . . . . 2. S. labyrinthica
  B. Thallus an ashy white or dull grayish coloration . . . . 3. S. medusulina
A. Spores not more than 16 μ in length . . . . 1. S. tricosa

1. **Sarcographa tricosa** (Ach.) Müll. Arg., Mém. Soc. Phys. Hist. Nat. Genève 29:63. 1887.

Graphis tricosa Ach., Lich. Univ. 674. 1810.

Thallus mainly or wholly within the substratum, indicated at the surface by a whitish or brownish gray coloration; stromata thin, scarcely raised, round to irregular, 2–4.5 mm. across, ashy white, blackish within; apothecia small to middle-sized, elongated, 0.3–1 × 0.2–0.35 mm., immersed, usually many in each stroma, much branched, the disk slightly concave to flat, dark brown to black; hypothecium dark brown; spores 8, brownish, oblong-ellipsoid, 3-septate, 12–16 × 5–7 μ.

On trees, from Maryland to Florida, and westward to Louisiana and Texas.

2. **Sarcographa labyrinthica** (Ach.) Müll. Arg., Mém. Soc. Phys. Hist. Nat. Genève 29:62. 1887.

Glyphis labyrinthica Ach., Syn. Meth. Lich. 107. 1814.

Thallus mainly or wholly within the substratum, indicated at the surface by an ashy green to brownish coloration; stromata raised, round to irregular, 2–6 mm. across, ashy white, black within; apothecia small to middle-sized, elongated, 0.3–1 × 0.2–0.3 mm., immersed many in each stroma, slightly curved, somewhat branched, the disk slightly concave to flat, black; hypothecium dark brown; spores 8, brownish to brown, oblong-ellipsoid, 3– rarely 5-septate, 15–23 × 6–7.5 μ.

On trees, Florida.

3. **Sarcographa medusulina** (Nyl.) Müll. Arg., Flora 70:77. 1887.

Glyphis medusulina Nyl., Act. Soc. Sci. Fenn. 7:485. 1863.

Thallus mainly within the substratum, indicated at the surface by an ashy white to dull grayish coloration; stromata slightly raised, ashy white, black within; apothecia small to middle-sized, elongated, 0.3–1.5 × 0.2–0.35 mm., immersed many in each stroma, branched, the disk slightly concave to flat, black; hypothecium dark brown; spores 8, brownish, oblong-ellipsoid, 3-septate, 16–20 × 6–9 μ.

On trees, Florida.

60. **Medusulina** Müll. Arg., Bull. Herb. Boiss. 2:93. 1894.

Thallus crustose, superficial, smooth to rough, rudimentary, commonly devoid of differentiation into layers, attached to the substratum by hyphal rhizoids; apothecia middle-sized to large, clustered in more or less raised stromata, immersed to superficial, round to oblong or irregular, branched, the disk closed to open, more or less concave to flat, the exciple colored like the disk or lighter; hypothecium and hymenium hyaline; paraphyses unbranched, free; asci oblong to clavate, with the apical wall somewhat thickened; spores 1–8, hyaline, oblong-ellipsoid to ellipsoid or fusiform, transversely and longitudinally septate, the cells spherical or lenticular.

The algal host is Trentepohlia.

1. **Medusulina texana** Müll. Arg., Bull. Herb. Boiss. 2:93. 1894.

Thallus thin, smooth to sometimes warty, ashy to pale yellowish or greenish gray; apothecia middle-sized to large, 0.6–1.2 × 0.1–0.25 mm., erumpent and surrounded by whitish, often sorediate areas of thallus, oblong to irregular, sometimes curved, rarely branched, the disk closed to open, concave to flat, black, the exciple thin, whitish; spores 1, oblong-ellipsoid, 15–19-septate transversely and 5–7-septate longitudinally, 120–150 × 50–60 μ.

On trees, Texas.

61. **Chiodecton** Ach., Syn. Meth. Lich. 108. 1814.

Thallus crustose, superficial, attached to the substratum by hyphal rhizoids; apothecia grouped in a stroma, immersed or superficial, circular, elongated, radiately or irregularly branched, the proper exciple well developed, brown to black,

or rudimentary or absent; hypothecium hyaline to black; paraphyses branched and interwoven; asci clavate; spores 8, hyaline, several-septate, elongated and variously shaped, the cells cylindrical.
The algal host is Trentepohlia.

A. Spores not more than 20 μ in length
  B. Spores 4–5-septate . . . . 5. C. ochroleucum
  B. Spores constantly 3-septate . . . . 4. C. inscriptum
A. Spores more than 20 μ in length
  B. Thallus deep red toward the margin . . . . 2. C. sanguineum
  B. Thallus not red toward the margin
    C. Thallus yellowish white . . . . 6. C. subochroleucum
    C. Thallus whitish or greenish gray
      D. Apothecia reaching 1 mm. across . . . . 3. C. perplexum
      D. Apothecia rarely more than 0.1 mm. across . . . . 1. C. sphaerale

1. **Chiodecton sphaerale** Ach., Syn. Meth. Lich. 108. 1814.
Thallus thin, smooth to rough, sometimes chinky and minutely granulose, greenish gray to whitish; apothecia minute, 0.04–0.1 mm. across, round to irregular, several to many immersed in each whitish, irregular, wartlike stroma, the disk concave to flat, black; hypothecium dark brown; spores fusiform to almost acicular, 3-septate, 23–35 × 2–3.5 μ.
On trees, Florida.

2. **Chiodecton sanguineum** (Swartz) Vainio, Act. Soc. Faun. Flor. Fenn. 7:143, 144. 1890.
Byssus sanguineum Swartz, Nov. Gen. & Sp. Pl. 148. 1788. *C. rubrocinctum* (Ehrh.) Nyl.
Thallus moderately thick, the central portions greenish gray to whitish or reddish, usually deep red toward the margins, commonly warty or coralloid; apothecia small, 0.4–0.6 mm. across, immersed in the whitish stromata, the disk flat, round to irregular, blackish or dirty whitish pruinose; hypothecium brownish black; spores fusiform-ellipsoid, 3-septate, 35–40 × 5–6.5 μ.
On trees, Florida, Alabama, Louisiana, and Mississippi. Apothecia unknown in the United States.

3. **Chiodecton perplexum** Nyl., Act. Soc. Sci. Fenn. 7:485, 486. 1863.
Thallus thin, smooth, whitish, becoming obscurely powdery and rarely disappearing, except between and about the apothecia, and over the depressed brownish black, irregular, and often shortly lobed stromata; apothecia small to middle-sized, 0.4–1 mm. across, immersed several in a group, round to irregular or more or less elongated; hypothecium brownish black; spores fusiform, often curved, 3-septate, 32–42 × 4.5–6.5 μ.
On trees, Texas.

4. **Chiodecton inscriptum** (Nyl.) Fink n. comb.
Stigmatidium inscriptum Nyl.; Eckf., Bull. Torr. Club 16:105. 1889. *Enterographa elegans* (Eschw.) Tuck. *Sclerophyton inscriptum* (Nyl.) Müll. Arg.
Thallus thin, whitish, often chinky and wrinkled; apothecia inconspicuous, very narrow and much elongated, flexuous and dendroid, more or less branched, 1–5 × 0.04–0.07 mm., the disk flat, brownish black, immersed in an often somewhat raised thalloid veil; hypothecium blackish brown, extended into a like-colored stroma; spores oblong-ellipsoid to finger-shaped, 3-septate, 11–15 × 4–5.5 μ.
On trees, Florida and Louisiana.

5. **Chiodecton ochroleucum** Zahlbr., Bull. Torr. Club 27:646. 1900.
Thallus thin, yellowish white, becoming thicker, chinky, and rough; apothecia small to middle-sized, 0.8–1.5 mm. across, usually clustered, becoming superficial, each seated on a separate brownish black stroma, round to irregular, the disk flat, blackish or more or less whitish pruinose, the exciple thick and raised, soon flex-

uous, of the same color as the thallus; asci oval-wedge-shaped; spores oblong-ovate, 4–5-septate, 14–18 × 7–9 μ.

On trees, Santa Catalina Island, California. Spores were uncertain in all the material seen.

6. **Chiodecton subochroleucum** Fink; Hedrick, Mycologia 25:313. 1933.

Thallus thin, yellowish white, smooth to rough and granulose-crumbling; apothecia small, 0.4–1 mm. across, scattered or clustered, adnate, round to irregular, the disk flat, rarely black, but much more commonly whitish pruinose, the exciple rarely flexuous, only moderately developed; hypothecium blackish brown, extending under each apothecium into a stroma of the same color; spores 3-septate, ellipsoid to ellipsoid-pointed, 19–27 × 5–6.5 μ.

On trees, southern California.

62. **Sclerophyton** Eschw., Syst. Lich. 14. 1824.

Thallus crustose, superficial, rudimentary, devoid of differentiation into layers, attached to the substratum by hyphal rhizoids; apothecia clustered in stromata, immersed to superficial, round to elongated, the disk flat, the exciple colored like the disk, well developed or rudimentary; hypothecium hyaline to brown; hymenium hyaline or brownish above; paraphyses branched; asci clavate; spores 8, brown, oblong to oblong-ellipsoid or spindle-shaped, 3–more-septate, the cells lenticular.

The algal host is Trentepohlia.

1. **Sclerophyton californicum** (Tuck.) Hasse, Bryologist 12:101. 1909.

Chiodecton californicum Tuck., Syn. N. A. Lich. 2:135. 1888.

Thallus moderately thick to thick, yellowish white and blackening, becoming rough and crumbling; apothecia small to middle-sized, 0.5–1.2 mm. across, adnate, round to irregular or elongated, 1–several more or less crowded on each small, blackish stroma, the disk slightly concave to flat, dull black or densely whitish pruinose, the exciple thick, colored like the thallus; hypothecium dark brown; spores ellipsoid to oblong-ellipsoid or fusiform, 3–7-septate, 20–30 × 5–8.5 μ.

On trees, southern California.

63. **Enterostigma** Müll. Arg., Flora 68:254. 1885.

Thallus crustose, superficial, rudimentary, devoid of differentiation into layers, attached to the substratum by hyphal rhizoids; apothecia clustered in rudimentary stromata, immersed to superficial, circular, the exciple rudimentary; hypothecium thin, hyaline; hymenium hyaline or brownish above; paraphyses few, sparingly branched; asci clavate or ovoid; spores 1–8, brown, oblong to oblong-ellipsoid or ellipsoid, transversely and longitudinally septate.

The algal host is Trentepohlia.

1. **Enterostigma Montagnaei** (Tuck.) Fink n. comb.

Chiodecton Montagnaei Tuck., Gen. Lich. 214, 215. 1872.

Thallus granulose, widespread, greenish gray with a white cottony border; stroma rudimentary; apothecia minute, 0.06–0.1 mm. across, immersed and inconspicuous when dry, round, closely clustered, the disk whitish to flesh-colored; hypothecium and exciple rudimentary; asci ovoid, carrying abundant epiplasm and a single spore; spores sometimes oblong, often curved and varying much in form, 15–23-septate transversely and 5–9-septate longitudinally, 50–60 × 17–24 μ.

On trees, Florida, Alabama, and Louisiana.

17. DIRINACEAE

Thallus crustose, showing little differentiation, attached to the substratum by hyphal rhizoids; apothecia round or irregular, somewhat immersed to adnate, the proper exciple surrounded by a thalloid one.

The algal host is Trentepohlia.

64. **Dirina** E. Fries, Syst. Orb. Veg. 244. 1825.

Thallus crustose, the cortex composed of erect, non-septate hyphae, the medulla attached to the substratum by hyphal rhizoids; apothecia round, irregular, or elongated, with thin proper exciple and thick thalloid one; hypothecium thick, black or dark brown, stroma-like; paraphyses unbranched or sparingly branched toward the apex; asci usually clavate; spores 8, hyaline, finger-shaped to spindle-shaped, several-septate.

The algal host is Trentepohlia.

A. Spores constantly 3-septate
  B. Spores less than 20 μ in length
    C. Thallus greenish gray to whitish . . . . 2. D. california
    C. Thallus cream-colored to whitish, sometimes lobed
      at the margin . . . . 4. D. Hassei
  B. Spores more than 20 μ in length . . . . 3. D. franciscana
A. Spores 3–9-septate . . . . 1. D. rediunta

1. **Dirina rediunta** (Stizenb.) Zahlbr., Ann. Naturh. Hofmus. Wien. 16:82. 1901.
Lecanora rediunta Stizenb., Erythea 4:107. 1896. *Lecidea sublugens* Nyl.
Thallus thin and smooth to thicker and chinky-areolate, greenish gray to ashy, finally crumbling more or less; apothecia small to middle-sized, 0.3–0.8 mm. across, sessile, the disk flat to convex, more or less whitish pruinose to black, the thalloid exciple colored like the thallus, rarely crenate and disappearing, exposing a proper exciple; hypothecium thick and dark brown; spores fusiform, bluntly pointed, 3–9-septate, 20–25 × 4–6 μ.
On trees, along the coast and on Santa Catalina Island, California.

2. **Dirina california** Tuck., Lich. Calif. 17. 1866.
Schizmatomma california (Tuck.) Herre.
Thallus moderately thick, greenish gray to whitish, becoming rough and chinky to subareolate; apothecia small to middle-sized, 0.5–1 mm. across, sessile, usually crowded, the disk flat to slightly convex, grayish pruinose and dirty black, the exciple wavy to crenulate and becoming more or less flexuous; hypothecium blackish brown, 2 or 3 times as thick as the hymenium, stroma-like; asci long-clavate; spores 3-septate, finger-shaped, 14–18 × 3–4.5 μ.
On trees, southern California.

3. **Dirina franciscana** Zahlbr.; Herre, Bot. Gaz. 43:270. 1907.
Thallus thick, irregularly tuberculate-warty, forming heaped patches, greenish gray to ashy or brownish yellow; apothecia middle-sized to large, 0.4–2.5 mm. across, sessile, becoming numerous and nearly covering the thallus, the disk flat to slightly convex, granulate or furrowed, grayish pruinose to dirty black, the exciple thick, prominent, colored like the thallus or more commonly whitish, becoming intricately flexuously irregular, and nearly disappearing; hypothecium dark brown, as thick as the hymenium, those of adjacent apothecia often coalescing in stroma-like fashion; spores finger-shaped, often curved, 3-septate, 25–34 × 5–8.5 μ.
On soil, southern California.

4. **Dirina Hassei** Zahlbr., Bull. Torr. Club 27:644, 645. 1900.
Thallus thin, often somewhat wrinkled, becoming chinky-areolate, dull cream-colored to whitish, the margin sometimes obscurely lobed; apothecia small, 0.3–0.7 mm. across, sessile, the disk flat to somewhat convex, more or less grayish pruinose or finally black, the exciple thin and whitish; hypothecium dark brown, reaching 2 or 3 times the thickness of the hymenium and stroma-like; asci cylindrico-clavate, becoming saccate or wedge-shaped; spores often slightly curved, fusiform with obtuse ends, 3-septate, 15–20 × 3–4 μ.
On trees, along the seashore near Santa Monica, California. Very close to *D. california* Tuck.

OTHER SPECIES REPORTED

Dirina Catalinariae Hasse—California.

18. ROCCELLACEAE

Thallus fruticose, erect, more or less branched, differentiated into a well-developed cortex surrounding the algal layer and the central medulla, attached to the substratum by a basal disk; apothecia round to elongated, immersed or sessile. The algal host is Trentepohlia.

A. Cortex of transversely extending hyphae
    B. Spores hyaline . . . . 66. ROCCELLA
    B. Spores brown . . . . 67. SCHIZOPELTE
A. Cortex of longitudinally extending hyphae . . . . 65. DENDROGRAPHA

65. Dendrographa Darbish., Ber. Deutsch. Bot. Ges. 13:321. pl. 25, f. 1–4. 1895.

Thallus fruticose, erect, dichotomously branched, the cortex indistinct, composed of longitudinal cohering hyphae, the medullary region tow-like, soralia present or absent, spherical to flattened; apothecia lateral, disk-shaped, the exciple colored like the disk or darker, surrounded by a decorticate thalloid one; hypothecium brownish black to black; paraphyses branched; asci clavate; spores 8, hyaline, 3-septate.
The algal host is Trentepohlia.

A. On shrubs, thallus branched . . . . 1. D. leucophaea
A. On rocks and soil, thallus much branched . . . . 2. D. minor

1. **Dendrographa leucophaea** (Tuck.) Darbish., Ber. Deutsch. Bot. Ges. 13:321. 1895.
Roccella leucophaea Tuck., Proc. Am. Journ. Sci. II. 25:423. 1858.
Thallus greenish gray to ashy or rarely brownish, dichotomously branched, erect and spreading, becoming much elongated and decumbent, flattened and rarely perforated with holes below, becoming narrower and often cylindrical above, soralia present; apothecia middle-sized to larger, 0.6–2 mm. across, lateral, sessile, more commonly on the basal, flattened portions of the thallus, the disk flat to convex, whitish pruinose or rarely blackish, the exciple thin, whitish; spores finger-shaped, 17–28 × 5–7 μ.
On shrubs, along the coast and coast islands of southern California.

2. **Dendrographa minor** Darbish., Ber. Deutsch. Bot. Ges. 16:13. 1898.
Thallus small, greenish gray to ashy, sometimes blackish below, erect to decumbent, dichotomously much-branched, the branches cylindrical throughout or more or less flattened below, becoming much entangled, soralia sparingly present or absent; apothecia middle-sized to large, 0.6–2.5 mm. across, lateral, mainly toward the basal portions of the thallus, sessile, the disk concave to slightly convex, whitish pruinose to blackish, the exciple thickish; spores finger-shaped, 19–28 × 5.5–7.5 μ.
On rocks and soil, near the coast, central and southern California.

66. Roccella Lam. & DC., Fl. Fr. III. 2:334. 1815.

Thallus fruticose, erect, more or less thickly branched, the branches flat, smooth or soraliate, more or less twisted, the cortex of transversely extending, cohering hyphae, the medullary tissue of longitudinally extending hyphae; apothecia lateral, sessile, the disk flat to convex, the exciple colored like the disk or lighter, surrounded by a thin, sometimes disappearing, thalloid one; hypothecium dark brown; hymenium hyaline or brownish above; paraphyses branched; asci clavate; spores 8, hyaline, oblong to oblong-fusiform or fusiform, 3-septate.
The algal host is Trentepohlia, found in the outer medullary tissue and the inner cortex.

A. On shrubs
    B. Spores not more than 20 μ in length . . . . 2. R. phycopsis
    B. Spores more than 20 μ in length . . . . 4. R. Montagnaei

A. On rocks
  B. Thallus whitish to yellowish gray, branches flattened . . . . 1. R. fuciformis
  B. Thallus greenish gray to whitish, branches round or flattened . . 3. R. tinctoria

1. **Roccella fuciformis** (L.) Lam. & DC., Fl. Fr. III. 2:335. 1815.
Lichen fuciformis L., Sp. Pl. 1147. 1753.
  Thallus erect, dull whitish to yellowish gray or grayish, dichotomously divided into long, slender, flattened, narrow, pointed, ribbon-like branches; apothecia middle-sized to large, 0.8–2 mm. across, marginal and terminal, sessile, the disk flat, grayish pruinose or rarely blackish, the exciple thin, colored like the thallus, becoming crenulate; asci clavate to inflated-clavate; spores fusiform, 20–28 × 4–7 μ.
  On rocks, California.

2. **Roccella phycopsis** Ach.; Weber & Mohr, Arch. Nat. 1:110. 1804.
Lichen fucoides Neck. *R. fucoides* (Neck.) Vainio.
  Thallus erect and spreading, dull ashy to whitish, becoming dichotomously much-branched, the branches long, flattened, pointed, more or less covered with whitish soralia; apothecia small, 0.4–0.8 mm. across, lateral, sessile, the disk flat, black or whitish pruinose, the exciple thin, colored like the thallus, rarely disappearing; spores oblong-fusiform, 12–16 × 3–4 μ.
  On shrubs, southern California.

3. **Roccella tinctoria** Lam. & DC., Fl. Fr. III. 2:334. 1815.
  Thallus tough, greenish gray to whitish, sparingly branched, the branches round to flattened, much elongated and intertangled, soralia present; apothecia middle-sized to large, 0.8–2 mm. across, sessile, the disk flat to slightly convex, black, the exciple thin, colored like the thallus, finally disappearing; spores oblong-fusiform, 20–26 × 5–8 μ.
  On rocks, southern California.

4. **Roccella Montagnaei** Bel, Voyage Indes-Orient. 2: Crypt. 117. 1846.
  Thallus erect, greenish gray to ashy, dichotomously much-branched, the branches short, more or less flattened, blunt or pointed, bearing numerous soralia; apothecia middle-sized to large, 1–2 mm. across, sessile, the disk flat to slightly convex, black, the exciple thin, colored like the thallus, finally disappearing; spores oblong-fusiform, 26–32 μ.
  On shrubs, southern California. (Description partly compiled from Nylander.)

OTHER SPECIES REPORTED
Roccella difficilis Darb.—North America.

67. Schizopelte T. Fries, Flora 58:143. 1875.

  Thallus foliose to fruticose, erect, more or less thickly lobed or branched, the lobes or branches round, smooth to rough, the cortex of transversely extending, cohering hyphae, a more or less distinct algal layer, the medullary tissue of longitudinally extending hyphae; apothecia lateral or terminal, irregular, the disk concave to flat, the exciple colored like the disk, soon disappearing, surrounded by an irregular thalloid one; hypothecium dark brown; hymenium hyaline or brownish above; paraphyses branched; asci clavate; spores 8, brown, oblong to fusiform, 3–many-septate.
  The algal host is Trentepohlia.

1. **Schizopelte californica** T. Fries, Flora 58:143, 144. 1875.
  Thallus composed of erect, clustered, whitish, rough to finally scaly, wrinkled, round, distinctly branched lobes; apothecia middle-sized to large, 2–8 mm. across, subpedicellate, lateral and terminal, becoming fan-shaped or irregular, the disk concave to rarely flat, dull black or thinly white-pruinose, the exciple thin, colored like the thallus, becoming crenate; spores oblong, 3–6-septate, 18–24 × 5–7.5 μ.
  On rocks and soil, California.

19. LECANACTIDACEAE

Thallus crustose, showing little or no differentiation, attached to the substratum by hyphal rhizoids; apothecia round to irregular, immersed to adnate, the proper exciple rudimentary or well developed, rarely wanting, sometimes surrounded by the thallus.
The algal host is Trentepohlia.

A. Apothecia with irregular thalloid exciple . . . . 70. SCHISMATOMMA
A. Apothecia with proper exciple rarely surrounded by a thin thalloid one
  B. Proper exciple well developed . . . . 68. LECANACTIS
  B. Proper exciple surrounded by a thin thalloid one . . . 69. PLATYGRAPHOPSIS

68. Lecanactis Eschw., Syst. Lich. 14. f. 7. 1824.

Thallus crustose, continuous or scattered, chinky, warty, or rarely areolate, devoid of differentiation into layers; apothecia small to middle-sized, round to more or less oblong, adnate to sessile, the disk flat to more or less convex, the exciple thin to rather thick, usually black; hypothecium dark brown to black; hymenium hyaline or rarely brownish above; paraphyses usually branched; asci clavate to cylindrical; spores usually 8, hyaline. fusiform or oblong-fusiform, 3–several-septate.
The algal host is Trentepohlia.

A. On trees and old wood
  B. Apothecia not more than 0.6 mm. across . . . . 1. .L. salicina
  B. Apothecia usually more than 0.6 mm. across
    C. Thallus more or less limited and dissected
    by a blackening hypothallus
      D. Spores 13–25 μ in length . . . . 2. L. premnea
      D. Spores 11–17 μ in length . . . . 2. L. premnea chloroconia
    C. Thallus not limited or dissected by a
    blackening hypothallus . . . . 4. L. illecebrosa megaspora
A. On rocks . . . . 3. L. Zahlbruckneri

1. **Lecanactis salicina** Zahlbr.; Hasse, Bryologist 11:7. 1906.
Thallus thin, minutely granulose or finely scaly, ashy to sometimes yellowish gray; apothecia small, 0.3–0.6 mm. across, round, subsessile, the disk flat to slightly convex, densely white-pruinose to black, the exciple thin, becoming crenulate, black; hypothecium dark brown; spores fusiform, 3-septate, 26–36 $\times$ 4–6.5 μ.
On trees, Santa Monica Range and Santa Catalina Island, California.

2. **Lecanactis premnea** (Ach.) Arn., Flora 44:664. 1861.
Lecidea premnea Ach., Lich. Univ. 173. 1810.
Thallus thin, smoothish to wrinkled, granulose or chinky, greenish to greenish gray or ashy, more or less limited and dissected by a blackening hypothallus, rarely disappearing; apothecia middle-sized, 0.7–1.5 mm. across, round to angular, sessile, the disk flat, greenish pruinose to black, the exciple black, becoming flexuous; hypothecium brownish black; spores fusiform-oblong, 3-septate, 13–25 $\times$ 3–6 μ.
On trees, from South Carolina to Florida, westward to Ohio and Minnesota, and recurring in California.
var. **chloroconia** Tuck., Gen. Lich. 194. 1872.
L. chloroconia Tuck., Proc. Am. Acad. 6:285. 1866.
The exciple thinner and the spores only 11–17 $\times$ 3–5 μ.
On trees and old wood, from New Hampshire to South Carolina, and westward to California.

3. **Lecanactis Zahlbruckneri** Herre, Bot. Gaz. 43:270. 1907.
Thallus thick, rough, pinkish to ashy gray, composed of coarse, irregular, sometimes folded granules; apothecia small to middle-sized, 0.5–1 mm. across, round, sessile, the disk flat to convex, grayish pruinose to black, the exciple rather thick,

black, finally disappearing; hypothecium dark brown; spores fusiform, sometimes slightly curved, 3-septate, 18–24 × 4.5–6 μ.
On maritime rocks, Santa Cruz Peninsula, California.

4. **Lecanactis illecebrosa** E. Fries, var. **megaspora** Merrill, Bryologist 16:59. 1913.
L. amylacea var. *megaspora* (Merrill) Zahlbr.
Thallus thin, more or less powdery or becoming granulose, white or grayish white; apothecia small to middle-sized or larger, 0.4–1 mm. across, round, adnate, the disk flat to convex, sometimes irregular, brown to black or whitish pruinose, the margin thin, black, sometimes disappearing; hypothecium brownish black; spores fusiform to oblong-fusiform, 3-septate, 24–30 × 4–6 μ.
On trees, Washington. (The species is limited to Europe.)

69. **Schismatomma** Flot. & Koerb., in Mass., Ric. Lich. 55. 1852.

Thallus crustose, thin, smooth to chinky, powdery, or minutely granulose, rudimentary, showing little or no differentiation into layers, attached to the substratum by rhizoids; apothecia minute or small to middle-sized or larger, round, oblong, or irregular, adnate to sessile, the disk flat to more or less convex, the exciple colored like the thallus, thin to thick, irregular; hypothecium dark brown to brownish black; hymenium hyaline to brownish above; paraphyses branched and netlike interwoven; asci clavate; spores 8, hyaline, fusiform to oblong-fusiform or acicular, sometimes curved, 3–13-septate, the cells cylindrical.
The algal host is Trentepohlia.

A. Spores 3–5-septate
   B. Spores constantly 3-septate
      C. Spores not more than 20 μ in length
         D. Apothecia 0.2–0.5 mm. across . . . . 2. S. ocellatum
         D. Apothecia more than 0.5 mm. across . . . . 6. S. vernans
      C. Spores more than 20 μ in length
         D. Thallus smooth to chinky, sometimes powdery . . . 1. S. abietinum
         D. Thallus chinky or granulose
            E. Apothecia 0.15–0.4 mm. across . . . . 3. S. pericleum
            E. Apothecia 0.6–1.3 mm. across . . . . 4. S. Ravenelii
   B. Spores 3–5-septate . . . . 5. S. subattingens
A. Spores 7–more-septate
   B. Spores 7-septate, 25–30 μ in length . . . . 7. S. hypothallinum
   B. Spores 7–13-septate, 40–50 μ in length . . . . 8. S. pluriloculare

1. **Schismatomma abietinum** (Ehrh.) Mass., Ric. Lich. 56. f. 102. 1852.
Lichen abietinus Ehrh., Plant. Crypt. Exsicc. 166. 1785. *Pyrenothea leucocephala* (Ach.) E. Fries. *Lecanactis abietina* (Ehrh.) Koerb.
Thallus thin, greenish gray, smooth to chinky, sometimes powdery; apothecia middle-sized or larger, 0.6–2 mm. across, round or becoming irregular or angular, sessile, the disk flat to convex, densely whitish pruinose or rarely becoming black, the exciple thick, thinly whitish pruinose; hypothecium dark brown; spores oblong-fusiform, 3-septate, 30–42 × 4–6 μ.
On trees, California.

2. **Schismatomma ocellatum** (Nyl.) Zahlbr., Cat. Lich. Univ. 2:560. 1924.
Platygrapha ocellata Nyl., Act. Soc. Sci. Fenn. 7:478. 1863.
Thallus thin, smooth and chinky to rarely thicker, rough and minutely granulose, pale greenish gray to whitish, upon a thin, blackening hypothallus; apothecia minute to small, 0.2–0.5 mm. across, partly immersed to adnate, round to oblong, the disk flat, brownish to black, the exciple thin, colored like the thallus, becoming crenate, covering a thin proper one; hypothecium brownish black; spores fusiform, 3-septate, 16–21 × 3.5–5 μ.
On trees, South Carolina and Florida.

3. **Schismatomma pericleum** (Ach.) Branth & Rostr., Bot. Tidss. 3:244. pl. 4, f. 51. 1869.

Lichen pericleus Ach., Lich. Suec. Prod. 78. 1798. *Platygrapha periclea* (Ach.) Nyl. *S. dolosum* (E. Fries) Flotow.

Thallus thin, composed of minute, whitish, scurfy granules, contiguous and finally forming a chinky crust; apothecia minute to small, 0.15–0.4 mm. across, round or oblong and rarely sparingly branched, the disk flat to convex, dark brown to black, the exciple thick, white, rarely disappearing, covering a very thin, inconspicuous, proper one; hypothecium dark brown; spores bluntly acicular, 3-septate, 30–38 × 2.5–4 μ.

On trees, New Hampshire, Massachusetts, and Tennessee.

4. **Schismatomma Ravenelii** (Tuck.) Zahlbr., Cat. Lich. Univ. 2:564. 1924.

Platygrapha Ravenelii Tuck., Gen. Lich. 196. 1872.

Thallus thin, ashy gray, smooth to rough and scurfy, becoming chinky or sometimes granulose; apothecia small to middle-sized, 0.6–1.3 mm. across, sessile, round or becoming flexuous or stellately lobed, the disk flat, chocolate brown and commonly whitish pruinose, the proper exciple erect, black, surrounded by a thick, whitish, powdery, more or less disappearing, thalloid one; hypothecium brownish black; spores fusiform, 3-septate, 24–40 × 4.5–6 μ.

On trees, Florida and Texas.

5. **Schismatomma subattingens** (Nyl.) Zahlbr., Cat. Lich. Univ. 2:565. 1924.

Platygrapha subattingens Nyl., Lich. Insul. Guin. 51. 1889.

Thallus thin, smooth to slightly rough, greenish white to ashy, sometimes becoming powdery; apothecia small to middle-sized, 0.5–1 mm. across, round to irregular, adnate to subsessile, the disk flat to slightly convex, brown, commonly whitish pruinose, the proper exciple thin, brown, often disappearing, surrounded by a thin, whitish, thalloid one; hypothecium dark brown; spores fusiform, some slightly curved, 3–5-septate, 30–35 × 3.5–4 μ, parallelly to irregularly arranged.

On trees, Florida.

6. **Schismatomma vernans** (Tuck.) Zahlbr., Cat. Lich. Univ. 2:566. 1924.

Platygrapha vernans Tuck., Syn. N. A. Lich. 2:116. 1888.

Thallus composed of minute, greenish gray granules, crowded at length into a thin, rough crust; apothecia small to middle-sized, 0.4–0.8 mm. across, adnate to sessile, round, the disk flat to convex, pale brown to black, somewhat grayish pruinose, the thalloid exciple thin, colored like the thallus, becoming flexuous and disappearing; hypothecium brownish black; spores ellipsoid to ellipsoid-fusiform, 3-septate, 13–18 × 4.5–6 μ.

On charred wood, Florida.

7. **Schismatomma hypothallinum** (Zahlbr.) Hasse, Cont. U. S. Nat. Herb. 17:32, 33. 1913.

Platygrapha hypothallina Zahlbr., Bull. Torr. Club 27:645. 1900. *Platygrapha pinguis* Tuck.

Thallus thick, whitish, warty, folded and wrinkled, becoming pulverulent; apothecia middle-sized to large, 0.5–1 mm. across or reaching 1.5 mm. across in one direction, partly immersed to adnate, round to more or less irregular, the disk flat to slightly convex, brownish to dull black, or more commonly whitish pruinose, the thalloid exciple thick, colored like the thallus, becoming flexuous; hypothecium dark brown to brownish black; spores oblong-fusiform, 7-septate, 25–30 × 3–5 μ.

On rocks and rarely on trees, southern California.

8. **Schismatomma pluriloculare** Zahlbr., in E. & P., Nat. Pfl. 1:116. 1907.

Platygrapha plurilocularis Zahlbr., Beih. Bot. Central. 13:156, 157. 1902.

Thallus thick, smooth to rough, whitish to ashy, becoming warty to chinky, often limited by a black hypothallus; apothecia small to middle-sized, 0.5–2 mm. across, sessile, often crowded, the disk flat, black or rarely whitish pruinose, the exciple thick, colored like the thallus, becoming crenate; hypothecium dark brown to blackish brown; spores fusiform, some slightly curved, 7–13-septate, 40–50 × 4.5–6 μ.

On trees, southern California.

70. Platygraphopsis Müll. Arg., Mém. Soc. Phys. Hist. Nat. Genève 29:15. 1887.

Thallus crustose, smooth to rough and chinky, rudimentary, showing little or no differentiation into layers, attached to the substratum by hyphal rhizoids; apothecia minute to small, rarely immersed to adnate, round to angular or elongated, sometimes branched, the disk concave to flat, the exciple colored like the disk, surrounded by a thin, irregular, thalloid one; hypothecium dark brown; hymenium hyaline to brownish above; paraphyses branched and interwoven; asci clavate; spores 8, hyaline to brown, dactyloid or blunt-acicular, 3–several-septate, the cells cylindrical.

The algal host is Trentepohlia.

1. **Platygraphopsis interrupta** (Fée) Müll. Arg., Mém. Soc. Phys. Hist. Nat. Genève 29:15. 1887.

Graphis interrupta Fée, Essai Crypt. 41. pl. 8, f. 1. 1824.

Thallus thin, smooth to somewhat rough and chinky, whitish; apothecia minute to small, 0.2–0.5 mm. across, immersed, round and punctiform to angular or elongated and rarely becoming 1 or more times branched, the disk flat, black, the proper exciple thin, black; spores hyaline to brownish, dactyloid, 3–4-septate, 16–22 × 5–7 μ.

On trees, southern Florida.

20. THELOTREMACEAE

Thallus crustose, showing little or no differentiation, attached to the substratum by hyphal rhizoids; apothecia more or less immersed to rarely superficial, single or rarely somewhat united in a stroma, round, the disk usually more or less concave, the proper exciple well developed and usually surrounded by a thalloid one.

The algal hosts are Trentepohlia, Phyllactidium, and Heterothallus.

A. Paraphyses numerous, unbranched and not interwoven
  B. Spores transversely several-septate
    C. Spores hyaline . . . . 71. OCELLULARIA
    C. Spores brown . . . . 72. PHAEOTREMA
  B. Spores transversely and longitudinally septate
    C. Spores hyaline . . . . 73. THELOTREMA
    C. Spores brown . . . . 74. LEPTOTREMA
A. Paraphyses few, branched and interwoven . . . . 75. GYROSTOMUM

71. Ocellularia Mey., Nebenstud. 327. 1825.

Thallus crustose, smooth to minutely granulose, warty, or chinky, rudimentary, commonly devoid of differentiation into layers, attached to the substratum by hyphal rhizoids; apothecia minute to small or rarely middle-sized, more or less immersed, the disk concave to flat, the exciple colored like the disk, thin, sometimes elevated, surrounded by a thicker, irregular, thalloid one; hypothecium and hymenium hyaline; paraphyses unbranched, free or coherent; asci clavate to broadly clavate; spores 1–8, hyaline, oblong to oblong-ellipsoid or fusiform, 3–many-septate, the cells lenticular.

The algal host is Trentepohlia.

A. Spores 3-septate
  B. Thallus greenish gray to ashy; apothecia dark flesh-colored . 6. O. micropora
  B. Thallus ashy white to whitish or pinkish
    white; apothecia black . . . . 7. O. carnea

A. Spores more than 3-septate
  B. Spores large, more than 100 μ in length
    C. Spores 1 in an ascus	2. O. domingensis
    C. Spores 8 in an ascus	3. O. floridensis
  B. Spores smaller, rarely more than 50 μ in length
    C. Apothecia minute, not more than 0.3 mm. across	5. O. lathraea
    C. Apothecia small, 0.3–0.8 mm. across
      D. Spores 5–7- or rarely 9-septate	4. O. granulosa
      D. Spores 7–15-septate	1. O. subtilis

1. **Ocellularia subtilis** (Tuck.) Riddle, Mycologia 15:79. 1923.

   Thelotrema subtilis Tuck., Am. Journ. Sci. II. 25:426. 1858.

   Thallus thin to somewhat thick, rough, chinky, greenish gray to ashy white; apothecia small to middle-sized, 0.4–0.8 mm. across, immersed to becoming superficial, the disk concave to almost flat, black or whitish pruinose, the proper exciple thin, surrounded by a thicker, raised, thalloid one; spores 8, fusiform, 7–15-septate, 26–54 × 6–13 μ.

   On trees, from New England to Florida, and westward to Texas.

2. **Ocellularia domingensis** (Fée) Müll. Arg., Flora 70:398. 1887.

   Ascidium domingense Fée; Nyl., Mém. Soc. Sci. Nat. Cherb. 5:118. 1857. *Thelotrema domingense* (Fée) Tuck. *Thelotrema domingense* var. *rhodostroma* (Mont.) Tuck. *O. rhodostroma* (Mont.) Zahlbr.

   Thallus thin, smooth to becoming rough and minutely granulose, sometimes chinky, greenish gray to ashy or whitish; apothecia small, 0.4–0.8 mm. across, immersed, the disk concave to flat, black or whitish pruinose, the proper exciple thin, black, becoming irregular and elevated, surrounded by a thicker thalloid one; spores 1, fusiform, 19–39-septate, 116–180 × 20–33 μ.

   On trees, from South Carolina to Florida, and westward to Louisiana and Mississippi.

3. **Ocellularia floridensis** Fink; Hedrick, Mycologia 25:314. 1933.

   Thallus thin to moderately thick, smooth to rough and chinky, ashy white; apothecia small, 0.5–0.8 mm. across, immersed to superficial, the disk deeply concave, black or whitish pruinose, the proper exciple thin, whitish, inflexed, surrounded by a thicker, irregular, thalloid one; spores 8, oblong-cylindrical, slightly flexuous, 15–29-septate, 118–180 × 16–20 μ.

   On trees, Florida.

4. **Ocellularia granulosa** (Tuck.) Zahlbr., Cat. Lich. Univ. 2:591. 1924.

   Thelotrema granulosum Tuck., Am. Journ. Sci. II. 25:426. 1858.

   Thallus thin, smooth to minutely granulose and warty, becoming chinky, greenish gray to ashy; apothecia small, 0.3–0.8 mm. across, immersed, the disk concave to almost flat, black or grayish pruinose, the proper exciple very thin, black, surrounded by a thin, elevated, thalloid one; spores 8, oblong-ellipsoid, 5–7- or rarely 9-septate, 17–24 × 6–7.5 μ.

   On trees, Florida and Louisiana.

5. **Ocellularia lathraea** (Tuck.) Zahlbr., Cat. Lich. Univ. 2:593. 1924.

   Thelotrema lathraeum Tuck., Syn. N. A. Lich. 1:224. 1882.

   Thallus thin, smooth to slightly rough, sometimes minutely warty, rarely becoming chinky, greenish gray to ashy or whitish; apothecia very minute, 0.08–0.12 mm. across, immersed, the disk concave, black or rarely grayish pruinose, the proper exciple thin, blackening, elevated, surrounded by a thalloid one; spores 8, oblong or oblong-ellipsoid, 5–7- or rarely 9-septate, 16–28 × 4–6.5 μ.

   On trees, Florida.

6. **Ocellularia micropora** (Mont.) Müll. Arg., Flora 74:112. 1891.

   Thelotrema microporum Mont., Ann. Sci. Nat. Bot. III. 10:130. 1848.

   Thallus thin, rough, chinky, greenish gray to ashy; apothecia minute to small, 0.1–0.3 mm. across, immersed, the disk deeply concave to almost flat, dark flesh-colored, the proper exciple thin, white, surrounded by a thicker, often disappearing, thalloid one; spores 8, ellipsoid, 3-septate, 11–14 × 6–8 μ.

On trees, Georgia, Florida, and Louisiana.

7. **Ocellularia carnea** (Eckf.) Zahlbr., Cat. Lich. Univ. 2:585. 1924.

Thelotrema carneum Eckf., Bull. Torr. Club 21:394. 1894.

Thallus thin, smooth to minutely granulose and warty, rarely somewhat chinky, ashy white to whitish or pinkish white, rarely bordered by and interspersed with a thin black hypothallus; apothecia minute to small, 0.25–0.6 mm. across, immersed, the disk becoming flat, black, slightly rough, the proper exciple thin, black, surrounded by a thick, irregular, thalloid one; spores 8, oblong-ellipsoid, 3-septate, 11–14 × 3–4 μ.

On trees, Louisiana.

72. **Phaeotrema** Müll. Arg., Mém. Soc. Phys. Hist. Nat.
Genève 29:10. 1887.

Thallus crustose, smooth to minutely granulose, warty or chinky, rudimentary, commonly devoid of differentiation into layers, attached to the substratum by hyphal rhizoids; apothecia minute to small, more or less immersed, the disk concave to flat, the exciple colored like the disk, thin, sometimes elevated, surrounded by a thicker, irregular, thalloid one; hypothecium and hymenium hyaline; paraphyses unbranched, free or coherent; asci clavate to broadly clavate; spores 1–8, brown, oblong to oblong-ellipsoid or fusiform, 3–many-septate.

The algal host is Trentepohlia.

1. **Phaeotrema californicum** (Tuck.) Zahlbr., Cat. Lich. Univ. 2:605. 1924.

Thelotrema californicum Tuck., Proc. Am. Acad. 12:177. 1877.

Thallus thin, smooth to warty and sometimes chinky, continuous or irregularly scattered, closely adnate, yellow to straw-colored; apothecia small, 0.3–0.7 mm. across, adnate to sessile, round, the disk flat, black, the exciple colored like the disk, thin, rarely prominent, surrounded by a thicker, entire to flexuous or stellate, thalloid one; spores 8, ellipsoid to subdactyloid, 3–7-septate, 20–30 × 5–8 μ.

On trees, San Diego, California. Description made from one by Zahlbruckner based on the cotype in Herbarium of Jean Müller.

73. **Thelotrema** Ach., Meth. Lich. 130. 1803.

Thallus crustose, smooth to warty, areolate, or chinky, partly within the substratum, commonly devoid of differentiation into layers, attached to the substratum by hyphal rhizoids; apothecia small to middle-sized, immersed to superficial, the disk closed to open, concave to flat, the exciple colored like the disk, thick to thinner, irregular, surrounded by a thin, usually persistent, thalloid one; hypothecium hyaline; hymenium hyaline or brownish above; paraphyses unbranched, free; asci clavate to broadly clavate; spores 1–8, hyaline, oblong-ellipsoid, ellipsoid or fusiform, transversely and longitudinally septate, the cells spherical or lenticular.

The algal host is Trentepohlia.

A. Spores 1, 128–180 μ in length . . . . 2. T. interpositum
A Spores 1–4 or rarely 8, 45–140 μ in length . . . . 1. T. lepadinum

1. **Thelotrema lepadinum** Ach., Meth. Lich. 132. 1803.

Lichen lepadinus Ach., Suec. Prod. 30. 1798.

Thallus thin to somewhat thick, smooth to rough, chinky, becoming areolate, gray to dull ashy or whitish; apothecia small to middle-sized, 0.4–1 mm. across, slightly immersed to superficial, the disk concave to flat, black or whitish pruinose, the proper exciple thin, brownish black, irregularly torn, surrounded by a thin thalloid one; spores 1–4 or rarely 8, fusiform or oblong-ellipsoid, 11–19-septate transversely and 1–3- or rarely 5-septate longitudinally, 45–140 × 10–25 μ.

On trees, New England, South Carolina, Florida, Louisiana, California, Oregon, and Washington.

2. **Thelotrema interpositum** (Nyl.) Müll. Arg., Flora 64:526. 1881.
Ascidium interpositum Nyl., Ann. Sci. Nat. Bot. IV. 19:335. 1863.

Thallus thin, rough, minutely warty, becoming chinky, greenish gray to dull white; apothecia small to middle-sized, 0.4–0.8 mm. across, slightly immersed to superficial, the disk flat, black, sometimes whitish pruinose, the proper exciple thick, black, surrounded by a thick, somewhat irregular, thalloid one; spores 1, hyaline to slightly brown, fusiform, 29–39-septate transversely and 3–7-septate longitudinally, 128–180 × 28–42 μ.

On trees, Georgia, Florida, Alabama, Louisiana, and Texas.

OTHER SPECIES REPORTED

Thelotrema compunctum (Smith) Nyl.—Louisiana and South Carolina.
Thelotrema Halei (Tuck.) Nyl.—Louisiana.
Thelotrema lepadodes Tuck.—Florida.

74. **Leptotrema** Mont. & Bosch., Lich. Jav. 57. 1855.

Thallus crustose, smooth to warty, areolate, or chinky, partly within the substratum, commonly devoid of differentiation into layers, attached to the substratum by hyphal rhizoids; apothecia minute to small or middle-sized, more or less immersed to superficial, the disk closed to more or less open, concave to flat, the exciple thin, colored like the disk, surrounded by a thicker, sometimes disappearing, thalloid one; hypothecium hyaline; hymenium hyaline or brownish above; paraphyses unbranched, free; asci clavate to broadly clavate; spores 1–8, brown, oblong to ellipsoid or ovoid-ellipsoid, transversely and longitudinally septate.

The algal host is Trentepohlia.

A. Thallus thin, smooth to slightly rough, wrinkled, or warty
  B. Apothecia not more than 0.6 mm. across
    C. Apothecia minute, not more than 0.2 mm. across .   . 6. L. laeviusculum
    C. Apothecia 0.2–0.6 mm. across
      D. Thallus greenish gray to ashy . . . . 7. L. glaucescens
      D. Thallus greenish to yellowish . . . . 2. L. Ravenelii
  B. Apothecia reaching 0.8–1 mm. across
    C. Spores 1, 80–135 μ in length . . . . 3. L. monosporum
    C. Spores 8, 14–26 μ in length . . . . 4. L. Wightii
A. Thallus thin to thick, granulose or bearing minute coralloid branchlets
  B. Thallus granulose . . . . 1. L. Auberianum
  B. Thallus bearing minute coralloid branchlets
    C. Thallus rough, sometimes crumbling; apothecia
      0.6–1.2 mm. across . . . . 5. L. santense
    C. Thallus smooth to rough; apothecia 0.8–2 mm. across . 8. L. heterosporum

1. **Leptotrema Auberianum** (Mont.) Fink n. comb.
Thelotrema Auberianum Mont., in Sagra, Hist. Nat. Cub. 163. pl. 8, f. 2. 1842.
Phaeotrema Auberianum (Mont.) Müll. Arg.

Thallus thin, chinky, somewhat wrinkled, becoming minutely granulose, greenish gray to ashy brown; apothecia small to middle-sized, 0.4–0.8 mm. across, immersed to almost superficial, the disk black, often covered by a perforate, whitish veil, the proper exciple thin, brown, more or less exposed by the disappearing of the thicker thalloid one; spores 8, oblong-ellipsoid, 3–5-septate transversely and 1– rarely 2-septate longitudinally, 16–24 × 7–9.5 μ.

On trees, Florida.

2. **Leptotrema Ravenelii** (Tuck.) Fink n. comb.
Thelotrema Ravenelii Tuck., Am. Journ. Sci. II. 25:426. 1858.

Thallus thin, smooth to minutely wrinkled and warty, greenish to yellowish; apothecia minute to small, 0.2–0.6 mm. across, immersed, the disk minute, the proper exciple colored like the thallus or becoming darker; spores 8, brownish, oblong-ellipsoid, 3–5-septate transversely and 1-septate longitudinally, 13–16 × 7–10 μ.

On trees, from South Carolina to Florida and Louisiana.

3. **Leptotrema monosporum** (Nyl.) Müll. Arg., Bull. Soc. Bot. Belg. 31:35. 1892.

Thelotrema monosporum Nyl., Ann. Sci. Nat. IV. 15:46. 1861.

Thallus thin, smooth to slightly rough, white to yellowish or ashy white; apothecia small to middle-sized, 0.3–0.8 mm. across, immersed, the disk minute, bordered by a firm, elevated, thalloid exciple, the proper exciple thin, black; spores 1, hyaline to brownish, oblong-ellipsoid, 17–35-septate transversely and 3–5-septate longitudinally, 80–135 × 20–36 μ.

On trees, Florida, Alabama, and Texas.

4. **Leptotrema Wightii** (Tayl.) Müll. Arg., Flora 65:499. 1882.

Endocarpon Wightii Tayl., in Hook., Journ. Bot. 155. 1847. *Thelotrema Wightii* (Tayl.) Nyl.

Thallus thin to moderately thick, smooth to minutely wrinkled, greenish gray to ashy; apothecia small to middle-sized, 0.4–1 mm. across, immersed, the disk minute, the proper exciple thin, black, the thalloid exciple thin, smooth, colored like the thallus or lighter; spores 8, ovoid-ellipsoid, 3–6-septate transversely and 1–2-septate longitudinally, 14–26 × 10–14 μ.

On trees, from South Carolina to Florida, and westward to Texas.

5. **Leptotrema santense** (Tuck.) Zahlbr., Cat. Lich. Univ. 2:639. 1924.

Thelotrema santense Tuck., Proc. Am. Acad. 5:406. 1862.

Thallus thick, rough, sometimes crumbling, often bearing minute coralloid branchlets, greenish gray to darker or ashy; apothecia small to middle-sized, 0.6–1.2 mm. across, immersed, the disk deeply concave to flat, black, often whitish pruinose, the proper exciple black, elevated, incurved and torn crenately, surrounded by a heavy, irregular, thalloid one; spores 8, ellipsoid, 2–5-septate transversely and 1- or rarely 2-septate longitudinally, 16–28 × 7–12 μ.

On trees, South Carolina, Florida, Louisiana, and Alabama.

6. **Leptotrema laeviusculum** (Nyl.) Zahlbr., Cat. Lich. Univ. 2:635. 1924.

Thelotrema laeviusculum Nyl., Ann. Sci. Nat. Bot. IV. 19:335. 1863.

Thallus thin to somewhat thick, rough, chinky and becoming areolate, greenish gray to ashy; apothecia minute, 0.08–0.2 mm. across, immersed, the disk concave, black, the proper exciple thin, black, surrounded by a thin thalloid one; spores 8, oblong, 3-septate transversely and 1-septate longitudinally, 12–18 × 7–10 μ.

On trees, South Carolina and Louisiana.

7. **Leptotrema glaucescens** (Nyl.) Müll. Arg., Flora 65:499. 1882.

Thelotrema glaucescens Nyl., Ann. Sci. Nat. Bot. IV. 19:332. 1863. *Thelotrema compunctum* var. *glaucescens* Nyl.

Thallus thin, rough, chinky, greenish gray to ashy; apothecia minute to small. 0.2–0.6 mm. across, immersed, the disk concave to almost flat, black, whitish pruinose, the proper exciple thin, whitish, surrounded by a thicker, irregular, raised, thalloid one; spores 8, ellipsoid, 3-septate transversely and becoming 1-septate longitudinally, 10–16 × 6–9 μ.

On trees, South Carolina, Georgia, Florida, Alabama, and Louisiana.

8. **Leptotrema heterosporum** (Knight) Zahlbr., Cat. Lich. Univ. 2:635. 1924.

Thelotrema heterosporum Knight, in Bailey, Syn. Queens. Flora Suppl. 1:72. pl. 1, f. 2. 1886. *L. mastoideum* Müll. Arg.

Thallus thin to somewhat thicker, smooth to rough, bearing minute coralloid branchlets, greenish gray to ashy white; apothecia middle-sized to large, 0.8–2 mm. across, immersed to superficial, the disk concave to flat, black or grayish pruinose, the proper exciple thin, surrounded by a thicker, irregularly torn and crenate. thalloid one; spores 8, ellipsoid, 3-septate transversely and 1-septate longitudinally, 17–23 × 7–10 μ.

On trees, Louisiana.

75. **Gyrostomum** E. Fries, Syst. Orb. Veg. 268. 1825.

Thallus crustose, smooth, rudimentary, commonly devoid of differentiation into layers, attached to the substratum by hyphal rhizoids; apothecia minute to small, more or less immersed to adnate or sessile, the disk concave to flat, the exciple colored like the disk, elevated, surrounded by a thin, usually disappearing, thalloid one; hypothecium hyaline; hymenium hyaline or brownish above; paraphyses few, branched and netlike interwoven; asci clavate to inflated-clavate; spores 2–8, hyaline to brown, oblong to oblong-ellipsoid, transversely and longitudinally septate.

The algal host is Trentepohlia.

1. **Gyrostomum scyphuliferum** (Ach.) E. Fries, Syst. Orb. Veg. 268. 1825.
Lecidea scyphulifera Ach., Syn. Meth. Lich. 27. 1814.
Thallus thin, smooth to very slightly rough, greenish ashy or olive-brown to lead-colored; apothecia minute to small, 0.25–0.9 mm. across, sessile, the disk flat, brown, varying toward dirty blackish, the exciple elevated, colored like the disk and becoming radiately striate, surrounded by a thin, disappearing, thalloid one; spores oblong-ellipsoid, 5–9-septate transversely and 1–2-septate longitudinally, 20–40 × 10–15 μ.

On trees, South Carolina, Florida, Louisiana, Alabama, and Texas.

OTHER SPECIES REPORTED

Gyrostomum Curtisii Tuck.—North America.

21. DIPLOSCHISTACEAE

Thallus crustose, rudimentary or showing more or less differentiation, attached to the substratum by hyphal rhizoids; apothecia round, immersed to superficial, the proper exciple well developed, usually surrounded by a heavy thalloid one.
The algal host is Protococcus.

A. Spores transversely septate . . . . 76. CONOTREMA
A. Spores transversely and longitudinally septate . . . . 77. URCEOLARIA

76. **Conotrema** Tuck., Syn. Lich. N. E. 86. 1848.

Thallus rudimentary, without distinct layers, sometimes forming a poorly developed, plectenchymatous layer, crustose, thin, smooth or somewhat rough, attached by hyphal rhizoids; apothecia small, more or less immersed to sessile, the disk concave, commonly whitish pruinose, the proper exciple blackish, surrounded by a thin, soon disappearing, thalloid one; hypothecium and hymenium hyaline; paraphyses branched toward the apices; asci cylindrical; spores 8, hyaline, cylindrical, many-septate, the cells spherical.
The algal host is Protococcus.

1. **Conotrema urceolatum** (Ach.) Tuck., Syn. Lich. N. E. 86. 1848.
Lecidea urceolata Ach., Lich. Univ. 671. 1810.
Thallus thin, smooth to scurfy, chinky or finally areolate, ashy whitish, sometimes partly disappearing; apothecia small, 0.4–0.75 mm. across, partly immersed to subsessile, the disk deeply concave, blackish or whitish pruinose, the proper exciple blackish, at first surrounded by a thin thalloid one; spores 29–39-septate, 100–160 × 3–4.5 μ. (PLATE 4.)

On trees, from New England to South Carolina, and westward to Iowa and Minnesota.

77. Urceolaria Ach., Meth. Lich. 141. 1803.

Thallus crustose, thick, areolate or warty, differentiated into a poorly developed upper cortex of entangled hyphae, more or less distinct algal and medullary layers, attached to the substratum by numerous hyphal rhizoids; apothecia minute to small or middle-sized, immersed to adnate, the disk closed to open, more or less concave, the exciple thick, colored like the disk, irregular, usually surrounded by a thin thalloid one; hypothecium brownish to brown; hymenium hyaline or brownish above; paraphyses sometimes branched toward the apices; asci cylindrico-clavate; spores 2–8, brown, ellipsoid to oblong-ellipsoid, transversely and longitudinally septate.

The algal host is Protococcus.

A. Not parasitic on lichens
 B. Spores not more than 35 μ in length
  C. Proper exciple thick, radiately striate . . . . 3. U. actinostoma
  C. Proper exciple thin, minutely toothed
   D. On soil and rocks among moss . . . . 1. U. scruposa bryophila
   D. On soil and rocks, but not among moss . . . . . 1. U. scruposa
 B. Spores 31–50 μ in length . . . . 2. U. albissima
A. Parasitic on lichens . . . . 1. U. scruposa parasitica

1. **Urceolaria scruposa** (Schreb.) Ach., Lich. Suec. 32. 1798.
 Lichen scruposus Schreb., Spic. Fl. Lips. 133. 1771. *Parmelia scruposa* (Schreb.) Hepp. *Diploschistes scruposus* (Schreb.) Norm. *U. ochroleuca* Tuck.

Thallus thin to thick, composed of minute to small, wartlike, uneven, continuous and crowded, greenish gray to ashy white areoles; apothecia small to middle-sized, 0.3–1 mm. across, commonly immersed to becoming adnate, the disk deeply concave, black or grayish pruinose, the proper exciple thin, black, minutely toothed, surrounded by a thick, swollen, sometimes crenate, more or less disappearing, thalloid one; spores 4–8, brownish to brown, oblong-ellipsoid, 5–7-septate transversely and 1–3-septate longitudinally, 20–34 × 10–15 μ.

On rocks and rarely on trees and old wood, throughout the United States.

var. **bryophila** (Ehrh.) Ach., Meth. Lich. 148. 1803.
 Lichen bryophilus Ehrh., Pl. Crypt. Exsicc. no. 236. 1774. *Parmelia scruposa* var. *bryophila* (Ehrh.) Hepp. *Diploschistes bryophilus* (Ehrh.) Zahlbr.

Thallus thin, smooth to slightly rough, becoming areolate, ashy gray to whitish; apothecia small, 0.3–0.6 mm. across; spores 8, brownish to brown, ellipsoid to oblong-ellipsoid, 5–7-septate transversely and 1–2-septate longitudinally, 26–28 × 10–12 μ.

On soil and rock among moss and species of Cladonia, West Virginia, Colorado, and California.

var. **parasitica** (Sommerf.) Tuck., Syn. N. A. Lich. 1:222. 1882.
 Lecanora scruposa var. *parasitica* Sommerf., Suppl. Flor. Lap. 100. 1826. *Diploschistes scruposus* var. *parasiticus* (Sommerf.) Zahlbr.

Thallus very thin and often disappearing; apothecia small, 0.3–0.6 mm. across; spores 8, oblong-ellipsoid, 5– rarely 7-septate transversely and 1– rarely 2-septate longitudinally, 18–21 × 7–9 μ.

On the thallus of species of Cladonia, Massachusetts, Ohio, and South Dakota.

2. **Urceolaria albissima** (Ach.) Fink n. comb.
 U. scruposa var. *albissima* Ach., Meth. Lich. 147. 1803. *U. gypsacea* Ach. *U. scruposa* var. *gypsacea* (Ach.) Koerb. *Diploschistes gypsaceus* (Ach.) Zahlbr. *Diploschistes albissimus* (Ach.) Dalla Torre & Sarnth.

Thallus thin to thick, continuous, wrinkled, uneven, minutely areolate, becoming powdery, ashy to whitish; apothecia small to middle-sized, 0.4–1 mm. across, immersed to becoming adnate, the disk deeply concave to concave, black or grayish pruinose, the proper exciple thin, black, somewhat wrinkled, surrounded by a thick, swollen, irregular, thalloid one; spores 2–4 or rarely 8, ellipsoid to oblong-ellipsoid, 5–7- or rarely 9-septate transversely and 1–3-septate longitudinally, 31–50 × 13–20 μ.

On soil and rocks, South Dakota, Iowa, and California.

3. **Urceolaria actinostoma** Pers., in Ach., Lich. Univ. 288. 1810.

Diploschistes actinostomus (Pers.) Zahlbr.

Thallus thin to somewhat thick, composed of minute to small, smooth to rough and finally wartlike, greenish gray to grayish or ashy white areoles; apothecia minute to small, 0.2–0.5 mm. across, immersed 1–several in an areole, the disk black, opened by a pore to becoming concave, the proper exciple thick, black or grayish pruinose, radiately striate, rarely surrounded by a thin thalloid one; spores 8, brownish to brown, ovoid-ellipsoid, 4–5-septate transversely and 1–2-septate longitudinally, 18–28 × 11–18 μ.

On rocks and rarely on soil, Connecticut, North Carolina, South Carolina, Florida, Kansas, Minnesota, Iowa, Washington, and California.

22. ECTOLECHIACEAE

Thallus crustose, showing little or no differentiation, attached to the substratum by hyphal rhizoids; apothecia round, immersed to superficial, the exciple usually wanting or poorly developed.

The algal host is Protococcus.

78. **Lopadiopsis** Vainio, Journ. Bot. 34:205. 1896.

Thallus crustose, thin, smooth to slightly rough, round to irregular, devoid of differentiation into layers and attached to the substratum by hyphal rhizoids; apothecia minute to small, round, immersed to adnate, the disk flat, the exciple colored like the thallus, somewhat prominent; hypothecium and hymenium hyaline; paraphyses unbranched, threadlike, free; asci ovoid-clavate; spores 1–2, hyaline, transversely and longitudinally septate.

The algal host is Protococcus.

1. **Lopadiopsis floridana** Zahlbr., Ann. Myc. 7:473, 474. 1909.

Thallus in minute to small, round to irregular areas, closely adnate, very thin, becoming rough toward the center, sometimes radiate toward the margin, pale greenish gray to silvery-white; apothecia minute, 0.18–0.24 mm. across, solitary or 2–3 in each thalloid area, immersed to adnate, the disk flat, brown, rarely whitish-pruinose, the exciple thin, entire, prominent, colored like the thallus; spores 1, hyaline, oblong-ellipsoid, 15–19-septate transversely and 2–5- or rarely 7-septate longitudinally, 50–70 × 18–28 μ.

On leaves, Florida.

The algal host was found to be Phyllactidium instead of the usual Protococcus.

23. GYALECTACEAE

Thallus crustose, with entire or lobed margins, devoid of differentiation into layers, attached to the substratum by hyphal rhizoids; apothecia round, immersed to superficial, single, the proper exciple usually well developed, sometimes covered by the thallus.

The algal hosts are Trentepohlia, Phyllactidium, and rarely Scytonema.

A. Spores 12–many in each ascus
  B. Spores 1-septate . . . . 82. RAMONIA
  B. Spores 3–several-septate . . . . 83. PACHYPHIALE
A. Spores 8 in each ascus
  B. Spores transversely septate
    C. Spores 1-septate . . . . 79. MICROPHIALE
    C. Spores 3–several-septate . . . . 81. SECOLIGA
  B. Spores transversely and longitudinally septate . . . . . . 80. GYALECTA

79. **Microphiale** Zahlbr., in E. & P., Nat. Pfl. 1:125. 1907.

Thallus crustose, very thin, smooth to scurfy, sometimes disappearing, partly within the substratum, rudimentary, rarely showing differentiation; apothecia minute to small, adnate to sessile, the disk more or less concave to flat, pale flesh-colored or yellowish orange or red, the exciple thick, colored like the disk, sometimes striate, often surrounded by a thin, soon disappearing, thalloid one; hypothecium hyaline; hymenium hyaline or brownish above; paraphyses unbranched; asci clavate to cylindrico-clavate; spores 8, hyaline, fusiform-ellipsoid, 1-septate.

The algal host is Trentepohlia.

A. Thallus greenish gray to ashy; apothecia pale yellow to yellowish orange   1. M. lutea
A. Thallus greenish to grayish white or lead-colored; apothecia
    pale flesh-colored to yellowish red . . . . 2. M. diluta

1. **Microphiale lutea** (Dicks.) Zahlbr., Sitzunb. Kais. Acad. Wiss. Math. Nat.
    Class. Wein. 111:392. 1902.
    Lichen luteus Dicks., Pl. Crypt. Brit. 1:11. pl. 2, f. 6. 1785. *Gyalecta lutea*
    (Dicks.) Horn.

Thallus thin, smooth to scurfy, greenish gray to ashy, sometimes disappearing; apothecia minute to small, 0.2–0.6 mm. across, sessile, the disk concave to flat, pale yellow to yellowish orange, the proper exciple lighter, becoming striate, bordered by a thin, disappearing, thalloid one; spores fusiform-ellipsoid, $8-12 \times 3-4.5 \mu$.

On trees, from New England to Florida, and westward to Nebraska and Minnesota.

2. **Microphiale diluta** (Pers.) Zahlbr., Ann. Naturhist. Hofmus. Wein. 19:413.
    1904.
    Peziza diluta Pers., Syn. Meth. Fung. 668. 1801. *Gyalecta Pineti* (Schrad.)
    Tuck.

Thallus very thin, smooth to scurfy, greenish to grayish white or lead-colored; apothecia minute, 0.15–0.45 mm. across, sessile, the disk deeply to slightly concave, pale flesh-colored to yellowish red, the proper exciple thick, colored like the disk; spores fusiform-ellipsoid, $10-13 \times 3-4.5 \mu$.

On trees, from New England to Florida, and westward to Illinois.

80. **Gyalecta** Ach., Lich. Univ. 30. pl. 1, f. 7–9. 1810. pr. p.

Thallus crustose, thin, smooth to chinky, granulose or powdery, sometimes disappearing, partly within the substratum, rudimentary, rarely showing differentiation; apothecia minute to small or rarely middle-sized, adnate to subsessile, the disk more or less concave, flesh-colored to reddish brown, the exciple colored like the disk, sometimes surrounded by an inconspicuous, soon disappearing, thalloid one; hypothecium hyaline; hymenium hyaline or rarely brownish above; paraphyses unbranched; asci cylindrico-clavate; spores 8, hyaline, ellipsoid to ovoid-ellipsoid, transversely and longitudinally septate, the cells cylindrical.

The algal host is Trentepohlia.

A. Thallus greenish gray to whitish; apothecia flesh-colored to red . . . 1. G. jenensis
A. Thallus grayish to whitish; apothecia flesh-colored . . . . 2. G. Flotowii

1. **Gyalecta jenensis** (Batsch.) Zahlbr., Cat. Lich. Univ. 2:720–724. 1924.
    Peziza jenensis Batsch., Elench. Fung. 219. f. 153. 1786. *Secoliga cupularis*
    (Hedw.) Norm. *G. cupularis* (Hedw.) Schaer.

Thallus very thin, smooth to scurfy, greenish gray to whitish; apothecia minute to small, 0.25–0.5 mm. across, adnate to subsessile, the disk concave, flesh-colored to brick-red, very small or finally larger, the proper exciple thick, whitish, becoming radiately striate, the thalloid one evanescent and seldom seen; spores ellipsoid, 3–5-septate transversely and 1-septate longitudinally, 15–19 × 6–9 μ.

On rocks, from Vermont to Alabama, and westward to Minnesota.

2. **Gyalecta Flotowii** Koerb., Syst. Lich. Germ. 171. pl. 3, f. 9 *a, b.* 1855.

Thallus thin, smooth to slightly chinky and scurfy, grayish to whitish, often disappearing; apothecia minute, 0.15–0.3 mm. across, adnate, the disk concave, pale flesh-colored, the proper exciple thick, whitish, becoming crenulate, covered by a thin, evanescent, thalloid one; spores ellipsoid to ovoid-ellipsoid, 3–9-septate transversely and 1–2-septate longitudinally, 12–15 × 7–9 μ.

On trees, near Amherst, Massachusetts.

OTHER SPECIES REPORTED

Gyalecta radiatilis Tuck.—Massachusetts and Rhode Island.

81. **Secoliga** Norm., Nyt Mag. Naturv. 1:230. pl. 1, f. 9 *b,* 10 *c, d*;
pl. 2, f. 24 *a.* 1853. pr. p.

Thallus crustose, thin, smooth to chinky, granulose or powdery, sometimes disappearing, partly within the substratum, rudimentary, rarely showing differentiation; apothecia minute, slightly immersed to adnate or sessile, the disk deeply concave to flat, flesh-colored to yellowish brown, the exciple thin, colored like the disk or lighter; hypothecium hyaline; hymenium hyaline or brownish above; paraphyses unbranched; asci cylindrico-clavate; spores 8, hyaline, oblong to ellipsoid, 3- or more-septate, the cells cylindrical.

The algal host is Trentepohlia.

A. On trees; apothecia flat, yellowish flesh-colored　.　.　.　.　.　2. S. carneoluteola
A. On soil and rocks; apothecia deeply concave, yellowish brown　.　.　.　1. S. geoica

1. **Secoliga geoica** (Wahl.) Koerb., Par. Lich. 111, 112. 1865.

Lichen geoicus Wahl., Vet. Akad. Handl. 142. pl. 4, f. 5. 1806. *Gyalecta geoica*
(Wahl.) Ach. *Gyalecta geoica* f. *trivialis* Willey.

Thallus thin, somewhat powdery, pale greenish gray to yellowish or whitish ashy, often disappearing; apothecia minute, 0.1–0.25 mm. across, immersed to adnate, the disk deeply concave, yellowish brown, the proper exciple thin, pale, becoming obscurely radiately striate; spores oblong to ellipsoid, 3-septate, 12–22 × 6–8 μ.

On soil and rocks, Massachusetts and Illinois.

2. **Secoliga carneoluteola** (Tuck.) Müll. Arg.; Engler, Bot. Jahr. 20:277. 1894.

Gyalecta carneoluteola Tuck., Proc. Am. Acad. 6:271. 1866.

Thallus very thin, scurfy to ashy gray; apothecia minute, 0.1–0.25 mm. across, adnate, flattened, the disk flat, yellowish flesh-colored, the proper exciple thin, lighter than the disk; spores 6–8, fusiform-ellipsoid, 3- or rarely 1-septate, 10–15 × 4–5.5 μ.

On trees, Florida. The material is doubtfully referred to this species.

82. **Ramonia** Stizenb., Ber. St. Gall. Nat. Gesell. 168. 1862.

Thallus crustose, granulose, rudimentary, showing little or no differentiation into layers, attached to the substratum by hyphal rhizoids; apothecia minute to small, immersed to adnate or sessile, the disk concave to flat, the exciple colored like the disk or whitish pruinose, striate, rather thick, surrounded by a thin thalloid one; hypothecium hyaline; hymenium hyaline or brownish above; paraphyses unbranched, spongy; asci clavate; spores 12–many, hyaline, ellipsoid or boat-shaped, 1-septate.

The algal host is Trentepohlia.

1. **Ramonia Valenzueliana** (Mont.) Stizenb., Ber. St. Gall. Nat. Gesell. 168. 1862.

Parmelia Valenzueliana Mont., in Sagra, Hist. Nat. Cub. 205. 1840. *Gyalecta Valenzueliana* (Mont.) Tuck. *R. Valenzueliana* f. *absconsa* (Tuck.) Zahlbr. *Gyalecta Valenzueliana* f. *absconsa* Tuck.

Thallus thin, chinky or densely granulose, greenish gray; apothecia minute, 0.15–0.3 mm. across, subsessile, the disk deeply concave to flat, blackish brown, the proper exciple flesh-colored to blackish, nearly closing over the disk but finally opening, radiately striate, covered laterally by a thalloid one; spores 12–30, ellipsoid, $12–16 \times 6–8 \mu$.

On trees, Florida.

83. **Pachyphiale** Lönnr., Flora 41:611, 612. 1858.

Thallus crustose, chinky, scurfy, or powdery, showing little or no differentiation into layers, attached to the substratum by hyphal rhizoids; apothecia minute to small, adnate to sessile, closed to open, the disk concave to more or less flat, the exciple colored like the disk, thin, sometimes surrounded by a thin, soon disappearing, thalloid one; hypothecium hyaline; hymenium hyaline or brownish above; paraphyses unbranched, spongy; asci clavate; spores 12–many, hyaline, fusiform to needle-shaped, 3–13-septate, the cells cylindrical.

The algal host is Trentepohlia.

1. **Pachyphiale fagicola** (Hepp) Zwackh., Flora 45:506. 1862.

Bacidia fagicola Hepp; Arn., Flora 41:504. 1858. *Secoliga fagicola* (Hepp) Koerb. *Gyalecta fagicola* (Hepp) Kremphl. *Gyalecta corticola* (Lönnr.) Tuck. *Gyalecta ceratina* Tuck. *Lecidea congruella* Nyl.

Thallus very thin, chinky or scurfy to powdery, pale greenish to brownish, sometimes disappearing; apothecia minute to small, 0.15–0.4 mm. across, subsessile, the disk concave, reddish flesh-colored to dark reddish and blackening, the proper exciple commonly of the same color, the thalloid one absent or disappearing; spores 12–20, 3–9-septate, $15–34 \times 3–6 \mu$.

On trees, Massachusetts and Minnesota.

24. COENOGONIACEAE

Thallus of septate branching hyphae forming a network about the filaments of the algal host, sometimes giving the appearance of a small, prostrate or upright, branched thallus; apothecia round, lateral or terminal, the proper exciple well developed.

The algal hosts are Trentepohlia or Cladophora.

A. Apothecia unknown . . . . 85. Racodium
A. Apothecia frequent . . . . 84. Coenogonium

84. **Coenogonium** Ehrh., in Nees, Hor. Phys. Berol. 120. 1820.

Thallus of elongated, many-celled, branched, hyaline hyphae, forming a more or less well-developed network over the surface of the monopodially branched algal host; apothecia biatoroid, pale within, usually subsessile but infrequently shortly stipitate, the exciple and the hypothecium plectenchymatous; paraphyses hyaline, unbranched, distinct and somewhat loosely arranged; asci clavate or more commonly varying toward cylindrical forms; spores 8, hyaline, ellipsoid, non- or 1-septate, usually more or less plainly uniseriately arranged.

The algal host is Trentepohlia.

A. Apothecia sessile or subsessile; spores scarcely more
  than 10 μ in length
  B. Algal host irregularly arranged; apothecia flesh-colored
    to yellow or reddish brown
    C. Apothecia reaching 0.8 mm. across, flesh-colored
      to yellow . . . .   3. C. interpositum
    C. Apothecia not more than 0.5 mm. across,
      flesh-colored to reddish or brownish . . . .   4. C. moniliforme
  B. Algal host commonly circularly arranged; apothecia
    pale yellowish to reddish . . . .   1. C. Linkii
A. Apothecia shortly stipitate; spores reaching 15 μ in length . . . .   2. C. disjunctum

1. **Coenogonium Linkii** Ehrh., in Nees, Hor. Phys. Berol. 120. pl. 27. 1820.
  C. Linkii var. *Leprieurii* Mont.

Hyphae 2–2.5 μ wide, the walls rather thick, variously disposed and forming
a loose network over the greenish gray, circularly or irregularly spreading algal
host; apothecia minute to small, 0.25–0.6 mm. across, subsessile, the disk flat
to slightly convex, pale yellowish to reddish, the exciple whitish; asci cylindrico-
clavate; spores becoming 1-septate, ellipsoid, 6–8 × 2–2.5 μ, usually obliquely uniseriate.

On trees, Florida.

2. **Coenogonium disjunctum** Nyl., Ann. Sci. Nat. Bot. IV. 16:91. 1861.

Hyphae about 1.5–2 μ wide, rather thick-walled, extending irregularly and
forming a loose network over the greenish gray, irregularly or circularly spreading
algal host; apothecia small, 0.3–0.6 mm. across, shortly stipitate, the exciple
whitish; asci cylindrico-clavate; spores ellipsoid, 1-septate, 10–15 × 2.5–3.5 μ, obliquely uniseriate or irregular.

On trees, Alabama.

3. **Coenogonium interpositum** Nyl., Ann. Sci. Nat. Bot. IV. 16:91. 1861.

Hyphae 2–2.5 μ wide, rather thick-walled, extending irregularly and forming
a loose network over the greenish gray, irregularly spreading algal host; apothecia
small, 0.3–0.8 mm. across, subsessile, the disk flesh-colored to yellow, the exciple
whitish; asci cylindrico-clavate; spores 1-septate, 7–10 × 2.5–3.5 μ, obliquely uniseriate or irregular.

On trees, from West Virginia to Florida, and westward to Texas.

4. **Coenogonium moniliforme** Tuck., Syn. N. A. Lich. 1:258. 1882.

Hyphae 2–2.5 μ wide, variously disposed in a network over the moniliform
cells of the algal host, forming a finely arachnoid, subareolate, yellowish to greenish
gray or olive-green crust; apothecia minute to small, 0.2–0.4 mm. across, sessile,
the disk flat to slightly convex, flesh-colored to reddish or brownish, the exciple
whitish; asci clavate; spores ellipsoid, 1-septate, 8–11 × 3–4 μ, irregularly arranged.

On trees, Florida.

85. Racodium Pers., Tent. Disp. Meth. Fung. 76. 1797.

Thallus of unbranched, dark-colored, septate hyphae, extending parallel in
longitudinal direction over the surface of the pale algal host, covering the latter
as a cylindrical sheath; apothecia unknown.

The algal host is Cladophora, and the filaments which support the lichen ascend
from the rocks and wood on which it grows.

1. **Racodium rupestre** Pers., Tent. Disp. Meth. Fung. 76. 1797.

Hyphae extending roughly longitudinally and parallel, 4–6 side by side, as a
dark brown to blackish layer, forming a complete or nearly complete cylindrical
sheath; apothecia unknown.

On shaded rocks, New Hampshire, Rhode Island, Pennsylvania, and North
Carolina.

25. EPHEBACEAE

Thallus of entangled hyphae, surrounding and ramifying through the filà-ments of the algal host, giving the appearance of a crustose to foliose or rarely fruticose thallus; apothecia minute, superficial or immersed in the swellings of the algal host.
The algal hosts are Scytonema and Stigonema.

A. Apothecia adnate to sessile
   B. Thallus appearing crustose to granulose . . . . ∴ 92. Porocyphus
   B. Thallus appearing dwarfish fruticose
      C. Spores many in an ascus . . . . 87. Zahlbrucknerella
      C. Spores 8 in an ascus
         D. Thallus devoid of differentiation into layers
            E. Paraphyses thickened; spores becoming 1-septate . . 88. Spilonema
            E. Paraphyses threadlike; spores non-septate . . . 86. Thermutis
         D. Thallus showing more or less differentiation
           into layers
            E. Spores 1-septate . . . . 91. Polychidium
            E. Spores non-septate . . . . 90. Leptogidium
A. Apothecia immersed . . . . 89. Ephebe

86. **Thermutis** E. Fries, Syst. Orb. Veg. 1:302. 1825.

Thallus of many, thin-walled, septate hyphae, extending longitudinally within the sheath of the host, appearing as many, densely crowded and matted, thread-like branches, devoid of differentiation into layers; apothecia small, adnate to sessile, the disk concave to flat, the exciple colored like the disk; hypothecium hyaline; hymenium hyaline or brownish above; paraphyses unbranched, threadlike; asci oblong-clavate; spores 8, hyaline, oblong to ellipsoid, non-septate.
The algal host is Scytonema.

1. **Thermutis velutina** (Ach.) E. Fries, Syst. Orb. Veg. 1:302. 1825.
Lichen velutinus Ach., Lich. Suec. 218. 1798.
Thallus dark brown, composed of many, slender, wrinkled, densely crowded and matted, threadlike branches; apothecia small, 0.4–0.8 mm. across, lateral, sessile, the disk slightly concave, black, the exciple thick, black, entire, swollen; spores ellipsoid, 10–12 × 5–6.5 µ.
On rocks, Minnesota.

87. **Zahlbrucknerella** Herre, Journ. Wash. Acad. Sci. 2:384. ·1912.

Thallus of many, thin-walled, septate hyphae, extending longitudinally within the sheath of the host, appearing as many, crowded and matted, short branches; apothecia small, closely adnate to sessile, the disk concave to flat, the exciple colored like the disk; hypothecium hyaline; hymenium hyaline or brownish above; paraphyses threadlike, rarely branched; asci oblong-clavate; spores 8–24, hyaline to brownish, spherical to ellipsoid, non-septate.
The algal host is Scytonema.

1. **Zahlbrucknerella calcarea** Herre, Journ. Wash. Acad. Sci. 2:384. 1912.
Zahlbrucknera calcarea Herre, Proc. Wash. Acad. Sci. 12:129. 1910.
Thallus as of the genus, appearing as many, crowded and matted, black or blackish brown branches; apothecia rare, minute, the disk concave, blackish brown to black, the exciple usually entire; spores 8–24, usually 18, hyaline to brownish or blackish, ovoid to ellipsoid, or rarely globose, 7.5–12.5 × 4.9–8.5 µ.
On rocks, California. (Description compiled.)

88. **Spilonema** Born., Mém. Soc. Sci. Nat. Cherb. 4:226. 1856.

Thallus of many, thin-walled, septate hyphae, extending longitudinally and often laterally within the sheath of the host, appearing as many suberect, more or less irregular, entangled branches, devoid of differentiation into layers; apothecia small, terminal, the disk flat to convex, the exciple thin, colored like the disk, soon disappearing; hypothecium brown to blackish brown; hymenium hyaline or brownish above; paraphyses thick, unbranched, jointed, enlarged and brownish toward the apices; asci oblong-clavate; spores 8, hyaline, oblong-ellipsoid to ellipsoid, non-septate or rarely 1-septate.

The algal host is Stigonema.

1. **Spilonema paradoxum** Born., Mém. Soc. Sci. Nat. Cherb. 4:226. pl. 1, 2. 1856.

Thallus minute to small, suberect, irregularly branched, blackish brown to black, the branches short, cylindrical, entangled, often much wrinkled; apothecia small, 0.4–0.5 mm. across, terminal, the disk convex, black; hypothecium blackish brown; spores oblong-ellipsoid, non-septate, 8–9.5 × 3.5–4 μ.

On rocks, Massachusetts.

89. **Ephebe** E. Fries, Syst. Orb. Veg. 1:256. 1825.

Thallus of few to many, thin-walled, many-celled, hyaline hyphae, extending longitudinally and less often laterally immediately within the sheath of the host, or sometimes in older conditions forming also in part a central axis of longitudinally extending hyphae, sometimes protruding through the hostal sheath, usually at raised places, in dense clusters, hyphae of older portions of the thallus sometimes becoming densely intertwined and forming a true plectenchyma toward the base of the hostal filaments; apothecia and spermagonia sometimes arising from the enlargements, apothecia minute, immersed in the host, often several in a group, and becoming semisuperficial and globose-discoid; hypothecium hyaline; paraphyses present or absent; asci short-clavate to cylindrico-clavate; spores 8, hyaline, non-septate or finally and obscurely 1-septate.

The algal host is Stigonema, plainly not the same species for all species of Ephebe. The detection of the mainly endoparasitic lichen requires careful microscopic study, and fruits are seldom seen.

A. Algal host rather small, uniformly and stoutly branched . . . . . 1. E. solida
A. Algal host longer, loosely and dichotomously branched . . . . . 2. E. lanata

1. **Ephebe solida** Born., Ann. Acad. Sci. Nat. III. 18:171. 1852.
E. Lesquereauxii Born.

Thallus that of the genus; apothecia minute, 0.09–0.2 mm. across, immersed laterally or terminally in the host; paraphyses distinct to coherent-indistinct, their apices somewhat thickened; asci cylindrico-clavate; spores oblong, often slightly curved, non-septate, 10–16 × 4–5 μ.

Occurs from New England to Georgia and Alabama, growing within black clusters of a smallish, rather uniformly and stoutly branched Stigonema, usually on exposed but frequently wet rocks. The form called *E. Lesquereauxii* grows on a much larger, less loosely branched Stigonema, and its fruit is unknown.

2. **Ephebe lanata** (L.) Vainio, Med. Soc. Faun. Flor. Fenn. 14:20. 1888.
Lichen lanatus L., Sp. Pl. 1155. 1753 pro parte. *E. pubescens* (Ach.) E. Fries.

Thallus that of the genus; apothecia minute, 0.1–0.25 mm. across, immersed several together, usually in swellings of the host, the disk punctiform; paraphyses absent; asci clavate; spores oblong, becoming 1-septate, 11–16 × 3–4 μ. (PLATES 5 and 6 a.)

Distributed throughout northern United States, mostly in mountainous regions. Also reported from Alabama. Growing within a rather long, loosely, dichotomously much-branched, brownish black Stigonema, which occurs in rather large clusters in moist, shady places.

OTHER SPECIES REPORTED

Ephebe mammillosum (Lyngb.) E. Fries—Massachusetts.

90. **Leptogidium** Nyl., Flora 56:195. 1873.

Transforming the algal colony into a minute to small, slender, densely branched body, the branches showing a thin cortex of many, thin-walled, septate, longitudinally extending hyphae, and a poorly developed, central cylinder of more or less septate, longitudinally extending medullary hyphae, surrounded by the algal layer; apothecia minute to small, terminal, adnate to sessile, the disk flat to convex, the exciple colored like the thallus or lighter; hypothecium hyaline; hymenium hyaline or brownish above; paraphyses more or less coherent, unbranched, septate; asci clavate; spores 8, hyaline, oblong-ellipsoid to fusiform, non-septate. The algal host is Scytonema.

1. **Leptogidium dendriscum** Nyl., Flora 56:195. 1873.
   Leptogium dendriscum Nyl., Syn. Lich. 1:135. 1858. *L. byssoides* (Carr.) Zahlbr.
   Transforming the algal colony into a minute, slender, dichotomously much-branched, pale green body, the branches very slender, cylindrical or obscurely flattened and interwoven; apothecia minute, 0.25–0.35 mm. across, adnate, the disk flat to slightly convex, pale to brownish red, the proper exciple thin, lighter colored than the disk; spores ellipsoid, 10–16 × 6–8 μ.
   On trees, Florida.

91. **Polychidium** Mass., Mem. Lich. 88. 1853.

Transforming the algal colony into a small to middle-sized, irregularly lobed, smooth to rough, rarely ciliate body, plectenchymatous throughout or showing plectenchymatous upper and lower cortices with indistinct algal and medullary layers; apothecia minute to small or middle-sized, scattered or terminal, adnate to sessile, the disk flat to more or less convex, the exciple thin, colored like the disk or lighter, often disappearing; hypothecium hyaline to yellowish; hymenium hyaline; paraphyses unbranched; asci clavate; spores 8, hyaline, oblong-ellipsoid to ellipsoid or fusiform, 1-septate. The algal host is Scytonema.

A. Thalloid body small, not bearing marginal cilia
  B. Thalloid body irregularly much-branched, greenish brown
     to olive-black . . . . 1. P. muscicola
  B. Thalloid body minutely lobed, greenish to lead-colored . . . . 2. P. rivale
A. Thalloid body rather large, bearing minute whitish
   marginal cilia . . . . 3. P. albociliatum

1. **Polychidium muscicola** (Swartz) S. F. Gray, Nat. Arr. Brit. Pl. 1:402. 1821.
   Lichen muscicola Swartz, Nov. Act. Acad. Upsal. 4:248. 1784. *Leptogium muscicola* (Swartz) E. Fries.
   Transforming the algal colony into a small, irregularly much-branched, greenish brown to olive-green body, the branches densely interwoven and more or less longitudinally striate; apothecia small to middle-sized, 0.3–0.8 mm. across, adnate to sessile, round to irregular, the disk flat to slightly convex, reddish brown, the proper exciple thin, lighter than the disk, rarely disappearing; spores oblong-ellipsoid to ellipsoid, 18–28 × 5–8 μ.
   On soil and mossy rocks, New Hampshire, Vermont, Alabama, California, Idaho, and Washington.

2. **Polychidium rivale** (Tuck.) Fink n. comb.
   Leptogium rivale Tuck., Proc. Am. Acad. 12:170, 171. 1877.
   Transforming the algal colony into a minutely and tufted-lobed, greenish to lead-colored body, the lobes crowded, imbricated, narrow, and flexuous; apothecia minute, 0.15–0.25 mm. across, immersed and indicated by an ostiole; hypothecium hyaline; spores oblong-ellipsoid, 16–23 × 5–8 μ.
   On pebbles, in a brook, California, growing with and on Hydrothyria.

3. **Polychidium albociliatum** (Desm.) Zahlbr., in E. & P., Nat. Pfl. 1:157. 1907.
Leptogium albociliatum Desm., Ann. Sci. Nat. Bot. IV. 4:132. 1855.

Transforming the algal colony into a middle-sized, irregularly lobed, greenish to blackish brown body, the lobes cut, crisped and crenate, bearing minute whitish marginal cilia, sometimes minutely granulose toward the center; lighter below with a more or less fleecy nap; apothecia small to middle-sized, 0.5–1.2 mm. across, sessile, scattered, the disk reddish brown, flat to convex, the proper exciple thin, scarcely lighter than the disk, soon disappearing; spores oblong-ellipsoid to ellipsoid, 18–26 × 6–9 μ.

On moss, Florida, California, and Oregon.

92. **Porocyphus** Koerb., Syst. Lich. 425, 426. 1855.

Thallus crustose, granulose or minutely branched, rudimentary, devoid of differentiation into layers; apothecia minute to small, immersed to adnate or sessile, the disk closed to open, concave, the exciple colored like the disk, indistinct, surrounded by a thicker, more or less irregular, thalloid one; hypothecium and hymenium hyaline; paraphyses threadlike, unbranched and free; asci cylindrico-clavate; spores 8, hyaline, ellipsoid to ovoid-ellipsoid, non-septate.

The algal host is Scytonema.

1. **Porocyphus furfurellus** (Nyl.) Forss., Nov. Act. Reg. Soc. Sci. Ups. III. 13:87. 1885.
Collema furfurellum Nyl., Not. Sällsk. Faun. Flor. Fenn. 1:229. 1858. *Pyrenopsis corallina* Willey.

Thallus thin, subareolate, composed of dark olive to brownish black, branched, coralloid granules; apothecia minute, 0.15–0.3 mm. across, sessile, the disk concave, brownish black, the exciple thick, colored like the thallus, finally crenulate; spores ellipsoid, 12–20 × 6–10 μ, uniseriately to irregularly arranged.

On rocks, Vermont, New Hampshire, Massachusetts, and Colorado.

26. PYRENOPSIDACEAE

Thallus crustose, foliose or fruticose, showing little or no differentiation into layers, attached to the substratum by hyphal rhizoids, rhizoids, or an umbilicus; apothecia commonly superficial, rarely somewhat immersed, with a proper or thalloid exciple.

The algal hosts are Gloeocapsa, Chroococcus, and Xanthocapsa.

A. Thallus crustose to squamulose
  B. Apothecia with proper and thalloid exciples . . . . . . 95. Psorotichia
  B. Apothecia with thalloid exciple
    C. Spores 8 in an ascus . . . . 93. Pyrenopsis
    C. Spores many in an ascus . . . . 96. Forssellia
A. Thallus foliose to fruticose
  B. Thallus attached to the substratum only at the center . . . . 97. Thyrea
  B. Thallus not attached to the substratum only at
    the center
    C. Thallus more or less branched; apothecia small to
      middle-sized . . . . 98. Peccania
    C. Thallus much branched; apothecia minute to small . . . 94. Synalissa

93. **Pyrenopsis** Nyl., Mém. Soc. Sci. Nat. Cherb. 5:143. 1857.

Thallus crustose, granulose, minutely warty, or with minute coralloid branches, devoid of differentiation into layers, attached to the substratum by hyphal rhizoids; apothecia minute to small, immersed to adnate, the disk more or less closed to open, concave to flat or convex, the exciple colored like the thallus; hypothecium hyaline to brownish; hymenium hyaline or brownish above; paraphyses more or less distinct, unbranched; asci clavate to cylindrico-clavate; spores commonly

8, hyaline, ellipsoid or somewhat spherical, non-septate to rarely becoming 1-septate.

The algal host is Gloeocapsa.

A. Spores rarely less than 14 μ in length
  B. On rocks; spores not more than 20 μ in length
    C. Apothecia 1–3 in each areole
      D. Thallus of coralloid granules, finally crowded
        into an areolate crust . . . . 8. P. phaeococca
      D. Thallus of minute granules, finally crowded
        into an irregular crust . . . . 3. P. phylliscina
    C. Apothecia 1 in each areole
      D. Thallus pale bluish to sage-green . . . . 5. P. viridirufa
      D. Thallus brownish black . . . . 6. P. fuscoatra
  B. On soil; spores 22–30 μ in length . . . . 4. P. compacta
A. Spores not more than 14 μ in length
  B. Spores more than 8 μ in length
    C. Thallus minutely granulose
      D. Apothecia very numerous . . . . 1. P. polycocca
      D. Apothecia 1 or more in an areole
        E. Granules crowded into a subareolate crust . . . 2. P. subfuliginea
        E. Granules compacted into substipitate areoles . . . 9. P. melambola
    C. Thallus minutely squamulose . . . . 10. P. haemaleella
  B. Spores 7–8 μ in length . . . . 7. P. lecideella

1. **Pyrenopsis polycocca** (Nyl.) Tuck., Syn. N. A. Lich. 1:136. 1882.
Synalissa polycocca Nyl., Syn. Meth. Lich. 1:96. 1858.
Thallus granulose, blackish, the granules minute, round, soon passing into a thin, broken, blackish to black crust; apothecia minute to small, 0.2–0.4 mm. across, globose, closely adnate, very numerous and sometimes nearly covering the thallus, the disk deeply concave and nearly closed, the thalloid exciple blackish or black; asci cylindrico-clavate; spores ellipsoid, 10–14 × 6–8 μ, uniseriately to irregularly arranged.
On rocks, Vermont, Massachusetts, and Minnesota.

2. **Pyrenopsis subfuliginea** Nyl., Flora 50:369. 1867.
Thallus minutely granulose, the granules convex, crowded into a thin, blackish, subareolate crust; apothecia minute, 0.15–0.3 mm. across, partly immersed, 1 or more in an areole, the disk concave to almost flat, the thalloid exciple thin, black; spores ovoid-ellipsoid, 9–14 × 6–9 μ, irregularly arranged.
On soil and rocks, Massachusetts.

3. **Pyrenopsis phylliscina** Tuck., Syn. N. A. Lich. 1:137. 1882.
Synalissa phylliscina Tuck., Gen. Lich. 80. 1872.
Thallus thin, composed of minute, brownish black granules, the granules finally crowded into an irregular crust; apothecia minute, 0.2–0.3 mm. across, partly immersed to adnate, 1–3 in each areole, the disk black, almost covered by a brownish black, thalloid exciple; paraphyses few and short; asci clavate-fusiform; spores ovoid-ellipsoid, rarely becoming 1-septate, 9–18 × 5–8 μ.
On granite rocks, near New Bedford, Massachusetts.

4. **Pyrenopsis compacta** Willey, in Nyl., Lich. Jap. 102. 1890.
Thallus thin, minutely granulose, the granules brownish black, flat to convex, forming an irregular, continuous, or more or less broken crust; apothecia minute to small, 0.25–0.4 mm. across, partly immersed, the disk finally convex, black, the exciple thin, black, soon disappearing; asci cylindrico-clavate; spores ellipsoid, 22–30 × 10–14 μ, biseriately to irregularly arranged.
On soil, Massachusetts and Illinois.

5. **Pyrenopsis viridirufa** Tuck., Syn. N. A. Lich. 1:137, 138. 1882.
Synalissa viridirufa Tuck., Proc. Am. Acad. 12:170. 1877.
Thallus granulose, pale bluish to sage-green, the granules small, round, becoming grouped into areole-like clusters and finally crowded into a thin chinky crust;

apothecia minute to small, 0.3–0.4 mm. across, more or less immersed, the disk flat to slightly convex, reddish brown to brown, the thalloid exciple lighter; spores ellipsoid, 16–18 × 8–10 μ.

On calcareous rocks, Kansas and Texas.

6. **Pyrenopsis fuscoatra** Fink, Proc. Ind. Acad. Sci. 267. 1918.

Thallus granulose, the granules minute, brownish black, flat or convex, usually scattered or forming a thin, irregularly broken crust; apothecia minute, 0.2–0.3 mm. across, partly immersed to closely adnate, finally more or less open, the disk concave to almost flat, brownish black, the thalloid exciple thin, black; spores oblong-ellipsoid, 13–20 × 7–10 μ, irregularly arranged.

On limestone, Indiana.

7. **Pyrenopsis lecideella** Fink; Hedrick, Mycologia 25:314. 1933.

Thallus minutely granulose, forming a thin, uneven, grayish to black, more or less continuous crust; apothecia very minute to minute, 0.1–0.2 mm. across, numerous, partly immersed to adnate, round, the disk slightly concave to flat and convex, black, the thalloid exciple thin, entire, black, soon disappearing; spores oblong-ovoid and flat on one side, 7–8 × 4–4.5 μ, irregularly arranged.

On limestone, near Oxford, Ohio.

8. **Pyrenopsis phaeococca** Tuck., Syn. N. A. Lich. 1:136, 137. 1882.

Synalissa phaeococca Tuck., Gen. Lich. 80. 1872. *Psorotichia phaeococca* (Tuck.) Hasse. *P. subareolata* Nyl.

Thallus composed of reddish brown to blackish, coralloid granules, the granules finally crowded into a thin or moderately thick, areolate crust; apothecia minute to small, 0.2–0.5 mm. across, immersed to adnate, 1–3 in each areole, the disk concave, brownish black to black, the thalloid exciple thin, black; spores ovoid-ellipsoid, rarely becoming 1-septate, 12–20 × 7–10 μ, irregularly arranged.

On rocks, from Vermont to South Carolina, westward to Illinois and Minnesota, and reappearing in California.

9. **Pyrenopsis melambola** Tuck., Syn. N. A. Lich. 1:136. 1882.

Synalissa melambola Tuck., Proc. Am. Acad. 12:170. 1877.

Thallus composed of minute, greenish black granules, compacted into thick and substipitate, rough, black areoles, forming a close crust; apothecia minute to small, 0.15–0.4 mm. across, immersed 1–6 in each areole, the disk concave, black, the thalloid exciple thin, black; spores ellipsoid, 8–12 × 5–8 μ, irregularly arranged.

On rocks, Alabama, Missouri, Minnesota, and California.

10. **Pyrenopsis haemaleella** (Nyl.) Blomb. et Forss., Enum. Pl. Scand. 110. 1880.

Euopsis haemaleella Nyl., Flora 60:457. 1877.

Thallus composed of minute, reddish brown to blackish squamules, finally crowded into a thin, rough, subareolate crust; apothecia minute to small, 0.2–0.5 mm. across, closely adnate, numerous and often crowded, the disk concave, reddish brown to black, the thalloid exciple thin, black; spores blunt-ellipsoid, rarely becoming 1-septate, 9–11 × 6–7 μ.

On rocks, Massachusetts.

94. **Synalissa** E. Fries, Syst. Orb. Veg. 1:297. 1825.

Thallus fruticose, erect, much branched, the branches cylindrical to club-shaped, clustered, nodular, devoid of differentiation into layers, attached to the substratum by rhizoids; apothecia minute to small, terminal, the disk closed to open and concave to convex, the exciple thick, colored like the thallus; hypothecium hyaline to brownish; hymenium hyaline and brownish above; paraphyses unbranched, slender; asci clavate; spores 8–32, hyaline, ellipsoid to spherical, non-septate.

The algal host is Gloeocapsa, growing in clusters in the upper portion of the thallus.

1. **Synalissa symphorea** (Ach.) Nyl., Act. Soc. Linn. Bord. 21:264. 1856.
Lichen symphoreus Ach., Lich. Suec. Prod. 135. 1798. *Omphalaria symphorea* (Ach.) Tuck. *S. sphaerospora* Nyl.
Thallus minute to small, dull black, parallel to becoming dichotomously branched, the branches short, round, obtuse, often densely clustered, becoming nodular; apothecia minute to small, 0.08–0.2 mm. across, terminal, partly immersed, the disk concave to flat or slightly convex, black, the exciple thick, colored like the thallus; spores 16–24, ellipsoid to spherical, 9–12 × 6–9 μ.
On calcareous rock, Alabama.

OTHER SPECIES REPORTED
Synalissa texana Tuck.—Texas.

95. Psorotichia Mass., Fram. Lich. 15. 1855.

Thallus crustose, granulose, becoming squamulose, devoid of differentiation into layers, attached to the substratum by hyphal rhizoids; apothecia minute to small or rarely middle-sized, immersed to adnate, the disk closed to open and concave to convex, the exciple thin, colored like the disk, often disappearing, commonly surrounded by a thicker thalloid one; hypothecium hyaline to yellowish brown; hymenium hyaline and brownish above; paraphyses unbranched, more or less coherent; asci clavate to cylindrico-clavate; spores 8–32, hyaline, oblong to ellipsoid or spherical, non-septate.
The algal host is Xanthocapsa.

A. Spores 8 in each ascus
   B. Apothecia minute, not more than 0.25 mm. across   . . . .   2. P. segregata
   B. Apothecia minute to small or larger, rarely less than 0.25 mm. across
      C. Thallus minutely granulose, olive-brown to blackish   . . . .   4. P. Hassei
      C. Thallus coarsely granulose, areolate-chinky, black   . . . .   1. P. Schaereri
A. Spores 16 in an ascus   . . . .   3. P. squamulosa

1. **Psorotichia Schaereri** (Mass.) Arn., Flora 52:265. 1869.
Pannaria Schaereri Mass., Ric. Lich. 114. f. 225. 1852. *Pyrenopsis Schaereri* (Mass.) Nyl. *Synalissa Schaereri* (Mass.) Tuck.
Thallus composed of minute granules, crowded into a thin, black, irregular, areolate-chinky, coarsely granulose to coralloid crust; apothecia small to middle-sized, 0.4–0.8 mm. across, sessile, very numerous and often crowded, the disk flat, brownish black to black, the exciple thin, black, becoming crenulate; hypothecium yellowish brown; spores 8, oblong-ellipsoid, 12–20 × 7–10 μ, uniseriately to irregularly arranged.
On rocks, New York, New Jersey, Alabama, Illinois, and California.

2. **Psorotichia segregata** (Nyl.) Hasse, Cont. U. S. Nat. Herb. 17:68, 69. 1913.
Collemopsis segregata Nyl., in Hasse, Lich. South. Calif. ed. 2. 6. 1898.
Thallus composed of small, thin, smooth to rough, irregular, greenish black to blackish nodules, sometimes forming a crust; apothecia minute, 0.15–0.25 mm. across, slightly immersed to adnate, numerous, nearly covering the thallus, the disk deeply concave to flat or slightly convex, dull reddish, the exciple colored like the thallus, finally disappearing; hypothecium yellowish brown; spores 8, oblong-ellipsoid, 16–19 × 9–10 μ, irregularly arranged.
On soil, Santa Monica Range, California.

3. **Psorotichia squamulosa** Zahlbr., Beih. Bot. Centralb. 13:158. 1902.
Thallus composed of small, tough, dark olive-green to dull black, broadly lobed squamules, sometimes forming a cushion-like mass; apothecia minute, 0.15–0.2 mm. across, immersed, the disk concave, brown, the exciple inconspicuous or absent; hypothecium brownish yellow; asci long-cylindrical; spores 16, ellipsoid, 9–13 × 5–6 μ, irregularly arranged.

On disintegrating granite, southern California.
The algal host as seen in material examined appears in groups as Gloeocapsa.

4. **Psorotichia Hassei** Fink; Hedrick, Mycologia 25:315. 1933.
Thallus composed of a thin, irregular, minutely granulose, olive-brown to blackish crust; apothecia minute to small, 0.15–0.6 mm. across, adnate, the disk concave to slightly convex, reddish brown, the proper exciple thin and often indistinct; hypothecium hyaline or tinged with yellowish brown; spores 8, oblong to ovoid-ellipsoid, 16–24 × 9–12 μ, irregularly arranged.
On soft, disintegrating sandstone among mosses, San Jacinto Mountains, California.

　　96. **Forssellia** Zahlbr., in E. & P., Nat. Pfl. 1:161. 1907.

Transforming the algal colony into a minute to small, irregular, minutely granulose, black body, devoid of differentiation into layers, near the edges appearing to be plectenchymatous, attached to the substratum by hyphal rhizoids; apothecia minute to small, immersed in wartlike elevations, the disk closed to more or less open, the exciple colored like the thallus; hypothecium hyaline to brownish; hymenium hyaline; paraphyses unbranched, loose; asci clavate; spores many, hyaline, subspherical to ellipsoid, non-septate.
The algal host is Xanthocapsa.

1. **Forssellia minnesotensis** Fink n. comb.
Omphalaria minnesotensis Fink, Cont. U. S. Nat. Herb. 14:145. 1910. *Thyrea minnesotensis* (Fink) Zahlbr.
Transforming the algal colony into a minute to small, irregular, smooth to more commonly uneven, slightly lobed, adnate to raised, rigid, black body; apothecia minute to small, 0.3–0.5 mm. across, immersed in plainly raised wartlike elevations of the thallus, 1 to several in each elevation, the disk punctiform, black; spores subspherical to ellipsoid, 3–6 × 2–3 μ.
On rocks, Minnesota.

　　97. **Thyrea** Mass., Flora 39:210. 1856.

Transforming the algal colony into a minute to small, more or less lobed and branched, adnate to ascending, grayish to black body, devoid of differentiation into layers, attached to the substratum at the center; apothecia minute to small, immersed to becoming adnate, the disk closed to open, deeply concave to becoming flat, the exciple colored like the thallus; hypothecium hyaline to brownish; hymenium hyaline; paraphyses unbranched; asci clavate; spores 8–24, hyaline, subspherical to ellipsoid, non-septate.
The algal host is Xanthocapsa.

A. On rocks
　　B. Thalloid body grayish pruinose or black ・・・・・・・ 1. T. pulvinata
　　B. Thalloid body black but not pruinose
　　　　C. Apothecia minute, 0.08–0.15 mm. across ・・・・・・ 4. T. pyrenoides
　　　　C. Apothecia minute to small, 0.2–0.5 mm. across ・・・・ 3. T. Demangeonii
A. On trees ・・・・・・・・・・・・・・・・・・・・ 2. T. Girardi

1. **Thyrea pulvinata** (Schaer.) Mass., Flora 39:211. 1856.
Parmelia stygia var. *pulvinata* Schaer., Lich. Helv. Spic. sec. 11. 544. 1842. *Omphalaria pulvinata* (Schaer.) Nyl.
Transforming the algal colony into a small, ascending to suberect, pulvinately lobed, marginally wavy to more or less deeply lobed, grayish pruinose or black body; apothecia minute to small, 0.2–0.5 mm. across, immersed to adnate, borne along the margins of the lobes, the disk almost closed to open, blackish to lighter, the algoid exciple very thin, colored like the thallus or lighter; spores 8, short-ellipsoid, 9–12 × 5–6 μ.
On rocks, New England and New York, and westward to Minnesota and Nevada.

2. **Thyrea Girardi** (Dur. & Mont.) Bagl. & Carr., Atti Soc. Critt. Ital. 2:349. 1881.

> *Collema Girardi* Dur. & Mont., in Dur., Fl. Alger. Crypt. 1:199. pl. 18, f. 4. 1846. *Omphalaria Girardi* (Dur. & Mont.) Nyl.

Transforming the algal colony into a small, tough, ascending to erect, widely lobed, marginally wavy to divided, ashy to blackening body; apothecia minute, 0.05–0.15 mm. across, immersed, the disk black, deeply urceolate, nearly closed to more or less open; hypothecium thin, hyaline to brownish; spores 8, short-ellipsoid, 9–12 × 6–8 μ.

On trees, Alabama. In the specimens examined the algal host seen was Gloeocapsa.

3. **Thyrea Demangeonii** (Mont. & Moug.) Fink n. comb.

> *Collema Demangeonii* Mont. & Moug., Ann. Sci. Nat. Bot. III. 12:291. 1849. *Omphalaria phyllisca* (Wahl.) Tuck. *Phylliscum Demangeonii* (Mont. & Moug.) Nyl.

Transforming the algal colony into a small, rigid, flat to slightly raised, irregularly cut-lobed, somewhat imbricated, black body; apothecia minute to small, 0.2–0.5 mm. across, immersed to slightly raised as warts, the disk punctiform, black, the algoid exciple moderately thick, colored like the thallus; spores 8–16, oblong-ellipsoid, 6–10 × 4–5 μ.

On rocks, New England, Minnesota, and Oregon. In the specimens examined the algal host seen was Trentepohlia.

4. **Thyrea pyrenoides** (Nyl.) Fink n. comb.

> *Omphalaria pyrenoides* Nyl., Syn. Meth. Lich. 1:100, 101. 1858.

Transforming the algal colony into a small, deeply lobed, marginally round and wavy black body, with lobes closely packed and ascending to erect; apothecia minute, 0.08–0.15 mm. across, immersed, the disk urceolate to finally dilated, black, the algoid exciple swollen, colored like the thallus; spores 8, spherical to ellipsoid, 8–12 × 6–9 μ.

On rocks, Minnesota, Texas, and New Mexico.

98. **Peccania** Mass., Atti Ist. Veneto III. 5:335. 1860.

Transforming the algal colony into a small, more or less branched, erect, fruticose body, devoid of differentiation into layers, attached to the substratum by rhizoids; apothecia small to middle-sized, subterminal, immersed to adnate, the disk closed to open, concave to convex, the exciple thick, colored like the thallus; hypothecium hyaline to brownish; hymenium hyaline; paraphyses firm, unbranched; asci clavate; spores 8 or more, hyaline, oblong to ellipsoid or almost spherical, non-septate.

The algal host is Xanthocapsa.

1. **Peccania kansana** (Tuck.) Forss., Nov. Act. Reg. Soc. Sci. Upsal. III. 13:90. 1885.

> *Omphalaria kansana* Tuck., Proc. Am. Acad. 12:170. 1877. *Pleoconis kansana* (Tuck.) Clements.

Transforming the algal colony into a small, rigid, black, fruticose body, composed of stipitate, erect, clavate, lobate divisions; apothecia small to middle-sized, 0.4–0.8 mm. across, subterminal, slightly immersed to adnate, the disk becoming convex, black, the algoid exciple thin, black, soon disappearing; spores 8–16, oblong to ellipsoid, 5–9 × 3–4 μ.

On rocks and soil, Minnesota, Kansas, and New Mexico.

27. LICHINACEAE

Thallus crustose, foliose or fruticose, showing little or no differentiation, attached to the substratum by a holdfast; apothecia immersed or superficial, terminal or lateral, with a proper or thalloid exciple.
The algal host is Rivularia, or Calothrix.

A. Spores non-septate . . . . 100. LICHINA
A. Spores septate   . . . . 99. PTERYGIUM

99. Pterygium Nyl., Bull. Soc. Bot. France 1:328. 1854.

Thallus crustose to scaly or squamulose, granulose to coralloid, the margin more or less lobed, showing poorly developed upper and lower cortices of longitudinally extending, septate hyphae, and more or less distinct algal and medullary layers between; apothecia minute to small, adnate to sessile, the disk flat to convex, the exciple colored like the disk; hypothecium brownish; hymenium hyaline or brownish above; paraphyses unbranched, septate; asci clavate; spores 8, hyaline, ovoid to ellipsoid, 1–3-septate.
The algal host is Calothrix.

1. Pterygium Petersii Nyl., Mém. Soc. Sci. Nat. Cherb. 5:332. 1857.

Pannaria Petersii (Nyl.) Tuck. *Placynthium Petersii* (Nyl.) Burnh.
Thallus composed of minute to small, flat, clustered or scattered, radiately lobed, greenish gray to brown or brownish black squamules, the central ones often disappearing; apothecia minute to small, 0.2–0.4 mm. across, sessile, the disk flat, black, the exciple thin, black, somewhat raised; hypothecium brownish; spores ellipsoid, becoming 1-septate, 12–20 × 4–6 μ.
On rocks, New York, Alabama, Tennessee, Iowa, and Minnesota.

100. Lichina C. A. Agardh, Spec. Alg. 1:104. 1821.

Thallus minutely fruticose, more or less erect, composed of densely clustered, slender branches, the cortex indistinctly plectenchymatous or of entangled hyphae, or rarely absent, the algal layer more or less irregular, joining the cortex and the central medullary tissue of thin-walled, septate, longitudinally extending hyphae; apothecia minute to small, more or less immersed in the tips of the branches, solitary or clustered, the disk closed to open, irregular, the exciple colored like the thallus; hypothecium brownish; hymenium hyaline or brownish above; paraphyses threadlike, sparingly branched; asci cylindrical; spores 8, hyaline, oblong, non-septate.
The algal host is Calothrix.

A. Cortex poorly developed or absent . . . . 1. L. confinis Willeyi
A. Cortex better developed   . . . . 1. L. confinis

1. Lichina confinis (Müll.) C. A. Agardh, Spec. Alg. 1:105. 1821.

Lichen confinis Müll., Icon. Pl. Danica 5:5. pl. 879, f. 121. 1782.
Thallus moderately thick, composed of slender, erect, tapering, densely clustered, dichotomously branched, greenish brown to black branches; apothecia small, 0.3–0.5 mm. across, immersed in the enlarged tips of the branches, the disk closed to slightly open, the exciple thick, prominent, colored like the thallus; hypothecium brownish; asci cylindrical; spores ellipsoid, 22–29 × 11–15 μ, uniseriately arranged.
On maritime rocks, Massachusetts.

f. Willeyi Tuck., Syn. N. A. Lich. 1:133. 1882.

Thamnidium Willeyi Tuck., in Schwend., Agentyp. Flechtengon. 19. pl. 1, f. 4–10. 1869.
The cortex poorly developed or absent.
On maritime rocks, near New Bedford, Massachusetts. The algal host is unusual, apparently one of the Rivulariaceae with thin walls and no heterocysts.

28. COLLEMACEAE

Thallus of septate, branching hyphae, ramifying through the algal host colony, giving the appearance of a foliose or fruticose structure, closely adhering to the substratum or attached by rhizoids, the cortex plectenchymatous or of interwoven hyphae; apothecia round, immersed to superficial, with a proper or thalloid exciple.

The algal host is Nostoc.

A. Reproduction by internal spermatia . . . . 104. COLLEMODES
A. Reproduction by external spermatia
   B. Spores non-septate . . . . 101. LEMPHOLEMMA
   B. Spores septate
      C. Spores transversely 1–several-septate . . . . 102. SYNECHOBLASTUS
      C. Spores transversely and longitudinally septate
         D. Cortex of interwoven hyphae . . . . 103. COLLEMA
         D. Cortex plectenchymatous . . . . 105. LEPTOGIUM

101. **Lempholemma** Koerb., Syst. Lich. 400. 1855.

Transforming the algal colony into small to middle-sized, irregular, lobed or branched, smooth to rough body, the thallus wholly mycelial, imbedded in the host and attached to the substratum by rhizoids; apothecia immersed to adnate, minute to small, sometimes lateral or terminal on the lobes or branches, the disk concave to flat or convex, the algoid exciple thin to thick; hypothecium hyaline; hymenium hyaline or brownish above; paraphyses unbranched, slender; asci clavate, rarely curved or twisted; spores 8, hyaline, spherical to ovoid or ellipsoid, non-septate.

The algal host is Nostoc.

A. Thallus foliose to somewhat erect, lobed or
cushion-like; spores oblong to ovoid
   B. Thallus small to middle-sized, lobed; spores 8–16 × 7–9 μ . 2. L myriococcum
   B. Thallus minute to small, cushion-like; spores 16–25 × 7–9 μ . . 3. L. umbella
A. Thallus subfruticose; spores spherical to ovoid, 15–20 μ across . . 1. L. cladodes

1. **Lempholemma cladodes** (Tuck.) Zahlbr., Cat. Lich. Univ. 3:23. 1924.

Collema cladodes Tuck., Gen. Lich. 89. 1872. *Physma cladodes* (Tuck.) Zahlbr.

Transforming the algal colony into a small, tough, subfruticose, blackish green, branched body, the branches longitudinally striate and marginally stellate; apothecia minute, 0.2–0.4 mm. across, borne terminally or laterally on the branches, the disk strongly convex, black; spores spherical, varying toward ovoid, 15–20 μ across. On calcareous rocks, near Trenton Falls, New York.

2. **Lempholemma myriococcum** (Ach.) T. Fries, Nov. Act. Reg. Soc. Sci. Upsal. III. 3:381. 1861.

Lichen myriococcus Ach., Lich. Suec. 127. 1798. *Collema myriococcum* Ach.
Physma myriococcum (Ach.) Koerb.

Transforming the algal colony into a small to middle-sized, blackish, round to irregular, closely attached, irregularly flexuously and complicatedly lobed body, the lobes warty, with more or less irregular margins; apothecia minute, 0.1–0.3 mm. across, partly immersed, crowded, the disk concave, pale to darker brown, the exciple thin, colored like the thallus; spores ovoid to ovoid-ellipsoid, 8–16 × 7–9 μ. Over mosses on calcareous rocks, New York, New Jersey, and Alabama.

3. **Lempholemma umbella** (Tuck.) Zahlbr., Cat. Lich. Univ. 3:22. 1924.

Omphalaria umbella Tuck., in Nyl., Syn. Lich. 1:105, 106. 1858. *Collema umbella* (Tuck.) Nyl.

Transforming the algal colony into a minute to small, thick, rigid, cushion-like, marginally crenulate and lobulate, minutely granulose, greenish brown to blackening body; below brownish to darker; apothecia minute to small, 0.1–0.3 mm. across, slightly immersed to adnate, the disk becoming flat, reddish brown to brown, the

algoid exciple thick, colored like the thallus; hypothecium hyaline to brownish; spores oblong, 16–25 × 7–9 μ.
On rocks, Alabama and Iowa.

102. **Synechoblastus** Trev., Caratt. Gen. Collem. 3. 1853.

Transforming the algal host colonies into small to large, irregularly lobed, foliose bodies, thallus wholly mycelial, imbedded in the host and usually attached to the substratum by hyphal rhizoids; apothecia small to middle-sized, somewhat immersed to adnate or sessile, the disk flat to slightly convex, brownish to brown, the algoid exciple usually present; hypothecium hyaline to brownish; hymenium hyaline to brownish above; paraphyses rarely branched; asci clavate; spores 8, hyaline, 1–several-septate, the cells cylindrical.
The algal host is Nostoc.

A. Spores 1–3-septate
  B. Spores constantly 1-septate
    C. On trees, old wood and soil
      D. Thalloid body of divided or deeply cut lobes
        E. Thalloid body small, lobes palmately divided . . . . . 6. S. texanus
        E. Thalloid body larger, lobes long and more or less
          branched . . . . 7. S. pycnocarpus
      D. Thalloid body of round lobules or stalked
        granules . . . . 5. S. coccophorus
    C. On rocks, sometimes with moss
      D. Thalloid lobes narrow, with rough nodular tips . . . . 3. S. laciniatus
      D. Thalloid lobes wider, with closely wrinkled margins . . 4. S. ohioensis
  B. Spores 1–3-septate
    C. On trees and soil
      D. Thalloid body of minute, erect, short branches . . . 8. S. fascicularis
      D. Thalloid body of narrow, fenestrate lobes . . . . . 10. S. cyrtaspis
    C. On rocks; spores 4–8 in an ascus . . . . 12. S. wyomingensis
A. Spores 3–5- or more-septate
  B. Spores rarely more than 40 μ in length
    C. Thalloid body cushion-like, very small . . . . . . 11. S. microptychius
    C. Thalloid body small to middle-sized, not cushion-like
      D. Spores rarely less than 25 μ in length
        E. Thalloid body small, lobes narrow, usually short
          F. Thalloid body densely wrinkled; spores 25–40
            × 2.5–5 μ . . . . 13. S. leptaleus
          F. Thalloid body somewhat wrinkled; spores
            22–34 × 4–7 μ . . . . 14. S. ryssoleus
        E. Thalloid body larger, lobes broad and expanded . . . 2. S. rupestris
      D. Spores 17–26 × 6–7.5 μ . . . . 9. S. polycarpus
  B. Spores rarely less than 40 μ in length
    C. Thalloid body expanded, lobes broad . . . . 1. S. nigrescens
    C. Thalloid body not expanded, lobes narrow
      D. Apothecia 0.4–0.8 mm. across; spores 5–7-septate . . 16. S. leucocarpus
      D. Apothecia 0.6–2 mm. across, crowded;
        spores 3–5-septate . . . . 15. S. aggregatus

1. **Synechoblastus nigrescens** (Huds.) Trev., Caratt. Gen. Collem. 3. 1853.
  Lichen nigrescens Huds., Fl. Angl. 450. 1762. *Collema nigrescens* (Huds.) DC.
  Collema nigrescens var. *leucopepla* Tuck. *S. nigrescens* var. *leucopeplus*
  (Tuck.) Fink. *S. vespertilio* (Lightf.) Hepp.
Transforming the algal colony into a small to middle-sized or larger, closely adnate, somewhat lobed, smooth to closely beset with pustules or radiately ridged, olive-green to greenish black body, the lobes round, short, with entire, slightly ascending margins; greenish below, marked with depressions; apothecia small to middle-sized, 0.4–1.25 mm. across, sessile, numerous, often crowded toward the center of the thallus, the disk flat to convex, brown or reddish brown or grayish

pruinose, the algoid exciple thin, sometimes disappearing; hypothecium cloudy; spores fusiform to acicular, 3–7-septate, 40–70 × 3.5–6.5 μ. (PLATE 6 b.)
On trees, throughout the United States.

2. **Synechoblastus rupestris** (Swartz) Trev., Caratt. Gen. Collem. 3. 1853.
   Lichen rupestris Swartz, Meth. Muscor. 37. 1781. *Collema rupestre* (Swartz) Rabh. *Collema flaccidum* Ach. *S. flaccidus* (Ach.) Koerb.
   Transforming the algal colony into a middle-sized, round to irregular, more or less lobed, smooth to minutely granulose, olive-green to greenish black body, the lobes broad, round, often imbricated, with entire, ascending margins; greenish below; apothecia small to middle-sized, 0.5–1.5 mm. across, sessile, scattered, the disk concave to slightly convex, brown or reddish brown, the algoid exciple thin, entire, often granulose; hypothecium cloudy to brownish; spores ellipsoid-pointed or acicular, 3–5- or rarely 7-septate, 28–40 × 5–9 μ.
   ·On trees and rarely on rocks, throughout the United States.

3. **Synechoblastus laciniatus** (Nyl.) Fink n. comb.
   Collema laciniatum Nyl., Syn. Meth. Lich. 1:116. 1858. *Collema Nylanderianum* Zahlbr.
   Transforming the algal colony into a small to middle-sized, tough, round, olive-green, stellately lobed body, the lobes long, narrow, ascending, irregularly divided, with rough, nodular tips; apothecia middle-sized, 0.8–1.5 mm. across, subsessile, the disk flat to slightly convex, reddish brown, the algoid exciple thin, becoming subcrenate; hypothecium cloudy; spores fusiform-ellipsoid, 1-septate, 15–18 × 5–6 μ.
   On calcareous rocks, Tennessee, Alabama, Kansas, Nebraska, Colorado, and California.

4. **Synechoblastus ohioensis** Fink, Ohio Biol. Surv. Bull. 5:46. 1915.
   Collema ohioense (Fink) Zahlbr.
   Transforming the algal colony into a small, irregularly lobed, olive-green to greenish black body, the lobes ascending with closely wrinkled margins; greenish brown below; apothecia small to middle-sized, 0.5–2.5 mm. across, sessile, scattered, the disk flat to convex, reddish brown to brown, the algoid exciple thin, entire or rarely disappearing; hypothecium cloudy; spores ovoid to ellipsoid-pointed, 1-septate, 12–24 × 5–8 μ.
   On limestone, Ohio.

5. **Synechoblastus coccophorus** (Tuck.) Fink, Mycologia 1:87. 1909.
   Collema coccophorum Tuck., Proc. Am. Acad. 5:385. 1862.
   Transforming the algal colony into a small, irregular, blackish green body, composed of minute, erect, round lobules or stalked granules, often run together into crenate, granulose lobes toward the circumference; apothecia middle-sized, 0.8–2 mm. across, sessile, more or less crowded, the disk flat, reddish brown, the algoid exciple thin, becoming granulose; hypothecium hyaline to cloudy; spores ovoid-ellipsoid, 1-septate, 11–20 × 5–8.5 μ.
   On soil, Texas, Arizona, and California.

6. **Synechoblastus texanus** (Tuck.) Müll. Arg., Rev. Mycol. 10:54. 1888.
   Collema texanum Tuck., Am. Journ. Sci. II. 28:200. 1859.
   Transforming the algal colony into a small, lobed, deep green and blackening body, the lobes rather narrow, prostrate or ascending, palmately much-divided and finally covered with wartlike lobules; apothecia small to middle-sized, 0.5–2 mm. across, adnate, the disk concave to flat or slightly convex, reddish brown, the algoid exciple thin, becoming crenate; hypothecium hyaline; spores ovoid, 1-septate, 10–18 × 5–8 μ.
   On old wood and soil, Virginia, Alabama, and Texas.

7. **Synechoblastus pycnocarpus** (Nyl.) Müll. Arg., Flora 69:308. 1886.
Collema pycnocarpum Nyl., Syn. Lich. 1:115. 1858. *Dicollema pycnocarpum* (Nyl.) Clements.
Transforming the algal colony into a small to middle-sized, irregularly lobed, smooth to minutely granulose, olive-green to greenish black body, the lobes long, more or less branched, with ascending to erect, densely wrinkled and minutely lobed margins; greenish to brownish green below; apothecia small, 0.4–0.8 mm. across, sessile, marginal on the erect or ascending lobes, the disk flat to convex, brown or reddish brown, the algoid exciple thin, sometimes disappearing; hypothecium cloudy; spores ovoid to ovoid-ellipsoid, 1-septate, 11–20 × 3.5–6.5 μ.
On trees, from New England to Florida, and westward to the Rocky Mountains.

8. **Synechoblastus fascicularis** (L.) A. L. Smith, Mono. Brit. Lich. 1:61. 1918.
Lichen fascicularis L., Mant. 133. 1767. *S. conglomeratus* (Hoffm.) Koerb. *Collema fasciculare* (L.) Wigg.
Transforming the algal colony into a small, round to somewhat irregular, minutely branched, blackish green body, the branches ascending or erect, short, crowded, clavate to fan-shaped; apothecia small to middle-sized, 0.6–1.7 mm. across, sessile, more or less crowded, 1–several toward the tip of each branch, the disk flat to convex, dull red to reddish brown, the algoid exciple thin, becoming crenulate; hypothecium hyaline to tinged brownish; spores fusiform, 1–3-septate, 18–26 × 5.5–7 μ.
On trees and soil, Nebraska and California.

9. **Synechoblastus polycarpus** (Hoffm.) Dalla Torre & Sarnth., Flecht. Tirol. 575. 1902.
Collema polycarpum Hoffm., Deutsch. Fl. 102. 1796. *Collema melaenum* var. *polycarpon* Nyl.
Transforming the algal colony into a small, dark green to reddish or blackish, radiately lobed body, the lobes short, narrow, folded and ascending toward the center, wider and less elevated toward the circumference; apothecia small to middle-sized, 0.5–1.5 mm. across, numerous, sessile, the disk flat to finally convex, dark red to blackish, the algoid exciple well developed, thick, becoming crenulate; hypothecium cloudy to tinged brownish; spores ellipsoid-pointed, 3–5-septate, 17–26 × 6–7.5 μ.
On rocks and trees, Georgia and Montana.

10. **Synechoblastus cyrtaspis** (Tuck.) Fink, Cont. U. S. Nat. Herb. 14:134. 1910.
Collema cyrtaspis Tuck., Proc. Am. Acad. 5:387. 1862.
Transforming the algal colony into a small to middle-sized, tough, round to irregular, much lobed, olive-green to greenish black body, the lobes narrow, fenestrate, bearing many ascending, marginal lobules; apothecia middle-sized, 1–2 mm. across, sessile, more or less clustered on the lobules, the disk flat to convex, dark chestnut-brown or reddish brown, the exciple thick, becoming crenulate, sometimes disappearing; hypothecium hyaline to cloudy; spores subfusiform, 3-septate, 16–25 × 3–7 μ.
On trees, from Massachusetts to Florida, and westward to Arkansas and Minnesota.

11. **Synechoblastus microptychius** (Tuck.) Fink n. comb.
Collema microptychium Tuck., Lich. Calif. 35. 1866.
Transforming the algal colony into a small, irregularly lobed, blackish green, cushion-like body, the lobes ascending, folded, deflexed, crowded, with crenate margins; apothecia minute to small, 0.2–0.8 mm. across, sessile, more or less scattered, the disk flat, reddish brown, the algoid exciple thin, entire; spores fusiform, several-septate, 30–44 × 4–6 μ.
On trees, Massachusetts.

12. **Synechoblastus wyomingensis** Fink; Hedrick, Mycologia 26:153. 1934.

Transforming the algal host into an irregular, ascending, much lobed, smooth, dark olive-green and blackening body, the lobes numerous, short, entire or sinuose; smooth and lighter colored below; apothecia small, 0,75–1.4 mm. across, sessile along the margins of the lobes, the disk flat to slightly convex, reddish brown and darker, the algoid exciple prominent, entire, colored like the thallus; hypothecium hyaline; spores 4– rarely 8, ellipsoid-pointed and occasionally extended into an appendage 3–5 μ long, 3-septate, 22–32 $\times$ 6.5–9.5 μ.

On limestone cliff, Wyoming.

13. **Synechoblastus leptaleus** (Tuck.) Fink n. comb.

Collema leptaleum Tuck., Proc. Am. Acad. 6:263. 1866.

Transforming the algal colony into a small, smooth to rough and densely wrinkled, somewhat lobed, dark green to greenish black body, the lobes short, with folded, ascending margins; apothecia small to middle-sized, 0.6–2 mm. across, sessile, more or less crowded, the disk flat, reddish brown, the algoid exciple thin, entire, becoming crenulate; hypothecium hyaline; spores acicular with blunt ends, sometimes curved, 3–5-septate, 25–40 $\times$ 2.5–5 μ.

On trees, from New England to Florida, and westward to Texas and Nebraska.

14. **Synechoblastus ryssoleus** (Tuck.) Fink, Cont. U. S. Nat. Herb. 14:135. 1910.

Collema nigrescens, ryssoleum Tuck., Lich. Calif. 34. 1866. *Collema ryssoleum* Tuck.

Transforming the algal colony into a small, irregularly lobed, smooth to somewhat wrinkled, olive-green to blackish brown body, the lobes round, imbricated, with folded, wavy, ascending margins; greenish brown below, reticulated; apothecia minute to middle-sized, 0.2–1.5 mm. across, sessile, scattered or more or less crowded, the disk flat to convex, reddish brown to brown, the algoid exciple thin, becoming wavy, sometimes disappearing; hypothecium hyaline to brownish; spores ellipsoid-pointed, 3–5- or rarely 7-septate, 22–34 $\times$ 4–7 μ.

On rocks and rarely on trees, from Maine to Maryland, and westward to Ohio and Minnesota.

15. **Synechoblastus aggregatus** (Ach.) T. Fries, Nov. Act. Reg. Soc. Sci. Ups. III. 3:380. 1861.

Collema fasciculare var. *aggregatum* Ach., Lich. Univ. 640. 1810. *Collema aggregatum* (Ach.) Röhl.

Transforming the algal colony into a middle-sized, round to irregular, lobed, smooth to minutely granulose, conspicuously ribbed, sometimes fenestrate, bright green to greenish black body, the lobes broad, short, with crenate, granulose margins; greenish below; apothecia small to middle-sized, 0.6–2 mm. across, irregular, sessile, crowded on the ridges of the thallus, the disk flat to convex, reddish brown, the algoid exciple thin, entire, rarely becoming granulose; hypothecium hyaline to cloudy; spores fusiform-cylindrical, sometimes curved, 3–5-septate, 35–60 $\times$ 4–5 μ.

On trees and rarely on rocks, Florida, Alabama, Nebraska, and California.

16. **Synechoblastus leucocarpus** (Hook. & Tayl.) Müll. Arg., Flora 70:113. 1887.

Collema leucocarpum Hook. & Tayl., Lond. Journ. Bot. 3:657. 1844. *Collema glaucophthalmum* Nyl. *Collema aggregatum* var. *glaucophthalmum* (Nyl.) Tuck.

Transforming the algal colony into a middle-sized, round to somewhat irregular, folded, ridged and fenestrate, somewhat lobed, light green to blackish body, the lobes round, with ascending margins; greenish below; apothecia small, 0.4–0.8 mm. across, subsessile, the disk slightly concave to flat, reddish brown or obscurely grayish pruinose, the algoid exciple becoming crenulate and disappearing; hypothecium hyaline to cloudy; spores long-fusiform, 5–7-septate, 40–65 $\times$ 4.5–7 μ.

On trees, southern California.

103. **Collema** (Hill.) Web., in Wigg., Prim. Fl. Hols. 89. 1780.

Transforming the algal colony into a small to large, round to irregular, lobed, greenish to blackish body, thallus wholly mycelial, imbedded in the host and attached to the substratum by rhizoids; apothecia small to large, more or less immersed to adnate or sessile, the disk concave to flat or slightly convex, flesh-colored to brown, the algoid exciple thin to thick, entire to irregular; hypothecium hyaline to brown; hymenium hyaline to brownish above; paraphyses rarely branched, commonly enlarged and brownish toward the apex; asci clavate; spores 8, hyaline, transversely and longitudinally septate.

The algal host is Nostoc.

A. Spores 1–3-septate transversely
  B. On trees and old wood
    C. Thalloid body very small, more or less crustlike
      D. Apothecia 0.15–0.25 mm. across . . . . 2. C. verruciforme
      D. Apothecia 0.4–0.8 mm. across . . . . 1. C. microphyllum
    C. Thalloid body larger, distinctly lobed . . . . 9. C. callibotrys
  B. On rocks and soil
    C. Thalloid lobes smooth above or rarely becoming granulose
      D. Apothecia 0.5–2 or 2.5 mm. across, more or less superficial
        E. Apothecia very numerous; spores oblong-ellipsoid,
          $16–30 \times 8–12 \mu$ . . . . 5. C. crispur`
        E. Apothecia rarely numerous; spores ovoid-ellipsoid,
          $16–24 \times 8–11 \mu$ . . . . 3. C. tenax
      D. Apothecia 0.2–0.7 mm. across, appearing like pustules . 4. C. pustulatum
    C. Thalloid lobes granulose above, or rarely somewhat smooth
      D. On rocks; thalloid body small to middle-sized
        E. Spores $24–34 \times 11–17 \mu$ . . . . 6. C. cheileum
        E. Spores $17–24 \times 9–11 \mu$ . . . . 8. C. furvum
      D. On soil; thalloid body minute; central lobes reduced
        and club-shaped; spores $16–30 \times 7–9 \mu$ . . . . . 7. C. cristatellum
A. Spores 3–5- or more sep ate transversely
  B. Spores rarely more than 25μ in length
    C. Thalloid body smooth to wrinkled above
      D. Apothecia more than 0.4 mm. across
        E. Thalloid margins usually plicate and crisped . . . 11. C. plicatile
        E. Thalloid margins wavy-crenate . . . . 10. C. pulposum
      D. Apothecia 0.1–0.3 mm. across . . . . 12. C. fayettensis
    C. Thalloid body granulose above . . . . 14. C. granosum
  B. Spores rarely less than 25μ in length
    C. Apothecia 1–3 mm. across; spores oblong-ellipsoid . . . 13. C. glaucescens
    C. Apothecia 0.2–0.7 mm. across; spores rarely
    becoming spheroidal . . . . 4. C. pustulatum heterosporum

1. **Collema microphyllum** Ach., Lich. Univ. 630. 1810.

Transforming the algal host into an olive-green to blackish, orbicular or irregular lobulate body, with the minute, sometimes scattered, ascending lobes reduced, subimbricated, and granulose-crenate toward the center, and those toward the margin larger and flat; apothecia small, 0.4–0.8 mm. across, numerous, sessile, the disk deeply concave to flat, red, the algoid exciple finally disappearing, and the pale proper exciple persisting; hypothecium hyaline to brownish; spores ovoid-ellipsoid, 3-septate transversely and 1-septate longitudinally, $16–25 \times 8–11 \mu$.

On trees, Massachusetts, Ohio, and Illinois.

2. **Collema verruciforme** (Ach.) Nyl., Syn. Meth. Lich. 1:112. pl. 4, f. 6. 1858.
Collema furvum var. *verruciforme* Ach., Lich. Univ. 650, 651. 1810.

Transforming the algal colony into a minute, olivaceous or darker brown body, composed of crowded, granulose, heaped or widespread, ascending, crenate lobules, and becoming broken and scattered; apothecia minute, 0.15–0.25 mm. across, numerous, 1–4 in each lobule, the disk deeply concave to flat, reddish brown, the algoid exciple thick and dark brown; hypothecium brownish; spores spheroidal to quadrangular or ellipsoid, 1–3-septate transversely and 1–2-septate longitudinally, 10–21 × 7–11 μ.

On trees and old wood, from Massachusetts westward to Illinois.

3. **Collema tenax** (Swartz) Ach., Lich. Univ. 635. 1810.

Lichen tenax Swartz, Nov. Act. Soc. Sci. Ups. 4:249. 1784.

Transforming the algal colony into a round or somewhat irregular, yellowish green or darker body, the lobes thin and closely adnate or rarely more loosely attached and folded; apothecia small to middle-sized, 0.5–2 mm. across, immersed to partly superficial, the disk concave to flat, reddish brown, the algoid exciple sometimes crenate; hypothecium brownish; spores ovoid-ellipsoid, 3-septate transversely and 1-septate longitudinally, 16–24 × 8–11 μ.

On calcareous soil, throughout eastern United States, and westward to Missouri and Minnesota.

4. **Collema pustulatum** Ach., Syn. Lich. 317. 1814.

Transforming the algal colony into a more or less irregular, brownish olive or darker, lobed body, the lobes becoming long and narrow and subdichotomously or irregularly divided and often ascending, the more closely attached central lobes commonly dying, leaving the marginal lobes often separately attached to the substratum; apothecia minute to small, 0.2–0.7 mm. across, immersed to adnate, appearing like pustules on the lobes, the disk concave to flat, reddish to blackish brown, the algoid exciple prominent; hypothecium hyaline to cloudy; spores ovoid-ellipsoid, 3-septate transversely and 1-septate longitudinally, 12–24 × 9–10 μ.

On calcareous rocks, from Pennsylvania to Alabama, and westward to Iowa and Minnesota.

var. **heterosporum** Fink; Hedrick, Mycologia 26:154. 1934.

Spores oblong-ellipsoid with one end slightly flattened, 3–5-septate transversely and 1–3-septate longitudinally, or rarely spheroidal and 3–5-septate transversely and longitudinally, 25–28 × 13–14 μ, irregularly or rarely uniseriately arranged.

On rocks, Florida.

5. **Collema crispum** (L.) Wigg., Prim. Fl. Hols. 89. 1780.

Lichen crispus L., Flora Suec. II. 406. 1755.

Transforming the algal colony into a small, rather thin, olive-green or darker, round or somewhat irregular, lobed body, the marginal lobes more or less expanded, those of the center raised and folded with dentate or granulate edges; apothecia middle-sized or larger, 0.7–2.5 mm. across, often numerous and nearly concealing the central part of the thallus, partly superficial, the disk concave, dark reddish brown, the algoid exciple entire to more commonly crenate-granulate; hypothecium brownish; spores oblong-ellipsoid, 3-septate transversely and 1–2-septate longitudinally, 16–30 × 8–12 μ.

On soil, throughout northern United States.

6. **Collema cheileum** Ach., Lich. Univ. 630, 631. 1810.

Lichen cheileus Ach., Lich. Suec. 134. 1798. *Collema cheileum* var. *monocarpon* (Duf.) Leight.

Transforming the algal colony into a greenish black to olive-green, lobed body, the lobes minute or small, loosely imbricated, round, entire to crenate, often undulate, folded, and granulate; apothecia small to middle-sized, 0.5–1 mm. across, immersed usually 1 in each lobe, the disk concave to slightly convex, reddish, the algoid exciple becoming crenulate or lobulate; hypothecium sometimes tinged with umber; spores oblong-ellipsoid, 3-septate transversely and 1-septate longitudinally, 24–34 × 11–17 μ.

On rocks, Santa Monica Range, California. The material is doubtfully referred to this species.

7. **Collema cristatellum** Tuck., Lich. Calif. 29. 1866.

Transforming the algal colony into a minute, blackish olive body with cut-crenate, usually scattered, ascending lobes having rough, granulose margins, the central lobes sometimes much reduced and club-shaped; apothecia small to middle-sized, 0.4–1 mm. across, the disk concave to slightly convex, the algoid exciple thin and granulose; hypothecium pale brownish; spores oblong-ellipsoid, 3-septate transversely and 1-septate longitudinally, 16–30 × 7–9 μ.

On soil, Illinois, New Mexico, and California.

8. **Collema furvum** (Ach.) DC., in Lam. & DC., Fl. Fr. ed. 3. 2:385. 1815.
   Lichen furvus Ach., Lich. Suec. 132. 1798.

Transforming the algal colony into a middle-sized, rather thin, lobed and folded, olive-green to blackish, dorsally granulose body, the lobes round to somewhat irregular, ascending, oblong, with entire to crenulate, deeply wavy margins; apothecia small to middle-sized, 0.3–1 mm. across, scattered or loosely clustered, the disk concave to flat, brown, the algoid exciple prominent; hypothecium brownish; spores ovoid-ellipsoid, 3-septate transversely and 1-septate longitudinally, 17–24 × 9–11 μ.

On calcareous rocks, from Vermont to Maryland, and westward to Iowa and Minnesota.

9. **Collema callibotrys** Tuck., Proc. Am. Acad. 5:386. 1862.

Transforming the algal colony into a middle-sized or larger, round to somewhat irregular, tough, pale green to blackish body, the lobes radiate, and often irregularly narrowed, ribbed and fenestrate, marginally ascending; apothecia small, 0.35–0.5 mm. across, numerous and often covering the lobes, the disk concave, red, the algoid exciple plainly visible; hypothecium hyaline to pale brownish; spores nearly square to ellipsoid, 3-septate transversely and 1-septate longitudinally, 10–22 × 7–12 μ.

On trees, from South Carolina to Florida, and westward to Texas.

10. **Collema pulposum** (Bernh.) Ach., Lich. Univ. 632. pl. 14, f. 9. 1810.
    Lichen pulposus Bernh., in Schrad., Syst. Samml. Krypt. Gewächse II. 11. 1797.

Transforming the algal colony into a more or less irregular, rather thick, light olive-green to blackish body, the lobes often radiately arranged, and wavy-crenate, often imbricate, especially over the thicker central portions, or the central lobes reduced to granules, the marginal ones somewhat flat; apothecia small to middle-sized, 0.7–2.5 mm. across, adnate to sessile, the disk concave to flat, reddish brown, the algoid exciple rarely crenate; hypothecium hyaline to brownish; spores ovoid-ellipsoid, 3–5-septate transversely and 1–3-septate longitudinally, 16–25 × 7–11.5 μ. (PLATE 7.)

On soil and mossy rocks, widely distributed throughout United States but scarcely well known. Externally similar to *Collemodes Bachmanianum* Fink.

11. **Collema plicatile** Ach., Lich. Suec. 129, 237. 1798.
    Lichen plicatilis Ach., Vet. Akad. Handl. 16:11. pl. 1, f. 2. 1795. *Leptogium plicatile* (Ach.) Leight.

Transforming the algal colony into a more or less irregular, olive-green to blackish body, the lobes more or less imbricated, commonly ascending or erect, their margins usually plicate and crisped; apothecia small, 0.4–1 mm. across, sub-sessile, the disk commonly concave, brown and darkening, the exciple algoid; hypothecium brownish; spores ovoid-ellipsoid, 3– rarely 5-septate transversely and 1-septate longitudinally, 18–28 × 7–10 μ.

On rocks, mostly calcareous, throughout northern United States from Vermont to California.

12. **Collema fayettensis** Fink; Hedrick, Mycologia 26:154. 1934.

Transforming the algal colony into a small, thin to somewhat thick, irregularly lobed, greenish to greenish brown body, the lobes smooth to somewhat wrinkled, becoming more or less imbricated, with crenate, ascending margins; lighter below and often minutely wrinkled, the hyphae often protruding in minute whitish areas commonly along the margin; apothecia minute to small, 0.1–0.3 mm. across, numerous, immersed, the disk concave to almost flat, brown, the algoid exciple rather thick and prominent; hypothecium hyaline or tinged brownish; spores oblong to ellipsoid-pointed, 3–4-septate transversely and 1-septate longitudinally, 18–22 × 9–11 μ, irregularly arranged.

On exposed limestone, near Big Rock, Fayette, Iowa.

13. **Collema glaucescens** Hoffm., Deutschl. Fl. 2:100. 1795.
    C. limosum Ach.

Transforming the algal colony into a somewhat thin, usually small, scattered, greenish to olivaceous, squamulose body, the large lobes crenate to serrate, narrow and ascending; apothecia small to middle-sized, 1–3 mm. across, immersed in the algal host body or becoming superficial and often obscuring its body, the disk concave to flat, becoming reddish brown, the algoid exciple thin, but finally prominent, sometimes crenulate; hypothecium brownish; spores usually 3–7-septate transversely and 1–3-septate longitudinally, 24–38 × 11–15 μ.

On soil, from New York to South Carolina, and westward across the United States.

14. **Collema granosum** (Schreb.) Rabh., Deutsch. Krypt. Fl. 2:53. 1845.
    Lichen granosus Schreb., Spic. Fl. Lips. 128. 1771. *C. auriculatum* Hoffm.

Transforming the algal colony into a rather large, rigid, irregularly wavy or cut-lobed, yellowish green to blackish, transversely or reticulately wrinkled or granulose body, with the lobes short and round to long and narrow; apothecia middle-sized, 0.4–0.7 mm. across, rarely present, immersed to adnate, the disk concave to flat, reddish brown, the algoid exciple thick and usually wrinkled or granulose; hypothecium brownish; spores oblong-ellipsoid, 3–5-septate transversely and 1–3-septate longitudinally, 23–26 × 10–13 μ.

Over mosses on rocks, Ohio and Illinois.

OTHER SPECIES REPORTED

Collema bermudiana Tuck.—Florida.
Collema stenophyllum Nyl.—North America.

104. **Collemodes** Fink, Mycologia 10:236, 237. 1918.

Transforming the algal host colonies into foliose bodies; thallus wholly mycelial, imbedded in the host and attached to the substratum by rhizoids; apothecia small to large, adnate to sessile; paraphyses often branched toward the apices, spores 8, hyaline, transversely and longitudinally septate; male reproductive organs internal spermatia, occurring in groups without spermagonial covering; female organs as in the Collemaceae generally, but the trichogynes passing to the groups of spermatia instead of rising above the surface of the algal-host colony.

The algal host is Nostoc.

1. **Collemodes Bachmanianum** Fink, Mycologia 10:235–38. pl. 13, f. 1–6. 1918.

Transforming the algal colony into a more or less irregular, closely attached, olive-green, bluish or blackish body, the lobes becoming wavy-crenate and sometimes imbricated, the marginal ones often ascending to suberect, the central ones usually flat; apothecia middle-sized to large, 0.5–4.5 mm. across, adnate to sessile, scattered or thickly disposed, the disk concave or rarely flat, reddish brown, the algoid exciple prominent, becoming wrinkled-crenate; spores ovoid-ellipsoid, 3–5-septate transversely and 1–3-septate longitudinally, 17–28 × 7.5–12 μ.

On soil and mossy rocks, New York, Ohio, Wisconsin, Iowa, Minnesota, and Missouri, scarcely distinguishable from *Collema pulposum* (Bernh.) Ach., except with respect to the very different sex organs and sexual behavior. The strong resemblance would lead one to suspect that the plants might be the same and bear both kinds of sex organs. However, careful study showed nothing of this kind.

105. **Leptogium** Ach.; S. F. Gray, Nat. Arr. Brit. Pl. 1:400. 1821.

Transforming the algal host colonies into small to large, more or less irregular, foliose bodies, thallus showing an upper and lower cortex, each commonly composed of a single layer of cells, rarely with poorly developed algal and medullary layers, adhering to the substratum or attached by short rhizoids; apothecia sometimes wanting, immersed to adnate or sessile, the disk flat to convex, brownish to brown, the algoid exciple sometimes disappearing; hypothecium hyaline to brownish; hymenium hyaline or brownish above; paraphyses rarely branched; asci clavate to broadly clavate; spores 8, hyaline, transversely and longitudinally septate.

The algal host is Nostoc.

A. Thalloid body very small to small, minutely lobed or more or
   less crustlike
   B. Thalloid body granulose or crustlike
      C. Spores 7–10 μ wide
         D. Thalloid body forming a broken areolate crust . . . 4. L. dactylinum
         D. Thalloid body crustlike, more or less covered
            with coralloid branchlets . . . . 9. L. perminutum
      C. Spores 8–15 μ wide
         D. Apothecia more than 0.4 mm. across, disk reddish brown
            E. Plectenchymatous throughout . . . . 1. L. byssinum
            E. Plectenchyma limited to the cortical regions . . . 8. L. caesiellum
         D. Apothecia 0.2–0.4 mm. across, disk dull brown
            or black . . . . 7. L. rhyparodes
   B. Thalloid body minutely squamulose, lobed, or
      coralloid, rarely becoming crustlike
      C. On rocks
         D. Thalloid body bearing coralloid branchlets along
            the margins . . . . 4. L. dactylinum
         D. Thalloid body with ascending margins . . . . . . 5. L. Schraderi
      C. On soil and old wood among moss
         D. Spores 24–36 × 9–15 μ . . . . 3. L. tenuissimum
         D. Spores 18–29 × 8–12 μ . . . . 6. L. minutissimum
A. Thalloid body small to middle-sized or large, more or less
   distinctly lobed
   B. Rhizoids conspicuous on the under surface
      C. Plectenchyma limited to the cortical regions
         D. Rhizoids scattered or clustered
            E. Bearing clustered rhizoids . . . . 12. L. Hildenbrandii
            E. More or less covered with delicate
               rhizoids below . . . . 11. L. Burgessii
         D. Rhizoids forming a densely tomentose nap below . . 10. L. saturninum
      C. Plectenchymatous throughout . . . . 2. L. plectenchymum
   B. Rhizoids inconspicuous or absent
      C. Spores usually less than 30 μ in length
         D. Thalloid body more or less granulose or coralloid above
            E. Thalloid body thicker, dark green to lead-colored
               F. Thalloid body much lobed
                  G. Margins crenate . . . . 13. L. chloromelum
                  G. Margins erect and curled or
                     wrinkled . . . . 13. L. chloromelum stellans
               F. Thalloid body less lobed, lobes gyrosely folded
                  and margins slashed . . . . . . 13. L. chloromelum conchatum
            E. Thalloid body thinner, lead-colored or sky-blue
               F. Thalloid body lead-colored . . . . 14. L. tremelloides
               F. Thalloid body sky-blue . . . . . . 14. L. tremelloides azureum
         D. Thalloid body smooth to more or less wrinkled above
            E. Thalloid body small, lobes more or less imbricated
               F. Lobes broad, usually much imbricated
                  G. Spores 3-septate transversely,
                     18–27 × 7–12 μ . . . . 15. L. arizonicum

G. Spores 3–5-septate transversely,
    15–22 × 7–9 μ . . . . 17. L. juniperinum
F. Lobes narrow, irregularly to radiately arranged . 16. L. apalachense
E. Thalloid body larger, lobes more or less folded
  F. Apothecia 1 or more mm. across
    G. Thalloid exciple thick and more or less folded
      H. Apothecia sessile, exciple folded and
        wavy . . . . 19. L. phyllocarpum
      H. Apothecia sessile to subpedicellate,
        exciple becoming lobed . . . . 18. L. bullatum
    G. Thalloid exciple thin, usually entire and
      often disappearing . . . . 22. L. pulchellum
  F. Apothecia rarely more than 1 mm. across
    G. Spores 16–22 × 7–9 μ . . . . 20. L. crenatellum
    G. Spores 20–30 × 10–12 μ . . . . 21. L. marginellum
C. Spores usually more than 30 μ in length
  D. Thalloid margins entire to crenate or rarely toothed
    E. Apothecia 0.2–0.5 mm. across
      F. Thalloid body wrinkled and pitted
        G. Margins toothed . . . . 23. L. palmatum
        G. Margins entire to subcrenate . . . . 26. L. scotinum
      F. Thalloid body more or less pustulate . . . . . 25. L. platynum
    E. Apothecia 0.4–0.8 mm. across . . . . 24. L. californicum
  D. Thalloid margins much jagged and fringed
    E. Lobes large, not densely crowded . . . . . . 27. L. lichenoides
    E. Lobes smaller, crowded, with finely fringed
      edges . . . . 27. L. lichenoides pulvinatum

1. **Leptogium byssinum** (Hoffm.) Zwackh.; Nyl., Act. Soc. Linn. Bord. 21:270. 1856.

Lichen byssinus Hoffm., Enum. Lich. 46. pl. 4, f. 7. 1784. *Pannaria byssina* (Hoffm.) Nyl.

Transforming the algal colony into a small, thin, rough, minutely squamulose, ashy gray to blackening body, the squamules coralloid and passing into very minute, scurfy granules, the internal structure plectenchymatous throughout; apothecia small to middle-sized, 0.4–1 mm. across, immersed to adnate, the disk concave to flat, brownish to reddish brown, the algoid exciple thin, colored like the thallus, finally disappearing; hypothecium hyaline to cloudy; spores ovoid-ellipsoid, 3–7-septate transversely and 1–2-septate longitudinally, 19–31 × 7–13.5 μ.

On soil, Massachusetts, New Jersey, North Carolina, and Illinois.

2. **Leptogium plectenchymum** Fink, Ohio Biol. Surv. Bull. 5:57, 58. pl. 4, f. 13 g. 1915.

Transforming the algal colony into a small to middle-sized, round to irregular, loosely adnate, irregularly lobed, lead-colored body, the lobes ascending, often imbricated with entire, irregular, or minutely lobulate margins, more or less of the internal structure plectenchymatous; lighter colored and bearing rhizoids below; apothecia small to middle-sized, 0.5–2 mm. across, sessile, scattered, the disk flat to convex, reddish brown, the algoid exciple colored like the thallus, entire or irregular; hypothecium hyaline to cloudy; spores ovoid-ellipsoid to ellipsoid-pointed, 3-septate transversely and becoming 1-septate longitudinally, 22–30 × 8–14 μ.

On damp clay soil, near Oxford, Ohio.

3. **Leptogium tenuissimum** (Dicks.) E. Fries, Corp. Fl. Prov. Suec. 1:293. 1835.
Lichen tenuissimus Dicks., Plant. Crypt. Brit. 1:12. pl. 2, f. 8. 1785.

Transforming the algal colony into a minute, minutely squamulose, digitately and unequally cut-lobed, greenish gray to greenish brown, crustlike body, with ascendant margins; apothecia minute to small, 0.2–0.6 mm. across, subsessile, the disk concave to finally flat, dull reddish to brown, the proper exciple thin, lighter colored than the disk; hypothecium hyaline to cloudy; spores ovoid-ellipsoid, 3–5-septate transversely and 1–2-septate longitudinally, 24–36 × 9–15 μ.

On soil and old wood among mosses, from New England to New Jersey, and westward to California and Oregon.

4. **Leptogium dactylinum** Tuck., in Nyl., Syn. Lich. 1:123. 1858.
Transforming the algal colony into a small, much-lobed, lead-colored to black body, with round lobules ascending or erect, the margins entire to crenate, or curled, and often beset above with coralloid branchlets, or the whole structure finally passing into a broken-areolate, granulose crust; apothecia small, 0.4–0.8 mm. across, subsessile, the disk flat, reddish brown, the proper exciple thin, lighter brown, soon disappearing; hypothecium hyaline or tinged with brown; spores ovoid-ellipsoid, 3-septate transversely and becoming 1-septate longitudinally, 16–24 × 7–10 μ.
On various rocks, from Vermont to New Jersey, and westward to Nebraska and South Dakota.

5. **Leptogium Schraderi** (Bernh.) Nyl., Act. Soc. Linn. Bord. 21:272. 1856.
Lichen Schraderi Bernh., Journ. Bot. 1:22. pl. 2, f. 5. 1799. *Collemodium Schraderi* (Bernh.) Nyl.
Transforming the algal colony into a very small, minutely subcylindrical, dichotomously or irregularly lobed, lead-colored to blackish, crustlike, often ascending body; apothecia minute to small, 0.2–0.5 mm. across, sessile, the disk somewhat concave to slightly convex, brownish to brown, the algoid exciple thin, soon disappearing, colored like the disk; hypothecium hyaline; spores ellipsoid to ellipsoid-pointed, 3–5-septate transversely and 1–2-septate longitudinally, 22–30 × 7–11 μ.
On rocks, southern California.

6. **Leptogium minutissimum** (Floerke) E. Fries, Sum. Veg. 122. 1846.
Collema minutissimum Floerke, Deutsch. Lich. part 5. 99. 1815.
Transforming the algal colony into a minutely lobed, lead-colored to dark brown or brownish body, the lobes or branches slender, elongated, crenate, finally crowded and imbricated; apothecia small to nearly middle-sized, 0.3–0.8 mm. across, sessile, the disk flat to slightly convex, reddish brown, the algoid exciple thin, pale; hypothecium hyaline to cloudy; spores ovoid-ellipsoid, 3–7-septate transversely and 1–2-septate longitudinally, 18–29 × 8–12 μ.
On soil among mosses, Massachusetts, Illinois, Washington, and California.

7. **Leptogium rhyparodes** Nyl., Flora 48:210. 1865.
Transforming the algal colony into a thin, brown to blackening, coarsely and unequally granulose, apparently crustose, scaly, or often minutely branched and sometimes ascending body; apothecia minute to small, 0.2–0.4 mm. across, subsessile, the disk concave to flat, dull brown or blackening, the algoid exciple elevated, lighter than the disk, finally disappearing; hypothecium pale yellowish; spores ellipsoid or ovoid-ellipsoid, 5–6-septate transversely and becoming 1-septate longitudinally, 22–34 × 10–15 μ.
On mosses and rocks, California.

8. **Leptogium caesiellum** Tuck., Syn. N. A. Lich. 1:156. 1882.
Transforming the algal colony into a flat, closely adnate, granulose, greenish gray to darker body, more or less covered with minute, scurfy, crenulate and subimbricate squamules; apothecia small to middle-sized, 0.5–0.8 mm. across, adnate, the disk slightly concave to flat, reddish brown, the proper exciple thin, lighter than the disk; hypothecium hyaline to cloudy; spores ovoid-ellipsoid, 3–7-septate transversely and 1-septate longitudinally, 18–34 × 8–14 μ.
On moist clay, Illinois.

9. **Leptogium perminutum** Fink; Hedrick, Mycologia 26:154. 1934.
Transforming the algal colony into a small, thin, wrinkled and irregular, closely adnate black body, more or less covered with minute coralloid branchlets, the cor-

tex plectenchymatous; apothecia minute, 0.1–0.3 mm. across, adnate to sessile, round, numerous, scattered or clustered, the disk concave to flat, brownish to reddish brown or brownish black, bright reddish brown when moistened, the algoid exciple thin to moderately thick, smooth to rarely somewhat rough or wavy; hypothecium hyaline; spores ellipsoid to pointed-ellipsoid, 5-septate transversely and 1–2-septate longitudinally, the cells almost cubical, $18–25 \times 8–10 \mu$, irregularly arranged.
On old wood, near Oxford, Ohio.

10. **Leptogium saturninum** (Dicks.) Nyl., Act. Soc. Linn. Bord. 21:272. 1856.
Lichen saturninus Dicks., Fasc. Pl. Crypt. Brit. 2:21. pl. 6, f. 8. 1790. *Collema saturninum* (Dicks.) DC. *L. myochroum* (Ehrh.) Nyl. *L. myochroum* var. *tomentosum* (Hoffm.) Tuck.
Transforming the algal colony into a large, irregularly lobed, smooth to wrinkled and somewhat granulose, marginally ascending and imbricated, lead-colored to greenish or blackish body; grayish to darker and densely tomentose below; apothecia middle-sized, 0.7–2 mm. across, subsessile, the disk flat, reddish brown, the algoid exciple thin, colored like the thallus, more or less irregular, often granulose; hypothecium hyaline to cloudy; spores ellipsoid, 3-septate transversely and partly 1-septate longitudinally, $20–29 \times 7–10 \mu$.
On trees and rocks, throughout the United States.

11. **Leptogium Burgessii** (L.) Mont., in Webb & Berth., Hist. Nat. Canar. 3^2: 129. 1840.
Lichen Burgessii L., Syst. Veg. ed. 13. 807. 1774.
Transforming the algal colony into a large, loosely aggregated, smooth to granulose, grayish green to lead-colored or purplish brown, marginally crenate or cut-lobed, imbricate, ascending body; ashy below and more or less covered with delicate rhizoids; apothecia large, 1.5–4 mm. across, sessile, the disk concave to flat, reddish to dark brown, the algoid exciple brown, moderately thick, irregularly lobed; hypothecium hyaline or tinged brownish; spores ellipsoid, often pointed toward the ends, 7–9-septate transversely and 3–4-septate longitudinally, $30–45 \times 15–18 \mu$.
On trees, New England, Virginia, and California.

12. **Leptogium Hildenbrandii** (Garov.) Nyl., Act. Soc. Linn. Bord. 21:272. 1856.
Collema Hildenbrandii Garov., Lich. Prov. Comens. 1:3. 1837.
Transforming the algal colony into a middle-sized to larger, round, irregularly lobed, smooth to densely granulose, lead-colored to greenish black body, the lobes rounded outward and irregularly cut at the margin; paler below, and wrinkled, sometimes bearing clustered rhizoids; apothecia small to middle-sized, 0.5–1.75 mm. across, sessile, the disk flat to convex, brownish red to brown, the algoid exciple colored like the thallus; hypothecium hyaline or tinged brownish; spores ellipsoid, 3-septate transversely and becoming 1-septate longitudinally, $16–24 \times 9–11 \mu$.
On trees, New Mexico and California. Our specimens are sterile.

13. **Leptogium chloromelum** (Swartz) Nyl., Syn. Lich. 1:128. 1858.
Lichen chloromelus Swartz, Fl. Ind. Acc. 3:1892. 1806.
Transforming the algal colony into a middle-sized or larger, somewhat rigid, strongly wrinkled, finally densely granulose, dark green to lead-colored body, with ascending crenately margined lobes, the central lobes folded and curled; apothecia small to middle-sized, 0.4–1 mm. across, sessile to subsessile, the disk concave to flat, red to brownish red, the algoid exciple thin, colored like the thallus, wrinkled to folded and granulose; hypothecium hyaline to cloudy; spores ovoid to ellipsoid-pointed, 3–5-septate transversely and 1-septate longitudinally, $18–32 \times 8–13 \mu$.
On trees, rocks, and mosses, throughout the United States.

var. **conchatum** Tuck., Syn. N. A. Lich. 1:163. 1882.
Thallus tending toward unlobed conditions with the lobes gyrosely folded and the margins slashed.
Substrata and distribution as for the species.

var. **stellans** Tuck., Syn. N. A. Lich. 1:163. 1882.
Thallus much narrower with the edges of the radiant lobes erect and curled or wrinkled; spores becoming 7–9-septate transversely.
Substrata and distribution as for the species.

14. **Leptogium tremelloides** (L.) S. F. Gray, Nat. Arr. Brit. Pl. 1:400. 1821.
Lichen tremelloides L., Suppl. Pl. 450. 1781.
Transforming the algal colony into a middle-sized, suborbicular, closely adnate, lead-colored, minutely coralline-granulose body, the lobes ascending, often imbricated, with entire or finely undulate or dentate, irregular margins; often somewhat lighter colored below; apothecia small to middle-sized, 0.5–1.7 mm. across, sessile to shortly stalked, the disk slightly concave to slightly convex, brown, the algoid exciple entire or irregular and colored like the thallus, sometimes disappearing; hypothecium hyaline to brownish; spores ovoid-ellipsoid to ellipsoid-pointed, 3–5-septate transversely and 2-septate longitudinally, $18–30 \times 7–11 \mu$. (PLATE 8)
On trees, from Maine to Florida, and westward to Texas and Washington.

var. **azureum** (Swartz) Nyl., Syn. Lich. 1:125. 1858.
Lichen azureus Swartz, in Ach., Lich. Suec. 137. 1798. *Collema tremelloides* var. *cyanescens* (Hoffm.) Ach.
Thallus sky-blue, smooth to finally pitted, round and more regularly lobed.
On trees and rocks, southern United States.

15. **Leptogium arizonicum** Zahlbr., Bull. Torr. Club 35:299. 1908.
Transforming the algal colony into a small, imbricately lobed, olive-greenish to darker body, the lobes broad and entire or incised, ascending and slender; apothecia middle-sized, 0.8–1.2 mm. across. sessile, the disk slightly concave to convex, brown to dull blackish, the proper exciple thin, entire, usually darker than the disk; hypothecium hyaline; spores ellipsoid to ovoid-ellipsoid, 3-septate and finally submuriform, $18–27 \times 7–12 \mu$.
On basaltic cliffs, near Tucson, Arizona.

16. **Leptogium apalachense** Nyl., Mém. Soc. .Sci. Nat. Cherb. 5:334. 1857.
Collema apalachense (Nyl.) Tuck.
Transforming the algal colony into a small to middle-sized, delicately wrinkled, irregularly to radiately many, narrowly, usually convexly lobed, olivaceous body, ascending at the margin; paler and slightly ridged below; apothecia small, 0.3–0.6 mm. across, scattered or clustered, immersed to sessile, the disk concave to flat, reddish to reddish brown, the exciple thick, externally algoid and colored like the thallus or becoming brownish, the algoid portion disappearing; hypothecium hyaline; spores ellipsoid, 3-septate transversely and 1-septate longitudinally, $18–26 \times 11–14.5 \mu$.
On rocks, Georgia, Alabama, Tennessee, and Missouri.

17. **Leptogium juniperinum** Tuck., Am. Journ. Sci. 28:200. 1859.
L. tremelloides var. *juniperinum* (Tuck.) Hue. *L. tremelloides* var. *microphyllum* Tuck.
Transforming the algal colony into a small, minutely and wavy-lobed, rosette-like, lead-colored to dark green body, the lobes ascending, much imbricated and folded; apothecia small to middle-sized, 0.4–1 mm. across, sessile, the disk flat, red to reddish brown, the algoid exciple thin, lighter colored to brown; hypothecium brownish; spores ovoid-ellipsoid, 3–5-septate transversely and 1-septate longitudinally, $15–22 \times 7–9 \mu$.
On soil, twigs, and rocks, from Massachusetts to Alabama, and westward to Texas and Illinois.

18. **Leptogium bullatum** (Ach.) Mont., Ann. Sci. Nat. II. 16:113. 1841.
   Lichen bullatus Ach., Lich. Suec. 137. 1798.
   Transforming the algal colony into a middle-sized to large, irregularly lobed or nearly entire, rigid, wrinkled, dull blue to lead-colored, marginally ascending and often folded body; apothecia middle-sized to large, 1–2 mm. across, sessile to subpedicellate, the disk concave to nearly flat, red, the exciple algoid and colored like the thallus, becoming lobed; hypothecium hyaline to brownish; spores ovoid-pointed, 3–5-septate transversely and 1-septate longitudinally, 24–36 × 8–14 μ.
   On trees, South Carolina, Florida, and Texas.

19. **Leptogium phyllocarpum** (Pers.) Mont., Ann. Sci. Nat. Bot. III. 10:134. 1848.
   Collema phyllocarpum Pers., Gaud. Voyag. Uran. 204. 1826. *L. bullatum* var. *phyllocarpum* (Pers.) Tuck.
   Transforming the algal colony into a small to middle-sized, strongly wrinkled, irregularly lobed, lead-colored body, the lobes round, wavy, or variously cut; paler below; apothecia middle-sized to large, 1–2.5 mm. across, sessile, the disk concave, dull red to brownish, the proper exciple brownish, thin, surrounded by a heavy, folded, and wavy algoid one; hypothecium hyaline to cloudy; spores ovoid to ellipsoid, 3–5-septate transversely and becoming 1-septate longitudinally, 23–34 × 6–12 μ.
   On trees, Florida and Texas.

20. **Leptogium crenatellum** Tuck., Am. Journ. Sci. II. 28:200. 1859.
   Transforming the algal colony into a small to larger, dilated, umbilically attached, greenish gray, yellowish, brownish, or ashy squamulose body, with ascending, smooth lobes and wavy to crenate margins; apothecia small to middle-sized, 0.5–1 mm. across, sessile, the disk flat to slightly convex, reddish, the proper exciple thin, colored like the thallus, crenulate, finally disappearing; hypothecium hyaline to brownish; spores ovoid-ellipsoid, 3-septate transversely and becoming 1-septate longitudinally, 16–22 × 7–9 μ.
   On trees, in swamps, Vermont and Illinois.

21. **Leptogium marginellum** (Swartz) S. F. Gray, Nat. Arr. Brit. Pl. 1:401. 1821.
   Lichen marginellus Swartz, Nov. Gen. et Spec. Pl. 147. 1788.
   Transforming the algal colony into a middle-sized, more or less strongly and reticulately wrinkled, cut-lobed, lead-colored body, the lobes becoming branchlike with folded, curled, entire to subentire margins; apothecia minute, 0.1–0.25 mm. across, borne on the margins of the lobes, sessile, the disk flat, brownish to reddish brown, the proper exciple rather thick, pale to brownish, somewhat granulose, and becoming narrowly lobed; hypothecium hyaline to cloudy; spores ovoid to ellipsoid, 3–5-septate transversely and becoming 1-septate longitudinally, 20–30 × 10–12 μ.
   On trees, Florida, Alabama, Louisiana, and Texas.

22. **Leptogium pulchellum** (Ach.) Nyl., Mém. Soc. Sci. Nat. Cherb. 5:90. 1857.
   Collema pulchellum Ach., Syn. Lich. 321. 1814.
   Transforming the algal colony into a middle-sized to large, closely adnate or marginally ascending, delicately folded and wrinkled, irregularly lobed, lead-colored body, the lobes imbricated, round with wavy margins; lighter-colored below, and more or less pitted and wrinkled; apothecia middle-sized to larger, 0.7–2 mm. across, sessile to shortly stalked, the disk flat to slightly convex, reddish brown to brown, the algoid exciple thin and colored like the thallus; hypothecium hyaline to brownish; spores ellipsoid or ellipsoid-pointed, 5-septate transversely and 1–3-septate longitudinally, 18–30 × 8–14 μ.
   On trees and rocks, from Vermont to Florida, and westward to Texas and Washington.

23. **Leptogium palmatum** (Huds.) Mont., in Webb & Berth., Hist. Nat. Canar. 3²:128. 1840.
Lichen palmatus Huds., Fl. Angl. ed. 2. 535. 1778.
Transforming the algal colony into a middle-sized or larger, irregularly cut-lobed, sharply wrinkled and pitted, lead-colored to chestnut-brown body, becoming narrow, involute, tubular toward the ends, with toothed margins; paler and wrinkled below; apothecia minute to small, 0.2–0.5 mm. across, sessile, crowded, the disk concave, reddish brown, the algoid exciple thin, paler than the disk, slightly elevated; hypothecium hyaline to cloudy; spores ovoid, 5–7-septate transversely and 1–3-septate longitudinally, 30–52 × 12–18 μ.
On soil among mosses, from Texas to Colorado, and westward to California and Washington.

24. **Leptogium californicum** Tuck., Syn. N. A. Lich. 1:159. 1882.
L. californicum var. *lophotum* Tuck. *L. scotinum* var. *platynum* Tuck.
Transforming the algal colony into a rather large, finely and sharply wrinkled and often granulose, irregularly lobed to sometimes erectly branched, marginally dilated, elongated and crenate, ascending, bluish to blackish brown body; apothecia small to middle-sized, 0.4–0.8 mm. across, sessile, the disk slightly concave, reddish brown, the proper exciple thick and brownish; hypothecium hyaline to cloudy; spores ovoid-ellipsoid, 5–9-septate transversely and 1–3-septate longitudinally, 30–54 × 11–19 μ.
On rocks, California.

25. **Leptogium platynum** (Tuck.) Herre, Proc. Wash. Acad. Sci. 12:144. 1910.
L. californicum var. *platynum* Tuck., Gen. Lich. 96. 1872.
Transforming the algal colony into a middle-sized to large, round, appressed, irregularly lobed, finely striate or wrinkled, more or less pustulate, black or greenish black body, the lobes elongated, expanded, imbricate, with crenate or dentate margins; paler and finely wrinkled below; apothecia minute to small, 0.2–0.5 mm. across, sessile, the disk concave, reddish brown, the exciple thin and elevated, paler than the disk; hypothecium hyaline to cloudy; spores ellipsoid, 7–9-septate transversely and 1–3-septate longitudinally, 28–52 × 10–17 μ.
On soil and rocks, in moist places, California.

26. **Leptogium scotinum** (Ach.) E. Fries, Corp. Fl. Prov. Suec. 1:293. 1835.
Lichen scotinus Ach., Lich. Suec. 128. 1798. *L. scotinum* var. *sinuatum* (Huds.) Forss.
Transforming the algal colony into a small, round or irregular, wrinkled, cut-lobed, lead-colored to brown body, the lobes round, crowded, suberect, with entire to subcrenate margins; apothecia minute to small, 0.2–0.5 mm. across, sessile, scattered, the disk concave, reddish brown to brown, the proper exciple slightly elevated, colored like the disk or paler; hypothecium hyaline to cloudy; spores ovoid to ellipsoid-pointed, 7–9-septate transversely and 1–5-septate longitudinally, 24–40 × 8–15 μ.
On soil, southern California.

27. **Leptogium lichenoides** (L.) Zahlbr., Cat. Lich. Univ. 3:136. 1924.
Tremella lichenoides L., Sp. Pl. 1157. 1753. *L. lacerum* (Swartz) S. Gray.
L. lacerum var. *lophaeum* (Ach.) Koerb.
Transforming the algal colony into a middle-sized, more or less round, reticularly wrinkled, irregularly lobed, greenish brown to lead-colored body, the lobes ascending, expanded toward the ends, and divided into jagged or fringed margins; scarcely lighter below; apothecia small, 0.3–0.6 mm. across, subsessile and rare, the disk concave to flattish, reddish to reddish brown, the algoid exciple rather thick, colored like the thallus, entire; hypothecium hyaline to cloudy; spores ellipsoid, 5–11-septate transversely and 1–3-septate longitudinally, 26–50 × 11–18 μ.
Among mosses on rocks and on trees, throughout the United States.

var. **pulvinatum** (Hoffm.) Zahlbr., Cat. Lich. Univ. 3:142. 1924.
Collema pulvinatum Hoffm., Deutschl. Fl. 2:104. 1796. *L. lacerum* var. *pulvinatum* (Hoffm.) Mont.
Transforming the algal colony into a smaller, brownish, lobed body, the lobes smaller, densely crowded with finely fringed edges, usually sterile.
On humus, mosses, and dead pine leaves, Maine, Massachusetts, Minnesota, and California.

OTHER SPECIES REPORTED

Leptogium fragile (Tayl.) Nyl.—California.
Leptogium intricatulum Nyl.—New Hampshire.
Leptogium microdium (Nyl.) Zahlbr.—Southern California.
Leptogium pulvillus Tuck.—Pennsylvania.

29. HEPPIACEAE

Thallus squamulose, foliose, or more or less fruticose, commonly differentiated into upper and lower cortices, algal and medullary layers, sometimes more or less plectenchymatous throughout, usually attached to the substratum at the center; apothecia more or less immersed, the proper exciple indistinct, sometimes surrounded by a thalloid one.
The algal host is a blue-green, usually Polycoccus.

A. Spores 8 in each ascus . . . . 107. SOLORINARIA
A. Spores many in each ascus . . . . 106. HEPPIA

106. **Heppia** Naeg., in Hepp, Spor. Flecht. Eur. pl. 7, f. 49. 1853.

Thallus foliose, attached to the substratum by rhizoids, plectenchymatous throughout, but differentiated into an upper cortex of 3 or more layers of horizontally elongated cells, algal and medullary regions of loosely arranged and vertically elongated cells, and a lower cortex of 1 or more layers of horizontally elongated cells; apothecia minute to middle-sized, more or less immersed to adnate, the disk more or less concave to flat or slightly convex, reddish brown to brown and black, the exciple very thin to thin, colored like the thallus, sometimes wanting; hypothecium hyaline to brownish; hymenium hyaline or brownish above; paraphyses unbranched, somewhat coherent; asci clavate to cylindrical; spores many, hyaline, non-septate, spheroidal to oblong or ellipsoid.
The algal host is usually Polycoccus.

A. Spores subspherical or globose
  B. Thallus yellowish to olive-green . . . . 6. H. leptopholis
  B. Thallus olive-green to brownish
    C. Apothecia immersed, 1–8 in each squamule . . . . . 9. H. Zahlbruckneri
    C. Apothecia immersed to adnate, 1 in each squamule
      D. Apothecia 0.4–0.75 mm. across . . . . 5. H. terrena
      D. Apothecia 0.1–0.25 mm. across . . . . 8. H. placodizans
A. Spores subspherical to ovoid or oblong
  B. Spores rarely more than 7 µ in length
    C. Thallus with sorediate and usually revolute margins . . . . 1. H. Guepini
    C. Thallus not sorediate
      D. Squamules minute, crowded, subimbricate . . . . . . 2. H. Bolanderi
      D. Squamules small, not imbricate
        E. Margins entire to irregular . . . . 3. H. polyspora
        E. Margins irregular and lobulate-crenate . . . . . . 7. H. Hassei
  B. Spores 7–10 µ in length
    C. Thallus of small clustered squamules . . . . 4. H. deserticola
    C. Thallus of smaller, more scattered and
    depressed squamules . . . . 4. H. deserticola minor

1. **Heppia Guepini** (Del.) Nyl., in Hue, Lich. Exot. 125. 1892.
Endocarpon Guepini Del., in Duby, Bot. Gall. 2:594. 1830. *Endocarpiscum Guepini* (Del.) Nyl.
Thallus thick, composed of large, flat to variously irregular, olive-green to brownish, foliose squamules with raised, sorediate, and usually revolute margins;

smooth to wrinkled, and flesh-colored to brown below; apothecia small, 0.3–0.5 mm. across, deeply immersed to adnate, the disk flat, dark brown, the exciple very thin, colored like the thallus; spores spheroidal to oblong, 3–5 × 1–2 μ.

On rocks, Massachusetts, Maryland, Arkansas, Minnesota, and California.

2. **Heppia Bolanderi** (Tuck.) Vainio, Act. Soc. Faun. Flor. Fenn. 7:215. 1890.
Pannaria Bolanderi Tuck., Gen. Lich. 51. 1872. *Endocarpiscum Bolanderi* Tuck.

Thallus thin, composed of minute, crowded, subimbricate, smooth, olive-green to dark brown squamules, with raised, crenate to lobate, sometimes obscurely powdery margins; apothecia minute to small, 0.3–0.6 mm. across, immersed to adnate, the disk flat to convex, reddish brown, the exciple thin, colored like the thallus; spores ellipsoid, 4–6 × 1.5–2 μ.

On rocks, Arizona and California.

3. **Heppia polyspora** Tuck., Syn. N. A. Lich. 1:115. 1882.
Endocarpiscum polyspora (Tuck.) Fink.

Thallus squamulose-foliose, thin, very small to small, olive-green to brownish, closely attached, round to irregular, flat or depressed, with raised margins; apothecia minute to small, 0.2–0.5 mm. across, immersed, the disk concave to flat, dull brown; hypothecium hyaline to yellowish; spores minute, subspherical to ovoid, 4–7.5 × 2–5 μ.

On soil and rocks, Minnesota, Nebraska, Arizona, Colorado, and California.

4. **Heppia deserticola** Zahlbr., Bull. Torr. Club 35:300. 1908.

Thallus thin, composed of more or less clustered, rather small, flat squamules with raised, incised to lobate margins, light to darker brown; apothecia small to middle-sized, 0.4–0.8 mm. across, immersed, 1 in each squamule, the disk slightly concave to flat, brownish black, the exciple very thin, colored like the thallus, soon disappearing; spores ovoid to oblong-ovoid, 7–10 × 3–5 μ.

On basaltic boulders, near Tucson, Arizona.

var. **minor** Zahlbr., Ann. Mycol. 7:474. 1909.

Thallus composed of minute to small, more or less clustered or scattered, flat or depressed toward the center, brownish to dark brown squamules; apothecia immersed to adnate.

On rocks, Arizona.

5. **Heppia terrena** Nyl.; Hasse, Bull. Torr. Club 24:445. 1897.

Thallus thin, composed of small, closely attached, usually scattered, flat, round to slightly irregular, dark olive-green squamules, with the margins usually slightly raised; apothecia small to middle-sized, 0.4–0.75 mm. across, partly immersed to adnate, solitary and often occupying nearly the whole squamule, the disk flat, reddish brown to brown, the exciple very thin, colored like the thallus, or turning brownish; spores globose, 3.5–4.5 μ across.

On soil, southern California.

6. **Heppia leptopholis** Nyl., in Hasse, Lich. South. Calif. 10. 1898.

Thallus composed of moderately thick, medium-sized, closely attached, concave to flat, often finely reticulated and fissured, yellowish to olive-green squamules; apothecia small, 0.35–0.5 mm. across, immersed, 1–4 or 5 in each squamule, the disk punctiform to concave or flat, reddish brown, the exciple rudimentary or absent; spores 16–24, globose, 4.5–6 μ across.

On soil, southern California.

7. **Heppia Hassei** Zahlbr., Beih. Bot. Centralb. 13:157. 1902.

Thallus thin, composed of small, appressed, round to somewhat irregular and lobulate-crenate, olive-green to brownish squamules, with slightly raised margins; apothecia minute, 0.1–0.4 mm. across, immersed 1 in each squamule, the disk flat, punctiform to plainly open and reddish brown, the exciple absent or very thin, colored like the thallus; spores ovoid-ellipsoid to subglobose, 5–7 × 3.5–4 μ.

On rocks, southern California.

8. **Heppia placodizans** Zahlbr., Bull. Torr. Club 35:297–300. 1908.
Endocarpiscum placodizans (Zahlbr.) Fink.

Thallus thin to rather thick, composed of small, wartlike, olive-green to umber-brown squamules, often becoming crowded, convex to semiglobose toward the center and lobed toward the margin; apothecia minute, 0.1–0.25 mm. across, deeply immersed, the disk punctiform, dull black; spores subspherical, 3–3.5 μ across.

On basaltic boulders, near Tucson, Arizona.

9. **Heppia Zahlbruckneri** Hasse, Bryologist 14:100, 101. 1911.

Thallus thin, composed of very short, erect, cylindrical to somewhat flattened, clustered, olive-green to darker, loosely attached lobules, with bulbous, flat, or clavate apices; apothecia minute, 0.2–0.3 mm. across, 1–8 immersed in the apex of each lobule, the disk punctiform or slightly open, dull brown; hypothecium hyaline to pale yellowish; spores 24–32, globose, 5–7 μ across.

On rocks, southern California.

OTHER SPECIES REPORTED

Heppia alumenensis Herre—California.
Heppia conchiloba Zahlbr.—Southern California.
Heppia planescens Nyl.—Texas.
Heppia psammophila Nyl.—California.

107. **Solorinaria** Vainio, Act. Soc. Faun. Fl. Fenn. 7:217. 1890.

Thallus crustose to minutely foliose, scaly or squamulose, closely attached, plectenchymatous throughout with upper and lower cortices of horizontally elongated hyphae; apothecia small to middle-sized, more or less immersed, the disk more or less concave to flat or rarely convex, the exciple colored like the thallus, often scarcely developed; hypothecium hyaline to brownish; hymenium hyaline or brownish above; paraphyses unbranched, becoming coherent; asci cylindrico-clavate; spores 8, hyaline, oblong to oblong-ellipsoid or ellipsoid, non-septate.

The algal host is usually Polycoccus.

1. **Solorinaria Despreauxii** (Mont.) Fink n. comb.
Solorina Despreauxii Mont., in Webb & Berth., Hist. Nat. Canar. 3:104. 1840.
Heppia virescens (Mont.) Nyl. *Heppia Despreauxii* (Mont.) Tuck.

Thallus moderately thick, composed of minute to small, closely attached, often clustered, round, flat, finally chinky and rough squamules, with raised, crenately lobed margins, olive to greenish or blackish; apothecia small to middle-sized, 0.6–2 mm. across, immersed, 1–many in each squamule, the disk deeply concave to rarely convex, reddish brown, the exciple scarcely developed; spores oblong-ellipsoid, 16–26 × 6–10 μ.

On soil, throughout the United States.

30. PANNARIACEAE

Thallus crustose, squamulose or foliose, entire or lobed at the margin, differentiated into upper and lower cortices, algal and medullary layers, usually attached to the substratum by rhizoids; apothecia round, sometimes marginal, with a proper or thalloid exciple.

The algal hosts are Dactylococcus, Nostoc, and Scytonema.

A. Thallus with blue-green algal host cells
  B. Under surface of thallus not veined
    C. Spores non-septate
      D. Apothecia with proper exciple
        E. Thallus with upper cortex only . . . . . . 111. PARMELIELLA
        E. Thallus with upper and lower cortices . . . . 114. COCCOCARPIA

     D. Apothecia with thalloid exciple　　. . . . . 112. PANNARIA
   C. Spores septate
     D. Lower cortex poorly developed　　. . . . . . . 109. MASSALONGIA
     D. Lower cortex wanting . . . . 110. PLACYNTHIUM
  B. Under surface of thallus veined . . . . 108. HYDROTHYRIA
A. Thallus with green algal host cells . . . . 113. PSOROMA

108. Hydrothyria Russell, Proc. Essex. Sust. 1:188–91. 1856.

Thallus foliose, composed externally of a plectenchymatous cortex, one to several layers thick, better developed above and under the apothecia; the medullary area composed of densely interwoven hyphae; apothecia sessile, subterminal, with proper exciple; hypothecium hyaline; paraphyses stout, several-septate, sometimes branched toward the enlarged, brownish apices; asci clavate; spores 8, hyaline, 3-septate.

The algal host is a short-chained form of Nostoc, and is scattered throughout the medulla.

1. Hydrothyria venosa Russell, Proc. Essex. Sust. 1:188–91. 1856.

Thallus large, thin and brittle, lead-colored to brownish or blackish, loosely lobed, the lobes fan-shaped, irregularly cut, obtusely crenate toward the ends; bearing prominent brown, branched veins below; apothecia small to middle-sized, 0.75–2.5 mm. across, sessile and submarginal, the disk flat to convex, reddish brown, the exciple becoming torn-dentate and disappearing; spores fusiform-ellipsoid, 24–32 × 7–8.5 μ.

On rocks in mountain brooks, from New England to North Carolina, and recurring in California.

109. Massalongia Koerb., Syst. Lich. 109. 1855.

Thallus foliose, squamulose, or becoming almost crustose, smooth, resting upon a well-developed, soon disappearing, black hypothallus, differentiated into a well-developed, thin, plectenchymatous upper cortex of vertically extending, septate hyphae, a thin irregular algal layer, and a more or less spongy medullary layer; apothecia marginal, sessile, the disk flat to convex, the exciple thin, colored like the thallus; hypothecium hyaline; hymenium hyaline or brownish above; paraphyses unbranched; asci clavate; spores 8, hyaline to somewhat brownish, ellipsoid to oblong-ellipsoid or spindle-shaped, 1-septate.

The algal host is Scytonema.

1. Massalongia carnosa (Dicks.) Koerb., Syst. Lich. 109, 110. 1855.

Lichen carnosus Dicks., Pl. Crypt. Br. 2:21. pl. 6, f. 7. 1790. Pannaria carnosa (Dicks.) Rabh.

Thallus composed of lobate, incised, suberect, often granular, imbricated, pale to dark brown squamules; whitish below; apothecia small, 0.4–0.6 mm. across, sessile, the disk flat to slightly convex, dark red to brown, the proper exciple thin, usually lighter colored than the disk; spores oblong-ellipsoid to ellipsoid, finally 1-septate, 19–26 × 6.5–12 μ.

Among mosses on boulders, Yosemite Valley, California.

110. Placynthium Ach.; S. F. Gray, Nat. Arr. Brit. Pl. 1:395. 1821.

Thallus foliose, squamulose or becoming almost crustose, smooth to more or less rough, irregularly lobed, sometimes resting upon a thin, soon disappearing, blue-black hypothallus, differentiated into a well-developed, plectenchymatous upper cortex, an irregular algal layer and a thin, poorly developed lower cortex, or appearing plectenchymatous throughout; apothecia minute to small or rarely middle-sized, slightly immersed to adnate or sessile, the disk concave or flat to more or less convex, the exciple thin, colored like the disk, sometimes disappearing;

hypothecium hyaline to brown; hymenium hyaline or bluish brown above; paraphyses unbranched; asci clavate; spores 8, hyaline, oblong to oblong-ellipsoid or ellipsoid, 1–3-septate.

The algal host is Scytonema.

A. Spores 1-septate . . . . 4. P. stenophylla
A. Spores 1–3-septate
  B. Thallus of minute squamules, passing into a thin, granulose crust
    C. Thallus lead-ashy   . . . . 1. P. nigrum
    C. Thallus dark gray to ashy white   . . . . 1. P. nigrum caesium
  B. Thallus more or less distinctly squamulose, the
    squamules more or less lobed
    C. The squamules sometimes covered with coralloid branchlets,
      the lobes narrow, much divided . . . . 3. P. flabellosum
    C. The squamules irregularly lobed, the lobes entire   . . 2. P. microphyllizum

1. **Placynthium nigrum** (Huds.) S. F. Gray, Nat. Arr. Brit. Pl. 1:395. 1821.
    Lichen niger Huds., Flora Angl. II. 2:524. 1778. *Pannaria nigra* (Huds.) Nyl.

Thallus composed of minute, lead-ashy, scattered and lobed squamules, or more often the squamules heaped into a thin, broken, granulose crust, on a thin, bluish black hypothallus; apothecia minute to small, 0.2–0.6 mm. across, sessile, the disk flat to convex, reddish brown to more commonly black, the proper exciple thin, brownish black to black, soon disappearing; hypothecium brownish to brown; hymenium hyaline below to bluish brown toward the top; spores oblong, 1–3-septate, 11–16 × 4.5–7 μ.

On rocks, throughout northern United States.

    var. **caesium** (Schaer.) Hue, Bull. Soc. Linn. Normand. V. 9:146. 1906.
    Lecidea triptophylla var. *caesia* Schaer., Enum. Lich. Eur. 99. 1850. (pr. p.)
      Pannaria nigra var. *caesia* (Schaer.) Malbr.

Thallus dark gray to ashy white.

On calcareous rocks, New York and Iowa.

2. **Placynthium microphyllizum** (Nyl.) Hasse, Cont. U. S. Nat. Herb. 17¹:81. 1913.
    Pannularia microphylliza Nyl.; Hasse, Lich. South. Calif. 9. 1898.

Thallus thin, composed of small, dark yellowish brown to cervine brown, closely clustered, irregularly somewhat lobed, marginally ascending squamules; pale below; apothecia small to middle-sized, 0.4–0.8 mm. across, sessile, the disk slightly concave to convex, dark reddish brown, the proper exciple thin, lighter colored than the disk, finally disappearing; hypothecium hyaline to yellowish; asci inflated-clavate; spores long-ellipsoid, 1–3-septate, 16–28 × 6–9 μ.

On rocks, southern California.

3. **Placynthium flabellosum** (Tuck.) Zahlbr., Cat. Lich. Univ. 3:227. 1925.
    Pannaria flabellosa Tuck., Proc. Am. Acad. 5:401. 1862.

Thallus thin, composed of small, pale lead-colored to ashy, irregularly lobed squamules, sometimes covered with coralloid branchlets, the lobes narrow, elongated, much divided, longitudinally striate and expanded toward the circumference, round and heaped toward the center, on an indistinct, bluish black hypothallus; apothecia minute to small, 0.2–0.4 mm. across, partly immersed to closely adnate, the disk flat to slightly convex, reddish brown to black, the proper exciple thin, becoming black, and rarely disappearing; spores oblong-ellipsoid, 1–3-septate, 16–20 × 5–7 μ.

On granite rocks, New Hampshire, Vermont, and Minnesota.

4. **Placynthium stenophylla** (Tuck.) Fink n. comb.
    Pannaria stenophylla Tuck., Proc. Am. Acad. 12:169. 1877. *Parmeliella stenophylla* (Tuck.) Zahlbr.

Thallus minute, round and stellate, greenish brown, the lobes round, branched toward the circumference, becoming squamulose or granulose, and sometimes dying toward the center; grayish to brownish below; apothecia minute, 0.15–0.25 mm. across, the disk concave to flat, brown, the exciple colored like the thallus, soon disappearing; spores 1-septate, oblong-ellipsoid, somewhat curved, 13–20 × 3–5 μ. On calcareous rocks, Alabama.

OTHER SPECIES REPORTED

Placynthium dubium Herre—California.

111. Parmeliella Müll. Arg., Mém. Soc. Phys. et Hist. Nat.
Genève 16:376. 1862.

Thallus squamulose to crustose, smooth to rough, more or less irregularly lobed, resting upon a well-developed, bluish black hypothallus or attached to the substratum by short rhizoids, differentiated into a plectenchymatous upper cortex of vertical-extending hyphae, and irregular algal and medullary layers; apothecia small to middle-sized, partly immersed to adnate or sessile, the disk flat to convex, the exciple colored like the disk, often disappearing; hypothecium hyaline to brownish; hymenium hyaline or brownish above; paraphyses unbranched; asci clavate; spores 8, hyaline, oblong or ellipsoid, non-septate.
The algal host is Nostoc.

A. On rocks and soil
  B. Thallus composed of squamules, often passing into a granulose crust
    C. Squamules and lobes dichotomously much-branched
      D. Thallus lead-gray . . . . 1. P. crossophylla
      D. Thallus greenish gray to straw-colored . . . . . . 3. P. cheiroloba
    C. Squamules and lobes more or less irregular
      D. Thallus more or less gray-sorediate
        E. Squamules marginally warty . . . . 2. P. lepidiota
        E. Squamules passing into irregularly swollen
          branchlets . . . . 2. P. lepidiota corallophora
      D. Thallus not sorediate
        E. Squamules greenish gray to ashy or ashy brown
          F. Squamules rather thin; apothecia not more than
            1 mm. across . . . . 5. P. microphylla
          F. Squamules thicker; apothecia reaching
            1.5 mm. across . . . . 5. P. microphylla californica
        E. Squamules dark yellowish brown . . . . 9. P. ruderatula
  B. Thallus composed of granules . . . . 6. P. cyanolepra
A. On trees
  B. Spores 14–24 μ in length
    C. Squamules irregularly lobed toward the circumference . . . 7. P. plumbea
    C. Squamules passing into a densely granulose crust . . . 4. P. corallinoides
  B. Spores 5–10 μ in length . . . . 8. P. stellata

1. **Parmeliella crossophylla** (Tuck.) Merrill & Burnh., Bryologist 25:36. 1922. *Pannaria crossophylla* Tuck., in Nyl., Ann. Sci. Nat. Bot. IV. 12:295. 1859.
Thallus composed of small, dichotomously much-branched, imbricated, marginally ascending, lead-gray squamules, passing centrally into a subsquamulose or granulose, warty crust; blackening toward the center below; apothecia small to middle-sized, 0.5–1 mm. across, immersed to partly superficial, the disk flat to convex, flesh-colored to chestnut-brown, the exciple thin, colored like the disk, soon disappearing; hypothecium hyaline; spores ellipsoid, 17–23 × 6–10 μ.
On rocks, from Vermont to Alabama, and westward to Illinois.

2. **Parmeliella lepidiota** (Sommerf.) Vainio, Term. Füz. 22:308. 1899.
Lecidea carnosa var. *lepidiota* Sommerf., Suppl. Fl. Lapp. 174. 1826. *Pannaria lepidiota* (Sommerf.) T. Fries.
Thallus composed of small to middle-sized, closely imbricated, crenately lobed, marginally warty and gray-sorediate, gray to brownish or blackening squamules, those of the central portion often ascending and passing into a granulose, gray, powdery crust; brownish to brown below, a bordering black hypothallus evident

in young plants; apothecia small to middle-sized, 0.5–2 mm. across, adnate to sessile, the disk flat to convex, reddish to blackish brown, the exciple thin, brownish to brown, disappearing; hypothecium hyaline to brownish; spores ovoid-ellipsoid to ellipsoid-pointed, 18–25 × 7–11 μ.

On soil and rocks, throughout northern United States and California.

  var. **corallophora** (Tuck.) Herre, Proc. Wash. Acad. Sci. 12:150, 151. 1910.
  Pannaria lepidiota var. *corallophora* Tuck., Syn. N. A. Lich. 1:122. 1882.
  Thallus passing into stout, short, irregularly swollen branchlets.
  On soil and rocks, southern California.

3. **Parmeliella cheiroloba** Müll. Arg., Hedwigia 34:140. 1895.
Thallus closely adnate throughout or marginally ascending, irregularly lobed, greenish gray to straw-colored, the lobes dichotomously much-branched, smooth to minutely wrinkled, passing into a thick, closely adnate, granulose to warty, brownish gray to darker crust; apothecia small to middle-sized, 0.5–1 mm. across, partly immersed to adnate, the disk flat to convex, flesh-colored to chestnut-brown and darker, the exciple very thin, colored like the disk, soon disappearing; hypothecium hyaline to pale brownish; spores ovoid-ellipsoid, 16–22 × 8–11 μ.
On soil, Montana.

4. **Parmeliella corallinoides** (Hoffm.) Zahlbr., Ann. Nat. Hofm. Wien. 13:462. 1899.
  Stereocaulon corallinoides Hoffm., Deutschl. Fl. 129. 1796. *Parmelia triptophylla* (Ach.) E. Fries. *Parmelia triptophylla* var. *corallinoides* (Hoffm.) Tuck. *Pannaria triptophylla* (Ach.) Mass.
Thallus composed of minute to small, pale yellowish to livid brownish, narrowly lobed, expanded squamules, often passing into a densely granulose crust, upon a bluish black hypothallus; apothecia small to middle-sized, 0.5–1 mm. across, sessile, the disk flat to convex, reddish to chestnut-brown, the proper exciple thin, brownish to chestnut-brown and disappearing; hypothecium hyaline to straw-colored; spores ellipsoid, 14–20 × 5–8 μ.
On trees, from New England and New York to South Carolina and Louisiana.

5. **Parmeliella microphylla** (Swartz) Müll. Arg., Flora 72:507. 1889.
  Lichen microphyllus Swartz; Westr., Vet. Akad. Handl. 301. 1791. *Parmelia microphylla* (Swartz) E. Fries. *Pannaria microphylla* (Swartz) Mass.
Thallus composed of small, greenish gray to ashy or ashy brown, closely adnate to marginally ascending, more or less imbricated, crenate squamules, often passing into a rather thick, rough crust; black below; apothecia small to middle-sized, 0.5–1 mm. across, adnate to subsessile, the disk flat to convex, pale reddish brown to black, the exciple thick, colored like the thallus, often disappearing; hypothecium hyaline; spores oblong-ellipsoid, 13–19 × 5–7 μ.
On rocks, throughout the United States.

  f. **californica** (Tuck.) Zahlbr., Cat. Lich. Univ. 3:216. 1925.
  Pannaria microphylla f. *californica* Tuck., Syn. N. A. Lich. 1:121. 1882.
  Thallus composed of usually thicker, rougher squamules; apothecia reaching 1.5 mm. across; spores 15–24 × 6–9 μ.
  On rocks, California.

6. **Parmeliella cyanolepra** (Tuck.) Herre, Proc. Wash. Acad. Sci. 12:151. 1910.
  Pannaria cyanolepra Tuck., Lich. Calif. 17. 1866. *Pannaria lepidiota* var. *cyanolepra* Tuck.
Thallus composed of minute, continuous and conglomerate, steel-blue granules; apothecia small to almost middle-sized, 0.3–0.7 mm. across, partly immersed to adnate, the disk flat to convex, dark reddish to blackish, the exciple thin, colored like the disk, soon disappearing; hypothecium brownish; spores ovoid-ellipsoid, 16–22 × 7–9 μ.
On soil and rocks, California.

7. **Parmeliella plumbea** (Lightf.) Müll. Arg., Bull. Herb. Boiss. 2: app. 1. 44.
1894.
Lichen plumbeus Lightf., Fl. Scot. 2:826. pl. 26. 1777. *Pannaria plumbea*
(Lightf.) Bory.

Thallus small to middle-sized, round, yellowish brown to brownish lead-colored,
composed of imbricated lobules toward the center, irregularly lobed toward the
circumference, the lobes radiately wrinkled, with round or round-crenate margins;
bearing pale to bluish black rhizoids below; apothecia small to middle-sized, 0.6–
2 mm. across, subsessile, the disk flat to convex, reddish brown to blackish, the
proper exciple thin, lighter colored and disappearing; spores ellipsoid, 16–24 ×
6–9 μ.

On trees, Maine and Louisiana.

8. **Parmeliella stellata** (Nyl.) Zahlbr., Cat. Lich. Univ. 3:224. 1925.
Pannaria stellata Nyl., Ann. Sci. Nat. Bot. IV. 12:295. 1859. *Coccocarpia*
stellata (Nyl.) Tuck.

Thallus composed of minute to small, lead-colored, linear and flattened lobes,
many-cleft and radiant at the circumference and becoming densely imbricated
toward the center; white below and bearing whitish rhizoids; apothecia minute to
small, 0.2–0.6 mm. across, sessile, the disk flat to convex, reddish brown, the
exciple thin, reddish brown, bearing minute white rhizoids below, often disappearing; spores ellipsoid, 5–10 × 3–4.5 μ.

On trees, South Carolina, Florida, and Alabama.

9. **Parmeliella ruderatula** (Nyl.) Hasse, Cont. U. S. Nat. Herb. 17:79. 1913.
Pannularia ruderatula Nyl., in Hasse, Lich. South. Calif. 10. 1898.

Thallus composed of minute to small, dark yellowish brown, imbricated, concave to slightly convex squamules, with minutely crenulate margins, upon an
obscure, brownish black hypothallus; apothecia small to middle-sized, 0.6–1 mm.
across, sessile, the disk flat, brownish to purplish brown, the proper exciple thin,
brownish to brown, rarely disappearing; asci inflated-clavate; hypothecium hyaline
to pale straw-colored; spores oblong-ellipsoid, 17–21 × 5.5–7 μ.

On rocks, southern California.

112. **Pannaria** Del., in Bory, Dict. Class. Hist. Nat. 13:20. 1828.

Thallus distinctly foliose or more commonly small and squamulose, quite
closely attached to the substratum by rhizoids, or resting upon a more or less distinct hypothallus, differentiated into a well-developed, distinctly cellular upper
cortex, distinct algal and medullary layers and a thin, distinctly cellular lower
cortex, or in the squamulose conditions appearing to be plectenchymatous throughout with algal cells scattered throughout except in the outer cells of the cortex;
apothecia minute to small or middle-sized, adnate to sessile, the disk concave to flat
or convex, red to brown or black, the exciple colored like the thallus, irregular,
sometimes disappearing; hypothecium hyaline to brown; hymenium hyaline or
brownish above; paraphyses rarely branched; asci clavate; spores 8, hyaline, oblong
to ellipsoid or ellipsoid-pointed, non-septate.

The algal host is Nostoc.

A. Apothecia not more than 0.5 mm. across
  B. Spores 9–13 × 4–5.5 μ . . . . 1. P. granatina
  B. Spores 20–33 × 2–3 μ . . . . 3. P. sonomensis
A. Apothecia more than .05 mm. across
  B. Hypothallus dark, more or less distinct
    C. Thallus plainly foliose, the lobes marginally ascending
      D. Thallus densely sorediate . . . . 6. P. rubiginosa lanuginosa
      D. Thallus smooth to minutely granulose . . . . . . 6. P. rubiginosa
    C. Thallus squamulose, closely adnate
      D. The margins white-powdery . . . . 4. P. leucosticta
      D. The margins not white-powdery . . . . 5. P. mariana

B. Hypothallus whitish or wanting
  C. Spores 13–18 × 7–9.5 µ . . . . 7. P. lurida
  C. Spores 17–29 × 8–13 µ . . . . 2. P. pezizoides

1. **Pannaria granatina** (Sommerf.) T. Fries, Nov. Act. Soc. Sci. Ups. III. 3:277. 1861.
Lecanora granatina Sommerf., Suppl. Fl. Lapp. 90. 1826.
Thallus minute, granular, becoming chinky, round to somewhat irregular, scarcely lobed, reddish brown, attached at a single point; blackening below; apothecia minute to small, 0.15–0.3 mm. across, adnate, the disk flat to convex, reddish brown, the thalloid exciple thin, subcrenulate, sometimes disappearing; spores oblong, 9–13 × 4–5.5 µ.
On rocks, Maine and New Hampshire.

2. **Pannaria pezizoides** (Weberi) Trevis., Lich. Vene. 98. 1869.
Lichen pezizoides Weberi, Spic. Fl. Goet. 200. 1778. *P. brunnea* (Swartz) Mass.
Thallus round, squamulose, brownish or grayish lead-colored to brown, the squamules minute to small, densely imbricated, crenate or deeply cut, often crowded into a granulose mass; a thin, whitish, cobwebby hypothallus sometimes persisting below; apothecia middle-sized, 0.6–1.5 mm. across, adnate, often crowded and irregular, the disk flat to convex, brick-red to reddish brown, the exciple thin, crenulate, colored like the thallus; hypothecium hyaline to brownish; spores ellipsoid to ellipsoid-pointed, 17–29 × 8–13 µ.
On soil and over moss, New England, New York, Colorado, Wyoming, Washington, and California.

3. **Pannaria sonomensis** Tuck., Proc. Am. Acad. 12:169. 1877.
Parmeliella sonomensis (Tuck.) Hasse. *Placynthium sonomense* (Tuck.) Herre.
Thallus small, composed of minute to small, linear, elongated, many-cleft, greenish brown lobes; whitish below, on a thin black hypothallus; apothecia minute to small, 0.1–0.3 mm. across, sessile, the disk flat to convex and rarely subglobose, reddish brown to black, the thalloid exciple thin, colored like the thallus or lighter, rarely disappearing; hypothecium hyaline to brownish; spores 8, hyaline, fusiform, sometimes curved, non-septate, 20–33 × 2–3 µ.
On rocks, southern California. (Description compiled, the algal host was Scytonema instead of Nostoc.)

4. **Pannaria leucosticta** Tuck.; Nyl., Ann. Sci. Nat. Bot. IV. 12:294. 1859.
Thallus squamulose, ashy to brownish or bluish brown, the squamules thick, small, closely adnate, the marginal ones expanded, elongated, crenate or pinnately lobed, the central ones smaller, densely imbricated, ascendant with entire or dentate-crenate, white-powdery margins; whitish below or darkened by the bluish black, also bordering hypothallus; apothecia middle-sized, 1–1.5 mm. across, adnate, the disk flat to convex, reddish brown, the exciple thin, colored like the thallus, crenate, often white-powdery; hypothecium hyaline to slightly brownish; spores ovoid-ellipsoid to ellipsoid-pointed, 16–22 × 8–13 µ. (PLATE 9.)
On trees and rocks, throughout the United States east of the Rocky Mountains.

5. **Pannaria mariana** (E. Fries) Müll. Arg., Flora 70:321. 1887.
Parmelia mariana E. Fries, Syst. Orb. Veg. 1:284. 1825. *P. pannosa* Nyl.
Thallus rather thin and smooth, middle-sized to large, round, bright greenish gray to ashy or brownish, composed of narrow, flattish, many-cleft, radiant-crowded to separate lobes with crenate to variously cut margins, upon a dense, bordering, black hypothallus; apothecia middle-sized, 0.7–1.5 mm. across, sessile, the disk flat, red to brownish red, the thalloid exciple thick, colored like the thallus, becoming crenate, or disappearing and exposing a thin, pale, proper one; spores ovoid-ellipsoid, 16–25 × 7–10 µ.
On trees, South Carolina, Florida, Alabama, and Louisiana.

6. **Pannaria rubiginosa** (Thunb.) Del., in Bory, Dict. Class. Hist. Nat. 13:20. 1828.

Lichen rubiginosus Thunb., in Ach., Lich. Suec. Prod. 99. 1798.

Thallus round, plainly foliose, middle-sized to large, smooth to minutely granulose, greenish gray to ashy, yellowish, or lead-colored, the lobes elongated, more or less imbricated, deeply waved or divided toward the raised and crenate margins; lighter to darkening below and covered with light to darkening rhizoids upon an obscure bluish black hypothallus; apothecia small to middle-sized, 0.5–2.5 mm. across, sessile, the disk flat to slightly concave, red to reddish brown, the exciple thick, crenulate, colored like the thallus; hypothecium brownish; spores ellipsoid-pointed, 14–26 × 6–11 μ.

On trees, throughout the United States.

var. **lanuginosa** (Hoffm.) Zahlbr., Cat. Lich. Univ. 3:258. 1925.

Lichen lanuginosus Hoffm., Enum. Lich. 82. pl. 10, f. 4. 1784. *Parmelia conoplea* (Pers.) Ach. *P. conoplea* (Pers.) Bory. *P. rubiginosa* var. *conoplea* (Pers.) Koerb.

Thallus bluish gray to darker, densely grayish sorediate, passing toward the center into a continuous crust; apothecia often without thalloid exciple.

On trees, New England, North Carolina, West Virginia, Minnesota, and California.

7. **Pannaria lurida** (Mont.) Nyl., Mém. Soc. Sci. Nat. Cherb. 5:109. 1857.

Collema luridum Mont., Ann. Sci. Nat. Bot. II. 18:266. 1842. *Parmelia Russellii* Tuck. *Physma luridum* (Mont.) Tuck.

Thallus middle-sized to large, wrinkled and powdery, greenish gray to yellowish or bluish gray, the lobes irregular, imbricated, with crenate or cut margins; pale below and covered more or less with pale or blackening rhizoids; apothecia small to middle-sized, 0.8–2.5 mm. across, adnate, the disk flat to convex, reddish brown to brownish black, the exciple thin, colored like the thallus, wrinkled to crenate; hypothecium hyaline to slightly brownish; spores ellipsoid to ellipsoid-pointed, 13–18 × 7–9.5 μ.

On trees and rocks, from Maine to Florida, and westward to Illinois and Missouri.

OTHER SPECIES REPORTED

Pannaria Halei Tuck.—Louisiana.
Pannaria melamphylla Tuck.—Vermont.

113. **Psoroma** Nyl., Mém. Soc. Sci. Nat. Cherb. 3:175. 1855.

Thallus squamulose, more or less irregular, commonly smooth, usually attached to the substratum by few rhizoids, differentiated into a well-developed cellular cortex of several rows of horizontal plectenchyma or rarely of irregular interwoven hyphae, more or less indistinct algal and medullary layers and a thin lower cortex composed of densely interwoven hyphae; apothecia middle-sized to large, adnate to sessile, the disk concave to flat, red to brown, the exciple colored like the thallus; hypothecium and hymenium hyaline; paraphyses unbranched, more or less coherent; asci clavate; spores 8, hyaline, ellipsoid to ovoid-ellipsoid or spherical, non-septate.

The algal host is Dactylococcus (?).

1. **Psoroma hypnorum** (Vahl.) S. F. Gray, Nat. Arr. Brit. Pl. 1:445. 1821.

Lichen hypnorum Vahl., Icon. Pl. Dan. fasc. 16. pl. 956. 1787. *Parmelia hypnorum* (Vahl.) Ach. *Pannaria hypnorum* (Vahl.) Koerb.

Thallus composed of minute, round, crenate, and imbricate, granulose, ascending, yellowish to reddish brown or finally grayish squamules; pale below; apothecia middle-sized to large, 1.5–5 mm. across, sessile, the disk concave to flat, reddish

brown to brown, the exciple thin, prominent, crenate and becoming granulose; spores ovoid-ellipsoid, 16–23 × 7–11 μ.
On soil among mosses, New Hampshire, from Montana to Washington, and southward to New Mexico.

114. **Coccocarpia** Pers., in Gaud., Voy. Uran. Bot. 206. 1826.

Thallus foliose or squamulose, smooth to rough, more or less lobed, differentiated into a well-developed, plectenchymatous upper cortex of longitudinally extending hyphae, an algal layer, and a more or less well-developed medullary layer passing into the plectenchymatous lower cortex of longitudinally extending hyphae; more or less densely clothed below with bluish black rhizoids; apothecia minute to small or larger, adnate, the disk flat to convex, the exciple colored like the disk, disappearing; hypothecium hyaline to brownish; hymenium hyaline or brownish above; paraphyses unbranched; asci clavate; spores 8, hyaline, ellipsoid to oblong-ellipsoid or spindle-shaped, non-septate.
The algal host is Scytonema.

A. Thallus smooth or bearing coralloid branchlets, the lobes entire . . 2. C. pellita
A. Thallus covered with minute coralloid branchlets, the
   lobes irregularly incised . . . . 1. C. incisa

1. **Coccocarpia incisa** Pers., in Gaud., Voy. Uran. Bot. 206. 1826.
C. molybdaea var. *incisa* (Pers.) Nyl. *Pannaria molybdaea* var. *incisa* (Pers.) Tuck. *C. pellita* var. *incisa* (Pers.) Müll. Arg. *C. cronia* (Tuck.) Vainio.
Thallus small to middle-sized, smooth to rough and covered with minute coralloid branchlets, irregularly lobed, grayish to lead-colored or greenish gray; whitish to brownish below and densely covered with bluish black rhizoids; apothecia minute to small, 0.4–0.8 mm. across, adnate, sometimes white-fibrillose below, the disk convex, reddish brown to black, the exciple colored like the disk, soon disappearing; hypothecium hyaline; spores ellipsoid to oblong-ellipsoid, 8–13 × 3.5–6.5 μ.
On trees, from New England to Florida, and westward to Illinois and Texas.

2. **Coccocarpia pellita** (Ach.) Müll. Arg., Flora 65:326. 1882.
Parmelia pellita Ach., Lich. Univ. 468. 1810. *Pannaria molybdaea* (Pers.) Tuck. *C. pellita* var. *cocoës* (Fée) Zahlbr.
Thallus medium-sized or larger, grayish lead-colored to light greenish gray, smooth above or bearing coralloid branchlets; heavily clothed below with bluish black rhizoids, or rarely in part naked and whitish; apothecia small to middle-sized, 0.5–1 mm. across, closely adnate, the disk yellowish brown to dull black, the exciple colored like the thallus and soon disappearing; hypothecium hyaline to yellowish; spores oblong-ellipsoid, 9–14 × 3–5 μ.
On trees, from Massachusetts to Florida, and westward to Illinois and Texas.

31. STICTACEAE

Thallus distinctly foliose, more or less lobed at the margin, loosely attached to the substratum, differentiated into well-developed upper and lower cortices, algal and medullary layers, the lower cortex more or less discontinued and interspersed with cyphellae; apothecia round, scattered or marginal, superficial, with a proper or thalloid exciple.
The algal hosts are Palmella, Protococcus, and Nostoc.

115. **Sticta** Schreb., Gener. Plant. 768. 1791.

Thallus foliose, small to middle-sized or large, smooth to wrinkled, more or less lobed, rather loosely attached to the substratum by short or long rhizoids, differentiated into a thick, well-developed, plectenchymatous upper cortex, distinct algal layer, medullary layer of loosely interwoven hyphae, and a thin, well-developed, plectenchymatous lower cortex, continuous or broken by cyphellae; apothecia small to middle-sized or large, adnate, sessile or substipitate, marginal, submarginal, or scattered, the disk concave to flat or more or less convex, the exciple colored like the thallus, irregular, sometimes disappearing; hypothecium hyaline to brownish; hymenium hyaline to brownish above; paraphyses unbranched; asci clavate to ovate-clavate; spores 8, hyaline to rarely brown, oblong-ovoid, fusiform or acicular, 1–3-septate.

The algal host is Protococcus or Nostoc.

A. Thallus without cyphellae or bare spots below
  B. Thallus clothed below with a spongy nap of short rhizoids . . 1. S. amplissima
  B. Thallus bearing few to many rhizoids
    C. Lobes small, round; spores 1-septate, 26–44 × 9–11 μ . . . . 2. S. herbacea
    C. Lobes somewhat elongated; spores 3-septate, 48–70 × 3–5 μ . . 3. S. erosa
A. Thallus with either cyphellae or bare spots below
  B. Thallus with bare spots below
    C. Thallus reticulately ribbed
      D. Sorediate or isidioid along the reticulations and margins;
        spores 18–33 × 5.5–9 μ . . . . 4. S. pulmonaria
      D Not sorediate or isidioid; spores 42–60 × 6–9 μ . . . . 6. S. oregana
    C. Thallus more or less pitted but not ribbed
      D. Thallus rather closely attached, brownish yellow to
        olive-green or brown . . . . 5. S. linita
      D. Thallus rather loosely attached, greenish gray to ashy
        and yellowish or brownish
        E. Soredia along the margins . . . . 8. S. verrucosa
        E. Soredia scattered . . . . 7. S. Hallii
  B. Thallus with cyphellae below
    C. Cyphellae sorediate
      D. Cyphellae yellowish
        E. Thallus greenish gray to brownish red or finally
          rose-red, soredia marginal . . . . 9. S. aurata
        E. Thallus greenish gray to brownish or greenish brown,
          soredia usually scattered . . . . 10. S. crocata
      D. Cyphellae whitish . . . . 11. S. anthraspis
    C. Cyphellae bare
      D. Thallus more or less covered with minute blackish
        granules . . . . 13. S. fuliginosa
      D. Thallus not granulose
        E. Thallus bearing isidia
          F. Isidia scattered . . . . 14. S. sylvatica
          F. Isidia usually marginal
            G. Lobes broad; spores 1–3-septate . . . . . 12. S. Weigelii
            G. Lobes elongated, narrow, more or less divided;
              spores 3-septate . . . . 15. S. quercizans
        E. Thallus bearing soredia . . . . 16. S. limbata

1. **Sticta amplissima** (Scop.) Rabh., Deutsch. Krypt. Fl. 2:64. 1845.
  Lichen amplissimus Scop., Fl. Carn. ed. 2. 2:386. 1772. *Lobaria amplissima* (Scop.) Forss. *S. glomulifera* (Lightf.) Del.

Thallus middle-sized to large, rather closely attached to the substratum, smooth to becoming more or less wrinkled, greenish gray to ashy or brownish, the lobes somewhat elongated, narrow to wider, sometimes more or less imbricated, with sinuate, or obscurely crenate margins; commonly lighter below, clothed with a spongy nap of short rhizoids interspersed with few longer ones or rarely bearing only long rhizoids; apothecia middle-sized, 1–3 mm. across, subsessile, scattered, the disk concave to flat, chestnut-brown, the exciple thin, becoming crenulate; spores acicular, 3-septate, 30–65 × 4.5–8 μ.

On trees, from Maine to Florida, and westward to Texas and Minnesota.

2. **Sticta herbacea** (Huds.) Ach., Syn. Lich. 341. 1814.
    Lichen herbaceus Huds., Fl. Angl. ed. 2. 2:544. 1778. *Lobaria laetevirens*
    (Lightf.) Zahlbr.
    Thallus small to middle-sized, closely attached to the substratum, smooth to
wrinkled, often shiny, greenish gray to brownish or greenish brown, the lobes
small, round, sometimes imbricated, with crenate, incised margins; brownish below,
sparingly tomentose, bearing short brownish to brown rhizoids; apothecia middle-
sized to large, 1–3 mm. or more across, scattered, the disk concave to flat, reddish
to brownish, the exciple sometimes granulose; spores hyaline to brownish, fusiform,
1-septate, 26–44 × 9–11 μ.
    On trees, from Maine to Florida, and Illinois (?).

3. **Sticta erosa** (Eschw.) Tuck., Syn. N. A. Lich. 1:93. 1882.
    Parmelia erosa Eschw., in Mart., Fl. Bras. 1:211. 1833. *S. Ravenelii* Tuck.
    Lobaria erosa (Eschw.) Trevis.
    Thallus small to middle-sized, closely attached to the substratum, smooth to
minutely rough and becoming much wrinkled, greenish gray to brownish or yellowish brown, the lobes somewhat elongated, often imbricated, incised, with crenate margins; brownish below, bearing many, short, scattered, brownish to brown
fibrils; apothecia small to middle-sized, 1.2–3 mm. across, scattered, sessile to
substipitate, the disk becoming flat, chestnut-brown, the exciple thin, becoming
wrinkled and crenate; hypothecium cloudy; spores acicular, 3-septate, 48–70 ×
3–5 μ.
    On trees, South Carolina, Georgia, Florida, Alabama, and Louisiana.

4. **Sticta pulmonaria** (L.) Bir., Fl. Ascon. 2:188. 1808.
    Lichen pulmonarius L., Sp. Pl. 1145. 1753. *S. pulmonacea* var. *hypomela* Del.
    Lobaria pulmonaria (L.) Hoffm.
    Thallus middle-sized to large, loosely attached to the substratum, plainly pitted
and reticulately ribbed, greenish gray to brownish or greenish brown, often grayish
sorediate or isidioid along the reticulations and margins, the lobes elongated, deeply
and narrowly divided, with somewhat blunt, notched apices; brownish to brown
below, clothed with a spongy nap of short rhizoids with many naked, raised, whitish spots interspersed; apothecia middle-sized to large, 1.5–4 mm. across, subsessile,
submarginal, the disk flat to convex, chestnut-brown to brown, the exciple thin,
sometimes becoming wrinkled, finally disappearing; spores boat-shaped, 3-septate,
18–33 × 5.5–9 μ.   (PLATE 10.)
    On trees and rocks, throughout northern United States and southward in the
mountains.

5. **Sticta linita** Ach., Syn. Lich. 234. 1814.
    S. pulmonaria var. *linita* (Ach.) Tuck. *Lobaria linita* (Ach.) Rabh.
    Thallus small to middle-sized, rather closely attached to the substratum, some-
what pitted, brownish yellow to olive-green or brown, the lobes round, crenate,
rarely sorediate or coralloid; greenish brown below, bearing short, brown fibrils in
veins with pale, naked spots between; apothecia small to middle-sized, 0.8–2 mm.
across, submarginal, the disk flat, reddish brown, the exciple thin, becoming
wrinkled, finally disappearing; spores boat-shaped, 1–3-septate, 16–30 × 5–10 μ.
    On rocks, New Hampshire.

6. **Sticta oregana** Tuck., Bull. Torr. Club 5:20. 1874.
    Lobaria oregana (Tuck.) Müll. Arg.
    Thallus large, loosely attached to the substratum, much lobed, smooth to pitted
and reticulately ribbed, greenish to yellowish gray or brownish, the lobes broad,
elongated, much divided, with incised, crenate margins; yellowish to brownish
below, reticulately marked with minute brown fibrils, naked whitish spots between;
apothecia middle-sized to large, 1.5–4 mm. across, scattered, the disk flat to slightly

convex, chestnut-brown to brownish black, the exciple thin, becoming crenate, finally disappearing; spores fusiform or acicular, 3-septate, 42–60 × 6–9 μ.

On trees, Washington, Oregon, and California.

7. **Sticta Hallii** Tuck., Proc. Am. Acad. 12:168. 1877.
Lobaria Hallii (Tuck.) Zahlbr. *Stictina Hallii* (Tuck.) Stizenb.

Thallus small to middle-sized, rather loosely attached to the substratum, reticulately pitted, obscurely chinky and granulose, finally more or less covered with lead-colored soredia, greenish gray to ashy, the lobes wide and round; brownish below, ribbed and bearing pale rhizoids between naked whitish spots; apothecia small to middle-sized, 0.8–3 mm. across, the disk becoming flat, reddish brown, the exciple thin, externally ciliate; spores brown, boat-shaped, 1-septate, 23–36 × 9–14 μ.

On trees and soil, Washington, Oregon, and Colorado.

8. **Sticta verrucosa** (Huds.) Fink n. comb.
Lichen verrucosus Huds., Fl. Angl. 445. 1762. *S. scrobiculata* (Scop.) Ach.
Lobaria scrobiculata (Scop.) Gärtner. *Stictina scrobiculata* (Scop.) Nyl.

Thallus middle-sized to large, rather loosely attached to the substratum, smooth to more or less pitted, bearing grayish soredia especially along the margins, greenish gray to yellowish or brownish, the lobes large, imbricated, with wavy-crenate margins; brownish below, or becoming darker toward the center, clothed with a spongy nap of short rhizoids interspersed with whitish naked spots; apothecia small to middle-sized, 0.8–2 mm. across, scattered, sessile, the disk flat, reddish brown, the exciple thin, becoming slightly wavy; spores acicular, 3–7-septate, 50–75 × 5–7 μ. (PLATE 11.)

On trees and over mosses, New England, New York, Minnesota, Washington, Oregon, and California.

9. **Sticta aurata** Ach., Meth. Lich. 277. 1803.

Thallus small to middle-sized, closely attached to the substratum, smooth, greenish gray to brownish red or at length rose-red, the lobes broad, somewhat imbricated, rather deeply cut, with crenate, yellowish, sorediate margins; bright yellow within; reddish to yellowish brown below or darkening toward the center, clothed with a spongy nap of short rhizoids interspersed with minute, yellowish, sorediate cyphellae; apothecia middle-sized to large, 1–2.5 mm. across, sessile, marginal or submarginal, the disk flat, purplish brown or brown, the exciple thin, becoming wavy; spores brownish, fusiform, 3-septate, 21–30 × 6–9 μ.

On trees, from Maine to Florida, and westward to Texas and Minnesota, and in Washington and Oregon.

10. **Sticta crocata** (L.) Ach., Meth. Lich. 277. 1803.
Lichen crocatus L., Mant. Alt. 310. 1771. *Stictina crocata* (L.) Nyl.

Thallus small to middle-sized or rarely larger, usually rather loosely attached to the substratum, smooth or becoming more or less pitted, greenish gray to brownish or greenish brown, bordered and more or less sprinkled with yellowish green soredia, the lobes usually wide, sometimes much divided, more or less imbricated, with crenate margins; brownish below or becoming darker toward the center, clothed with a soft nap of short rhizoids interspersed with minute, yellowish, sorediate cyphellae; apothecia middle-sized, 1–1.5 mm. across, sessile, marginal or scattered, the disk flat, becoming black, the exciple thin, crenate, disappearing; spores brown, oblong-fusiform, 1-septate, 20–32 × 8.5–10 μ.

On trees and over mossy rocks, from Maine to Florida and Alabama, and in Minnesota, Washington, and Oregon.

11. **Sticta anthraspis** Ach., Meth. Lich. 280. 1803.
Stictina anthraspis (Ach.) Nyl.

Thallus middle-sized to large, loosely attached to the substratum, reticulately veined, irregularly pitted, greenish gray to greenish brown or brown, the lobes wide, somewhat imbricated, with crenate margins; brownish below and becoming darker toward the center, clothed with a spongy nap of short rhizoids interspersed with minute, whitish, sorediate cyphellae; apothecia middle-sized to large, 1.5–4 mm. across, scattered, sessile, the disk flat to convex, reddish brown to black, the exciple thin, usually disappearing; spores fusiform, 3-septate, 23–31 × 7–10 μ.

On trees and over moss, Maine, Washington, Oregon, and California.

12. **Sticta Weigelii** (Ach.) Vainio, Lich. Bres. 1:189, 190. 1890.

   S. damaecornis var. *Weigelii* Ach., Lich. Univ. 446. 1810. *Stictina Weigelii* (Ach.) Stizenb.

Thallus small to middle-sized, rather closely attached to the substratum, smooth to rarely somewhat wrinkled, greenish gray to brownish or lead-colored, the lobes broad, somewhat imbricated, with crenate, commonly isidioid margins; brownish to brown below, clothed with a soft nap of short rhizoids interspersed with small to larger, concave, whitish cyphellae; apothecia middle-sized, 0.8–2 mm. across, scattered, sessile, the disk flat, reddish brown, the exciple thin, soon disappearing; spores fusiform, 1–3-septate, 26–36 × 6–9 μ.

On trees and soil, North Carolina and Florida.

13. **Sticta fuliginosa** (Dicks.) Ach., Meth. Lich. 280, 281. 1803.

   Lichen fuliginosus Dicks., Pl. Crypt. Brit. 1:13. 1875. *Stictina fuliginosa* (Dicks.) Nyl.

Thallus middle-sized to large, loosely attached to the substratum, smooth to more or less pitted, greenish brown to brownish or lead-colored, more or less covered with minute, blackish granules, the lobes round, somewhat imbricate, with cut, crenate margins; brownish below, clothed with a soft nap of short rhizoids interspersed with concave whitish cyphellae; apothecia small to middle-sized, 0.6– 1 mm. across, usually marginal, the disk flat to convex, reddish brown, the exciple thin, soon disappearing; spores fusiform, 1–3-septate, 25–46 × 7–9 μ.

On trees and rocks, New England, North Carolina, Georgia, Minnesota, Oregon, and California.

14. **Sticta sylvatica** (Huds.) Ach., Meth. Lich. 281. 1803.

   Lichen sylvaticus Huds., Fl. Angl. 453. 1762. *Stictina sylvatica* (Huds.) Nyl.

Thallus small to middle-sized, rather closely attached to the substratum, sometimes more or less pitted, smooth or bearing scattered grayish to darker isidia, greenish brown to brownish or reddish brown, the lobes somewhat imbricate, with wavy, crenate margins; brownish below and darker toward the center, clothed with a soft nap of short rhizoids interspersed with minute to small, concave, whitish cyphellae; apothecia small to middle-sized, 0.5–2 mm. across, marginal, sessile, the disk flat to convex, reddish brown, the exciple thin, soon disappearing; spores fusiform, 1–3-septate, 25–46 × 7–9 μ.

On trees and rocks over moss, Maine, New York, New Jersey, North Carolina, and Alabama.

15. **Sticta quercizans** Ach., Syn. Lich. 234, 235. 1814.

   Parmelia quercizans Ach., Lich. Univ. 464. 1810. *Lobaria quercizans* (Ach.) Michx.

Thallus small to middle-sized, rather closely attached to the substratum, smooth or more or less isidioid especially along the margins, greenish gray to brown or rarely reddish brown, the lobes somewhat elongated, rather narrow, more or less divided, often imbricated, with irregular, ascending, crenate margins; brownish to darker below, clothed with a spongy nap of short rhizoids interspersed by the concave, whitish cyphellae; apothecia middle-sized, 1.5–3 mm. across, submarginal or scattered, the disk flat, reddish brown, the exciple thin, becoming wavy; spores fusiform, 3-septate, 26–40 × 7–10 μ.

On trees and over mosses, from Vermont to Florida, and westward to New Mexico and Minnesota, and in Oregon.

16. **Sticta limbata** Ach., Meth. Lich. 280. 1803.
Stictina limbata (Ach.) Nyl.

Thallus small to rarely middle-sized, rather loosely attached to the substratum, smooth to becoming reticulately veined and more or less pitted, greenish brown to brown or lead-colored, the lobes broad, with wavy, crenate margins, more or less grayish sorediate toward or along the margins; brownish below, clothed with a soft nap of short rhizoids interspersed with few, concave, whitish cyphellae; apothecia small to middle-sized, 0.6–2 mm. across, scattered, adnate to sessile, the disk flat to convex, dull black, the exciple thin, soon disappearing; spores brown, oblong-ovoid, 1-septate, slightly constricted, 15–22 × 5–8 μ.

On trees, Minnesota, Oregon, and California.

32. PELTIGERACEAE

Thallus squamulose or foliose, differentiated into well-developed plectenchymatous cortex on one or both sides, algal layer and well-developed medulla, cephalodia sometimes present and well developed, attached to the substratum by rhizoids; apothecia round to irregular, closely adnate, marginal or scattered on the upper or lower surface of the thallus, without exciple.

The algal hosts are Palmella, Nostoc, and Dactylococcus.

A. Thallus with cortex only above; apothecia borne
    on under surface . . . . 117. NEPHROMA
A. Thallus with cortex above and below; apothecia borne
    on upper surface
    B. Spores brownish to brown . . . . 116. SOLORINA
    B. Spores hyaline . . . . 118. PELTIGERA

116. Solorina Ach., Vet. Akad. Nya Handl. 228. 1808.

Thallus foliose, more or less lobed, sometimes squamulose, loosely attached to the substratum by rhizoids, differentiated into a well-developed, thin to thick, plectenchymatous upper cortex, an algal layer, a well-developed medullary layer of interwoven hyphae, and sometimes a poorly developed lower cortex of closely interwoven hyphae; apothecia small to middle-sized or large, partly immersed to adnate, the disk more or less concave to flat or convex, the exciple thin, colored like the thallus, sometimes disappearing; hypothecium hyaline to brownish; hymenium hyaline or brownish above; paraphyses unbranched; asci cylindrical; spores 2–8, brown, oblong, ellipsoid to fusiform, 1-septate.

The algal host is Palmella or Nostoc.

A. Thallus minutely squamulose, passing into a rough crust . . . . . 2. S. spongiosa
A. Thallus foliose, irregularly lobed, more or less loosely attached
    B. Bright orange or saffron-colored below . . . . 3. S. crocea
    B. Grayish to brownish below . . . . 1. S. saccata

1. **Solorina saccata** (L.) Ach., Vet. Akad. Nya Handl. 228. 1808.
Lichen saccatus L., Fl. Suec. ed. 2. 419. 1755.

Thallus small to middle-sized, smooth, irregularly lobed, rather loosely attached to the substratum, greenish gray to ashy or brownish, and rarely whitish pruinose, the lobes rather short, with more or less crenate margins, lighter below and bearing long, scattered rhizoids; apothecia middle-sized, 2–6 mm. across, sunken in the thallus, the disk more or less concave, dark brown, the exciple thin, colored like the thallus, sometimes disappearing; hypothecium brownish; asci cylindrical; spores 4, brown, ellipsoid, 1-septate, 36–60 × 16–24 μ. (PLATE 12 a.)

On' soil and over moss, throughout the United States.

2. **Solorina spongiosa** (J. E. Smith) Anzi, Comm. Soc. Critt. Ital. 1:136. 1862.
Lichen spongiosus J. E. Smith, Engl. Bot. 20: pl. 1374. 1805. *S. saccata* var.
    spongiosa (J. E. Smith) Nyl.

Thallus minutely squamulose, dark green to grayish brown, the squamules suberect, minutely lobed and crenate, finally passing into a rough, granulose crust;

apothecia small to middle-sized, 1.5–4 mm. across, partly immersed to adnate, the disk deeply concave to rarely flat, chestnut-brown to brownish black, the exciple thin, brownish to colored like the thallus, becoming granulate; hypothecium brownish; asci long-clavate; spores 4, brown, ellipsoid, 1-septate, 30–50 × 15–22 μ. On soil, Colorado and Washington.

3. **Solorina crocea** (L.) Ach., Vet. Akad. Nya Handl. 228. 1808.
Lichen croceus L., Sp. Pl. 1149. 1753.
Thallus middle-sized, smooth, lobed, brownish to cinnamon-brown or rarely reddish brown, the lobes more or less imbricated, with wavy margins; bright orange or saffron-colored below with concolorate or brownish branched veins, and bearing few, clustered, brownish rhizoids; apothecia middle-sized to large, 4–10 mm. across, adnate, round to irregular, the disk flat to slightly convex, reddish brown to brownish black; hypothecium hyaline to brownish; asci long, cylindrical; spores 8, brown, oblong to fusiform-oblong, 1-septate, 30–44 × 10–14 μ. On soil, Montana, Idaho, Washington, Oregon, and Colorado.

117. **Nephroma** Ach., Lich. Univ. 101. pl. 11, f. 1. 1810.

Thallus foliose, small to large, irregularly lobed, more or less closely attached to the substratum by rhizoids, distinctly differentiated into a rather thick, cellular upper cortex, well-developed algal and medullary layers and a thin, cellular lower cortex; apothecia middle-sized to large, marginal or submarginal, adnate or sessile on the under surface of the lobes of the thallus, the disk more or less turned upward, flat, reddish brown to brown, the exciple thin, colored like the thallus, often disappearing; hypothecium hyaline or brownish; hymenium hyaline; paraphyses unbranched, enlarged, and brownish toward the apices; asci clavate; spores 8, brownish to brown, ellipsoid to oblong-ellipsoid or fusiform, 1–3- or rarely 5-septate.

The algal host is Nostoc or Palmella.

A. Thallus more or less tomentose below
  B. Without pits or tubercles below
    C. Lobes large . . . . 1. N. arcticum
    C. Lobes small to middle-sized . . . . 2. N. helveticum
  B. With pits or tubercles below
    C. Lobes middle-sized to large, margins commonly and
      deeply wavy . . . . 3. N. resupinatum
    C. Lobes small to middle-sized, margins crenate . . . . 4. N. rameum
A. Thallus smooth to wrinkled below
  B. Sorediate above, especially toward the margin . . . . 6. N. parile
  B. Not sorediate above
    C. Whitish within . . . . 5. N. laevigatum
    C. Yellowish within . . . . 7. N. lusitanicum

1. **Nephroma arcticum** (L.) Torss., Enum. Lich. et Byssac. Scand. 7. 1843.
Lichen arcticus L., Sp. Pl. 1148. 1753.
Thallus large to very large, smooth to infrequently more or less undulate or wrinkled, irregularly lobed, the margins round and often undulate, greenish to yellowish straw-colored; black below with paler margins and bearing black rhizoids; apothecia large to very large, 4–20 mm. across, adnate, the disk flat, brick-red to reddish brown; spores brownish, oblong-ellipsoid, 3-septate, 20–31 × 3.5–5 μ.
On soil, New England and New York.

2. **Nephroma helveticum** Ach., Lich. Univ. 523. 1810.
N. resupinatum f. *helveticum* (Ach.) Rabh.
Thallus small to middle-sized, narrowly and deeply lobed, smooth to slightly wrinkled, grayish to yellowish brown, the lobes round, wavy, or irregularly cut, and fringed with toothlike lobules; dark and blackening below and finally tomentose; apothecia middle-sized to large, 1.5–6 mm. across, the disk flat, reddish

brown to brown, the exciple thin, colored like the thallus, becoming wavy; spores brown, 3-septate, ellipsoid to subfusiform, 15–22 × 5–8.5 μ.

On trees and rocks and over mosses, throughout the United States.

3. **Nephroma resupinatum** (L.) Ach., Lich. Univ. 522. 1810.

Lichen resupinatus L., Sp. Pl. 1148. 1753. *N. tomentosum* (Hoffm.) Flot.

Thallus middle-sized to large, smooth to more or less tomentose, greenish gray to lead-colored or brown, the lobes round, with margins commonly and deeply waved; whitish below, brownish tomentose, and bearing minute whitish tubercles; apothecia middle-sized to large, 2–12 mm. across, the disk reddish brown, the exciple colored like the thallus, becoming irregularly crenate; spores brownish, 3- rarely 5-septate, fusiform to oblong, 19–26 × 4.5–7 μ.

On trees, throughout northern United States.

4. **Nephroma rameum** (Schaer.) Mass., Mem. Lich. 23. 1853.

N. resupinatus f. *rameum* Schaer., Enum. Lich. Eur. 18. pl. 2, f. 3. 1850. *Ne- phromium tomentosum* var. *rameum* (Schaer.) Nyl.

Thallus small to middle-sized, smooth to minutely granulose, finally imbricated, greenish gray to grayish brown, the lobes irregular with crenate margins; brown- ish below, and sometimes bearing whitish tubercles and pits; apothecia middle- sized to large, 2–7 mm. across, borne on the margins of the lobes, the disk flat, reddish to dark brown, the exciple thin, colored like the thallus, becoming wavy; spores brownish, oblong, 3-septate, 17–24 × 6.5–8.5 μ.

On trees, Washington and California.

5. **Nephroma laevigatum** Ach., Syn. Meth. Lich. 242. 1814.

Thallus small to middle-sized, with small, roundish lobes, smooth to finely wrinkled and pitted, marginally crenate and wavy, greenish gray to chestnut- brown; wrinkled and naked, and white or whitish below, or rarely tinged with brown; apothecia middle-sized to large, 2–5.5 mm. across, adnate, the disk flat, reddish to dark brown, the exciple thin, colored like the thallus; spores brownish, fusiform-ellipsoid, 3-septate, 16–23 × 4–7 μ.

On trees and rocks, throughout northern United States and in California.

6. **Nephroma parile** Ach., Lich. Univ. 522. 1810.

Lichen parilis Ach., Lich. Suec. 164. 1798. *N. laevigatum* f. *parile* (Ach.) Mudd.

Thallus small to middle-sized, smooth, becoming sorediate, greenish gray to chestnut-brown, the lobes round, curled, strongly grayish sorediate toward the margin; wrinkled and blackening below; apothecia middle-sized to large, 2–4.5 mm. across, borne on the margins of the lobes, the disk flat, reddish brown to dark brown, the exciple very thin, colored like the thallus; spores brownish, fusiform- ellipsoid, 3-septate, 16–24 × 5–6 μ.

On trees, New England, New York, Minnesota, and Montana.

7. **Nephroma lusitanicum** Schaer., Enum. Lich. Eur. 323. 1850.

Nephromium lusitanicum (Schaer.) Nyl.

Thallus small to middle-sized, smooth to more or less reticulately wrinkled, slightly to deeply lobed, with crenate margins, greenish gray to chestnut-brown, yellowish within; smooth to finely wrinkled below, and pale to brown or darker; apothecia middle-sized to large, 2–5 mm. across, borne on the margin of the lobes, the disk flat, reddish brown to chestnut-brown; spores brownish, 3-septate, fusi- form-oblong, 19–24 × 5–8 μ.

On trees and rocks, Maine, Washington, Oregon, and California.

118. **Peltigera** Willd., Fl. Berol. Prod. 347. 1787.

Thallus foliose, usually large, more or less lobed, rather loosely attached to the substratum, differentiated into a well-developed, cellular upper cortex, a distinct algal layer, and a medullary layer with horizontal hyphae below bearing numerous rhizoids, more or less veined below, the upper surface sometimes more or less covered with minute hyphae; apothecia small to more commonly middle-sized or large, borne on the margins of the lobes, the disk reddish brown to brown, the exciple colored like the thallus, becoming more or less irregular; hypothecium hyaline to brown; hymenium hyaline or brownish above; paraphyses commonly unbranched; asci clavate to cylindrico-clavate; spores 8, rarely only 6, hyaline to brownish, fusiform or acicular, frequently more or less curved, 3–7-septate.

The algal host is Nostoc or Dactylococcus.

A. Without trichomatic hyphae, smooth above
  B. Bearing irregular cephalodia above . . . . 1. P. aphthosa
  B. Cephalodia absent
    C. Lobes small, fan-shaped to triangular . . . . 2. P. venosa
    C. Lobes larger, broad and irregular
      D. Spores 3-septate, 30–48 μ in length
        E. Margins smooth . . . . 3. P. horizontalis
        E. Margins isidioid . . . . 4. P. Zopfii
      D. Spores 3–7-septate, 60–100 μ in length . . . . . . 5. P. polydactyla
A. With trichomatic hyphae or granulose above
  B. Thallus brownish to dark brown or black below
    C. Uniformly covered with a dense nap below . . . . . . 7. P. malacea
    C. More or less reticulated or veined below
      D. Margins crenate and smooth . . . . 8. P. rufescens
      D. Margins irregular, often isidioid-granulose to sorediate . . 6. P. scutata
  B. Thallus white to brownish below
    C. Thallus powdery or bearing coralloid branchlets or masses of soredia above
      D. Thallus powdery . . . . 13. P. pulverulenta
      D. Thallus bearing coralloid branchlets . . . . 9. P. praetextata
      D. Thallus bearing masses of soredia . . . . 12. P. sorediata
    C. Thallus uniform above
      D. Thallus small to middle-sized . . . . 11. P. spuria
      D. Thallus middle-sized to large
        E. Rhizoids running together into a conspicuous spongy nap . . . . 10. P. canina spongiosa
        E. Rhizoids scattered or absent
          F. Thallus thinner, expanded
            G. Trichomatic hyphae very prominent . 10. P. canina leucorrhiza
            G. Smooth or minutely pitted . . . 10. P. canina membranacea
          F. Thallus thicker, less expanded . . . . 10. P. canina

1. Peltigera aphthosa (L.) Willd., Fl. Berol. Prod. 347. 1787.

Lichen aphthosus L., Sp. Pl. 1148. 1753. *P. aphthosa* var. *minor* Tuck.

Thallus middle-sized to large, smooth, somewhat closely attached, sprinkled more or less with small, irregular cephalodia, greenish gray to green or brownish, the lobes broad, round, sometimes more or less imbricated, strongly ascending at least toward the margins; white to blackening below, reticulated with whitish to blackened veins, bearing scattered, black rhizoids; apothecia middle-sized to large, 4–8.5 mm. across, borne on somewhat extended lobules, rolled backward, the disk reddish brown, the exciple thin, colored like the thallus, becoming crenulate; hypothecium brownish; spores hyaline to pale brownish, 3–7-septate, acicular, 45–75 × 4–7 μ. (PLATE 13.)

On soil and over humus-covered rocks, throughout northern United States, and occasionally occurring farther southward.

2. Peltigera venosa (L.) Baumg., Fl. Lips. 561. 1790.

Lichen venosus L., Sp. Pl. 1148. 1753.

Thallus small, composed of scattered to rarely confluent, fan-shaped to triangular, smooth, ascending, greenish gray to ashy or brownish, marginally wavy lobes; whitish below, reticulated with coarse brownish black veins bearing small rhizoids and often spreading together into a close nap; apothecia middle-sized, 2–5 mm. across, borne on the margins of the lobes, superficial, round to horizontal, the disk flat, reddish to blackish brown, the exciple becoming crenate or finely toothed and disappearing; hypothecium brownish to rarely brown; spores fusiform, brownish to hyaline, 3– rarely 4-septate, 28–45 × 6–9 μ. (PLATE 12 b.)

On soil, throughout the United States.

3. **Peltigera horizontalis** (Huds.) Baumg., Fl. Lips. 562. 1790.

Lichen horizontalis Huds., Fl. Angl. 453. 1762.

Thallus middle-sized to large, somewhat closely adnate, smooth and shining, greenish gray to ashy or reddish brown, the lobes broad and ascending with round to irregular margins; white below, reticulated with blackening veins passing into a continuous close nap; apothecia middle-sized, 3–5 mm. across, borne on narrowed lobules or submarginal, sometimes superficial, horizontal, the disk reddish brown, transversely oblong, the exciple becoming subcrenulate; hypothecium brownish; spores hyaline to pale brownish, 3-septate, long-ellipsoid, 30–48 × 5–7.5 μ.

On soil and over mossy rocks, throughout the United States.

4. **Peltigera Zopfii** Gyelnik, Bot. Közlem 24:134, 135. 1927.

Thallus middle-sized to large, rather closely adnate, smooth and shining to bearing isidia along the ascending, irregular margins of the broad lobes, greenish gray to ashy or rarely reddish brown; white or whitish below, reticulated with few to many brownish to brown veins bearing few brownish rhizoids; apothecia middle-sized, 2–5 mm. across, borne on narrowed lobules, adnate, horizontal, the disk flat to convex, dark brown; hypothecium yellowish to brownish; spores hyaline, oblong, straight or curved, 3-septate, 40–45 × 6–6.5 μ.

On soil, Connecticut.

Very close to *Peltigera horizontalis* but separated by the isidioid margins of the upper surface of the thallus and fewer veins and rhizoids of the lower. Description compiled.

5. **Peltigera polydactyla** (Neck.) Hoffm., Descript. & Adumbr. Pl. Lich. 1:19, 20. pl. 4, f. 1. 1790.

Lichen polydactylon Neck., Meth. Musc. 85. 1771.

Thallus middle-sized to large, closely adnate, smooth and shining, greenish gray to lead-colored and brownish, the lobes broad and variously irregular, ascending toward the margins; whitish to blackening below, reticulated with brownish to blackened veins, and bearing small to large, brownish to black rhizoids; apothecia middle-sized, 3–5 mm. across, borne on narrow, extended, digitately clustered lobules, commonly rolled backward, the disk reddish to dark brown, the exciple becoming irregularly crenulate; hypothecium brownish; spores hyaline, 3–7-septate, acicular, sometimes slightly curved, 60–100 × 3–4 μ.

On soil, widely distributed throughout the United States.

6. **Peltigera scutata** (Dicks.) Duby, Bot. Gall. 2:599. 1830.

Lichen scutatus Dicks., Fasc. Pl. Crypt. Brit. 3:18. 1793. *P. polydactyla* var. *scutata* (Dicks.) E. Fries.

Thallus rather thin, small to middle-sized, adnate, bearing scattered trichomatic hyphae, sinuately lobed, greenish gray to ashy or brownish, ascending toward the irregular, often isidioid-granulose to sorediate margins; brownish to dark brown below, with many brown veins; apothecia small to middle-sized, 2–5 mm. across, borne on short lobules, round to oblong, sometimes rolled backward, the disk reddish brown, the margin inflexed and soon crenate; hypothecium brownish; spores hyaline, 3–7-septate, acicular, 48–68 × 3–4.5 μ.

On trees and soil, widely distributed throughout northern United States.

7. **Peltigera malacea** (Ach.) Funck, Crypt. Gëwach 33. Heft. 5. 1827.

Peltidea malacea Ach., Syn. Lich. 240. 1814.

Thallus loosely adnate, middle-sized to large, somewhat soft and spongy, finely granulose or rarely downy, greenish gray to ashy or rarely brownish, with narrow, round, or wavy lobes, usually ascending toward the margins; brownish to blackish below, often lighter toward the margins, bearing few long rhizoids, but uniformly covered with a dense nap; apothecia middle-sized to large, 3–7.5 mm. across, borne on narrow, extended lobules, round and rolled backward, the disk reddish brown, the exciple becoming crenulate; hypothecium dark brown; spores hyaline, 3–5-septate, acicular, 50–72 $\times$ 4–6 μ.

On soil and over mossy rocks, from New England westward to the Rocky Mountains.

8. **Peltigera rufescens** (Weis.) Humb., Flor. Frib. Specim. 2. 1793.

   Lichen caninus, rufescens Weis., Pl. Crypt. Flor. Goett. 79. 1770.

   Thallus small to middle-sized, closely adnate, smooth to somewhat downy, greenish gray to brown, the lobes crowded, narrow, with crenate, much-elevated margins; brownish to dark brown below, thickly reticulated with brown veins with numerous brown rhizoids; apothecia middle-sized to large, 3.5–7.5 mm. across, borne on narrow, extended lobules, rolled backward, the disk brown to blackish brown, the exciple becoming crenulate or toothed; hypothecium brownish; spores hyaline, 3–7-septate, acicular, sometimes curved, 40–68 $\times$ 3.5–5 μ.

   On soil, throughout northern United States, and southward west of the Mississippi River.

9. **Peltigera praetextata** (Sommerf.) Vainio, Term. Füz. 22:306. 1899.

   Peltidea ulorrhiza var. *praetextata* Sommerf., Suppl. Fl. Lapp. 123. 1826.

   P. rufescens var. *praetextata* (Sommerf.) Nyl.

   Thallus middle-sized to large, adnate toward the center, more or less covered with coralloid branchlets, especially toward the margin, greenish gray to brown, with broad, wavy lobes, ascending toward the irregular margins; whitish below, bearing numerous whitish to brown veins and rhizoids; apothecia middle-sized, 2–5 mm. across, borne on narrow, extended lobules, rolled backward, the disk brown to brownish black, the exciple usually denticulate; hypothecium brownish to brown; spores hyaline, 3–5-septate, sometimes slightly curved, 42–56 $\times$ 3–5 μ.

   On soil, old logs, and over mosses, Ohio and Michigan.

10. **Peltigera canina** (L.) Willd., Fl. Berol. Prod. 347. 1787.

    Lichen caninus L., Sp. Pl. 1149. 1753.

    Thallus middle-sized to large, closely adnate, greenish gray to ashy and brownish, with broad ascending lobes, and round to irregular or crenate margins, partly covered with trichomatic hyphae; whitish below or rarely brownish toward the center, bearing many whitish to darkening veins and rhizoids; apothecia middle-sized to large, 4–8 mm. across, borne on extended, suberect lobules, round to commonly rolled backward, the disk reddish to dark brown, the exciple sometimes becoming crenulate or irregular; hypothecium brownish; spores hyaline, 5–7-septate, acicular, sometimes curved, 38–72 $\times$ 3–5 μ.

    On soil and over mosses, throughout the United States.

    f. **spongiosa** Tuck., Syn. N. A. Lich. 1:109. 1882.

    The veins of the lower side pale, the rhizoids whitish or darkening and running together into a conspicuous spongy nap.

    On soil, rocks, or at the base of old trees, throughout the United States.

    f. **leucorrhiza** Floerke; Flot., 28. Jahresber. Schesisch. Gesellsch. Kultur. 124. 1850.

    Peltidea leucorrhiza Floerke, in Hepp, Flecht.-Fl. von Würzburg, 54. 1824.

    Thallus very large, slightly thinner, the trichomatic hyphae very prominent; whitish below, bearing conspicuous white veins and scattered rhizoids.

    On soil, Minnesota.

    f. **membranacea** (Ach.) Duby, Bot. Gall. 2:598. 1830.

    Peltidea canina var. *membranacea* Ach., Lich. Univ. 518. 1810.

    Thallus thinner, smooth to minutely pitted; white below and reticulated with whitish veins; apothecia smaller, borne on short lobules.

    On soil, logs, and mossy rocks, California and Oregon.

11. **Peltigera spuria** (Ach.) DC., in Lam. & DC., Fl. Franc. III. 2:406. 1815.
Lichen spurius Ach., Lich. Suec. 159. 1798. *P. canina* var. *spuria* (Ach.) Schaer.

Thallus small to rarely middle-sized, ascending to suberect, greenish gray to ashy and brownish, partly covered with trichomatic hyphae, the lobes small with round to crenate margins; whitish to cream-colored below, reticulated with whitish veins bearing few rhizoids; apothecia small to middle-sized, 2–5 mm. across, borne on short, somewhat digitately clustered lobules, rolled backward, the disk reddish brown, the exciple crenulate or finely toothed; hypothecium brownish; spores hyaline, 3–7-septate, acicular, 45–75 × 3.5–4.5 μ.

On soil, throughout the United States.

12. **Peltigera sorediata** (Schaer.) Fink; Corring., Ohio State Univ. Bull. 25: no. 6. 356, 357. 1921.

P. canina var. *spuria* f. *sorediata* Schaer., Enum. Lich. Eur. 21. 1850. *P. canina* var. *sorediata* (Schaer.) Fink. *P. leptoderma* Nyl.

Thallus small, adnate, greenish gray to deep gray or ashy, thickly covered with trichomatic hyphae and round areas of grayish soredia, the scattered lobes irregular, round to crenate, and slightly ascending toward the margins; ashy white to cream-colored below, reticulated with whitish veins, bearing whitish rhizoids; apothecia small, 1.5–3.5 mm. across, rare, borne on narrow, extended, digitately clustered lobules, round to horizontal to partly rolled backward, the disk dark brown, the exciple becoming crenulate; hypothecium brownish; spores hyaline, 5–7-septate, acicular, 50–66 × 3–3.5 μ.

On soil and over mossy rocks, throughout the United States, preferring mountains southward.

13. **Peltigera pulverulenta** (Tayl.) Nyl., Syn. Lich. 1:325. 1860.

Peltidea pulverulenta Tayl.; Hook., Lond. Journ. Bot. 6:184. 1847.

Thallus middle-sized to large, closely adnate, smooth to chinky and granulose to powdery, sometimes more or less pitted, greenish gray to ashy and lurid brown, with broad, slightly imbricated, round to irregular lobes, often slightly ascending toward the margins; whitish to brownish below, reticulated with brownish, confluent veins; apothecia middle-sized, 4–6 mm. across, borne on short, digitately clustered lobules, round, often horizontal, the disk dark brown, the exciple often obscurely irregular or crenulate; hypothecium hyaline to brownish; spores hyaline, 3–7-septate, acicular, 60–100 × 3–4 μ.

On soil, New Hampshire, sterile and uncertainly included.

OTHER SPECIES REPORTED

Peltigera Evansiana Gyelnik—New Hampshire, Vermont, Connecticut, and Michigan.

33. LECIDEACEAE

Thallus crustose, granulose to squamulose, entire to lobed at the margin, differentiated into cortical, algal, and medullary layers or showing little differentiation, attached to the substratum by hyphal rhizoids; apothecia round, immersed to sessile or rarely pedicellate, the proper exciple well developed.

The algal hosts are Gloeocapsa, Pleurococcus, and Protococcus.

A. Spores non-septate
  B. Parasitic on other lichens . . . . 121. Nesolechia
  B. Not parasitic on other lichens
    C. Spores very large, thick-walled . . . . 122. Mycoblastus
    C. Spores not large, thin-walled
      D. Thallus crustose . . . . 119. Lecidea
      D. Thallus squamulose . . . . 120. Psora
A. Spores septate
  B. Spores transversely 1–many-septate
    C. Spores 1-septate
      D. Spores large, thick-walled . . . . 124. Megalospora
      D. Spores small, thin-walled . . . . 123. Catillaria

C. Spores 1–3- or several- to many-septate
   D. Spores 3- or rarely more septate, fusiform . . . . 125. B<small>ILIMBIA</small>
   D. Spores 1–3- or commonly more septate, acicular
      E. Thallus crustose . . . . 126. B<small>ACIDIA</small>
      E. Thallus squamulose . . . . 127. T<small>ONINIA</small>
B. Spores transversely and usually longitudinally septate
   C. Spores hyaline . . . . 128. L<small>OPADIUM</small>
   C. Spores brown . . . . 129. R<small>HIZOCARPON</small>

119. **Lecidea** Ach., Meth. Lich. 32. pl. 2, f. 1, 2. 1803.

Thallus crustose, granulose, warty or areolate, rudimentary, devoid of differentiation into layers and attached to the substratum by hyphal rhizoids; apothecia minute to middle-sized, more or less immersed to adnate or sessile, the disk flat to convex, light-colored to black, the exciple colored like the disk, usually disappearing; hypothecium hyaline to brown or black; hymenium hyaline to brownish or brown above; paraphyses unbranched or enlarged and branched toward the apices; asci clavate to cylindrico-clavate; spores 8 to rarely more, hyaline, nonseptate to rarely appearing 1-septate, usually oblong or ellipsoid.

The algal host is Protococcus.

A. Apothecia light-colored to brownish or rarely brownish black
  B. Hypothecium hyaline
    C. Thallus often disappearing
      D. On old wood
        E. Disk brown to brownish black; spores 7–9.5 $\times$ 3–3.5 μ . 3. L. misella
        E. Disk pale lead-colored to black; spores 5–7.5 $\times$ 2.5–3 μ 1. L. punctella
      D. On rocks; spores 8–12 $\times$ 4–7 μ . . . . 2. L. phaeophora
    C. Thallus usually persistent
      D. Thallus greenish gray to ashy, whitish, yellowish or rarely darker
        E. On trees and old wood, rarely over moss
          F. Thallus distinctly granulose
            G. Spores ovoid-ellipsoid or long-ovoid
              H. Thallus greenish gray to yellowish green, usually
                 bordered and decussated by black lines . . 7. L. varians
              H. Thallus greenish gray to white . . . . . 4. L. paddensis
            G. Spores globose, 4.5–7 μ across . . . . . 9. L. Nylanderi
          F. Thallus smooth to chinky, scurfy or sorediate
            G. Apothecia flesh-colored to yellow or whitish . 10. L. carneoalbens
            G. Apothecia pale yellowish to reddish brown . . . 5. L. vernalis
            G. Apothecia scarlet . . . . 8. L. cinnabarina
        E. On rocks and soil
          F. Thallus granulose-areolate . . . . . . 6. L. leucophaeoides
          F. Thallus squamulose . . . . 11. L. glebulosa
      D. Thallus rarely greenish gray, more or less brownish,
      reddish brown or darker
        E. On trees and old wood
          F. Spores less than 16 μ in length
            G. Apothecia 0.2–0.3 mm. across; spores
              10–15 $\times$ 3–5 μ . . . . 12. L. furvonigrans
            G. Apothecia 0.3–1.5 mm. across; spores
              9–14 $\times$ 4–7 μ . . . . 13. L. holopolia
          F. Spores 17–23 $\times$ 11–16 μ . . . . 15. L. tornoensis
        E. On rocks
          F. Spores oblong-ellipsoid, 9–12 $\times$ 3–5 μ . . . . . 16. L. rivulosa
          F. Spores subglobose to ovoid, 6–9 $\times$ 5–6 μ . . . 14. L. mollis
  B. Hypothecium hyaline to yellowish or rarely darker
    C. Apothecia rarely more than 0.5 mm. across
      D. Apothecia lemon-colored; spores 4–7 $\times$ 2–3 μ . . . . 19. L. lucida
      D. Apothecia pale to reddish brown or black; spores
      13–16 $\times$ 7–9 μ . . . . 17. L. mutabilis

    C. Apothecia rarely less than 0.5 mm. across
       D. Disk flat to convex, smooth
          E. Apothecia dark reddish or nearly black . . . . . 21. L. furfuracea
          E. Apothecia reddish brown to dark purplish . . . . 20. L. rufofusca
       D. Disk slightly convex, irregular and furrowed, appearing as many
          conglomerate apothecia . . . . 18. L. congesta
  B. Hypothecium hyaline to brownish or pale brown
    C. On trees and old wood
       D. Thallus greenish or bright yellow or brownish
          E. Thallus greenish yellow to brownish . . . . . . 23. L. quernea
          E. Thallus yellowish green or sulphur-colored . . . . 22. L. cadubriae
       D. Thallus greenish gray to brownish . . . . 24. L. carnulenta
    C. On rocks, soil, over moss and rarely on wood
       D. Disk pale flesh-colored to black; spores 13–23 $\times$ 7–13 μ 27. L. coarctata
       D. Disk flesh-colored to olive-green or black;
          spores 9–16 $\times$ 4.5–5 μ . . . . 26. L. granulosa
       D. Disk flesh-colored to yellowish brown;
          spores 5–7 $\times$ 2.5–3 μ . . . . 25. L. intropallida
  B. Hypothecium reddish or brownish to dark brown or black
    C. Thallus greenish gray to ashy or black
       D. Spores rarely more than 12 μ in length
          E. Thallus chinky-areolate to wrinkled and granulose
             F. Disk pale brownish to black . . . . 31. L. turgidula
             F. Disk bright or dull red . . . . 32. L. russula
          E. Thallus obscurely rough and becoming smooth and
            disappearing . . . . 29. L. peliaspis
       D. Spores rarely less than 12 μ in length .
          E. On trees, soil, moss, or old wood
             F. Spores 9–20 $\times$ 3.5–6 μ . . . . 34. L. sanguineoatra
             F. Spores 12–16 $\times$ 6–8 μ . . . . 30. L. furfurosa
          E. On rocks . . . . 28. L. calcivora
    C. Thallus greenish gray to more or less brownish or darker
       D. Thallus chinky-areolate to granulose
          E. Apothecia rarely more than 0.4 mm. across
             F. Thallus olive-green to blackish brown . . . . . 36. L. uliginosa
             F. Thallus greenish to yellowish brown . . . . 35. L. flavidolivens
          E. Apothecia 0.5–1.2 mm. across . . . . 33. L. hypomela
       D. Thallus subgranulose to squamulose . . . . . . 37. L. parvifolia
A. Apothecia reddish brown or brown to black, rarely pruinose
  B. Hypothecium hyaline
    C. Thallus soon disappearing
       D. On old wood . . . . 38. L. myriocarpella
       D. On rocks . . . . 40. L. plana
    C. Thallus usually persistent
       D. Thallus greenish gray to ashy, whitish or yellowish
          E. Black hypothallus more or less conspicuous
             F. Thallus more or less yellowish
                G. Apothecia 0.2–0.7 mm. across . . . . . . 46. L. tessellina
                G. Apothecia 0.7–1.8 mm. across . . . . . . 47. L. amylacea
             F. Thallus greenish gray to ashy or whitish, but not yellowish
                G. On rocks
                    H. Exciple thick, becoming wavy . . . . 44. L. tennessensis
                    H. Exciple thin, finally curled-flexuous . . . . 45. L. cyanea
                G. On trees . . . . 42. L. fuscescens
          E. Black hypothallus rarely conspicuous
             F. On rocks and soil
                G. Thallus greenish gray to dirty yellowish . . . 41. L. Brandegei
                G. Thallus ashy to whitish . . . . 43. L. subplebeia
             F. On old wood . . . . 39. L. melancheima
       D. Thallus pale to dark green or blackening
          E. Thallus chinky to areolate . . . . 48. L. tenebrosa
          E. Thallus of erect crowded trunks . . . . 49. L. Pringlei

B. Hypothecium hyaline to dusky or yellowish or darker
  C. Hypothecium hyaline to dusky
    D. Thallus thin, powdery . . . . 50. L. floridensis
    D. Thallus thicker, chinky- or squamulose-areolate
      E. Thallus grayish yellow to tan . . . . 55. L. atrolutescens
      E. Thallus pale yellowish to yellowish red . . . . . 54. L. armeniaca
  C. Hypothecium tinged yellowish or darker
    D. On trees or old wood
      E. Thallus greenish gray to yellowish or bright yellow . . 53. L. aitema
      E. Thallus dark ashy to whitish . . . . . . 59. L. parasema achrista
    D. On rocks
      E. Hypothecium hyaline to yellowish
        F. Spores $10–12 \times 2–3.5 \mu$ . . . . 52. L. Hassei
        F. Spores $12–17 \times 6–9 \mu$ . . . . 51. L. catalinariae
      E. Hypothecium yellow to blackish . . . . 59. L. parasema theioplaca
B. Hypothecium hyaline to brownish or brown
  C. Thallus greenish gray to ashy, whitish, or yellowish
    D. Apothecia solitary and scattered
      E. Black hypothallus not conspicuous
        F. Thallus very thin to thin, smooth to chinky and
          finally areolate
          G. Apothecia rarely less than 0.5 mm. across
            H. Apothecia yellowish to blackish and obscurely
              grayish pruinose . . . . . . 59. L. parasema ambigua
            H. Apothecia black . . . . 59. L. parasema
          G. Apothecia rarely more than 0.5 mm. across . 61. L. virginiensis
        F. Thallus moderately thick . . . . 68. L. pantherina
      E. Black hypothallus conspicuous
        F. Thallus greenish white to ashy gray
          G. Thallus very thin, scurfy . . . . . . 62. L. cruciaria
          G. Thallus moderately thick, granulose to warty-
            areolate . . . . 67. L. panaeola
        F. Thallus yellowish . . . . 59. L. parasema flavens
    D. Apothecia more or less clustered or confluent
      E. On rocks, soil, and over moss
        F. On soil and over moss . . . . . . 59. L. parasema muscorum
        F. On rocks
          G. Spores rarely more than 15μ in length
            H. Black hypothallus usually conspicuous
              I. Exciple lighter colored than the disk . . 57. L. pruinosa
              I. Exciple same color as the disk
                J. Thallus chinky-areolate, greenish gray
                  to ashy . . . . 58. L. polycarpa
                J. Thallus squamulose-areolate, yellowish to
                  copper or chestnut-brown . . . 104. L. atrobrunnea
            H. Black hypothallus not conspicuous
              I. Disk flat to strongly convex . . . . . 64. L. pacifica
              I. Disk slightly concave to slightly convex . 63. L. lithophila
          G. Spores rarely less than 15μ in length
            H. Disk black . . . . 56. L. Brujeriana
            H. Disk thinly gray-pruinose . . . . . . 69. L. arctica
      E. On old wood
        F. Thallus more or less granulose
          G. Thallus thin, granules sometimes forming
            a thin crust . . . . 65. L. viridescens
          G. Thallus thicker, granules more often forming
            a crust . . . . 66. L. gelatinosa
        F. Thallus smooth to slightly rough . . . . . 60. L. torquens
  C. Thallus greenish gray to olive-brown, or reddish brown to
  darker, squamulose . . . . 70. L. lugubris
B. Hypothecium brownish to brown and black
  C. Thallus soon disappearing
    D. Spores rarely more than 10μ in length . . . . . . 74. L. micytho

D. Spores rarely less than 10 μ in length
  E. On rocks and soil
    F. Apothecia 0.4–0.8 or 1 mm. across
      G. Exciple thin, finally disappearing . . . . 73. L. promiscens
      G. Exciple thick, ashy pruinose . . . . 71. L. cinerata
    F. Apothecia 0.2–0.4 mm. across . . . . . . 98. L. humosa
  E. On old wood . . . . 72. L. diapensiae
C. Thallus usually persistent
  D. Thallus greenish gray to ashy, whitish or yellowish, rarely darker
    E. Spores rarely less than 10 μ in length
      F. Thallus more or less distinctly areolate
        G. Disk more or less pruinose
          H. Thallus continuous
            I. Spores rarely less than 15 μ in length
              J. Thallus moderately thick, chinky to
                indistinctly areolate . . . 103. L. albocaerulescens
              J. Thallus smooth, then warty, chinky
                or subareolate . . . . . . 79. L. cinereoatra
            I. Spores 10–14 × 6–7 μ . . . . 90. L. grisella
          H. Thallus scattered or irregularly spread
            I. Thallus thin; apothecia 0.4–2.5 mm. across 77. L. platycarpa
            I. Thallus thicker; apothecia 0.5–1.5 mm.
              across . . . . 91. L. contigua
        G. Disk never pruinose
          H. Apothecia rarely clustered
            I. Thallus without a black hypothallus
              J. Disk becoming irregular and lobed
                K. Thallus thick, granulose to areolate . 88. L. latypea
                K. Thallus thin, smooth to chinky
                  or subareolate . . . . 88. L. latypea aequata
              J. Disk regular and entire
                K. Showing a whitish hypothallus . . 78. L. speirea
                K. Areoles more or less plainly lobed 94. L. mamillana
            I. Thallus with a black hypothallus
              J. Thallus ashy to ashy brown . . 93. L. fuscocinerea
              J. Thallus pale yellow . . . . . . 89. L. aglaea
          H. Apothecia clustered and irregular
            I. Thallus ashy to whitish . . . . . 81. L. vorticosa
            I. Thallus greenish gray to ashy or rust-red . 80. L. lapicida
      F. Thallus smooth to warty or granulose
        G. On trees and over moss
          H. On trees . . . . 75. L. euphorea
          H. Over moss
            I. Apothecia sometimes crowded, disk black . 85. L. limosa
            I. Apothecia rarely crowded, disk brown
              to blackish . . . . 86. L. fusca
        G. On rocks
          H. Thallus minutely granulose; spores
           10–13 × 5–6 μ . . . . 76. L. fuscorubens
          H. Thallus warty to granulose; spores
           10–14 × 6–10 μ . . . . 83. L. goniophila
    E. Spores rarely more than 10 μ in length
      F. On rocks and moss
        G. Apothecia less than 0.5 mm. across
          H. Spores 5–8 × 2–3.5 μ . . . . . . 87. L. planetica
          H. Spores 8–11 × 3–4 μ . . . . . . 84. L. neglecta
        G. Apothecia more than 0.5 mm. across . . 82. L. auriculata
      F. On old wood . . . . 92. L. flexuosa
  D. Thallus greenish gray to olivaceous, reddish, brownish, or blackening
    E. Spores rarely less than 10 μ in length
      F. Thallus granulose to areolate
        G. On trees
          H. Thallus wrinkled-granulose to warty;
           apothecia 0.3–0.4 mm. across . . . 102. L. xanthococcoides

H. Thallus granulose; apothecia 0.4–1 mm. across . 96. L. olivacea
G. On rocks . . . . 97. L. Manni
F. Thallus more or less squamulose
  G. Hypothallus not distinct
    H. Apothecia not less than 0.5 mm. across
      I. Thallus reddish brown . . . . . 108. L. protabacina
      I. Thallus brownish gray . . . . . 109. L. fuscatoatra
    H. Apothecia not more than 0.6 mm. across . 107. L. intumescens
  G. Hypothallus distinct and black
    H. Thallus reddish brown to blackish . . . 105. L. fuscoatra
    H. Thallus yellowish to copper or
      chestnut-brown . . . . 104. L. atrobrunnea
E. Spores rarely more than 10 μ in length
  F. Spores ellipsoid or ovoid-ellipsoid
    G. Thallus granulose
      H. On rocks
        I. Hypothecium blackish brown . . . . 99. L. cyrtidia
        I. Hypothecium bluish black . . . . . 100. L. sylvicola
      H. On old wood . . . . 101. L. myriocarpoides
    G. Thallus granulose-squamulose . . . . . 106. L. fuliginosa
  F. Spores globose, 7–9 μ across . . . . 95. L. dolodes

1. **Lecidea punctella** (Willey) Zahlbr., Cat. Lich. Univ. 3:815. 1925.
Biatora punctella Willey, in Tuck., Syn. N. A. Lich. 2:23. 1888.
Thallus disappearing; apothecia minute, 0.1–0.2 mm. across, adnate, the disk convex, pale lead-colored to black, the exciple disappearing; hypothecium hyaline; spores ellipsoid, 5–7.5 × 2.5–3 μ.
On old wood, near New Bedford, Massachusetts.

2. **Lecidea phaeophora** Stizenb.; Hasse, Bull. Torr. Club 24:448. 1897.
Biatora phaeophora Stizenb.; Hasse, Erythea 4:108. 1896.
Thallus powdery, ashy white, sometimes disappearing; apothecia minute to middle-sized, 0.2–0.6 mm. across, sessile, sometimes crowded, the disk slightly convex, reddish brown, exciple indistinct, surrounded by a thin, powdery, thalloid one; hypothecium hyaline; asci becoming inflated; oblong-ellipsoid, 8–12 × 4–7 μ.
On calcareous rocks, southern California.

3. **Lecidea misella** Nyl., Not. Sällsk. Faun. Flor. Fenn. 8:177. 1866.
L. anomala var. *misella* Nyl., Not. Sällsk. Faun. Flor. Fenn. 5:202. 1861.
Thallus thin, ashy to greenish gray, minutely granulose, becoming scurfy and disappearing; apothecia minute, 0.15–0.25 mm. across, slightly immersed to sessile, scattered, the disk convex, brown to blackish brown; hypothecium hyaline; spores oblong-ellipsoid, 7–9.5 × 3–3.5 μ.
On old wood, southern California.

4. **Lecidea paddensis** (Tuck.) Zahlbr., Cat. Lich. Univ. 3:808. 1925.
Biatora paddensis Tuck., Syn. N. A. Lich. 2:25. 1888.
Thallus granulose, granules scattered, tough, finally flattened, greenish gray to white; apothecia middle-sized, 0.5–1 mm. across, sessile, the disk flat to slightly convex, dull yellowish brown to lead-colored to dark red or blackish, the exciple becoming flexuous, finally disappearing; hypothecium hyaline; spores globose or long-ovoid, 6–12 × 4–7 μ.
On old wood of conifers, Montana and Washington.

5. **Lecidea vernalis** (L.) Ach., Meth. Lich. 68. 1803.
Lichen vernalis L., Syst. Nat. ed. 12. 234. 1768. *Biatora vernalis* (L.) E. Fries.
Thallus rather thin, widespread, greenish gray to ashy, the granules very minute, irregular or hemispherical, sometimes compacted into a smoother, less granular, chinky crust; apothecia minute to small, 0.3–0.7 mm. across, often clustered and conglomerate, the disk becoming strongly convex, pale yellowish to reddish brown, and blackening, the exciple of same color, disappearing; hypothe-

cium hyaline; spores ellipsoid, varying toward fusiform, sometimes 1-septate, 12–17 × 4–6 μ.

On mosses, trees, and rarely wood, throughout northern United States westward to Minnesota.

6. **Lecidea leucophaeoides** Nyl., Flora 53:35. 1870.
　　L. lulensis Helb.

Thallus granulose-areolate, the areoles minute and indistinct, or larger, distinct, and convex, whitish to ashy or dirty gray, continuous or scattered, hypothallus black, visible here and there and at the margin; apothecia middle-sized, 0.5–0.8 mm. across, adnate, the disk flat to strongly convex, appearing finely roughened under the lens, pale, soon dusky or dull black, the exciple soon disappearing; hypothecium hyaline; spores ovoid to ellipsoid, 9–15 × 5–9 μ.

On rocks, Maryland.

7. **Lecidea varians** Ach., Syn. Meth. Lich. 38. 1814.
　　Biatora varians (Ach.) Eschw., Syst. Lich. 26. 1824. *L. exigua* Chaub. *L. atrorubens* E. Fries as det. Merrill from Maine.

Thallus granulose, greenish gray to yellowish green, or the minute granules passing into a thin but continuous, smooth or rough, often chinky crust, usually bordered and decussated by black lines; apothecia minute, 0.12–0.25 mm. across, adnate, often clustered and confluent, the disk flat to convex, pale yellowish to black, the exciple of same color, thin, finally disappearing; hypothecium hyaline; spores ovoid-ellipsoid, 7–15 × 5–7 μ.

On trees and old wood, throughout the United States.

8. **Lecidea cinnabarina** Fée, Essai Crypt. 108. 1824.
　　Biatora cinnabarina (Fée) E. Fries.

Thallus widespread, thin, chinky, sometimes sorediate, whitish to greenish gray; apothecia small to middle-sized, 0.2–1 mm. across, adnate, sometimes flexuously lobed, rarely proliferous, the disk flat to convex, scarlet, the exciple lighter colored, soon disappearing; hypothecium hyaline; spores oblong, 8–12 × 2–3 μ.

On trees, Washington, Oregon, and California.

9. **Lecidea Nylanderi** (Anzi) T. Fries, Lich. Scand. 2:462. 1874.
　　Biatora Nylanderi Anzi, Cat. Lich. Sandr. 75. 1860.

Thallus thin, widespread, granulose, the granules very minute, often forming scattered clusters, greenish ashy to whitish; apothecia middle-sized, 0.4–1 mm. across, adnate, the disk flat to convex, reddish brown and darkening, the exciple pale, becoming flexuous, soon disappearing; hypothecium hyaline; spores globose, 4.5–7 μ across.

On trees, Massachusetts.

10. **Lecidea carneoalbens** Nyl., Lich. Ins. Guin. 46. 1889.

Thallus thin, somewhat scurfy, continuous, greenish gray; apothecia minute to small, 0.2–0.5 mm. across, adnate, the disk concave to convex, flesh-colored, varying toward yellow or white, the exciple lighter colored, slightly raised or sometimes disappearing; hypothecium hyaline; spores oblong-ellipsoid, 11–14 × 6 μ.

On oaks, Florida.

11. **Lecidea glebulosa** (E. Fries) Clemente, Colm. Enum. Crypt. Esp. Port. 138. 1868.
　　Biatora glebulosa E. Fries, Lich. Eur. 252. 1831.

Thallus squamulose, greenish to whitish, the squamules thickish, closely attached to substratum, becoming crowded and imbricated, lobulate and crenate, convex, irregular; apothecia middle-sized, 0.5–1.5 mm. across, adnate, often confluent, the disk flat to convex, slightly pruinose, pale or reddish to brownish or black, the exciple thin, paler, sometimes finally disappearing; hypothecium hyaline; spores ovoid-ellipsoid, 10–12 × 5–6 μ.

On soil, Washington, Oregon, and California.

12. **Lecidea furvonigrans** (Tuck.) Zahlbr., Cat. Lich. Univ. 3:762. 1925.
Biatora furvonigrans Tuck., Syn. N. A. Lich. 2:129. 1888.
Thallus thin, widespread, unequal, brown, the hypothallus black; apothecia minute, 0.2–0.3 mm. across, sessile, the disk convex, brown to blackish, the exciple disappearing; hypothecium hyaline; spores oblong, 10–15 × 3–5 μ.
On trees, Washington.

13. **Lecidea holopolia** (Tuck.) Zahlbr., Cat. Lich. Univ. 3:782. 1925.
Biatora holopolia Tuck., Syn. N. A. Lich. 2:26. 1888. *Biatora pullata* Tuck.
Thallus granulose, olive-brown to blackening, the granules coarse, tough, round, scattered or finally crowded; apothecia middle-sized, 0.3–1.5 mm. across, adnate, the disk flat, becoming convex, rusty red and blackening, the exciple blackish, thick, becoming wavy-lobed; hypothecium hyaline; spores ovoid, 9–14 × 4–7 μ.
On old wood, Washington and California.

14. **Lecidea mollis** (Wahl.) Nyl., Not. Sällsk. Faun. Flor. Fenn. 5:223. 1861.
L. rivulosa var. *mollis* Wahl., Fl. Lapp. 472. 1812.
Thallus rough or slightly scurfy, chinky-areolate, becoming verrucose, greenish- or reddish-gray to brownish gray or blackish brown, bordered and dissected by a black hypothallus; apothecia middle-sized, 0.7–1.2 mm. across, adnate to sessile, the disk flattish, from flesh-colored soon brown to black, sometimes white-pruinose, the exciple black, soon flexuous, rarely disappearing; hypothecium hyaline; spores subglobose to ovoid, 6–9 × 5–6 μ.
On rocks, New Hampshire.

15. **Lecidea tornoensis** Nyl. et Saelan, Herb. Musc. Fenn. 110. 1859.
Biatora tornoensis (Nyl. et Saelan) T. Fries.
Thallus granulose, olive-greenish brown, the granules flattened, crowded and passing into an irregular, sometimes chinky-areolate crust; apothecia small, 0.3–0.8 mm. across, adnate to subsessile, clustered and confluent into variously irregular masses, the disk becoming strongly tuberculate, reddish brown to blackish, the exciple evanescent; hypothecium hyaline; spores short-ellipsoid, 17–23 × 11–16 μ.
On trees, shrubs, and old wood, New Hampshire, Washington, and California.

16. **Lecidea rivulosa** Ach., Meth. Lich. 38. 1803.
Biatora rivulosa (Ach.) E. Fries.
Thallus rough, chinky-areolate to granulose or verrucose, greenish gray to reddish brown to blackish brown or mouse-colored, the hypothallus black; apothecia middle-sized, 0.7–1.3 mm. across, sessile to adnate, the disk flattish, slightly rough, becoming flexuous and irregular, dusky flesh-colored to brown or black, the exciple thin, paler, rarely disappearing; hypothecium hyaline; spores oblong-ellipsoid, slightly curved, 9–12 × 3–5 μ.
On rocks, New England, Pennsylvania, North Carolina, South Carolina, Tennessee, and Washington.

17. **Lecidea mutabilis** Fée, Mém. Mus. Hist. Nat. Strasb. 2E:105. 1835.
Biatora mutabilis (Fée) Mont.
Thallus rather thin, granulose, continuous, ashy gray, the granules small, closely crowded and becoming scurfy; apothecia minute to small, 0.2–0.5 mm. across, adnate, the disk flat or finally convex, pale to reddish brown or black, the exciple thin, soon disappearing; hypothecium hyaline to yellowish; spores ovoid-ellipsoid, 13–16 × 7–9 μ.
On trees, Florida, Louisiana, Minnesota, and California.

18. **Lecidea congesta** Fink; Hedrick, Mycologia 26:155. 1934.
Thallus of small, round to slightly irregular, often scattered, greenish gray to dirty brown or darker warts; apothecia small to middle-sized, 0.4–1.8 mm. across, adnate, the disk slightly to strongly convex, light to darker brown, the exciple

thin, surrounded by a very thin thalloid veil, exciple and veil obscurely visible at the basal margins of very young hymenia, but disappearing very early; the mature apothecia becoming variously irregular in form and furrowed above with 1 to 4 or rarely more furrows, running in various directions, sometimes intersecting, at first shallow, but finally splitting the apothecium into about 2–5 variously shaped, closely placed portions, giving the appearance of so many peculiarly shaped, conglomerate apothecia; hypothecium hyaline to pale yellowish; spores oblong-ellipsoid to ellipsoid, 9.5–11 $\times$ 4.5–5 μ.

On a granite boulder, Ohio.

19. **Lecidea lucida** Ach., Meth. Lich. 74. 1803.
    Lichen lucidus Ach., Lich. Suec. 39. 1798. *Biatora lucida* (Ach.) E. Fries.

Thallus rather thin, widespread, greenish yellow, minutely granulose, soon powdery, continuous or scattered, sometimes forming small heaps; apothecia minute to small, 0.15–0.35 mm. across, adnate, sometimes clustered to conglomerate, the disk convex, lemon-colored, becoming brownish, the exciple soon disappearing; hypothecium pale yellowish; spores 4–7 $\times$ 2–3 μ.

On shaded rocks and exposed roots of trees, New York, Massachusetts, and Minnesota.

20. **Lecidea rufofusca** (Anzi) Nyl., Flora 52:409. 1869.
    Biatora rufofusca Anzi, Cat. Lich. Sondr. 76. 1860.

Thallus rather thick, widespread, granulose-verrucose, whitish to brownish, hypothallus whitish; apothecia small to middle-sized, 0.5–1.2 mm. across, subsessile, the disk flat to convex, reddish brown to dark purplish, the exciple of the same color, thin, finally disappearing; hypothecium pale yellow; spores oblong-ellipsoid, 13–18 $\times$ 6–9 μ.

On turfy soil and trees, Colorado.

21. **Lecidea furfuracea** Pers., in Gaudich., Bot. Voy. Uran. 192. 1826.

Thallus thin, smooth to scurfy, obscurely chinky, ashy gray; apothecia small to middle-sized, 0.5–1 mm. across, the disk flat to convex, dark reddish or nearly black, the exciple disappearing; hypothecium yellowish and darkening; spores hyaline, ellipsoid, 10–16 $\times$ 5–8 μ.

On trees, Florida and Louisiana.

22. **Lecidea cadubriae** (Mass.) Nyl., Not. Sällsk. Faun. Flor. Fenn. 13:335. 1868.
    Biatora cadubriae Mass., Sched. Crit. 176. 1855. *Biatora aitema* Mass.

Thallus thin, rough, composed of minute, irregularly shaped, scattered, yellowish green or sulphur-colored granules on a white cobwebby hypothallus; apothecia minute to small, 0.1–0.3 mm. across, immersed to adnate, the disk flat to slightly convex, yellowish to dark brown, the exciple thin, dirty brown, soon disappearing; hypothecium brownish; spores oblong-ellipsoid, 8–11 $\times$ 3–4 μ.

On trees, California.

23. **Lecidea quernea** (Dicks.) Ach., Meth. Lich. 62. 1803.
    Lichen querneus Dicks., Pl. Crypt. Brit. 1:9. pl. 2, f. 3. 1785. *Biatora quernea* (Dicks.) E. Fries.

Thallus of minute granules, greenish yellow to brownish, scattered, or crowded and forming a thin, chinky crust; apothecia minute to middle-sized, 0.3–1 mm. across, partly immersed to adnate, the disk flat to convex, becoming irregular, reddish brown to blackish, the exciple paler, soon disappearing; hypothecium pale brownish; spores ovoid-ellipsoid, 7–11 $\times$ 4–6 μ.

On trees and old wood, Minnesota, Montana, and California.

24. **Lecidea carnulenta** (Tuck.) Fink, Cont. U. S. Nat. Herb. 14[1]:73. 1910.
    Biatora carnulenta Tuck., Proc. Am. Acad. 12:179. 1877.

Thallus rudimentary or entirely disappearing, when present consisting of a very thin and· scattered crust, greenish gray to brownish; apothecia minute to small, 0.2–0.6 mm. across, adnate, the disk flat to convex, pale flesh-colored to darkening, sometimes faintly pruinose, the exciple darker, finally disappearing; hypothecium hyaline to brownish; spores ovoid-ellipsoid, 7–12 × 3–5.5 μ.

On old wood, from New England to Iowa and Minnesota, and in Washington.

25. **Lecidea intropallida** Fink, Ohio Biol. Surv. 2:338. 1921.

Thallus continuous, smooth or slightly roughened, ashy gray and darkening; apothecia minute, 0.15–0.25 mm. across, adnate or partly immersed, the disk flat to slightly convex, flesh-colored to yellowish brown, the exciple of the same color and soon disappearing; hypothecium pale brown; spores ellipsoid, 5–7 × 2.5–3 μ.

On pebbles, Ohio.

26. **Lecidea granulosa** (Hoffm.) Ach., Meth. Lich. 65. 1803.

Verrucaria granulosa Hoffm., Descr. Pl. Crypt. 2:21. pl. 30, f. 3. 1794. *Biatora granulosa* (Hoffm.) Flot. *L. granulosa* var. *phyllizans* Zahlbr. *L. decolorans* (Hoffm.) Floerke.

Thallus widespread, greenish gray to ashy, granulose, the granules hemispherical, or irregular and sublobate, usually closely crowded and subimbricate, often forming sorediate heaps; apothecia middle-sized, 0.3–2 mm. across, adnate, frequently clustered to confluent and irregular, the disk flat to convex, flesh-colored to olive-green or black, the exciple raised, often paler, soon disappearing; hypothecium pale brown; spores ovoid-ellipsoid, 9–16 × 4.5–5 μ. (PLATE 15 *b*.)

On soil, dead moss, and old wood, throughout northern United States.

27. **Lecidea coarctata** (J. E. Smith) Nyl., Act. Soc. Linn. Bord. 21:358. 1856.

Lichen coarctatus J. E. Smith, in Sowerby, Engl. Bot. 8: pl. 534. 1799. *Biatora coarctata* (J. E. Smith) T. Fries. *L. coarctata* var. *ornata* (Sommerf.) T. Fries. *Lecanora coarctata* (J. E. Smith) Ach.

Thallus of squamulaceous areoles, these minute, scattered or clustered, round, angular, or minutely and irregularly crenate, greenish gray to ashy or brownish, sometimes passing into an areolate or subcontinuous and chinky crust; apothecia minute to small, 0.2–0.4 mm. across, adnate, the disk concave to flat or irregular, pale flesh-colored to black, the exciple of the same color, sometimes surrounded by a more or less developed thalloid veil; hypothecium hyaline to brown; spores ellipsoid or ovoid, 13–23 × 7–13 μ.

On rocks and rarely on soil, throughout northern United States.

28. **Lecidea calcivora** (Ehrh.) Nyl., Act. Soc. Linn. Bord. 21:381. 1856.

Lichen calcivorus Ehrh., Crypt. Exsicc. 244. 1793.

Thallus widespread, scurfy, light gray to white, usually confused with the substratum and disappearing; apothecia small, 0.3–0.5 mm. across, immersed in pits, finally superficial, flat to convex, blackish, dark red when wet, sometimes gray-pruinose, the exciple thin, soon disappearing; hypothecium pale to darker brown; spores ovoid-ellipsoid, 12–20 × 6–9 μ.

On calcareous rocks, Alabama.

29. **Lecidea peliaspis** (Tuck.) Zahlbr., Cat. Lich. Univ. 3:809. 1925.

Biatora peliaspis Tuck., Proc. Am. Acad. 12:179. 1877.

Thallus thin, obscurely roughened-verrucose, greenish gray to ashy, becoming smooth and disappearing; apothecia minute to small, 0.15–0.4 mm. across, the disk flat to strongly convex, sometimes slightly pruinose, dusky to blackish brown, the exciple thin, darker, becoming flexuous, finally disappearing; hypothecium blackish brown; spores various in shape and size, finally pointed-ellipsoid, 6–12 × 3–6 μ.

On trees and old wood, New Hampshire, Massachusetts, South Carolina, Florida, Illinois, and Iowa.

30. **Lecidea furfurosa** Tuck., Proc. Am. Acad. 6:274. 1866.

Biatora furfurosa Tuck.

Thallus widespread, granulose, the granules minute, round, sometimes scattered, ashy to dusky gray, the hypothallus thin and inconspicuous, blackening; apothecia middle-sized, 0.4–0.9 mm. across, sessile, the disk light yellowish brown and blackening, the exciple thin, black, transversely striated, finally disappearing; hypothecium blackish browñ; spores ovoid, 12–16 × 6–8 μ.

On trees, Florida and Louisiana.

31. **Lecidea turgidula** E. Fries, Sched. Crit. Lich. Exsicc. Suec. fasc. 1. 10. 1827.

Biatora turgidula (E. Fries) Nyl.

Thallus granulose, greenish gray to whitish, the granules commonly inconspicuous, irregular, usually more or less scattered, forming a very thin, subareolate or subcontinuous, sometimes disappearing crust; apothecia minute to small, 0.2–0.8 mm. across, sessile, the disk flat to strongly convex, pale brownish to black, sometimes slightly white-pruinose, the exciple soon disappearing; hypothecium brown; spores oblong to ellipsoid, 7–12 × 3–5 μ.

On trees and old wood, throughout the United States.

32. **Lecidea russula** Ach., Meth. Lich. 61. 1803.

Biatora russula (Ach.) Mont.

Thallus thin, smoothish to chinky-areolate, becoming wrinkled and granulose, greenish ashy to pale cream-colored, more or less limited by a dark hypothallus; apothecia small to middle-sized, 0.5–1.5 mm. across, sessile, the disk slightly concave to convex, becoming flexuous and lobed, bright or dull red, the exciple of same color or lighter, thin, finally disappearing; hypothecium yellow to reddish; spores oblong-ellipsoid, 8–12 × 3–4 μ.

On trees, from New York to Florida, and westward to the Rocky Mountains.

33. **Lecidea hypomela** Nyl., Mém. Soc. Sci. Nat. Cherb. 5:121. 1857.

Biatora hypomela (Nyl.) Tuck.

Thallus continuous, becoming roughened and minutely chinky-areolate or granulose, greenish gray to ashy or brownish; apothecia middle-sized, 0.5–1.2 mm. across, adnate, the disk flattish, finally convex and proliferous, bright to dark brownish or black, the exciple thick, blackening; hypothecium brownish black; spores ovoid-ellipsoid, 10–18 × 5–9 μ.

On trees, from Florida to Texas.

34. **Lecidea sanguineoatra** (Wulf.) Ach., Meth. Lich. 50. 1803.

Lichen sanguineoatra Wulf., in Jacq., Coll. Bot. 3:116. 1789. *Biatora sanguineoatra* (Wulf.) Tuck. *L. fusca* var. *atrofusca* (E. Fries) T. Fries.

Thallus thickish, widespread, granulose, the granules irregular or subhemispherical, usually closely aggregated and heaped, greenish gray to ashy gray; apothecia small to middle-sized, 0.4–1.2 mm. across, adnate, usually scattered, the disk flattish, becoming strongly convex, dark rusty brown through sanguineous and finally black, the exciple thin, black, finally disappearing; hypothecium brown; spores ellipsoid varying toward fusiform, 9–20 × 3.5–6 μ.

On dead moss, especially at bases of trees, on soil, and rarely on wood, throughout the United States.

35. **Lecidea flavidolivens** (Tuck.) Fink, Cont. U. S. Nat. Herb. 14[1]:76. 1910.

Biatora flavidolivens Tuck., Syn. N. A. Lich. 2:28. 1888.

Thallus granulose, greenish to yellowish brown, the minute, irregular, usually crowded and heaped granules forming a commonly widespread, continuous or somewhat scattered crust; apothecia minute, 0.2–0.3 mm. across, immersed to adnate, the disk flat to convex, olive-green to black, the exciple pale, soon disappearing; hypothecium brownish to brown; spores rarely 1-septate, 7–14 × 3–4 μ.

On cedar stumps, Minnesota, New Hampshire, and Massachusetts.

36. **Lecidea uliginosa** (Schrad.) Ach., Meth. Lich. 43. 1803.

Lichen uliginosus Schrad., Spic. Fl. Germ. 88. 1794. *Biatora uliginosa* (Schrad.) E. Fries. *L. uliginosa* var. *fuliginea* (Ach.) Link.

Thallus granulose, olive-green to blackish brown, or the minute, irregular, rarely coralloid granules forming a scattered or continuous crust; apothecia minute to small, 0.2–0.4 mm. across, immersed to adnate, often clustered, the disk flat to convex, brown to brownish black, the exciple thin, raised and lighter colored to black, disappearing; hypothecium brown; spores oblong-ellipsoid, 8–15 × 4–8 μ. On earth and old wood, widely distributed throughout the United States.

37. **Lecidea parvifolia** Pers., in Gaudich., Bot. Voy. Uram. 192. 1826.
Biatora parvifolia (Pers.) Tuck. *Biatora parvifolia* var. *corallina* Tuck. *Biatora parvifolia* var. *subgranulosa* Tuck. *L. santensis* Tuck.
Thallus squamulose, sometimes subgranulose, the squamules small, thin, ascending, crenate, becoming palmately or pinnately many-lobed, passing more or less completely into irregular coralloid branchlets, greenish gray or whitish to reddish brown or brown, hypothallus whitish through reddish to black; apothecia middle-sized to large, 0.6–1.4 mm. across, irregular, proliferous, the disk flat to strongly convex, yellowish brown to brown or blackish, the exciple of same color or paler, thick, finally disappearing; hypothecium brown; spores ellipsoid, becoming oblong, 7–15 × 2–4 μ.
On trees, from New Jersey to Florida, and westward to California.

38. **Lecidea myriocarpella** (Merrill) Zahlbr., Cat. Lich. Univ. 3:803. 1925.
Biatora myriocarpella Merrill, Bryologist 16:58. 1913.
Thallus very thin and inconspicuous or disappearing; apothecia minute, 0.1–0.25 mm. across, very numerous, adnate, the disk flat to strongly convex, dark brown to dull black, the exciple very thin, dull black, soon disappearing; hypothecium hyaline; spores ellipsoid or ellipsoid-oblong, rarely 1-septate, 7–8.5 × 3–4 μ.
On old wood, Washington.

39. **Lecidea melancheima** Tuck., Syn. Lich. N. E. 68. 1848.
L. elabens T. Fries.
Thallus thick, rough, wrinkled and warty, rarely subareolate, greenish gray to ashy, usually irregularly spread over the substratum, at first as a continuous crust, becoming scattered and finally disappearing; apothecia small to middle-sized, 0.25–1.25 mm. across, adnate, frequently clustered and irregular, the disk flat to convex, black, frequently shining, the exciple disappearing; hypothecium hyaline; spores oblong-ellipsoid, 7–13 × 3–4.5 μ. (PLATE 14.)
On old wood, New England, Iowa, Colorado, and Minnesota.

40. **Lecidea plana** (Lahm) Nyl., Flora 55:552. 1872.
Lecidella plana Lahm, in Koerb., Par. Lich. 211–213. 1865.
Thallus thin, chinky-areolate, gray, often disappearing, hypothallus black; apothecia small to middle-sized, 0.4–1 mm. across, adnate, often crowded and variously irregular, the disk concave to flat, black, the exciple paler, thin, raised; hypothecium hyaline; spores long-ellipsoid, 10–13 × 2.5–4 μ.
On rocks, Nevada and southern California.

41. **Lecidea Brandegei** Tuck., Bull. Torr. Club 10:21. 1883.
Thallus composed of minute, convex, round to irregular, greenish gray to dirty yellowish areoles, running together into a rather thick, wrinkled crust; apothecia middle-sized to large, 0.6–1.6 mm. across, adnate, the disk flat to slightly convex, dull black, the exciple thin, becoming black and wavy, then disappearing; hypothecium hyaline; spores ovoid-ellipsoid, 6–11 × 4–6 μ.
On rocks, Arizona and Colorado, and doubtfully in California.

42. **Lecidea fuscescens** Sommerf., Vet. Akad. Handl. 1823:114. 1823.
Biatora fuscescens (Sommerf.) E. Fries.
Thallus of minute, whitish, scattered granules, and a more or less apparent black hypothallus; apothecia minute to small, 0.3–0.6 mm. across, adnate to sessile, the disk flat to slightly convex, brown to black, the exciple thin, dark,

soon disappearing; hypothecium hyaline; spores short-ellipsoid to subspherical or spherical, 5–10 × 4–8 μ.
On trees, New York, Michigan, Washington, and California.

43. **Lecidea subplebeia** Nyl.; Hasse, Bull. Torr. Club 24:447. 1897.
Thallus widespread, powdery, chinky-areolate, sometimes slightly wrinkled, ashy to whitish; apothecia minute to small, 0.25–0.6 mm. across, closely adnate, the disk flat to slightly convex, black, the exciple also black, thin; hypothecium dusky or paler;.spores ovoid-ellipsoid, 9–12 × 6–7 μ.
On adobe soil and small pebbles, southern California.

44. **Lecidea tennessensis** Nyl., Lich. Lab. Sing. 41. 1891.
Thallus chinky-areolate, ashy gray to whitish, the areoles becoming more or less orbicular, swollen and convex, limited by the black hypothallus; apothecia small to middle-sized, 0.4–0.9 mm. across, partly immersed to closely adnate, becoming variously irregular, the disk flat, black, the exciple also black, thick, becoming wavy, rarely disappearing; hypothecium hyaline; spores short-ellipsoid to ellipsoid, 7–11 × 4.5–6 μ.
On sandstone, Tennessee.

45. **Lecidea cyanea** (Ach.) Röhling, Deutschl. Fl. 3:32. 1813.
L. lapicida var. *cyanea* Ach., Meth. Lich. 38. 1803. *L. tessellata* (Ach.) Floerke. *L. spilota* E. Fries.
Thallus more or less roughened, chinky-areolate, in round areas or irregularly widespread, greenish gray to ashy, the hypothallus black; apothecia small to middle-sized, 0.3–1 mm. across, or larger, immersed to adnate, the disk flat to convex, slightly pruinose, soon black, the exciple also black, thin, raised, finally curled-flexuous; hypothecium hyaline; spores ellipsoid, 8–12 × 4–7 μ.
On rocks, widely distributed throughout the United States.

46. **Lecidea tessellina** Tuck., Proc. Am. Acad. 12:181. 1877.
Thallus rough, chinky-areolate, greenish gray, varying toward yellowish, the areoles flat to sometimes convex, angular, the black hypothallus showing between the areoles; apothecia minute to small, 0.2–0.7 mm. across, immersed in the areoles, becoming confluent and irregular, the disk concave to slightly convex, black, the exciple paler, thin, acute, often disappearing; hypothecium hyaline; spores ellipsoid, 9–13 × 5–7 μ.
On rocks, from New England to the Gulf, and westward to Kansas and Nebraska, and also in Washington.

47. **Lecidea amylacea** (Ach.) Tuck., Syn. N. A. Lich. 2:78, 79. 1888.
Lichen amylaceus Ach., Vet. Akad. Nya Handl. 2:191. 1794.
Thallus thick, rough, continuous, becoming chinky to areolate, somewhat mealy, pale yellow to white, the hypothallus black; apothecia middle-sized to large, 0.7–1.8 mm. across, adnate, the disk flat, black, somewhat pruinose, the exciple black, thick, raised, finally disappearing; hypothecium hyaline; spores ellipsoid, 7–10 × 4–6 μ.
On rocks, Utah, Montana, and California; doubtfully reported also from the mountains of New Hampshire.

48. **Lecidea tenebrosa** Flot.; Nyl., Not. Sällsk. Faun. Flor. Fenn. 5:231. 1861.
Thallus rough, chinky, becoming areolate, the areoles distinct, smooth, slightly convex to swollen, pale green to blackish lead-colored, the hypothallus black; apothecia minute to small, 0.3–0.6 mm. across, immersed to adnate, the disk flat, black, the exciple also black, thin, rarely disappearing; hypothecium hyaline; spores ellipsoid, 12–18 × 7–10 μ.
On granite, New Hampshire.

49. **Lecidea Pringlei** Tuck., Bull. Torr. Club 10:22. 1883.
Thallus composed of crowded, erect, thick, dark green to blackening trunks, the branches dilated above, often densely rough and folded and passing into rootlike branches below; apothecia large, 1.5–5 mm. across, sessile, the disk flat

to convex, reddish brown to black, becoming wrinkled, the exciple thick, brownish to black and shining, finally becoming irregular and disappearing; hypothecium hyaline; spores oblong-ellipsoid, non-septate to appearing 1-septate, 10–12 × 3–6 μ. On rocks, Washington and California.

50. **Lecidea floridensis** Nyl.; Eckf., Bull. Torr. Club 16:104. 1889.
Thallus thin, continuous, slightly powdery, ashy to darker; apothecia middle-sized, 0.5–1 mm. across, adnate, the disk flat to slightly convex, black, the exciple thick, raised, black; hypothecium dusky; spores ellipsoid, 11–15 × 6–8 μ. On trees, Florida.

51. **Lecidea catalinariae** Stizenb.; Hasse, Bull. Torr. Club 24:447, 448. 1897.
Thallus warty, greenish yellow, the warts distinct, crowded or scattered, small, round, smooth, sometimes larger, and then oblong and distinctly lobulate; apothecia middle-sized, 0.6–1.2 mm. across, immersed to adnate, often clustered and angular, the disk flat to slightly convex, black, the exciple rather thick, black, finally partially disappearing; hypothecium hyaline to yellowish; spores ovoid-ellipsoid, 12–17 × 6–9 μ. On sandstone, Santa Catalina Island, California.

52. **Lecidea Hassei** Zahlbr., Ann. Mycol. 10:374. 1912.
Thallus rather thick, yellowish ashy, widespread, continuous, somewhat roughened, and chinky; apothecia large, 0.5–1.5 mm. across, sessile, the disk concave to flat, black, the exciple blackish, rather thick, becoming irregular and cut-wavy to strongly flexuous; hypothecium yellowish; spores long-oblong-ellipsoid, 10–12 × 2–3.5 μ. On sandstone, southern California.

53. **Lecidea aitema** Ach., Lich. Univ. 178. 1810.
Lecanora varia var. *aitema* (Ach.) Cromb., Lich. Brit. 52. 1870.
Thallus moderately thick, smooth to scurfy or powdery, light or greenish gray to yellowish or bright yellow; apothecia minute to small, 0.3–0.6 mm. across, adnate, often closely clustered, the disk flat to strongly convex, dull black, the exciple thin and inconspicuous, black, finally disappearing, surrounded at first by a thin, evanescent, thalloid veil; hypothecium and hymenium hyaline to yellowish; asci broadly clavate; spores oblong-ellipsoid, 9–14 × 3.5–5.5 μ. On old wood, New England and Illinois.

54. **Lecidea armeniaca** (Lam. & DC.) E. Fries, Syst. Veg. 286. 1825.
Rhizocarpon armeniacum Lam. & DC., Fl. France ed. 3. 2:366. 1815.
Thallus thick, pale yellowish to yellowish red, chinky-areolate, the areoles flat to convex, wrinkled, the hypothallus black, usually showing between the areoles; apothecia middle-sized to large, 1–3 mm. across, immersed, the disk flat to convex, black, the exciple soon disappearing; hypothecium hyaline to dusky; spores ellipsoid, 9–13 × 4–6 μ. On granite rocks, the Rocky Mountains, Montana, and Washington.

55. **Lecidea atrolutescens** Nyl.; Herre, Proc. Wash. Acad. Sci. 12:84, 85. 1910.
Thallus squamulose-areolate, the areoles scattered or overlapping, flat to convex, round to wavy or crenate, grayish yellow to tan; apothecia small to middle-sized, 0.75–2 mm. across, sessile, scattered to clustered, the disk flat to convex, dull black, becoming whitish pruinose, the exciple slightly paler, raised, entire to deeply wavy; hypothecium cloudy to yellowish; spores oblong-ellipsoid, 12–16 × 5–8 μ. On granite rocks, southern California.

56. **Lecidea Brujeriana** (Schaer.) Leight., Brit. Lich. 281. 1871.
Lecanora coarctata var. *Brujeriana* Schaer., Enum. Lich. Eur. 77. 1850. *Biatora coarctata* var. *Brujeriana* (Schaer.) Tuck.
Thallus granulose, passing into an areolate crust, continuous, scattered, or finally disappearing, greenish gray to ashy; apothecia small to middle-sized, 0.3–1

mm. across, adnate, frequently clustered, the disk concave to convex, sometimes irregular, black, the exciple of the same color, often raised, sometimes disappearing; hypothecium more or less brownish; spores oblong-ellipsoid, 12–21 × 6–10 μ. On sandstone, South Carolina, Wisconsin, and Minnesota.

57. **Lecidea pruinosa** Ach., Meth. Lich. 55. 1803.
L. lithophila Ach. in Fink, Cont. U. S. Nat. Herb. 14¹:77. 1910.
Thallus widespread, smoothish, continuous, becoming rough, chinky-areolate, greenish gray to ashy, sometimes disappearing, hypothallus black; apothecia small to middle-sized, 0.4–1.5 mm. across, sometimes closely clustered and angular, adnate or rarely sessile, the disk almost flat, blackish brown to black, rarely slightly pruinose, the exciple paler, rarely disappearing; hypothecium hyaline, finally brownish; spores oblong-ellipsoid, 9–15 × 5–7 μ.
On rocks, Minnesota, Tennessee, Texas, and California.

58. **Lecidea polycarpa** Floerke, in Sommerf., Suppl. Fl. Lapp. 149. 1826.
Thallus thin, minutely chinky-areolate, the areoles flat, greenish gray to ashy, sometimes disappearing, hypothallus black, sometimes absent; apothecia small to middle-sized, 0.6–1.5 mm. across, adnate, usually crowded into groups and angular, the disk slightly concave to flat, black, the exciple thin, black, raised; hypothecium hyaline, finally brownish; spores ellipsoid, 9–13 × 4–6 μ.
On rocks, New Hampshire, Nebraska, South Dakota, and the Rocky Mountains.

59. **Lecidea parasema** Ach., Meth. Lich. 35. 1803.
Lichen parasemus Ach., Lich. Suec. 64. 1798. *L. enteroleuca* Ach.
Thallus very thin to thin, smoothish to somewhat rough, becoming chinky to areolate, and sometimes minutely granulose, greenish gray to ashy; apothecia minute to middle-sized, 0.3–1 mm. across, adnate, scattered, the disk flat to more or less convex, black, the exciple thin, black, becoming flexuous and soon disappearing; hypothecium hyaline to brown; spores ovoid-ellipsoid, 8–17 × 5–9 μ.
On rocks and trees, throughout the United States.
The relationship between *L. parasema* and *L. enteroleuca* (Ach.) T. Fries is not clear, and it has seemed best to place our material under *L. parasema* and varieties thereof.

var. **ambigua** (Mass.) Boist., Nouv. Fl. Lich. 221. 1903.
Biatora ambigua Mass., Ric. Lich. 124. 1852. *L. enteroleuca* var. *ambigua* (Mass.) Tuck.
Thallus thin, smooth to slightly rough, ashy; apothecia yellowish to blackish and obscurely grayish pruinose.
On old wood, Minnesota, Oregon, and Washington.

var. **flavens** Nyl., Not. Sällsk. Faun. Flor. Fenn. 5:217. 1861.
L. enteroleuca var. *flavida* E. Fries.
Thallus yellowish, smooth to chinky, surrounded and dissected by a black hypothallus; the disk somewhat grayish pruinose, the exciple thin, commonly persistent.
On trees, New England and Minnesota, and perhaps generally distributed.

var. **muscorum** (Wulf.) Fink n. comb.
Lichen muscorum Wulf., in Jacq., Coll. Bot. 4:232. 1790. *L. enteroleuca* var. *muscorum* (Wulf.) T. Fries. *L. enteroleuca* var. *Wulfenii* Koerb.
Thallus warty, white to ashy; apothecia very black, confluent, the disk flat to convex, the exciple pale yellow to darker and finally brown.
On soil and mosses, New Hampshire.

var. **achrista** (Sommerf.) Mong., Bull. Acad. Géogr. Bot. 9:201. 1900.
L. elaeochroma var. *achrista* Sommerf., Suppl. Fl. Lapp. 150. 1826. *L. enteroleuca* var. *achrista* (Sommerf.) Tuck.
Thallus thin and smooth to chinky, warty, dark ashy to whitish; apothecia flat to tardily convex, becoming flexuous; hypothecium pale yellow to darker and brownish.
On trees, throughout the United States.

var. **theioplaca** (Tuck.) Zahlbr., Cat. Lich. Univ. 3:664. 1925.
L. enteroleuca var. *theioplaca* Tuck., Gen. Lich. 179. 1872.
Thallus thicker, rough, chinky to warty, pale yellowish or at least tinged with yellow; hypothecium yellow to blackish.
On rocks, New Jersey, South Carolina, Iowa, Minnesota, and California.

60. **Lecidea torquens** Müll. Arg., Hedwigia 34:141, 142. 1895.
Thallus very thin, smooth to sometimes slightly rough, greenish gray to ashy; apothecia minute, 0.1–0.25 mm. across, adnate, sometimes clustered, the disk flat to convex, brownish black to black, the exciple dull blackish, thin, indistinct, and evanescent; hypothecium hyaline to brownish; spores minute, ellipsoid, 7–9 × 2–3 μ.
On old wood, Illinois.

61. **Lecidea virginiensis** Nyl., Bot. Gaz. 22:333. 1896.
Thallus thin, smooth, becoming chinky and finally areolate, greenish gray to dull yellow; apothecia minute, 0.2–0.5 mm. across, subsessile, the disk flat to convex, brownish black to black, the exciple like the disk, soon disappearing; hypothecium brownish; asci somewhat broadly clavate, the apical wall somewhat thickened; spores oblong-ellipsoid, 9–12 × 4–5 μ, irregularly arranged.
On sandstone, West Virginia.

62. **Lecidea cruciaria** Tuck., Syn. N. A. Lich. 2:67. 1888.
Thallus very thin, scurfy, greenish white, intersected by black lines when wet; apothecia middle-sized, 0.5–0.9 mm. across, sessile, the disk flat to slightly convex, black, the exciple black, rather thick, wrinkled or wavy, finally disappearing; hypothecium hyaline to brownish; spores oblong-ellipsoid, 10–20 × 3–6 μ.
On rocks, Oregon and southern California.

63. **Lecidea lithophila** Ach., Syn. Meth. Lich. 14. 1814.
L. lapicida var. *lithophila* Ach., Lich. Univ. 160. 1810.
Thallus thin, rough and crumbly, chinky-areolate, ashy to whitish, sometimes disappearing; apothecia middle-sized, 0.5–1 mm. across, adnate, frequently clustered and angular, the disk slightly concave to slightly convex, black, the exciple pale, finally black, thin, raised, sometimes disappearing; hypothecium hyaline to brownish; spores ellipsoid, 10–14 × 4.5–6.5 μ.
On rocks, California.

64. **Lecidea pacifica** Herre, Proc. Wash. Acad. Sci. 2:264. 1910.
Thallus thin, minutely rough and becoming chinky or subareolate, ashy white; apothecia middle-sized to large, 0.6–1 mm. across, adnate to subsessile, sometimes clustered and irregular, the disk flat to strongly convex, brownish black, the exciple thin, colored like the disk, disappearing; hypothecium brownish; spores short-ellipsoid, 10–13 × 5–7 μ.
On rocks, California.

65. **Lecidea viridescens** (Schrad.) Ach., Meth. Lich. 62. 1803.
Lichen viridescens Schrad., Spic. Fl. Germ. 88. 1794. *Biatora viridescens* (Schrad.) Mann.
Thallus granulose, ashy to grayish green, the minute, smooth or deliquescent and powdery granules often forming a thin or rarely thicker crust; apothecia minute to small, 0.2–0.5 mm. across, adnate, frequently clustered or even conglomerate, the disk flat to convex, black, the exciple thin, pale lead-colored or darker, finally disappearing; hypothecium hyaline to pale brown; spores oblong-ellipsoid, 9–12 × 4–5.5 μ.
On old wood, from New England to Alabama, and westward to Ohio and Minnesota, and in California.

66. **Lecidea gelatinosa** Floerke, Ges. Naturf. Freund. Mag. 3:201. 1809.
Biatora viridescens var. *gelatinosa* (Floerke) E. Fries.
Thallus moderately thick, composed of minute, smooth and sometimes powdery, ashy to greenish gray granules passing into a continuous crust or tending to disappear; apothecia small to middle-sized, 0.3–0.7 mm. across, adnate, often clustered and irregular, the disk flat to convex, black, the exciple thin, pale lead-colored, soon disappearing; hypothecium hyaline to brownish; spores ovoid to ovoid-ellipsoid, 7–11 $\times$ 4–5.5 μ.
On rotten wood, New Hampshire and New Jersey.

67. **Lecidea panaeola** Ach., Vet. Akad. Nya Handl. 267. 1808.
L. leucophaea (Floerke) T. Fries. *Biatora leucophaea* Floerke.
Thallus moderately thick, granulose, widespread, ashy gray, the granules somewhat raised and irregular, scattered or continuous, often becoming verrucose-areolate; hypothallus black; apothecia small to middle-sized, 0.3–1 mm. across, partly immersed to adnate, the disk flat to slightly convex, dark brown to black, whitish within, the exciple thin, often lighter, finally disappearing; hypothecium hyaline to pale brownish; spores oblong-ellipsoid, 10–15 $\times$ 6–8 μ.
On rocks, New Hampshire and Minnesota.

68. **Lecidea pantherina** (Hoffm.) Ach., Meth. Lich. 37. 1803.
Verrucaria pantherina Hoffm., Deutschl. Fl. 184. 1796. *L. lactea* (Flot.) Schaer.
L. variegata E. Fries.
Thallus moderately thick, ashy, varying toward whitish or greenish gray, smooth, continuous, becoming roughened and chinky or areolate; apothecia small to large, 0.4–1.5 mm. across, partly immersed to rarely adnate, the disk flattish, black, often pruinose, the exciple also black, thin, becoming wavy, often finally disappearing; hypothecium brownish; spores ellipsoid, 9–14 $\times$ 5–8 μ. (PLATE 15 *a*.)
On rocks, Minnesota.

69. **Lecidea arctica** Sommerf., Suppl. Fl. Lapp. 156. 1826.
L. arctica var. *pallida* Tuck.
Thallus widespread, granulose, brownish ash-colored, the granules minute, globular, at first scattered, then heaped; apothecia small, 0.4–1 mm. across, immersed, sometimes conglomerate, the disk strongly convex to hemispherical, round to irregular, black, thinly gray-pruinose, the exciple soon disappearing; hypothecium brownish; spores oblong-ellipsoid, 12–24 $\times$ 7–9 μ.
On rocks, New Hampshire, Colorado, and Washington.

70. **Lecidea lugubris** Sommerf., Suppl. Fl. Lapp. 143. 1826.
Thallus thick, widespread, tough, squamulose, reddish brown to blackish gray, the squamules becoming lobed, crowded, often breaking up into granulose areas; hypothallus black; apothecia middle-sized, 0.5–1 mm. across, sessile, the disk flat, black, the exciple blackish, thick, raised, sometimes flexuous; hypothecium brownish; spores globose, 6–9 μ across.
On rocks, New Hampshire.

71. **Lecidea cinerata** Zahlbr., Bull. Torr. Club 27:644. 1900.
Thallus white, absent except under the apothecia; apothecia small, 0.4–1 mm. across, adnate, more or less clustered, the disk concave to flat, round, angular or flexuous, black, at first lightly pruinose, the exciple thick, raised, ashy pruinose; hypothecium brown; spores 12–14 $\times$ 5–6 μ.
On disintegrated granite, southern California.

72. **Lecidea diapensiae** T. Fries, Nov. Act. Soc. Sci. Ups. III. 2:209. 1860.
Biatora diapensiae (T. Fries) Hellb.
Thallus very thin, whitish, sometimes disappearing; apothecia small, 0.2–1 mm.
across, sessile, the disk flat to convex, reddish black to black, shining, the exciple
black, uneven to flexuous, finally disappearing; hypothecium dark reddish brown;
spores oblong to ellipsoid, 10–14 × 4–6 μ.
On old wood, New Hampshire.

73. **Lecidea promiscens** Nyl., Flora 55:358. 1872.
Thallus very thin, becoming chinky and finally areolate, whitish to ashy, often
disappearing; apothecia small to middle-sized, 0.4–0.8 mm. across, adnate, rarely
clustered and irregular, the disk flat to slightly convex, black, the exciple thin,
black, finally disappearing; hypothecium dark brown; spores ellipsoid to oblong-
ellipsoid, 9–14 × 3–5 μ.
On sandstone, Ohio.

74. **Lecidea micytho** Tuck., Syn. N. A. Lich. 2:131. 1888.
Thallus thin, verrucose-areolate, reddish yellow, scattered and disappearing;
apothecia minute, 0.1–0.15 mm. across, the disk flat to convex, black, the exciple
black and soon disappearing; hypothecium reddish brown; spores ovoid-ellipsoid,
7–10.5 × 3–4.5 μ.
On quartz, Pennsylvania, North Carolina, South Carolina, and Florida.

75. **Lecidea euphorea** (Floerke) Nyl., Flora 64:187. 1881.
L. sabuletorum var. *euphorea* Floerke, Ges. Naturf. Freund. Mag. 2:311. 1808.
Thallus widespread, smooth, pale greenish gray; apothecia minute to small,
0.25–0.8 mm. across, sessile, the disk flat to slightly convex, brownish black to
black, the exciple raised, finally disappearing, brownish black; hypothecium pale
or darker brown; spores oblong-ellipsoid, 11–16 × 6–8 μ.
On trees, southern California.

76. **Lecidea fuscorubens** Nyl., Not. Sällsk. Faun. Flor. Fenn. 5:199. 1861.
Biatora fuscorubens Nyl., Nya Bot. Notis. 183. 1853.
Thallus thin, smooth to minutely granulose or somewhat areolate, grayish to
dull ashy, sometimes almost disappearing; apothecia minute to small, 0.3–0.8 mm.
across, sessile, the disk flat to convex, brownish black to black, rarely grayish
pruinose, the exciple thin, colored like the disk, soon disappearing; hypothecium
dark brown; spores ellipsoid, 10–13 × 5–6 μ.
On rocks, Washington.
Very similar to *L. sanguineoatra* and may be a subspecies of it, depending on
thallus and substratum.

77. **Lecidea platycarpa** Ach., Lich. Univ. 173. pl. 2, f. 5. 1810.
L. platycarpa var. *steriza* (Ach.) Rabh. *L. macrocarpa* (Lam. & DC.) Stend.
Biatora phaea Flot.
Thallus thin, obscurely or more or less roughened, greenish gray to ashy, usually
chinky to subareolate, continuous, scattered, or sometimes disappearing; apothecia small to large, 0.4–2.5 mm. across, adnate to sessile, the disk flat to convex,
round to irregular, brownish black to black, rarely slightly whitish pruinose, the
exciple black, raised, sometimes disappearing; hypothecium blackish brown; spores
ellipsoid, 11–20 × 5–10 μ.
On rocks, from New England to North Carolina, and westward to California.

78. **Lecidea speirea** Ach., Meth. Lich. 52. 1803.
Lichen speireus Ach., Lich. Suec. 59. 1798.
Thallus subdeterminate, irregular, rather smooth, becoming chinky to areolate,
sometimes roughened, sometimes mealy, white to ashy white, hypothallus whitish;
apothecia small to middle-sized, 0.4–1.2 mm. across, immersed to rarely adnate, the
disk flat to convex, black, the exciple black or whitish pruinose, often disappearing; hypothecium brown to blackish; spores ellipsoid, 9–14 × 5–8 μ. (PLATE 16 a.)

On rocks, New England, West Virginia, Minnesota, Wyoming, Idaho, Washington, and California.

79. **Lecidea cinereoatra** Ach., Lich. Univ. 167. 1810.
Thallus usually thin, at first smooth, then warty or chinky to subareolate, whitish to greenish gray, the black hypothallus usually absent; apothecia small, 0.2–1 mm. across, partly immersed to adnate, the disk concave to slightly convex, black, often grayish pruinose, the exciple of the same color, raised; hypothecium brownish black; spores oblong-ellipsoid, 12–17 × 6–9 μ.
On sandstone, Ohio.

80. **Lecidea lapicida** Ach., Meth. Lich. 37. 1803.
Lichen lapicida Ach., Lich. Prod. 61. 1798. *L. lapicida* f. *oxydata* Rabh. *L. silacea* Ach.
Thallus widespread, rather thin, verrucose-areolate, roughened, greenish gray to ashy, varying toward rust-red, a black hypothallus sometimes present; apothecia small to middle-sized, 0.3–1 mm. across, partly immersed to adnate, sometimes clustered, the disk flat to convex and irregular, black, the exciple also black, raised, becoming strongly flexuous, often finally disappearing; hypothecium dark brown; spores short-ellipsoid, 8–12 × 4–7 μ.
On rocks, Maine, Minnesota, South Dakota, and southern California.

81. **Lecidea vorticosa** (Floerke) Koerb., Syst. Lich. 251, 252. 1855.
L. sabuletorum var. *vorticosa* Floerke, Ges. Naturf. Freund. Mag. 2:311. 1808.
Thallus thin, granulose to chinky-areolate, ashy to whitish, the granules crowded and heaped, or scattered, sometimes disappearing; apothecia minute to middle-sized, 0.3–0.8 mm. across, subsessile, often closely crowded, irregular and confluent in heaps, the disk flattish, very black, the exciple also black, thick, prominent, becoming flexuous and lobed, rarely disappearing; hypothecium brownish black; spores linear-ellipsoid, 9–13 × 4–5 μ.
On sandstone, Arizona.

82. **Lecidea auriculata** T. Fries, Nov. Act. Soc. Sci. Ups. III. 3:313. 1861.
L. diducens Nyl. *L. auriculata* f. *paupera* T. Fries.
Thallus chinky-areolate to warty, whitish to brownish, or sometimes disappearing; apothecia middle-sized to large, 0.6–1.4 mm. across, adnate, the disk flat to convex, often becoming finally lobed, or variously irregular, black, the exciple of the same color, slightly raised, finally disappearing; hypothecium brown; spores 6–12 × 2.5–4 μ.
On rocks, mountains of New Hampshire, Nevada, and California.

83. **Lecidea goniophila** (Floerke) Schaer., Enum. Lich. Eur. 127. 1850.
L. immersa var. *goniophila* Floerke, Ges. Naturf. Freund. Mag. 3:311. 1809. *L. elaechroma* var. *pilularis* (Dav.) T. Fries. *L. enteroleuca* var. *pilularis* (Dav.) T. Fries. *L. pungens* (Koerb.) Nyl.
Thallus thin, greenish gray to ashy or whitish, verrucose or areolate-verrucose, becoming granulose, scattered and disappearing; apothecia small to middle-sized, 0.2–0.8 mm. across, adnate, the disk concave, becoming flat or slightly convex, black, the exciple also black, thickish, raised, finally disappearing; hypothecium dark brown; spores ovoid-ellipsoid to ellipsoid, 10–14 × 6–10 μ.
On rocks, Maine, Minnesota, Utah, and California.

84. **Lecidea neglecta** Nyl., Not. Sällsk. Faun. Flor. Fenn. 1:233. 1859.
Thallus thin, rough, composed of minute, whitish to ashy white, subconfluent granules; apothecia minute, 0.15–0.25 mm. across, adnate, the disk flat, brownish black to black, the exciple rather thick, finally disappearing; hypothecium brownish to brown; spores oblong to fusiform-oblong, 8–11 × 3–4 μ.
On rocks and mosses over rocks, New Hampshire and Massachusetts. Specimens seen were infertile but agree with European material.

85. **Lecidea limosa** Ach., Lich. Univ. 182. 1810.
Thallus composed of minute, convex, scattered or heaped, greenish gray to ashy granules; apothecia small to middle-sized, 0.5–1 mm. across, adnate, sometimes crowded, the disk strongly convex, black, the exciple very thin, black, soon disappearing; hypothecium brownish to reddish brown; spores ovoid, 10–18 × 4–6 μ.
Over mosses on soil, Colorado.

86. **Lecidea fusca** (Schaer.) T. Fries, Nov. Act. Soc. Sci. Ups. III. 3:283. 1861.
L. sphaeroides var. *fusca* Schaer., Lich. Helv. Spic. 166. 1833.
Thallus thin, greenish to grayish white, minutely granular and rough, finally disappearing; apothecia small to middle-sized, 0.5–1 mm. across, adnate to sessile, the disk flat to strongly convex, brown to blackish, the exciple thin and disappearing; hypothecium light or darker brown; spores oblong-fusiform, 10–16 × 4–6 μ.
On mosses, Maine.

87. **Lecidea planetica** Tuck., Syn. N. A. Lich. 2:131. 1888.
Thallus thin, widespread, verrucose, greenish gray; apothecia minute to small, 0.2–0.4 mm. across, numerous, the disk convex, black, the exciple inconspicuous and disappearing; hypothecium dark brown and blackish; spores ovoid-ellipsoid, 5–8 × 2–3.5 μ.
On rocks, Pennsylvania and New Jersey.

88. **Lecidea latypea** Ach., Meth. Lich. Suppl. 10. 1803.
Thallus thickish, verrucose-areolate, whitish to pale ashy, the areoles small, flattish or becoming round and subglobular, scattered or crowded, sometimes minutely granulose; apothecia small to middle-sized, 0.4–1.5 mm. across, partly immersed to adnate, becoming irregular and lobed, the disk flat to finally convex, black, the exciple paler, thin, finally disappearing; hypothecium brown; spores short-ellipsoid, 10–15 × 5–8 μ.
On rocks, southern California, and, according to Hasse, in the eastern and southern states.

f. **aequata** (Ach.) Arn., Flora 67:562. 1884.
L. coniops var. *aequata* Ach., Lich. Univ. 171. 1810. *L. enteroleuca* var. *aequata* (Ach.) Tuck.
Thallus thin and smooth, becoming chinky and subareolate, or tending to disappear, ashy.
On rocks, widely distributed throughout the United States.

89. **Lecidea aglaea** Sommerf., Suppl. Fl. Lapp. 144. 1826.
Thallus thick, widespread, rough, verrucose-areolate, the areoles becoming swollen, convex and wrinkled, crowded, forming an unequal pale yellow crust, the hypothallus black; apothecia middle-sized to large, 0.7–1.5 mm. across, immersed to adnate, the disk becoming convex, black, the black exciple disappearing; spores ellipsoid, 10–16 × 5–8 μ.
On rocks, New Hampshire and New York.

90. **Lecidea grisella** Floerke, in Flot., Siles. nos. 141, 142. 1829.
Thallus moderately thick, greenish gray to ashy, composed of small, flat to convex areoles, making a continuous crust; apothecia middle-sized to larger, 0.5–1.3 mm. across, partly immersed, often clustered and angular, the disk flat or slightly convex, black or obscurely gray-pruinose, the exciple entire, black; hypothecium dark brown; spores oblong-ellipsoid, 10–14 × 6–7 μ.
On rocks, Santa Cruz Peninsula, California.

91. **Lecidea contigua** E. Fries, Sched. Crit. Lich. Exsicc. Suec. fasc. 13, 14. 1827.
L. contigua var. *convexella* (Vainio) Fink. *L. contigua* var. *hydrophila* E. Fries. *L. crustulata* (Ach.) Floerke.
Thallus more or less rough, chinky to subareolate, greenish gray to ashy, irregularly spread over the substratum, sometimes thin and scattered; apothecia

small to middle-sized, 0.5–1.5 mm. across, more or less immersed to adnate or sub-sessile, the disk flat to convex, black, rarely and faintly pruinose, the exciple thin, black, raised, sometimes finally disappearing; hypothecium brownish black; spores ovoid-ellipsoid, 11–20 × 6–9 μ.

On granite rocks, bricks, and old wood, from New England to Florida, and westward to Nebraska, also in Washington.

92. **Lecidea flexuosa** (E. Fries) Nyl., Act. Soc. Linn. Bord. 21:356. 1856.

Biatora flexuosa E. Fries, Vet. Akad. Handl. 1822. 268. 1822.

Thallus granulose, ashy to greenish gray, the small granules scattered or clus-tered, or sometimes passing into a flattened to wrinkled, moderately thick, finally areolate crust; apothecia minute to small, 0.2–0.4 mm. across, adnate, becoming flexuous, the disk flat, black, the exciple thin, pale lead-colored or darker; hypo-thecium brown; spores oblong-ellipsoid, 5–10 × 3–5 μ.

On old wood, widely distributed throughout the United States.

93. **Lecidea fuscocinerea** Nyl., Nya Bot. Not. 1852:177. 1852.

Thallus thickish, widespread, unequal, chinky-areolate, the areoles often wart-like, ashy to ashy brown, the hypothallus black; apothecia middle-sized, 0.5–1.2 mm. across, sessile to adnate, irregular, the disk flattish, black, the exciple lighter, thin, raised, strongly and variously flexuous; hypothecium brown; spores ellipsoid, 9–14 × 7–10 μ.

On rocks, New Hampshire.

94. **Lecidea mamillana** Tuck., Proc. Am. Acad. 12:180. 1877.

Thallus moderately thick, more or less plainly squamulose-areolate, greenish gray to brownish white, the areoles swollen, continuous or scattered, more or less plainly lobed, sometimes radiately striate; apothecia minute to small, 0.2–0.5 mm. across, slightly immersed to superficial in the center of the areole, the disk flat to convex, black, the exciple thin, black, disappearing; hypothecium brownish to brown; spores ovoid-ellipsoid, 9–16 × 5–8.5 μ.

On calcareous rocks, Alabama.

95. **Lecidea dolodes** Nyl.; Hasse, Bull. Torr. Club 24:447. 1897.

Thallus moderately thick, composed of small, convex, light brown, somewhat crenate, finally imbricated squamules; apothecia minute to small, 0.2–0.5 mm. across, adnate, sometimes clustered, the disk flat to slightly convex, black, the exciple brownish to blackish, soon disappearing; hypothecium brown to blackish brown; spores globose, 7–9 μ across.

On trees, California.

96. **Lecidea olivacea** (Hoffm.) Mass., Ric. Lich. 71. 1852.

Verrucaria olivacea Hoffm., Deutschl. Fl. 2:192. 1791. *L. olivacea* var. *geo-graphica* Bagl. *L. elaeochroma* var. *geographica* (Bagl.) Zahlbr.

Thallus thin and smooth to thick and rough, composed of scattered or con-tinuous, olivaceous to yellowish or greenish gray or reddish granules, sometimes limited by a black border; apothecia minute, 0.4–1 mm. across, partly immersed to adnate, the disk concave to flat, or even convex, rusty black to black, the exciple thin, black, and finally disappearing; hypothecium brown; spores ovoid-ellipsoid, 12–14 × 7–8 μ.

On trees, California.

97. **Lecidea Manni** Tuck., Syn. N. A. Lich. 2:75. 1888.

Thallus thick, rough, composed of small, convex, crowded, greenish brown areoles on a black hypothallus; apothecia middle-sized to large, 0.5–1.5 mm. across, adnate, the disk flat to slightly convex, grayish pruinose, the exciple black and strongly developed; hypothecium becoming brownish to brown; spores ellipsoid, 11–16 × 5–6 μ.

On volcanic rocks, California.

98. **Lecidea humosa** (Ehrh.) Röhling, Deutschl. Fl. 3:36. 1813.
Lichen humosus Ehrh., in Hoffm., Deutschl. Fl. 191. 1796. *L. uliginosa* var.
humosa (Ehrh.) Ach. *L. humicola* (Ach.) Fink, Ohio Biol. Surv. 2:339.
1921 by error in spelling.
Thallus very minutely and inconspicuously granulose, brownish black, evanescent; apothecia minute to small, 0.2–0.4 mm. across, scattered or clustered, the disk flat to convex, dark brown to black, the exciple thin, of the same color, finally disappearing; hypothecium dark brown; spores oblong-ellipsoid, 9–15 × 5–7 μ.
On soil and shaded rock, moist woods, Ohio and Kentucky.

99. **Lecidea cyrtidia** Tuck., Proc. Am. Acad. 12:181. 1877.
Thallus of minute granules, inconspicuous, scattered to crowded, scurfy, greenish gray to olive-green, frequently widespread; apothecia minute, 0.2–0.5 mm. across, closely adnate, the disk flat to convex, black, the exciple black, thick, soon disappearing; hypothecium blackish brown; spores ovoid-ellipsoid, 5–9 × 2–4 μ.
On rocks, from New England to Delaware, and westward to Illinois and Minnesota.

100. **Lecidea sylvicola** Flot., Lich. Sil. Exsicc. no. 171. 1829.
Thallus granulose, greenish gray to olive-brown or darker, or the minute, flattened to hemispherical granules passing into a thin, continuous or scattered, scurfy, verrucose or subareolate crust; apothecia minute to small, 0.2–0.5 mm. across, immersed to more commonly adnate, the disk flat to convex, dark brown to black, the exciple black, soon disappearing; hypothecium blackish brown or bluish black; spores ellipsoid, 5–9 × 2.5–4 μ.
On rocks, Ohio and Minnesota.

101. **Lecidea myriocarpoides** Nyl., Flora 48:355. 1865.
Biatora myriocarpoides (Nyl.) Tuck.
Thallus rather thin, granulose, somewhat scurfy, widespread, scattered or disappearing, olive-brown, the granules minute, irregular, somewhat flattened to rarely hemispherical; apothecia minute to small, 0.15–0.4 mm. across, adnate, the disk flat to convex and swollen, dark brown to black, the exciple thin, soon disappearing; hypothecium brown to blackish brown; spores ellipsoid, 6–9 × 3–5 μ.
On old wood, in eastern United States, Illinois, Iowa, Minnesota, and California.

102. **Lecidea xanthococcoides** Zahlbr., Bull. Torr. Club 27:644. 1900.
Thallus thin, grayish to yellowish brown, wrinkled-granulose to verrucose; apothecia minute to small, 0.3–0.4 mm. across, sessile, the disk slightly concave to finally convex, black, the exciple thin, black, finally disappearing; hypothecium dark brown; spores ovoid to ovoid-oblong, 12–15 × 5.5–6 μ.
On trees, San Bernardino Mountains, California.

103. **Lecidea albocaerulescens** (Wulf.) Ach., Meth. Lich. 52. 1803.
Lichen albocaerulescens Wulf., in Jacq., Coll. Bot. 2:184. pl. 15, f. 1. 1788.
L. albocaerulescens var. *flavocaerulescens* Schaer. *L. hebescens* Nyl.
Thallus smooth or somewhat rough, ashy to greenish gray or olive-green, more or less chinky or becoming obscurely small-areolate, continuous, moderately thick; apothecia small to large, 0.4–1.5 mm. across, immersed to adnate, round to irregular, the disk usually flat, black or brownish black, commonly more or less whitish pruinose, the exciple black, rarely disappearing; hypothecium dark brown to blackish; spores ellipsoid, 15–24 × 7–10 μ. (PLATE 16 *b*.)
On rocks, northeastern United States, southward to Florida and Alabama at high elevations, westward to Illinois and Missouri, and reappearing in Washington. (Thallus sometimes tinged red by iron.)

104. **Lecidea atrobrunnea** (Ram.) Schaer., Lich. Helv. Spic. 134. 1828.
Rhizocarpon atrobrunneum Ram., in Lam. & DC., Fl. France 2:367. 1815.
Thallus squamulose-areolate, the areoles tough, scattered or clustered, flat to convex, lobed, appressed toward the center and ascending and wavy at the margin, at length wrinkled, the outer ones sometimes elongated, smooth, shining to dull, yellowish to copper- or chestnut-brown, the margins blackening, the hypothallus black; apothecia small to middle-sized, 0.5–1.5 mm. across, sessile, sometimes clustered, the disk concave to sometimes slightly convex, black, the exciple also black, thick, raised, flexuous; hypothecium finally brown; spores ellipsoid, 7–12 × 3–6 μ.
On granite rocks, mountains of Colorado, Wyoming, Nevada, California, Oregon, and Washington.

105. **Lecidea fuscoatra** (L.) Ach., Meth. Lich. 44. 1803.
Lichen fuscoatra L., Sp. Pl. 1140. 1753. *L. fumosa* Ach.
Thallus squamulose-areolate, the areoles thin, scattered or crowded, flat to slightly concave, sometimes becoming imbricated, the blackening margins ascending and wavy to lobulate, reddish brown to blackish, the hypothallus black, often distinct; apothecia middle-sized to large, 0.6–1.5 mm. across, adnate to sessile, the disk flat to strongly convex, slightly pruinose, finally black, the exciple thin, black, finally disappearing; hypothecium blackish brown; spores oblong-ellipsoid, 9–16 × 5–7 μ.
On rocks, usually alpine, from New England to California and Oregon.

106. **Lecidea fuliginosa** Tayl., in Mack., Fl. Hibern. 2:131. 1836.
Thallus granulose-squamulose, conglomerate, occurring in small, thickish areas, dark reddish brown, the hypothallus brownish black; apothecia small, 0.4–0.8 mm. across, often clustered, the disk somewhat convex, black, the exciple also black, thin, soon disappearing; hypothecium brownish black; spores ovoid-ellipsoid, 8–10 × 5–6 μ.
On rocks, West Virginia and Tennessee.

107. **Lecidea intumescens** (Floerke) Nyl., Act. Soc. Linn. Bord. 21:373. 1856.
L. petraea var. *intumescens* Floerke; Flot., Flora 11:690. 1828. *L. insularis* Nyl.
Thallus rough, the warts running together into a convex, tawny-brown to brownish ashy crust, composed of areoles or folded squamules; apothecia minute to small, 0.3–0.6 mm. across, flat, partly immersed to adnate, often clustered and angular, the disk black, the exciple thin, black; hypothecium brown; spores broadly ellipsoid, 10–13 × 5–7 μ.
On sandstone, California.

108. **Lecidea protabacina** Nyl.; Hasse, Bull. South. Calif. Acad. 2:60. 1903.
Thallus squamulose, reddish brown, the squamules swollen, strongly convex, smooth, shining, round, sometimes lobulate, or angular, crowded or rarely scattered; apothecia middle-sized to large, 0.5–2 mm. across, often clustered, sessile, becoming flexuous, the disk flat to convex, smooth, shining, black, the exciple blackish, thin and disappearing; hypothecium dark brown; spores oblong-ellipsoid, 10–12 × 4–5 μ.
On granite, Washington and California.

109. **Lecidea fuscatoatra** Nyl., in Hasse, Lich. South. Calif. ed. 2. 20. 1898.
Thallus thickish, squamulose, the squamules continuous, concave to convex or undulate, round or angular to lobulate, brown varying toward gray; apothecia middle-sized, 0.7–1.6 mm. across, adnate, irregularly round, the disk flat to slightly convex, black, the exciple also black, thin, raised, entire to wavy or deeply lobulate; hypothecium brown; spores long-ellipsoid, 8–12 × 3–4 μ.
On rocks, southern California.

OTHER SPECIES REPORTED

Lecidea admiscens Nyl.—Southern California.
Lecidea assimilata Nyl.—California.
Lecidea glaucopholis Nyl.—California.
Lecidea griseoatra (Hoffm.) Flot.—California.
Lecidea gyrophoroides Spreng.—Pennsylvania.
Lecidea Michenerii (Tuck.)—Pennsylvania.
Lecidea microps Tuck.—North Carolina.
Lecidea mundula Müll. Arg.—New England.
Lecidea recedens Nyl.—North and South Carolina.
Lecidea Tuckeii Herre—Nevada.

120. **Psora** Hoffm., Descr. Pl. Crypt. 1:37. pl. 8, f. 1. 1790.

Thallus crustose to more or less subfoliose, squamulose, differentiated into a well-developed, more or less gelatinized, cellular upper cortex, an algal layer and an indistinctly medullary layer or sometimes a lower cortex composed of hyphae extending in a horizontal direction, attached to the substratum by more or less numerous hyphal rhizoids; apothecia small to middle-sized or rarely large, adnate or sessile, the disk flat to more or less convex, reddish brown to black, the exciple usually colored like the disk, thin and disappearing; hypothecium hyaline to brown or black; hymenium hyaline to brownish; paraphyses unbranched; asci clavate to cylindrico-clavate; spores 8, hyaline, ellipsoid to oblong, non-septate.
The algal host is Protococcus.

A. On old wood or over moss
  B. On old wood
    C. Apothecia reaching 0.8–1 mm. across
      D. Spores 8–10 × 2.5–3 μ . . . . 14. P. ostreata
      D. Spores 7–8.5 × 3–4 μ . . . . 8. P. Friesii
    C. Apothecia 0.2–0.5 mm. across . . . . 7. P. anthracophila
  B. On moss over rocks . . . . 4. P. Petri
A. On rocks and soil
  B. Hypothecium hyaline to yellowish or brownish
    C. Black hypothallus conspicuous
      D. Squamules brownish gray to ashy white . . . . 1. P. demissa
      D. Squamules blackish chestnut-brown . . . . 5. P. scotopholis
    C. Hypothallus not conspicuous
      D. Squamules white-edged . . . . 6. P. Russellii
      D. Squamules not white-edged
        E. Squamules brownish or greenish to blackish . . . . 3. P. rufonigra
        E. Squamules dull brownish yellow to dark red . . . . 2. P. luridella
  B. Hypothecium brownish to dark brown
    C. Squamules white-edged
      D. Squamules smooth or furrowed, flesh-colored to brick-colored
        or whitish . . . . 13. P. decipiens
      D. Squamules smooth, pale to darker fawn-colored . . . 12. P. rubiformis
    C. Squamules not white-edged, or only rarely so
      D. Squamules greenish gray to ashy or greenish yellow to tawny
        E. Squamules middle-sized, ascending to erect, stipitate . 11. P. caulophylla
        E. Squamules small, closely adnate to marginally ascending . 9. P. icterica
      D. Squamules greenish or reddish to brownish and brown
        E. Squamules middle-sized, greenish to lurid brown . . . 15. P. lurida
        E. Squamules larger, more or less reddish brown
          F. Apothecia 0.5–1.5 mm. across, disk strongly convex . 16. P. globifera
          F. Apothecia 0.3–0.8 mm. across, disk convex . . . 10. P. crenata

1. **Psora demissa** (Rutström) Stein., in Cohn, Krypt. Flora 2:171. 1879.
   Lichen demissus Rutström, Spic. Pl. Crypt. Suec. 8. 1794. *Lecidea demissa*
   (Rutström) Ach. *Biatora atrorufa* (Dicks.) E. Fries. *P. atrorufa* (Dicks.)
   Hook.

Thallus composed of minute to small, round, adnate, crenate and lobulate, brownish gray to ashy white, often imbricate squamules, or the squamules run together into a rough, warty, irregular crust, on a black hypothallus; apothecia small to middle-sized, 0.4–1 mm. across, adnate, sometimes confluent, the disk flat to convex, dark reddish brown to black, the exciple thin, darker, and soon disappearing; hypothecium hyaline; spores ovoid-ellipsoid, 10–18 × 5–8 μ.
On soil, Vermont, New Hampshire, Colorado, and Washington.

2. **Psora luridella** (Tuck.) Fink n. comb.
   Lecidea luridella Tuck., Proc. Am. Acad. 5:418. 1862. *Biatora luridella* Tuck.
   Thallus composed of small, rather thick, closely adnate, round, finally crenate-lobed, subimbricate, dull brownish yellow to dark red squamules, the margins and rarely whole squamules whitish pruinose; white below; apothecia minute to small, 0.4–0.8 mm. across, adnate, the disk convex, dark brown to black, the exciple thin and disappearing; hypothecium hyaline; spores ovoid-ellipsoid, 7–12 × 4–6 μ.
   On soil, Colorado, New Mexico, California, and Washington, usually in mountains.

3. **Psora rufonigra** (Tuck.) Schneid., Guide Study Lich. 119. 1898.
   Biatora rufonigra Tuck., Proc. Am. Acad. 1:250. 1848. *Lecidea rufonigra* (Tuck.) Nyl.
   Thallus composed of small, smooth, rather thick, concave, irregular and lobed, commonly ascendant, more or less imbricated, brownish or greenish to blackish squamules; commonly darker below and clothed with dark rhizoids; apothecia small to middle-sized, 0.3–0.9 mm. across, adnate, the disk flat to convex, dark brownish to black, the exciple colored like the disk, soon disappearing; hypothecium hyaline; spores oblong-ellipsoid, 8–15 × 5–7 μ.
   On rocks, throughout the United States.

4. **Psora Petri** (Tuck.) Fink n. comb.
   Biatora Petri Tuck., Proc. Am. Acad. 12:179. 1877. *Lecidea Petri* (Tuck.) Zahlbr.
   Thallus composed of small to middle-sized, rough, round to oblong or irregular, concave, undulately lobed, loosely imbricated, pale greenish gray to brownish squamules, on a thin brownish hypothallus; apothecia middle-sized to large, 0.6–2.5 mm. across, sessile to somewhat elevated, the disk flat, reddish to blackish, the exciple thick, dark brown, flexuous and finally disappearing; hypothecium hyaline to yellowish; hymenium hyaline to bluish black toward the top; spores ovoid-ellipsoid, 9–11 × 4–5 μ.
   On mosses of calcareous areas, Alabama and Tennessee.

5. **Psora scotopholis** (Tuck.) Fink n. comb.
   Biatora scotopholis Tuck., Lich. Calif. 24. 1866. *Lecidea scotopholis* (Tuck.) Herre.
   Thallus composed of minute, thin, round, convex, glistening, blackish chestnut-brown, often areolate squamules upon a black fringing hypothallus, the squamules becoming elevated at the crenately lobed, crowded, and subimbricated margins; apothecia middle-sized, 0.5–1 mm. across, adnate-sessile, the disk flat to convex, reddish to dull black, the exciple thick, brownish black, becoming crenulate and finally disappearing; hypothecium hyaline to brownish; spores ellipsoid, 7–12 × 3–5 μ.
   On rocks, California and Oregon.

6. **Psora Russellii** (Tuck.) Schneid., Gen. Lich. 141. pl. 25. 1897.
   Biatora Russellii Tuck., Lich. Calif. 23. 1866. *Lecidea Russellii* Tuck. *Biatora Russellii* f. *dealbata* Tuck.
   Thallus composed of small to middle-sized, rather thick, round or irregular, more or less lobed, dull or reddish brown or finally whitish, sometimes reticulately

furrowed, scattered or clustered, closely adnate or marginally ascendant, white-edged squamules; white below with a few rhizoids; apothecia small to middle-sized, 0.3–1 mm. across, sessile, the disk convex, reddish brown to darker, the exciple thin, lighter brown, finally disappearing; hypothecium yellowish to brownish; hymenium pale yellowish to brownish; spores ellipsoid, 9–13 × 4–6 μ. (PLATE 17.)

On calcareous rocks, throughout the United States.

7. **Psora anthracophila** (Nyl.) Arn., Flora 53:471. 1870.
   Lecidea anthracophila Nyl., Flora 48:603. 1865. *Lecidea cladonioides* (E. Fries) T. Fries.

Thallus composed of minute to small, rather thick, polished, round to irregular, greenish gray to dull brownish yellow, finally ascending, imbricated finally and obscurely crenate squamules; apothecia minute to small, 0.2–0.5 mm. across, adnate, the disk flat to convex, reddish brown, the exciple lighter, thin and disappearing; hypothecium brownish; spores oblong, 7–13 × 2–4 μ, irregularly arranged.

On old wood, Vermont, Massachusetts, New Jersey, and North Carolina.

8. **Psora Friesii** (Ach.) Hellb., Sven. Vet. Akad. Handl. 9:61. no. 11. 1870.
   Lecidea Friesii Ach., in Liljebl., Utk. Svensk. Flora ed. 3. 610. 1816. *Biatora Friesii* (Ach.) Tuck.

Thallus composed of minute to small, subadnate, convex, crowded and sub-imbricate, greenish gray to brownish squamules; apothecia small to middle-sized, 0.3–0.8 mm. across, sessile, the disk flat to slightly convex, black, the exciple thin, black, persistent and becoming more or less flexuous; hypothecium brownish to dark brown; hymenium yellowish; spores ellipsoid, 7–8.5 × 3–4 μ.

On old wood, Vermont, Massachusetts; doubtfully reported from California.

9. **Psora icterica** (Mont.) Müll. Arg., Flora 71:45. 1888.
   Biatora icterica Mont., Ann. Sci. Nat. Bot. II. 2:373. 1834. *Lecanora Wrightii* Tuck. *Biatora Wrightii* Tuck. *Lecidea icterica* (Mont.) Tayl. *Lecidea endo-chlora* Tayl.

Thallus composed of small, smooth or furrowed, round to extended, scattered or crowded and imbricated, closely adnate, greenish yellow to tawny, sometimes marginally ascending squamules; white below; apothecia small to middle-sized, 0.4–1.2 mm. across, sessile, the disk soon convex, dark brown to black, the exciple thin and disappearing; hypothecium brownish to brown; hymenium hyaline to pale brownish; spores ovoid-ellipsoid, 12–18 × 4–7.5 μ.

On soil, New York and throughout the United States west of the Mississippi River.

10. **Psora crenata** (Tayl.) Reinke; Prings., Jahrbück. Bot. 28:96. f. 33, II. 1895.
   Endocarpon crenatum Tayl., Lond. Journ. Bot. 6:156. 1847. *Biatora crenata* (Tayl.) Tuck. *Lecidea crenata* (Tayl.) Stizenb. *Lecidea crenata* f. *dealbata* (Tuck.) Zahlbr.

Thallus composed of thick, middle-sized to large, closely adnate, round to irregular, brownish red or whitish squamules, the squamules depressed at the margins and hollowed at the center; whitish below; apothecia small to middle-sized, 0.3–0.8 mm. across, sessile, borne on the margins of the squamules, sometimes clustered, the disk flat to convex, brownish black, the exciple thin and disappearing; hypothecium brownish to dark brown; hymenium hyaline to yellowish; spores oblong-ellipsoid, 11–17 × 5–7 μ.

On soil, Texas, Oklahoma, New Mexico, Arizona, Colorado, and Montana.

11. **Psora caulophylla** (Tuck.) Fink n. comb.
   Biatora caulophylla Tuck., Proc. Am. Acad. 12:178. 1877. *Lecidea caulophylla* (Tuck.) Zahlbr.

Thallus composed of middle-sized, ascending to erect, sometimes stipitate, greenish gray to ashy squamules, the squamules dilated and lobed above or crowded together into an irregularly folded crust; apothecia middle-sized to large, 0.8–2 mm. across, sessile, sometimes clustered, the disk flat to convex, reddish brown to black, the exciple rather thick, lighter to finally black; hypothecium brownish to dark brown; spores ovoid-ellipsoid, 7–13 × 4–6 μ.
On soil and rocks, Sierra Nevada Mountains, California.

12. **Psora rubiformis** (Wahl.) Hook., in J. E. Smith, Engl. Fl. 5:193. 1833.
   Baeomyces rubiformis Wahl., in Ach., Meth. Lich. 324. pl. 7, f. 5. 1803.
   Lecidea rubiformis Wahl. *Biatora globifera* var. *rubiformis* (Wahl.) Torss.
   Thallus composed of middle-sized, rather thick, smooth, ascending, imbricated, crenate or lobed, pale to darker fawn-colored, white-margined squamules; whitish below; apothecia middle-sized to large, 0.8–1.8 mm. across, sessile, often clustered, the disk strongly convex, purplish black to black, the exciple thin and disappearing; hypothecium brownish to brown; hymenium pale yellowish to brownish; spores oblong-ellipsoid, 11–15 × 5–7 μ.
   On rocks and soil, Colorado, Washington, and California.

13. **Psora decipiens** (Ehrh.) Hoffm., Descr. Pl. Crypt. 2:63. pl. 43, f. 1–3. 1794.
   Lichen decipiens Ehrh., in Hedw., Descr. Musc. Frond. 2:7. 1789. *Biatora decipiens* (Ehrh.) E. Fries. *P. decipiens* f. *dealbata* (Torss.) Mass. *Biatora decipiens* f. *dealbata* Torss. *Lecidea decipiens* (Ehrh.) Zahlbr.
   Thallus composed of thin, small to middle-sized, closely adnate, round or irregular and lobed, more or less concave, smooth or sometimes furrowed, rarely clustered, flesh-colored to brick-colored or whitish, white-edged squamules; white below; apothecia small to middle-sized, 0.3–1.2 mm. across, becoming sessile, commonly borne along the margins of the squamules, the disk strongly convex, brown to black, the lighter exciple thin, soon disappearing; hypothecium brownish to brown; hymenium pale brownish; spores oblong-ovoid, 10–16 × 5–7 μ.
   On soil, throughout the United States except in the extreme southern part.

14. **Psora ostreata** Hoffm., Deutschl. Fl. 2:163. 1795.
   Lecidea ostreata (Hoffm.) Schaer. *Biatora ostreata* (Hoffm.) E. Fries.
   Thallus composed of small, smooth, crenately lobed, imbricated, soon ascending, light to darker fawn-colored squamules; whitish and sometimes powdery below; apothecia small to middle-sized, 0.6–1 mm. across, adnate, the disk flat, black or more or less whitish pruinose, the exciple rather thick, grayish to blackening, becoming flexuous; hypothecium brownish to blackish brown; spores oblong-ellipsoid, 8–10 × 2.5–3 μ.
   On old wood, Maine, Vermont, Colorado, Washington, and California.

15. **Psora lurida** (Dill.) Lam. & DC., Fl. Fr. III. 2:370. 1815.
   Lichen luridus Dill., in Wither., Bot. Arr. Brit. Pl. 2:720. 1776. *Lecidea lurida* (Dill.) Ach. *Biatora lurida* (Dill.) E. Fries.
   Thallus composed of small to middle-sized, rather thick, closely adnate, round, imbricated, irregularly lobed, greenish to dull lurid brown squamules; white below; apothecia small to middle-sized, 0.5–1.4 mm. across, adnate, sometimes clustered, the disk flat to convex, reddish brown to black, the exciple thin, brown to black, soon disappearing; hypothecium brownish to brown; spores oblong-ellipsoid, varying toward ovoid, 12–15 × 5–7 μ.
   On rocks, Michigan, Colorado, Washington, and California.

16. **Psora globifera** (Ach.) Mass., Ric. Lich. 91. f. 186. 1852.
   Lecidea globifera Ach., Syn. Lich. 51. 1814. *Biatora globifera* Ach.
   Thallus composed of middle-sized to large, thick, smooth to slightly rough and chinky, irregularly lobed, often imbricated, greenish gray to reddish brown, ascending squamules; paler or white below; apothecia small to middle-sized, 0.5–1.5

mm. across, sessile, sometimes clustered, the disk flat to strongly convex, brown to black, the exciple lighter and soon disappearing; hypothecium brownish to brown; hymenium hyaline to yellowish; spores ovoid-ellipsoid, 9–14 × 5–6.5 μ.

On soil, Vermont, Michigan, Montana, Arizona, California, Oregon, and Washington.

121. Nesolechia Mass., Misc. Lich. 13. 1856.

Thallus imbedded in that of the host and therefore invisible; apothecia minute to small, immersed to adnate or sessile, the disk flat to more or less convex, the exciple colored like the disk, thin, soon disappearing; hypothecium hyaline or brownish to brown; hymenium hyaline or brownish above; paraphyses branched, often swollen toward the apices, becoming coherent; asci clavate; spores 8, hyaline, ovoid, ellipsoid to fusiform, non-septate.

The algal host is Pleurococcus or Protococcus. (Zahlbruckner and Lindau omit from lichen classification, regarding these as non-lichen fungi.)

A. Spores less than 15μ in length
  B. Disk yellowish flesh-colored . . . . 4. N. Papillariae
  B. Disk black
    C. Spores 9–12 μ in length
      D. Exciple moderately thick; spores 9–11 × 6.5–7 μ . . . . 3. N. vitellinaria
      D. Exciple inconspicuous; spores 9–12 × 3–4.5 μ . . . . 5. N. cladoniscum
    C. Spores 6–8 × 2–3 μ . . . . 2. N. oxysporella
A. Spores 15–20 × 5–7.5 μ . . . . 1. N. oxyspora

1. Nesolechia oxyspora (Tul.) Mass., Misc. Lich. 13. 1856.

Abrothallus oxysporus Tul., Ann. Sci. Nat. Bot. III. 17:116. pl. 16, f. 27. 1852.
    Lecidea oxyspora (Tul.) Nyl. *Biatora oxyspora* (Tul.) Tuck.

Thallus disappearing or not distinguishable from that of the host, the latter deformed by the parasite and passing into small tufts of hemispherical or irregular lobules; apothecia minute, 0.16–0.3 mm. across, more or less immersed in the deformed thallus of the host, the disk flat to slightly convex, pale brown to black, the exciple disappearing; hypothecium pale brownish to brown; spores ellipsoid to fusiform, 15–20 × 5–7.5 μ.

On species of Parmelia, especially *Parmelia borreri*, on trees, New England to Minnesota.

2. Nesolechia oxysporella (Nyl.) Arn., Flora 57:99. 1874.

Lecidea oxysporella Nyl., Enum. Lich. 127. 1850. *N. punctum* Mass.

Thallus imbedded in the host and invisible; apothecia very minute, 0.05–0.15 mm. across, partly immersed to adnate, the disk strongly convex, black, the exciple disappearing and seldom seen; hypothecium brownish; paraphyses slender, branched, often swollen toward the tips; asci clavate; spores ellipsoid, 6–8 × 2–3 μ.

On species of Cladonia, Iowa.

3. Nesolechia vitellinaria (Nyl.) Rehm, in Rabenh., Krypt. Flora 1³:318. 1890.

Lecidea vitellinaria Nyl., Bot. Not. 1852:177. 1852.

Thallus wholly or for the most part imbedded in host and invisible, possibly sometimes scantily developed superficially; apothecia minute to small, 0.1–0.4 mm. across, sessile, the disk concave to flat, black, the exciple moderately thick, black, slightly elevated; hypothecium brownish to brown; spores ellipsoid or oblong-ellipsoid, 9–11 × 6.5–7 μ.

On the thallus of *Candelariella vitellina*, Colorado.

4. Nesolechia Papillariae (Willey) Fink n. comb.

Biatora Papillariae Willey, Enum. Lich. New Bedford, Mass. 22. 1892.

Thallus mostly within the lichen host, appearing as grayish areas; apothecia very minute, 0.06–0.1 mm. across, the disk convex, yellowish flesh-colored, the exciple disappearing; hypothecium hyaline; spores ellipsoid, 5–10 × 2–3.5 μ.

On podetia of *Cladonia Papillaria*, near New Bedford, Massachusetts.

5. **Nesolechia cladoniscum** (Willey) Fink n. comb.
  Biatora cladoniscum Willey, Enum. Lich. New Bedford, Mass. 22. 1892.
  Thallus within the lichen host and invisible; apothecia minute, 0.1–0.2 mm.
across, adnate, often clustered, the disk convex, becoming black, the exciple inconspicuous, soon disappearing; hypothecium hyaline to brownish; spores ellipsoid,
9–12 × 3–4.5 μ.
  On *Cladonia Papillaria,* near New Bedford, Massachusetts.

122. **Mycoblastus** Norm., Nyt Mag. Naturv. 7:24. 1853.

  Thallus crustose, rough, wrinkled and warty, rudimentary, devoid of differentiation into layers and attached to the substratum by hyphal rhizoids; apothecia
middle-sized to large, adnate or sessile, the disk more or less convex, usually
black, the exciple soon disappearing; hypothecium hyaline to reddish or brown;
hymenium hyaline to brownish; paraphyses unbranched; asci clavate; spores 1 or
rarely 2, hyaline, large, non-septate, with thick wall.
  The algal host is Protococcus.

A. Apothecia with red coloration; hypothecium
  resting upon a blood-red layer . . . . 1. M. sanguinarius
A. Apothecia without red coloration; hypothecium
  resting upon a hyaline layer . . . . 1. M. sanguinarius alpinus

1. **Mycoblastus sanguinarius** (L.) Norm., Nyt Mag. Naturv. 7:237. 1853.
  Lichen sanguinarium L., Sp. Pl. 1140. 1753. *Lecidea sanguinaria* (L.) Ach.
  Megalospora sanguinaria (L.) Mass. *Heterothecium sanguinarium* (L.)
  Tuck.
  Thallus of flattened, greenish gray to ashy granules, commonly running together into a rough, wrinkled to verrucose or chinky, somewhat polished crust;
apothecia middle-sized to large, 1–3 mm. across, adnate, sometimes clustered and
irregular, the disk usually convex, black and more or less shining, the exciple pale
to reddish or darkening, soon disappearing; hypothecium hyaline above, usually
reddish below, resting upon a blood-red layer; spores oblong-ellipsoid, hyaline or
slightly tinged, 56–90 × 22–46 μ. (PLATE 18.)
  On trees, throughout the northern United States.

  var. **alpinus** (E. Fries) Stein, in Cohn, Krypt. Fl. 2:256. 1879.
  Lecidea sanguinarius var. *alpina* E. Fries, Lich. Eur. 335. 1831. *Megalospora
  sanguinaria* var. *affinis* (Schaer.) Krempelh. *Heterothecium sanguinarium*
  var. *affine* (Schaer.) Tuck.
  Apothecia without red coloration; hypothecium hyaline, resting upon a hyaline
layer.
  On trees and old wood, Minnesota (probably much more widely distributed).

123. **Catillaria** T. Fries, Lich. Scand. 1:563. 1874.

  Thallus crustose, granulose, chinky, warty, or areolate, rudimentary, devoid
of differentiation into layers and attached to the substratum by hyphal rhizoids;
apothecia minute to middle-sized or rarely large, somewhat immersed to adnate
or sessile, the disk flat to more or less convex, yellowish flesh-colored to brown
or black, the exciple usually colored like the disk, often disappearing; hypothecium
hyaline to brown; hymenium hyaline to brownish; paraphyses unbranched; asci
usually clavate; spores 8, hyaline, ellipsoid to oblong-ellipsoid or fusiform, 1-septate
or rarely non-septate.
  The algal host is Protococcus.

A. Parasitic on other lichens . . . . 7. C. Herrii
A. Not parasitic on other lichens
  B. On rocks and soil
    C. Apothecia not more than 0.2 mm. across
      D. Spores 7–12 × 2–3 μ . . . . 3. C. flavens
      D. Spores 14–18 × 3.5–5.3 μ . . . . 2. C. terrena

C. Apothecia more than 0.2 mm. across
   D. Spores not more than 14 μ in length
      E. Thallus granulose . . . . 16. C. lenticularis
      E. Thallus chinky-areolate . . . . 15. C. chalybeia
   D. Spores 14–22 × 3–5 μ . . . . 8. C. franciscana
B. On trees and old wood
   C. Hypothecium hyaline to yellowish or brownish
      D. Thallus greenish gray, ashy white, to ashy or yellowish
         E. Apothecia pale yellow or lead-colored . . . . . 1. C. micrococca
         E. Apothecia flesh-colored or lead-colored to brown
            or black
            F. Apothecia small, not more than 0.5 mm. across
               G. Apothecia 0.25–0.5 mm. across, lead-colored
                  or dull brown to black . . . . 5. C. globulosa
               G. Apothecia 0.15–0.25 mm. across, flesh-colored
                  to brown or blackish . . . . 4. C. tricolor
            F. Apothecia large, 1–1.8 mm. across . . . . . 10. C. endochroma
      D. Thallus greenish gray to brownish or blackish green
         E. Apothecia not more than 0.7 mm. across
            F. Apothecia pale to reddish brown, finally black . . . 6. C. prasina
            F. Apothecia purplish black to black . . . . 11. C. atropurpurea
         E. Apothecia 0.8–1.5 mm. across . . . . 9. C. leptocheila
   C. Hypothecium brownish to brown or black
      D. Spores not more than 18 μ in length
         E. Apothecia 0.2–0.45 mm. across . . . . 13. C. glauconigrans
         E. Apothecia 0.4–1 mm. across . . . . 12. C. Laureri
      D. Spores 20–28 × 8–16 μ . . . . 14. C. grossa

1. **Catillaria micrococca** (Koerb.) T. Fries, Lich. Scand. 1:571. 1874.
   Biatora micrococca Koerb., Par. Lich. 155. 1865.
   Thallus thin, scurfy or minutely granulose, pale greenish to ashy; apothecia
very minute, 0.1–0.3 mm. across, adnate, often clustered to confluent, the disk
strongly convex, pale yellow or lead-colored, the exciple absent or soon disappearing; hypothecium hyaline; spores oblong-ellipsoid, rarely non-septate, 8–14 × 2.5–
4.5 μ.
   On trees, Massachusetts.

2. **Catillaria terrena** (Willey) Zahlbr., Cat. Lich. Univ. 4:79. 1926.
   Biatora terrena Willey, Enum. Lich. New Bedford, Mass. 23. 1892.
   Thallus thin, composed of large, coarse, crenate, yellowish to reddish yellow
granules; apothecia minute, 0.1–0.2 mm. across, sessile, the disk convex, yellowish
flesh-colored, the exciple absent or soon disappearing; hypothecium hyaline; spores
ellipsoid, 14–18 × 3.5–5.5 μ.
   On soil, Massachusetts and Illinois.

3. **Catillaria flavens** (Willey) Fink n. comb.
   Biatora flavens Willey, in Tuck., Syn. N. A. Lich. 2:34. 1888. *Bacidia flavens*
     (Willey) Zahlbr.
   Thallus thin, chinky, yellowish ashy; apothecia minute, 0.1–0.2 mm. across,
adnate, the disk flat to convex, wax-colored, the exciple thin, soon disappearing;
hypothecium hyaline; spores ellipsoid to oblong-ellipsoid, 7–12 × 2–3 μ, rarely
2-septate.
   On granitic rocks, near New Bedford, Massachusetts.

4. **Catillaria tricolor** (With.) T. Fries, Lich. Scand. 1:574, 575. 1874.
   Lichen tricolor With., Arr. Brit. Pl. ed. 3:20. 1796. *Biatorina tricolor* (With.)
     Stein. *Biatorina tricolor* var. *atlantica* (Tuck.) Fink. *Biatora mixta* E. Fries.
     Biatorina griffithii (Sm.) Mass. *Biatora mixta* var. *atlantica* Tuck. *C. tri-*
     color var. *atlantica* (Tuck.) Zahlbr.
   Thallus thin, ashy white, smooth, becoming minutely granulose, chinky, or
wrinkled-verrucose; apothecia minute, 0.15–0.25 mm. across, adnate, the disk flat
to slightly convex, flesh-colored to brown and blackish, the exciple paler, thick,

finally disappearing; hypothecium pale yellow; spores sometimes non-septate, oblong-ellipsoid to fusiform, sometimes curved, 9–15 × 3–4.5 μ.
On trees, rarely dead wood, from New England to Florida, and westward throughout northern United States.

5. **Catillaria globulosa** (Floerke) T. Fries, Lich. Scand. 1:575. 1874.
Lecidea globulosa Floerke, Deutsch. Lich. part 10. 181. 1821. *Biatora globulosa* (Floerke) E. Fries.
Thallus thin, ashy white to dirty gray, smooth, becoming minutely granulose, sometimes disappearing; apothecia minute to small, 0.25–0.5 mm. across, adnate, the disk flat to strongly convex, pale lead-colored or dull brown to black, the exciple of the same color, thin, soon disappearing; hypothecium hyaline; spores long-ellipsoid, the septum often indistinct or absent, 7–13 × 2–4 μ.
On old wood, New Hampshire and California.

6. **Catillaria prasina** (E. Fries) T. Fries, Lich. Scand. 1:572, 573. 1874.
Micorea prasina E. Fries, Syst. Orb. Veg. 257. 1825. *Biatorina prasina* (E. Fries) Stein. *C. prasina* f. *byssacea* (Zwackh.) T. Fries. *C. prasina* f. *prasiniza* (Nyl.) Zahlbr.
Thallus thin, of very minute, round, frequently heaped granules, sometimes somewhat scurfy, pale or dark greenish gray to blackish green; apothecia minute to small, 0.2–0.5 mm. across, adnate, the disk convex, pale to reddish brown, finally black, the exciple soon disappearing; hypothecium hyaline to brownish; spores oblong-ovoid, frequently non-septate, 8–12 × 3–5 μ.
On old wood, from Massachusetts to Georgia, and westward throughout northern United States.

7. **Catillaria Herrii** (Hepp) Fink n. comb.
Biatora Herrii Hepp, Spor. Flecht. Eur. pl. 16, f. 135. 1853. *Biatorina Herrii* (Hepp) Fink.
Thallus of minute, round, frequently heaped granules, greenish gray, sometimes disappearing; apothecia minute, 0.1–0.3 mm. across, adnate to sessile, the disk flat to slightly convex, flesh-colored and darkening to black, the exciple at first darker, then of the same color; hypothecium hyaline to light brown; spores ovoid-ellipsoid, 7–12 × 3–5.5 μ.
On the thallus of *Peltigera canina,* Massachusetts, Ohio, Illinois, and Minnesota.

8. **Catillaria franciscana** (Tuck.) Herre, Proc. Wash. Acad. Sci. 10:95. 1910.
Biatora franciscana Tuck., Syn. N. A. Lich. 2:32. 1888.
Thallus thick, becoming warty and crumbling, ashy white to gray; apothecia middle-sized, 0.5–0.8 mm. across, sessile, the disk flat to strongly convex, black, or commonly more or less whitish pruinose, the exciple dull black, soon disappearing; hypothecium hyaline; spores oblong, 14–22 × 3–5 μ.
On various rocks, California.

9. **Catillaria leptocheila** (Tuck.) Riddle, Mycologia 4:128. 1912.
Lecidea leptocheila Tuck.; Nyl., Ann. Sci. Nat. Bot. IV. 19:351. 1863. *Heterothecium leptocheilum* Tuck.
Thallus thin, minutely granulose, chinky and finally warty, whitish to brownish, bordered by a thin, black, fibrillose hypothallus; apothecia middle-sized to large, 0.8–1.5 mm. across, sessile, the disk flat to strongly convex, black, the exciple thin, black, soon disappearing; hypothecium brownish; spores boat-shaped to ellipsoid, 12–16 × 4–5 μ.
On trees, Florida and Alabama.

10. **Catillaria endochroma** (Fée) Zahlbr., in E. & P., Nat. Pfl. 1¹:134. 1907.
Lecanora endochroma Fée, Essai Crypt. 114. pl. 29, f. 1. 1824. *Heterothecium endochromum* (Fée) Flot. *Biatora endochroma* (Fée) Merrill.
Thallus moderately thick, rough, wrinkled, minutely granulose, greenish gray to yellowish or ashy; apothecia middle-sized to large, 1–1.8 mm. across, sessile,

the disk flat to convex, black, the exciple thin, yellowish green, becoming black, irregular and finally disappearing; hypothecium brownish; spores 8, ellipsoid, slightly curved, 15–18 × 4.5–6 μ.
On trees, California.

11. **Catillaria atropurpurea** (Schaer.) T. Fries, Lich. Scand. 1:565. 1874.
Lecidea sphaeroides var. *atropurpurea* Schaer., Enum. Lich. Eur. 140. 1850.
Biatorina atropurpurea (Schaer.) Mass.
Thallus thin, minutely granulose to slightly chinky or scurfy, rarely sorediate, ashy, varying toward greenish or brownish, sometimes disappearing; apothecia minute to small, 0.2–0.7 mm. across, slightly immersed to adnate, the disk flat to strongly convex, purplish black to black, the exciple soon disappearing; hypothecium hyaline; spores ellipsoid, 10–16 × 3.5–6 μ.
On trees, New England, Florida, Alabama, Illinois, Minnesota, and California.

12. **Catillaria Laureri** Hepp, in Arn., Exsicc. no. 353. 1867.
Biatora Laureri (Hepp) Tuck.
Thallus thin to thickish, smooth to wrinkled, scurfy, or chinky, dusky gray to ashy white; apothecia small to middle-sized, 0.4–1 mm. across, sessile, the disk flat to convex, often roughened, black, the exciple paler, thin, soon disappearing; hypothecium blackish brown; spores ellipsoid to fusiform, 10–18 × 3–7 μ.
On trees, rarely old wood, New England, Florida, Oregon, and California.

13. **Catillaria glauconigrans** (Tuck.) Hasse, Bryologist 12:102. 1909.
Biatora glauconigrans Tuck., Proc. Am. Acad. 12:179, 180. 1877.
Thallus thin, composed of continuous or scattered, small, round, greenish gray to ashy granules; apothecia minute to small, 0.2–0.45 mm. across, adnate to sessile, the disk flat to convex, pale lead-colored to black, the exciple colored like the disk, soon disappearing; hypothecium brown to brownish black; spores oblong-ellipsoid, 6–12 × 2.5–4 μ.
On trees, Massachusetts and California.

14. **Catillaria grossa** (Pers.) Blomb., Vet. Akad. Fordhandl. 24:122. 1867.
Lecidea grossa Pers., in Nyl., Act. Soc. Linn. Bord. 21:385. 1857. *Heterothecium grossum* (Pers.) Tuck.
Thallus thin, smooth to wrinkled or chinky-areolate, greenish gray to ashy, sometimes disappearing; apothecia middle-sized, 0.7–1.5 mm. across, sessile, the disk flat to strongly convex, black, the exciple paler, thick, finally disappearing; hypothecium black; spores ovoid-ellipsoid, 20–28 × 8–16 μ.
On trees, Nebraska.

15. **Catillaria chalybeia** (Borr.) Mass., Ric. Lich. 79. f. 161. 1852:
Lecidea chalybeia Borr., in Hook. and Sowerby, Engl. Bot. Suppl. 1: pl. 2687, f. 2. 1831. *Biatorina chalybeia* (Borr.) Mudd.
Thallus thin, smooth to finely chinky-areolate, ashy gray to darkening, becoming inconspicuous and rarely disappearing; apothecia minute to small, 0.3–0.5 mm. across, adnate to sessile, the disk concave to slightly convex, black, the exciple of the same color, rarely covered; hypothecium dark brown; spores long-ellipsoid, 9–12 × 3–4.5 μ.
On rocks, Maine, Ohio, and southern California.

16. **Catillaria lenticularis** (Ach.) T. Fries, Lich. Scand. 1:567. 1874.
Lecidea lenticularis Ach., Syn. Meth. Lich. 28. 1814. *Biatorina lenticularis* (Ach.) Koerb. *C. lenticularis* f. *acrustacea* (Hepp) Hasse.
Thallus thin, smooth to slightly rough and granulose, ashy white to greenish or brownish gray, sometimes disappearing; apothecia minute to small, 0.25–0.5 mm. across, adnate, numerous, the disk flat to slightly convex, black, the exciple of the same color, thin, finally disappearing; hypothecium pale brown to dark brown; spores long-ellipsoid, 8–14 × 2.5–5 μ. ˙
On rocks, Ohio and California.

OTHER SPECIES REPORTED

Catillaria subnigrata (Nyl.) Blombg. et Forss.—California.
Catillaria superflua (Müll. Arg.) Zahlbr.—New England.

124. **Megalospora** Meyer, Nov. Act. Acad. Caes. Leop. Car. Suppl. 19:228. 1843.

Thallus crustose, rough and warty, rudimentary, devoid of differentiation into layers and attached to the substratum by hyphal rhizoids; apothecia middle-sized or large, adnate or almost sessile, the disk more or less convex, usually black, the exciple light-colored to black, usually disappearing; hypothecium hyaline to brownish or brown; hymenium hyaline; paraphyses unbranched or branched and netlike interwoven; asci clavate; spores 1–8, hyaline, large, 1-septate. The algal host is Protococcus.

1. **Megalospora versicolor** (Fée) Zahlbr., in E. & P., Nat. Pfl. 1:134. 1907.
Lecanora versicolor Fée, Essai Crypt. 115. pl. 28, f. 4. 1824. *Heterothecium versicolor* (Fée) Flot. *M. sulphurata* var. *genuina* Riddle.

Thallus thin to moderately thick, smooth to chinky-areolate and wrinkled, greenish gray to ashy, rarely disappearing; apothecia middle-sized to large, 1–3 mm. across, sessile, the disk flat to convex, brownish black to black, the exciple thin, light-colored to black, finally disappearing; hypothecium brownish to blackish brown; paraphyses slender, flexuous, becoming enlarged at the apices; asci long-clavate; spores 2–4 or rarely 8, ellipsoid, slightly curved, 45–65 × 18–30 μ. On trees, Florida.

125. **Bilimbia** De Not., Giorn. Bot. Ital. 2¹:190, 191. 1846.

Thallus crustose, smooth to warty or minutely granulose or rarely squamulose, rudimentary and rarely differentiated into layers; apothecia minute to small, rarely somewhat immersed to adnate or sessile, scattered or clustered, round to irregular, the disk flat to convex, flesh-colored or yellow to red, brown or black, the proper exciple usually disappearing; hypothecium hyaline to brownish black; hymenium hyaline; paraphyses unbranched; asci clavate; spores 8 or rarely more, hyaline, oblong-ellipsoid to fusiform, 3–7-septate, rarely only 1-septate. The algal host is Protococcus.

A. On rocks and soil
  B. Hypothecium hyaline to yellowish
    C. Spores 3-septate
      D. Apothecia pale to yellowish or reddish . . . . . . 4. B. cupreorosella
      D. Apothecia reddish to brownish black . . . . . 8. B. gyalectiformis
    C. Spores 3–5-septate
      D. Apothecia pale flesh-colored . . . . 14. B. Ravenelii
      D. Apothecia brownish red to blackish . . . . . . 15. B. rubidofusca
  B. Hypothecium brownish or reddish brown to brownish black
    C. Spores 3-septate
      D. Hypothecium pale brownish to brown
        E. Thallus thin, chinky to areolate . . . . 12. B. Pammellii
        E. Thallus thicker, granules becoming sublobulate . . . . 18. B. artyta
      D. Hypothecium reddish brown to brown
        E. Thallus scurfy or granulose, forming a thin
          chinky crust . . . . 22. B. trachona
        E. Thallus granulose, often disappearing
          F. Thallus thin; disk flat to convex . . . . . . 21. B. granosa
          F. Thallus thicker; disk convex to subglobose . . 20. B. microcarpa
    C. Spores 3–7-septate . . . . 24. B. caudata
A. On trees, old wood, soil, and moss
  B. On trees
    C. Hypothecium hyaline
      D. Apothecia yellowish to reddish or flesh-colored
        E. Spores 10–15 × 2.5–4 μ . . . . 1. B. floridana

E. Spores rarely less than 12 μ in length
  F. Thallus greenish to grayish; apothecia pale
    yellowish to reddish . . . . 2. B. caloosensis
  F. Thallus greenish gray to lead-colored; apothecia
    yellowish flesh-colored . . . . 3. B. molybditis
 D. Apothecia flesh-colored or red to brown or black
  E. Spores more than 8, 10–16 × 5–6 μ . . . . . . 7. B. gyalizella
  E. Spores 8, more than 18 μ in length
    F. Spores 18–26 × 4.5–5.5 μ . . . . 6. B. Naegelii
    F. Spores 33–36 × 3.5–5 μ . . . . 13. B. rubricosa
 C. Hypothecium yellowish or reddish brown to darker
  D. Spores 8–16 in an ascus . . . . 11. B. acclinis
  D. Spores 8 in an ascus
   E. Spores less than 15 μ in length
     F. Hypothecium brownish . . . . 9. B. declinis
     F. Hypothecium blackish brown . . . . . . 17. B. tricholoma
   E. Spores 14–21 × 3.5–5 μ . . . . 10. B. trisepta
 B. On old wood, moss, or soil
  C. Spores 3-septate
   D. On old logs; apothecia coal black . . . . 19. B. melaena
   D. On moss; apothecia pale flesh-colored to reddish
     brown . . . . 5. B. sphaeroides
  C. Spores 3–7-septate
   D. Thallus brownish to ashy; spores 18–38 × 4.5–8 μ . . . 16. B. lignaria
   D. Thallus greenish gray to ashy; spores 15–30 ×4–7.5 μ . 23. B. sabuletorum

1. **Bilimbia floridana** (Tuck.) Riddle, Bull. Torr. Club 43:162. 1916.
Biatora floridana Tuck., Syn. N. A. Lich. 2:39. 1888. *Bacidia floridana* (Tuck.)
Zahlbr.
Thallus thin, of subsquamulose, confluent, yellowish green granules; apothecia
minute, 0.01–0.35 mm. across, adnate, often clustered, the disk flat to slightly convex, sometimes becoming irregular, reddish flesh-colored, the exciple paler, thin,
and sometimes disappearing; hypothecium hyaline; spores hyaline, oblong-ellipsoid
to finger-shaped, 3-septate, 10–15 × 2.5–4 μ.
On trees, Florida.

2. **Bilimbia caloosensis** (Tuck.) Fink n. comb.
Biatora caloosensis Tuck., Syn. N. A. Lich. 2:41. 1888. *Bacidia caloosensis*
(Tuck.) Zahlbr.
Thallus thin, minutely granulose, pale greenish to grayish, often forming a
granulose crust; apothecia minute to small, 0.2–0.5 mm. across, adnate, often
clustered, the disk flat to convex, pale yellowish to reddish, the exciple of same
color and disappearing; hypothecium hyaline; spores hyaline, oblong-ellipsoid to
finger-shaped, 3-septate, 12–22 × 2.5–4 μ.
On trees, Florida.

3. **Bilimbia molybditis** (Tuck.) Fink n. comb.
Biatora molybditis Tuck., Syn. N. A. Lich. 2:34. 1888. *Bacidia molybditis*
(Tuck.) Zahlbr.
Thallus minutely granulose, greenish gray to lead-colored, forming a thin,
chinky crust; apothecia minute to small, 0.2–0.45 mm. across, sessile, often clus-
tered, the disk flat to slightly convex, yellowish flesh-colored, the exciple stout,
of same color; hypothecium hyaline; spores fusiform, 3-septate, 12–21 × 2.5–4.5 μ.
On trees, Florida.

4. **Bilimbia cupreorosella** (Nyl.) Bausch, Verh. Nat. Vere. Carls. 4:124. 1869.
Lecidea cupreorosella Nyl., Mém. Soc. Sci. Nat. Cherb. 122. 1857. *Biatora
cupreorosella* (Nyl.) Tuck.
Thallus granulose, greenish gray to whitish, passing into chinky and verrucose
conditions; apothecia minute to small, 0.2–0.5 mm. across, adnate, often irregular,

the disk flat to commonly convex, pale to yellowish and reddish, the exciple incon-spicuous and soon disappearing; hypothecium hyaline; spores fusiform-ellipsoid to finger-shaped, 3-septate, 12–20 × 2–3.5 μ.

On limestone, Orange County, New York.

5. **Bilimbia sphaeroides** (Dicks.) Koerb., Syst. Lich. 213. 1855.
   Lichen sphaeroides Dicks., Pl. Crypt. Brit. 1:9. pl. 2, f. 3. 1785. *Biatora sphae-roides* (Dicks.) Horn. *Bacidia sphaeroides* (Dicks.) Zahlbr.

Thallus minutely granulose, greenish gray, often forming a thin, chinky and scurfy crust, sometimes largely disappearing; apothecia small to middle-sized, 0.25–0.9 mm. across, adnate, sometimes clustered, the disk convex to subspherical, pale flesh-colored to reddish brown, the exciple of same color and soon disappear-ing; hypothecium hyaline to light brown; spores ellipsoid to fusiform, 3-septate, 14–22 × 3.5–6.5 μ.

On mossy bases of trees, from New England to Florida, and westward to the Rocky Mountains.

6. **Bilimbia Naegelii** (Hepp) Kremphl., Bay. Bot. Ges. 4:223. 1861.
   Biatora Naegelii Hepp, Spor. Flecht. Eur. pl. 4, f. 1, 19. 1853. *Bacidia Naegelii* (Hepp) Zahlbr.

Thallus granulose, greenish gray, forming a chinky, more or less roughened crust; apothecia small to middle-sized, 0.4–0.8 mm. across, adnate, usually clus-tered, the disk convex, from flesh-colored to reddish brown or black, the exciple thin, lighter colored and soon disappearing; hypothecium hyaline; spores ellipsoid to fusiform, 3-septate, 18–26 × 4.5–5.5 μ.

On trees, from New England to Florida, and westward to Minnesota. Also known in California.

7. **Bilimbia gyalizella** (Nyl.) Fink n. comb.
   Lecidea gyalizella Nyl., Lab. Sing. 38. 1891. *Biatora gyalizella* (Nyl.) Willey. *Bacidia gyalizella* (Nyl.) Zahlbr.

Thallus very thin, minutely granulose, ashy; apothecia minute, 0.15–0.25 mm. across, adnate to sessile, the disk deeply concave, dark red, the exciple entire, dark red to dusky brown; hypothecium hyaline; spores about 24, oblong-ellipsoid, 1–3-septate, 10–16 × 5–6 μ.

On trees, near New Bedford, Massachusetts.

8. **Bilimbia gyalectiformis** Zahlbr., Beih. Bot. Centralb. 13:158,159. 1902.
   Bacidia gyalectiformis (Zahlbr.) Hasse.

Thallus thin, somewhat rough, chinky, grayish to ashy white, becoming pow-dery; apothecia small to middle-sized, 0.3–0.8 mm. across, partly immersed, the disk deeply concave to flat, reddish to brownish black, the exciple absent and the disk surrounded by a thalloid veil; hypothecium pale yellowish; spores oblong-ellipsoid, 3-septate, 18–24 × 5–7 μ.

On sandy soil among rocks, San Jacinto Mountains, California.

9. **Bilimbia declinis** (Tuck.) Fink n. comb.
   Lecidea declinis Tuck., Gen. Lich. 182. 1872. *Biatora declinis* Tuck. *Bacidia declinis* (Tuck.) Zahlbr.

Thallus thin, scurfy, greenish brown; apothecia minute to small, 0.15–0.3 mm. across, adnate, the disk flat to slightly convex, brownish to black, the exciple of same color and soon disappearing; hypothecium hyaline to brownish; spores ellip-soid to finger-shaped, 1–3-septate, 9–12 × 3–5 μ.

On trees, Massachusetts. Spores of material seen, collected by Tuckerman and Willey, have the size of European specimens and not the much smaller size of Tuckerman's descriptions.

10. **Bilimbia trisepta** (Naeg.) Arn., Lich. Monac. Exsicc. 118. 1890.
Lecidea trisepta Naeg., in Müll. Arg., Mém. Soc. Phys. Hist. Nat. Genève
16:404. 1862. *Bacidia trisepta* (Naeg.) Zahlbr. *Biatora trisepta* (Naeg.)
Willey.
Thallus thin, minutely granulose, grayish to ashy or brownish; apothecia
minute, 0.08–0.2 mm. across, adnate, scattered or clustered, the disk convex, black,
the exciple of same color and soon disappearing; hypothecium pale brown; spores
fusiform-ellipsoid, 3-septate, 14–21 × 3.5–5 μ.
On trees, Massachusetts.

11. **Bilimbia acclinis** (Mass.) Trevis., Linn. 28:293. 1856.
Arthrosporum accline Mass., Gen. Lich. 20. 1854. *Bacidia acclinis* (Mass.)
Zahlbr.
Thallus thin, verrucose to scaly or granulose, greenish gray to ashy, often disappearing; apothecia minute to small, 0.3–0.7 mm. across, adnate, the disk flat to
convex, black, the exciple thin, of same color and often disappearing; hypothecium
pale yellowish; spores 8–16, oblong-ellipsoid, somewhat curved, 3-septate, 9–18 ×
4–5 μ.
On trees, from New England to Minnesota, Iowa, and Nebraska.

12. **Bilimbia Pammellii** Fink; Hedrick, Mycologia 26:156. 1934.
Thallus granulose, continuous, scattered, greenish gray, becoming a thin,
chinky crust; apothecia small to middle-sized, 0.3–0.7 mm. across, adnate, scattered
or rarely clustered, the disk slightly to strongly convex, black, the exciple of the
same color and soon disappearing; hypothecium pale brown; spores oblong-ellipsoid,
3-septate, 15–24 × 3–4.5 μ.
On sandstone, Iowa.

13. **Bilimbia rubricosa** (Müll. Arg.) Fink n. comb.
Patellaria rubricosa Müll. Arg., Hedwigia 34:142, 143. 1895. *Bacidia rubricosa*
(Müll. Arg.) Zahlbr.
Thallus thin, widespread, minutely granulose or granulose-scurfy, whitish or
yellowish white; apothecia middle-sized to large, 1–1.5 mm. across, sessile, more or
less scattered, the disk flat, red to reddish brown, the exciple thin, somewhat
lighter than the disk; hypothecium hyaline; spores oblong to dactyloid-oblong,
curved, 3-septate, 33–36 × 3.5–5 μ.
On trees, Idaho (description was made from the original description and one
prepared by A. Zahlbruckner, who studied the original specimen).

14. **Bilimbia Ravenelii** (Tuck.) Fink n. comb.
Biatora Ravenelii Tuck., Syn. N. A. Lich. 2:34. 1888. *Bacidia Ravenelii* (Tuck.)
Zahlbr.
Thallus thin, minutely granulose, greenish gray; apothecia minute to small,
0.15–0.5 mm. across, sessile, the disk concave to flat, pale flesh-colored, the exciple
elevated, thin and lighter in color; hypothecium hyaline; spores oblong-ellipsoid
to fusiform, 3–5-septate, 16–25 × 4–5 μ.
On sandstone, Florida.

15. **Bilimbia rubidofusca** (Willey) Fink n. comb.
Biatora rubidofusca Willey, Enum. Lich. New Bedford, Mass. 23. 1892. *Bacidia
rubidofusca* (Willey) Zahlbr.
Thallus thin, granulose, greenish gray, often forming a continuous, scarcely
granulose crust; apothecia minute to small, 0.15–0.25 mm. across, adnate to sessile,
scattered or sometimes clustered, the disk concave, brownish red to blackish, the
exciple of same color or darker; hypothecium hyaline; spores ellipsoid to fusiform,
3–5-septate, 13–22 × 4–5.5 μ.
On soil, near New Bedford, Massachusetts.

16. **Bilimbia lignaria** (Ach.) Mass., Ric. Lich. 121. f. 236. 1852.
    Lecidea lignaria Ach., Vet. Akad. Nya Handl. 236. 1808. *Biatora milliaria* (E.
        Fries) Tuck. *Bacidia milliaria* (E. Fries) Sandst. *Bacidia milliaria* f. *lignaria*
        (Ach.) Hasse. *Bacidia lignaria* (Ach.) Lettau.
    Thallus thin, brownish to ashy, granulose, sometimes becoming roughly verru-
culose or scurfy, or disappearing; apothecia minute to small, 0.25–0.65 mm. across,
partly immersed to sessile, commonly clustered or confluent, the disk convex to
spherical, brownish black to black, the exciple black, disappearing; hypothecium
hyaline; spores finger-shaped to fusiform, 3–7-septate, 18–38 × 4.5–8 μ.
    On rotten wood and dead mosses, from New England to Florida, and recurring
in California.

17. **Bilimbia tricholoma** (Mont.) Fink n. comb.
    Biatora tricholoma Mont., Ann. Sci. Nat. Bot. III. 16:53. 1851. *Biatora leuco-
        blephara* Nyl.
    Thallus thin, scurfy, grayish green to greenish ashy; apothecia minute to
small, 0.15–0.4 mm. across, adnate, rarely clustered, the disk flat to convex, pale
brown to blackish, the exciple pale, exteriorly often whitish cobwebbed, soon disappearing; hypothecium blackish brown; spores fusiform-ellipsoid to finger-shaped,
3-septate, 10–15 × 3–5 μ.
    On trees, Florida, South Carolina, and Georgia.

18. **Bilimbia artyta** (Ach.) Fink n. comb.
    Lecidea artyta Ach., Lich. Univ. 170, 171. 1810. *Biatora artyta* (Ach.) Tuck.
    Thallus rather thick, granular, greenish gray to ashy, the granules flat, often
becoming dilated and sublobulate, sometimes more or less scattered; apothecia
small, 0.3–0.7 mm. across, sessile and often clustered, the disk convex to hemispherical, pale lead-colored to blackish brown or finally black, the exciple soon
disappearing; hypothecium brown; spores finger-shaped, 3-septate, 12–24 × 4–6 μ.
    On soil, Rocky Mountains of Colorado.

19. **Bilimbia melaena** (Nyl.) Arn., Flora 48:596. 1865.
    Lecidea melaena Nyl., Bot. Not. 182. 1853. *Biatora melaena* (Nyl.) Tuck.
        Bacidia melaena (Nyl.) Zahlbr.
    Thallus very thin, granulose to scurfy, grayish green to brownish and often
disappearing; apothecia minute, 0.2–0.5 mm. across, sessile, clustered, the disk
soon very convex, coal black, the exciple of same color, soon disappearing; hypothecium pale reddish-brown; spores oblong-ellipsoid, 3-septate, 12–18 × 3–5 μ.
    On old logs, New England to Florida, and westward to Louisiana and Ohio.

20. **Bilimbia microcarpa** T. Fries, Bot. Not. 1863:8. 1863.
    B. obscurata var. *microcarpa* T. Fries, Nov. Act. Soc. Sci. Ups. III. 3:283. 1861.
        Bacidia microcarpa (T. Fries) Lettau.
    Thallus thin to moderately thick, granulose, greenish gray to ashy, becoming
scattered and often disappearing; apothecia minute to small, 0.25–0.7 mm. across,
adnate, sometimes clustered, the disk soon convex or subglobose, dirty brown to
black, the exciple pale and soon disappearing; hypothecium pale reddish brown;
asci often inflated; spores fusiform, 3-septate, 15–23 × 3.5–6 μ.
    On shaded sandstone, Hocking County, Ohio.

21. **Bilimbia granosa** (Tuck.) Fink n. comb.
    Lecidea granosa Tuck., Proc. Am. Acad. 5:420. 1862. *Toninia granosa* (Tuck.)
        B. de Lesd.
    Thallus thin, minutely granulose, greenish to ashy, forming a broken crust or
scattered, scurfy and disappearing; apothecia minute to small, 0.2–0.5 mm. across,
adnate, the disk flat to slightly convex, black or rarely pale livid, the exciple black,
finally disappearing; hypothecium reddish brown; spores oblong-ellipsoid to finger-
shaped, 3-septate, 10–20 × 2.5–4.5 μ.
    On bricks, mortar and calcareous rocks, from New York to Florida, and west-
ward to California.

22. **Bilimbia trachona** (Ach.) Trevis., Linnaea 28:293. 1856.
   Verrucaria trachona Ach., Meth. Lich. Suppl. 16. 1803. *Biatora trachona* (Ach.)
   Koerb. *Bacidia trachona* (Ach.) Lettau.
   Thallus scurfy or granulose, greenish gray to ashy, becoming a thin, chinky
crust; apothecia small to middle-sized, 0.4–0.8 mm. across, adnate, the disk flat
to strongly convex, brownish black to black, the exciple entire and of same color,
often disappearing; hypothecium dark brown; spores fusiform-ellipsoid, 3-septate,
12–19 × 2.5–5.5 μ.
   On shaded rocks, Massachusetts, New York, Ohio, Illinois, and Iowa.

23. **Bilimbia sabuletorum** (Schreb.) Arn., Verh. Ges. Wien. 19:637. 1869.
   Lichen sabuletorum Schreb., Spic. Fl. Lips. 134. 1771. *Bacidia sabuletorum*
   (Schreb.) Lettau. *Biatora hypnophila* (Ach.) Lönnr. *Lecidea hypnophila*
   Ach. *B. hypnophila* (Ach.) T. Fries. *Bacidia obscurata* (Sommerf.) Zahlbr.
   Thallus thin, greenish gray to ashy, of crowded granules, sometimes confluent,
and forming a crust, or sometimes disappearing; apothecia small to middle-sized,
0.2–0.7 mm. across, adnate to sessile, often clustered, the disk flat to strongly
convex, light brown to black, the exciple black and soon disappearing; hypothecium
pale to darker brown; spores ellipsoid to fusiform, 3–7-septate, 15–30 × 4–7.5 μ.
   On moss and soil, distributed throughout the United States.

24. **Bilimbia caudata** (Nyl.) Fink n. comb.
   Lecidea caudata Nyl., Bot. Notis. 176. 1852. *Bacidia lugubris* (Sommerf.)
   Zahlbr.
   Thallus moderately thick, granulose to chinky-areolate, brownish to ashy, on a
black hypothallus; apothecia small to middle-sized, 0.1–0.6 mm. across, sessile, the
disk flat to convex, black, the exciple of the same color, entire, becoming flexuous
or lobed, or finally disappearing; hypothecium brownish black; spores hyaline,
oblong-ellipsoid with caudate appendage, 3–7-septate, 30–45 × 4–6 μ.
   On rocks, White Mountains, New Hampshire.

OTHER SPECIES REPORTED

Bilimbia Meadii (Tuck.)—Biatora Meadii Tuck.—Florida.

126. Bacidia De Not., Giorn. Bot. Ital. 2¹:189. 1846.

   Thallus crustose, granulose, sometimes inconspicuous, rarely disappearing, often
passing into chinky, warty, subareolate, and even subsquamulose conditions, rudimentary, usually devoid of differentiation, attached to the substratum by hyphal
rhizoids; apothecia usually adnate but sometimes sessile or rarely immersed, the
disk usually becoming convex, flesh-colored to more commonly darker or even
black, the exciple of the same color and usually becoming covered; hypothecium
usually yellowish to brown, but rarely persistently hyaline; hymenium hyaline to
brownish; paraphyses rarely branched; asci long-clavate to cylindrico-clavate;
spores 8, hyaline, acicular, several-septate, the septa often indistinct, the cells
cylindrical.
   The algal host is Protococcus.

A. Hypothecium hyaline, yellowish to brown or rarely becoming darker
  B. On rocks and rarely on wood
    C. Spores 3–7-septate, 1.5–3 μ in width
      D. Hypothecium hyaline to brown; spores 20–40 × 1.5–2.5 μ   10. B. inundata
      D. Hypothecium pale yellow; spores 18–30 × 2.5–3 μ . . . . 22. B. umbrina
    C. Spores 5–9-septate, 0.75–1.25 μ in width . . . . . . 8. B. egenuloidea
  B. On trees, old wood, and rarely on rocks
    C. Spores rarely more than 40 μ in length
      D. Hypothecium hyaline
        E. Thallus scaly or squamulose
          F. Spores 18–28 × 2–3 μ . . . . 7. B. microphyllina
          F. Spores 30–40 × 1.5–2 μ . . . . 6. B. Augustini

E. Thallus granulose, powdery or chinky-areolate
  F. Apothecia not more than 0.5 mm. across
    G. Disk light pink to pale reddish . . . . . . 2. B. albescens
    G. Disk yellowish to reddish or finally
      leaden-brown . . . . 4. B. stigmatella
  F. Apothecia 0.8–1.2 mm. across . . . . 5. B. Herrei
D. Hypothecium hyaline to yellowish or brownish
  E. Apothecia not more than 1 mm. across
    F. Thallus ashy to whitish
      G. Apothecia always black . . . . 11. B. akompsa
      G. Apothecia brownish to blackish . . . . . 12. B. bacillifera
    F. Thallus greenish gray to greenish or brownish
      G. Thallus scurfy or powdery . . . . 15. B. effusa
      G. Thallus coarsely granulose . . . . 13. B. chlorantha
  E. Apothecia 1–2.5 mm. across . . . . 9. B. subgranulosa
C. Spores rarely less than 40 μ in length
  D. Hypothecium hyaline
    E. Disk flesh- to rose-colored, sometimes obscurely
      pruinose . . . . 3. B. rosella
    E. Disk yellowish to reddish brown . . . . . 1. B. leucophyllina
  D. Hypothecium hyaline to yellowish or brownish to darker
    E. Disk light brown or reddish to brown or black
      F. Apothecia rarely less than 0.6 mm. across
        G. Disk pale brown or reddish to darker and
          black; spores 40–75 × 3–4 μ . . . . . 17. B. fuscorubella
        G. Disk reddish yellow to reddish brown or
          obscurely white-pruinose; spores 45–65 × 3-4 μ . 16. B. luteola
      F. Apothecia 0.2–0.6 mm. across . . . . 19. B. arceutina
    E. Disk dark brown to black
      F. Apothecia rarely more than 0.8 mm. across
        G. Spores 30–60 × 2.5–4.5 μ . . . . 14. B. atrogrisea
        G. Spores 60–80 × 4–5 μ . . . . 18. B. Clementis
      F. Apothecia 0.6–1.75 mm. across . . . . . . 21. B. Schweinitzii
A. Hypothecium brownish or reddish brown to brownish black
  B. On trees and old wood
    C. Spores rarely more than 40 μ in length
      D. Thallus very thin and inconspicuous . . . . . 24. B. endocyanea
      D. Thallus scurfy or powdery to granulose
        E. Hypothecium reddish brown . . . . 25. B. incompta
        E. Hypothecium blackish brown
          F. Spores 1–3-septate . . . . 23. B. chlorosticta
          F. Spores 3–7-septate . . . . 26. B. Jacobi
    C. Spores rarely less than 40 μ in length
      D. Apothecia less than 1 mm. across
        E. Spores 5–9-septate . . . . 27. B. abductans
        E. Spores 15–29-septate . . . . 29. B. dryina
      D. Apothecia 1.5–2.5 mm. across . . . . 28. B. suffusa
  B. On soil, moss, rocks, and other lichens, rarely on trees
    C. Spores 25–40 × 2–3 μ . . . . 20. B. muscorum
    C. Spores 35–85 × 3–4 μ . . . . 30. B. flavovirescens

1. **Bacidia leucophyllina** (Nyl.) Fink n. comb.
    Lecidea leucophyllina Nyl., Ann. Sci. Nat. Bot. IV. 19:347. 1863. *Biatora leucophyllina* (Nyl.) Tuck. *Psorella leucophyllina* (Nyl.) Zahlbr.
    Thallus composed of minute, irregular, greenish gray to whitish granules; apothecia small, 0.3–0.5 mm. across, adnate, the disk flat to convex, yellowish to reddish brown, the exciple thin, colored like the disk; hypothecium hyaline; spores 8, hyaline, acicular, slightly curved, 7–9-septate, 38–60 × 2–4 μ.
    On trees, Florida.

2. **Bacidia albescens** Zwackh., Flora 45:495. 1862.
    Thallus thin, minutely granulose or powdery, greenish gray to whitish, sometimes indistinct; apothecia minute to small, 0.15–0.5 mm. across, sessile, often numerous, the disk flat to convex, light pink to pale reddish, the exciple paler,

finally disappearing; hypothecium hyaline; spores 3–14-septate, long-cylindrical to acicular, 27–40 × 1.8–2.3 μ.
On trees, New England, California, and Washington.

3. **Bacidia rosella** (Pers.) De Not., Giorn. Bot. Ital. 2¹:190. 1846.
Lichen rosellus Pers., Ann. Bot. Usteri 1:25. 1794.
Thallus thin, subgranulose, greenish gray to white; apothecia small to middle-sized, 0.1–0.8 mm. across, adnate to subsessile, the disk slightly concave to convex, flesh- to rose-colored, sometimes obscurely pruinose, the exciple thick and slightly paler, finally disappearing; hypothecium hyaline; spores 5–9-septate, 45–75 × 3–5 μ.
On trees, Maine and Vermont.

4. **Bacidia stigmatella** (Tuck.) Zahlbr., Cat. Lich. Univ. 4:241. 1926.
Biatora stigmatella Tuck., Gen. Lich. 167. 1872.
Thallus powdery-granular, pale greenish to ashy; apothecia minute to small, 0.2–0.5 mm. across, adnate to sessile, the disk flat to convex, yellowish to reddish or finally leaden-brown, the exciple slightly darker, finally disappearing; hypothecium hyaline; spores 3-, rarely 5–7-septate, 22–40 × 1.5–2.5 μ.
On trees, Louisiana, Texas, and Illinois.

5. **Bacidia Herrei** Zahlbr., Ann. Mycol. 6:130, 131. 1908.
Thallus thin, granulose to subgranulose or approaching chinky-areolate, pale greenish yellow, bordered by gray; apothecia middle-sized, 0.8–1.2 mm. across, sessile, somewhat angular when clustered, the disk flat to convex, dark purplish red, the exciple of the same color, thin, often flexuous, sometimes finally disappearing; hypothecium hyaline; spores fusiform-acicular, 4–7-septate, 35–40 × 1.7–1.8 μ.
On dead twigs, California.

6. **Bacidia Augustini** (Tuck.) Zahlbr., Cat. Lich. Univ. 4:102. 1926.
Biatora Augustini Tuck., Syn. N. A. Lich. 2:42. 1888.
Thallus of greenish gray to brownish, imbricated or expanded, and stellate squamiform scales, upon a black hypothallus; apothecia small to middle-sized, 0.5–1 mm. across, subsessile, solitary or clustered, the disk flat to convex, pale lead-colored to dark reddish, the exciple blackish to black, and soon disappearing; hypothecium hyaline; spores acicular, becoming 3-septate, 30–40 × 1.5–2 μ.
On trees, Florida.

7. **Bacidia microphyllina** (Tuck.) Riddle, Mycologia 15:80. 1923.
Lecidea microphyllina Tuck., Proc. Am. Acad. 6:278. 1866. *Biatora microphyllina* Tuck.
Thallus of minute, cut-crenate, greenish ashy to brownish, ascendant squamules; apothecia small to middle-sized, 0.2–0.8 mm. across, adnate, the disk flat to convex, yellowish to reddish, the exciple of same color, becoming flexuous and disappearing; hypothecium hyaline; spores 3–5-septate, 18–28 × 2–3 μ.
On trees, Florida.

8. **Bacidia egenuloidea** Fink, Ohio Biol. Surv. 2:346. 1921.
Thallus of minute, crowded granules, forming a rather thick, wrinkled and obscurely chinky, dirty olive and darkening crust; apothecia minute to small, 0.25–0.4 mm. across, subsessile, the disk flat, yellowish brown and darkening, the exciple darker; hypothecium hyaline or tinged brown; spores obscurely 5–9-septate, variously curved, 25–40 × 0.75–1.25 μ.
On granite, Ohio.

9. **Bacidia subgranulosa** (Tuck.) Riddle, Mycologia 4:131. 1912.
Lecidea microphyllina var. *subgranulosa* Tuck., Proc. Am. Acad. 6:278. 1866.
Thallus thin to moderately thick, composed of minute granules, forming a rough, greenish gray to brownish crust; apothecia middle-sized to large, 1–2.5 mm.

across, sessile, the disk flat to slightly convex, dark flesh-colored to reddish or brownish, the exciple thin, becoming flexuous and soon disappearing; hypothecium hyaline to tinged brownish; spores 8, hyaline, acicular, indistinctly many-septate, $25–38 \times 1.5–2.5\,\mu$.

On trees, Georgia and Louisiana.

10. **Bacidia inundata** (E. Fries) Koerb., Syst. Lich. 187. 1855.
   Biatora inundata E. Fries, Vet. Akad. Handl. 1822:270. 1822.
   Thallus minutely granulose or chinky to subareolate, greenish gray to ashy or darkening; apothecia minute to small, 0.3–0.7 mm. across, adnate or rarely partly immersed, the disk flat to convex, pale brown, lead-colored, reddish brown, to finally black, the exciple at first paler, then of the same color, finally disappearing; hypothecium pale to brown; spores 3–7-septate, $20–40 \times 1.5–2.5\,\mu$.

On rocks, rarely on wood, throughout United States east of Rocky Mountains.

11. **Bacidia akompsa** (Tuck.) Fink, Cont. U. S. Nat. Herb. 14[1]:90. 1910.
   Biatora akompsa Tuck., Syn. N. A. Lich. 2:47, 48. 1888.
   Thallus of minute granules, forming a scurfy, or compacted and chinky, smooth or rough-verrucose, ashy crust; apothecia minute to small, 0.2–0.5 mm. across, adnate to sessile, the disk flat to subhemispherical, rough, black, the exciple paler, uneven; hypothecium hyaline to brownish; spores 3–5-septate, $19–30 \times 2–3\,\mu$.

On trees, Minnesota, California, and Washington.

12. **Bacidia bacillifera** (Nyl.) Fink, Cont. U. S. Nat. Herb. 14[1]:91, 92. 1910.
   Lecidea bacillifera Nyl., Not. Sällsk. Faun. Flor. Fenn. 5:210. 1861.
   Thallus of minute granules forming a thin, rough, ashy to whitish crust, sometimes disappearing; apothecia minute to small, 0.3–0.8 mm. across, adnate to subsessile, the disk flat to convex, brownish to blackish, the exciple thick, soon disappearing; hypothecium hyaline to pale brownish; spores 3–7-septate, $19–32 \times 1.7–2.3\,\mu$.

On trees, Massachusetts.

13. **Bacidia chlorantha** (Tuck.) Fink, Cont. U. S. Nat. Herb. 14[1]:91. 1910.
   Biatora chlorantha Tuck., Syn. Lich. New Eng. 60. 1848.
   Thallus of rather coarse, scattered granules, becoming flattened and crowded, then forming a bright green or paler to brownish, somewhat chinky crust, the hypothallus black; apothecia small to middle-sized, 0.4–1 mm. across, sessile, the disk flat to slightly convex, dark reddish brown to black, the exciple thick, blackish, often flexuous; hypothecium hyaline to pale brownish; spores 30–50, indistinctly 3–7-septate, $20–35 \times 2–3\,\mu$.

On trees, New England, New York, Ohio, Illinois, and Minnesota.

14. **Bacidia atrogrisea** (Hepp) Koerb., Par. Lich. 133. 1865.
   Biatora atrogrisea Hepp, Spor. Flecht. Eur. 26. 1853. *B. endoleuca* (Nyl.)
      Kickx.
   Thallus thin, smoothish, becoming granulose or chinky-verrucose, greenish ashy to ashy white, hypothallus blackening; apothecia small, 0.5–0.75 mm. across, adnate to sessile, the disk slightly concave to convex, blackish brown to black, the exciple of the same color, thick, finally disappearing; hypothecium hyaline to reddish brown or brown; spores 7–15-septate, $30–60 \times 2.5–4.5\,\mu$.

On trees, Massachusetts to Florida, and westward to Kansas and Minnesota.

15. **Bacidia effusa** (J. E. Smith) Trevis., Linn. 28:293. 1856.
   Lichen effusus J. E. Smith, in Sowerby, Engl. Bot. 26:1863. *Biatora effusa*
      (J. E. Smith) Tuck.
   Thallus thin, scurfy or powdery, becoming chinky, greenish ashy to whitish; apothecia small, 0.4–0.8 mm. across, adnate, the disk flat to convex, pale flesh-colored to reddish brown, the exciple of the same color, soon disappearing; hypothecium pale yellowish; spores indistinctly many-septate, $25–45 \times 1.5–2\,\mu$.

On trees, Massachusetts, Iowa, and California.

16. **Bacidia luteola** (Schrad.) Mudd, Man. Brit. Lich. 183. 1861.
   Lichen luteolus Schrad., Spic. Fl. Germ. 85. 1794. *Biatora luteola* (Schrad.)
   E. Fries. *Biatora rubella* (Hoffm.) Rabh. *B. rubella* (Hoffm.) Mass. *Biatora
   rubella* var. *porriginosa* (Ach.) Tuck.
   Thallus of minute, scattered or continuous and subscurfy or chinky, greenish
gray to yellowish or whitish granules, sometimes disappearing; apothecia small to
middle-sized, 0.5–1.35 mm. across, adnate to sessile, the disk flat to convex, reddish
yellow to reddish brown or obscurely white-pruinose, the exciple paler, thick,
finally disappearing; hypothecium hyaline to yellowish brown; spores 5–11- and
rarely 15-septate, 45–65 × 3–4 μ.
   On trees, New England, and westward to Missouri, Minnesota, and Oregon.

17. **Bacidia fuscorubella** (Hoffm.) Bausch, Verh. Ver. Carls. 4:107. 1869.
   Verrucaria fuscorubella Hoffm., Deutschl. Fl. 2:175. 1795.
   Thallus granulose, becoming wrinkled and chinky, greenish gray to ashy, hypothallus finally blackening; apothecia small to middle-sized, 0.6–1.5 mm. across,
subsessile, the disk flat to slightly convex, pale brown or reddish to darker and
black, the exciple of the same color or white-pruinose, often transversely striate,
finally disappearing; hypothecium yellow to brown; spores about 6–13-septate,
40–75 × 3–4 μ.
   On trees and rarely on rocks, throughout the United States.

18. **Bacidia Clementis** Hasse, Bryologist 13:61. 1910.
   Thallus thin to moderately thick, ashy to whitish, coarsely granulose, becoming
chinky; apothecia small to middle-sized, 0.2–0.8 mm. across, sessile, the disk flat
to convex, brownish black to black, the exciple thin, black, soon disappearing;
hypothecium yellowish to brownish; spores 8, hyaline, cylindrical with round ends,
curved, 14–17-septate, 60–80 × 4–5 μ.
   On trees, southern California.

19. **Bacidia arceutina** (Ach.) Rehm; Arn., Verh. Gesell. Wien. 29:624. 1869.
   Lecidea luteola var. *arceutina* Ach., Meth. Lich. 61. 1803. *Biatora luteola* var.
   arceutina (Ach.) Tuck. *Biatora effusa* var. *arceutina* (Ach.) Tuck.
   Thallus very thin, smooth to granulose or scurfy, sometimes chinky, ashy to
whitish; apothecia minute to small, 0.2–0.6 mm. across, sessile, the disk flat to
strongly convex, light brown to blackish, the exciple darker, finally disappearing;
hypothecium yellowish; spores indistinctly many-septate, flexuous, 35–50 × 1.2–2 μ.
   On trees, Massachusetts and Oregon.

20. **Bacidia muscorum** (Swartz) Mudd, Man. Brit. Lich. 184, 185. 1861.
   Lichen muscorum Swartz, Meth. Musc. 36. 1781. *Biatora muscorum* (Swartz)
   E. Fries. *B. atrosanguinea* (Hepp) Anzi.
   Thallus of minute granules, usually compacted and wrinkled-verrucose, greenish
gray to whitish; apothecia small to middle-sized, 0.4–1.2 mm. across, adnate to
sessile, often conglomerate, the disk flat to convex, black or rarely reddish brown,
the exciple of the same color, thin, often flexuous, finally disappearing; hypothe-
cium yellowish to reddish brown; spores 5–9-septate, 25–40 × 2–3 μ.
   On soil, moss, and rarely bark, New England and westward to Nebraska and
Minnesota.

21. **Bacidia Schweinitzii** (Tuck.) Schneid., Guide Study Lich. 110. 1898.
   Biatora Schweinitzii Tuck., in Darl., Fl. Cestr. ed. 3. 447. 1853.
   Thallus of rounded, often crowded or heaped granules, sometimes becoming
compacted and chinky-verrucose, greenish to olive-gray or ashy; hypothallus
finally blackening; apothecia middle-sized to rather large, 0.6–1.75 mm. across,
adnate to sessile, the disk flat to slightly convex, dark brown to black, the exciple
thick, of the same color or paler, often flexuous-lobulate; hypothecium yellowish
to dark brown; spores 7–15-septate, 40–70 × 2–3.5 μ.
   On trees, eastern United States, and westward to Texas and Minnesota.

22. **Bacidia umbrina** (Ach.) Branth & Rostr., Bot. Tidssk. 3:235. 1869.
    Lecidea umbrina Ach., Lich. Univ. 183. 1810. *Biatora umbrina* (Ach.) Tuck.
    Biatora umbrina var. *compacta* (Koerb.) T. Fries.
    Thallus of minute granules, usually flattened, thickish and continuous, or thinner and scattered, often becoming scurfy, chinky, or subareolate, greenish gray or ashy to blackish, sometimes disappearing; apothecia minute to small, 0.25–0.6 mm. across, partly immersed to adnate, the disk flat to convex, light brown to black, the exciple paler, soon disappearing; hypothecium pale yellow; spores 3–7-septate, 18–30 × 2.5–3 µ.
    On rocks, and rarely on wood, widely distributed throughout northern United States, southward to North Carolina, and westward to California.

23. **Bacidia chlorosticta** (Tuck.) Schneid., Guide Study Lich. 109. 1898.
    Lecidea chlorosticta Tuck., Proc. Am. Acad. 5:419. 1862. *Biatora substipitata* Stizenb. *Biatora chlorosticta* Tuck.
    Thallus of minute, smooth, greenish to ashy granules, thinly scattered, or crowded and forming a rough granulose crust; apothecia minute, 0.1–0.3 mm. across, raised-sessile to short-stipitate, usually clustered, the disk convex, pale lead-colored to black, the exciple evanescent; hypothecium blackish brown; spores 1–3-septate, 18–29 × 1.3–2.2 µ.
    On trees, Massachusetts, South Carolina, and Illinois.

24. **Bacidia endocyanea** (Tuck.) Zahlbr., Cat. Lich. Univ. 4:192. 1926.
    Biatora endocyanea Tuck., in Willey, Enum. Lich. New Bedford, Mass. 24. 1892.
    Thallus thin and inconspicuous, greenish gray; apothecia minute to small, 0.15–0.55 mm. across, the disk soon strongly convex, brownish black to black, the exciple disappearing very soon; hypothecium dark brown to blackish; hymenium bluish; asci narrowly clavate; spores 3–5-septate, 22–35 × 2.5–4 µ.
    On holly, near New Bedford, Massachusetts.

25. **Bacidia incompta** (Borr.) Anzi, Cat. Lich. Sondr. 70. 1860.
    Lecidea incompta Borr., in Sowerby, Engl. Bot. Suppl. 2: pl. 2699. 1834. *Biatora incompta* (Borr.) Hepp. *Biatora luteola* var. *incompta* (Borr.) Tuck.
    Thallus minutely granulose, thin, smooth, and powdery, to thicker, wrinkled, and subareolate, greenish gray; apothecia minute to small, 0.35–0.75 mm. across, adnate, the disk flat to convex, brownish black to black, the exciple of the same color, thin, flexuous, finally disappearing; hypothecium reddish brown; spores 3–7-septate, 17–32 × 2–3 µ.
    On trees, New England, and westward to Illinois and Minnesota.

26. **Bacidia Jacobi** (Tuck.) Hasse, Cont. U. S. Nat. Herb. 17:51. 1913.
    Biatora Jacobi Tuck., Syn. N. A. Lich. 2:48. 1888.
    Thallus scurfy or powdery, widespread, white to ashy gray, becoming somewhat rough and finally verrucose; apothecia minute to small, 0.2–0.6 mm. across, adnate, the disk flat to slightly convex, black, the exciple also black, thin and often disappearing; hypothecium blackish brown; spores 3–7-septate, 20–38 × 2–3.5 µ.
    On trees, California.

27. **Bacidia abductans** (Nyl.) Zahlbr., Cat. Lich. Univ. 4:166. 1926.
    Lecidea abductans Nyl., Lich. Jap. 68. 1890.
    Thallus very thin to thin, composed of minute granules forming a chinky, smooth to warty, ashy crust; apothecia small to middle-sized, 0.5–1 mm. across, adnate to sessile, the disk flat to strongly convex, dull brownish black to black, the exciple thin, black, soon disappearing; hypothecium brown; spores 8, acicular, 5–9-septate, 48–60 × 3–3.5 µ.
    On trees, Florida.

28. **Bacidia suffusa** (E. Fries) Schneid., Guide Study Lich. 110. 1898.
Biatora suffusa E. Fries, Syst. Orb. Veg. 285. 1825. *B. fuscorubella* var. *suffusa* (E. Fries) Fink.

Thallus granulose, becoming wrinkled and chinky, greenish gray to ashy, hypothallus finally blackening; apothecia middle-sized to large, 1.5–2.5 mm. across, the disk flat to convex, reddish brown and finally blackening, white-pruinose at the margin or throughout, the exciple thick, usually white-pruinose, often transversely striate, disappearing; hypothecium finally dark; spores 5–11-septate, 40–70 × 2.5–3.5 μ.

On trees, from New England to New Jersey, and westward to Texas and Iowa.

29. **Bacidia dryina** (Ach.) Fink n. comb.
Lecidea dryina Ach., Meth. Lich. 34. 1803. *Biatora dryina* (Ach.) Tuck.

Thallus very thin, slightly rough and scurfy or mealy, ashy white to white; apothecia minute to small, 0.3–0.6 mm. across, sometimes angular, the disk flat to slightly convex, black, often finely roughened, the exciple also black, thin, sometimes finally disappearing; hypothecium brownish to dark brown; spores 15–29-septate, 46–76 × 2.5–4 μ.

On trees and old wood, Washington and California.

30. **Bacidia flavovirescens** (Dicks.) Anzi, Cat. Lich. Sondr. 71. 1860.
Lichen flavovirescens Dicks., Pl. Crypt. Brit. 3:13. pl. 8, f. 9. 1793. *Lecidea flavovirescens* (Dicks.) Vainio.

Thallus thin, widespread, greenish yellow, finely granulose to powdery, absent when parasitic; apothecia minute to small, 0.2–0.6 mm. across, sessile, sometimes clustered, the disk concave to flat, black, the exciple thick, black; hypothecium brownish black; spores several–many-septate, 35–85 × 3–4 μ.

On soil, rocks, and other lichens; on *Baeomyces byssoidea,* White Mountains, New Hampshire.

OTHER SPECIES REPORTED

Bacidia ioëssa Herre—California.
Bacidia Kingmani Hasse—Southern California.

127. **Toninia** Mass., Ric. Lich. 107. f. 212–214. 1852.

Thallus crustose to squamulose, or subareolate, differentiated into a thin, more or less gelatinized, indistinctly cellular upper cortex, more or less distinct algal and medullary layers, attached to the substratum by hyphal rhizoids; apothecia small to middle-sized or large, adnate or sessile, the disk flat to more or less convex, usually black, the exciple colored like the disk, usually disappearing; hypothecium hyaline to dark brown; hymenium hyaline to brownish; paraphyses unbranched, often coherent; asci clavate or cylindrico-clavate; spores 8, hyaline, ellipsoid to oblong or fusiform, 1–7- or rarely more-septate.

The algal host is Pleurococcus.

A. Spores 1-septate
  B. Spores not more than 15 μ in length . . . . 5. T. massata
  B. Spores commonly more than 15 μ in length
    C. Thallus greenish gray to olive-brown or
       darker, usually whitish pruinose . . . . . . 4. T. caeruleonigricans
    C. Thallus whitish to white, powdery . . . . 7. T. candida
A. Spores more than 1-septate
  B. Spores 3-septate
    C. On mosses over rocks . . . . 8. T. aromatica
    C. On soil and rocks
      D. Apothecia minute, 0.08–0.3 mm. across . . . . . . 3. T. cumulata
      D. Apothecia larger, 1.2–3 mm. across . . . . 2. T. ruginosa
  B. Spores 3–many-septate
    C. The disk flat to convex . . . . 1. T. squarrosa
    C. The disk deeply concave, papillate . . . . 6. T. caulescens

1. **Toninia squarrosa** (Ach.) T. Fries, Lich. Scand. 1:331. 1874.
   Lecidea atrorufa var. *squarrosa* Ach., Kgl. Vet. Akad. Nya Handl. 267. 1808.
   Lecidea squalida Ach. *T. squalida* (Ach.) Mass. *T. squarrosa* f. *persimilans*
   (Nyl.) Hasse.
   Thallus composed of thick, lobed, wrinkled, adnate to ascending, imbricate,
   crowded, yellowish brown to blackening squamules; apothecia middle-sized to
   large, 0.8–2.5 mm. across, subsessile, irregular, usually confluent, the disk flat to
   convex, black, the exciple thin, black, soon disappearing; hypothecium yellowish;
   spores acicular to fusiform, thicker toward one end, 3–many-septate, 23–68 ×
   2–5 µ.
   On soil, Washington and California.

2. **Toninia ruginosa** (Tuck.) Herre, Proc. Wash. Acad. Sci. 12:103. 1910.
   Lecidea ruginosa Tuck., Lich. Calif. 25. 1866.
   Thallus composed of round, swollen, greenish to yellowish brown, more or
   less crowded, wavy, rough, folded, finally perforate squamules; apothecia middle-
   sized to large, 1.2–3 mm. across, the disk flat to slightly convex, dull black, the
   exciple thick, black, becoming flexuous, finally disappearing; hypothecium brownish; spores acicular, 3-septate, 25–40 × 2–3.5 µ.
   On soil and rocks, Washington and California.

3. **Toninia cumulata** (Sommerf.) T. Fries, Lich. Scand. 1:341. 1874.
   Lecidea cumulata Sommerf., Suppl. Flor. Lapp. 157. 1826. *Biatora cumulata*
   (Sommerf.) Tuck.
   Thallus composed of small, irregular, ashy gray to white squamules, scattered
   or crowded into a rough, chinky crust; apothecia minute to small, 0.08–0.3 mm.
   across, adnate, usually numerous and confluent, the disk flat to slightly convex,
   black, the exciple thick, black, finally almost disappearing; hypothecium yellowish
   to reddish brown; spores ellipsoid-fusiform, 3-septate, 14–18 × 4.5–6 µ.
   On sandy soil, California.

4. **Toninia caeruleonigricans** (Lightf.) T. Fries, Lich. Scand. 1:336. 1874.
   Lichen caeruleonigricans Lightf., Fl. Scot. 2:805. 1777. *Lecidea caeruleonigricans* (Lightf.) Schaer. *T. vesicularis* (Hoffm.) Mong. *Psora vesicularis*
   Hoffm.
   Thallus composed of middle-sized to large, often substipitate, expanding and
   sublobate, greenish gray to olive-brown or darker, usually whitish pruinose, somewhat crowded and imbricated squamules; apothecia middle-sized to large, 0.75–2
   mm. across, sessile, shield-shaped, the disk flat to slightly convex, black, the exciple thick, black or whitish pruinose, finally disappearing; hypothecium brownish
   to brown; spores fusiform, 1-septate, 14–25 × 2–4 µ.
   On soil, New England, and westward throughout northern United States.

5. **Toninia massata** (Tuck.) Herre, Proc. Wash. Acad. Sci. 12:103. 1910.
   Lecidea massata Tuck., Lich. Calif. 25. 1866.
   Thallus composed of small, continuous or scattered, swollen, pale greenish to
   greenish gray, finally folded squamules; apothecia small to middle-sized, 0.3–1.3
   mm. across, partly immersed, the disk flat to strongly convex, black, the exciple
   thin, black, wavy, becoming irregular and disappearing; hypothecium reddish
   brown; spores boat-shaped, 1-septate, 10–15 × 3.5–5 µ.
   On soil and rocks, Colorado and California.

6. **Toninia caulescens** Anzi, Cat. Lich. Sondr. 67. 1860.
   Lecidea caulescens (Anzi) Tuck. *Lecidea squalida* var. *caulescens* (Anzi) Nyl.
   Thallus composed of tawny brown, turgid, convolute, scattered or more commonly crowded and imbricate squamules, the squamules often extending downward in stout brownish stems; apothecia small to middle-sized, 0.4–1.5 mm. across,
   closely sessile, round to lobulate, the disk deeply concave, dull black, papillate, the
   exciple prominent, turgid, becoming wavy; hypothecium dark reddish brown; asci

spatulate; spores acicular to somewhat fusiform, 3–7- or 9-septate, 24–50 ×
2.5–5 μ.
On soil and rocks, Washington and California.

7. **Toninia candida** (Web.) T. Fries, Kgl. Svensk. Vet. Akad. Handl. 7:33. 1867.
Lichen candidus Web., Spic. Flor. Goett. 193. 1776. *Lecidea candida* (Web.)
Ach. *Diphloeis candida.* (Web.) Clements.
Thallus composed of middle-sized, swollen, lobulate, powdery, whitish to white
squamules, sometimes crowded into an uneven or wrinkled crust; apothecia middle-sized to large, 0.8–2 mm. across, adnate, irregular, the disk flat, grayish pruinose, the exciple thin, grayish pruinose, becoming flexuous; hypothecium brown;
spores fusiform, 1-septate, 16–23 × 2–4.5 μ.
On soil, Utah.

8. **Toninia aromatica** (Turn.) Mass., Fram. Lich. 24. 1855.
Lichen aromaticus Turn., Linn. Trans. 9:140. 1808. *Lecidea aromatica* Turn.
Thallus composed of small, thick, closely clustered or more or less scattered,
greenish gray to brownish or ashy squamules, the squamules sometimes running
together into a thick, warty, irregular crust; apothecia small to middle-sized, 0.4–1
mm. across, adnate, often irregular and clustered, the disk flat to convex, black,
the exciple thin, black, soon disappearing; hypothecium brown to blackish brown;
spores fusiform, 3-septate, 15–27 × 3–4.5 μ.
On mosses over rocks, Minnesota and California.

128. **Lopadium** Koerb., Syst. Lich. Germ. 210. 1855.

Thallus crustose, granulose or warty, rudimentary, devoid of differentiation
into layers and attached to the substratum by hyphal rhizoids; apothecia rarely
minute to small or middle-sized and large, sessile, the disk flat to more or less
convex, light-colored to black, the exciple thin to thick, usually colored like the
disk, often disappearing; hypothecium hyaline to brown or black; hymenium
hyaline to brownish; paraphyses usually unbranched and somewhat coherent; asci
clavate or cylindrico-clavate; spores 1–8, hyaline, transversely and longitudinally
septate.
The algal host is Protococcus.

A. On leaves, mosses, and rocks
 B. On leaves; apothecia pale brownish to greenish and
  finally black . . . . 7. L. phyllocharis
 B. On mosses and rocks; apothecia reddish yellow to dirty
  orange, sometimes grayish pruinose . . . . 6. L. fuscoluteum
A. On trees
 B. Spores rarely more than 50 μ in length
  C. Apothecia small, 0.25–0.5 mm. across . . . . 1. L. Augustini
  C. Apothecia larger, more than 0.5 mm. across
   D. Spores 1–4 in each ascus, 1–3-septate longitudinally . . . 3. L. vulpinum
   D. Spores 2–8 in each ascus, 1-septate
    longitudinally . . . . 2. L. domingense
 B. Spores commonly more than 60 μ in length
  C. Apothecia black . . . . 4. L. pezizoideum
  C. Apothecia yellow or rust-colored to dark green . . . 5. L. leucoxanthum

1. **Lopadium Augustini** (Tuck.) Zahlbr., Cat. Lich. Univ. 4:299. 1926.
Heterothecium Augustini Tuck., Syn. N. A. Lich. 2:59. 1888.
Thallus thin, often scanty, granulose, greenish gray; apothecia minute to small,
0.25–0.5 mm. across, sessile, the disk flat to slightly convex, blackish, the exciple
thin, hanging, white; hypothecium reddish brown; spores 1, long oblong-ellipsoid,
9–13-septate transversely and 3–5-septate longitudinally, 40–60 × 14–20 μ.
On trees, Florida, Mississippi, Louisiana, and Texas.

2. **Lopadium domingense** (Pers.) Fink n. comb.
　　Patellaria domingense Pers., Act. Soc. Wett. 2:12. 1810. *Heterothecium domin-*
　　　gense (Pers.) Flot.
　　Thallus of flattened granules, running into a thin, smooth, greenish gray to
yellowish or orange crust, becoming uneven, and finally thickened and wrinkled-
warty; apothecia middle-sized to large, 0.7–1.5 mm. across, sessile, the disk flat
to slightly convex, sanguineous and blackening, the exciple swollen, becoming flexuous to deep-wavy, orange-yellow; hypothecium dusky reddish; spores 2–8, ellipsoid, 5–9-septate transversely and 1-septate longitudinally, 20–45 × 6–18 μ.
　　On trees, South Carolina, Alabama, Florida, Louisiana, and Texas.

3. **Lopadium vulpinum** (Tuck.) Zahlbr., Cat. Lich. Univ. 4:316. 1926.
　　Lecidea vulpina Tuck., Proc. Am. Acad. 6:281, 282. 1864. *Heterothecium vul-*
　　　pinum Tuck.
　　Thallus of flattened granules, running into a thin, smooth crust, becoming
uneven, and finally thickened and wrinkled-warty, greenish gray to bright yellow
or orange; apothecia middle-sized to large, 0.7–1.5 mm. across, sessile, the disk
flat to slightly convex, reddish and darkening, the exciple swollen, becoming flexuous to deep wavy, orange, finally red; hypothecium dusky reddish; spores 1–4,
subspherical to oblong-ellipsoid, 5–9-septate transversely and 1–3-septate longitudinally, 25–50 × 14–20 μ.
　　On trees, South Carolina and Florida.

4. **Lopadium pezizoideum** (Ach.) Koerb., Syst. Lich. 211. 1855.
　　Lecidea pezizoidea Ach., Lich. Ann. 182. 1810. *Heterothecium pezizoideum*
　　　(Ach.) Stiz.
　　Thallus of scattered, usually flattened squamules or granules, sometimes warty
or coralloid, greenish to dusky and blackening; apothecia small to large, 0.5–1.5
mm. across, sessile, the disk concave to flat, black, the exciple thick, brownish
to black; hypothecium dusky; spores 1, oblong-ellipsoid, 13–23-septate transversely
and 3–5-septate longitudinally, 44–100 × 18–40 μ.
　　On trees, Massachusetts, Florida, and Washington.

5. **Lopadium leucoxanthum** (Spreng.) Zahlbr., in E. & P., Nat. Pfl. 1[1]:137.
　　　1907.
　　Lecidea leucoxanthum Spreng., Nat. Akad. Handl. 46. 1826. *Heterothecium*
　　　leucoxanthum (Spreng.) Mass.
　　Thallus smooth, becoming chinky, granulose, or wrinkled-warty, greenish or
yellowish to whitish; apothecia middle-sized to large, 0.8–1.8 mm. across, sessile,
the disk flat to slightly convex, yellow or rust-colored to dark green, the exciple
swollen, flexuous to deeply sinuate, orange-yellow to rust-colored or reddish brown;
hypothecium reddish brown; spores 1, oblong-ellipsoid, 19–21-septate transversely
and 5–9-septate longitudinally, 45–90 × 28–40 μ.
　　On trees, Maine, North Carolina, South Carolina, Florida, Alabama, Mississippi,
Louisiana, Texas, and Ohio.

6. **Lopadium fuscoluteum** (Dicks.) Mudd, Man. Brit. Lich. 190. pl. 3, f. 73.
　　　1861.
　　Lichen fuscoluteus Dicks., Pl. Crypt. Brit. 2:18. pl. 6, f. 2. 1790. *Biatora fusco-*
　　　lutea (Dicks.) E. Fries. *Heterothecium fuscoluteum* (Dicks.) Tuck.
　　Thallus thin, minutely granulose to warty, ashy white to light greenish gray;
apothecia middle-sized, 0.4–0.9 mm. across, sessile, the disk concave to flat, reddish
yellow to dirty orange, sometimes grayish pruinose, the exciple thick, prominent,
bright orange, becoming inflexed; hypothecium hyaline to brownish; spores 1,
hyaline or tinged brownish, oblong-ellipsoid, 23–35-septate transversely and 7–15-
septate longitudinally, 50–110 × 22–56 μ.
　　On mosses and rocks, Washington.

7. **Lopadium phyllocharis** (Mont.) Fink n. comb.

Biatora phyllocharis Mont., Ann. Sci. Nat. Bot. III. 10:128. 1848. *Heterothecium phyllocharis* (Mont.) Tuck. *Sporopodium phyllocharis* (Mont.) Mass.
Thallus very thin, smooth or slightly granulose, greenish gray, usually in small areas; apothecia minute, 0.25–0.5 mm. across, sessile, the disk convex, pale brownish varying toward greenish, finally black, the exciple thin, white, soon disappearing; hypothecium brownish; spores 1, oblong-ellipsoid, 11–29-septate transversely and 2–5-septate longitudinally, 30–75 × 12–36 μ.
On leaves, Alabama and Florida.

129. **Rhizocarpon** Lam., in Lam. & DC., Fl. Franc. ed. 3. 2:365. 1815.

Thallus crustose to subsquamulose, commonly areolate or warty, not distinctly differentiated and attached to the substratum by hyphal rhizoids; apothecia circular or flexuous, immersed to sessile, the disk flat to convex, usually black, the exciple colored like the disk, usually disappearing; hypothecium brown to blackish brown; hymenium hyaline to brownish above; paraphyses unbranched or branched; asci clavate to inflated-clavate; spores 1–8, large, hyaline to more commonly brown, transversely and longitudinally septate.
The algal host is Pleurococcus.

A. Spores transversely septate and sometimes becoming
   longitudinally septate
  B. Spores transversely septate
    C. Spores 3-septate
      D. Spores 14–18 × 5–7 μ . . . . 3. R. vernicomoideum
      D. Spores 16–26 × 7–12 μ . . . . 2. R. Oederi
    C. Spores 1-septate . . . . 1. R. alpicolum
  B. Spores transversely and becoming longitudinally septate
    C. Thallus ashy gray to white, sometimes circular . . . . 6. R. alboatrum
    C. Thallus ashy to grayish brown, more or less irregular
      D. Thallus thin, sometimes disappearing . . . . . . 4. R. postumum
      D. Thallus thin, bordered and intersected by a
        black hypothallus . . . . 5. R. cinereovirens
A. Spores transversely and longitudinally septate
  B. Thallus greenish gray, ashy to whitish or brownish
   to rarely black
    C. Spores rarely more than 40 μ in length
      D. Thallus smooth to chinky or areolate
        E. Spores rarely more than 25 μ in length
          F. On trees; thallus thin . . . . 13. R. penichrum
          F. On rocks; thallus moderately thick . . . . . 15. R. albineum
        E. Spores commonly more than 25 μ in length
          F. Apothecia irregularly arranged
            G. Thallus thin to moderately thick; apothecia
              0.3–1.5 mm. across
              H. Thallus smooth or chinky to areolate,
                greenish gray to ashy or brownish black . . 10. R. petraeum
              H. Thallus areolate, ashy to purplish or
                brownish . . . . 9. R. grande
            G. Thallus thin; apothecia 0.4–0.75 mm. across . . 12. R. ambiguum
          F. Apothecia concentrically arranged . . . . 16. R concentricum
      D. Thallus minutely to coarsely granulose
        E. Thallus minutely granulose, ashy or grayish brown
          to ashy
          F. Apothecia 0.2–0.5 mm. across; spores
            20–36 × 8–14 μ . . . . 14. R. interponens
          F. Apothecia 0.2–0.8 mm. across; spores
            20–46 × 10–18 μ . . . . 11. R. obscuratum
        E. Thallus coarsely granulose, brownish gray to
         brown . . . . 10. R. petraeum confervoides
    C. Spores commonly more than 40 μ in length
      D. Thallus areolate or warty, ashy gray to reddish or
        brownish . . . . 7. R. disporum

D. Thallus squamulose, chestnut-brown to black . . . . 8. R. Bolanderi
B. Thallus dirty white to light or darker yellow
  C. Spores rarely more than 35 μ in length
    D. Spores 3-septate transversely . . . . 18. R. viridiatrum
    D. Spores 3–5- or 7-septate transversely
      E. Thallus greenish to bright yellow
        F. Thallus chinky to scattered areolate; apothecia
          immersed to adnate . . . . 20. R. geographicum
        F. Thallus areolate; apothecia immersed . . . 19. R. lecanorinum
      E. Thallus dirty white to yellowish . . . . . . 17. R. athalloides
  C. Spores 30–78 $\times$ 16–24 μ . . . . 21. R. oidaleum

1. **Rhizocarpon alpicolum** (Wahl.) Rabh., Flecht. Eur. fasc. 22. no. 618. 1861.
Lecidea atrovirens var. *alpicola* Wahl., Fl. Lapp. 474. 1812. *Lecidea geographica*
var. *alpicola* (Wahl.) Schaer. *Lecidea alpicola* (Wahl.) Hepp. *Buellia alpicola* (Wahl.) Anzi.
Thallus moderately thick, bright yellow to yellowish gray, chinky to areolate,
the areoles rough, flat to slightly convex, continuous or scattered upon a black
hypothallus; apothecia small to middle-sized, 0.6–1.8 mm. across, partly immersed
to adnate, often clustered, the disk flat to slightly convex, black, the exciple thin,
black, finally disappearing; hypothecium dark brown; asci clavate; spores 8, hyaline
to dark brown, ellipsoid, 1-septate, 15–28 $\times$ 9–14 μ.
On rocks, Maine and New Hampshire.

2. **Rhizocarpon Oederi** (Web.) Koerb., Par. Lich. 232. 1861.
Lichen Oederi Web., Spic. Flor. Goett. 182. 1778. *Buellia Oederi* (Web.) Rostr.
Thallus thin, yellowish or reddish brown, chinky to areolate or finally warty;
apothecia minute, 0.15–0.5 mm. across, partly immersed to adnate, the disk flat
to slightly convex, dull black, sometimes wrinkled, the exciple thin, black, flexuous; hypothecium dark brown; asci clavate to inflated-clavate; spores 8, hyaline
to rarely brownish, oblong-ellipsoid, 3-septate, slightly constricted at the septa,
16–26 $\times$ 7–12 μ.
On rocks, at high elevations, Maine, New Hampshire, Oregon, and California.

3. **Rhizocarpon vernicomoideum** Fink, Ohio Biol. Surv. 2:350. 1921.
Thallus thin, straw-colored, minutely granulose, the granules convex, scattered
or clustered, covering small areas and usually resting upon and bordered wholly
or in part by a black hypothallus; apothecia minute to small, 0.2–0.6 mm. across,
partly immersed to adnate, the disk flat to convex, black, the exciple thin, prominent, black, finally disappearing; hypothecium dark brown; paraphyses branched,
semi-distinct; asci clavate; spores 8, brown, oblong-ellipsoid, 3-septate, slightly
constricted at the septa, 14–18 $\times$ 5–7 μ.
On rocks, Ohio.

4. **Rhizocarpon postumum** (Nyl.) Arn., Flora 53:478. 1870.
Lecidea postuma Nyl., Flora 51:345. 1868.
Thallus thin, ashy to grayish brown, becoming minutely granulose or warty,
sometimes disappearing; apothecia minute to small, 0.2–0.6 mm. across, adnate,
the disk flat to convex, black, the exciple thin, black, finally disappearing; hypothecium brown to brownish black; paraphyses semi-distinct; asci clavate; spores
8, hyaline to brown, ellipsoid to fusiform-ellipsoid, 3-septate transversely and becoming 1-septate longitudinally, 12–18 $\times$ 5–8.5 μ.
On rocks, Alabama.

5. **Rhizocarpon cinereovirens** (Müll. Arg.) Vainio, Act. Soc. Faun. Flor. Fenn.
   53:336. 1922.
Patellaria cinereovirens Müll. Arg., Flora 51;49. 1868. *R. ignobile* T. Fries.
   Buellia concreta (Koerb.) Eckf.
Thallus thin, smooth to rough, ashy to grayish brown, becoming minutely
granulose, bordered and intersected by the black hypothallus; apothecia minute

to small, 0.3–0.7 mm. across, partly immersed to adnate, sometimes clustered, the disk flat to slightly convex, dull black, the exciple thin, black, becoming flexuous, finally disappearing; hypothecium dark brown; spores 8, hyaline to brown, 1–3-septate transversely and becoming 1-septate longitudinally, 14–20 × 6–11 μ.

On rocks, Minnesota.

6. **Rhizocarpon alboatrum** (Hoffm.) Anzi, Cat. Lich. Sondr. 92. 1860.

    Lichen alboater Hoffm., Enum. Lich. Icon. 30. 1784. *Buellia alboatra* var. *ambigua* (Ach.) T. Fries. *R. alboatrum* f. *saxicola* (E. Fries) Fink. *Lecidea alboatrum* var. *epipolia* (Ach.) Schaer.

Thallus smooth, or chinky to warty-areolate, sometimes becoming powdery, ashy gray to white, continuous or sometimes scattered; apothecia small to middle-sized, 0.35–1 mm. across, immersed to adnate, the disk flat to convex, dull black or whitish pruinose, the exciple thin, black, finally disappearing; hypothecium dark brown; asci clavate; spores 8, brown, oblong-ellipsoid, 3–4-septate transversely and becoming 1–2-septate longitudinally, 12–22 × 6–9 μ.

On trees and rocks, throughout the United States; when on rocks, the thallus is more circular and commonly bordered by a blackish hypothallus.

7. **Rhizocarpon disporum** (Naeg.) Müll. Arg., Revue Mycolog. 1:170. 1879.

    Lecidea dispora Naeg., in Hepp, Flecht. Eur. 28. 1853. *R. geminatum* Koerb. *R. disporum* var. *Montagnei* (Flot.) Zahlbr. *Buellia Montagnei* (Flot.) Tuck. *Buellia petraea* var. *Montagnei* (Flot.) Willey. *R. petraeum* var. *Montagnei* (Flot.) Boist.

Thallus thin to moderately thick, ashy gray to reddish or brownish, becoming areolate or warty, continuous or scattered upon a black hypothallus; apothecia small, 0.4–0.8 mm. across, subsessile, the disk flat to slightly convex, black, the exciple thin, black, rarely disappearing; hypothecium dark brown; asci inflated-clavate; spores 1 or rarely 2, hyaline to dark brown, ellipsoid to oblong-ellipsoid, 7–13-septate transversely and 3–5-septate longitudinally, 28–60 × 10–30 μ.

On rocks, throughout northern United States; also Florida and California.

8. **Rhizocarpon Bolanderi** (Tuck.) Herre, Proc. Wash. Acad. Sci. 12:106. 1910.

    Buellia Bolanderi Tuck., Gen. Lich. 189. 1872. *Buellia Bolanderi* var. *sulphurosa* Tuck. *R. Bolanderi* var. *sulphurosa* (Tuck.) Zahlbr.

Thallus chestnut-brown to black, becoming squamulose, the squamules small, adnate to sessile, becoming wavy or lobed, the margins ascending and black below, sometimes sulphur-colored within, commonly scattered upon a black hypothallus; apothecia small to middle-sized, 0.35–1.2 mm. across, adnate to sessile, the disk flat to convex, dull black, the exciple thick, black, wavy, finally disappearing; hypothecium dark brown; asci inflated-clavate; spores 2, ellipsoid, hyaline to grayish and dark brown, 7–11-septate transversely and 2–4-septate longitudinally, with a dense halo, 30–72 × 18–34 μ.

On rocks, Washington, Oregon, and California.

9. **Rhizocarpon grande** (Floerke) Arn., Flora 54:149. 1871.

    Lecidea petraea var. *fuscoatra* f. *grandis* Floerke; Flot., Flora 11:690. 1828. *Buellia petraea* var. *grandis* (Floerke) Tuck. *R. petraeum* var. *grande* (Floerke) Fink.

Thallus thin to moderately thick, areolate, the areoles small, convex, ashy to purplish or brownish, commonly scattered upon a conspicuous black hypothallus; apothecia small to middle-sized, 0.4–1.1 mm. across, the disk convex to subglobose, black, the exciple thin, black, soon disappearing; hypothecium dark brown; asci clavate or inflated-clavate; spores 8, hyaline to blackish brown, oblong-ellipsoid, 3–7-septate transversely and 1–3-septate longitudinally, 25–42 × 12–20 μ.

On rocks, throughout northern United States, and southward in the mountains.

10. **Rhizocarpon petraeum** (Wulf.) Mass., Ric. Lich. 102. f. 206. 1852.

    Lichen petraeus Wulf., Ges. Naturf. Fr. Berl. 2:89. 1788. *Buellia petraea* (Wulf.) Branth & Rostr. *Buellia petraea* var. *vulgaris* Tuck. *R. eupetraeum* (Nyl.) Arn.

Thallus thin to moderately thick, smooth to rough, chinky to areolate, greenish gray to ashy or becoming brownish black, continuous or scattered upon a black hypothallus; apothecia small to middle-sized, 0.3–1.5 mm. across, partly immersed to adnate, round to sometimes irregular and clustered, the disk flat to slightly convex, blackish brown to black, the exciple thick, black, rarely whitish pruinose, finally disappearing; hypothecium blackish brown; paraphyses semi-distinct; asci clavate to inflated-clavate; spores 8, hyaline to dark brown, oblong-ellipsoid, 3–7- or rarely 9-septate transversely and 1–3-septate longitudinally, 16–40 × 8–18 μ.

On rocks, and rarely on old wood, throughout northern United States, and southward in the mountains.

var. **confervoides** (DC.) Zahlbr., Cat. Lich. Univ. 4:388. 1926.
R. confervoides DC., in Lam. & DC., Fl. Fr. ed. 3. 2:366. 1815.

Thallus moderately thick, brownish gray to brown, coarsely granulose, the granules strongly convex, commonly scattered upon a conspicuous black hypothallus; apothecia irregular, the disk commonly convex, the exciple seldom disappearing.

On rocks, Vermont.

11. **Rhizocarpon obscuratum** (Ach.) Mass., Ric. Lich. 103. f. 207. 1852.
Lecidea petraea var. *obscurata* Ach., Lich. Univ. 156. 1810. *R. petraeum* var. *obscuratum* (Ach.) Krempelh. *Lecidea panaeola* var. *obscurata* (Ach.) E. Fries.

Thallus thin, grayish brown to ashy, minutely granulose, the granules flat, continuous or rarely scattered on a poorly developed black hypothallus; apothecia minute to small, 0.2–0.8 mm. across, partly immersed to adnate, the disk flat, black, the exciple rather thick, black, becoming crenulate, rarely disappearing; hypothecium blackish brown; asci inflated-clavate; spores 8, hyaline to brownish, oblong-ellipsoid, 3–7-septate transversely and 1–3-septate longitudinally, 20–46 × 10–18 μ.

On rocks, Maine and Minnesota.

12. **Rhizocarpon ambiguum** (Schaer.) Zahlbr., Cat. Lich. Univ. 4:344. 1926.
Lecidea petraea var. *ambigua* Schaer., Lich. Helv. Spic. sec. 3. 137. 1828. *R. distinctum* T. Fries.

Thallus thin, whitish to gray or brownish, minutely areolate or sometimes warty, the areoles continuous or scattered upon a conspicuous black hypothallus; apothecia small, 0.4–0.75 mm. across, adnate, the disk flat to convex, black, rough, the exciple thin, slightly raised, finally disappearing; hypothecium dark brown; asci clavate to inflated-clavate; spores 8, hyaline to brownish, oblong-ellipsoid, 5–7-septate transversely and 1–2-septate longitudinally, 21–36 × 11–16 μ.

On rocks, Virginia and southern California.

13. **Rhizocarpon penichrum** (Tuck.) Merrill; Millsp. & Nutt., Flora St. Catal. Island 367. 1923.
Buellia oidalea var. *penichra* Tuck., Syn. N. A. Lich. 2:99, 100. 1888. *Buellia penichra* (Tuck.) Hasse.

Thallus thin, smooth to rough, becoming minutely areolate, ashy to whitish, bordered and sometimes intersected by the black hypothallus; apothecia small to middle-sized, 0.35–1 mm. across, sessile, the disk flat to slightly convex, dull black, the exciple thick, black, somewhat raised, finally disappearing; hypothecium dark brown; paraphyses semi-distinct, appearing to be branched; asci clavate to inflated-clavate; spores 6–8, brownish to dark brown, oblong to oblong-ellipsoid, 3–5-septate transversely and 1–2-septate longitudinally, 14–28 × 8–15 μ.

On trees, Montana, Washington, and California.

14. **Rhizocarpon interponens** (Nyl.) Zahlbr., Cat. Lich. Univ. 4:374. 1926.
Lecidea interponens Nyl., Lich. Lab. Sing. 42. 1891.

Thallus very thin, ashy to gray, minutely granulose, the granules flat, continuous or rarely scattered; apothecia minute, 0.2–0.5 mm. across, partly immersed to adnate, numerous, sometimes crowded, the disk flat, dull black, the exciple thick, black, becoming wavy; hypothecium dark brown; asci inflated-clavate; spores 8, hyaline to rarely brownish, oblong-ellipsoid, 3–7-septate transversely and 1–3-septate longitudinally, 20–36 × 8–14 μ.

On rocks, Tennessee.

15. **Rhizocarpon albineum** (Tuck.) Fink n. comb.

Buellia petraea f. *albinea* Tuck., Syn. N. A. Lich. 2:102. 1888. *R. petraeum* f. *albineum* (Tuck.) Zahlbr.

Thallus moderately thick, chinky-areolate, whitish to ashy, the areoles flat, rather large, commonly in dense groups upon a black hypothallus; apothecia small to middle-sized, 0.35–1 mm. across, partly immersed to adnate, the disk flat to convex, black, the exciple thin, black, finally disappearing; hypothecium dark brown; asci clavate to inflated-clavate; spores 8, hyaline to dark brown, oblong-ellipsoid, 3–7-septate transversely and 1–2-septate longitudinally, 21–26 × 10–15 μ.

On rocks, from New England to Virginia, and in Indiana.

16. **Rhizocarpon concentricum** (Davies) Beltr., Lich. Bass. 187. pl. 4, f. 9–12. 1858.

Lichen concentricus Davies, Trans. Linn. Soc. Lond. 2:284. 1794. *R. calcareum* var. *concentricum* (Davies) T. Fries. *R. subconcentricum* (E. Fries) Koerb.

Thallus thin, more or less circular, smooth to chinky and finally areolate, the areoles minute, ashy to whitish, continuous; apothecia small to middle-sized, 0.3–1.5 mm. across, partly immersed to adnate, commonly showing a well-defined concentric arrangement, the disk concave to slightly convex, dull black, rarely whitish pruinose, the exciple rather thick, black, finally disappearing; hypothecium dark brown; asci clavate to inflated-clavate; spores 8, oblong to oblong-ellipsoid, hyaline to dark brown, 5–9-septate transversely and 2–3-septate longitudinally, 22–39 × 10–16 μ. (PLATE 19 *a*.)

On rocks, Alabama and Minnesota.

17. **Rhizocarpon athalloides** (Nyl.) Hasse, Cont. U. S. Nat. Herb. 17:57. 1913.

Lecidea athalloides Nyl., Bull. Soc. Bot. France 7:503. 1860.

Thallus dirty white to yellowish, composed of loosely interwoven hyphae, becoming minutely granulose, or continuous and finally becoming chinky; apothecia small to middle-sized, 0.4–1.5 mm. across, partly immersed to adnate, the disk flat to slightly convex, dull black, the exciple thin, black, obscurely crenulate, finally disappearing; hypothecium brownish; asci clavate to inflated-clavate; spores 4–6, ovoid and sometimes pointed at one end, hyaline to brown, 3–5-septate transversely and 1–3-septate longitudinally, 22–38 × 10–18 μ.

On soil, mountains of southern California.

18. **Rhizocarpon viridiatrum** (Wulf.) Koerb., Syst. Lich. 262. 1855.

Lichen viridiater Wulf., in Jacq., Coll. Bot. 2:186. 1788.

Thallus granulose-areolate, greenish yellow, continuous or scattered upon an inconspicuous black hypothallus; apothecia small, 0.4–0.8 mm. across, adnate to subsessile, the disk flat to convex, rough, dull black, the exciple black, crenulate, rarely disappearing; hypothecium dark brown; asci becoming inflated-clavate; spores 8, dark brown, fusiform to ellipsoid, 3-septate transversely and 1-septate longitudinally, 18–25 × 8–11 μ.

On rocks and boulders, California.

19. **Rhizocarpon lecanorinum** (Koerb.) Anders, Hedwigia 64:261. 1923.

R. geographicum var. *lecanorinum* Koerb., Syst. Lich. 263. 1855. *Buellia geographica* var. *lecanorina* (Koerb.) Tuck. *R. geographicum* f. *lecanora* (Floerke) Arn.

Thallus thin, greenish to bright yellow, becoming areolate, the areoles small, slightly raised, usually scattered upon a conspicuous black hypothallus; apothecia small to middle-sized, 0.4–1 mm. across, sometimes clustered, usually immersed in the areoles of the thallus, the disk flat to slightly convex, black, the exciple thin, black, finally disappearing; hypothecium dark brown; asci clavate or inflated-clavate; spores 8, hyaline to dark brown, ellipsoid, 3–7-septate transversely and 1–3-septate longitudinally, 17–40 × 10–16 μ.

On rocks, throughout northern United States, and southward in the mountains.

20. **Rhizocarpon geographicum** (L.) Lam. & DC., Fl. Fr. ed. 3. 2:365. 1815.
    Lichen geographicus L., Sp. Pl. 1140. 1753. *Lecidea geographica* (L.) Rebent. *Buellia geographica* (L.) Tuck. *R. geographicum* f. *contiguum* (Schaer.) Mass. *Lecidea geographica* var. *contigua* Schaer.

Thallus thin to moderately thick, greenish to bright yellow, chinky to sometimes areolate or warty, continuous or more commonly scattered upon a conspicuous black hypothallus; apothecia small to middle-sized, 0.4–1 mm. across, partly immersed between the areoles of the thallus, sometimes clustered and irregular, the disk flat to slightly convex, black, the exciple thin, black, finally disappearing; hypothecium dark brown; asci clavate to inflated-clavate; spores 8, hyaline to dark brown, oblong-ellipsoid, 5–7-septate transversely and 1–3-septate longitudinally, 20–38 × 11–18 μ. (PLATE 19 b.)

On rocks, throughout northern United States, and southward in the mountains.

21. **Rhizocarpon oidaleum** (Tuck.) Fink, Mycologia 21:306. 1919.
    Lecidea oidalea Tuck., Proc. Am. Acad. 4:405. 1860.

Thallus thin, smooth to rough, yellowish to greenish gray or ashy, chinky to minutely areolate, bordered by the black hypothallus; apothecia small to middle-sized, 0.5–1.5 mm. across, sessile, the disk flat to convex, dull black, the exciple thick, black, soon disappearing; hypothecium dark brown; paraphyses semi-distinct, appearing to be branched; asci clavate to inflated-clavate; spores 2–6 or rarely 8, brownish to dark brown, oblong-ellipsoid, 7–11-septate transversely and 2–3-septate longitudinally, 30–78 × 16–24 μ.

On trees, Montana, Washington, Oregon, and California.

34. CLADONIACEAE

Thallus commonly twofold, the primary thallus crustose, granulose to squamulose, often disappearing soon, showing more or less differentiation and attached to the substratum by hyphal rhizoids, the secondary thallus forming upright podetia, more or less branched, short to elongated and well developed, with or without cortex, solid or hollow within; apothecia round to irregular, scattered or clustered, commonly borne on the tips of the podetia, rarely lateral, with a more or less well-developed exciple.

The algal host is Pleurococcus.

A. Podetia short, unbranched
    B. Hypothecium hyaline; spores non- or 1–3-septate   .   .   .   130. BAEOMYCES
    B. Hypothecium dark; spores non-septate   . . . . . 131. PILOPHORUS
A. Podetia short to long, more or less branched
    B. Podetia mostly hollow; spores non-septate   . . . . . 132. CLADONIA
    B. Podetia solid; spores 3- or more-septate   . . . . . 133. STEREOCAULON

130. **Baeomyces** Ehrh., Beitr. Nat. 4:149. 1789.

Thallus commonly crustose to granulose and sometimes becoming subfoliose, differentiated into a thin upper layer of gelatinized hyphae, distinct algal and medullary layers, and attached to the substratum by hyphal rhizoids; stipes composed of loosely interwoven hyphae within and closely packed, longitudinally placed hyphae without; apothecia borne singly or conglomerate on the stipes or very rarely sessile on the thallus, the disk flat to convex, the exciple colored like the disk, often becoming covered; hypothecium hyaline; hymenium hyaline or brownish above; paraphyses unbranched; asci clavate to cylindrico-clavate; spores 8, hyaline, non-septate, ellipsoid to oblong-ellipsoid.

The algal host is Pleurococcus or rarely Gloeocapsa-like.

A. Thallus granulose to scurfy-squamulose
  B. Spores not more than 16 μ in length
    C. Thallus smooth to somewhat scurfy . . . . 3. B. absolutus
    C. Thallus granulose to scurfy-squamulose . . . . 2. B. rufus
  B. Spores reaching 20–26 μ in length
    C. Stipes of medium length or shorter; apothecia 1.5–2.5 mm. across   4. B. roseus
    C. Stipes rather long; apothecia 2–4 mm. across . . . . . 5. B. fungoides
A. Thallus subfoliose, more or less lobed . . . . 1. B. placophyllus

1. **Baeomyces placophyllus** Ach., Meth. Lich. 323. 1803.

Thallus rather thick, greenish to greenish gray or whitish, subfoliose, wrinkled, folded, and lobed, the lobes short, round, sometimes imbricate, the margins subcrenulate; stipes often flattened, commonly short, whitish, sprinkled with round and elevated squamules; apothecia small to middle-sized and large, 1.5–4 mm. across, the disk flat to convex, reddish brown, the exciple soon disappearing; spores long-ellipsoid to fusiform, 10–15 × 2.5–3.5 μ.

On sterile soil of slides or banks of streams, White Mountains, New Hampshire.

2. **Baeomyces rufus** (Huds.) Rebent., Prod. Fl. Neom. 315. 1804.

Lichen rufus Huds., Fl. Angl. 443. 1762. *B. byssoides* (L.) Ach. *B. rufus* f. *sessilis* Nyl. *Biatora byssoides* (L.) E. Fries.

Thallus rather thin, greenish gray to whitish, granulose, the round granules passing into a scurfy-squamulose and crenate-lobulate, continuous or more or less scattered crust; stipes often flattened and furrowed, rarely divided above, sometimes granulose or corticate, reaching 3–4 mm. long, or rarely very short or wanting, of the same color as the thallus, naked portions tan to brown; apothecia small, 0.7–1.75 mm. across, round to irregular, the disk flat to strongly convex, brownish flesh-colored to dark brown, the exciple soon disappearing; spores ellipsoid, 8–15 × 3–4 μ. (PLATE 20 a.)

On soil and rocks, from New England to Florida, and westward to Minnesota, Oregon, and Washington.

3. **Baeomyces absolutus** Tuck., Am. Journ. Sci. 28:201. 1859.

Thallus thin, greenish, smooth to somewhat scurfy; stipes short, whitish; apothecia small to middle-sized, 1.5–2 mm. across, becoming flexuous, the disk pale flesh-colored, flat, the exciple loose and usually basal, disappearing; spores oblong-ellipsoid to ellipsoid, 10–16 × 4–6 μ.

On sand, wet rocks, and soil, North Carolina, Florida, and Alabama.

4. **Baeomyces roseus** Pers., Ann. Bot. Usteri 1:19. 1794.

Dibaeis rosea (Pers.) Clements.

Thallus granulose, greenish gray to whitish, the granules raised and becoming spheroidal, often passing into a continuous, more or less roughened crust; stipes stout, of medium length, or rarely very short, sometimes furrowed, rarely divided toward the top, whitish; apothecia middle-sized, 1.5–2.5 mm. across, subspherical to flattened, becoming flexuous, the disk strongly convex, flesh-colored, the exciple soon disappearing; asci cylindrico-clavate; spores oblong-fusiform to fusiform, 11–26 × 2–3 μ.

On sterile soil, from New England westward to Ohio and Kentucky, and southward to Florida.

5. **Baeomyces fungoides** (Swartz) Ach., Meth. Lich. 320. 1803.

Lichen fungoides Swartz, Prod. Lich. Ind. 146. 1788. *B. roseus* var. *fungoides* Tuck.

Thallus granulose, the granules raised and sometimes spheroidal, passing finally into a crust; stipes rather long, often granulose, whitish; apothecia middle-sized to large, 2–4 mm. across, the disk strongly convex, flesh-colored, the exciple soon covered; spores oblong-fusiform to fusiform, 11–23 × 3–4 μ.

On sterile soil, Florida.

131. Pilophorus T. Fries, Ster. Pil. Comm. 40. 1857.

Primary thallus crustose, minutely granulose, rudimentary, devoid of differentiation into layers, attached to the substratum by hyphal rhizoids, often disappearing; podetia arising from the primary thallus, cylindrical, rarely branched, solid or hollow, decorticate and commonly granulose and covered with thalloid warts, the central portion composed of loosely interwoven, longitudinally extending hyphae, surrounded by mechanical tissue of densely packed hyphae; apothecia small to middle-sized, borne at the apices of the podetia, the disk subglobose to subconical, commonly black, the exciple soon disappearing; hypothecium brownish to dark brown; hymenium brown; paraphyses unbranched, becoming indistinct; asci clavate; spores 8, hyaline, ellipsoid to oblong-ellipsoid, non-septate.

The algal host is Pleurococcus.

A. Apothecia large, vertically elongated, 2–3 × 1 mm. . . . . 3. P. Hallii
A. Apothecia smaller, round, not more than 2 mm. across
   B. Podetia unbranched, granulose to subsquamulose . . . . . . 2. P. Fibula
   B. Podetia rarely branched, warty-granulose or somewhat powdery . 1. P. cereolus

1. **Pilophorus cereolus** (Ach.) T. Fries, Lich. Scand. 1:55. 1871.

   Lichen cereolus Ach., Lich. Suec. 89. 1798. *P. cereolus* var. *acicularis* (Ach.) Tuck.

Primary thallus effuse at the base, forming a warty-granulose or powdery, grayish white crust; podetia arising from the primary thallus, short, erect, cylindrical, rarely branched, clustered or scattered, warty-granulose or somewhat powdery, greenish gray to ashy or rarely greenish; apothecia small, 0.6–2 mm. across, borne on the tips of the podetia, subglobose to subconical, black; spores ellipsoid-fusiform, 16–23 × 5–8 μ.

On rocks, Minnesota, California, Oregon, and Washington, and eastward into the Rocky Mountains.

2. **Pilophorus Fibula** (Tuck.) T. Fries, Ster. Pil. Comm. 42. 1857.

   Stereocaulon Fibula Tuck., Syn. Lich. 46. 1848. *P. cereolus* var. *Fibula* Tuck.

Primary thallus minutely granulose to somewhat areolate, greenish gray to brownish, soon disappearing; podetia arising from the primary thallus, solid, erect, unbranched, very short to somewhat elongated, granulose to subsquamulose; apothecia small, 0.6–1 mm. across, borne on the tips of the podetia, subglobose, black; spores ellipsoid to ellipsoid-fusiform, 17–26 × 5–8 μ.

On rocks, Vermont and northern New York.

3. **Pilophorus Hallii** (Tuck.) Vainio, Bot. Mag. Tokyo. 35:59. 1921.

   P. acicularis f. *Hallii* Tuck., Proc. Am. Acad. 12:177. 1877.

Primary thallus warty-granulose or powdery, greenish gray to ashy or brownish; podetia arising from the primary thallus, erect, solid, scarcely ever branched, short and stout, minutely granulose or powdery; apothecia small to middle-sized, vertically elongated, 2–5 × 0.5–1 mm., almost cylindrical, black, borne on the tips of the podetia; spores ellipsoid to ellipsoid-pointed, 18–24 × 5–8 μ.

On rocks, Washington and Oregon.

132. **Cladonia** Hill; Web., in Wigg., Prim. Fl. Hols. 90. 1780.

Primary thallus composed of squamules, persistent or dying, ascending and foliose or horizontal and crustose, becoming rough and warty, the upper side corticate, the lower side and rarely the upper decorticate and sorediate; podetia arising from the squamules of the primary thallus or from old podetia, often dying at the base, cylindrical, trumpet-shaped, or variously irregular, with or without

branching, with or without cups, with or without squamules, often bearing secondary and tertiary podetia, corticate or decorticate and sorediate, the cortex when present continuous, warty, areolate, or scattered-areolate; apothecia of various sizes, forms, and arrangement, terminal on the podetia or on their cups or branches, or on short apothecial stalks, the disk commonly flat to convex, scarlet or brown, the exciple thin and soon disappearing; hymenium above colored like the disk and hyaline below; hypothecium hyaline; paraphyses rarely branched; asci clavate or cylindrico-clavate, with the apical wall almost uniformly more or less thickened; spores 8, hyaline, ellipsoid, non-septate, 6–24 $\times$ 2–4.5 μ.
The algal host is Pleurococcus.

A. Primary thallus crustose, persistent or evanescent . . . . SECTION 1
A. Primary thallus granulose or squamulose, usually persistent
   B. Apothecia scarlet . . . . SECTION 2
   B. Apothecia brown . . . . SECTION 3

SECTION 1
A. Primary thallus persistent; podetia very small . . . . 5. Cl. papillaria
A. Primary thallus evanescent; podetia large
   B. Podetia greenish gray to grayish brown, large . . . . . 1. Cl. rangiferina
   B. Podetia straw-colored or whitish, smaller
      C. Podetia loosely branched, the tips usually nodding
         D. Podetia densely cobwebby-tomentose, especially
            toward the tips . . . . 2. Cl. sylvatica sylvestris
         D. Podetia decorticate and somewhat powdery
            but not tomentose . . . . 2. Cl. sylvatica
      C. Podetia repeatedly branched, the tips erect
         D. Podetia repeatedly much-branched; southern . . . . 3. Cl. pycnoclada
         D. Podetia radiately branched; northern . . . . 4. Cl. alpestris

SECTION 2
A. Cups present and usually well developed
   B. Cups broad, short relative to width
      C. Cups sorediate or granulose, at least above
         D. Primary squamules minute, white, often granulose . . . 13. Cl. Ravenelii
         D. Primary squamules small to middle-sized, greenish 12. Cl. coccifera pleurota
      C. Cups not sorediate
         D. Proliferations in part from the diaphragm of the
            cup, podetia elongated . . . . 12. Cl. coccifera asotea
         D. Proliferations from the margin of the cup, podetia
            abruptly or gradually dilated . . . . 12. Cl. coccifera
   B. Cups narrow, long relative to width
      C. Podetia corticate, often squamulose . . . . 15. Cl. bellidiflora
      C. Podetia decorticate, at least in part
         D. Podetia slender, whitish, granulose-sorediate . . . 10. Cl. flabelliformis
         D. Podetia stouter, greenish-yellow, farinose-sorediate
            E. Podetia commonly branched, KOH plus . . . . . 11. Cl. digitata
            E. Podetia commonly simple, KOH minus . . . . . 14. Cl. deformis
A. Cups lacking, the podetia subulate or branched, abortive or absent
   B. Podetia very short or lacking
      C. Apothecia seated on the minute, white squamules 13. Cl. Ravenelii epiphylla
      C. Apothecia usually on short podetia, the squamules
      larger, yellowish green
         D. Squamules sorediate . . . . 16. Cl. cristatella paludicola
         D. Squamules not sorediate
            E. Podetia densely squamulose . . . . . 16. Cl. cristatella densissima
            E. Podetia without squamules . . . . . . 17. Cl. abbreviatula
   B. Podetia usually well developed
      C. Podetia repeatedly branched . . . . 18. Cl. leporina
      C. Podetia simple or sparingly branched above
         D. Podetia usually sorediate, simple or rarely branched
            E. Podetia rarely branched, KOH minus . . . . . 7. Cl. bacillaris
            E. Podetia more often branched above
               F. Primary thallus rarely persistent; podetia
               slender, KOH plus . . . . 8. Cl. macilenta

   F. Primary thallus usually persistent, podetia stouter,
    KOH minus (in ours) . . . . 9. Cl. didyma
  D. Podetia corticate, sometimes decorticate, usually branched
   E. Primary squamules yellowish green; podetia
    always corticate . . . . 16. Cl. cristatella
   E. Primary squamules usually greenish gray; podetia
    sometimes decorticate . . . . 6. Cl. Floerkeana

SECTION 3

A. Cups, axils, or tips of the podetia usually perforate
 B. Podetia usually yellowish green, rarely pallid; apothecia pallid;
 primary thallus usually soon disappearing
  C. Podetia slender or slightly turgid, elongate or
   repeatedly branched . . . . 19. Cl. amaurocraea
  C. Podetia more or less turgid, usually short
   D. Sides of the podetia often perforate . . . . . . 22. Cl. reticulata
   D. Sides never perforate
    E. Podetia thick and bulbous . . . . 21. Cl. caroliniana
    E. Podetia more slender
     F. Tips of podetia usually subulate . . . . . . 20. Cl. uncialis
     F. Tips short and obtuse . . . . . . 20. Cl. uncialis obtusata
 B. Podetia whitish, greenish white, or brownish, rarely yellowish;
 apothecia usually dark
  C. Podetia always corticate throughout
   D. Primary squamules large; podetia usually more or less
   irregular and cups often absent . . . . 37. Cl. turgida
   D. Primary squamules smaller; podetia usually regular
    E. Podetia small to medium size . . . . 29. Cl. floridana
    E. Podetia usually long and repeatedly branched
     F. Axils of the podetia not conspicuously dilated,
      narrowly perforate or sometimes imperforate
      G. Podetia whitish or greenish gray
       H. Podetia not conspicuously squamulose, at least
       not throughout
        I. Podetia elongated, much branched 23. Cl. furcata racemosa
        I. Podetia shorter, less branched . . . . 23. Cl. furcata
       H. Podetia usually more or less squamulose throughout
        I. Podetia slender . . . . . . 23. Cl. furcata pinnata
        I. Podetia rather stout . . . . . 23. Cl. furcata Finkii
      G. Podetia often brownish or olive-brown above
       H. Podetia with cups . . . . 24. Cl. palamaea
       H. Podetia usually without cups
        I. Apices of the podetia pointed, KOH
        plus (yellow)
         J. Cortex scattered and forming small
         patches . . . . 26. Cl. rangiformis
         J. Cortex subcontinuous . . 26. C. rangiformis pungens
        I. Apices usually blunt, KOH plus (brown) . 25. Cl. Herrei
     F. Axils of podetia dilated, perforations gaping
      G. Cups usually wide; podetia stout, the ranks short
       H. Podetia squamulose . . . . . . 30. Cl. crispata divulsa
       H. Podetia usually without squamules . . . 30. Cl. crispata
      G. Cups very narrow or absent; podetia slender,
       the ranks long . . . . 30. Cl. crispata gracilescens
  C. Podetia more or less decorticate, or coralloid, or granulose
   D. Podetia short
    E. Podetia granulose or coralloid; primary squamules
    esorediate or granulose
     F. Podetia short, cupless; cortex granulose . . . . 27. Cl. santensis
     F. Podetia longer, often with cups; cortex usually with
      coralloid squamules . . . . 28. Cl. exasperatula
    E. Podetia more or less decorticate; primary squamules sorediate
     F. Podetia abortive, decorticate, KOH minus . . 33. Cl. caespiticia

        F. Podetia always evident, partly decorticate,
            KOH plus . . . . 34. Cl. delicata
    D. Podetia becoming long
       E. Primary thallus usually soon disappearing; podetia
          becoming more or less decorticate above . . 23. furcata scabriuscula
       E. Primary thallus usually persistent; podetia
          decorticate throughout, or becoming so
         F. Podetia usually simple, or somewhat branched,
            farinose-sorediate
           G. Podetia usually with cups, the apices commonly
              perforate
             H. Podetia much elongated . . ' . . 35. Cl. cenotea exaltata
             H. Podetia short to medium-long
               I. Podetia rarely branched . . . . . 35. Cl. cenotea
               I. Podetia usually branched . . . 35. Cl. cenotea crossota
           G. Podetia usually without cups, the sterile
              apices usually subulate . . . . 36. Cl. glauca
         F. Podetia more or less branched, the cortex becoming
            granulose, or lacking
           G. Podetia plainly squamulose
             H. Squamules small . . . . 31. Cl. squamosa
             H. Squamules larger
               I. Podetia regularly cup-bearing 31. Cl. squamosa phyllocoma
               I. Podetia rarely cup-bearing . . 31. Cl. squamosa frondosa
           G. Podetia not plainly squamulose
             H. Podetia squamulose-scaly or sorediate-
                granulose, KOH plus
               I. Podetia squamulose-scaly above, squamulose
                  toward the base . . . . 32. Cl. subsquamosa
               I. Podetia sorediate-granulose, without
                  squamules . . . . . . 32. Cl. subsquamosa granulosa
             H. Podetia granulose or cortex more or less
                continuous, KOH minus
               I. Podetia without cups . . . 31. Cl. squamosa muricella
               I. Podetia regularly cup-bearing
                 J. Podetia densely granulose . . 31. Cl. squamosa rigida
                 J. Podetia smooth, cortex almost continuous
                    or absent
                   K. Cortex absent or scattered, at
                      least above . . . . 31. Cl. squamosa denticollis
                   K. Cortex more or less continuous, rarely
                      slightly sorediate . 31. Cl. squamosa multibrachiata
A. Cups, apices, or axils of podetia usually imperforate
  B. Podetia yellowish or yellowish green; apothecia pallid
    C. Podetia sorediate, more or less decorticate
      D. Regularly forming cups . . . . 65. Cl. carneola
      D. Regularly cupless, sterile apices subulate . . . . . 64. Cl. cyanipes
    C. Podetia corticate, not sorediate
      D. Podetia slender; on old wood . . . . 62. Cl. botrytes
      D. Podetia stouter; on soil, rarely on old wood . . . 63. Cl. piedmontensis
  B. Podetia greenish gray; apothecia pallid, or brownish
    C. Podetia becoming long
      D. Podetia commonly proliferating from the center
         of the cups
        E. Ranks rather long, the apices beaklike or cornute,
           KOH plus . . . . 52. Cl. gracilescens
        E. Ranks shorter, apices terminated by cups or apothecia,
           KOH minus
          F. Podetia usually whitish green . . . . . . 56. Cl. calycantha
          F. Podetia darker
            G. Proliferations from the center of the cups . 55. Cl. verticillata
            G. Proliferations in part from the margins of the
               cups and from the sides of the
               podetia . . . . 55. Cl. verticillata cervicornis

D. Podetia simple or proliferating from the margins of the cups
  E. Podetia always corticate
    F. Podetia subtomentose between the scattered areoles, the
      tips often fastigiately branched; often spotted at
      the base . . . . 50. Cl. degenerans
    F. Podetia subtomentose between the scattered areoles,
      tips not fastigiately branched; base not spotted
      G. Cups dilated and rather broad; podetia rather stout
        H. Podetia without squamules or with squamules
          toward the base . . . . 48. Cl. gracilis
        H. Podetia squamulose throughout, cups more
          irregular . . . . 48. Cl. gracilis dilacerata
      G. Cups narrow or wanting; podetia slender
        H. Podetia much elongated . . . . 48. Cl. gracilis elongata
        H. Podetia medium-sized
          I. Podetia squamulose . . . . . 48. Cl. gracilis aspera
          I. Podetia not squamulose . . . 48. Cl. gracilis chordalis
  E. Podetia always wholly or partly decorticate
    F. Podetia not uniformly decorticate above
      G. Podetia sorediate toward the apex, sometimes
        bearing cups . . . . 49. Cl. cornuta
      G. Podetia variously sorediate and decorticate,
        never bearing cups . . . . 46. Cl. decorticata
    F. Podetia uniformly decorticate above
      G. Primary squamules densely covered with minute
        coralloid branchlets or squamules . . . 59. Cl. microphylliza
      G. Primary squamules smooth or rarely
        sorediate . . . . . 57. C. fimbriata (and subspecies below)
        H. Cups usually well developed
          I. Podetia proliferating . . . . 57. Cl. fimbriata prolifera
          I. Podetia not proliferating . . . 57. Cl. fimbriata simplex
        H. Cups absent, or narrow and abortive
          I. Podetia elongated
            J. Cups never present . . . 57. Cl. fimbriata subulata
            J. Cups usually present
              K. Cups better developed . 57. Cl. fimbriata radiata
              K. Cups very poorly
                developed . . . . 57. Cl. fimbriata nemoxyna
          I. Podetia usually short
            J. Podetia usually cupless . 57. Cl. fimbriata coniocraea
            J. Podetia with narrow and abortive
              cups . . . . . . 57. Cl. fimbriata ochrochlora
C. Podetia short or lacking
  D. Apothecia seated on the primary squamules . . . 40. Cl. apodocarpa
  D. Apothecia on longer or shorter podetia
    E. Primary squamules medium-sized to large
      F. Podetia cupless . . . . 61. Cl. strepsilis
      F. Podetia with small cups . . . . 60. Cl. foliacea
    E. Primary squamules small to medium-sized
      F. Podetia always or sometimes forming cups
        G. Cups broad, always corticate, the ranks short
          H. Squamules rather large . . . . . 54. Cl. mateocyatha
          H. Squamules smaller
            I. Squamules of the primary thallus thinner
              and more incised . . . . 53. Cl. pyxidata
           I. Squamules thicker and less incised, closely
              packed into a brownish or olivaceous
              crust . . . . 53. Cl. pyxidata pocillum
        G. Cups narrow or sometimes absent; ranks elongated
          H. Primary thallus persistent; cortex
            dispersed, soon scattered . . . . . 45. Cl. Beaumontii
          H. Primary thallus disappearing; cortex subcontinuous
            or areolate . . . . 58. Cl. pityrea

F. Podetia never forming cups
  G. Podetia slender, unbranched or the branching at the
    tips irregular, short, and along the sides of the podetia
    H. Branches short, more or less spinous and
      swollen . . . . 44. Cl. leptothallina
    H. Branches slender, irregular, or podetia simple
      I. Primary squamules crenate or incised-
        crenate . . . . 47. Cl. acuminata
      I. Primary squamules usually subdigitate or laciniate
        J. Podetia with squamules . 58. Cl. pityrea phyllophora
        J. Podetia without squamules . 58. Cl. pityrea subacuta
  G. Podetia stouter, branches of medium length and
    more or less radiate
    H. Apothecia unknown, the sterile tips
      pointed . . . . 51. Cl. cerasphora
    H. Apothecia regularly formed, usually terminating
    the tips
      I. Sides of the podetia usually fissured
        J. Podetia squamulose . . . 43. Cl. cariosa squamulosa
        J. Podetia with few or no squamules
          K. Podetia pierced by openings, the
            cortex dispersed . . . . 43. Cl. cariosa cribrosa
          K. Podetia fissured but hardly pierced
            by openings . . . . . . 43. Cl. cariosa
      I. Sides of the podetia smooth, rarely fissured
        J. Branched above, the branches suberect
          and spreading . . . . 39. Cl. mitrula
        J. Unbranched, or the branches short or parallel
          K. Podetia usually squamulose, sometimes
            corymbosely or erectly parallel-
            branched . . . . 38. Cl. corymbosula
          K. Podetia without squamules
            L. Podetia usually short; primary
              squamules middle-sized . . 41. Cl. symphycarpa
           L. Podetia longer; primary squamules
              middle-sized to large . . . 42. Cl. subcariosa

1. **Cladonia rangiferina** (L.) Web., in Wigg., Prin. Fl. Hols. 90. 1780.
    Lichen rangiferinus L., Sp. Pl. 1153. 1753. *Cl. rangiferina* var. *tenuior* (Del.)
    Vainio.
    Primary thallus soon dying, crustose when present, and composed of subglobose, depressed or irregular, clustered or scattered, ashy white warts; podetia arising from the primary thallus, or from branches or free fragments of old or dying podetia, subcylindrical and cupless, subdichotomously or subradiately branched, the axils somewhat dilated and frequently perforate, the apices pointed or forked, clustered or subsolitary, erect or rarely ascending or even reclining, the sterile apices commonly brownish, the remainder of the podetium greenish gray to gray or grayish brown, the cortex commonly scattered, rough; apothecia small to middle-sized, 0.5–2 mm. across, solitary or clustered on the apices of the branches, the disk convex, brown.
    On soil, throughout northern United States, and southward to Florida and Alabama.

2. **Cladonia sylvatica** (L.) Hoffm., Deutschl. Fl. 114. 1795.
    Lichen rangiferinus var. *sylvaticus* L., Sp. Pl. 1153. 1753.
    Primary thallus rarely persistent, composed, when present, of subglobose, scattered or clustered, straw-colored warts, these forming a thin crust; podetia arising from the branches of old or dying podetia or rarely from the primary thallus, dying at the base, cylindrical or subcylindrical, cupless, often dilated in the axils, dichotomously or sympodially or radiately branched, the apices subulate and sometimes minutely radiate or furcate-spinose, erect, subsolitary or clustered, the axils frequently perforate, whitish or yellowish straw-colored to greenish gray,

the cortex scattered or decorticate and somewhat powdery; apothecia small to middle-sized, 0.5–1.2 mm. across, solitary or clustered at the apices of the branches, the disk depressed-convex, brown to rarely brick-red.

On soil, throughout the United States.

var. **sylvestris** (Oed.) Vainio, Act. Soc. Faun. Flor. Fenn. 4:20–32. 1887.
  Lichen rangiferinus var. *sylvestris* Oed., Fl. Dan. 3:28. pl. 539. 1770. *Cenomyce sylvatica* var. *laxiuscula* Del. *Cenomyce sylvatica* var. *morbida* Del. *Cl. squarrosa* (Wallr.) Flot. *Cl. tenuis* (Floerke) Harm. *Cl. mitis* Sandst.

Podetia commonly slender, smooth, densely cobwebby-tomentose, especially toward the tips of the branches.

On soil, from New England to Florida, and westward to Iowa and Minnesota.

3. **Cladonia pycnoclada** (Gaudich.) Nyl., Lich. Nov. Zel. 244. 1866.
  Cenomyce pycnoclada Gaudich., Ann. Sci. Nat. 5:97. 1825. *Cl. pycnoclada* var. *exalbescens* Vainio. *Cl. pycnoclada* var. *flavida* Vainio. *Cl. rangiferina* f. *minor* Harm.

Primary thallus rarely persistent, when present, subglobose, scattered or clustered, straw-colored to yellowish warts forming a thin crust; podetia arising from branches or loose fragments of dying podetia or rarely from the primary thallus, dying at the base, cylindrical to subcylindrical, cupless, somewhat dilated at axils, repeatedly much-branched, the axils often perforate, upper branches then short and closely aggregated, often subarachnoid, with pointed, sometimes brownish apices, decorticate or all or lower part warty, straw-colored to whitish or yellowish straw-colored to greenish gray or ashy white; apothecia rare and small, 0.3–0.7 mm. across, solitary or somewhat clustered on the apices of branches, the disk flat to convex, brown or brick red.

On soil, Florida.

4. **Cladonia alpestris** (L.) Rabenh., Clad. Eur. Exsicc. pl. 39. no. 11. 1860.
  Lichen rangiferinus var. *alpestris* L., Sp. Pl. 1153. 1753.

Primary thallus crustose, dying soon, composed of delicate, medium-sized, subglobose or irregular, clustered or scattered, straw-colored warts; podetia arising from the primary thallus, from old or dying podetia, of medium length, subcylindrical, radiately branched, 1 or more branches becoming larger and erect, commonly decorticate, rarely somewhat sorediate, the upper branches short, the apices radiately spinose, mostly straight, clustered, erect, colored like the primary thallus, cupless; apothecia small, 0.3–0.5 mm. across, rare, solitary, clustered, or confluent on the apices of the branches, the disk convex, light to darker brown.

On soil, rarely on wood, throughout the United States. Smaller toward the south.

5. **Cladonia papillaria** (Ehrh.) Hoffm., Deutschl. Fl. 2:117. 1796.
  Lichen papillaria Ehrh., Phyt. Ehrh. no. 100. 1780. *Cl. papillaria* f. *molariformis* (Hoffm.) Schaer.

Primary thallus persistent or finally dying, composed of small, contiguous or confluent, subglobose or depressed-convex, irregular warts, white to ashy white or greenish; podetia arising from the primary thallus, short and subglobose to cylindrical and club-shaped or irregularly swollen about the axils, cupless, more or less branched, the branches papillaeform or short, and suberect to diverging, clustered or crowded into clumps, the sides smooth or warty, colored like the primary thallus; apothecia small, 0.3–0.7 mm. across, clustered or heaped on the apices of podetia, the disk flat to convex, reddish brown.

On sandy or gravelly soil, throughout eastern United States and westward to Ohio.

6. **Cladonia Floerkeana** (E. Fries) Sommerf., Suppl. Fl. Lapp. 128. 1826.
  Cenomyce Floerkeana E. Fries, Sched. Crit. Lich. Exsicc. Suec. fasc. 3. 18. 1824.

Primary thallus commonly persistent, composed of small to middle-sized, laciniate or incised and crenate, commonly flat to somewhat inward-rolled, scattered or clustered and clumped, greenish gray to ashy or olive-green squamules; white below or becoming yellowish and darker toward the base, rarely sorediate at the margin and below; podetia arising from the primary thallus, erect, subcylindrical or somewhat top-shaped, commonly rather slender and cupless, broader or branched toward the apex, the branches short, obtuse, often sorediate or coralloid-squamulose, usually terminated by perfect or imperfect apothecia, rarely by imperfect cups, the lower part of all corticate, ashy green to greenish brown or these colors variegated; apothecia middle-sized, 1–2.5 mm. across, solitary or rarely aggregate, the disk flat to convex, scarlet to reddish brown.

On soil, New Hampshire, Florida, and Wisconsin.

7. **Cladonia bacillaris** (Del.) Nyl., Lich. Lapp. 179. 1866.

Cenomyce bacillaris Del., in Duby, Bot. Gall. ed. 2. 2:634. 1830. *Cl. bacillaris* f. *clavata* (Ach.) Vainio.

Primary thallus persistent or rarely dying, composed of middle-sized, laciniate-lobate or crenate, flat or ascending, scattered or clustered, greenish gray to olive-green squamules; whitish and sometimes sorediate below, or turning darker toward the base of the squamules; podetia arising from the primary thallus, slender, subcylindrical, sorediate, rarely enlarged at the apex, cupless or infrequently bearing imperfect cups, rarely branched, often sterile or terminated by imperforate, solitary or clustered apothecia, erect, corticate toward the base and below the apothecia, colored like the primary thallus; apothecia middle-sized, 1–4 mm. across, solitary or clustered, the disk commonly convex, scarlet.

On old stumps and logs, rarely on earth, New Hampshire, New York, Minnesota, Washington, and California.

8. **Cladonia macilenta** Hoffm., Deutschl. Fl. 2:126. 1795.

Primary thallus persistent or finally dying, composed of small to middle-sized, laciniate, lobed-laciniate, crenate, or subentire, flat or somewhat inward-rolled, scattered or clustered, greenish gray to whitish or greenish squamules; white below or darker or rarely yellow toward the base; podetia arising from the primary thallus, short or somewhat elongated, rather slender, subcylindrical or club-shaped, cupless, often somewhat branched, the apices obtuse or impressed, sterile or terminated by apothecia, erect, sorediate, squamulose toward the base or rarely throughout, often corticate toward the base and below the apothecia, whitish to greenish gray; apothecia small to middle-sized, 0.5–2.5 mm. across, solitary or clustered on the apices of the podetia, the disk convex, scarlet.

On soil or rotten wood, throughout the United States.

9. **Cladonia didyma** (Fée) Vainio, Act. Soc. Faun. Flor. Fenn. 4:137. 1887.

Scyphophorus didymus Fée, Essai Crypt. Intro. 98. pl. 3, f. 13. 1824. *Cl. didyma* var. *muscigena* (Eschw.) Vainio. *Cl. pulchella* Schwein.

Primary thallus rarely persistent, composed of middle-sized, laciniate, incised, or crenate, flat or somewhat inward-rolled, scattered or clustered, greenish gray to olive-green or whitish squamules; white below or turning yellowish or darker toward the base; podetia arising from the primary thallus, cylindrical, cupless, becoming branched, the branches erect or diverging, aggregate or subsolitary, sorediate, granulose or minutely squamulose, rarely corticate toward the base, greenish brown to whitish; apothecia small to middle-sized, 0.3–2.5 mm. across, solitary or clustered and conglomerate on the apices of the podetia, the disk convex, scarlet.

On old wood, from Maine to Florida, and westward to Texas and Nebraska.

10. **Cladonia flabelliformis** (Floerke) Vainio, Act. Soc. Faun. Fenn. 4:113–16. 1887.

Capitularia flabelliformis Floerke, Mag. Ges. Naturf. Freunde. Berlin 2:216. 1808.

Primary thallus commonly persistent, composed of small to middle-sized, laciniate, incised or lobed, flat or somewhat inward-rolled, scattered or crowded, greenish gray to pale greenish squamules; white and rarely sorediate below or turning darker toward the base; podetia arising from the primary thallus, commonly top-shaped, solitary or crowded and clustered, the lower part corticate, rarely squamulose, colored like the primary thallus; cups narrow, gradually dilated, rather regular, the margins subentire to radiate and sometimes one or more times proliferate, the cavity sorediate or rarely corticate; apothecia middle-sized, 1–2.5 mm. across, borne on the margins or on the proliferations of the cups, solitary or clustered, the disk convex, scarlet.

On old wood, California.

11. **Cladonia digitata** Hoffm., Deutschl. Fl. 2:124, 125. 1796.

Primary thallus persistent or finally dying, composed of lobed or incised, middle-sized, flat or inward-rolled, scattered or clustered, greenish gray to rarely greenish squamules; white and often sorediate below, dull or yellowish toward the base; podetia arising from the primary thallus, rather short, cylindrical, rarely cupless, erect or ascending, commonly branched, the upper part sorediate, the lower part and sometimes the whole covered with a continuous cortex, whitish to yellowish or greenish gray; cups middle-sized, abruptly dilated, regular to irregular, the margin somewhat curved, subentire, dentate, radiate, or proliferate; apothecia small to middle-sized, 0.5–5 mm. across, solitary or clustered on the apices of the proliferations, or rarely on the margin of the cups, the disk convex, scarlet.

On old logs and stumps, northern United States.

12. **Cladonia coccifera** (L.) Willd., Fl. Berol. Prodr. 361. 1787.

Lichen cocciferus L., Sp. Pl. 1151. 1753. *Cl. cornucopioides* (L.) E. Fries. *Cl. coccifera* var. *ochrocarpia* Floerke. *Cl. coccifera* var. *stemmatina* Ach. *Cl. coccifera* f. *phyllocoma* Floerke.

Primary thallus usually persistent, composed of irregularly incised, crenate or lobate, small or larger, flat or somewhat inward-rolled, clustered or scattered, light to reddish or greenish gray squamules; whitish below or yellowish toward the base, rarely sorediate below and at the margins; podetia arising from the primary thallus, short, cylindrical, hollow, erect, corticate, the cortex subcontinuous or areolate, colored like the primary thallus, rarely squamulose; cups gradually or abruptly dilated, 1–4 proliferations from a cup, bearing cups or apothecia; apothecia middle-sized to large, 1–6 mm. across, clustered or solitary, the disk depressed-convex to convex, scarlet.

On soil, over rocks, and rarely on old wood, throughout the United States.

var. **asotea** (Ach.) Arn., Flora 67:81. 1884.

Baeomyces cocciferus var. *asoteus* Ach., Meth. Lich. 332. 1803.

Podetia elongated, tubular, destitute of squamules, the cortex areolate or warty, scattered, or continuous toward the base; cups large, gradually dilated, the margin becoming proliferate; apothecia commonly stalked, the disk convex.

On soil, Massachusetts and Washington.

var. **pleurota** (Floerke) Schaer., Lich. Helv. Spic. 1:25. 1823.

Capitularia pleurota Floerke, Ges. Nat. Freund. Mag. 2:218. 1808. *Cl. cornucopioides* var. *pleurota* (Floerke) Nyl.

Squamules of the primary thallus sometimes sorediate below and along the margin; podetia corticate below, but upper part more or less decorticate and sorediate.

On soil, throughout northern United States.

13. **Cladonia Ravenelii** Tuck., Syn. N. A. Lich. 1:254, 255. 1882.

Cl. Ravenelii f. *simplex* Merrill. *Cl. Ravenelii* f. *bractiata* Merrill.

Primary thallus composed of very minute, disk-shaped, subentire to finely torn-laciniate, white squamules, often breaking down to form granules; podetia small, short, cylindrical to more or less top-shaped, the cortex usually continuous, smooth to granulose or granulose-warty, greenish gray to more commonly yellowish green or whitish, rarely branched and usually cup-bearing; cups dilated, for the most

part deeply concave, the margin usually proliferate; apothecia small, 0.5–0.8 mm. across, borne on the apices of proliferations, the disk flat to convex, scarlet.
On old wood, South Carolina, Florida, and Alabama.

 f. **epiphylla** Merrill, Bryologist 27:23. 1924.
 Podetia absent and the apothecia seated on the squamules.
 On old wood, near Sanford, Florida.

 14. **Cladonia deformis** (L.) Hoffm., Deutschl. Fl. 2:120. 1795.
 Lichen deformis L., Sp. Pl. 1152. 1753. *Scyphophorus sulphurius* Michx.
 Primary thallus usually dying, composed of incised, crenate or lobed, middle-sized, depressed or ascending, flat, convex, or somewhat inward-rolled, scattered or clustered, greenish gray to light reddish brown squamules; pale or brownish and sometimes sorediate below; podetia arising from the primary thallus, sub-cylindrical or rarely elongated-turbinate, scattered or clustered, erect, rarely cupless, sorediate, the lower part corticate, the cortex continuous or chinky, sometimes squamulose, yellowish straw-colored to greenish gray; cups middle-sized, gradually or abruptly dilated, imperforate, the margin dentate or often irregularly proliferate, the ranks 1–3, the cavity of the cups minutely sorediate; apothecia middle-sized, 0.5–5 mm. across, scattered on the margins of the cups or clustered at the dilated apices of the proliferations, the disk depressed-convex to convex, scarlet. (PLATE 22 *a*.)
 On soil, throughout the United States.

 15. **Cladonia bellidiflora** (Ach.) Schaer., Lich. Helv. Spic. 21. 1823.
 Lichen bellidiflora Ach., Lich. Suec. 194. 1798.
 Primary thallus rarely persistent, composed of middle-sized, sorediate, thin, ascending, flat to slightly inward-rolled, scattered or clustered, straw-colored to greenish gray squamules; whitish below, the bases turning brownish or darker; podetia arising from the primary thallus, or from dying podetia, elongated, sub-cylindrical, branched, erect or somewhat flexuous, the cortex continuous or chinky and dispersed-areolate, colored like the primary thallus; cups small, abruptly dilated, the margin plane, dentate, or proliferate; apothecia middle-sized to large, 0.5–4 mm. across, clustered or rarely confluent, the disk flat to convex, scarlet. (PLATE 22 *b*.)
 On earth and rocks, California, Washington, and Oregon.

 16. **Cladonia cristatella** Tuck., Am. Journ. Sci. 25:428. 1858.
 Cl. cristatella f. *Beauvoisii* (Del.) Vainio. *Cl. cristatella* var. *ochrocarpia* Tuck. *Cl. cristatella* var. *vestita* Tuck. *Cl. cristatella* var. *ramosa* Tuck. *Cl. cristatella* f. *minuta* Sandst. *Cl. substraminea* Nyl.
 Primary thallus composed of small, incised or crenate, usually persistent, commonly flat but sometimes inward-rolled, scattered or clustered, sometimes sorediate, greenish gray or straw-colored squamules; whitish and sometimes sorediate below; podetia arising from the primary thallus, erect, becoming squamulose, subcylindrical or somewhat enlarged toward the apex, without cups, often more or less digitately branched toward the apex, the branches short and obtuse, the axils sometimes perforate, the cortex continuous or areolate, smooth or roughened, colored like the primary thallus; apothecia small to middle-sized, 0.3–3 mm. across, solitary or clustered on the apices of branches, the disk convex, scarlet or rarely light yellowish brown.
 On soil, throughout the United States east of the Rocky Mountains.

 var. **paludicola** Tuck., Syn. N. A. Lich. 1:255. 1882.
 Cl. paludicola (Tuck.) Merrill.
 Squamules sorediate, and the podetia short or wanting.
 On rotten wood, New England, and southward to Virginia.

 var. **densissima** Fink; Hedrick, Mycologia 26:157. 1934.
 The squamules thicker, rather smaller and less lobed than usual, closely packed and becoming imbricated in 3 or 4 layers; podetia abortive or very short, scarcely

surpassing 3 or 4 mm. in length, densely covered with squamules, the basal ones of ordinary size and the upper ones reduced and sometimes passing into wartlike bodies toward the apex; apothecia minute, 0.1–0.4 mm. across, mostly grouped at the apex of the podetia but sometimes occurring on the sides as well and sometimes even seated on squamules of the primary thallus.

On top of fence post, near Oxford, Ohio.

17. **Cladonia abbreviatula** Merrill, Bryologist 27:21. 1924.

Primary thallus persistent, composed of small, at first round, then crenate, lobulate, or dissected, imbricate, usually ascending, greenish yellow squamules; white below; podetia arising from the primary squamules, very short, 0.5 mm. or less in length, sometimes almost lacking, erect, cylindrical or enlarged toward the apex, cupless, unbranched or branched at the apex, cortex continuous, smooth, colored like the primary thallus; apothecia very small, 0.1–0.15 mm. across, solitary, the disk convex, scarlet.

On soil or over wood, Sanford, Florida.

18. **Cladonia leporina** E. Fries, Lich. Eur. 243. 1831.

Primary thallus rarely persistent, composed of small, somewhat outward-rolled, narrowly lobed, greenish gray squamules; white below; podetia arising from the primary thallus or from fragments of old podetia, subcylindrical, swollen, often wrinkled, cupless, subdichotomously or irregularly much-branched, the branches spreading, the axils often open, clustered and entangled, suberect or ascending, rarely curved or flexuous, the cortex continuous to fissured, yellowish or greenish gray to pale straw-colored; apothecia small to middle-sized, 0.7–1.5 mm. across, subsolitary or clustered on the apices of branches, the disk more or less convex, scarlet.

On soil, from New Jersey to Florida, and westward to Texas and Arkansas.

19. **Cladonia amaurocraea** (Floerke) Schaer., Lich. Helv. Spic. 1:34. 1823.

Capitularia amaurocraea Floerke, in Web. & Mohr., Beitr. Naturk. 2:334. 1810.

Primary thallus composed of small, crenate or digitately incised, clustered or scattered, ascending or flat, greenish gray, rarely persistent squamules; white below; podetia arising from branches or fragments of dying podetia, or rarely from the surface of the primary thallus, dying at the base, cupless and subcylindrical or cup-bearing, dichotomously, radiately, or irregularly branched, the axils closed or perforate, the branches divaricate, forming clusters, erect, ascending, or prostrate, the cortex continuous or areolate and frequently scattered, smooth or the areoles elevated, straw-gold-colored or greenish gray, the apices straight, usually brownish; cups commonly abrupted, dilated, regular or oblique, margin spinulose and proliferate; apothecia middle-sized, 0.7–3.5 mm. across, solitary or clustered at the apices of the podetia, the disk flat to convex, brown to brick-red or lighter.

On soil, throughout the United States.

20. **Cladonia uncialis** (L.) Hoffm., Deutschl. Fl. 2:117. 1796.

Lichen uncialis L., Sp. Pl. 1153. 1753. *Cl. unciclis* f. *adunca* (Ach.) Flot. *Cl. uncialis* f. *dicraea* (Ach.) Scriba. *Cl. uncialis* f. *soraligera* Robb.

Primary thallus rarely present, composed of small, crenate or incised, ascending or flat, scattered or clustered, greenish gray to straw-colored squamules with continuous cortex; white below; podetia arising from branches or fragments of dying podetia or rarely from the primary thallus, dying at the base, subcylindrical, cupless, but the apices frequently dilated and somewhat cup-shaped, dichotomously, sympodially, or radiately branched, densely crowded and clustered, erect or rarely prostrate, the axils mostly perforate, the cortex subcontinuous or areolate and scattered, smooth or the areoles more or less raised, destitute of squamules, the apices straight, pointed or radiately or furcately spinose, colored like the primary thallus with the apices rarely becoming brown; apothecia small, 0.5–0.8 mm. across, solitary or clustered on the apices of short branches, the disk flat to convex, brown to brick-red.

On soil, throughout the United States.

f. **obtusata** (Ach.) Nyl., Syn. Lich. 215. 1860.

Cenomyce obtusata Ach., in Floerke, Arn. Wett. Ges. 1:100. 1809.

Podetia short, thick, with short branches obtuse at the ends, but with short spinous ultimate branchlets.

On soil, Massachusetts, Maryland, New York, Minnesota, and Washington.

21. **Cladonia caroliniana** Tuck., Am. Journ. Sci. II. 25:427. 1858.

Cenomyce caroliniana Schwein. in herb. *Cl. uncialis* var. *caroliniana* (Schwein.) Tuck.

Primary thallus soon dying; podetia thick and bulbous, swollen, without squamules, obscurely pitted, dichotomously branched above, the branches obconical-dilated, erect, cupless, the cortex subcontinuous or areolate and scattered, smooth or the areoles more or less raised, yellowish straw-colored or greenish gray, apices obtuse and dentate; apothecia small, 0.3–0.5 mm. across, solitary or clustered on the ends of the branches; the disk flat to convex, flesh-colored to brownish.

On soil, Vermont, North Carolina, Georgia, Alabama, and Tennessee.

22. **Cladonia reticulata** (Russell) Vainio, Act. Soc. Faun. Flor. Fenn. 4:280. 1887.

Cl. uncialis var. *reticulata* Russell, Journ. of Essex Natur. Hist. Soc. 1:100. 1839. *Cl. Boryi* Tuck. *Cl. Boryi* var. *lacunosa* Tuck.

Primary thallus indistinct; podetia arising from dying podetia and from free branches of old podetia, dying at the base, of medium length, cylindrical, dichotomously much-branched, upper branches erect and slender, lower branches short and thick, the axils and sides often perforate, the latter sometimes sievelike, decorticate, indistinctly tomentose, uneven, straw-colored to whitish; cups small, infrequent, the margins commonly proliferate, often disappearing; apothecia small, 0.3–0.6 mm. across, the disk flat to convex, brown to brownish black.

On soil, New England and New York.

23. **Cladonia furcata** (Huds.) Schrad., Spic. Fl. Germ. 107. 1794.

Lichen furcatus Huds., Fl. Angl. 458. 1762.

Primary thallus rarely persistent, composed of middle-sized, subentire to irregularly lobed or crenate, ascending or flat, scattered or clustered, greenish gray to brownish or whitish squamules; white below; podetia arising from primary thallus, cylindrical or subcylindrical, the lower part sometimes dying, rarely squamulose toward the base, rarely cup-bearing, dichotomously or frequently radiately branched, erect or rarely prostrate or decumbent, rarely somewhat soredeate, the cortex continuous or more or less dispersed, colored like the primary thallus; apothecia small to middle-sized, 0.5–1.5 mm. across, irregularly or cymosely borne on the apices of the branches, the disk convex, brown to brick-red or lighter.

On soil, frequently over rocks, and rarely on old wood, throughout the United States.

var. **racemosa** (Hoffm.) Floerke, Clad. Comm. 152. 1828.

Cl. racemosa Hoffm., Deutschl. Fl. 2:114. 1795. *Cl. furcata* f. *fissa* Floerke. *Cl. furcata* var. *corymbosa* (Ach.) Nyl.

Podetia becoming elongated, dichotomously much-branched, rarely squamulose toward the base.

On soil, throughout the United States.

var. **pinnata** (Floerke) Vainio, Act. Soc. Faun. Flor. Fenn. 4:332. 1887.

Cenomyce racemosa var. *pinnata* Floerke, in Schleich., Cat. Pl. Helv. 47. 1821.

Podetia squamulose throughout, the squamules incised or lobate-crenate, commonly smoothed; apothecia subentire.

On soil, Maine, New York, West Virginia, South Carolina, and Minnesota.

var. **scabriuscula** (Del.) Vainio, Act. Soc. Faun. Flor. Fenn. 4:338. 1887.
   Cenomyce scabriuscula Del., in Duby, Bot. Gall. ed. 2:623. 1830. *Cl. furcata* f.
   recurva (Ach.) Hoffm.
Podetia more or less coralloid or sorediate, sometimes squamulose, the cortex
more or less broken, partly wanting toward the top, whitish.
On soil, New Hampshire, Massachusetts, Minnesota, and Iowa.

var. **Finkii** Vainio, Minn. Bot. Stud. 3:217. 1903.
Podetia rather stout, irregularly branched, more or less squamulose; cups
irregular and sometimes perforate, the margins subentire to dentate or proliferate,
the ranks usually 2 or 3, the upper ones often without cups.
On soil, Massachusetts and Minnesota.

24. **Cladonia palamaea** (Ach.) Fink n. comb.
   Baeomyces spinosus var. *palamaeus* Ach., Meth. Lich. 359. 1803. *Cl. furcata*
      var. *palamaea* (Ach.) Nyl. *Cl. furcata* f. *paradoxa* (Vainio) Fink. *Cenomyce*
      furcata var. *subulata* Floerke. *Cl. multiformis* Merrill.
Primary thallus rarely persistent, composed of commonly middle-sized, irregularly lobed or crenate, flat to ascending, scattered or clustered, greenish gray to
yellowish squamules; white below; podetia arising from the primary thallus, cylindrical, becoming thickened at the axils, irregularly and dichotomously much-
branched, erect, often squamulose toward the base, sometimes fissured and gaping, the cortex continuous or subcontinuous and areolate, greenish gray to commonly brownish to olive-brown, or remaining greenish gray below; cups gradually
or abruptly dilated, sometimes perforate, or finely sievelike, the margin dentate to
repeatedly proliferate; apothecia small to middle-sized, 0.5–1.5 mm. across, solitary
or clustered on the margins of the cups or the apices of the branches, the disk
depressed-convex to strongly convex, sometimes perforate, brown.
On soil, from New England to Minnesota, and recurring in Washington.

25. **Cladonia Herrei** Fink; Hedrick, Mycologia 26:157. 1934.
Primary thallus composed of small to middle-sized, usually elongated and finally
several times deeply lobed, commonly ascending, flat or slightly inward-rolled,
clustered or scattered and sometimes disappearing, greenish gray to brownish
squamules, their lobes often crenate; whitish below; podetia arising from
squamules of the primary thallus or from dying podetia, long and slender, erect
or ascending, subdichotomously much-spreading-branched, without squamules or
more or less squamulose, sometimes throughout, the upper squamules much
smaller and round, with little or no lobing, cylindrical, the cortex subcontinuous
to chinky or rough and subareolate, the areoles continuous or finally and rarely
somewhat scattered, the sides and axils rarely perforate, the sterile tips forked and
spinous-pointed, sometimes perforate, greenish gray to olive-brown, very rarely cup-
bearing; cups small; apothecia small, 0.3–0.6 mm. across, on or below the ends of
obtuse branches, or very rarely on the margins of cups, commonly clustered or
conglomerate, the disk strongly convex to subspherical, light to darker brown, or
finally blackish.
In crevices of rocks, California.

26. **Cladonia rangiformis** Hoffm., Deutschl. Fl. 2:114. 1796.
Primary thallus composed of middle-sized, irregularly crenate or incised-crenate, ascending, flat, scattered or clustered, greenish gray to whitish greenish gray
or olive-brown, finally dying squamules; white below; podetia arising from the
primary thallus, dying at the base, cylindrical, cupless, dichotomously much-
branched, the axils rarely dilated, the branches spreading and commonly suberect,
the apices slender and pointed or rarely obtuse and thickened, the sides entire
to subentire, crowded or clustered, rarely sorediate in part, corticate, the cortex
scattered and forming small patches, smooth or rarely warty to chinky, rarely
more or less squamulose, colored like the primary thallus; apothecia small,
0.5–0.7 mm. across, solitary or clustered on the apices of the branches, the disk
convex, brown.
On soil, Virginia.

var. **pungens** (Ach.) Vainio, Act. Soc. Faun. Flor. Fenn. 4:361, 362. 1887.
Lichen pungens Ach., Lich. Suec. Prod. 202. 1798. *Cl. furcata* var. *pungens*
(Ach.) E. Fries.

Podetia slender, the axils sometimes perforate or shortly fissured, the lower
part of the cortex subcontinuous, destitute of squamules, occasionally whitish.
On soil, New England, Florida, Alabama, and Minnesota.

27. **Cladonia santensis** Tuck., Am. Journ. Sci. 25:427. 1858.

Primary thallus commonly persistent, composed of thickened, short to elongated, laciniate and crenate, ascending, crowded to clumped, granulose, greenish
gray to whitish squamules; white below; podetia arising from the primary thallus,
fragile, subcylindrical with tips dilated and swollen but cupless, rarely branched,
the apices perforated, the cortex becoming more or less granulose, colored like
the primary thallus; apothecia small, 0.3–0.7 mm. across, clustered and heaped on
the apices of podetia and branches, the disk convex, brown or reddish brown.
On soil, North Carolina, South Carolina, Alabama, and Texas.

28. **Cladonia exasperatula** Merrill, Bryologist 27:22. 1924.

Primary thallus persistent, composed of small, becoming elongated, crenate
or often digitately lobed, usually ascending, grayish white squamules; white below;
podetia arising from the primary squamules, rather short, 0.5–2 cm. long, erect,
slender, cylindrical and cupless, or enlarged at the tips to form cups, the cortex
strongly verrucose, verrucae often elongated into coralloid squamules; cups
narrow, perforate, often gaping, proliferate, the tips of the proliferations sterile,
black, or with apothecia; apothecia small, 0.5 mm. across or smaller, round to
irregular, usually clustered, the disk convex, pale brown to dark brown.
On old wood, Sanford, Florida.

29. **Cladonia floridana** Vainio, in Sandst., Clad. Exsicc. no. 1196. 1925. *Cl.*
daytoniana Merrill.

Primary thallus composed of abundant and persistent, small to middle-sized,
long, slender, and cylindrical, deeply and usually crenately lobed, commonly
ascending, flat or inward-rolled, greenish gray squamules; white below; podetia
arising from squamules of the primary thallus, of medium length, rather slender,
erect, much branched above and often sparingly so below, without squamules or
squamulose below, the cortex continuous and smooth to smoothly and obscurely
areolate, the areoles finally more or less scattered, the axils sometimes perforate,
the tips rarely and obscurely spinous, but commonly obtuse and fruit-bearing,
cupless, but the perforate fruit-bearing tips rarely simulating cups, colored like
the primary thallus; apothecia small, 0.3–0.7 mm. across, solitary or clustered
on the ends of branches, the disk convex to strongly convex, brown.
On palmetto roots, near Sanford, Florida.

30. **Cladonia crispata** (Ach.) Flot., in Wendt., Therm. Warmbr. 96. 1839.
Baeomyces turbinatus var. *crispata* Ach., Meth. Lich. 341. 1803. *Cl. furcata*
var. *crispata* (Ach.) Floerke. *Cl. crispata* var. *infundibulifera* (Schaer.)
Vainio. *Cl. crispata* var. *virgata* (Ach.) Vainio.

Primary thallus composed of middle-sized, digitate-laciniate or crenate, ascending, flat or inward-rolled, scattered or rarely clustered squamules, forming a
compact, greenish gray or olive-brown, persistent or dying crust; white below
or turning brownish or reddish toward the base; podetia arising from the primary
thallus, often dying at the base, subcylindrical or irregularly turgescent, radially
or sympodially branched, the branches suberect to spreading, solitary or clustered,
forming clumps, erect, the cortex subcontinuous or dispersed-areolate, the areoles
more or less raised, greenish gray or variously whitish, reddish or brownish green;
cups small, abruptly dilated, borne at the apices of the branches, the margin
repeatedly proliferate, sometimes perforate or sievelike; apothecia small to
middle-sized, 0.5–0.7 mm. across, subsolitary or clustered at the apices of the

short branches or at the ends of the proliferations of the cups, the disk flat or convex, brown or rarely brick-red.

On soil, from New England to Delaware, and westward to the Pacific Coast.

var. **divulsa** (Del.) Arn., Lich. Tirol. XXI. 106. 1880.
Cenomyce divulsa Del., in Duby, Bot. Gall. 625. 1830.
Podetia commonly squamulose, the squamules narrowly laciniate and crenate.
On soil, New York and Michigan.

var. **gracilescens** (Rabenh.) Vainio, Act. Soc. Faun. Flor. Fenn. 4:395, 396. 1887.
Cl. rangiferina var. *gracilescens* Rabenh., Clad. Eur. Suppl. pl. 31, f. 22, 23. 1863.
Podetia dying below and slowly growing above, cupless or bearing very narrow, open cups; the cupless apices closed and pointed or open and obtuse; apothecia small, on the margins of the cups or at the ends of branches.
On soil, New Hampshire.

31. **Cladonia squamosa** (Scop.) Hoffm., Deutschl. Fl. 2:125. 1796.
Lichen squamosus Scop., Fl. Carn. ed. 2. 2:368. 1772.
Primary thallus commonly persistent, composed of middle-sized or rarely large, crenate, irregularly subdigitate or subpinnate-laciniate, ascending, flat or inward-rolled, scattered or clustered, greenish gray to ashy or brownish squamules, rarely forming a compact crust; white below; podetia arising from the primary thallus, rarely dying at the base, subcylindrical or rarely trumpet-shaped or top-shaped, clustered, erect, ascending, reclining or irregularly flexuous, commonly more or less irregularly or radiately branched, the branches erect or spreading, the axils frequently open, the cortex areolate or subcontinuous toward the base, commonly squamulose, sorediate above, ashy, greenish gray, olive-green, or brown, or these colors variegated; cups common, abruptly dilated, middle-sized or small, usually perforate, the margin repeatedly proliferate; apothecia small, 0.5–0.7 mm. across, subsolitary or clustered on the margin of the cups or the apices of the branches or proliferations, the disk flat to convex, pale or darker brown.

On soil and old wood, throughout the United States.

var. **denticollis** (Hoffm.) Floerke; Vainio, Act. Soc. Faun. Flor. Fenn. 4:421. 1887.
Cl. denticollis Hoffm., Deutschl. Fl. 2:125. 1796.
Podetia cup-bearing, cortex absent or scattered, at least above, rarely bearing scattered granules.
On soil, usually over rocks, New England, New York, Minnesota, and Washington.

f. **rigida** (Del.) Sandst., Abhandl. Naturw. Verein. Bremen 18:427. pl. 24, f. 3. 1906.
Cenomyce squamosa f. *rigida* Del., in Duby, Bot. Gall. 625. 1830.
Podetia rigid, erect, mostly cup-bearing, gray to olive-green, densely granulose and bearing scattered, minute to small squamules.
On soil, Ohio.

var. **muricella** (Del.) Vainio, Act. Soc. Faun. Flor. Fenn. 4:431, 432. 1887.
Cenomyce squamosa var. *muricella* Del. in Duby, Bot. Gall. ed. 2. 626. 1830.
Podetia cupless, commonly decorticate, almost destitute of squamules above, or the squamules small.
On soil, New Hampshire, California, and Washington.

var. **multibrachiata** (Floerke) Vainio, Act. Soc. Faun. Flor. Fenn. 4:437. 1887.
Cl. squamosa var. *asperella* f. *multibrachiata* Floerke, Clad. Comm. 133. 1828.
Cl. squamosa f. *phyllopoda* Vainio. *Cl. squamosa* f. *pityrea* Arn.

Podetia cup-bearing, almost destitute of squamules.
On soil, Massachusetts, New York, Iowa, and Minnesota.
var. **phyllocoma** (Rabenh.) Vainio, Act. Soc. Faun. Flor. Fenn. 4:441, 442. 1887.
Cl. squamosa var. *macrophylla* f. *phyllocoma* Rabenh., Clad. Eur. Exsicc. pl. 26, no. 20. 1860.
Podetia cup-bearing, squamulose even to the apices, the squamules commonly large.
On soil, New York, Virginia, and Minnesota.
f. **frondosa** (Del.) Harm., Bull. Soc. Sci. Nancy II. 14:357. pl. 7, f. 23. 1896.
Cenomyce squamosa f. *frondosa* Del., in Duby, Bot. Gall. 625. 1830.
Primary thallus composed of large, elongated, ascending, much branched and irregularly margined squamules; whitish below, turning yellowish brown toward the base of the squamules; podetia whitish to ashy, commonly decorticate and sorediate, often densely squamulose, especially toward the apices, rarely cup-bearing.
On old logs, Washington.

32. **Cladonia subsquamosa** (Nyl.) Vainio, Act. Soc. Faun. Flor. Fenn. 4:445. 1887.
Cl. delicata var. *subsquamosa* Nyl., Ann. Mag. Nat. Hist. III. 18:407. 1866.
Primary thallus rarely persistent, when present composed of small to middle-sized, oblong to variously irregular, entire or lobed, greenish gray to olive-brown squamules; white below; podetia arising from the primary thallus, dying at the base, subcylindrical and often hollow, sometimes cup-bearing, irregularly branched, the axils sometimes perforate, the apices cup-bearing, obtuse, perforate or rarely pointed, erect, the cortex warty or areolate or almost all decorticate, squamulose toward the base and squamulose-scaly higher up, whitish or greenish gray to brownish; cups perforate, the margin becoming repeatedly proliferate; apothecia commonly small, 0.5–0.7 mm. across, subsolitary or clustered on the apices of branches, the disk flat to convex, brown.
On soil over rocks, Kentucky, Minnesota, California, Oregon, and Washington.
f. **granulosa** Vainio, Act. Soc. Faun. Flor. Fenn. 4:448, 449. 1887.
Podetia destitute of squamules, sorediate-granulose; cups small, often oblique.
On soil, Oregon.

33. **Cladonia caespiticia** (Pers.) Floerke, Clad. Comm. 8. 1828.
Baeomyces caespiticius Pers., Ann. Bot. Usteri 7:155. 1794.
Primary thallus persistent, composed of subdigitately laciniate, incised, or crenate, ascending, flat or rarely inward-rolled, commonly clustered, greenish gray to whitish or olive-green squamules; white and sorediate below; podetia arising from the primary thallus, subcylindrical or clavate, cupless, scattered, erect, rarely branched, the apices obtuse and always bearing apothecia, decorticate, rarely squamulose, usually ashy; apothecia middle-sized to large, 0.75–3 mm. across, solitary or clustered, the disk flat to convex, brown to reddish brown.
On rocks and old wood, throughout the United States east of the Rocky Mountains.

34. **Cladonia delicata** (Ehrh.) Floerke, Clad. Comm. 7. 1828.
Lichen delicatus Ehrh., Pl. Crypt. 247. 1793. *Cl. delicata* f. *querina* (Pers.) Vainio.
Primary thallus commonly persistent, composed of small, laciniate, incised, or crenate, ascending, flat or inward-rolled, clustered squamules, frequently forming a crust, ashy to greenish gray or greenish; white and more or less sorediate below; podetia arising from the primary thallus, cupless, subcylindrical, clavate or irregularly top-shaped, sometimes slightly branched, scattered or clustered, erect, commonly sorediate and decorticate, the sides more or less fissured, the apices obtuse and terminated by apothecia, or rarely sterile and pointed: apothecia small to

middle-sized, 0.3–1.5 mm. across, solitary or clustered on the apices of the podetia or branches, the disk flat to convex, brown or rarely reddish brown.

On old wood, throughout eastern United States.

35. **Cladonia cenotea** (Ach.) Schaer., Lich. Helv. Spic. 1:35. 1823.

Baeomyces cenoteus Ach., Meth. Lich. 345. pl. 7, f. 7. 1803.

Primary thallus usually persistent, composed of small to middle-sized, irregularly laciniate, incised or subentire, ascending, flat or inward-rolled, scattered or clustered, ashy, greenish gray, brownish, or olive-green squamules; whitish and more or less sorediate below; podetia arising from the primary thallus, of medium length, subcylindrical, decorticate, sorediate, or corticate toward the base, irregularly swollen, rarely branched, sometimes squamulose toward the base, erect, commonly clustered, colored like the primary thallus; cups middle-sized, perforate, the margins commonly proliferate; apothecia small to middle-sized, 0.5–1.5 mm. across, subsolitary or clustered, the disk flat to convex, flesh-colored to brown.

On old logs and on earth, New England, Minnesota, and Washington.

var. **crossota** (Ach.) Nyl., Not. Sällsk. Faun. Flor. Fenn. 5:57. 1861.

Cenomyce cenotea var. *crossota* Ach., Syn. Lich. 272. 1814.

Podetia of medium length, or elongated, more branched than the species, cylindrical or irregularly swollen, erect, the apices commonly bearing cups.

On soil, over rotten wood, and among mosses, Maine and Washington.

f. **exaltata** Nyl.; Vainio, Act. Soc. Faun. Flor. Fenn. 4:481–83. 1887.

Podetia much elongated, subcylindrical, or slender top-shaped.

On soil, Vermont and New Hampshire.

36. **Cladonia glauca** Floerke, Clad. Comm. 140. 1828.

Cl. brachiata var. *furcellata* (Hoffm.) E. Fries.

Primary thallus commonly persistent, composed of middle-sized, irregularly or subdigitately laciniate or incised and crenate, ascending, flat or inward-rolled, scattered or clustered, greenish gray squamules; white below; podetia arising from the primary thallus, cylindrical and elongated, often hollow, cupless or rarely bearing minute cups, variously branched, the branches suberect or rarely spreading, clustered into small clumps, all densely powdery-sorediate and decorticate or rarely corticate and squamulose toward the base, ashy or greenish gray or rarely ashy brown, the apices thin and pointed or rarely obtuse; cups small, commonly perforate, the margin radiate or proliferate; apothecia small, 0.3–0.7 mm. across, more or less crowded on the apices of irregular branches, the disk flat to convex, often perforate and lobed, brown to bluish brown.

On rotten logs or soil, New Hampshire and Massachusetts.

37. **Cladonia turgida** (Ehrh.) Hoffm., Deutschl. Fl. 2:124. 1796.

Lichen turgidus Ehrh., Pl. Crypt. W. 297. 1793. *Cl. turgida* var. *grypea* Tuck.

Cl. turgida var. *conspicua* Del.

Primary thallus commonly persistent, composed of large, foliose, laciniate or irregularly or dichotomously lobed, ascending or nearly erect, flat, convex and canaliculately rolled or concave and inward-rolled, often crowded, greenish gray to ashy squamules; white below; podetia arising from the primary thallus, sometimes dying at the base, turbinate or subcylindrical, more or less branched, the branches suberect, the axils more or less open, scattered or clustered in clumps, erect or ascending, the cortex areolate or continuous, the apices cupless, obtuse and branched, or bearing imperfect cups, more or less squamulose, colored like the primary thallus, with apices frequently becoming brown; cups somewhat dilated, shallow, perforate to sievelike, the margin radiately proliferate; apothecia small to middle-sized, 0.5–2 mm. across, borne on the apices of the branches or proliferations, frequently short-stalked, the disk flat to convex, brown to rarely reddish brown, often perforate.

On soil, throughout northern United States.

38. **Cladonia corymbosula** Nyl., Flora 59:560. 1876.
    Cl. pileolata Nyl.
    Primary thallus composed of small to middle-sized, narrowly cut-lobed, flat
or ascending, clustered, greenish gray to grayish, finally disappearing squamules;
white below; podetia arising from squamules of the primary thallus, very short to
short, cylindrical, without cups but always finally fruited, sometimes corymbosely
or erectly parallel-branched, the sides often chinky, obscurely ribbed, or warty,
or finally minutely areolate, the areoles sometimes scattered, usually squamulose;
apothecia small to middle-sized, 0.5–1.5 mm. across, sessile on the ends of
podetia or their branches, commonly clustered, the disk convex to subspherical,
brick-red or infrequently brown.
    On soil, Lookout Mountain, Tennessee (doubtfully included).

39. **Cladonia mitrula** Tuck., in Darl., Fl. Cestr. ed. 3. 444. 1853.
    Cl. mitrula f. *imbricatula* (Nyl.) Vainio.
    Primary thallus commonly persistent, composed of small to middle-sized,
irregularly or subdigitately laciniate or crenate, flat, ascending or suberect, clustered, ashy to greenish gray squamules; white below; podetia arising from the
primary thallus, cylindrical, cupless, always terminated by apothecia, somewhat
branched toward the apex, the branches suberect and spreading, the sides sometimes fissured, the axils sometimes open, subsolitary to crowded, erect, the cortex
continuous or composed of contiguous areoles, rarely in part decorticate and
sorediate, sometimes more or less squamulose, colored like the primary thallus;
apothecia small to middle-sized, 0.5–2 mm. across, sometimes perforate, solitary or
clustered on the apices of podetia and branches, the disk flat to convex, brown
to lighter or reddish brown.
    On soil, throughout the United States.

40. **Cladonia apodocarpa** Robbins, Rhodora 27:211. 1925.
    Primary thallus persistent, composed of middle-sized to large, broad to
elongated, entire to sinuate or crenate, ascending, greenish white squamules;
podetia arising from the primary squamules, very short, 0.5 cm. or less in length,
or apparently lacking, abruptly enlarged from the base, cupless; apothecia middle-
sized to large, 1–2 mm. across, solitary to aggregated on the tips of the podetia,
the disk flat to convex, brown or rarely brownish black.
    On soil, from Massachusetts to Virginia.

41. **Cladonia symphycarpa** (Ach.) E. Fries, Lich. Suec. Exsicc. fasc. 8. 20. 1826.
    Lichen symphycarpus Ach., Lich. Suec. 198. 1798. *Cl. symphycarpa* var. *epi-
        phylla* Tuck.
    Primary thallus persistent, composed of middle-sized, round-lobed to crenate,
ascending, greenish gray to brownish squamules; white below; podetia arising from
the primary thallus or rarely wanting, subcylindrical to subclavate, short or
rarely longer, unbranched or branched with short and commonly pointed branches,
cupless, erect, the cortex subcontinuous or partly areolate, colored like the primary
thallus; apothecia small to middle-sized, 0.5–2 mm. across, solitary or clustered on
the branches of the podetia or rarely sessile on the squamules of the primary
thallus, the disk flat to convex, brown.
    On soil, from Maine to Florida, and westward to Texas and Minnesota.

42. **Cladonia subcariosa** Nyl., Flora 59:560. 1876.
    Cl. gracilis var. *symphocarpea* Tuck. *Cl. clavulifera* Vainio.
    Primary thallus persistent, composed of middle-sized to large, subdichoto-
mously or irregularly laciniate, wavy to crenate, flat, ascending to suberect,
clustered, greenish gray to ashy or olive-brown squamules; white below or becoming dark toward the base; podetia arising from the primary thallus, short and
stout, subcylindrical or the upper part becoming thickened, rarely and but sparingly branched, the sides entire or very rarely fissured, the axils entire or becoming

perforate, subsolitary to clustered, suberect or rarely ascending, the cortex sub-continuous to areolate, the areoles subcontiguous, destitute of squamules, cupless, colored like the primary thallus; apothecia middle-sized to rather large, 0.5–4 mm. across, always present, clustered or conglomerate on the apices of podetia and branches, the disk flat to convex, brown or rarely reddish brown.

On soil, from New England to Tennessee, and in Minnesota, Colorado, and California.

43. **Cladonia cariosa** (Ach.) Spreng., Syst. Veg. 4:272. 1827.
Lichen cariosus Ach., Lich. Suec. 198. 1798. *Cl. sobolescens* Nyl. nomen nudum.
Primary thallus persistent or replaced by new squamules, composed of irregu-larly laciniate, incised, or crenate, concave, flat, inward- to outward-rolled, as-cending or suberect, clustered or rarely scattered, greenish gray to olive-green squamules; whitish and sorediate below, or brownish toward the base; podetia arising from the primary thallus, subcylindrical, sorediate, becoming laterally grooved and fissured, freely branched, clustered or subsolitary, usually suberect, cupless, the cortex subcontinuous or areolate, the areoles frequently scattered, pale greenish gray to whitish; apothecia middle-sized to large, 1–3 mm. across, clustered to conglomerate, the disk flat to convex, brown to rarely reddish brown.

On earth or rarely on old wood, throughout the United States.

f. **cribrosa** (Wallr.) Vainio, Act. Soc. Faun. Flor. Fenn. 10:50. 1894.
Patellaria fusca f. *cribrosa* Wallr., Naturg. Flecht. Cen. 121. 1829.
Podetia pierced with short or longer openings, destitute of squamules, the cortex dispersed.
On soil, Tennessee, New Mexico, and Washington.

f. **squamulosa** (Müll. Arg.) Vainio, Act. Soc. Faun. Flor. Fenn. 10:57. 1894.
Cl. symphycarpa f. *squamulosa* Müll. Arg., Flora 65:298. 1882.
The podetia squamulose, densely so in ours.
On soil, Colfax County, New Mexico.

44. **Cladonia leptothallina** Merrill, Bryologist 27:21, 22. 1924.
Primary thallus persistent, composed of small, round, appressed or imbricate, ashy green squamules, the margins sinuous, crenate, or cleft; white below; podetia arising from the primary thallus, short to somewhat elongated, cylindrical to sub-cylindrical, ashy, branched toward the apices, the branches short, more or less spinous and swollen, corticate, the cortex becoming areolate and the areoles sepa-rated by decorticate areas, rarely squamulose toward the base; apothecia small, 0.3–0.5 mm. across, solitary or rarely clustered on the tips of podetia and branches, the disk convex, brown.

On soil, at the base of palmetto trees, Sanford, Florida.

45. **Cladonia Beaumontii** (Tuck.) Fink n. comb.
Cl. santensis var. *Beaumontii* Tuck., Syn. Lich. 1:245. 1882. *Cl. stenophylliza*
Vainio nomen nudum. *Cl: stenophyllia* Merrill.
Primary thallus persistent, composed of numerous, small to middle-sized, irregular, clustered, crenate or digitately incised, pale greenish gray to whitish, erect or ascending squamules; white below; podetia arising from the primary thallus, short to elongated, slender, cylindrical, cupless, dichotomously branched, the branches sometimes much entangled, more or less squamulose, the cortex minutely areolate, scattered, colored like the primary thallus; apothecia minute to small, 0.1–0.3 mm. across, solitary or clustered on the apices of the branches, the disk convex, brownish to brown.

On soil, Massachusetts, North Carolina, Florida, and Alabama.

46. **Cladonia decorticata** (Floerke) Spreng., Syst. Veg. 4:271. 1827.
Capitularia decorticata Floerke, in Web. & Mohr, Beitr. Naturk. 2:297. 1810.
Primary thallus finally dying and usually more or less replaced by small, laciniate or crenate, somewhat concave or inward-rolled, scattered or clustered,

light greenish gray to greenish white squamules; white below, or brownish toward the base; podetia arising from the primary thallus, cylindrical, cupless, more or less dichotomously or irregularly branched, the branches commonly erect or spreading, the fertile apices often dilated, the sterile ones obtuse or pointed, clustered or subsolitary, erect or rarely ascending, variously sorediate, areolate, and squamulose, decorticate toward the base, greenish gray to brownish; apothecia middle-sized to large, 0.75–4.5 mm. across, clustered to conglomerate, borne at the apices of the podetia or branches, the disk flat to convex, brown or rarely reddish brown.

On soil, New Hampshire and Minnesota.

47. **Cladonia acuminata** (Ach.) Norrl.; Vainio, Act. Soc. Faun. Flor. Fenn. 10:73. 1894.
    Cenomyce pityrea var. *acuminata* Ach., Syn. Lich. 254. 1814. *Cl. Norrlini* Vainio.

Primary thallus persistent or rarely dying, composed of minute to small or middle-sized, smooth to somewhat granulose, crenate or incised-crenate, scattered or crowded, marginally ascending, greenish gray squamules; white below; podetia arising from the primary thallus, cylindrical, slender, short to more or less elongated, clustered or rarely solitary, more or less irregularly branched toward the apices and rarely so below, the branches short, erect, the apices acuminate, more or less minutely granulose, becoming squamulose below, decorticate above, the cortex subcontinuous and warty or composed of minute, scattered areoles, colored like the primary thallus or grayish white; apothecia minute to small, 0.2–0.7 mm. across, solitary or clustered on the apices of the podetia and branches, the disk convex, reddish brown.

On soil, New Hampshire.

48. **Cladonia gracilis** (L.) Willd., Fl. Berol. Prodr. 363. 1787.
    Lichen gracilis L., Sp. Fl. 1152. 1753. *Cl. gracilis* var. *ecmocyna* (Ach.) Scriba. *Cl. gracilis* var. *dilatata* (Hoffm.) Vainio pro parte.

Primary thallus commonly persistent, composed of middle-sized, irregularly laciniate or crenate, somewhat flat, inward- or outward-rolled, ascending, clustered or scattered, greenish gray to greenish squamules; white below or turning brownish toward the base; podetia arising from the primary thallus, cylindrical and cupless or trumpet-shaped and cup-bearing, commonly in clusters, erect or ascending, the cortex subcontinuous or composed of contiguous or scattered areoles, rarely squamulose toward the base, greenish gray, ashy, greenish or rarely reddish brown, more or less branched, sometimes dying below; cups middle-sized, abruptly or gradually dilated, regular or subregular, shallow or deep, the margin dentate or proliferate, rarely proliferate from the center; apothecia middle-sized to large, 1–4.5 mm. across, commonly borne on short stalks, solitary or in clusters on the margins of the cups, the disk flat to convex, pale to darker brown.

On soil or rarely on rotten wood, throughout the United States.

var. **dilacerata** Floerke, Clad. Comm. 37. 1828.
    Cl. gracilis var. *dilatata* (Hoffm.) Vainio pro parte. *Cl. gracilis* f. *anthocephala* Floerke.

Podetia irregularly top-shaped and often hollow, more or less squamulose even toward the top; cups rather abruptly dilated, at first somewhat regular but becoming very irregular.

On soil and old logs, throughout northern United States.

var. **chordalis** (Floerke) Schaer., Lich. Helv. Spic. 32. 1823.
    Capitularia gracilis var. *chordalis* Floerke, Ges. Naturf. Freund. Mag. 4:264. 1810. *Cl. gracilis* f. *hybrida* (Hoffm.) Schaer.

Podetia cylindrical and cupless, or in part hollow and cup-bearing, much branched; usually dying toward the base.

On soil, from New England westward throughout northern United States.

var. **aspera** Floerke, Clad. Comm. 40. 1828.
Capitularia gracilis var. *aspera* Floerke, in Web. & Mohr. Beitr. Naturk. 2:259.
  1810.
Podetia slender, proliferously branched, cylindrical and cupless or cup-bearing,
frequently hollow, more or less squamulose; cups few.
On soil, New Hampshire, New York, and Montana.

var. **elongata** (Jacq.) E. Fries, Lich. Eur. 219. 1831.
Lichen elongatus Jacq., Misc. II. 368. pl. 11, fig. 1. 1781. *Cl. gracilis* f. *laontera* Arn. *Cl. gracilis* f. *macroceras* Floerke.
Podetia much elongated, cylindrical and cupless or in part hollow and cup-
bearing, sometimes branched, the sides rarely perforate, branched, the branches
ascending; cups narrow, regular or rarely more or less oblique.
On soil, New England and New York.

49. **Cladonia cornuta** (L.) Schaer., Lich. Helv. Spic. 299. 1833.
Lichen cornutus L., Sp. Pl. 1152. 1753.
Primary thallus composed of middle-sized, irregularly lobate or laciniate,
scattered or crowded, flat or inward- or outward-rolled, rarely dying, greenish
gray squamules; white below, or turning brownish toward the base; podetia arising from the primary thallus, cylindrical, pointed, elongated, hollow, becoming
freely branched, commonly crowded and forming clumps, erect or rarely flexuous,
the upper part of the branches commonly sorediate, the cortex subcontinuous or
subareolate, areoles elevated, rarely squamulose toward the base, greenish gray
to ashy to ashy brown; cups small, gradually or abruptly dilated, the margin
dentate and then proliferate, the cavity deep and sorediate; apothecia middle-
sized to large, 1.5–6 mm. across, solitary or clustered and confluent on the margins of the cups, the stalks short, the disk flat to convex, brown to brick-red or
lighter, commonly pruinose.
On soil, New Hampshire, Ohio, Wisconsin, Minnesota, Nebraska, Montana,
and California.

50. **Cladonia degenerans** (Floerke) Spreng., Syst. Veg. 4:273. 1827.
Baeomyces degenerans Floerke, Ges. Naturf. Freund. Mag. 1:283. 1807. *Cl.
  degenerans* f. *euphorea* (Ach.) Floerke. *Cl. degenerans* f. *cladomorpha* (Ach.)
  Vainio.
Primary thallus soon dying, composed of usually middle-sized, irregularly
laciniate-lobed, ascending, flat, or slightly inward- or outward-rolled, scattered or
clustered, greenish gray or rarely olive-green squamules; white below and turning
brownish toward the base; podetia arising from the primary thallus, more or
less top-shaped, and cup-bearing, or subcylindrical and cupless, branched, the
sides rarely more or less grooved, commonly crowded into large or smaller clumps,
erect or ascending, the cortex areolate, the areoles elevated, scattered or in part
continuous, more or less squamulose, colored like the primary thallus or variegated; cups middle-sized, gradually or abruptly dilated, usually more or less
irregular, the cavity rather deep, the margin and often the center of the cups
proliferate, the ranks 1–5; apothecia small to middle-sized, 0.5–2 mm. across,
solitary or clustered on the apices of podetia or proliferations, the disk flat to
convex, brown to pale or reddish brown.
On soil, from New Hampshire to Virginia, and westward to Washington.

51. **Cladonia cerasphora** Vainio, Act. Soc. Faun. Flor. Fenn. 10:167. 1894.
Cl. degenerans f. *hypophylla* Nyl.
Primary thallus sometimes disappearing, composed of middle-sized, flat, somewhat elongated, more or less crenate or lobed squamules, greenish gray, varying
toward whitish; white or dirty whitish below; podetia arising from the primary
thallus, short and squamulose, subcylindrical, erect, ascending, or flexuous, cupless and pointed, sometimes sparingly branched, the axils frequently open, the
cortex subcontinuous, but often chinky-areolate; apothecia unknown.
On soil, New York.

52. **Cladonia gracilescens** (Floerke) Vainio, Act. Soc. Faun. Flor. Fenn. 10:159. 1894.

Capitularia gracilescens Floerke, Ges. Naturf. Freund. Mag. 4:321. 1810.

Primary thallus rarely persistent, composed of middle-sized, subentire to slightly lobed and crenate, flat, scattered, greenish gray to rarely greenish brown squamules; white below; podetia arising from squamules of primary thallus, elongated, cylindrical, often hollow, crowded and forming dense clusters, erect or ascending, more or less branched toward the apex, the sides subentire or becoming more or less fissured, cortex subcontinuous or areolate, the areoles elevated and irregular, squamulose, colored like the primary thallus; cups more or less regular, gradually or rather abruptly dilated, the cavity deep, the center and rarely the margin repeatedly proliferate; apothecia small to middle-sized, 0.5–1.5 mm. across, borne on short stalks on the margin of the cups, the disk flat to convex, dark brown or rarely reddish brown.

On soil, New Hampshire and Colorado.

53. **Cladonia pyxidata** (L.) Hoffm., Deutschl. Fl. 2:121. 1795.

Lichen pyxidatus L., Sp. Pl. 2:1151. 1753. *Cl. pyxidata* var. *neglecta* (Floerke) Mass. *Cl. pyxidata* var. *chlorophaea* (Spreng.) Floerke. *Cl. pyxidata* f. *costata* Floerke. *Cl. pyxidata* var. *chlorophaea* f. *lepidophora* Floerke.

Primary thallus commonly persistent, composed of irregularly or digitately incised or lobate, flat, concave, or rarely convex, commonly ascending, clustered or scattered, greenish gray to whitish or greenish squamules; lighter and sorediate below; podetia arising from the primary thallus, top-shaped and often hollow, erect, closely clustered, the cortex areolate or verrucose or subcontinuous toward the base, sometimes decorticate and sorediate toward the top, rarely more or less squamulose, greenish gray to ashy or olive-green; cups regular or irregular, gradually or abruptly dilated, the cavity sorediate or corticate, the margin dentate or proliferate; apothecia middle-sized, 1–4 mm. across, solitary to conglomerate, sessile or shortly stalked on the margin of the cups, the disk flat to convex, brown. (PLATE 21.)

On soil or rotten wood, throughout the United States.

var. **pocillum** (Ach.) Flot., Linnaea 17:19. 1843.

Baeomyces pocillum Ach., Meth. Lich. 336. pl. 8, f. 6. 1803.

Primary thallus composed of thick, round-lobed or incised, closely adnate or slightly ascending, more or less imbricated squamules, closely packed into a greenish or brownish crust; podetia commonly sterile.

On soil, throughout the United States.

54. **Cladonia mateocyatha** Robbins, Rhodora 27:50. 1925.

Primary thallus persistent or disappearing, composed of middle-sized to large, elongated, entire to crenate, usually ascending, greenish gray or olive-green squamules; white or sordid below; podetia arising from the primary thallus, short, 0.5–3 cm. long, erect, rather slender to stout, enlarged at the apex to form the cup, the cortex continuous or areolate, smooth to slightly roughened, greenish gray to olivaceous or darker; cups imperforate, narrow to rather broad, shallow, simple to several-ranked, proliferations usually from the sides of the cups, rarely central, the apices usually terminated by apothecia; apothecia small to middle-sized, 0.5–1 mm. across, usually round, the disk convex, pale brown to dark brown.

On soil, Massachusetts, Connecticut, and the District of Columbia.

55. **Cladonia verticillata** Hoffm., Deutschl. Fl. 2:122. 1796.

Cl. verticillata var. *evoluta* T. Fries. *Cl. verticillata* f. *phyllocephala* Oliv.

Primary thallus commonly persistent, composed of middle-sized or larger, irregularly subcuneate or crenately lobed, or even incised-lobate, flat or somewhat inward-rolled, ascending, clustered or scattered, greenish gray to ashy, olive, or brownish squamules; white below or darkening toward the base; podetia arising from the primary thallus, hollow and rarely turbinate, subsolitary or clustered

into small clumps, erect or rarely ascending, the sides rarely somewhat chinky, the cortex subcontinuous, grooved or areolate with commonly closely contiguous and somewhat raised areoles, destitute of squamules or rarely more or less squamulose at the base of the podetia or at .the margins of the cups, greenish gray to ashy, yellowish or brownish, or these colors variegated; cups middle-sized to large, usually abruptly dilated, shallow, the margin subentire to dentate, the closed cavity of the cup commonly proliferate, and the proliferations cup-bearing; apothecia small to middle-sized, 0.5–2.5 mm. across, round or irregular and perforate, sessile or on short stalks, solitary or clustered on the margin of the cups, the disk flat to convex, pale or darker brown. (PLATE 23.)
On soil, throughout the United States.

var. **cervicornis** (Ach.) Flot., Linnaea 22:380. 1849.
Lichen cervicornis Ach., Lich. Suec. 184. 1798. *Cl. verticillata* var. *subcervicornis* Vainio.
Primary thallus persistent; podetia rather short; cups becoming one or rarely more times proliferate from the center or from the margin of the cups, or even from the sides of the podetia.
On soil, throughout the United States.

56. **Cladonia calycantha** Del.; Nyl., Flora 38:673. 1855.
Primary thallus persistent, or finally dying, composed of middle-sized, lobate, incised or crenate, ascending, concave and often slightly inward-rolled, commonly clustered, greenish gray to whitish green squamules; white below, commonly turning dark toward the base; podetia arising from primary thallus, cylindrical, hollow, clustered, sometimes branched, commonly erect or rarely somewhat curved, the cortex subcontinuous or areolate, colored like the primary thallus; cups small, abruptly dilated, the margin commonly several times proliferate; apothecia small to middle-sized, 0.3–1.5 mm. or more across, solitary or rarely clustered and confluent, shortly stalked on the margins of the cups, the disk flat to convex, brown to reddish brown.
On soil, Florida.

57. **Cladonia fimbriata** (L.) E. Fries, Lich. Eur. 222. 1831.
Lichen fimbriatus L., Sp. Pl. 1152. 1753.
Primary thallus commonly persistent, composed of digitately or irregularly incised or lobed, flat or concave, frequently inward- or outward-rolled, ascending, clustered or scattered, middle-sized squamules, greenish gray to greenish or whitish; white below or darkening toward the base, rarely sorediate below and along the edges; podetia arising from the primary thallus, cylindrical or rarely top-shaped, usually clustered into groups, erect, or rarely ascending or irregularly curved, commonly decorticate and more or less sorediate, or corticate toward the base and below the cups, the cortex areolate, warty or subcontinuous, destitute of squamules or more or less squamulose toward the base, colored like the primary thallus, the apices frequently forked or pointed; cups well developed or abortive, abruptly or gradually dilated, regular or irregular, the cavity deep and sorediate, the margin usually dentate or proliferate; apothecia middle-sized, 0.8–2 mm. across, solitary and rounded or irregularly conglomerate, sessile or stalked on the margins of the cups or on the apices of podetia, the disk flat to convex, brown or reddish brown.
On soil and old wood, throughout the United States.

var. **simplex** (Weiss) Flot.; Vainio, Act. Soc. Faun. Flor. Fenn. 10:256. 1894.
Lichen pyxidatus var. *simplex* Weiss, Pl. Crypt. Gott. 84. 1770. *Cl. fimbriata* var. *simplex* f. *minor* (Hag.) Vainio.
Podetia rather short, erect and straight, cylindrical or narrowly top-shaped; cups well developed, the margin entire or dentate.
On soil, throughout the United States.

var. **prolifera** (Retz.) Mass., Sched. Crit. Lich. Exsicc. no. 155. 1855.
Lichen fimbriatus var. *prolifer* Retz., Fl. Scand. Prodr. 232. 1779.
Podetia long; cups middle-sized, the margin repeatedly proliferate, usually more than one proliferation from each cup, the ranks all cup-bearing, but the terminal cups commonly narrowed; apothecia usually borne on the cups of the higher ranks.
On soil, Maine and Minnesota.

var. **radiata** (Schreb.) E. Fries, Lich. Eur. 223. 1831.
Lichen radiatus Schreb., Spic. Fl. Lips. 122. 1771. *Cl. fimbriata* var. *cornutoradiata* Coem. pro parte.
Podetia commonly long, tubular or elongated top-shaped, commonly cup-bearing; cups small, the margin dentate or proliferate, the ranks 2 or 3, the apices horn-shaped, awl-shaped, or rarely and imperfectly cup-bearing; apothecia sessile or shortly stalked on the margins of the cups.
On soil and old wood, throughout the United States.

var. **subulata** (L.) Vainio, Act. Soc. Faun. Flor. Fenn. 10:282. 1894.
Lichen subulatus L., Sp. Pl. 1153. 1753. *Cl. fimbriata* f. *furcellata* (Hoffm.) Sandst. *Cl. fimbriata* f. *clavata* (Arnold) Hasse. *Cl. fimbriata* var. *cornutoradiata* Coem. pro parte.
Podetia much elongated, usually cupless, rarely and variously branched, erect, and straight or flexuous toward the horn-shaped or awl-shaped apex; apothecia at the apices of the podetia, rather rare.
On soil, especially over rocks, Massachusetts, Maine, New Hampshire, Minnesota, and California.

var. **nemoxyna** (Ach.) Vainio, Act. Soc. Faun. Flor. Fenn. 10:295. 1894.
Baeomyces radiata var. *nemoxyna* Ach., Meth. Lich. 342. 1803. *Cl. fimbriata* f. *fibula* (Hoffm.) Ach.
Podetia becoming very long, cylindrical, cup-bearing, 2- or 3-ranked from the margins of the cups, the sterile apices abortively cup-bearing, horn-shaped, or awl-shaped, erect, suberect, or flexuous; apothecia sessile on the margins of the cups or on short pedicels.
On soil, Massachusetts, Pennsylvania, and Minnesota.

var. **coniocraea** (Floerke) Vainio, Act. Soc. Faun. Flor. Fenn. 10:308. 1894.
Cenomyce coniocraea Floerke, Deutsch. Lich. part 7. 11. 1821. *Cl. coniocraea* f. *tubaeformis* (Hoffm.) E. Fries. *Cl. ochrochlora* f. *ceratodes* Floerke. *Cl. fimbriata* f. *apolepta* (Ach.) Vainio. *Cl. fimbriata* f. *ceratodes* Floerke.
Podetia rather short, cupless and cylindrical, sometimes abortively cup-bearing, rarely short-branched toward the apex, commonly straight and erect; cups rare and small, the margin usually entire. (PLATE 20 *b*.)
On old and rotting wood, throughout the United States.

var. **ochrochlora** (Floerke) Vainio, Act. Soc. Faun. Flor. Fenn. 10:319–22. 1894.
Cl. ochrochlora Floerke, Clad. Comm. 75. 1828.
Podetia often hollow, the sides sometimes more or less fissured, greenish gray to whitish or olive-green; cups narrow and abortive, commonly irregular.
On old wood, New England, Florida, California, and Washington.

58. **Cladonia pityrea** (Floerke) E. Fries, Sched. Crit. Lich. Exsicc. Suec. fasc. 8. 21. 1826.
Capitularia pityrea Floerke, Ges. Naturf. Freund. Mag. 2:15. 1808. *Cl. pityrea* f. *cladomorpha* Floerke.
Primary thallus disappearing, when present composed of subdigitate, laciniate, or crenate, inward-rolled, concave or flat, ascending, clustered or scattered, greenish gray to green squamules; white below; podetia arising from the primary thallus, subcylindrical to top-shaped, and often hollow, scattered or clustered in small clumps, usually erect, more or less irregularly branched, the cortex sub-

continuous and warty or composed of small, raised and contiguous areoles, sometimes squamulose, often cupless, the sterile apices obtuse or pointed, colored like the primary thallus; cups narrow, gradually or abruptly dilated, more or less irregular, the cavity rather shallow, the margin dentate, lacerate or proliferate; apothecia small to middle-sized, 0.5–2.5 mm. across, often conglomerate, borne on short stalks on the margin of the cups or at the cupless apices of podetia, the disk flat to convex, brick-red to brown.

On soil, widely distributed throughout northern United States.

var. **phyllophora** (Mudd) Vainio, Act. Soc. Faun. Flor. Fenn. 10:355. 1894.

Cl. pyxidata var. *pityrea* f. *phyllophora* Mudd. Mon. Brit. Clad. 15. 1865.

Podetia cupless and squamulose.

On soil over rocks, northern Minnesota.

var. **subacuta** Vainio, Act. Soc. Faun. Flor. Fenn. 10:355. 1894.

Podetia always cupless, wholly granulate or sorediate-granulate, or corticate toward the base, seldom squamulose.

On old wood, Minnesota.

59. **Cladonia microphylliza** Merrill, Bryologist 27:22. 1924.

Primary thallus persistent, densely covering the substratum, composed of middle-sized, narrow, long, ascending, irregularly branched, pale greenish gray to whitish or pale brownish squamules, the branches densely covered with minute coralloid branchlets or granules; scarcely lighter below; podetia arising from the primary thallus, whitish, erect or ascending, of moderate length, cylindrical to somewhat irregular, cupless, commonly two or three times branched toward the apex, the branches short, the main axils and sometimes portions of the branches without cortex, the former and sometimes the latter more or less clothed with minute squamules, coralloid branchlets, or granules; apothecia middle-sized, 0.5–1 mm. across, solitary or sometimes clustered on the ends of branches, the disk convex, often irregular, flesh-colored to light brown.

On a rotten cypress log, near Sanford, Florida.

60. **Cladonia foliacea** (Huds.) Schaer., Lich. Helv. Spic. 294. 1833.

Lichen foliaceus Huds., Fl. Angl. 457. 1762. *Cl. alcicornis* (Lightf.) Willd. *Cl. endiviaefolia* E. Fries.

Primary thallus commonly persistent, composed of long, narrow, palmately cleft, irregularly crenate or lobed and incised, ascending, clustered, greenish squamules, the tips and sides bearing darkening fibrils, greenish gray to brownish; white below; podetia arising from the primary thallus, short, cylindrical and often hollow, rarely branched, erect, the cortex subcontinuous or areolate, colored like the primary thallus, rarely squamulose toward the base; cups small, somewhat irregular, the margin subentire to dentate and sometimes proliferate; apothecia middle-sized, 0.8–1.5 mm. across, the disk flat to convex, brick-colored to brown.

On soil, from Massachusetts to Florida, and westward to California and Washington.

61. **Cladonia strepsilis** (Ach.) Vainio, Act. Soc. Faun. Flor. Fenn. 10:403–12. 1894.

Baeomyces strepsilis Ach., Meth. Lich. Suppl. 52. 1803. *Cl. sobolifera* (Del.) Nyl.

Primary thallus persistent or finally dying, composed of middle-sized to large, irregularly or subdichotomously laciniate, plane or concave or slightly inward-rolled, ascending, clustered, rather fragile, greenish gray to olive squamules; white below; podetia arising from the primary thallus, irregularly subcylindrical or dilated toward the apex, cupless, terminated by perfect or imperfect apothecia, sometimes irregularly branched toward the apices, the apices and axils closed or fissured, the sides smooth to chinky, sometimes fissured, the cortex areolate and warty or in part subcontinuous, the warts and areoles often elevated, commonly more or less squamulose, colored like the primary thallus; apothecia small to middle-sized, 0.3–1.2 mm. across, solitary or clustered and heaped on the apices of the branches, the disk flat to convex, becoming dark brown.

On soil, Massachusetts, Tennessee, Florida, and Alabama.

62. **Cladonia botrytes** (Hag.) Willd., Fl. Berol. Prodr. 365. 1787.

Lichen botrytes Hag., Tent. Hist. Lich. 121. pl. 2, f. 9. 1782.

Primary thallus commonly persistent, composed of small, crenate, incised, or various-laciniate, flat, inward-rolled, or rarely convex, commonly ascending, scattered or rarely clustered, greenish gray to straw-colored or olive-green squamules; white below; podetia arising from the primary thallus, slender, cylindrical or subcylindrical, usually branched toward the apex, or rarely toward the base, erect or variously curved or flexuous, the cortex warty or divided into rather small contiguous or scattered areoles, colored like the primary thallus; cups rare and abortive, in the axils of branches when present; apothecia small to middle-sized, 0.4–2 mm. across, round to irregular, frequently clustered or conglomerate, the disk flat to convex, pale flesh-colored to pale brown, rarely somewhat pruinose.

On old wood, from New York to Florida, and westward to Minnesota and Nebraska.

63. **Cladonia piedmontensis** Merrill, Bryologist 27:22, 23. 1924.

Cl. substraminea Nyl., Syn. Lich. 204. 1860 (in part); *Cl. lepidota* E. Fries, in Tuck., Syn. N. A. Lich. 249. 1882 (in part); *Cl. cristatella* f. *lepidifera* Vainio.

Primary thallus persistent or disappearing, composed of small to middle-sized, entire to irregularly incised and lobed, flat, greenish gray to yellowish squamules; white or whitish below; podetia arising from the primary thallus, small to middle-sized, erect, cylindrical to somewhat top-shaped, unbranched or branched above, the axils closed, strongly corticate, the cortex sometimes broken, more or less beset with small, irregularly incised squamules, colored like the primary thallus; cups commonly abortive, irregular; apothecia terminal on the margin of the cups or apices of the podetia, commonly clustered, the disk flat to convex, light brown to brown.

On soil or rarely on old wood, from Massachusetts to Alabama.

64. **Cladonia cyanipes** (Sommerf.) Vainio, Act. Soc. Faun. Flor. Fenn. 10:431. 1894.

Cenomyce cyanipes Sommerf., Phys. Beckr. Saltd. 62. 1826. *Cl. Despreauxii* (Bory.) Tuck. *Cl. carneola* var. *cyanipes* (Sommerf.) E. Fries.

Primary thallus composed of middle-sized or small, laciniate, incised or crenate, ascending, flat or concave, scattered or clustered, often dying, straw-colored to greenish gray squamules; straw-colored below and sometimes sorediate here and along the margins; podetia arising from the primary thallus, elongated, cylindrical, slender and rarely irregularly branched, clustered or scattered, erect or rarely flexuous and curved, the lower part frequently corticate, the cortex dispersed-areolate and warty, the apices pointed or blunt, rarely terminated by apothecia, colored like the primary thallus; apothecia small, 0.3–0.5 mm. across, solitary on the apices of normal branches, the disk commonly convex, pale brown to tinged with brick-red.

On soil, White Mountains, New Hampshire.

65. **Cladonia carneola** E. Fries, Lich. Eur. 233. 1831.

Cenomyce carneola E. Fries, Sched. Crit. fasc. 4. 23. 1824.

Primary thallus persistent or dying, composed of lobate, closely laciniate, or crenate, middle-sized, flat or inward-rolled, ascending, aggregate or scattered, greenish gray or straw-colored squamules; whitish or rarely straw-colored below, turning dark toward the base, sorediate and often slightly granulose; podetia arising from the primary thallus, of medium length, sorediate, cylindrical to top-shaped, hollow, commonly branched, the apices terminated by cups or apothecia, aggregate or subsolitary, erect, colored like the primary thallus, lower part wholly or partly corticate, the cortex areolate or rarely subcontinuous, sorediate above; cups small to middle-sized, abruptly dilated, the margin entire to lobate or repeatedly proliferate; apothecia small to middle-sized, 0.5–1.5 mm. across, solitary or clustered, the disk flat to convex, flesh-colored to livid and rarely brick-red.

On old wood, Oregon and Washington.

OTHER SPECIES REPORTED

Cladonia Blakei Robbins—Washington, D.C.
Cladonia botryocarpa Merrill—Florida.
Cladonia caespiticia f. plumosa Ach.—Maine.
Cladonia cetrarioides Schwein.—North America.
Cladonia chlorophaea f. prolifera (Arn.) Herre—California.
Cladonia digitata var. monstrosa (Ach.) Vainio—New Mexico.
Cladonia endoxantha Vainio—Florida.
Cladonia fimbriata var. Balfourii (Cromb.) Vainio—New Hampshire, South Carolina, Georgia, and Florida.
Cladonia Floerkeana var. intermedia Hepp.—Florida.
Cladonia heteromorpha Merrill—North Carolina.
Cladonia hypoxantha Tuck.—Maryland and Florida.
Cladonia mitis f. prostrata Sandst.—Massachusetts.
Cladonia mitrula f. dissectula Merrill—Florida.
Cladonia pachycladodes Vainio—Florida.
Cladonia papillaria var. stipata (Floerke) Merrill—Maine.
Cladonia squamosa f. murina Scriba—New Hampshire.
Cladonia stenophyllodes Vainio—Florida.
Cladonia uncialis f. turgescens Del.—Massachusetts.

133. **Stereocaulon** Schreb., Gen. Pl. 2:768. 1791.

Primary thallus crustose, granulose, warty, rudimentary, devoid of differentiation into layers, soon disappearing; podetia arising from the primary thallus, much branched, twisted and irregular, solid, decorticate, the central portion composed of closely interwoven, longitudinally extending hyphae, the medullary layer of tangled hyphae, surrounded by the irregular, warty, algal layer of loosely interwoven hyphae; apothecia small to middle-sized, lateral or terminal, the disk flat to convex, reddish brown to brown or black, the exciple colored like the disk, soon disappearing; hypothecium hyaline; hymenium hyaline or brownish to brown above; paraphyses unbranched; asci clavate; spores commonly 8, hyaline, fusiform to acicular, 3– rarely 7-septate.

The algal host is Protococcus.

A. Branches of podetia smooth and naked below
  B. Squamules passing into minute granules
    C. More or less squamulose above
      D. Squamules grayish white to brownish . . . . . . 8. S. denudatum
      D. Squamules greenish gray to ashy or chalky white . . . 3. S. albicans
    C. Densely squamulose above . . . . 7. S. alpinum botryosum
  B. Squamules passing into tiny coralloid branchlets . . . . . 4. S. coralloides
A. Branches of podetia not always smooth and naked below
  B. Podetia more or less tomentose
    C. Branches thinly tomentose
      D. Branches more or less squamulose
        E. Podetia much branched, densely clustered . . . . 5. S. paschale
        E. Podetia becoming branched, clustered . . . . . . 7. S. alpinum
      D. Branches densely squamulose . . . . 1. S. condensatum
    C. Branches densely tomentose
      D. Podetia moderately long, squamules densely crowded
        above, few below . . . . 6. S. tomentosum

D. Podetia elongated, squamules more or less
    scattered . . . . 6. S. tomentosum simplex
  B. Podetia densely sorediate at the tips . . . . 2. S. pileatum

1. **Stereocaulon condensatum** Hoffm., Deutschl. Fl. 130. 1796.

Podetia very short, stout, sparingly branched, the branches sometimes thinly tomentose, densely squamulose, the squamules small, ashy gray to brownish or whitish, conglomerate, passing into minute, blunt branchlets; apothecia small to middle-sized, 0.6–2 mm. across, terminal, clustered, the disk flat to convex, rough, brownish to dark reddish brown; spores acicular, 3-septate, 20–36 × 1.5–3 μ.

On soil, New Hampshire, Massachusetts, and Connecticut.

2. **Stereocaulon pileatum** Ach., Lich. Univ. 582. 1810.

Podetia very short, erect, slender, sparingly branched, squamulose, the tips densely sorediate, the squamules small, ashy to gray, more or less scattered, passing into minute coralloid granules; apothecia small to middle-sized, 0.6–2 mm. across, terminal, the disk flat to slightly convex, reddish brown to brown; spores acicular, 3-septate, 18–30 × 3–4.5 μ.

On soil, New England and New York.

3. **Stereocaulon albicans** T. Fries, Ster. Pil. Comm. 36. 1857.

S. nanum Tuck. *S. nanodes* Tuck. *S. tenellum* Tuck.

Podetia short, slender, clustered to conglomerate, branched, the branches slender, more or less entangled, smooth and sometimes blackening below, more or less squamulose above, the squamules greenish gray to ashy or chalky white, passing into powdery granules; apothecia small to middle-sized, 0.6–1.2 mm. across, terminal, the disk flat to convex, reddish brown; spores acicular, 3-septate, 24–41 × 2.5–3 μ.

On rocks and soil, New Hampshire, South Dakota, Colorado, Arizona, California, and Washington.

4. **Stereocaulon coralloides** E. Fries, Lich. Exsicc. no. 118. 1817.

Podetia short to moderately long, stout, solitary or clustered, erect or ascending, much branched, the branches smooth below, squamulose above, the squamules more or less scattered, greenish gray to ashy, passing into numerous, tiny, crowded, coralloid branchlets; apothecia small to middle-sized, 0.5–2 mm. across, lateral or terminal, rarely clustered, the disk flat to convex, reddish brown to brownish black, smooth to slightly rough; spores acicular, 3- rarely 5–7-septate, 22–40 × 2.5–4 μ. (PLATE 24.)

On soil, New England, New York, North Carolina, and South Carolina.

5. **Stereocaulon paschale** (L.) Hoffm., Deutschl. Fl. 130, 131. 1796.

Lichen paschale L., Sp. Pl. 1153. 1753. *S. paschale* var. *conglomeratum* E. Fries.

Podetia short to moderately long, erect or ascending, slender to stout, more or less densely clustered, much branched, the branches rarely somewhat tomentose, more or less bare below, squamulose above, the squamules greenish gray to ashy white, minutely granulose, passing into short, crenate branchlets; apothecia small to middle-sized, 0.7–2 mm. across, terminal or lateral, often clustered, the disk flat to convex, reddish brown to brownish black, the exciple thin, brownish to brown, soon disappearing; spores acicular, 3-septate, 18–40 × 2.5–4.5 μ.

On soil and rocks, throughout northern United States.

6. **Stereocaulon tomentosum** E. Fries, Sched. Crit. fasc. 3. 20. 1824.

Podetia moderately long, stout, usually cylindrical, erect or ascending, densely whitish tomentose, branched, the branches much divided above, squamulose, the squamules greenish gray to ashy white, few below, densely crowded above, passing into many blunt, crenate branchlets; apothecia small, 0.6–1 mm. across, subterminal or lateral, more or less clustered, the disk flat to convex, brownish to brown, the exciple thin, brown, soon disappearing; spores acicular, 3-septate, 22–35 × 2–3.5 μ.

On soil over rocks, throughout northern United States, and in New Mexico.

var. **simplex** Riddle, Bot. Gaz. 50:298. 1910.

Podetia elongated, slender, sparingly branched, the squamules more or less scattered; apothecia rarely terminal.

On sandy soil, Washington and Oregon.

7. **Stereocaulon alpinum** Laurer, in Funck, Crypt. Gewächse 33. Heft. 6. 1827.

S. tomentosum var. *alpinum* (Laurer) T. Fries.

Podetia short, stout, erect or decumbent, clustered, becoming branched, the branches thinly tomentose, squamulose, the squamules small, ashy to whitish or brownish, becoming warty and conglomerate or passing into minute, coralloid branchlets; apothecia small to middle-sized, 0.6–2 mm. across, terminal or rarely lateral, the disk flat to convex, reddish brown to brownish black, the exciple thin, colored like the disk, commonly disappearing; spores acicular, 3-septate, 20–35 × 2.5–4.5 μ.

On rocks, Maine, New Hampshire, Minnesota, Wyoming, Washington, and Oregon.

var. **botryosum** (Ach.) Laurer, in E. Fries, Lich. Eur. 204. 1831.

S. botryosum Ach., in Lam. & DC., Fl. Franc. ed. 3. 6:178. 1805. *S. tomentosum* var. *botryosum* (Ach.) Nyl.

Podetia densely clustered, much branched, the branches smooth below, densely squamulose above, the squamules small, ashy gray to brownish, passing into minute, warty, or conglomerate granules.

On rocks, Maine.

8. **Stereocaulon denudatum** Floerke, Deutsch. Lich. part 4. 13. 1819.

S. glaucescens Tuck.

Podetia short to moderately long, erect or ascending, slender, loosely or sometimes densely clustered, becoming much branched, the branches smooth, squamulose above, the squamules grayish white to brownish, passing into minute, irregular, confluent granules; apothecia small, 0.3–0.7 mm. across, lateral or sometimes terminal, rarely clustered, the disk flat to slightly convex, brownish black to black; spores acicular, 3-septate, 22–40 × 2.5–4 μ.

On soil, New England, New York, New Jersey, Pennsylvania, Minnesota, Washington, and California.

OTHER SPECIES REPORTED

Stereocaulon chlorellum Tuck.—North America.

Stereocaulon ramulosum (Swartz) Ach.—Oregon.

35. GYROPHORACEAE

Thallus distinctly foliose, differentiated into well-developed plectenchymatous cortices, algal and spongy medullary layers, attached to the substratum by an umbilicus; apothecia round, scattered, sessile to shortly pedicellate, the disk grooved, giving the appearance of a compound apothecium, the proper exciple wanting or more or less developed, sometimes surrounded by a thalloid one. The algal host is Pleurococcus.

A. Spores non-septate . . . . 134. GYROPHORA
A. Spores septate
  B. Spores transversely septate . . . . 136. DERMATISCUM
  B. Spores transversely and longitudinally septate . . . . . 135. UMBILICARIA

134. **Gyrophora** Ach., Meth. Lich. 100. pl. 2, f. 6. 1803.

Thallus foliose, attached by an umbilicus, the margin entire to variously lobed and torn, having a strongly developed plectenchymatous cortex above and below, that of the lower side especially well developed; apothecia immersed to shortly stalked, black or blackish, usually thrown into closely packed, elongated or roundish folds, each fold apparently a shortly stalked apothecium as seen in section, the whole apothecium surrounded by a black, proper exciple; hypothecium brownish to black; paraphyses loosely arranged, usually unbranched; asci usually clavate; spores 8, hyaline, non-septate.

The algal host is Pleurococcus.

A. Thallus usually bearing rhizoids below
  B. Thallus black below, more or less covered with rhizoids
    C. Thallus very large
      D. Upper surface ashy colored . . . . 17. G. vellea
      D. Upper surface brown or darker . . . . 18. G. Dillenii
    C. Thallus small to middle-sized
      D. Rhizoids black; spores 8–13 × 4.5–7 μ . . . . . 16. G. polyrrhiza
      D. Rhizoids usually lighter; spores 14–22 × 6–11 μ . . . 15. G. angulata
  B. Thallus ashy to grayish or darker below
    C. Upper surface smooth
      D. Margins bearing rhizoids . . . . 10. G. cylindrica
      D. Margins not bearing rhizoids . . . . 14. G. grisea
    C. Upper surface more or less wrinkled and furrowed or reticulated
      D. Thallus reticulated above
        E. Thallus smooth below, light colored
          F. Blackish brown or rarely pruinose above;
            apothecia 0.6–1.5 mm. across . . . . 9. G. proboscidea
          F. Pale ashy to darker or olive-brown above;
            apothecia 1–4 mm. across . . . . 11. G. rugifera
        E. Thallus reticulated below, dark colored . . . . . 12. G. erosa
      D. Thallus rough and furrowed above, slightly
        punctured . . . . 13. G. torrefacta
A. Thallus without rhizoids below
  B. Thallus reticulated or pitted below
    C. More or less pitted below
      D. Upper surface more or less pustulate and wrinkled . . 5. G. hyperborea
      D. Upper surface smooth . . . . 6. G. deusta
    C. Reticulated below . . . . 8. G. Mühlenbergii
  B. Thallus smooth to minutely granulose below
    C. Thallus always smooth above
      D. Thallus deeply lobed and somewhat imbricated . . . 7. G. polyphylla
      D. Thallus lobed but not deeply so . . . . 4. G. phaea
    C. Thallus more or less granulose or reticulated above
      D. Granulose to wrinkled or rarely reticulated toward the center.
        E. Thallus smooth to chinky-areolate above; spores
          12–18 × 4.5–7 μ . . . . 1. G. anthracina
        E. Thallus much wrinkled above; spores
          11–19 × 6–10 μ . . . . 3. G. arctica
      D. Reticulated over the whole upper surface . . . . . 2. G. decussata

1. **Gyrophora anthracina** (Wulf.) Koerb., Syst. Lich. 99. 1855.
    Lichen anthracinus Wulf., in Jacq., Coll. Bot. 2:84. 1788. *Umbilicaria anthracina* (Wulf.) Schaer.
Thallus middle-sized, becoming irregular and sometimes deeply lobed, smooth to chinky-areolate, blackish brown; lighter to dark brown, or sometimes blackish pruinose below, and becoming minutely granulose; apothecia middle-sized to large, 1–2 mm. across, sessile to substipitate, round, the disk concave to flat, black, the blackish exciple well developed, raised and becoming crenulate; hypothecium brown; spores oblong-ellipsoid, rarely somewhat curved, 12–18 × 4.5–7 μ.
On rocks at high elevation, New Hampshire and Yellowstone National Park.

2. **Gyrophora decussata** (Vill.) Zahlbr., Cat. Lich. Univ. 4:678. 1927.
    Lichen decussatus Vill., Hist. Pl. Douph. 3:964. pl. 55. 1789. *G. reticulata* (Schaer.) T. Fries. *Umbilicaria anthracina* var. *reticulata* (Schaer.) Tuck.
Thallus small to middle-sized, ashy to blackish brown, or becoming whitish

granulose, finely chinky-areolate and more or less reticulated by finally coalescing ridges; brownish to darker brown below, and smooth to minutely granulose; apothecia small to middle-sized, 0.6–1.5 mm. across, round, sessile, the disk concave to slightly convex, black, rarely becoming obscurely folded, the blackish exciple strongly developed; hypothecium brown; spores ovoid-ellipsoid, 12–15 × 5.5–8 μ.

On rocks at high elevation, New Hampshire, Colorado, Nevada, California, Oregon, and Washington.

3. **Gyrophora arctica** Ach., Meth. Lich. 106. pl. 2, f. 6. 1803.
Umbilicaria proboscidea var. *arctica* (Ach.) E. Fries.
Thallus small to middle-sized, thick, becoming much wrinkled and somewhat granulose, grayish brown to brownish black, the margin irregularly crenate to torn-lobed, and reflexed; pale yellowish or brownish to brownish black and minutely chinky to granulose below; apothecia small to middle-sized, 1–2 mm. across, adnate to subsessile, round to rarely ellipsoid, the disk flat to slightly convex, black, becoming closely folded, the blackish exciple becoming flexuous and disappearing; hypothecium brown; spores ellipsoid, 11–19 × 6–10 μ.
On rocks at high elevation, New England and California.

4. **Gyrophora phaea** (Tuck.) Nyl.; Hue, Nouv. Arch. III. 3:37. 1891.
Umbilicaria phaea Tuck., Lich. Calif. 15. 1866.
Thallus small to middle-sized, smooth, ashy to tawny brown and blackening, the margin becoming unevenly crenulate to rarely torn-lobed; paler to rarely dull black below, and minutely granulose; apothecia small to middle-sized, 0.6–1.2 mm. across, immersed to subadnate, angulate and often crowded into clusters near the margin, the disk convex, black, becoming closely folded; hypothecium brown; spores ellipsoid, finally brown, 10–15 × 5.5–8.5 μ.
On rocks, Montana, Nevada, California, Oregon, and Washington. Reported also from North Carolina.

5. **Gyrophora hyperborea** Ach., Meth. Lich. 104. 1803.
Lichen hyperboreus Ach., Vet. Akad. Handl. 15:89. 1794. *Umbilicaria hyperborea* (Ach.) Hoffm.
Thallus middle-sized, round to irregular, smooth to more or less pustular-wrinkled, olive-brown to brown, often perforate here and there, the margin sparingly lobed and becoming jagged; grayish brown to blackish below and more or less pitted; apothecia small to middle-sized, 0.4–2.4 mm. across, subsessile, round to oblong or angulate, the disk convex and black, becoming folded, the exciple thin and black; hypothecium dark brown; spores ellipsoid, 12–17 × 5.5–8.5 μ. (Plate 25.)
On rocks at high elevation, from New Hampshire to Minnesota and Nevada, thence westward to Washington, Oregon, and California.

6. **Gyrophora deusta** (L.) Ach., Meth. Lich. 102. 1803.
Lichen deustus L., Sp. Pl. 1150. 1753. *G. flocculosa* (Wulf.) Borr. & Turn.
Umbilicaria flocculosa (Wulf.) Hoffm.
Thallus small to middle-sized, sometimes deeply lobed, thin, smooth to somewhat scurfy, olive to blackish brown, the margin reflexed; blackish brown and more or less reticulately pitted below; apothecia small, 0.6–0.9 mm. across, rare, sessile, round, the disk flat to convex, black, becoming slightly folded, the exciple thin and disappearing; hypothecium brown; spores ellipsoid, sometimes slightly curved, 18–28 × 6–9.5 μ.
On rocks, usually at high elevations, Maine, Vermont, New Hampshire, Minnesota, and South Dakota.

7. **Gyrophora polyphylla** (L.) Funck, Crypt. Gewächse 4. 1804.
Lichen polyphyllus L., Sp. Pl. 1150. 1753. *Umbilicaria polyphylla* (L.) Baumg.
Thallus small and irregular, usually crinkled, sometimes deeply lobed and somewhat imbricated, smooth, dark olive-brown to black, the margin crenate to

cut-lobate; light brown to dull black and smooth to minutely rough below; apothecia small to middle-sized, 0.5–1.5 mm. across, rare, immersed to adnate, round, becoming slightly folded, the disk flat to convex, black, the blackish exciple thin and finally disappearing; hypothecium hyaline to brownish; spores ellipsoid, 12–18 × 6–8 μ.

On rocks, from New England to North Carolina, and westward to California and Washington.

8. **Gyrophora Mühlenbergii** Ach., Lich. Univ. 227. pl. 2, f. 11. 1810.
   Umbilicaria Mühlenbergii (Ach.) Tuck.

Thallus middle-sized to large, smooth, more or less reticulately pitted, sometimes becoming perforate, olive-brown, the margin irregularly lobed and commonly more or less jagged; olive-brown to black, granulose, and reticulated below, with plates of branched or united supporting tissue, infrequently bearing rhizoid-like extensions; apothecia small to middle-sized, 0.5–3 mm. across, round to irregular, adnate, the disk convex, black, becoming closely folded, the blackish exciple soon disappearing; hypothecium brownish or darker; spores oblong to ellipsoid, 11–13 × 4–5 μ.

On rocks, throughout the northern United States.

9. **Gyrophora proboscidea** (L.) Ach., Meth. Lich. 105. 1803.
   Lichen proboscideus L., Sp. Pl. 1150. 1753. *Umbilicaria proboscidea* (L.)
   Schrad. *G. deusta* Turn. & Borr.

Thallus small to middle-sized, reticulately wrinkled, especially toward the center, blackish brown or rarely grayish pruinose, the margin irregularly scalloped or torn; pale to darker grayish or grayish pruinose, smooth to pitted below, and sometimes bearing scattered black rhizoids; apothecia small to middle-sized, 0.6–1.5 mm. across, adnate, round, becoming much folded, the disk flat to convex, black, the dark exciple thin and finally disappearing; hypothecium brown; spores ellipsoid to oblong-ellipsoid, 12–18 × 6–8.5 μ.

On rocks, mountains of New England, and westward to Arizona and Washington.

10. **Gyrophora cylindrica** (L.) Ach., Meth. Lich. 107. 1803.
    Lichen cylindricus L., Sp. Pl. 1144. 1753. *Umbilicaria cylindrica* (L.) Delise.

Thallus middle-sized, smooth, irregular, gray, varying toward bluish or brownish, more or less deeply lobed, the margins commonly fringed with black rhizoids; pale to blackening below and bearing few black rhizoids; apothecia small to middle-sized, 0.6–2.5 mm. across, subsessile to shortly stalked, round, the disk flat to strongly convex, becoming much folded, the margin well developed; hypothecium brown; spores ellipsoid, 10–14 × 6–9 μ.

On rocks, high elevation, South Dakota and Washington.

11. **Gyrophora rugifera** (Nyl.) T. Fries, Lich. Scand. 1:156. 1871.
    Umbilicaria rugifera Nyl., Not. Sällsk. Faun. Flor. Fenn. 5:117. 1861.

Thallus middle-sized to larger, more or less furrowed with coarse, reticulated, more or less evident ridges, pale ashy to darker to rarely olive-brown, the margin irregular and sometimes more or less lobed, the lobes often folded together; pale to rosy ash-colored below and more or less covered with short pale rhizoids; apothecia middle-sized to large, 1–4 mm. across, adnate to sessile, round, becoming closely folded, the disk flat to convex, black, the dark exciple very thin, becoming flexuous; hypothecium brown; asci becoming ventricose; spores ellipsoid, 8–15 × 7.5–8.5 μ.

On rocks, high elevation, California, Oregon, and Washington, and reported eastward to South Dakota and New Mexico.

12. **Gyrophora erosa** (Weberi) Ach., Meth. Lich. 103. 1803.
    Lichen erosus Weberi, Spic. Fl. Goett. 259. 1778. *Umbilicaria erosa* (Weberi)
    Ach.

Thallus middle-sized, minutely wrinkled, becoming reticulated, olive-brown to brownish black, variously open or punctured toward the irregularly torn-lobed margin; brownish to rarely blackening and more or less ridged below, often bearing few black rhizoids on the ridges; apothecia small to middle-sized, 0.5–1.2 mm. across, subsessile, round and much folded, the disk flat to convex, black, the black exciple thin and finally disappearing; hypothecium brown; spores ellipsoid, 9–12 × 5–7 μ.

On rocks, Nevada, Montana, Idaho, Washington, and California.

13. **Gyrophora torrefacta** (Lightf.) Cromb., Grevillea 12:74. 1884.
　　Lichen torrefactus Lightf., Fl. Scot. 2:862. 1777. *G. erosa* var. *torrefacta* (Lightf.) T. Fries.

Thallus small, rather thick, rough and furrowed, scarcely or slightly punctured, dark reddish to blackish brown, the margins sometimes slightly torn-lobed; pale to brownish black below, granulate and pitted with few scattered rhizoids; apothecia small to middle-sized, 0.5–1.2 mm. across, infrequent, sessile, round, becoming wavy-folded, the disk flat to convex, black, the dark exciple thin and finally disappearing; hypothecium brown; asci becoming inflated; spores ovoid-ellipsoid, 9–13 × 6–8 μ.

On rocks, South Dakota and southern California.

14. **Gyrophora grisea** Swartz; Billb. et Swartz, Sven. Bot. 8:546. 1819.
　　Lichen griseus Swartz, Vet. Akad. Handl. 1793:53. 1793. *G. hirsuta* var. *grisea* (Swartz) T. Fries.

Thallus small to middle-sized, thin, smooth, minutely powdery, ashy white to pale mouse-colored, the margin sometimes more or less lobed and crenate; ashy to blackish, rough, finely granulose below, or with few black rhizoids; apothecia minute to small, 0.2–0.6 mm. across, adnate, the disk flat to convex, black, becoming closely folded, the exciple evanescent; hypothecium brown; spores ellipsoid, 13–17 × 7.5–10 μ.

On rocks, usually at high elevation, Maine and California.

15. **Gyrophora angulata** (Tuck.) Herre, Cont. U. S. Nat. Herb. 13:318. 1911.
　　Umbilicaria angulata Tuck., Proc. Am. Acad. 1:266. 1848.

Thallus small to middle-sized, smooth, irregular, ashy to blackish brown or with a purple or blackish bloom, variously crenate, lobed and torn; black, granulose and more or less covered with paler rhizoids below; apothecia middle-sized to large, 1–3.5 mm. across, adnate to subsessile, round to angular, the disk flat to convex, black, becoming closely folded, the exciple thick, rarely disappearing; hypothecium brown; spores ovoid-ellipsoid, 14–22 × 6–11 μ.

On rocks, Minnesota, Washington, Oregon, and California.

16. **Gyrophora polyrrhiza** (L.) Koerb., Par. Lich. 41. 1859.
　　Lichen polyrrhizus L., Sp. Pl. 1151. 1753. *G. diabolica* Zahlbr. *Umbilicaria Mühlenbergii* var. *alpina* Tuck.

Thallus small to middle-sized, smooth, sometimes deeply lobed, the lobes folded together, greenish copper-colored, the margins irregularly crenate or unequally torn-lobed; black below, reticulated and densely covered with short black rhizoids; apothecia middle-sized to large, 2–7 mm. across, infrequent, immersed to adnate, round to angular or oblong, the disk flat to convex, becoming folded, dark brown to black, the exciple evanescent; hypothecium brownish to brown; spores ellipsoid, 8–13 × 4.5–7 μ.

On rocks, usually at high elevation, South Dakota, Washington, Oregon, and California.

17. **Gyrophora vellea** (L.) Ach., Meth. Lich. 109. 1803.
　　Lichen velleus L., Sp. Pl. 1150. 1753. *Umbilicaria vellea* (L.) Ach.

Thallus large to very large, thick, smooth, or rarely rough, variously round to irregular, ashy to ashy brownish, or more or less whitish or bluish pruinose, the margin becoming more or less torn; brown to blackish below, with strong dark

brown or black rhizoids; apothecia small to middle-sized, 0.4–2.5 mm. across, infrequent, closely adnate, rare, usually near the margin, the disk convex, black, becoming closely folded, the blackish exciple disappearing; hypothecium dark brown; spores short-ellipsoid, 8–14 × 5.3–8 μ.
On rocks, usually at high elevation, throughout the United States.

18. **Gyrophora Dillenii** (Tuck.) Müll. Arg., Flora 72:364. 1889.
Umbilicaria Dillenii Tuck., Proc. Am. Acad. 1:264. 1848.
Thallus large to very large, smooth, brown to dark or ashy brown, the margin torn and irregular; black below with strong black rhizoids; apothecia middle-sized to large, 1–4 mm. across, infrequent, subsessile, round, the disk convex and black, becoming closely folded, the dark exciple disappearing; hypothecium light to darker brown; spores ellipsoid, 17–24 × 9–14 μ. (PLATE 26.)
On rocks, from Maine to South Carolina, and westward to Oklahoma and Minnesota (at high elevation southward).

OTHER SPECIES REPORTED
Gyrophora hirsuta Ach.—California.

135. **Umbilicaria** Hoffm., Descr. Pl. Crypt. 1:7. pl. 2, f. 1–4. 1790.

Thallus foliose, irregular or lobed, smooth to very rough, attached to the substratum by an umbilicus, differentiated into well-developed, plectenchymatous, upper and lower cortices, the upper much thinner, distinct algal and medullary layers; apothecia small to middle-sized, closely adnate to substipitate, the disk flat to more or less convex, becoming folded and irregular, the exciple colored like the disk; hypothecium brownish to brown; hymenium brownish; paraphyses branched; asci clavate; spores 1–8, brown or rarely hyaline, ellipsoid to oblong-ellipsoid, transversely and longitudinally septate.
The algal host is Pleurococcus.

A. Thallus very black below, covered here and there with
     strong black rhizoids . . . . 2. U. caroliniana
A. Thallus grayish to brownish black below, rarely
     with few scattered rhizoids
     B. Thallus more or less coarsely papillose above;
         pitted below
         C. Brownish black below . . . . 3. U. pennsylvanica
         C. Grayish to rarely dark brown below . . . . 4. U. pustulata
     B. Thallus smooth above; not pitted below . . . . 1. U. semitensis

1. **Umbilicaria semitensis** Tuck., Gen. Lich. 31. 1872.
U. angulata var. *semitensis* Tuck.
Thallus small to middle-sized, smooth to finely areolate or granulose, ashy gray, varying toward brown, becoming several-lobed with undulate margins; grayish black to black below, granulose to lacerate and ridged, with scattered rhizoids rising from the ridges; apothecia small to middle-sized, 0.5–3 mm. across, closely adnate, round to irregular, the disk flat to convex, becoming closely folded, the exciple well developed, becoming flexuous; hypothecium brown; spores usually 1–2, oblong-ellipsoid, hyaline to finally brown, 5–7-septate transversely and 1–3-septate longitudinally, 20–30 × 13–21 μ.
On rocks, southern California.

2. **Umbilicaria caroliniana** Tuck., Proc. Am. Acad. 12:167. 1877.
U. mammulata Tuck. (non Ach.)
Thallus small to middle-sized, olive to blackish brown, becoming deeply lobed, thin, very smooth, irregularly or inconspicuously papillose; very black, pitted and granulose below, and covered here and there with strong black rhizoids; apothecia small to middle-sized, 0.4–1 mm. across, round to elongated, substipitate, the disk flat, black, soon folded and finally proliferous; spores 1 or rarely 2, ellipsoid, brown, 11–19-septate transversely and 3–7-septate longitudinally, 30–42 × 20–24 μ.
On rocks, mountains of North Carolina.

3. **Umbilicaria pennsylvanica** Hoffm., Pl. Lich. 3:5. pl. 69, f. 1, 2. 1801.

Thallus middle-sized to large, coarsely papillose, ashy to smoky-brown, often white-powdery at the center, the margin somewhat irregular, torn; often slightly brownish black and granulose below; apothecia small to middle-sized, 0.5–1.2 mm. across, sessile, round to irregular, the disk flat, black, becoming proliferous, the exciple thin, black, becoming striate and flexuous; spores 1, ellipsoid, becoming blackish brown, 15–23-septate transversely and 7–11-septate longitudinally, 46–70 × 23–35 μ.

On rocks, from Maine to Florida, and westward to Pennsylvania and Tennessee.

4. **Umbilicaria pustulata** (L.) Hoffm., Descr. Pl. Crypt. 2:13. pi. 28, f. 1, 2, pl. 29, f. 4. 1794.

Lichen pustulatus L., Sp. Pl. 1150. 1753. *U. pustulata* var. *papulosa* (Ach.) Tuck. *U. dictyiza* Nyl.

Thallus small to middle-sized, papillose, brown or ashy brown, often becoming chinky, often powdery, the margin more or less irregular and sometimes irregularly lobed; grayish to dark brown, granulose and reticulately pitted below; apothecia small to middle-sized, 0.5–1 mm. across, sessile, the disk flat, black, becoming folded, the exciple thin, black, and irregular; spores 1, ellipsoid to oblong-ellipsoid, brown or sometimes hyaline, 9–19-septate transversely and 7–13-septate longitudinally, 48–85 × 23–42 μ. (PLATE 27 *a*.)

On rocks, from Maine to Florida, and westward to Minnesota and New Mexico (confined to high elevations southward).

136. Dermatiscum Nyl., Bot. Zeitung 133. 1867.

Thallus squamulose to foliose; plectenchymatous cortex poorly developed and pale above, well developed and black below, the medullary region well developed with the hyphae loosely interwoven in the upper part and closely interwoven in the lower part; without rhizoids and attached by a ventral umbilicus; apothecia immersed to superficial, the exciple colored like the disk, often wanting; hypothecium hyaline to brown; paraphyses sometimes branched toward the apices; asci cylindrico-clavate; spores 8, brown, 1-septate, somewhat constricted.

The algal host is Pleurococcus, distributed throughout the medulla, but more abundant in the upper part.

1. **Dermatiscum catawbensis** (Willey) Nyl.; Willey, Bull. Torr. Club 14:222. 1887.

Buellia catawbensis Willey, Int. Stud. Lich. 49. 1887. *D. porcellaneum* Nyl.

Thallus foliose, rather thick, whitish, round to somewhat irregular, small, scarcely exceeding 1 cm. across, the margin sometimes obscurely lobed; black below; apothecia small, 0.5–1.3 mm. across, immersed to semisuperficial, scattered or clustered, circular to somewhat irregular in outline, the disk flat, black, the exciple rudimentary or wanting; hypothecium dark brown; spores oblong-ellipsoid, 13–16 × 7.5–8.5 μ.

On rocks, South Carolina.

36. ACAROSPORACEAE

Thallus crustose, scaly or squamulose, devoid of differentiation or showing poorly or well-developed plectenchymatous cortex, rarely plectenchymatous throughout, with algal and poorly developed medullary layers, attached to the substratum by hyphal rhizoids or rarely by an umbilicus; apothecia round, immersed to adnate or rarely somewhat pedicellate, single or aggregate, with proper or thalloid exciple.

The algal hosts are Pleurococcus and Protococcus.

A. Horizontal thallus well developed
  B. Apothecia with thalloid exciple
    C. Apothecia immersed, spores non-septate . . . . . . 140. ACAROSPORA

C. Apothecia adnate to sessile, spores non–1-septate . . . . . 139. MARONEA
B. Apothecia with proper exciple . . . . 138. BIATORELLA
A. Horizontal thallus almost wanting . . . . 137. THELOCARPON

137. Thelocarpon Nyl., Mém. Soc. Sci. Nat. Cherb. 2:15, 338. 1854.

Thallus rudimentary, devoid of differentiation into layers, the superficial portion absent or forming a very thin crust over the substratum; apothecia minute, globose, scattered or rarely aggregate, entirely covered by a thin thalloid exciple except a tiny pore at the more or less depressed apex; hypothecium and hymenium hyaline; paraphyses short, unbranched or branched and interwoven; asci long, more or less distended toward the center; spores numerous, minute, hyaline, spherical to oblong, non-septate or rarely appearing 1-septate.

The algal host is Pleurococcus or Protococcus.

A. On rocks, trees, and old wood
  B. Spores not more than 8 μ in length
    C. Apothecia scattered or aggregate
      D. Spores 2.5–4 × 1.5–2 μ . . . . 1. T. Laureri
      D. Spores 3.5–6 × 1.5–2.5 μ . . . . 5. T. epilithellum
    C. Apothecia scattered
      D. Spores 2–3.5 × 1–1.5 μ . . . . 2. T. majusculum
      D. Spores 4–7 × 2.5–4 μ . . . . 6. T. prasinellum
  B. Spores more than 8 μ in length . . . . 7. T. superellum
A. On soil or dung
  B. On soil; apothecia covered by a yellowish green exciple . 3. T. intermediellum
  B. On dung; apothecia covered by a greenish exciple . . . . . 4. T. fimicola

1. **Thelocarpon Laureri** (Flot.) Nyl., Mém. Soc. Sci. Nat. Cherb. 3:191. 1855.
Sphaeropsis Laureri Flot., Bot. Zeit. 5:65. 1847.

Thallus rudimentary, the superficial portion absent or rarely visible; apothecia minute, 0.05–0.2 mm. across, globose, scattered or rarely aggregate, entirely covered by a thin, yellowish green, thalloid exciple except a tiny pore at the somewhat depressed apex; hyaline within; paraphyses slender, short, somewhat branched; asci distended toward the center; spores oblong, 2.5–4 × 1.5–2 μ.

On old wood, Pennsylvania and Illinois (?).

2. **Thelocarpon majusculum** Nyl., Flora 68:300. 1885.

Thallus rudimentary, the superficial portion absent or scarcely visible; apothecia minute, 0.1–0.25 mm. across, globose, more or less scattered, entirely covered by a thin, yellowish green thalloid exciple except a tiny pore at the apex; hyaline within; paraphyses slender, threadlike; asci distended toward the center; spores oblong-ellipsoid, 2–3.5 × 1–1.5 μ.

On old trees and rarely on rocks, Massachusetts, Florida, Pennsylvania (?), and Illinois (?).

3. **Thelocarpon intermediellum** Nyl., Flora 48:261. 1865.

Thallus rudimentary, the superficial portion absent or rarely visible; apothecia minute, 0.05–0.15 mm. across, globose, scattered, entirely covered by a thin, yellowish green, thalloid exciple except a tiny black pore at the slightly depressed apex; hyaline within; paraphyses absent; asci distended toward the center; spores oblong, 3.5–5 × 1.5–2 μ.

On soil, Massachusetts.

4. **Thelocarpon fimicola** Fink, Mycologia 14:95, 96. 1922.

Thallus rudimentary, the superficial portion absent or rarely visible; apothecia minute, 0.05–0.15 mm. across, globose, scattered, covered entirely by a thin, greenish thalloid exciple except a tiny pore at the apex; hyaline within; paraphyses indistinct and disappearing; asci cylindrical to becoming distended toward the center and tapering toward both ends; spores spherical to oblong, 2–4 × 1.5–2 μ.

On cow dung, Kentucky.

5. **Thelocarpon epilithellum** Nyl., Flora 48:605, 606. 1865.

Thallus rudimentary, the superficial portion absent or scarcely visible; apothecia minute, 0.05–0.1 mm. across, globose, scattered or rarely aggregate, entirely covered by a thin, greenish yellow, thalloid exciple except a tiny black pore at the depressed apex; hyaline within; paraphyses slender, short; asci long, cylindrical to broadly distended toward the center; spores oblong, $3.5–6 \times 1.5–2.5 \mu$.

On rocks, Illinois.

6. **Thelocarpon prasinellum** Nyl., Flora 64:451. 1881.

Thallus rudimentary, the superficial portion a very thin greenish crust over the substratum, commonly disappearing; apothecia minute, 0.1–0.2 mm. across, globose, scattered, entirely covered by a thin, greenish, thalloid exciple except a minute black pore at the apex; hyaline within; paraphyses slender and branched; asci cylindrical, becoming distended toward the center; spores oblong-ellipsoid, $4–7 \times 2.5–4 \mu$.

On old wood and rocks, Massachusetts, Ohio, Iowa, and Minnesota.

7. **Thelocarpon superellum** Nyl., Flora 48:261, 262. 1865.

Thallus rudimentary, the superficial portion absent or scarcely visible; apothecia minute, 0.05–0.15 mm. across, globose, scattered, entirely covered by a thin, greenish yellow, thalloid exciple except a minute pore at the subconical apex; hyaline within; paraphyses slender, threadlike; asci distended toward the middle; spores small, oblong or oblong-ellipsoid, non-septate or appearing 1-septate, $8–12 \times 3–4.5 \mu$.

On old wood, New Hampshire, Massachusetts, and New York.

OTHER SPECIES REPORTED

Thelocarpon albomarginatum Herre—California.

138. **Biatorella** De Not., Giorn. Bot. Ital. 2^1:192. 1846.

Thallus crustose, often inconspicuous and evanescent, but sometimes granular, warty, or subareolate, devoid of differentiation and attached to the substratum by hyphal rhizoids; apothecia usually minute to small, immersed to sessile, the disk flat to convex, the exciple colored like the disk, sometimes becoming covered; hypothecium hyaline to brown; hymenium hyaline to brown; paraphyses unbranched or inconspicuously branched, often somewhat enlarged above; asci broadly clavate or ventricose; spores minute and numerous, rarely only 12 or 8, hyaline, non-septate, spherical to oblong or ellipsoid.

The algal host is Pleurococcus.

A. On trees, old wood, soil, and over moss
  B. On trees
    C. Spores spherical
      D. Thallus yellowish or orange-yellow
        E. Thallus lemon-yellow . . . . 3. B. nannaria
        E. Thallus yellowish gray to orange-yellow . . . . 5. B. conspersa
      D. Thallus greenish gray to whitish or brownish
        E. Thallus minutely granulose . . . . 6. B. moriformis
        E. Thallus very thin, smooth . . . . 4. B. Rappii
    C. Spores oblong to short-ellipsoid
      D. Apothecia 0.4–0.9 mm. across
        E. Spores $5–11 \times 2–2.5 \mu$ . . . . 15. B. camptocarpa
        E. Spores $3–4 \times 2–3 \mu$ . . . . 14. B. cyphalea
      D. Apothecia 0.05–0.1 mm. across . . . . 13. B. albidula
  B. On old wood and soil and over moss
    C. Spores spherical
      D. Apothecia 0.15–0.3 mm. across . . . . 1. B. geophana
      D. Apothecia 0.4–1 mm. across . . . . 2. B. resinae
    C. Spores oblong to oblong-cylindrical or ellipsoid
      D. Apothecia 0.2–0.5 mm. across . . . . 8. B. campestris
      D. Apothecia 0.7–1 mm. across . . . . 9. B. fossarum

A. On rocks
  B. Thallus poorly developed and rarely persistent except
     under the apothecia
    C. Spores numerous, not more than 8 μ in length
      D. Apothecia pruinose . . . .   11. B. simplex pruinosa
      D. Apothecia not pruinose
        E. Apothecia 0.2–1 mm. across, red when wet . . . .   11. B. simplex
        E. Apothecia 0.7–2 mm. across, not red when wet . . .   10. B. clavus
    C. Spores not numerous, 8–16 × 3–6.5 μ . . . .   12. B. revertens
  B. Thallus well developed and persistent
    D. Thallus granulose, greenish gray to gray . . . . .   16. B. hypophaea
    D. Thallus areolate, yellowish copper-colored and
       blackening   . . . .   7. B. testudinea

1. **Biatorella geophana** (Nyl.) Rehm, in Rabh., Krypt. Flora Deutsch. ed. 2.
   1:307. 1890.
   Lecidea geophana Nyl., Not. Sällsk. Faun. Flor. Fenn. 5:212. 1861. *Biatora geophana* (Nyl.) T. Fries.
   Thallus greenish gray, very thin, evanescent; apothecia minute, 0.15–0.3 mm. across, the disk convex, black, the exciple soon disappearing; hypothecium yellowish brown; asci ventricose; spores 12–18, spherical, 5–7.5 μ in diameter.
   On soil and rotten wood, Massachusetts, New Jersey, and Illinois.

2. **Biatorella resinae** (E. Fries) T. Fries, Nov. Act. Soc. Sci. Ups. III. 3:299.
   1861.
   Peziza resinae E. Fries, Syst. Myc. 2:149. 1822. *Biatora difformis* (E. Fries) Tuck.
   Thallus thin, yellowish to grayish or brownish, scurfy, evanescent; apothecia small to middle-sized, 0.4–1 mm. across, sessile, the disk flat to convex, pale to yellowish and finally blackening, the exciple of the same color, and soon disappearing; hypothecium from yellowish to brown; asci clavate-ventricose; spores spherical, 2–3.5 μ in diameter.
   On pine resin, Vermont, Massachusetts, New York, and New Jersey.

3. **Biatorella nannaria** (Tuck.) Zahlbr., Cat. Lich. Univ. 5:44. 1927.
   Heterothecium nannarium Tuck., Gen. Lich. 176. 1872.
   Thallus thin, scurfy-granular, pale lemon-colored; apothecia minute, 0.15–0.25 mm. across, sessile, the disk flat to slightly convex, reddish brown, the exciple thin, yellow; hypothecium dusky brown; asci short and swollen; spores spherical, 2–2.5 μ in diameter.
   On trees, Texas.

4. **Biatorella Rappii** Zahlbr., Ann. Mycol. 29:82. 1931.
   Thallus very thin, smooth, widespread, continuous, dirty brown; apothecia minute, 0.3–0.5 mm. across, adnate to sessile, slightly constricted at the base, more or less scattered, the disk deeply concave to concave or rarely flat, reddish brown, the exciple thick, colored like the disk; hypothecium hyaline to yellowish or tinged reddish brown; asci fusiform to clavate; spores globose, 2–3 μ across.
   On trees, near Mecca, Florida.

5. **Biatorella conspersa** (Fée) Vainio, Act. Soc. Faun. Fl. Fenn. 7:62. 1890.
   Lecidea conspersa Fée, Essai Crypt. 108. pl. 27, f. 4. 1824.
   Thallus of very minute, crowded or scattered, yellowish gray to orange-yellow granules; apothecia small, 0.5–1 mm. across, sessile, the disk orange to black, powdery-granular, flat to strongly convex, the exciple pale yellow, becoming blackish where rubbed, soon disappearing; hypothecium reddish to blackish brown; spores spherical, 1.5–2.5 μ in diameter.
   On trees, southern Alabama.

6. **Biatorella moriformis** (Ach.) T. Fries, Lich. Scand. 1:401, 402. 1874.
   Arthonia moriformis Ach., Syn. Meth. Lich. 5. 1814.
   Thallus of minute granules, commonly compacted into a thin, smooth, wide-

spread, sometimes scurfy and chinky, grayish green, varying toward whitish or brownish, rarely disappearing crust; apothecia minute, 0.2–0.4 mm. across, adnate, the disk flat to slightly convex, light brown to black, the exciple soon covered; hypothecium hyaline; spores spherical, 1.5–3 μ in diameter.

On trees, Massachusetts, Minnesota, Washington, and California.

7. **Biatorella testudinea** (Ach.) Mass., Ric. Lich. 131. f. 258. 1852.
Lecidea fumosa var. *testudinea* Ach., Vet. Akad. Nya Handl. 232. 1808. *Lecidea morio* E. Fries. *Lecidea morio* var. *coracina* (Hoffm.) Schaer.

Thallus well developed, of yellowish copper-colored and blackening, flat or slightly convex, marginally lobed areoles, resting on or more or less immersed in a black hypothallus; apothecia minute to middle-sized, 0.3–1 mm. across, partly or wholly immersed, round to irregular, the disk flat to convex, black, the exciple black, becoming indistinct; hypothecium hyaline to dark reddish brown; spores spherical to ellipsoid, 3–5 × 2–3 μ.

On alpine rocks, the White, Rocky, and Sierra Nevada mountains.

8. **Biatorella campestris** (E. Fries) T. Fries, Gen. Heterol. Eur. 86. 1861.
Biatora campestris E. Fries, Vet. Akad. Handl. 1822:273. 1822.

Thallus scattered and inconspicuous, pale greenish, fading to whitish, scurfy-granular, disappearing; apothecia minute or small, 0.2–0.5 mm. across, sessile, the disk concave to slightly convex, amber-colored to reddish black, slightly white-pruinose; hypothecium hyaline; spores oblong-ellipsoid, 5–8 × 2–3 μ.

On soil, mosses, and old wood, from Massachusetts to New Jersey, and westward to Illinois.

9. **Biatorella fossarum** (Nyl.) T. Fries, Lich. Scand. 2:397. 1874.
Lecidea fossarum Nyl., Ann. Sci. Nat. III. 20:320. 1853. *Biatora fossarum* Mont.

Thallus scurfy, greenish gray, thin and disappearing, or compacted into an uneven crust; apothecia small, 0.7–1 mm. across, adnate to sessile, the disk convex to hemispherical, pale yellow to reddish brown; exciple soon disappearing; hypothecium yellowish brown; spores oblong to oblong-cylindrical, 7–11 × 3 μ.

On soil, New Jersey, Florida, Illinois, and Washington.

10. **Biatorella clavus** (Lam. & DC.) T. Fries, Lich. Scand. 1:409. 1874.
Patellaria clavus Lam. & DC., Fl. Fr. ed. 3. 2:348. 1805.

Thallus inconspicuous and evanescent, sometimes seen under the apothecia; apothecia middle-sized to large, 0.7–2 mm. across, sessile to substipitate, scattered or clustered, round or variously irregular, the disk dark red to black, concave to slightly convex, the exciple thick, often chinky and wrinkled, or finally disappearing; asci cylindrico-clavate, often saccate; hypothecium hyaline to pale brown; spores oblong-ellipsoid, 4–6.5 × 2 μ.

On rocks, from New England to Georgia, and westward to California.

11. **Biatorella simplex** (Dav.) Branth & Rostr., Bot. Tidssk. 3:241. 1869.
Lichen simplex Dav., Trans. Linn. Soc. Lond. 2:283. pl. 28, f. 2. 1794. *Lecanora privigna* (Ach.) Nyl.

Thallus thin and evanescent, seldom seen; apothecia minute to small or middle-sized, 0.2–1 mm. across, adnate, scattered or crowded, round to irregular, the disk brownish to black, reddish when wet, the exciple raised, black; hypothecium hyaline to yellowish; spores oblong-ellipsoid, 3–6 × 1–1.5 μ.

On rocks, throughout the United States.

var. **pruinosa** (Ach.) Fink, Cont. U. S. Nat. Herb. 14:66. 1910.
Lichen pruinosus Ach., Lich. Suec. Prod. 77. 1798. *Lecanora privigna* var. *pruinosa* (Ach.) Tuck. *Lecidea albocoerulescens* var. *immersa* E. Fries. *B. pruinosa* (Ach.) Mudd.

Thallus thin; apothecia middle-sized, 0.8–1.3 mm. across, partly immersed in the substratum, the disk whitish or grayish pruinose.

On rocks, throughout the United States.

12. **Biatorella revertens** (Tuck.) Herre, Proc. Wash. Acad. Sci. 12:121, 122. 1910.
Lecanora privigna var. *revertens* Tuck., Syn. N. A. Lich. 1:204, 205. 1882.

Thallus light greenish gray to ashy, evanescent, seen occasionally under the apothecia, very rarely elsewhere; apothecia small to middle-sized, 0.5–1.5 mm. across, sessile, the disk concave to somewhat convex, dark reddish to black, the exciple thin, of same color as the thallus, sometimes becoming flexuous and disappearing; hypothecium hyaline; spores 8–16 × 3–6.5 μ, not numerous and sometimes only 8.

On rocks, Colorado, Nevada, and California.

13. **Biatorella albidula** (Willey) Zahlbr., Cat. Lich. Univ. 5:34. 1927.
Biatora albidula Willey, in Tuck., Syn. N. A. Lich. 2:130. 1888.

Thallus very thin, smooth, white to ashy; apothecia very minute, 0.05–0.1 mm. across, adnate, the disk convex, white to light brown, the exciple very thin, color similar to that of the disk, soon disappearing; hypothecium hyaline; spores 6–7 × 2–3 μ.

On beech trees, near New Bedford, Massachusetts.

14. **Biatorella cyphalea** (Tuck.) Zahlbr., Cat. Lich. Univ. 5:36. 1927.
Biatora cyphalea Tuck., Gen. Lich. 168. 1872.

Thallus thin, grayish to grayish white, granular, or finally wrinkled-verrucose; apothecia small, 0.5–0.8 mm. across, sessile and often clustered, the disk flat to convex, pale to dark reddish and rusty brown, the exciple paler or darkening, soon disappearing; hypothecium yellowish or brownish; asci ventricose; spores short-ellipsoid, 3–4 × 2–3 μ.

On elm bark, Illinois.

15. **Biatorella camptocarpa** (Tuck.) Fink n. comb.
Biatora camptocarpa Tuck., Syn. N. A. Lich. 2:18, 19. 1888.

Thallus thin, scurfy to granulose, greenish gray; apothecia small to middle-sized, 0.4–0.9 mm. across, sessile, concave to slightly convex, the disk reddish to dark livid brown, the darker, well-developed exciple rising higher than the disk and finally becoming flexuous and disappearing; spores 30 or more, narrow-oblong, 5–11 × 2–2.5 μ.

On trees, Florida.

16. **Biatorella hypophaea** (Nyl.) Blombg. & Forss., Pl. Scand. 83. 1880.
Lecanora hypophaea Nyl., Flora 53:34. 1870.

Thallus thin, smooth to slightly rough, granulose, greenish gray to gray; apothecia small to middle-sized, 0.3–1 mm. across, sessile, round to somewhat irregular, the disk flat to convex, reddish to brownish black, the exciple entire to wavy, black and disappearing; hypothecium yellowish; spores oblong, apparently thickened slightly at both ends, 5–7 × 1–1.5 μ.

On crumbling sandstone, Santa Monica Range, California.

139. **Maronea** Mass., Flora 39:291. 1856.

Thallus crustose, granulose, rudimentary, devoid of differentiation into layers, attached to the substratum by hyphal rhizoids; apothecia minute to small or middle-sized, partly immersed to adnate or sessile, the disk commonly flat, the exciple thin to thick, colored like the thallus, irregular, rarely disappearing; hypothecium hyaline; hymenium hyaline and becoming indistinct; paraphyses unbranched or more or less forked at the apices; asci clavate to cylindrico-clavate;

spores numerous, minute, hyaline, oblong, ellipsoid or spherical, non-septate, or rarely becoming 1-septate.

The algal host is Pleurococcus or Protococcus.

A. Apothecia small, not more than 0.5 mm. across; the
exciple granulose . . . . 1. M. constans sublecideina
A. Apothecia larger, reaching 1 mm. across; the exciple
becoming crenulate . . . . 1. M. constans

1. **Maronea constans** (Nyl.) Hepp, Flecht. Eur. No. 771. 1860.

Lecanora constans Nyl., Mém. Soc. Imp. Sci. Nat. Cherb. 3:199. 1855. *Rinodina constans* (Nyl.) Tuck.

Thallus thin, granulose, greenish gray to brownish or ashy, the granules minute, becoming wartlike, commonly forming small, round to irregular areas; apothecia small to middle-sized, 0.4–1 mm. across, sessile, the disk flat, brownish black to black, the exciple thick, colored like the thallus, becoming crenulate; hypothecium hyaline to yellowish; asci clavate; spores numerous, minute, oblong, hyaline, non-septate to becoming 1-septate, 3–6 × 1.5–2.5 μ.

On trees, from New England to South Carolina, and westward to Alabama and Illinois.

var. **sublecideina** Zahlbr.; Hasse, Bryologist 16:1, 2. 1913.

Apothecia usually smaller than in the species, 0.3–0.5 mm. across, the exciple thin, granulose, colored like the thallus, sometimes almost disappearing.

On trees, southern California.

140. **Acarospora** Mass., Ric. Lich. 27. f. 43–46. 1852.

Thallus squamulose, the squamules forming areoles, especially toward the center, frequently lobed toward the margin, commonly closely adnate and plectenchymatous throughout, whitened (dealbate) conditions occurring in some of the species, and often segregated as subspecies; apothecia minute to middle-sized or larger, immersed or infrequently becoming superficial, 1–3 or more to each areole, a thalloid exciple frequently differentiated; hymenium and hypothecium commonly hyaline; paraphyses hyaline, usually unbranched, coherent and semidistinct; asci frequently becoming inflated-ventricose; spores minute, non-septate, spherical to ellipsoid, numerous. (PLATE 28.)

The algal host is Protococcus.

A. Thallus yellow or white, rarely clay-colored
  B. On soil
    C. Thallus white or whitish pruinose
      D. Apothecia brownish black or gray-pruinose . . . 5. A. thelococcoides
      D. Apothecia blackish red . . . . 3. A. reagens
    C. Thallus sulphur-colored or finally dirty white . . . . . 1. A. Schleicheri
  B. On rocks
    C. Thallus bright yellow
      D. Thallus squamulose
        E. Apothecia yellow to reddish or rarely blackening . . . . 9. A. flava
        E. Apothecia reddish brown to brownish black . . . 8. A. rhabarbarina
      D. Thallus areolate . . . . 7. A. citrina
    C. Thallus white, grayish, or rarely brownish
      D. Spores spherical
        E. Apothecia 0.4–1.2 mm. across . . . . 2. A. saxicola
        E. Apothecia 0.7–3 mm. across . . . . 6. A. scabra
      D. Spores subspherical to ovoid or ellipsoid
        E. Thallus of irregular squamules . . . . 4. A. peltasticta
        E. Thallus of short, branched stipes . . . . . 11. A. thermophila
A. Thallus greenish gray to brown or darker
  B. Thallus areolate, rarely wanting or of branched stipes
    C. Thallus not areolate
      D. Thallus wanting . . . . 24. A. glaucocarpa depauperata
      D. Thallus of branched stipes . . . . 27. A. thamnina

C. Thallus distinctly areolate
  D. Apothecia more or less pruinose
    E. Thallus greenish brown . . . . . .   24. A. glaucocarpa verrucosa
    E. Thallus dark greenish gray to black . . . . . . 13. A. immersa
  D. Apothecia not pruinose
    E. Apothecia 0.1–0.2 mm. across . . . .   12. A. Heppii
    E. Apothecia 0.3–0.7 mm. across . . . .   17. A. arenosa
B. Thallus more or less distinctly squamulose
  C. Apothecia rarely more than 0.4 mm. across
    D. Apothecia minute, rarely more than 0.2 mm. across
      E. Apothecia brown . . . .   14. A. california
      E. Apothecia greenish or bluish pruinose . . . . . 10. A. aeruginosa
    D. Apothecia rarely less than 0.2 mm. across
      E. Thallus light brown or white-pruinose . . . . . 16. A. cineracea
      E. Thallus grayish white to light gray or brown . . 15. A. epilutescens
  C. Apothecia rarely less than 0.4 mm. across
    D. Apothecia rarely more than 0.6 mm. across
      E. Apothecia more or less pruinose
        F. Thallus light brown . . . .   20. A. obpallens
        F. Thallus reddish brown . . . . 21. A. Carnegiei
      E. Apothecia not pruinose
        F. Thallus pale greenish gray to dusky yellowish or
          brown . . . .   18. A. Hassei
        F. Thallus light to blackish brown . . . . . . 26. A. molybdina
    D. Apothecia reaching 0.8–1.25 mm. across
      E. Spores not more than 6 μ in length
        F. Apothecia more or less pruinose
          G. Thallus yellowish brown to dark chestnut . . . 19. A. cervina
          G. Thallus pale greenish brown . . . . . 24. A. glaucocarpa
        F. Apothecia not pruinose
          G. Disk flat . . . . 22. A. squamulosa
          G. Disk rough and often papillose . . . . . . 23. A. fuscata
      E. Spores 8–15 × 7–10 μ. . . . . 25. A. glebosa

1. **Acarospora Schleicheri** (Ach.) Mass., Ric. Lich. 27, f. 43. 1852.
   Urceolaria Schleicheri Ach., Lich. Univ. 332, 333. 1810. *Lecanora Schleicheri*
   (Ach.) Nyl.
   Thallus of fairly conspicuous, sulphur-colored or finally dirty white, continuous
and areolate, convex, rugulose, sublobate squamules; apothecia small to middle-
sized, 0.3–1.2 mm. across, immersed 1 in a squamule, the disk flat, reddish brown
to brownish black, sometimes papillate, a crenate thalloid exciple sometimes visible; spores subspherical, 3–5 × 3 μ.
   On soil, Rocky Mountains and westward to California and Washington.

2. **Acarospora saxicola** Fink; Hedrick, Mycologia 26:159. 1934.
   Thallus squamulose, the squamules small to middle-sized, irregular, sometimes
lobed, becoming imbricated and passing into a thick, irregular, areolate, grayish
or dirty white crust, more or less closely attached to the substratum; apothecia
small to middle-sized, 0.4–1.2 mm. across, immersed to adnate, 1 or more in an
areole or squamule, the disk flat to slightly convex, brown to brownish black or
grayish pruinose, the exciple thin, colored like the thallus, entire to slightly irregular and crenulate; spores spherical, 2.5–4.5 μ in diameter, irregularly arranged.
   On rocks, Colorado.

3. **Acarospora reagens** Zahlbr., Beih. Bot. Centralb. 13:162. 1902.
   Thallus whitish and white-pruinose, centrally areolate and marginally squamulose, the squamules often scattered; apothecia immersed to semi-immersed, 1 or
more in each areole or squamule, middle-sized to large, 0.4–1.8 mm. across, the
disk flat, blackish red; spores spherical, 4–6 μ in diameter.
   On sandy soil, southern California.

4. **Acarospora peltasticta** Zahlbr., Beih. Bot. Centralb. 13:161. 1902.
   Thallus of rounded or irregular, raised, dull ivory-white, chinky-areolate squam-

ules; apothecia small, spreading, 0.5–0.8 mm. or more across, immersed 1–3 in each squamule, the disk flat, black; spores spherical to ovoid, $3.5–5 \times 4–6 \mu$.
On rocks, California, Arizona, and Nevada.

5. **Acarospora thelococcoides** (Nyl.) Zahlbr., Cat. Lich. Univ. 5:98. 1927.
   Lecanora thelococcoides Nyl., Lich. Lab. et Sing. 37. 1891. *A. pleistospora*
   (Nyl.) Hasse. *A. pleiospora* Zahlbr. *Lecanora pleistospora* Nyl.
   Thallus of small, sordid white to ashy gray, entire, subglobular, usually crowded squamules, the margin coarsely white-pruinose; apothecia minute to middle-sized, 0.3–0.75 mm. across, immersed 1 in each squamule, the disk concave, brownish black or grayish pruinose; asci ventricose; spores 24 or more, spherical, $4–6 \mu$ in diameter.
   On soil, near Los Angeles, California.

6. **Acarospora scabra** (Pers.) T. Fries, Scand. Lich. 1:208. 1871.
   Urceolaria scabra Pers., Ann. Wett. Ges. 2:10. 1811. *A. rhagadiosa* (Ach.)
   T. Fries. *Glypholecia scabra* (Pers.) Müll. Arg.
   Thallus well developed, of a single white or grayish white, or rarely brownish yellow squamule, centrally chinky-areolate, and marginally lobed; apothecia middle-sized to large, 0.7–3 mm. across, partly immersed to almost superficial, several in the squamule, round to difform, the disk flat to convex, reddish to blackish brown, surrounded by a thalloid exciple, and the disk mottled with persistent lines of cortical tissue, giving a falsely compound appearance; spores spherical, $2.5–3.5 \mu$.
   On sandstone, near the Great Falls of the Missouri River, Montana.

7. **Acarospora citrina** (Tayl.) Zahlbr., Rech. Denk. Akad. Wiss. Wien. 88:28.
   1913.
   Urceolaria citrina Tayl.; Hook., Lond. Journ. Bot. 6:158. 1847. *Lecanora chrysops* Tuck. *Lecanora xanthoplana* Nyl. *A. xanthoplana* (Nyl.) Jatta. *Lecanora xanthoplana* f. *dealbata* Tuck. *Lecanora bella* Ach.
   Thallus well developed of lemon-yellow to white, continuous, flat to slightly convex, angulate-areolate, or marginally distinct and lobed squamules; apothecia minute to small, 0.2–0.6 mm. across, immersed often 4 or more in each squamule, the flat to concave disk reddish to blackish brown and often irregular, an entire thalloid exciple often evident; spores ovoid, $3–5 \times 1.5–2 \mu$.
   On rocks other than calcareous, generally distributed throughout the United States.

8. **Acarospora rhabarbarina** Hue, Nouv. Arch. Museum V. 1:117. 1909.
   A. bella (Nyl.) Jatta. *Lecanora bella* Nyl.
   Thallus composed of thin to somewhat thick, small to middle-sized, irregular, bright to greenish yellow squamules, these scattered or more commonly imbricated and crowded into a thick uneven crust, the outer squamules becoming lobed; apothecia small to rarely middle-sized, 0.3–0.6 mm. across, immersed 1 or rarely more in a squamule, the disk concave to flat, sometimes uneven, reddish brown to brownish black, the exciple thin, colored like the thallus, becoming irregular and wavy; spores ovoid to ovoid-ellipsoid, $4–6 \times 1.5–2.5 \mu$.
   On rocks, southern California.

9. **Acarospora flava** (Bell.) Trev., Riv. Per. Acc. Padova 262. 1851–52.
   Lichen flavus Bell., Appen. Fl. Pede 261. 1792. *A. chloroplana* (Wahl.) Mass.
   Thallus of conspicuous, plicate, bright lemon-colored, strongly convex, areolate-verrucose, or elongated and lobed squamules, the lobing especially marked toward the margin; apothecia small to middle-sized, 0.4–0.9 mm. across, immersed to superficial, 1–3 or more in each squamule, the disk concave to flat, from yellow to reddish and rarely blackening, the thalloid exciple entire; spores oblong-ellipsoid, $4–4.5 \times 1.5–2.5 \mu$.
   On alpine rocks and at lower elevations, from Texas to Utah, and westward to California and Oregon.

10. **Acarospora aeruginosa** Hasse, Cont. U. S. Nat. Herb. 17[1]:67, 68. 1913.
Thallus of minute, clay-colored, flattened to convex, continuous or scattered squamules; apothecia very minute, 0.1–0.15 mm. across, immersed 1–3 in each squamule, the disk punctiform to round or irregular, concave to flat, pale greenish or bluish pruinose; spores oblong, 3–4 × 1–2 μ.
On argillaceous clay and granite, southern California.

11. **Acarospora thermophila** Herre, Bot. Gaz. 55:394. 1913.
Thallus of short, black, often branched stipes, and small, surmounting, pale yellowish to clay-brown, orbicular to lobulate squamule-like expansions; apothecia small to middle-sized, 0.3–0.8 mm. across, 1–several in each expansion, the disk flat, more or less rough and sometimes fissured, yellowish brown, the exciple narrow but plainly visible; spores subglobose to short-ellipsoid, 2–4.5 × 1–2 μ.
Common on rocks, at 4,000 to 8,000 feet, mountains about Reno and Mt. Rose, Nevada.

12. **Acarospora Heppii** Naeg., in Koerb., Par. Lich. 61, 62. 1859.
Thallus very thin, minutely warty, sometimes scarcely visible, greenish gray to brick-red or dusky brown or rarely grayish white; apothecia minute, 0.1–0.2 mm. across, solitary, semi-immersed to adnate, the disk concave to flat, reddish brown to dusky, the exciple prominent, rising above the disk, brownish black; spores ellipsoid, 4–6 × 1.5–2 μ, said to be sometimes globose.
On rocks, along a stream, Montgomery County, Indiana. Differing considerably from the type and doubtfully included here.

13. **Acarospora immersa** Fink; Hedrick, Mycologia 26:158. 1934.
Thallus thin, smooth to minutely chinky and areolate, dark greenish gray to black; apothecia minute, 0.1–0.15 mm. across, immersed 1 or rarely more in an areole, the disk flat, grayish pruinose, the exciple thin, colored like the thallus, entire; asci clavate and becoming inflated; spores ellipsoid, 3–4 × 1.5–2 μ, irregularly arranged.
On limestone, near Oxford, Ohio.

14. **Acarospora california** Zahlbr.; Hasse, Bryologist 17:62. 1914.
Thallus of small, continuous or scattered, light tan to pale chocolate colored, sometimes obscurely pruinose areoles or squamules; apothecia minute, 0.15–0.25 mm. across, the disk concave and brown, deeply immersed, 1 or rarely 2 or 3 in each areole or squamule; asci narrowly flask-shaped to cylindrico-clavate; spores oblong-ellipsoid, 3–4 × 1.5–2 μ.
On granite, San Jacinto Mountains, California.

15. **Acarospora epilutescens** Zahlbr., Beih. Bot. Centralb. 13:161. 1902.
Thallus of grayish white to light steel gray or finally light brown, turgid, roughened, round to irregular, continuous or scattered squamules; apothecia 1 or rarely more in a squamule, minute or small, 0.2–0.5 mm. across, immersed, the disk flat and black, the thalloid exciple moderately thick, entire or subentire, inflexed; spores subspherical to ovoid, 4–5 × 2.5–4 μ.
On granite, San Jacinto Mountains, California.

16. **Acarospora cineracea** (Nyl.) Wedd., Bull. Soc. Bot. France 21:342. 1874.
Lecanora cervina f. *cineracea* Nyl., Act. Soc. Linn. Bordeaux, 21:440. 1856.
Lecanora cineracea Nyl.
Thallus of conspicuous, light brown to white-pruinose, flat or convex, clustered and areolate or scattered and round, irregular, or lobed squamules; apothecia minute, 0.2–0.4 mm. across, immersed, 1–several in each squamule, the disk concave or flat, dark brown; spores oblong-ellipsoid, 4.5–6 × 2–3 μ.
On shaded basalt, near Tucson, Arizona.

17. **Acarospora arenosa** Herre, Proc. Wash. Acad. Sci. 12:128. 1910.
Thallus thin, composed of small, flat to slightly convex, rough, greenish gray to brownish, scale-like areoles, sometimes crowded into an uneven, chinky crust;

apothecia small to middle-sized, 0.3–0.7 mm. across, 1 or rarely more partly immersed in an areole, the disk flat to slightly convex, black, the proper exciple thin, black, becoming irregular, surrounded by a very thin, soon disappearing, thalloid one; hypothecium hyaline to brownish; spores numerous, hyaline, ellipsoid, nonseptate, 2.5–4 × 1–1.5 μ.
On sandstone, southern California.

18. **Acarospora Hassei** Herre, Proc. Wash. Acad. Sci. 12:128. 1910.
Thallus of irregular, thick, sometimes lobate, often scattered areoles or squamules, pale greenish gray to dusky yellowish or brown, beneath pale yellowish to brown; apothecia small, 0.4–0.6 mm. across, immersed 1–several in each areole, the disk slightly concave to flat, reddish brown; hypothecium hyaline to yellowish; spores 3–5 × 1–1.5 μ.
On sandstone, at 3,000 feet, Santa Cruz Peninsula, California.

19. **Acarospora cervina** (Ach.) Mass., Ric. Lich. 28. f. 46. 1852.
Lecanora cervina Ach., Syn. Lich. 188, 189. 1814. *Parmelia cervina* (Ach.) Hepp. *A. cervina* var. *cinereoalba* Fink. *A. cervina* var. *pruinosa* Mass. *A. smaragdula* (Wahl.) Mass.
Thallus of small, yellowish brown to dark chestnut, subpellate or crenate-lobate, closely adnate, scattered or contiguous-areolate and often imbricated squamules, sometimes becoming ashy white; apothecia small to middle-sized, 0.3–0.8 mm. across, 1–3 or 4 in each areole, immersed or becoming superficial, the disk flat and reddish brown or very rarely pruinose, the entire thalloid exciple disappearing; spores subspherical to oblong, 3–5 × 1.5–3 μ.
On rocks other than calcareous, throughout northern United States.

20. **Acarospora obpallens** (Nyl.) Zahlbr., Beih. Bot. Centralb. 13:161, 162. 1902.
Lecanora obpallens Nyl.; Hasse, Bull. Torr. Club 24:446. 1897.
Thallus of shining, light chestnut, crowded or scattered, somewhat wrinkled and pitted, convex and rounded squamules; apothecia small to middle-sized, 0.4–0.6 mm. across, partly immersed, 1–several in each squamule, the disk concave to flat, papillate, reddish brown and sometimes obscurely pruinose, the thalloid exciple prominent, moderately thick, crenulate; spores oblong-ellipsoid, 3–6 × 1.5–2 μ.
On soil and crumbling sandstone, southern California.

21. **Acarospora Carnegiei** Zahlbr., Bull. Torr. Club 35:297. 1908.
Thallus of small, angular or reddish brown and darkening, round, clustered or more or less scattered squamules; apothecia immersed, middle-sized, 0.4–0.7 mm. across, 1–3 in each squamule, the disk flat to slightly convex, pruinose; spores oblong, 5–6 × 1.5–2.5 μ.
On blocks of basalt, near Tucson, Arizona.

22. **Acarospora squamulosa** (Schrad.) Trevis., Riv. Per. Acc. Padova 263. 1851–52.
Lichen squamulosus Schrad., Ann. Bot. Usteri, 22:84. 1797. *Parmelia cervina* var. *squamulosa* (Schrad.) E. Fries. *Lecanora cervina* var. *squamulosa* (Schrad.) Willey.
Thallus brown to grayish brown, squamulose, the squamules round, entire to lobulate, flat to convex, crowded to scattered; apothecia small to middle-sized, 0.25–1 mm. across, immersed to semi-immersed, 1–12 or more in each squamule, the disk flat, chestnut-brown to dull black; spores oblong-ellipsoid, 3–5 × 1.8–2.5 μ.
On various rocks, Santa Monica Range, California.

23. **Acarospora fuscata** (Schrad.) Arn., Verh. Ges. Wien. 22:279. 1872.
Lichen fuscatus Schrad., Spic. Fl. Germ. 83. 1794. *A. cervina* var. *fuscata* Fink. *Lecanora fuscata* (Schrad.) Röhl. *Lecanora fuscata* var. *rufescens* (Ach.) Tuck. *Lecanora fuscata* f. *sinopica* (Wahl.) Nyl.
Thallus of pale to dark chestnut, clustered and areolate or scattered and often lobulate squamules; apothecia small to middle-sized, 0.3–0.9 mm. across, immersed

to superficial, 1–several in the areoles, the disk concave to convex, reddish to dark brown, becoming rough and often papillose, the thalloid exciple thin, disappearing; spores subspherical to oblong, 3–5 × 1.8–2.7 μ.

On rocks other than calcareous, throughout the northern and middle states.

24. **Acarospora glaucocarpa** (Ach.) Koerb., Par. Lich. 57. 1859.
Parmelia glaucocarpa Ach., Meth. Lich. 182. 1803. *Lecanora glaucocarpa* Ach.

Thallus of small, pale greenish brown, round, scattered or more rarely clustered and imbricated, entire or crenate squamules; apothecia middle-sized to large, 0.5–1.25 mm. across, 1 or more on each squamule, the disk flat to slightly convex, reddish brown, usually grayish pruinose, the thalloid exciple rather thick, entire; spores oblong-ellipsoid, 4–5 × 1.5–2.5 μ.

On calcareous rocks, from Vermont to Washington, and southward.

f. **depauperata** (Koerb.) Hazel., Verh. Vere. Nat. Presb. 4:90. 1859.
A. cervina var. *glaucocarpa* f. *depauperata* Koerb., Syst. Lich. Germ. 155. 1855.

Thallus wanting; apothecia variable in size, scattered or clustered, the disk sometimes pruinose, the thalloid exciple sometimes disappearing.

On calcareous rocks, Washington.

var. **verrucosa** (Anzi) Magn., Mono. Acar. 240. 1929.
Lecanora glaucocarpa var. *verrucosa* Anzi, Lich. Lang. Exsicc. 8:329. 1863.
A. glaucocarpa var. *distans* Arn.

Thallus reduced to minute, scattered, round, convex, greenish brown areoles; the disk of the apothecium only evanescently pruinose.

On calcareous rocks, Kansas, Texas, and California.

25. **Acarospora glebosa** (Flot.) Koerb., Syst. Lich. 156. 1855.
Zeora cervina var. *glebosa* Flot., Jahr. Schl. Ges. 122. 1849. *Lecanora fuscata* var. *oligospora* (Nyl.) Tuck.

Thallus of dirty greenish brown, appressed and rounded, scattered or rarely clustered areoles or separate or marginal squamules; apothecia small to middle-sized, 0.4–0.9 mm. across, immersed, 1 in each areole or squamule, the disk concave or flat, reddish brown, the exciple wide, entire or obscurely crenulate, of same color as the thallus; spores oblong-ovoid, 8–15 × 7–10 μ, 20–40 in each saccate ascus.

On granite and sandstone, California and Iowa.

26. **Acarospora molybdina** (Wahl.) Trevis., Riv. Per. Ist. Padova 262. 1851–52.
Parmelia molybdina Wahl., in Ach., Meth. Lich. Suppl. 42. 1803. *Lecanora molybdina* (Wahl.) Ach. *Lecanora molybdina* var. *vulgaris* Schaer. *A. molybdina* var. *microcyclos* (Ach.) Mass. *Lecanora molybdina* var. *microcyclos* Ach.

Thallus of thick or thin, light to blackish brown, convex squamules, continuous and verrucose-areolate toward the center, but linear-lobed toward the margin; apothecia small, 0.4–0.6 mm. across, immersed to semi-immersed, 1 or rarely more in each squamule; the disk concave, brownish black, a thalloid exciple sometimes evident; spores oblong, 3–5 × 1.5–2 μ.

On rocks, Maine (poorly developed).

27. **Acarospora thamnina** (Tuck.) Herre, Bot. Gaz. 55:395, 396. 1913.
Lecanora cervina var. *thamnina* Tuck., Syn. N. A. Lich. 1:202. 1882.

Thallus of small, branched stipes, rising 10 to 15 mm. high and expanding into small, brown to grayish pruinose, closely aggregated, often lobulate and even imbricate, areole-like areas; apothecia minute to small, 0.2–0.8 mm. across, usually solitary in the areoles, the disk flat, reddish brown, the entire exciple disappearing; spores ellipsoid, 3.3–4.5 × 0.75–1.25 μ.

On rocks, mountains of California, and eastward to Montana and Nevada.

OTHER SPECIES REPORTED
Acarospora pelioscypha (Wahl.) T. Fries—Nevada.

37. PERTUSARIACEAE

Thallus crustose, showing differentiation into upper and lower cortical layers, algal and medullary layers, attached to the substratum by hyphal rhizoids; apothecia immersed to adnate, single or clustered, the disk sometimes becoming a sorediate mass, the exciple usually thalloid.

The algal hosts are Pleurococcus and Protococcus.

141. **Pertusaria** Lam. & DC., Fl. Fr. ed. 3. 2:319. 1815.

Thallus crustose, thin to thick, partly within the substratum, differentiated into a poorly developed, plectenchymatous upper cortex or a thin gelatinized layer of interwoven hyphae, distinct algal and medullary layers, attached to the substratum by hyphal rhizoids; apothecia minute to small, commonly 1–several immersed in wartlike elevations of thallus, opening by a small pore or becoming open and disklike, thalloid covering often breaking up into a sorediate mass; hypothecium hyaline; hymenium hyaline or brownish above; paraphyses branched and netlike interwoven; asci clavate or cylindrico-clavate; spores 1–8, hyaline, ellipsoid or oblong-ellipsoid, non-septate, with thick wall.

The algal host is Protococcus.

A. On trees, rocks, and old wood
  B. Spores 1–4 or rarely 8 in an ascus, more than 50 μ in length
    C. Thallus greenish gray to ashy white, brownish or rarely
      yellowish gray
      D. Spores rarely more than 170 μ in length
        E. Margins not swollen or raised
          F. Spores 1 or 2 in an ascus
            G. Apothecia passing into sorediate heaps
              H. Apothecia 1–several immersed in each wartlike
                elevation . . . . 1. P. multipuncta
              H. Apothecia 1 immersed in each wartlike
                elevation . . . . 1. P. multipuncta ophthalmiza
            G. Apothecia persistent, ostiole opening into a disk
              H. Thallus ashy, smooth to chinky; exciple
                thin . . . . 12. P. Finkii
              H. Thallus ashy to brownish, smooth to
                rough and areolate; exciple thicker,
                irregular . . . . 10. P. pustulata
          F. Spores 2–4 or 8 in an ascus
            G. Ostioles minute . . . . 8. P. tetrathalamia
            G. Ostioles prominent, or opening into a blackening
              disk . . . . 13. P. leioplaca
         E. Margins swollen and raised . . . . 14. P. marginata
      D. Spores reaching 200–250 μ in length
        E. Thallus lighter and zonate toward the circumference;
          disk becoming sorediate . . . . 4. P. velata
        E. Thallus rarely zonate, wartlike elevations often
          crowded . . . . 15. P. pertusa
    C. Thallus sulphur-colored to more or less yellowish gray
      D. Thallus yellow to ashy or yellowish gray   .
        E. Thallus smooth to wrinkled, minutely areolate or
          granulose
            F. Disk white-pruinose to pale flesh-colored . . . . 2. P. lecanina
            F. Disk dull black or blackish pruinose . . . . 2. P. lecanina nigra
        E. Thallus becoming minutely granulose and powdery . 11. P. lutescens
      D. Thallus sulphur-colored or ashy yellow
        E. On trees; disk blackish, exciple thick, wavy to
          flexuous . . . . 16. P. Wulfenii
        E. On rocks; disk yellowish pruinose to blackish,
          exciple thinner . . . . 3. P. flavicunda
  B. Spores 8 in an ascus, less than 50 μ in length
    C. On trees; disk flesh-colored to greenish or grayish pruinose

D. Exciple thin, entire . . . . 7. P. carneopallida
D. Exciple irregular, appearing as 2 or 3 layers . . . . . 6. P. ambigens
    C. On rocks; disk brownish to blackening . . . . 9. P. nolens
A. On soil and over moss
    B. Thallus of coralloid branchlets
        C. Apothecia flesh-colored to blackish; spores 2–4
            in an ascus . . . . 18. P. globularis
        C. Apothecia flesh-colored, more or less covered by a thalloid
            veil; spores 1 in an ascus . . . . 5. P. dactylina
    B. Thallus of confluent, wartlike elevations . . . . 17. P. glomerata

1. **Pertusaria multipuncta** (Turn.) Nyl., Not. Sällsk. Faun. Flor. Fenn. 5:179,
180. 1861.
Variolaria multipuncta Turn., Trans. Linn. Soc. Lond. 9:137. pl. 10, f. 1. 1808.
P. communis var. *sorediata* E. Fries. *P. faginea* Tuck.
Thallus thin, smooth to chinky or warty-areolate, greenish gray to pale ashy;
apothecia small to middle-sized, 0.3–0.6 mm. across, 1–several immersed in each
wartlike elevation, with a minute, depressed, blackened ostiole, or becoming open
with a flat, pale to blackish disk and thin, irregular exciple, the apothecia finally
passing into powdery-sorediate heaps; spores 1 or rarely 2, ellipsoid to oblong-
ellipsoid, 75–170 × 25–65 µ.
On trees, throughout the United States.

var. **ophthalmiza** Nyl., Not. Sällsk. Faun. Flor. Fenn. 5:180. 1861. *P. multipuncta* var. *laevigata* Turn.
Thallus thin and smooth; apothecia usually 1 in each wartlike elevation, becoming open, with a flat, blackened disk and thin, irregular, thalloid exciple.
On trees, Minnesota and Washington.

2. **Pertusaria lecanina** Tuck., Gen. Lich. 127. 1872.
Thallus thin, smooth to slightly wrinkled, becoming granulose, yellowish to
ashy, sometimes bordered by a thin, black hypothallus; apothecia small to middle-
sized, 0.5–1 mm. across, adnate to sessile, the disk flat to slightly concave, thickly
white-pruinose to pale flesh-colored, the exciple thick, colored like the thallus,
slightly wavy; spores 2, ellipsoid, 96–140 × 34–48 µ.
On trees, California.

var. **nigra** Fink; Hedrick, Mycologia 26:966. 1934.
Apothecia becoming dull black or blackish pruinose; spores 100–128 × 40–50 µ.
On dead yew tree, at 3,000 feet, Montana.

3. **Pertusaria flavicunda** Tuck., Proc. Am. Acad. 12:176, 177. 1877.
Thallus thin, smooth to chinky-areolate, granulose or minutely warty, sulphur-
colored, the areoles becoming lobed toward the margin; apothecia small to middle-
sized, 0.6–1.5 mm. across, adnate, round to irregular, sometimes in groups of 2 or
more, the ostiole soon opening and the disk concave to flat, yellowish pruinose or
becoming blackish, the exciple colored like the thallus, becoming thin; hypothecium
hyaline to pale brownish; spores 2 or 3, oblong-ellipsoid, 60–90 × 38–52 µ.
On rocks, California.

4. **Pertusaria velata** (Turn.) Nyl., Not. Sällsk. Faun. Flor. Fenn. 5:179. 1861.
Parmelia velata Turn., Trans. Linn. Soc. Lond. 9:142. pl. 12, f. 1. 1808.
Thallus round, rather thin to thick, smooth to folded, wrinkled, chinky or
irregularly roughened and warty, greenish gray to ashy, commonly lighter and frequently zonate toward the circumference; apothecia small, 0.3–0.5 mm. across, 1–2
or 3 immersed in small to middle-sized, wartlike elevations, the disk concave to flat,
irregular, yellowish to flesh-colored, sometimes white-powdery-sorediate, the thalloid
exciple thick, very rarely disappearing; spores 1 or rarely 2, oblong-ellipsoid, 150–
250 × 42–84 µ. (PLATE 27 b.)
On trees and rocks, throughout the United States east of the Rocky Mountains (California?).

5. **Pertusaria dactylina** (Ach.) Nyl., Act. Soc. Sci. Fenn. 7:447. 1863.
   Lichen dactylinus Ach., Lich. Suec. 89. 1798.
   Thallus thin, smooth to wrinkled and uneven, ashy white, producing many finger-shaped, erect, sometimes divided, cylindrical branchlets; apothecia minute to small, 0.15–0.5 mm. across, borne in the tips of the branchlets, the disk concave to flat, pale flesh-colored, more or less covered by a thalloid veil; spores 1, 125–200 × 65–85 μ.
   On soil over mosses, New Hampshire.

6. **Pertusaria ambigens** (Nyl.) Tuck., Proc. Am. Acad. 12:176. 1877.
   Lecanora ambigens Nyl., Act. Soc. Sci. Fenn. 7:449. 1863.
   Thallus thin, smooth to wrinkled and warty, greenish gray; apothecia small to middle-sized, 0.4–1 mm. across, sessile or becoming slightly elevated, the disk concave to flat, flesh-colored to dark greenish, often grayish pruinose, the exciple colored like the thallus, irregularly crenate, at length appearing as 2 or 3 layers; spores 8, ellipsoid to ovoid-ellipsoid, 17–24 × 8–13 μ.
   On trees, Washington, Oregon, and California.

7. **Pertusaria carneopallida** Nyl., Flora 51:478. 1868.
   Lecidea carneopallida Nyl., Bot. Not. 183. 1853.
   Thallus very thin to thin, smooth to slightly rough, greenish gray to ashy, sometimes disappearing; apothecia minute to small, 0.1–0.5 mm. across, immersed to adnate, the disk flat to convex, pale flesh-colored, the exciple thin, colored like the thallus, irregular and finally disappearing; spores 8, ellipsoid to broad-ellipsoid, 16–32 × 11–18 μ.
   On trees, Washington.

8. **Pertusaria tetrathalamia** (Fée) Nyl., Act. Soc. Sci. Fenn. 7:448. 1863.
   Trypethelium tetrathalamia Fée, Essai Crypt. 69. 1824. *P. leioplacoides* Müll. Arg.
   Thallus thin to moderately thick, smooth to becoming wrinkled and chinky or warty, pale greenish gray to whitish; apothecia minute to small, 0.1–0.5 mm. across, 1 or more commonly several immersed in each convex or slightly depressed, irregular, wartlike elevation, the ostioles minute, papillate or scarcely prominent; spores 2–4 or rarely 8, ellipsoid, 65–120 × 24–36 μ.
   On trees, Florida.

9. **Pertusaria nolens** Nyl., Flora 47:489. 1864.
   Thallus thin, smooth to finely chinky-areolate, lead-gray to dull ashy; apothecia minute to small, 0.25–0.5 mm. across, 1 or rarely 2 immersed in an areole, the ostioles black, opening to form round or more commonly irregular, flat, brownish to blackening disks, the exciple rarely substellate; spores 8, ellipsoid, 28–42 × 14–22 μ.
   On schistose rocks, Santa Monica Range, California.

10. **Pertusaria pustulata** (Ach.) Duby, Bot. Gall. 2:673. 1830.
    Porina pustulata Ach., Lich. Univ. 309. 1810.
    Thallus thin, smooth to rough and chinky or finally somewhat warty, greenish gray to yellowish or brownish; apothecia minute to small, 0.15–0.4 mm. across, 1–4 or 5 immersed in each small, hemispherical, and irregular wartlike elevation, the ostioles becoming prominent and often opening separately or converging into a flat, blackish disk with a rather thick, irregular exciple; spores 2, ellipsoid, 50–135 × 25–56 μ.
    On trees, throughout the United States.

11. **Pertusaria lutescens** (Hoffm.) Lam., Bull. Soc. Bot. 25:427. 1878.
    Lepra lutescens Hoffm., Enum. Lich. 3. 1784.
    Thallus thin, smooth to minutely wrinkled, becoming powdery, yellow to yellowish gray, sometimes thinly zonate toward the circumference; apothecia rare,

minute to small, 0.15–0.3 mm. across, 1– rarely 3 or 4 immersed in wartlike elevations, with minute black ostioles or becoming superficial and open, with the disk
concave to flat, blackish, the exciple thick, irregular, colored like the thallus, the
whole apothecium sometimes passing into a powdery-sorediate heap; spores 1 or
2, ellipsoid, 64–96 × 28–40 μ.
On trees, Florida.

12. **Pertusaria Finkii** Zahlbr., in Fink, Minn. Bot. Stud. 2:696. 1901.
Thallus thin, smooth or becoming chinky and somewhat warty, ashy to whitish,
the wartlike elevations small, irregular, and flattened; apothecia small to middle-
sized, 0.3–0.6 mm. across, immersed 1–5 in each flat and inconspicuous elevation
with minute, irregular, brown or blackish ostiole, or becoming open with a concave,
brown to blackish disk; spores 2 or rarely 1, oblong-ellipsoid, sometimes constricted
along the sides, 70–140 × 28–53 μ.
Qn trees, Minnesota.

13. **Pertusaria leioplaca** (Ach.) Lam. & DC., Fl. Fr. ed. 3. 6:173. 1815.
Porina leioplaca Ach., Lich. Univ. 309. pl. 7, f. 2. 1810.
Thallus thin, smooth to slightly chinky and warty, greenish gray to yellowish, or
rarely imbedded in the substratum and invisible; apothecia small, 0.25–0.4 mm.
across, 1– rarely 5 immersed in each small to middle-sized, round, irregular, wartlike elevation, the ostioles minute, black, becoming prominent, or the apothecia
rarely becoming open with blackening disk and thick, irregular exciple; spores
4–8, oblong-ellipsoid, 44–180 × 20–50 μ.
On trees and rocks, throughout the United States.

14. **Pertusaria marginata** Nyl., Lich. Jap. 53. 1890.
P. torquata Müll. Arg. *P. propinqua* Müll. Arg.
Thallus thin, smooth to wrinkled, becoming chinky-areolate and warty, grayish
white to whitish, the wartlike elevations irregular, with margins wholly or in part
swollen and raised; apothecia small, 0.3–0.5 mm. across, 1–several immersed in each
wartlike elevation, the ostioles black, subdepressed, commonly converging and appearing disklike with a thick, irregular, swollen exciple; spores 4–8, ellipsoid, 72–
110 × 28–42 μ.
On trees and rocks, from Massachusetts to the Carolinas.

15. **Pertusaria pertusa** (L.) Tuck., Enum. N. A. Lich. 56. 1845.
Lichen pertusus L., Mant. Pl. 131. 1767. *P. communis* Lam. & DC. *Porina*
pertusa (L.) Ach. *P. rupestris* (DC.) Schaer.
Thallus thin to rarely moderately thick, smooth, becoming wrinkled or warty
and subareolate, greenish gray or lighter colored, and rarely zonate toward the
circumference, the wartlike elevations subglobose, somewhat depressed, variously
irregular; apothecia small to middle-sized, 0.4–0.6 mm. across, 2–several immersed
in each elevation, the ostioles minute and often inconspicuous, sunken, blackish to
black; spores 2 or rarely 3 or 4, oblong-ellipsoid, 90–200 × 40–70 μ.
On trees and rocks, throughout the United States.

16. **Pertusaria Wulfenii** Lam. & DC., Fl. Fr. ed. 3. 2:320. 1805.
Porina fallax Ach.
Thallus thin to rather thick, smooth to wrinkled and warty, sulphur-colored to
ashy yellow; apothecia small to middle-sized, 0.4–1 mm. across, 1–several immersed
in small to middle-sized wartlike elevations, the few to many black ostioles running
together into a depressed but flat blackish disk with a thick, wavy to flexuous,
thalloid exciple; spores 8, ellipsoid, 58–110 × 28–42 μ.
On trees, throughout the United States.

17. **Pertusaria glomerata** (Ach.) Schaer., Lich. Helv. Spic. 66. 1826.
Porina glomerata Ach., Lich. Univ. 310, 311. 1810.
Thallus thin to moderately thick, round, composed of minute to small, sub-

globose, greenish gray to ashy, confluent wartlike elevations; apothecia small to middle-sized, 0.3–0.6 mm. across, 1–several immersed in each wartlike elevation, solitary and protuberant or at length clustered or united into crowded, irregular groups, the ostioles black; hypothecium hyaline to cloudy; spores 2– rarely 4, 6, or 8, yellowish, oblong-ellipsoid to ellipsoid-pointed, 95–195 × 25–68 μ.

On soil and over mosses, New Hampshire, New York, and Minnesota.

18. **Pertusaria globularis** (Ach.) Tuck., Proc. Am. Acad. 1:277. 1848.
Porina globularis Ach., Syn. Meth. Lich. 112. 1814.

Thallus thin, minutely granulose to densely covered with short or sometimes longer and branched coralloid branchlets, greenish gray to ashy; apothecia small, 0.25–0.5 mm. across, subsessile, sometimes united in groups of 2–several, the ostioles sunken and flesh-colored to blackish; hypothecium hyaline to pale brownish; spores 2–4, oblong-ellipsoid, 65–110 × 34–52 μ.

Over mosses, from New England to Alabama, and westward to Arkansas.

OTHER SPECIES REPORTED

Pertusaria amara (Ach.) Nyl.—Maine and Washington.
Pertusaria globulifera (Turn.) Mass —California.
Pertusaria rhexostoma Nyl.—North America.
Pertusaria scutellaris Hue—Maine.
Pertusaria texana Müll. Arg.—Texas.
Pertusaria xanthodes Müll. Arg.—Texas.

38. LECANORACEAE

Thallus crustose, scaly, squamulose, or rarely even fruticose, differentiated into cortical, algal, and medullary layers, rarely plectenchymatous throughout, attached to the substratum by hyphal rhizoids; apothecia round, immersed to adnate or sessile, with a well-developed thalloid exciple and rarely a poorly developed proper one.

The algal hosts are Pleurococcus and Protococcus.

A. Spores non-septate
  B. Spores large . . . . 143. OCHROLECHIA
  B. Spores small
    C. Thallus yellow to orange . . . . 151. CANDELARIELLA
    C. Thallus rarely yellow or orange . . . . 142. LECANORA
A. Spores septate
  B. Spores transversely 1–many-septate
    C. Spores 1–3-septate
      D. Spores constantly 1-septate or rarely becoming 3-septate
        E. Thallus yellow to orange . . . . 151. CANDELARIELLA
        E. Thallus not yellow or orange
          F. Thallus crustose . . . . 145. LECANIA
          F. Thallus squamulose . . . . 146. SOLENOPSORA
      D. Spores 1–3-septate . . . . 144. ICMADOPHILA
    C. Spores 3–many-septate
      D. Apothecia more or less immersed
        E. Paraphyses unbranched . . . . 149. PHLYCTELLA
        E. Paraphyses branched and interwoven . . . . . 150. PHLYCTIDIA
      D. Apothecia adnate to sessile . . . . 147. HAEMATOMMA
  B. Spores transversely and longitudinally septate . . . . . . 148. PHLYCTIS

142. **Lecanora** Ach., Lich. Univ. 77. pl. 7, f. 3–7. 1810.

Thallus crustose to rarely subfoliose or foliose, the crustose forms showing no differentiation or poorly developed indistinct upper cortex, algal and medullary layers, and attached to the substratum by hyphal rhizoids, the foliose forms differentiated into a well-developed, gelatinized pseudocellular upper cortex, well-developed algal and medullary layers, and a thin, poorly developed lower cortex;

apothecia small to large, immersed to adnate or sessile, the disk flat to convex, the exciple colored like the thallus; hypothecium hyaline to brownish; hymenium hyaline or brownish above; paraphyses unbranched; asci clavate; spores 2–8 or rarely 16–32, hyaline, non-septate.

The algal host is Protococcus.

A. Thallus dwarfish-fruticose
  B. Thallus pale or greenish straw-colored
    C. Apothecia 0.5–4 mm. across, disk flesh-colored to
      yellowish and brownish . . . . 66. L. Bolanderi
    C. Apothecia 0.6–1.5 mm. across, disk pale yellowish to
      tawny red . . . . 67. L. thamnitis
  B. Thallus reddish yellow or lighter . . . . 68. L. phryganitis
A. Thallus crustose to more or less foliose
  B. Thallus foliose or more or less lobed, at least toward
  the circumference
    C. Thallus foliose or squamulose
      D. Apothecia present
        E. Apothecia large, 1.5–5 mm. across
          F. Thallus smooth to rough . . . . 63. L. rubina
          F. Thallus chinky and wrinkled . . . . 63. L. rubina heteromorpha
        E. Apothecia smaller, rarely more than 2.5 mm. across
          F. Thallus foliose, attached by an umbilicus . . . 53. L. marginalis
          F. Thallus squamulose . . . . 49. L. thamnoplaca
      D. Apothecia unknown . . . . 65. L. Haydenii
    C. Thallus areolate or squamulose toward the circumference
      D. Apothecia immersed to adnate
        E. Spores 8, rarely more than 16 μ in length
          F. Apothecia 0.3–0.8 mm. across
            G. Disk olive-brown to blackish . . . . . 50. L. intricata
            G. Disk buff to darker brownish . . . . . 56. L. versicolor
          F. Apothecia 0.6–1.5 mm. across
            G. Disk light to dark brown . . . . . . 55. L. circinata
            G. Disk flesh-colored to livid black, usually
              whitish pruinose . . . . 54. L. rupicola
        E. Spores 4–10, 14–24 × 9–20 μ . . . . 52. L. glaucopsina
      D. Apothecia adnate to subsessile or sessile
        E. Disk more or less pruinose
          F. Thallus ashy to whitish or light brown to brownish
            G. Thallus pruinose in scattered areas . . . 64. L. bipruinosa
            G. Thallus not pruinose . . . . 51. L. melanaspis
          F. Thallus straw-colored, dull greenish gray to
          sulphur-yellow
            G. Thallus sulphur-yellow within . . . . . . 60. L. pinguis
            G. Thallus whitish within . . . . 62. L. semitensis
        E. Disk not pruinose
          F. Thallus not pruinose
            G. Disk light-colored to darker or black
              H. Apothecia adnate, disk concave to flat
                I. Thallus pale greenish gray to whitish,
                  bearing soredia . . . . 61. L. gelida
                I. Thallus greenish gray to yellowish
                  brown . . . . 48. L. melanophthalma
              H. Apothecia adnate to subsessile or sessile,
              disk flat
                I. Thallus greenish gray to yellowish or
                rarely brownish
                  J. Thallus long- or shorter-lobed . . . 57. L. muralis
                  J. Thallus lobes elongated . . 57. L. muralis Garovaglii
                I. Thallus more or less brownish . . 57. L. muralis saxicola
            G. Disk reddish brown or brown to black
               H. Thallus greenish gray to ashy or
                 yellowish . . . . 47. L. frustulosa
              H. Thallus yellowish brown to reddish and
               darker . . . . 58. L. diffracta

    F. Thallus more or less whitish pruinose . . . . 59. L. lentigera
B. Thallus crustose, not lobed toward the circumference
  C. Apothecia immersed to adnate, disk concave to flat
    D. Spores rarely more than 15 μ in length
      E. Disk light-colored to becoming darker
        F. Spores usually more than 10 μ in length
          G. Thallus finely whitish pulverulent . . . . . 2. L. iowensis
          G. Thallus chinky to areolate
            H. Spores 10–13 × 4–6 μ . . . . 11. L. odora
            H. Spores 11–17 × 6–9 μ . . . . 13. L. epulotica
        F. Spores 10 × 6 μ . . . . 14. L. lavata
      E. Disk reddish brown or black
        F. Thallus blackish olive . . . . . . 8. L. cinerea microspora
        F. Thallus not blackish olive
          G. Thallus pale brick color or yellowish green . . 12. L. lacustris
          G. Thallus greenish gray to ashy . . . . . 9. L. deplanans
    D. Spores rarely less than 15 μ in length
      E. Spores rarely more than 30 μ in length
        F. Spores constantly 8 in an ascus
          G. Disk black
            H. Apothecia 0.5–1.5 mm. across
              I. Thallus thin to thick, ashy white to
                greenish or rarely blackening . . . . . 8. L. cinerea
              I. Thallus thick, greenish to brownish gray . 4. L. gibbosa
            H. Apothecia 0.2–0.6 mm. across . . . . . . 7. L. laevata
          G. Disk reddish to reddish brown . . . 10. L. cinereorufescens
        F. Spores 2–4 or 8 in an ascus
          G. Thallus greenish gray to rarely whitish . . . . 1. L. calcarea
          G. Thallus greenish lead-colored or grayish
            white . . . . 3. L. contorta
      E. Spores commonly more than 30 μ in length
        F. On trees; thallus dark ashy gray to yellowish . . 6. L. mutabilis
        F. On soil and moss; thallus greenish gray to
          whitish or ashy . . . . 5. L. verrucosa
  C. Apothecia adnate to more or less sessile
    D. Spores rarely more than 17 μ in length
      E. Apothecia dark red, reddish brown to brown, or black
        F. Thallus greenish gray to ashy, brownish, or more
        or less yellowish
          G. Confined to rocks
            H. Thallus greenish ashy to grayish or lead-colored
              I. Apothecia 0.4–0.9 mm. across . . . . . 17. L. melaena
              I. Apothecia 0.8–1.8 mm. across . . . . . 22. L. alpina
            H. Thallus greenish yellow . . . . 42. L. oregana
          G. Not confined to rocks
            H. On trees, old wood, and rocks
              I. Thallus rather thick, more or less granulose
                J. Disk very black . . . . 15. L. atra
                J. Disk brown to brownish black . . . . 23. L. rugosa
              I. Thallus thin, becoming wrinkled and
                broken . . . . 26. L. subfusca coilocarpa
            H. On trees and old wood
              I. Apothecia 0.1–0.6 mm. across
                J. Thallus yellowish to ashy or darkening;
                  disk reddish brown . . . . . . 38. L. effusa
                J. Thallus greenish gray to ashy; disk
                  reddish brown to brown and grayish
                  pruinose . . . . 19. L. hypoptoides
              I. Apothecia 0.5–1 or 1.6 mm. across
                J. Disk reddish brown to brownish black
                  or rarely grayish pruinose; spores
                  10–16 × 5–7.5 μ . . . . 36. L. parisensis
                J. Disk reddish brown and commonly grayish
                  pruinose; spores 11–18 × 6–9 μ . . 20. L. miculata

F. Thallus greenish ashy to olive-green or brown
  G. On rocks
    H. Thallus thin, greenish ashy to olive-green . . 43. L. badia
    H. Thallus thicker, coppery or duller brown . 44. L. atriseda
  G. On trees . . . . 46. L. phaeobola
E. Apothecia light-colored to becoming brownish or black
  F. Apothecia yellowish, flesh-colored, or orange to
  rarely pale brown
    G. On trees and rarely on rocks
      H. Disk more or less pruinose
        I. Apothecia 0.7–3 mm. across
          J. Apothecia sometimes smaller
            K. Apothecia crowded and irregularly
              angular . . . . . . 35. L. pallida angulosa
            K. Apothecia scattered . . . . . 35. L. pallida
          J. Apothecia larger
            K. Apothecia becoming pro-
              liferate . . . . . . 35. L. pallida prolifera
            K. Apothecia swollen, exciple crenate
              and lobed . . . . . 35. L. pallida cancriformis
        I. Apothecia 0.5–0.8 mm. across . . . . 37. L. orosthea
      H. Disk not pruinose
        I. Thallus greenish gray . . . . 34. L. cupressi
        I. Thallus pale greenish, yellowish, or
          whitish . . . . 39. L. varia
    G. On rocks
      H. Apothecia 0.5–1.5 mm. across
        I. Apothecia crowded, irregular . 41. L. polytropa alpigena
        I. Apothecia scattered . . . . . . 41. L. polytropa
      H. Apothecia smaller, 0.3–0.7 mm.
        across . . . . 41. L. polytropa illusoria
  F. Apothecia pale yellow, flesh-colored, red or
  brownish, or darkening
    G. On trees, old wood, moss, and rarely on rocks
      H. Spores 8 in an ascus
        I. Apothecia 0.1–0.25 mm. across
          J. Spores 3–5 × 2–3 μ . . . . . . 18. L. minutella
          J. Spores 8–12 × 4–5.5 μ . . . . . 32. L. piniperda
        I. Apothecia usually more than 0.2 mm. across
          J. Disk more or less pruinose
            K. Spores 7–14 × 4–6 μ . . . . . 28. L. Hageni
            K. Spores 12–16 × 6.5–10 μ . . . 27. L. pacifica
          J. Disk not pruinose
            K. Thallus more or less granulose
              L. On old wood . . . . . . 40. L. symmicta
              L. On moss . . . 26. L. subfusca hypnorum
            K. Thallus chinky or warty to areolate
              L. Thallus sorediate . . 26. L. subfusca variolosa
              L. Thallus not sorediate
                M. Spores 11–20 × 7–10 μ
                  N. Disk flat to somewhat
                    convex . . . . . 26. L. subfusca
                  N. Disk strongly and irregularly
                    convex . . . 26. L. subfusca campestris
                M. Spores 8–15 × 5–8 μ . . . .
                  . . . . . . 26. L. subfusca argentata
      H. Spores 8–32, usually 12–16 in an ascus
        I. Disk flat to convex . . . . 29. L. Sambuci
        I. Disk broken into 2–8 convex
          areas . . . . . . 29. L. Sambuci minnesotensis
    G. On rocks
      H. Disk light-colored to darker
        I. Spores 10–17 × 5–8.5 μ
          J. Disk thinly pruinose . . . . . . 24. L. cenisia

J. Disk not pruinose . . . . 25. L. atrynea
   I. Spores 8–13 × 3.5–5.5 μ . . . . . . 33. L. dispersa
H. Disk dark red . . . . 31. L. Willeyi
D. Spores rarely less than 16 μ in length
  E. Spores ellipsoid or ovoid-ellipsoid
    F. On trees
      G. Thallus lemon-yellow within . . . . . 21. L. granulifera
      G. Thallus whitish within . . . . 16. L. glaucomela
    F. On rocks . . . . 45. L. Bockii
  E. Spores spherical . . . . 30. L. praecrenata

1. **Lecanora calcarea** (L.) Nyl., Not. Sällsk. Faun. Flor. Fenn. 5:154. 1861.
Lichen calcareus L., Sp. Pl. 1140. 1753. *Parmelia calcarea* (L.) Hepp.

Thallus rough, chinky to areolate or warty, greenish gray to rarely whitish, often disappearing; apothecia small to middle-sized, 0.5–1 mm. across, immersed to rarely adnate, the disk flat, light brown to blackish, and commonly more or less grayish pruinose, the exciple thin, colored like the thallus, becoming wrinkled; spores 2–8, subglobose to ellipsoid, 15–27 × 9–22 μ.

On rocks, throughout northern United States, and extending southward through California.

2. **Lecanora iowensis** Fink; Hedrick, Mycologia 26:161. 1934.

Thallus thin, greenish gray to ashy, finely whitish pulverulent, chinky to areolate, the areoles small and flat, rarely lobed toward the margins; apothecia minute to small, 0.25–0.7 mm. across, immersed to adnate, 1–2 in each areole, the disk slightly concave to flat, light to darker brown or blackish, beneath a persistent grayish white-pruinose cover, the exciple entire, becoming somewhat flexuous, colored like the thallus or darkening; spores oblong-ellipsoid, 10–14 × 5–8 μ.

On calcareous rocks, near Fayette, Iowa.

3. **Lecanora contorta** (Hoffm.) Stiz.; Reching., Verh. Gesell. Vien. 65:199. 1915.
Verrucaria contorta Hoffm., Descr. Pl. Crypt. 1:97. pl. 22, f. 1–4. 1790. *L. calcarea* var. *contorta* (Hoffm.) Hepp. *L. calcarea* var. *monstrosa* Lamy.

Thallus thick, composed of irregular, centrally elevated and marginally depressed, greenish lead-colored or grayish white, sometimes scattered areoles; apothecia minute to small, 0.3–0.8 mm. across, immersed to scarcely adnate, the disk flat and sometimes punctiform, commonly grayish pruinose, the exciple thick, colored like the thallus; spores 2–4, subglobose, 16–30 × 12–20 μ.

On rocks, throughout the United States, but not common.

4. **Lecanora gibbosa** (Ach.) Nyl., Mém. Soc. Imp. Sci. Nat. Cherb. 5:113. 1857.
Lichen gibbosus Ach., Lich. Suec. 30. 1798. *L. cinerea* var. *gibbosa* (Ach.) Nyl.

Thallus thick, rough, often crumbling, warty-areolate, greenish to brownish gray, on a blackening hypothallus; apothecia small to middle-sized, 0.6–1.5 mm. across, immersed to adnate, the disk concave to flat, black, the exciple thin, colored like the thallus, becoming slightly crenulate, often blackening; spores subspherical to ellipsoid, 16–30 × 10–18 μ.

On rocks, from New Hampshire to Alabama, westward to Iowa and Minnesota, and recurring in California.

5. **Lecanora verrucosa** Ach., Lich. Univ. 354. 1810.
Urceolaria verrucosa Ach., Lich. Univ. 339. 1810. *Parmelia verrucosa* (Ach.) Sprengl.

Thallus rather thick, composed of minute to small, greenish gray to whitish or ashy warts; apothecia small to middle-sized, 0.6–1.2 mm. across, immersed to adnate and subsessile, the disk concave to flat, black and sometimes grayish pruinose, often nearly closed, the exciple thin to rather thick, colored like the thallus, often inflexed, becoming flexuous; spores ellipsoid, 30–45 × 16–30 μ.

On soil and mosses, New Hampshire, North Carolina, Rocky Mountains, California, and Washington.

6. **Lecanora mutabilis** (Ach.) Nyl., Mém. Soc. Sci. Nat. Cherb. 2:324. 1854.
    Urceolaria mutabilis Ach., Lich. Univ. 335. 1810. *L. verrucosa* f. *mutabilis* (Ach.) Blombg. et Forss.

Thallus moderately thick, warty, chinky to subareolate, dark ashy gray, varying toward yellowish; apothecia small to middle-sized, 0.5–1 mm. across, immersed, varying toward superficial, the disk deeply to slightly concave, commonly black, opening tardily, the exciple thick and inflexed, colored like the thallus; spores ellipsoid, 30–52 $\times$ 16–34 μ.

On trees, Massachusetts, New York, and Minnesota.

7. **Lecanora laevata** (Ach.) Nyl., Not. Sällsk. Faun. Flor. Fenn. 8:137. 1866.
    Sagedia laevata Ach., Vet. Akad. Nya Handl. 164. 1809. *L. cinerea* var. *laevata* (Ach.) Tuck.

Thallus thin, smooth to slightly rough, chinky to subareolate, greenish to dirty gray, sometimes showing a black hypothallus; apothecia minute to small, 0.2–0.6 mm. across, immersed, the disk concave, black, the exciple thin, colored like the thallus, becoming swollen, sometimes scarcely differentiated from the thallus; spores ellipsoid, 15–26 $\times$ 9–16 μ.

On rocks, Maine, Massachusetts, Alabama, Minnesota, Missouri, California, and Washington.

8. **Lecanora cinerea** (L.) Röhling, Deutschl. Fl. 3:90. 1813.
    Lichen cinereus L., Mant. Pl. 1:132. 1767. *Parmelia cinerea* (L.) Hepp.

Thallus thin to moderately thick, rough, chinky-areolate, ashy white to greenish and rarely blackening, on a black hypothallus; apothecia small to middle-sized, 0.5–1 mm. across, immersed, the disk concave to flat, black, the exciple thin, colored like the thallus or sometimes blackening, rarely disappearing; spores ellipsoid or rarely subglobose, 13–27 $\times$ 8–16 μ.

On rocks, throughout the United States.

    var. **microspora** Fink, Cont. U. S. Nat. Herb. 14[1]:184. 1910.

Thallus thin, rough, blackish olive; apothecia small, 0.4–0.6 mm. across; spores oblong-ellipsoid, 11–16 $\times$ 6–10 μ.

On rocks, Minnesota.

9. **Lecanora deplanans** Nyl., Bot. Gaz. 22:334. 1896.

Thallus thin, smooth, chinky to areolate, greenish gray to ashy; apothecia minute to small, 0.25–0.6 mm. across, immersed, the disk slightly concave to flat, reddish brown, the exciple thin, colored like the thallus, and finally somewhat raised; spores short-ellipsoid, 13–16 $\times$ 8–10 μ.

On rocks, West Virginia.

10. **Lecanora cinereorufescens** (Ach.) Nyl., Not. Sällsk. Faun. Flor. Fenn. 5:154, 155. 1861.
    Urceolaria cinereorufescens Ach., Lich. Univ. 677. 1810.

Thallus thin, smooth to warty and chinky to areolate, the areoles sometimes scattered, pale to darker grayish on a black hypothallus; apothecia small to middle-sized, 0.4–0.8 mm. across, immersed to adnate, the disk concave to flat, reddish to reddish brown, the exciple colored like the thallus; spores ellipsoid, 12–20 $\times$ 7–10 μ.

On rocks, Utah and Oregon. Our spore measurements are much larger than Tuckerman's and agree well with European material examined.

11. **Lecanora odora** (Ach.) Tuck., Syn. N. A. Lich. 1:199, 200. 1882.
    Gyalecta odora Ach., in Schaer., Lich. Helv. Spic. 80. 1826.

Thallus thin, becoming somewhat rough, chinky-areolate, sometimes crumbling, grayish to ashy; apothecia minute to small, 0.2–0.5 mm. across, immersed, the disk concave, yellowish flesh-colored, the exciple thin, colored like the thallus or paler, becoming flexuous; spores ovoid-ellipsoid, 10–13 $\times$ 4–6 μ.

On rocks, New Hampshire.

12. **Lecanora lacustris** (With.) Nyl., Not. Sällsk. Faun. Flor. Fenn. 5:155. 1861.
Lichen lacustris With., Arr. Brit. Pl. ed. 3. 21. 1796.
Thallus thin to rather thick, smooth, chinky to subareolate, pale brick-color or yellowish green; apothecia minute to small, 0.2–0.6 mm. across, immersed, the disk concave, reddish brown, the exciple rather thick, colored like the thallus, becoming flexuous, often scarcely differentiated from the thallus; spores oblong-ellipsoid, 11–17 $\times$ 5–6.5 μ.
On rocks, New England, New York, New Jersey, North Carolina, South Carolina, Alabama, and Minnesota.

13. **Lecanora epulotica** (Ach.) Leighton, Lich. Fl. Great Brit. 212. 1871.
Gyalecta epulotica Ach., Lich. Univ. 151. pl. 1, f. 7. 1810. *L. subepulotica* (Nyl.) Fink.
Thallus thin, smooth to more or less rough, chinky to areolate, greenish gray to yellowish or whitish gray; apothecia minute to small, 0.2–0.5 mm. across, immersed, the disk slightly concave, pale flesh-colored to darker, the exciple thick, colored like the thallus, not always differentiated from the thallus; spores ellipsoid to ovoid-ellipsoid, 11–17 $\times$ 6–9 μ.
On rocks, New England and Minnesota.

14. **Lecanora lavata** (Magn.) Fink n. comb.
Jonaspis lavata Magn., Meddel. Got. Bot. Trädgärd 3:15. 1927.
Thallus thin, smooth to somewhat irregular and minutely chinky, creamy yellow or tinged with rose; apothecia minute to small, 0.2–0.3 or rarely 0.6 mm. across, very numerous, immersed, often crowded and confluent, the disk slightly concave, light reddish or yellowish brown, the exciple colored like the thallus; spores 8, hyaline, oval, non-septate, 10 $\times$ 6 μ.
On submerged rocks, Mt. Rainier, 8,000 feet, near Paradise Glacier, Washington. (Description compiled.)

15. **Lecanora atra** (Huds.) Ach., Lich. Univ. 344. 1810.
Lichen ater Huds., Fl. Angl. 445. 1762. *Parmelia atra* (Huds.) Ach.
Thallus of moderate thickness, composed of granules usually run together into a smoothish, warty, or areolate crust, greenish gray to ashy white; apothecia small to middle-sized, 0.9–2 mm. across, more or less immersed to adnate, the disk flat to somewhat convex, very black, the exciple rarely crenate and flexuous, occasionally becoming black and rarely disappearing; hypothecium and hymenium brown to brownish black; spores ellipsoid, 10–15 $\times$ 5–8 μ.
On rocks and trees, throughout the United States.

16. **Lecanora glaucomela** Tuck., Gen. Lich. 118. 1872.
Thallus thin, smooth to somewhat rough, becoming wrinkled and somewhat chinky, greenish gray; apothecia small to middle-sized, 0.6–1.2 mm. across, subsessile, the disk flat to slightly convex, blackish brown to black, the exciple thin, colored like the thallus, becoming crenulate and rarely disappearing; spores ellipsoid, 17–23 $\times$ 9–12 μ.
On trees, California and Oregon.

17. **Lecanora melaena** (Hedlund) Fink n. comb.
L. polytropa var. *melaena* Hedlund, Bih. Svensk. Vet. Akad. Handl. 18. III[3]. 3:38. 1892.
Thallus thin to rather thick, greenish gray to ashy, chinky to areolate, the areoles sometimes obscurely crenate, sometimes scattered; apothecia small, 0.4–0.9 mm. across, immersed to partly superficial, the disk flat to strongly convex, olive-blackish to dull black, the exciple of the same color as the thallus and commonly disappearing; spores oblong-ellipsoid to ellipsoid, 8.5–11.5 $\times$ 5–6.5 μ.
On rocks, northeastern Minnesota.

18. **Lecanora minutella** Nyl., Lich. Jap. 105, 106. 1890.
Thallus very thin, smooth, pale greenish gray to ashy or whitish, sometimes disappearing; apothecia minute, 0.1–0.25 mm. across, subsessile, the disk concave or flat to slightly convex, yellowish to reddish brown, the exciple thin, colored like the thallus, sometimes disappearing; spores ovoid, 3–5×2–3μ.
On trees, Tennessee.

19. **Lecanora hypoptoides** Nyl., Flora 55:249. 1872.
Lecidea hypoptoides Nyl., Flora 50:371. 1867.
Thallus very thin, smooth to slightly rough, minutely granulose, greenish gray to ashy, sometimes disappearing; apothecia minute to small, 0.1–0.6 mm. across, closely adnate, the disk flat to slightly convex, reddish brown to brown, sometimes grayish pruinose, the exciple thin, colored like the thallus, becoming crenulate or sometimes disappearing; spores 8, hyaline, ovoid to ovoid-ellipsoid, non-septate, 8–12×4.5–5.5μ.
On old wood, New York.

20. **Lecanora miculata** Ach., Syn. Meth. Lich. 164. 1814.
Thallus thin, composed of dirty white, commonly scattered granules or warts; apothecia small to middle-sized, 0.5–1 mm. across, adnate, the disk flat to slightly convex, reddish brown and commonly grayish pruinose, the exciple rather thick, colored like the thallus, becoming crenate; spores ellipsoid, 11–18×6–9μ.
On trees, from Pennsylvania to Florida, and westward to Texas and Arkansas. The plants are poorly known and doubtfully included.

21. **Lecanora granulifera** (Ach.) Nyl., Bull. Linn. Soc. Norm. II. 2:67. 1868.
Parmelia granulifera Ach., Syn. Meth. Lich. 212. 1814 pro parte.
Thallus thin, papilliform-granulose to rugged-warty, greenish gray to ashy, upon a blackening hypothallus, more or less lemon-yellow within; apothecia minute to small, 0.3–0.8 mm. across, sessile, the disk flat to convex, reddish brown to black, the exciple thick, colored like the thallus, rarely becoming crenate and disappearing; spores ellipsoid, 15–26×9–15μ.
On trees, Florida. Material so named from California was incorrectly determined.

22. **Lecanora alpina** Sommerf., Suppl. Fl. Lapp. 91. 1826.
Thallus thin, composed of round or irregular, commonly scattered, grayish or lead-colored, warty areoles, upon a thin, black hypothallus; apothecia middle-sized to large, 0.8–1.8 mm. across, partly immersed to superficial, the disk flat, reddish to reddish black, the exciple thin, elevated, colored like the thallus, rarely disappearing; spores 8, hyaline, ellipsoid or ovoid-ellipsoid, 9–13×6–8μ.
On rocks, Washington, Oregon, and California.

23. **Lecanora rugosa** (Pers.) Nyl., Flora 55:250. 1872.
Lichen rugosus Pers., in Ach., Lich. Univ. 394. 1810. *L. subfusca* var. *rugosa* (Pers.) Nyl.
Thallus rather thick, greenish gray to whitish, warty or granulose and finally wrinkled; apothecia middle-sized to large, 0.5–2.6 mm. across, subsessile to finally sessile, the disk concave to slightly convex, sometimes undulate, brown to brownish black, often obscurely whitish pruinose, the exciple thick, elevated, becoming wrinkled-crenate; spores 10–15×6–8μ.
On living and old wood, and rarely on rocks, Maine, New York, Minnesota, and California.

24. **Lecanora cenisia** Ach., Lich. Univ. 361. 1810.
L. atrynea var. *cenisia* (Ach.) Nyl.
Thallus thick, composed of coarse, greenish gray granules, sometimes scattered or frequently forming a warty-areolate crust; apothecia small to middle-sized, 0.6–2 mm. across, sessile, the disk flat to convex, livid or yellowish brown and blacken-

ing, thinly grayish pruinose, the exciple thick, colored like the thallus, becoming crenate and sometimes disappearing; spores ellipsoid, 10–17 × 5–8.5 μ.

On rocks, Vermont, Ohio, and California.

25. **Lecanora atrynea** (Ach.) Röhl., Deutschl. Fl. 3:82. 1813.

L. subfusca var. *atrynea* Ach., Lich. Univ. 395. 1810.

Thallus thick, roughly granulose to coarsely warty, chinky to areolate, ashy to grayish white; apothecia small to middle-sized, 0.6–1.5 mm. across, adnate to subsessile, the disk flat to slightly convex, lurid brown to black, the exciple thin, colored like the thallus, becoming crenulate and flexuous; spores ellipsoid, 11–16 × 6–8 μ.

On rocks, Minnesota.

26. **Lecanora subfusca** (L.) Ach., Lich. Univ. 393. pl. 7, f. 6. 1810.

Lichen subfuscus L., Sp. Pl. 1142. 1753. *L. subfusca* var. *allophana* Ach. *L. subfusca* var. *discolor* (E. Fries) Willey. *Parmelia subfusca* (L.) Ach.

Thallus becoming moderately thick, smooth to chinky or warty-areolate, greenish gray to ashy; apothecia small to middle-sized, 0.5–2.5 mm. across, adnate to sessile, sometimes clustered, the disk flat to somewhat convex, light brown to darker, the exciple thin, colored like the thallus, becoming crenate and rarely flexuous; spores ellipsoid, 11–20 × 7–10 μ.

On trees or old wood, rarely on rocks or over mosses, throughout the United States. There is much diversity of opinion about the disposition of the subspecies recorded below.

var. **argentata** Ach., Lich. Univ. 393. 1810.

L. subfusca var. *distans* (Pers.) Dietrich. *L. subfusca* var. *chlarona* Ach. *L. chlarona* (Ach.) Nyl.

Thallus rather thin and smooth, finally somewhat chinky, ashy to white; apothecia minute to small, 0.3–1.5 mm. across, the exciple becoming crenulate and rarely disappearing; spores 8–15 × 5–8 μ.

On trees, throughout the United States.

var. **campestris** Rabh., Deutschl. Krypt. Flora 2:33. 1845.

Thallus at first granulose, later becoming very thick, rough, and areolate; apothecia becoming strongly and often irregularly convex, the exciple often disappearing.

On trees and rarely on rocks, New England, Maryland, Minnesota, and California.

var. **coilocarpa** Ach., Lich. Univ. 393. 1810.

L. coilocarpa (Ach.) Nyl.

Thallus rather thin, becoming wrinkled and broken, usually whitish; apothecia minute to small, 0.4–1.5 mm. across, the disk black, the exciple usually entire; spores 9–15 × 5.5–9 μ.

On trees and rocks, throughout the United States.

var. **hypnorum** (Wulf.) Rabh., Deutschl. Krypt. Flora 2:34. 1845.

Lichen hypnorum Wulf., in Jacq., Coll. Bot. 4:233. pl. 7, f. 2. 1790.

Thallus running over mosses, rough and granulose, white or whitish.

On mosses of high areas, northern Minnesota and Montana.

var. **variolosa** Koerb., Syst. Lich. 141. 1855.

L. subfusca var. *sorediifera* T. Fries. *L. variolascens* Nyl.

Thallus warty, becoming more or less whitish sorediate; apothecia few, rather small, the exciple rarely disappearing.

On trees, Minnesota.

27. **Lecanora pacifica** Tuck., Syn. N. A. Lich. 1:191. 1882.

Thallus thin, smooth to slightly rough, becoming chinky and areolate, dirty white to grayish; apothecia small to middle-sized, 0.6–1.2 mm. across, adnate to subsessile, the disk flat to convex, yellowish to brownish black, commonly greenish to whitish pruinose, the exciple thick, colored like the thallus, becoming flexuous and crenulate; spores ovoid-ellipsoid, 12–16 × 6.5–10 μ.

On trees and rarely on rocks, California, Oregon, and Washington.

28. **Lecanora Hageni** Ach., Lich. Univ. 367. 1810.

Lichen Hageni Ach., Lich. Suec. 57. 1798. *L. Hageni* var. *umbrina* Ach.

Thallus thin, smooth, becoming warty, the warts sometimes scattered, or rarely disappearing, dirty greenish to ashy white; apothecia small to middle-sized, 0.4–1 mm. across, adnate, the disk flat to slightly convex, more or less grayish pruinose or pale brown to blackish, the exciple white or colored like the thallus, usually more or less crenate, rarely flexuous or disappearing; spores ellipsoid, 7–14 × 4–6 μ.

On trees, old wood, and rocks, throughout the United States.

29. **Lecanora Sambuci** (Pers.) Nyl., Not. Sällsk. Faun. Flor. Fenn. 5:168. 1861.

Lichen Sambuci Pers., Ann. Bot. Usteri 7:26. 1794. *L. Hageni* var. *Sambuci* (Pers.) Tuck.

Thallus thin, smooth, becoming granulose to minutely scaly, whitish to ashy gray, rarely disappearing; apothecia minute to small, 0.3–1 mm. across, adnate, the disk flat to slightly convex, flesh-colored to light brown or darker, often grayish pruinose, the exciple thin, colored like the thallus, becoming crenulate and rarely disappearing; spores 8–32, usually 12–16, ellipsoid, 8–12 × 4.5–6.5 μ.

On trees, Massachusetts, Illinois, and Minnesota.

var. **minnesotensis** Fink; Hedrick, Mycologia 26:161. 1934.

Exciple becoming flexuous and disappearing, the disk in this condition strongly convex and broken into 2 to 8 convex areas, giving the appearance of as many very minute conglomerate apothecia.

On balsam trunks, Grand Portage, Minnesota.

30. **Lecanora praecrenata** Nyl., in Hasse, Lich. South. Calif. 12. 1898.

Thallus very thin, dirty white, disappearing; apothecia small, 0.5–0.8 mm. across, sessile, the disk flat, dusky brown, the exciple slightly elevated, colored like the thallus, crenulate, the crenules globose, necklace-like; spores 4–6, spherical, 18–21 μ in diameter.

On rocks, southern California.

31. **Lecanora Willeyi** Tuck., Syn. N. A. Lich. 1:191. 1882.

Thallus very thin, warty, rough and heaped, dark greenish gray to ashy; apothecia minute to small, 0.3–0.8 mm. across, adnate, the disk flat to strongly convex, dark red, the exciple thin, colored like the thallus or olive-green, becoming crenulate, sometimes disappearing; spores ellipsoid, 8–11 × 4–7 μ.

On rocks, Massachusetts and New Jersey.

32. **Lecanora piniperda** Koerb., Par. Lich. 81. 1865.

Thallus thin, becoming scurfy or somewhat warty or granulose, greenish gray to whitish, often disappearing; apothecia minute, 0.1–0.25 mm. across, adnate, the disk flat to convex, flesh-colored to brownish, often obscurely pruinose, the exciple usually thin, colored like the thallus or lighter, becoming subcrenulate, often disappearing; spores ellipsoid, 8–12 × 4–5.5 μ.

On stumps, Ohio and Minnesota.

33. **Lecanora dispersa** (Pers.) Röhl., Deutschl. Fl. 3:91. 1813.

Lichen dispersus Pers., Ann. Bot. Usteri 7:27. 1794.

Thallus composed of small, scattered, dirty greenish to whitish granules, sometimes persisting under the apothecia but disappearing elsewhere; apothecia minute to small, 0.3–1.2 mm. across, often clustered, adnate, the disk flat, yellowish brown to olivaceous, the exciple thin, colored like the thallus, more or less crenate; spores ellipsoid, 8–13 × 3.5–5.5 μ.

On rocks, Ohio, Iowa, and Minnesota.

34. **Lecanora cupressi** Tuck., in Nyl., Flora 55:251. 1872.
Thallus thin, granulose to densely warty, greenish gray; apothecia small to middle-sized, 0.4–1 mm. across, sessile, the disk flat to slightly convex, bright yellow to brownish orange, the exciple thick, colored like the thallus, crenulate; spores oblong-ellipsoid, 10–16 × 4–5 μ.
On trees, from Massachusetts to Florida, and in Louisiana.

35. **Lecanora pallida** (Schreb.) Rabh., Deutschl. Krypt. Flora 2:34. 1845.
Lichen pallidus Schreb., Spic. Fl. Lips. 133. 1771. *L. albella* (Pers.) Ach. *Parmelia albella* (Pers.) Ach.
Thallus thin, usually smooth, or becoming thicker and chinky to warty, whitish or pale cream-colored, or darkening; apothecia small to middle-sized, 0.7–3 mm. across, adnate to sessile, the disk flat to convex, whitish buff to darker, white-pruinose, the exciple thick, colored like the thallus, sometimes becoming obscurely crenulate and flexuous or disappearing; spores ellipsoid, 8–18 × 6–10 μ.
On trees, throughout the United States.

var. **angulosa** (Schreb.) Koerb., Syst. Lich. 145. 1855.
Lichen angulosus Schreb., Spic. Fl. Lips. 136. 1771. *L. angulosa* (Schreb.) Ach.
Apothecia crowded, smaller, and irregularly angular.
On trees, throughout the United States, but not common.

var. **cancriformis** (Hoffm.) Tuck., Syn. N. A. Lich. 1:186. 1882.
Verrucaria cancriformis Hoffm., Deutschl. Fl. 171. 1796. *L. albella* var. *cancriformis* (Hoffm.) Herre. *L. caesiorubella* Ach.
Thallus becoming thicker and more warty; apothecia becoming swollen and larger, the disk flesh-colored to reddish, and gray-pruinose, the exciple flexuous, becoming crenate and lobed.
On trees, throughout the United States.

var. **prolifera** Fink; Hedrick, Mycologia 26:161. 1934.
Apothecia middle-sized, becoming proliferate.
On trees, South Carolina.

36. **Lecanora parisensis** Nyl., Bull. Soc. Bot. France 13:368. 1866.
L. subfusca f. *parisensis* (Nyl.) Stizenb.
Thallus moderately thick, roughly granulate or warty, chinky to areolate, yellowish ashy to grayish; apothecia middle-sized to large, 0.6–1.6 mm. across, adnate to subsessile, the disk slightly concave to flat, reddish brown to brownish black, or rarely grayish pruinose, the exciple thin to moderately thick, colored like the thallus, becoming wrinkled, crenulate, and sometimes flexuous; spores ellipsoid, 10–16 × 5–7.5 μ.
On trees, New Mexico.

37. **Lecanora orosthea** Ach., Lich. Univ. 400. 1810.
Lichen orosthea Ach., Lich. Suec. 38. 1798. *L. expallens* Ach.
Thallus thin, chinky-areolate, frequently becoming powdery, greenish to sulphur-yellow; apothecia small to middle-sized, 0.5–0.8 mm. across, adnate to sessile, the disk flat to slightly convex, buff to yellowish flesh-color, sometimes whitish pruinose, the exciple thin to rather thick, colored like the thallus, becoming flexuous and crenulate, often disappearing; spores ellipsoid, 10–17 × 6–7.5 μ.
On trees, New England, New Jersey, and California.

38. **Lecanora effusa** (Pers.) Ach., Lich. Univ. 386. 1810.
Lichen effusus Pers., in Hoffm., Deutschl. Fl. 2:174. 1795.
Thallus thin, widespread, scurfy to granulose or warty-areolate, yellowish to ashy or darkening, sometimes becoming scattered and disappearing; apothecia minute to small, 0.2–0.6 mm. across, the disk flat to convex, reddish brown, the exciple thin, obscurely powdery or subcrenulate, sometimes disappearing; spores ellipsoid, 8–13 × 5–6.5 μ.
On old wood, Nebraska.

39. **Lecanora varia** (Hoffm.) Ach., Lich. Univ. 377. 1810.
Patellaria varia Hoffm., Descr. Pl. Crypt. 1:102. pl. 23, f. 4. 1790. *Parmelia varia* (Hoffm.) Ach.
Thallus thin to rather thick, smooth to warty-areolate, pale greenish, yellowish, or whitish; apothecia minute to small, 0.4–1 mm. across, adnate to subsessile, the disk flat to convex, flesh-colored to yellowish or buff, the exciple thin, colored like the thallus, becoming crenulate and sometimes disappearing; spores oblong-ellipsoid to ellipsoid, 10–14 × 4–7 μ. (PLATE 29 a.)
On trees and rocks, throughout the United States.

40. **Lecanora symmicta** Ach., Syn. Meth. Lich. 340. 1814.
L. varia var. *symmicta* Ach. *L. varia* var. *saepincola* (Ach.) Link. *L. symmicta* var. *saepincola* (Ach.) T. Fries.
Thallus thin to moderately thick, smooth to scurfy or subgranulose, yellowish to whitish, rarely disappearing; apothecia minute to small, 0.2–1 mm. across, adnate, the disk flat to strongly convex, round to variously irregular, pale yellowish to reddish and blackening, the exciple thin, colored like the thallus, evanescent or disappearing later; spores ellipsoid, 9–14 × 3.5–5.5 μ.
On old wood, throughout the United States.

41. **Lecanora polytropa** (Ehrh.) Rabh., Deutschl. Krypt. Flora 2:37. 1845.
Verrucaria polytropa Ehrh., in Hoffm., Deutschl. Fl. 196. 1796. *Parmelia varia* var. *polytropa* (Ehrh.) E. Fries. *L. varia* var. *polytropa* (Ehrh.) Dietrich.
Thallus thin to moderately thick, somewhat rough, chinky to areolate, sub-squamulose, or rarely granulose, greenish to yellowish or whitish, sometimes scattered and disappearing; apothecia small to middle-sized, 0.5–1.3 mm. across, adnate to subsessile, the disk flat to convex, yellowish flesh-colored to brownish, the exciple thin, colored like the thallus, flexuous, subcrenulate, sometimes disappearing; spores ellipsoid, 10–15 × 5–7 μ.
On rocks, New England, New York, Minnesota, Montana, Washington, and California.

var. **alpigena** (Ach.) Rabh., Deutschl. Krypt. Flora 2:37. 1845.
L. varia var. *alpigena* Ach., Lich. Univ. 379. 1810.
Thallus thin, sometimes disappearing; apothecia small to middle-sized, 0.5–1.5 mm. across, adnate, clustered or crowded, often irregular from pressure, the exciple thin, colored like the thallus, disappearing, and the proper exciple becoming conspicuous.
On alpine rocks, Oregon.

f. **illusoria** (Ach.) Leight., Lich. Flora Great Brit. 198. 1871.
L. varia var. *illusoria* Ach., Lich. Univ. 380. 1810.
Thallus very inconspicuous and evanescent; apothecia minute to small, 0.3–0.7 mm. across, subsessile on the substrata or minute subtended thallus areas, the disk flat to convex, pale brown, the thin thalloid veil very inconspicuous and evanescent, never seen in mature apothecia, but replaced by a pale proper exciple.
On rocks, Wyoming, Washington, and California. Its position with the present species or even the genus is doubtful.

42. **Lecanora oregana** Tuck., Syn. N. A. Lich. 1:193. 1882.
Thallus thick, composed of coarse, crowded and sometimes heaped or confluent, strongly convex, greenish yellow, sometimes centrally stalked areoles; apothecia middle-sized to large, 1.5–3 mm. across, subsessile, the disk flat to convex, reddish brown, the exciple rather thin, colored like the thallus, incurved, soon crenulate, and often flexuous; spores ellipsoid to subglobose, 10–14 × 6–8 μ.
On rocks, Idaho and Oregon.

43. **Lecanora badia** (Hoffm.) Ach., Lich. Univ. 407. 1810.
Lichen badia Hoffm., Deutschl. Fl. 182. 1796. *Parmelia badia* (Hoffm.) Hepp.
Thallus thin, warty and chinky to areolate, or subsquamulose, greenish ashy to

olive-green, often shining; apothecia small to middle-sized, 0.5–1.5 mm. across, adnate to sessile, the disk flat to convex, chestnut-brown to brown, shining, the exciple thick, sometimes becoming flexuously crenate, colored like the thallus or becoming black; spores fusiform-ellipsoid, 9.5–14 × 3–5 μ.

On rocks, Maine and New Hampshire.

44. Lecanora atriseda (E. Fries) Nyl., Mém. Soc. Sci. Nat. Cherb. 5:115. 1857.
Parmelia badia var. *atriseda* E. Fries, Lich. Eur. 149. 1831.

Thallus of moderate thickness, composed of sometimes scattered, more or less convex, coppery or duller brown areoles, each bordered by a thin black line, and the whole thallus resting on a more or less apparent black hypothallus; apothecia small to middle-sized, 0.4–1.2 mm. across, partly immersed to adnate, the disk flat to convex, chestnut-brown to brown, the exciple thin, colored like the thallus, and soon disappearing; spores ellipsoid, 8–13 × 5–7 μ.

On rocks, New Hampshire.

45. **Lecanora Bockii** Rodig., in E. Fries, Syst. Orb. Veg. 1:285. 1825.

Thallus thin, composed of subglobose, minute, sometimes crumbling or areolate granules, brownish gray to olive-brown, on a thin black hypothallus; apothecia small, 0.5–0.8 mm. across, adnate to sessile, the disk flat, black, sometimes punctiform, the exciple thick, colored like the thallus; spores ovoid-ellipsoid, 16–24 × 11–15 μ.

On rocks, New England.

46. **Lecanora phaeobola** Tuck., Gen. Lich. 115, 116. 1872.

Thallus thin, olive-brown, becoming wrinkled and papillate-granulose, the granules minute and polished; apothecia small to middle-sized, 0.6–1 mm. across, adnate, the disk flat to convex, reddish brown to black, shining, the exciple thin, colored like the thallus, disappearing; spores ellipsoid, 9–16 × 3–5 μ.

On trees, California and Washington.

47. **Lecanora frustulosa** (Dicks.) Ach., Lich. Univ. 405. 1810.
Lichen frustulosa Dicks., Pl. Crypt. Brit. 3:13. pl. 8, f. 10. 1793.

Thallus of moderate thickness, rough, composed of crowded and imbricate to somewhat scattered, much raised and irregular, greenish gray to ashy or yellowish, smoothish to wartlike areoles, the margin squamulose, flattish and lobed, often appearing subfoliose; apothecia small to middle-sized, 0.6–2 mm. across, sessile, the disk flat to convex, reddish brown to black, the exciple colored like the thallus, becoming subcrenulate; spores ellipsoid, 9–15 × 5–7.5 μ. (PLATE 29 *b*.)

On rocks, throughout northern United States.

48. **Lecanora melanophthalma** (Lam. & DC.) Ramond, Mém. Mus. Nat. Hist. Paris, 13:249. 1825.
Squamaria melanophthalma Lam. & DC., Fl. Fr. ed. 3. 2:376. 1815. *Parmelia rubina* var. *opaca* (Ach.) Schaer.

Thallus rather thick, warty or areolate, or passing into lobed, crenately cut squamules, greenish gray to yellowish brown; apothecia small to middle-sized, 0.6–2 mm. across, adnate, the disk concave, pale olivaceous to black, the exciple rather thick, colored like the thallus, becoming crenate and flexuous; spores ellipsoid, 9–15 × 5–7.5 μ.

On rocks, from South Dakota to Texas, and westward to California and Washington.

49. **Lecanora thamnoplaca** Tuck., Gen. Lich. 113. 1872.

Thallus composed of rough, crumbling, dull brownish to yellowish, crowded, convex and swollen, crenate squamules, passing at the circumference into narrow, convex, wavy-margined lobes; apothecia middle-sized to large, 0.8–2.5 mm. across, immersed to adnate, the disk slightly concave to flat, reddish brown to black, the

exciple thick, colored like the thallus, becoming flexuous; spores ovoid-ellipsoid, 9–15 × 5–7.5 μ.
On rocks, Montana, Utah, Nevada, and California.

50. **Lecanora intricata** Ach., Lich. Univ. 380. 1810.
L. varia var. *intricata* (Ach.) Nyl.
Thallus moderately thick, areolate, the areoles sometimes chinky, often scattered and obscurely lobed, greenish gray to whitish or yellowish, upon a more or less visible blackish hypothallus; apothecia minute to small, 0.3–0.8 mm. across, partly immersed to adnate, 1–several on each areole, the disk flat to slightly convex, olive-brown to blackish, the exciple prominent, colored like the thallus; spores oblong-ellipsoid to ellipsoid, 10–13 × 4.5–6.5 μ.
On rocks, mountains of New Hampshire.

51. **Lecanora melanaspis** Ach., Lich. Univ. 427. 1810.
Parmelia melanaspis Ach., Meth. Lich. 196. 1803. *L. alphoplaca* var. *melanaspis* (Ach.) Nyl.
Thallus thick, becoming warty, chinky or subareolate, or subfoliose, and showing linear, branched, or more or less imbricated lobes, ashy to whitish or brownish; apothecia small to middle-sized, 0.8–2 mm. across, adnate to subsessile, the disk flat to more or less convex, dark brown to blackish and rarely pruinose, the exciple thin, colored like the thallus, becoming irregular, and rarely disappearing; spores ellipsoid, 8–14 × 5–9 μ.
On rocks, from Minnesota to Kansas, and westward to California and Washington.

52. **Lecanora glaucopsina** Nyl., in Hasse, Lich. South. Calif. 12. 1898.
Thallus thin, pale greenish gray, areolate-squamulose, the squamules small, somewhat wrinkled, subimbricate, loosely attached, angular or with wavy or lobate margins; apothecia minute to small, 0.3–0.8 mm. across, immersed to adnate, often clustered, the disk flat, black, brick-red when wet, the exciple thin, colored like the thallus, becoming subcrenulate; asci becoming saccate, the apical wall greatly thickened; spores 4–10, subspherical to ovoid, 14–24 × 9–20 μ.
On clay, Santa Monica Range, California.

53. **Lecanora marginalis** Hasse, Bryologist 13:112. 1910.
Thallus foliose, entire or obscurely lobed, moderately thick, smooth to wrinkled and warty, the circumference sometimes rolled downward, white or finely white-pruinose above; tawny flesh-colored below, attached by an umbilicus; apothecia small to middle-sized, 0.7–1.6 mm. across, adnate, marginal or submarginal, sometimes crowded and often irregular from pressure, the disk concave to flat, grayish pruinose or black, the exciple thick, colored like the thallus, becoming flexuous; spores ovoid-ellipsoid, 10–14 × 6.5–8.5 μ.
On rocks, southern California.

54. **Lecanora rupicola** (L.) Zahlbr., Cat. Lich. Univ. 5:525–29. 1928.
Lichen rupicola L., Mant. Pl. 132. 1767. *L. sordida* (Pers.) T. Fries. *L. sordida* var. *bicincta* (Ramond) T. Fries. *L. glaucoma* Ach.
Thallus thin to moderately thick, greenish gray to brownish white, smooth to chinky or areolate, the areoles becoming somewhat raised and irregular, often subsquamulose toward the circumference; apothecia small to middle-sized, 0.65–1.5 mm. across, partly immersed to adnate, the disk flat to convex, flesh-colored to livid black, usually whitish pruinose, the exciple thin, colored like the thallus, becoming flexuous and rarely disappearing; spores ellipsoid, 8–15 × 5.5–7.5 μ.
On rocks, throughout the northern United States, and southward on the Pacific Coast.

55. **Lecanora circinata** (Pers.) Ach., Lich. Univ. 425. 1810.
Lichen circinatus Pers., Ann. Bot. Usteri 7:25. 1794. *L. subcircinata* Nyl.
Thallus thick, chinky or warty-areolate in the center, radiately and plicately

lobed toward the circumference, light brown; apothecia small to middle-sized, 0.6–1.5 mm. across, immersed to adnate, the disk slightly concave to flat, light to dark brown, the exciple thin, colored like the thallus, becoming somewhat flexuous; spores ellipsoid, 11–16 × 6.5–8.5 μ.

On rocks, Arizona.

56. **Lecanora versicolor** (Pers.) Ach., Lich. Univ. 426. 1810.
  Lichen versicolor Pers., Ann. Bot. Usteri 7:24. 1794. *L. muralis* var. *versicolor* (Pers.) Tuck.

Thallus thin, areolate toward the center, radiate-plicate toward the shortly lobed margin, often dying in part and rejuvenating in the form of new lobes or complete small thallus within the boundaries of larger partly dead old ones, yellowish or whitish gray and sometimes more or less whitish powdery; apothecia minute to small, 0.3–0.8 mm. across, partly immersed to adnate, the disk slightly concave to flat, buff to darker brownish, the exciple thin, colored like the thallus, becoming subcrenulate and flexuous, rarely and obscurely whitish powdery; spores ellipsoid, 9–15 × 4.5–7 μ. (PLATE 30.)

On calcareous rocks, Iowa, Minnesota, Nebraska, Kansas, and Missouri.

57. **Lecanora muralis** (Schreb.) Rabh., Deutschl. Krypt. Flora 2:42. 1845.
  Lichen muralis Schreb., Spic. Fl. Lips. 130. 1771.

Thallus thin, closely adnate, greenish gray or sometimes yellowish or brownish, the central portions more or less areolate or crenate-scaly, long- or shorter-lobed toward the circumference, and the margin deeply wavy or irregularly crenate; apothecia small to middle-sized, 0.65–2 mm. across, adnate to subsessile, the disk flat, yellowish to tawny brown, the exciple thin, colored like the thallus, becoming crenate and flexuous; spores ellipsoid, 9–15 × 4.5–7 μ.

On rocks, throughout the United States.

var. **Garovaglii** (Koerb.) Tuck., Syn. N. A. Lich. 1:184. 1882.
  Placodium Garovaglii Koerb., Par. Lich. 54. 1865. *L. Garovaglii* (Koerb.) Zahlbr.

Thallus lobes elongated, flexuous, convex, radiately folded.

On rocks, Minnesota, Nebraska, and Nevada.

var. **saxicola** (Poll.) Tuck., Syn. N. A. Lich. 1:184. 1882.
  Lichen saxicola Poll., Hist. Plant. 3:225. 1777. *Parmelia saxicola* (Poll.) Ach.
  L. saxicola (Poll.) Ach.

Thallus better developed, showing more tendency toward brown coloration, and more flattish lobes; apothecia less closely attached to the thallus.

On rocks, throughout northern United States, and southward in the mountains.

58. **Lecanora diffracta** Ach., Lich. Univ. 432. 1810.
  Lichen diffractus Ach., Lich. Suec. 63, 64. 1798. *L. muralis* var. *diffracta* (Ach.) Rabh. *L. saxicola* var. *diffracta* (Ach.) Jatta.

Thallus mainly or wholly areolate, or the margins short-lobed, yellowish brown or reddish and darker, the areoles and squamules usually black-edged; apothecia small to middle-sized, 0.6–1.5 mm. across, adnate, the disk flat to slightly convex, brown or rarely reddish brown, the exciple thin, colored like the thallus, crenate or minutely flexuous; spores ellipsoid, 9–14 × 4–6 μ.

On rocks, Minnesota and California.

59. **Lecanora lentigera** (Web.) Ach., Lich. Univ. 423. 1810.
  Lichen lentigerus Web., Spic. Fl. Goett. 192. 1778.

Thallus moderately thick, greenish to yellowish white, commonly more or less whitish pruinose, chinky to subareolate toward the center, deeply wavy and crenately lobed toward the circumference; apothecia small to middle-sized, 0.6–2 mm. across, adnate, clustered, the disk flat, buff-colored, the exciple thin, colored like the thallus; spores ellipsoid, 9–13 × 4.5–5.5 μ.

On soil, Nevada, Colorado, Nebraska, and Montana.

60. **Lecanora pinguis** Tuck., Proc. Am. Acad. 6:268. 1866.

Thallus at first thin, but becoming very thick, chinky-areolate and warty toward the center and radiate to radiately folded toward the circumference, dull greenish gray to sulphur-yellow as always internally; apothecia middle-sized to large, 0.8–2.5 mm. across, adnate, the disk concave to flat, yellowish flesh-colored, usually subpruinose, the exciple thin, colored like the thallus, crenate to flexuously lobed; spores oblong-ellipsoid, 12–18 × 4–6 μ.

On rocks, California.

61. **Lecanora gelida** (L.) Ach., Lich. Univ. 428, 429. 1810.

Lichen gelidus L., Mant. Pl. 2:133. 1771.

Thallus moderately thick, pale greenish gray to whitish, chinky to areolate toward the center, bearing cephalodia and usually whitish soredia, the margin closely and deeply lobed; apothecia small to middle-sized, 0.6–1.4 mm. across, adnate, the disk concave to flat, pale brick-colored and blackening, the exciple thick, colored like the thallus; spores ellipsoid, 14–18 × 6–8 μ.

On rocks, New Hampshire, California, Oregon, and Washington.

62. **Lecanora semitensis** Tuck., Proc. Am. Acad. 12:172. 1877.

L. muralis var. *semitensis* Tuck. *L. saxicola* var. *semitensis* (Tuck.) Hasse.

Thallus composed of small, rather thick, round or angular, straw-colored, sometimes crenate-lobulate, black-edged areoles or squamules; apothecia small to middle-sized, 0.5–1.6 mm. across, subsessile, the disk flat to strongly convex and irregular, whitish pruinose to livid brown, the exciple of same color as the thallus or becoming black, soon disappearing; spores ellipsoid, 9–14 × 5–7 μ.

On rocks, California.

63. **Lecanora rubina** (Vill.) Ach., Lich. Univ. 412. 1810.

Lichen rubinus Vill., Hist. Plant. Dauphin. 3:977. 1789. *L. rubina* var. *campestris* Tuck.

Thallus subfoliose to rarely foliose and attached by an umbilicus, or composed of more or less round-lobed, irregular and elongated, frequently imbricated squamules, rarely reduced toward the center to flattened, irregularly lobed areoles or squamules, greenish straw-colored; commonly black below; apothecia middle-sized to large, 1.5–5 mm. across, rarely clustered, subsessile to sessile, the disk flat to convex, pale yellow to reddish or brownish, the exciple thin, colored like the thallus, becoming flexuous and disappearing; spores ellipsoid, 8–15 × 4.5–8 μ.

On rocks, throughout the United States.

var. **heteromorpha** Ach., Lich. Univ. 412. 1810.

Thallus chinky and wrinkled, less distinctly lobed; apothecia colored like the thallus or becoming brownish.

On rocks, Montana, Oregon, and Texas.

64. **Lecanora bipruinosa** Fink; Hedrick, Mycologia 26:160. 1934.

Thallus thick, closely adnate, light brown, whitish pruinose over small portions here and there, the central portions partly chinky to subareolate or warty, and in part lobulate, distinctly lobed toward the margins, the lobes slightly to strongly convex, transversely more or less broken-furrowed, rather short, their borders entire to irregularly and coarsely wavy-crenate, the tips sometimes tinged blackish; apothecia small to middle-sized, 0.5–2 mm. across, subsessile, the disk flat to slightly convex, pale yellowish green pruinose, the exciple colored like the thallus, at first thick, raised, entire and round, becoming cracked-crenulate, flexuous, and partly or nearly disappearing; spores oblong-ellipsoid, 10–14 × 6–7.5 μ.

On northward-facing rocks, near Tucson, Arizona.

65. **Lecanora Haydenii** Tuck., Proc. Am. Acad. 6:267. 1866.

Thallus foliose, thick and tough, greenish straw-colored, irregularly long-lobed, the lobes variously dissected above by obscure furrows, usually imbricated and often convolute, their margins irregularly torn-lobed or crenate, and usually whitish, especially toward the tips; paler below than above to reddish brown, the lobes sometimes longitudinally furrowed; apothecia unknown.

On soil, Nebraska, South Dakota, and Wyoming. Usually unattached, blown about, and sometimes drifting when dry. Fruiting condition needed to decide finally the relationships of the plant.

66. **Lecanora Bolanderi** Tuck., Proc. Am. Acad. 6:266. 1866.

Thallus loosely tufted and dichotomously much-branched, the branches erect or ascending, cylindrical, with obtuse papilliform tips, greenish straw-colored; apothecia middle-sized to large, 0.5–4 mm. across, terminal or subterminal, the disk concave to flat, flesh-colored to yellowish and brownish, the exciple swollen and becoming crenulate, colored like the thallus; spores ovoid-ellipsoid, 10–16 × 5–7.5 μ.

On rocks, California.

67. **Lecanora thamnitis** Tuck., Lich. Calif. 20. 1866.

Thallus made up of short, erect or ascending, more or less divided, crowded, pale straw-colored branchlets, often forming a crust; apothecia middle-sized to large, 0.6–1.5 mm. across, subterminal, the disk concave to flat, pale yellowish to tawny red, the exciple thick, colored like the thallus, crenate; spores ovoid-ellipsoid, 10–14 × 6–8 μ.

On rocks, along the coast, California.

68. **Lecanora phryganitis** Tuck., Lich. Calif. 19. 1866.

Thallus reddish yellow or fading to lighter shades, appearing very rough and often tuberculate, but really composed of many closely clustered branches, those toward the center short and erect, the marginal ones longer and ascending to prostrate; apothecia middle-sized to large, 1.5–4 mm. across, subsessile, the disk concave to flat, pale brick-colored to brownish, the exciple thin, colored like the thallus, becoming flexuously lobed; spores oblong-ellipsoid, 10–15 × 5–6.5 μ.

On rocks, California.

OTHER SPECIES REPORTED

Lecanora castanea (Hepp) T. Fries—Colorado.
Lecanora cinerea var. obscurata E. Fries—Maryland.
Lecanora conizaea (Ach.) Nyl.—Tennessee.
Lecanora constipans Nyl.—California.
Lecanora erythrantha Tuck.—California.
Lecanora fulva Schw.—New York.
Lecanora galactina (Ach.) Nyl.—Maine.
Lecanora glaucophana Nyl.—California.
Lecanora holophaea (Mont.) Nyl.—California.
Lecanora myrina Fée—South Carolina.
Lecanora olivacea (Bagl. & Car.) Steiner—Nevada.
Lecanora spodophaeiza Nyl.—California.

143. Ochrolechia Mass., Ric. Lich. 30. 1852.

Thallus crustose, smooth to more or less rough, chinky, areolate, warty or rarely minutely branched, often sorediate, the upper cortex thin or sometimes wanting, composed of vertically or irregularly septate, coherent, thin-walled hyphae, the algal layer distinct, the medullary layer of loosely interwoven, thin-walled hyphae, attached to the substratum by hyphal rhizoids; apothecia middle-sized to large, immersed to adnate or sessile, the disk concave to flat or convex, the exciple colored like the thallus, more or less irregular; hypothecium hyaline; hymenium hyaline; paraphyses branched and interwoven; asci clavate, with apical wall slightly thickened; spores 2–8, hyaline, ellipsoid to ovoid- or oblong-ellipsoid, non-septate.

The algal host is Pleurococcus.

A. Disk divided by inward extensions of the exciple . . . . 2. O. pallescens rosella
A. Disk not so divided
   B. Thallus of conglomerate granules or short coralloid branchlets . 1. O. tartarea
   B. Thallus chinky to areolate, becoming folded and wrinkled . . 2. O. pallescens

1. **Ochrolechia tartarea** (L.) Mass., Ric. Lich. 30. 1852.
   Lichen tartareus L., Sp. Pl. 1141. 1753. *Lecanora tartarea* var. *gonatodes* Ach.
   Lecanora tartarea (L.) Ach.

Thallus thick, composed of rough, uneven, conglomerate and often heaped, whitish to darker ashy granules or short coralloid branchlets; apothecia middle-sized to large, 1–3 mm. across, adnate to sessile, the disk concave to flat, yellowish brown to brick-colored, the exciple thick, colored like the thallus, becoming flexuous; spores ellipsoid to oblong-ellipsoid, 30–65 × 20–35 μ.
On trees and rocks, throughout the United States.

2. **Ochrolechia pallescens** (L.) Mass., Ann. Sci. Nat. Bot. 7:212. 1853.
   Lichen pallescens L., Sp. Pl. 1142. 1753. *Lecanora pallescens* (L.) Röhl.
   Lecanora pallescens var. *upsaliensis* (L.) Flot. *O. upsaliensis* (L.) Mass.

Thallus moderately thick, smooth, chinky to areolate, becoming folded and wrinkled, rarely warty or tuberculate, whitish to darker gray; apothecia middle-sized, 1–2.5 mm. across, adnate, the disk more or less concave to flat, flesh-colored to whitish or yellowish, usually more or less whitish pruinose, the exciple thick, colored like the thallus, sometimes rough and warty; spores ellipsoid to ovoid-ellipsoid, 40–75 × 20–35 μ. (PLATE 31.)
On trees, throughout the United States.

   var. **rosella** (Tuck.) Zahlbr., Cat. Lich. Univ. 5:686. 1928.
   Lecanora pallescens var. *rosella* Tuck., Gen. Lich. 125. 1872.
The disk divided into areas by inward extensions of the exciple.
On trees and rarely on rocks, throughout northern United States. Not common.

144. **Icmadophila** Ehrh., Beitr. Naturk. 4:147. 1789.

Thallus crustose, closely attached to the substratum, devoid of differentiation into layers; stipes very short or wanting; apothecia middle-sized to large, sessile or on apex of stipe, the disk flat to convex, the exciple thin, colored like the disk, surrounded by a thin to thick, soon disappearing, thalloid one; hypothecium hyaline; hymenium hyaline or brownish above; paraphyses unbranched; asci cylindrical; spores 8, hyaline, 1–3-septate.
The algal host is Pleurococcus.

1. **Icmadophila ericetorum** (L.) Zahlbr., Wiss. Mitteil. Bosn. Herc. 3:605. 1895.
   Lichen ericetorum L., Sp. Pl. 1141. 1753. *I. aeruginosa* (Scop.) Trevis. *Baeomyces aeruginosus* (Scop.) DC. *Lecidea icmadophila* (L.) Ach.

Thallus thin to moderately thick, rough, granulose or somewhat warty, rarely becoming scurfy, greenish gray to greenish or whitish; apothecia middle-sized to large, 0.6–3.5 mm. across, sessile or borne on very short stipes, the disk flat to slightly convex, pale to rosy flesh-colored, becoming more or less wrinkled, surrounded by a thin proper exciple, the thalloid exciple thin to rather thick, becoming flexuous and sometimes disappearing; spores oblong, fusiform, 1–3-septate, 14–28 × 4–6 μ. (PLATE 32.)
On soil and old wood, from New England westward to the Pacific coast.

145. **Lecania** Mass., Gen. Lich. 12. 1855.

Thallus crustose, uniform, devoid of differentiation into layers, or showing poorly developed, indistinct upper cortex, algal and medullary layers, and attached to the substratum by hyphal rhizoids; apothecia minute to small or middle-sized, adnate to sessile, the disk concave to flat or more or less convex, the exciple colored like the thallus, often disappearing; hypothecium hyaline; hymenium hyaline or brownish above; paraphyses unbranched; asci clavate; spores 8, rarely 16–32, hyaline, 1-septate.

The algal host is Pleurococcus.

A. On trees
  B. Spores constantly 1-septate . . . . 1. L. syringea dimera
  B. Spores 1–3-septate
    C. Thallus chinky to sometimes warty, ashy brown to whitish . 1. L. syringea
    C. Thallus chinky to granulose or warty, greenish gray to darker . 2. L. cyrtella
A. On rocks and soil
  B. Thallus dark gray to brownish or reddish brown to darker
    C. Thallus of squamules or squamiform granules
      D. Granules imbricated . . . . 10. L. subdispersa
      D. Granules bearing round elevations . . . . 9. L. Brunonis
    C. Thallus of scattered or clustered warts
      D. Warts light to reddish brown . . . . 7. L. Dudleyi
      D. Warts dark gray to blackish . . . . 11. L. fructigena
  B. Thallus greenish gray to ashy or white
    C. Thallus of clustered squamules . . . . 12. L. toninioides
    C. Thallus of minute granules or areoles
      D. Apothecia more or less whitish pruinose
        E. Spores 1–3-septate . . . . 8. L. Nylanderiana
        E. Spores 1-septate
          F. Thallus smooth to chinky-areolate . . . . . . 5. L. albariella
          F. Thallus of minute granules . . . . 6. L. californica
      D. Apothecia not pruinose
        E. Apothecia 0.2–0.6 mm. across . . . . . . 3. L. perproxima
        E. Apothecia 0.4–1 mm. across . . . . 4. L. erysibe

1. **Lecania syringea** (Ach.) T. Fries, Lich. Scand. 1:290, 291. 1871.
Parmelia Hagenii var. *syringea* Ach., Meth. Lich. 163. 1803. *L. fuscella* (Schaer.) Koerb. *Lecanora athroocarpa* Duby. *Lecanora metabolica* Ach. *Lecanora athroocarpa* var. *Macounii* Tuck.
Thallus thin to very thin, smooth to chinky and sometimes warty, frequently disappearing, ashy brown to whitish; apothecia minute to small, 0.25–0.6 mm. across, subsessile, the disk flat to convex, pale brown to darker and finally black, the exciple thin, colored like the thallus, sometimes disappearing; spores 8–16, ellipsoid, 1–3-septate, 12–20 × 4.5–7 μ.
On trees, Massachusetts, New Hampshire, Ohio, Illinois, Nebraska, and California.

  var. **dimera** (Nyl.) Oliv., Fl. Lich. Orne 2:164. 1884.
  Lecanora dimera Nyl., Not. Sällsk. Faun. Flor. Fenn. 5:169. 1861. *L. dimera* (Nyl.) T. Fries.
  Spores said to be constantly 1-septate, a doubtful distinction.
  On trees, California and Washington.

2. **Lecania cyrtella** (Ach.) T. Fries, Lich. Scand. 1:294–96. 1871.
Lecidea cyrtella Ach., Meth. Lich. 67. 1803.
Thallus very thin, smooth to chinky, becoming granulose or warty, greenish gray to darker, sometimes disappearing; apothecia minute to small, 0.2–0.7 mm. across, adnate to subsessile, the disk flat to convex, brick-red to brown and lurid blackish, the exciple thin, colored like the thallus, disappearing; spores 8–16, oblong to fusiform-oblong, 1–3-septate, 9–16 × 3.5–5 μ.
On trees, Vermont, New York, Colorado, California, and Washington.

3. **Lecania perproxima** (Nyl.) Zahlbr., Cat. Lich. Univ. 5:739. 1928.
Lecanora perproxima Nyl.; Calkins, Bull. Chicago Acad. Sci. 1:29. 1896.
Thallus thin, minutely granulose, becoming chinky, ashy white to grayish; apothecia minute to small, 0.2–0.6 mm. across, adnate, the disk concave to slightly convex, black, the exciple thin, colored like the thallus, becoming flexuous; spores ellipsoid, becoming 1-septate, 14–18 × 5–7 μ.
On rocks, Illinois.

4. **Lecania erysibe** (Ach.) Mudd, Man. Brit. Lich. 141. pro parte pl. 2, f. 47. 1861.
Lichen erysibe Ach., Lich. Suec. 50. 1798. *Lecanora erysibe* (Ach.) Nyl.

Thallus thin, composed of rarely scattered, irregular, olive to greenish gray granules, or becoming scurfy or subareolate; apothecia minute to small, 0.5–1 mm. across, adnate, the disk flat to more or less convex, brown to blackish brown, the exciple colored like the thallus, becoming crenulate and sometimes disappearing; spores ellipsoid, becoming 1-septate, 10–14 × 4–6 μ.
On rocks, Illinois, Iowa, and Minnesota.

5. **Lecania albariella** (Nyl.) Müll. Arg., Rev. Mycol. 2:76. 1880.
Lecanora albariella Nyl., Act. Soc. Linn. Bord. 21:63. 1856.

Thallus thin, smooth to chinky-areolate, dirty creamy-white, becoming scattered and disappearing; apothecia minute, 0.1–0.25 mm. across, adnate, the disk flat to convex, brown to brownish black, or whitish pruinose, the exciple thin, colored like the thallus, soon disappearing; spores ovoid-ellipsoid, 1-septate, 10–15 × 4.5–6.5 μ.
On calcareous rocks, Ohio. Material doubtfully included.

6. **Lecania californica** (Zahlbr.) Fink n. comb.
L. turicensis var. *californica* Zahlbr., Beih. Bot. Centralb. 13:159. 1902.

Thallus very thin, composed of minute, scattered, ashy white, soon disappearing granules; apothecia minute to small, 0.15–0.4 mm. across, adnate, the disk flat to strongly convex, white-pruinose or flesh-brown to darker, the exciple very thin, scarcely conspicuous and becoming flexuous, soon disappearing; spores ellipsoid 1-septate, 9–13 × 3–4.5 μ.
On calcareous rocks, southern California.

7. **Lecania Dudleyi** Herre, Proc. Wash. Acad. Sci. 12:188. 1910.

Thallus rather thick, composed of small, tough, semiglobular, somewhat clustered, light to reddish brown warts; apothecia small to middle-sized, 0.6–1.2 mm. across, immersed to partly immersed, the disk flat to slightly convex, dark brown, the exciple becoming thin and disappearing, colored like the thallus, soon flexuous; spores oblong-ellipsoid, 1-septate, 12–16 × 6–7.5.μ.
On soil and rocks, California.

8. **Lecania Nylanderiana** Mass., Sched. Crit. Lich. Exsicc. 152. 1855.

Thallus thin, granulose, becoming chinky-areolate, dirty grayish to ashy white; apothecia minute to small, 0.2–0.6 mm. across, adnate, the disk flat to convex, brown to brownish black or grayish pruinose, the exciple thin, colored like the thallus, often disappearing; spores 1–3-septate, oblong-ellipsoid, 12–18 × 4–5.5 μ.
On rocks, Iowa.

9. **Lecania Brunonis** (Tuck.) Herre, Proc. Wash. Acad. Sci. 12:188, 189. 1910.
Lecanora Brunonis Tuck., Gen. Lich. 116. 1872.

Thallus thin, composed of minute, usually confluent, imbricated, pale to darker brown squamaceous granules, bearing round elevations; apothecia small to middle-sized, 0.4–1 mm. across, adnate to sessile, the disk concave to flat or slightly convex, rusty brown to dull black, the exciple thin, colored like the thallus or blackening, becoming crenulate and finally disappearing; spores oblong-ellipsoid, 1-septate, 10–17 × 4.5–7 μ.
On rocks, Nebraska and California.

10. **Lecania subdispersa** (Nyl.) Hasse, Cont. U. S. Nat. Herb. 17:97. 1913.
Lecanora subdispersa Nyl., in Hasse, Lich. South. Calif. 12. 1898.

Thallus thin, composed of minute, greenish gray to brownish, somewhat imbricated squamules or squamiform granules; apothecia small to middle-sized, 0.4–1 mm. across, sessile, the disk flat, reddish brown to brownish black, the exciple thin, colored like the thallus, rarely disappearing; spores ellipsoid, 1-septate, 15–21 × 3–4.5 μ.
On rocks, California.

11. **Lecania fructigena** Zahlbr., Bryologist 17:61. 1914.

Thallus thin, composed of small, dark gray to blackish, more or less scattered warts, sometimes flattening into crenate to lobate squamules; apothecia small, 0.4–0.75 mm. across, sessile to slightly elevated, sometimes clustered, the disk flat to slightly convex, brownish black to black, the exciple thin, colored like the thallus, and appearing like a proper exciple, rarely disappearing; spores 8, oblong to oblong-ellipsoid, sometimes slightly curved, 1-septate, 12–18 × 4.5–5.5 μ.

On rocks, California.

12. **Lecania toninioides** Zahlbr., Beih. Bot. Centralb. 13:160. 1902.

Thallus thin, composed of small, round to angular, or wavy-lobed, ashy gray, clustered and often subimbricated squamules; apothecia middle-sized, 0.6–1.5 mm. across, adnate to subsessile, the disk flat to slightly convex, black or grayish pruinose, the exciple thin, colored like the thallus, becoming irregular and disappearing; spores ellipsoid, 1-septate, 15–21 × 4–6 μ.

On rocks and soil, near Santa Monica, California.

OTHER SPECIES REPORTED

Lecania shastensis Herre—California.

146. **Solenopsora** Mass., Framm. Lich. 20. 1855.

Thallus crustose to squamulose, more or less lobed, irregular and rough, the upper cortex very thin or wanting, composed of coherent, septate, thin-walled hyphae, indistinct algal and medullary layers, attached to the substratum by hyphal rhizoids; apothecia small to middle-sized, immersed to adnate or sessile, the disk concave to flat or convex, the exciple colored like the thallus, thin to thick, somewhat irregular; hypothecium hyaline; hymenium hyaline; paraphyses unbranched; asci clavate; spores 8, hyaline, oblong to oblong-ellipsoid or fusiform, 1–3-septate, rarely non-septate.

The algal host is Pleurococcus.

A. Thallus of yellowish or whitish squamules
   B. Squamules yellowish or yellowish ashy; whitish to blackening below   2. S. crenata
   B. Squamules whitish   .   .   .   .   1. S. candicans
A. Thallus of dark blackish brown squamules   .   .   .   .   3. S. Hassei

1. **Solenopsora candicans** (Dicks.) Sten., Oest. Bot. Zeit. 65:288. 1915.

Lichen candicans Dicks., Pl. Crypt. Brit. 3:15. pl. 9, f. 5. 1793. *Placolecania candicans* (Dicks.) Zahlbr.

Thallus thin, composed of small, convex, crenate to lobed, whitish squamules, the squamules toward the margin more distinctly lobed and often radiately extended; apothecia small to middle-sized, 0.4–1 mm. across, adnate to subsessile, the disk flat to convex, brownish black, often more or less pruinose, the thalloid exciple thick, becoming crenate and rarely disappearing; spores 8, hyaline, 1-septate, oblong-ellipsoid, 10–16 × 4–6 μ.

On rocks, southern California.

2. **Solenopsora crenata** (Herre) Zahlbr., Cat. Lich. Univ. 5:755. 1928.

Placolecania crenata Herre, Proc. Wash. Acad. Sci. 12:190. 1910.

Thallus thin, composed of small, convex, somewhat imbricated, crenate-lobed, pale yellowish to yellowish gray squamules; whitish to blackening below; apothecia small to middle-sized, 0.3–0.8 mm. across, closely adnate to sessile, the disk flat to slightly convex, brownish to black, often whitish pruinose, the thalloid exciple thick, becoming crenate, rarely disappearing; hypothecium hyaline; spores 8, nonseptate to 1-septate and very rarely 3-septate, ellipsoid, sometimes curved, 11–20 × 4–5.5 μ.

On rocks and soil, southern California.

3. **Solenopsora Hassei** Zahlbr., Cat. Lich. Univ. 5:755. 1928.

Placolecania Hassei Zahlbr.; Hasse, Bryologist 17:61, 62. 1914.

Thallus thick, composed of small, convex, irregularly lobed, often imbricated, shining, dark blackish brown squamules, the squamules toward the circumference more distinctly lobed; apothecia small to middle-sized, 0.4–1 mm. across, sessile, the disk slightly concave to flat, dark brown to dull black, the thalloid exciple thin, becoming crenate; hypothecium hyaline; spores 8, hyaline, oblong to oblong-ellipsoid, non-septate to more frequently 1-septate, 15–25 × 4.5–6 μ.

On rocks, southern California.

147. Haematomma Mass., Ric. Lich. 32. f. 53, 54. 1852.

Thallus crustose, thin to thick, smooth to wrinkled, chinky, minutely granulose or powdery, with a more or less developed upper cellular cortex or a thin layer of gelatinized, scarcely distinct hyphae, other layers not often differentiated, attached to the substratum by hyphal rhizoids; apothecia minute to small or middle-sized, rarely larger, adnate to sessile, the disk flat to more or less convex, brownish to red or brown, the exciple thin, colored like the thallus, becoming more or less irregular and sometimes disappearing; hypothecium hyaline; hymenium hyaline or brownish above; paraphyses unbranched, commonly thickened and brownish toward the apex; asci clavate; spores 8, hyaline, acicular, several-septate, the cells cylindrical.

The algal host is Pleurococcus.

A. Spores 3–7-septate
  B. On trees; apothecia red to reddish brown
    C. Thallus sulphur-colored, greenish yellow or ashy . . . . 2. H. ventosum
    C. Thallus greenish gray to ashy or faintly yellowish
      D. Thallus wrinkled and minutely granulose . . . . 4. H. cismonicum
      D. Thallus chinky to densely granulose-powdery or warty
        E. Thallus thin; apothecia sessile . . . . . . 3. H. elatinum
        E. Thallus thick; apothecia substipitate . . 3. H. elatinum ochrophaeum
  B. On rocks; apothecia scarlet to reddish brown . . . . . . 5. H. coccineum
A. Spores 7–15-septate . . . . 1. H. puniceum

1. **Haematomma puniceum** (Ach.) Mass., Atti Ist. Veneto III. 5:253. 1860.
Lecanora punicea Ach., Syn. Meth. Lich. 174. 1814.
Thallus thin, chinky to wrinkled and granulose, greenish gray to pale yellowish green; apothecia minute to small, 0.2–0.6 mm. across, closely sessile, the disk flat, scarlet, the exciple thin, colored like the thallus, becoming flexuous and crenulate; spores needle-shaped, 7–15-septate, 38–65 × 4–5 μ.

On trees and rarely on rocks, from New Jersey to Florida, and westward to Texas and Iowa.

2. **Haematomma ventosum** (L.) Mass., Ric. Lich. 33. 1852.
Lichen ventosus L., Sp. Pl. 1141. 1753. *Lecanora ventosa* (L.) Ach.
Thallus thick, smooth to wrinkled and warty, becoming areolate, greenish yellow to sulphur-colored, or rarely varying toward ashy; apothecia middle-sized to large, 0.8–2 mm. across, adnate, the disk flat to convex, blood-red, the exciple thin, colored like the thallus, rarely wrinkled-crenate, becoming flexuous and soon disappearing; spores needle-shaped, 3–7-septate, curved, 35–50 × 3–5 μ.

On trees, New England, California, and Washington.

3. **Haematomma elatinum** (Ach.) Mass., Gen. Lich. 21. 1854.
Lecanora elatina Ach., Lich. Univ. 387. 1810.
Thallus thin, smooth and somewhat chinky to densely granulose or powdery, ashy white to faintly yellowish; apothecia small to middle-sized, 0.5–1.5 mm. across, sessile, the disk flat to convex and knobby, light to dark reddish brown, or somewhat pruinose, the exciple thin, colored like the thallus, becoming irregular and soon disappearing; spores fusiform-needle-shaped, curved, 3–5-septate, 38–55 × 4–5.5 μ.

On trees, New England, New York, North Carolina, Illinois, Iowa, and Minnesota.

var. **ochrophaeum** (Tuck.) Merrill & Burnh., Bryologist 25:73. 1922.
Biatora ochrophaea Tuck., Syn. Lich. N. E. 61, 62. 1848.
Thallus thick, smooth to rough, wrinkled and warty, finally crumbling more or less; apothecia substipitate, the disk but slightly convex, the exciple seldom disappearing.
On trees, distribution as in the species.

4. **Haematomma cismonicum** Belts., Lich. Bassam. 127. pl. 4, f. 1–4. 1858.
Lecanora elatina var. *minor* Tuck.
Thallus very thin, smooth to wrinkled and minutely granulose, pale greenish gray to ashy white; apothecia minute to small, 0.3–0.8 mm. across, sessile, the disk flat to somewhat convex, white-pruinose, or rarely pale brownish, the exciple thin, colored like the thallus, becoming somewhat flexuous and rarely disappearing; spores fusiform-needle-shaped, curved, 3–5-septate, 30–45 × 4–5.5 μ.
On trees, New England, New York, and North Carolina.

5. **Haematomma coccineum** (Dicks.) Koerb., Syst. Lich. 153. 1855.
Lichen coccineus Dicks., Crypt. Brit. 1:8. 1785. *Lecanora haematomma* Ach.
Thallus thin to moderately thick, smooth to powdery, whitish sulphur-colored to whitish; apothecia small to middle-sized, 0.5–1.4 mm. across, adnate, the disk flat to strongly convex, scarlet to reddish brown, the exciple thin, colored like the thallus, becoming subcrenate and disappearing; spores needle-shaped, curved, 3–7-septate, 28–60 × 5–7 μ.
On rocks, Colorado.

OTHER SPECIES REPORTED

Haematomma Rappii Zahlbr.—Florida.

148. **Phlyctis** Flot., Bot. Zeit. 8:571. 1850.

Thallus crustose, smooth to rough, chinky, areolate or powdery, the upper cortex usually wanting, the algal layer indistinct, the medullary layer of loosely interwoven, thin-walled hyphae, attached to the substratum by hyphal rhizoids; apothecia minute to small or middle-sized, immersed to adnate, the disk concave to flat, the exciple colored like the thallus, thin to thick, irregular; hypothecium hyaline to yellowish or brownish; hymenium hyaline or brownish above; paraphyses unbranched and free or somewhat branched toward the apices; asci clavate; spores 1–8, hyaline, oblong to oblong-ellipsoid or ellipsoid, transversely and longitudinally septate.
The algal host is Pleurococcus.

A. Spores not more than 90 μ in length . . . . 1. P. agelaea
A. Spores more than 90 μ in length
    B. Apothecia not more than 0.25 mm. across . . . . 3. P. Willeyi
    B. Apothecia more than 0.25 mm. across . . . . 2. P. argena

1. **Phlyctis agelaea** (Ach.) Flot., Bot. Zeit. 8:574. 1850.
Lichen agelaeus Ach., Lich. Suec. 30. 1798.
Thallus thin, smooth or becoming obscurely chinky and areolate, white or grayish white; apothecia minute to small, 0.2–0.5 mm. across, the disk flat, black or whitish pruinose, the exciple thin, colored like the thallus, becoming powdery; hypothecium yellowish; spores 1–2, hyaline to pale brownish, oblong-ellipsoid, pointed at both ends, 15–21-septate transversely and 5–9-septate longitudinally, 48–85 × 14–20 μ.
On trees, southern California.

2. **Phlyctis argena** (Ach.) Flot., Bot. Zeit. 8:572. 1850.
Lichen argenus Ach., Lich. Suec. 8. 1798.
Thallus thin, round, smooth to slightly wrinkled, becoming powdery, white throughout or creamy white toward the circumference; apothecia small to middle-sized, 0.25–0.6 mm. across, adnate, the disk flat, brownish black to black or thickly

pruinose, the exciple thin, colored like the thallus, becoming powdery; hypothecium hyaline to pale brownish; spores 1, hyaline to brownish, oblong with round ends, 19–35-septate transversely and 5–9-septate longitudinally, 100–170 × 32–46 μ.
On trees, New Hampshire, Oklahoma, Washington, Oregon, and California.

3. **Phlyctis Willeyi** Tuck., in Nyl., Lich. Jap. 106. 1890.
Thallus thin, smooth to slightly uneven, becoming chinky, ashy gray to whitish; apothecia minute, 0.15–0.25 mm. across, immersed, the disk concave to flat, black, the exciple rather thick, colored like the thallus, becoming wavy; hypothecium hyaline to yellowish; spores 1, hyaline, oblong, 9–25-septate transversely and 4–6-septate longitudinally, 92–130 × 32–60 μ.
On trees, Florida and Texas.

149. **Phlyctella** Kremph., Verh. Zool. Bot. Gesell. 26:452. 1876.

Thallus crustose, smooth to rough, chinky, areolate or powdery, the upper cortex usually wanting, the algal layer indistinct, the medullary layer of loosely interwoven, thin-walled hyphae, attached to the substratum by hyphal rhizoids; apothecia minute to small or middle-sized, immersed to adnate, the disk concave to flat, the exciple colored like the thallus, thin to thick, irregular; hypothecium hyaline to yellowish or brownish; hymenium hyaline or brownish above; paraphyses unbranched and free; asci clavate; spores 1–8, hyaline, several–many-septate, the cells lenticular.
The algal host is Pleurococcus.

1. **Phlyctella andensis** Nyl., Lich. Nov. Zeal. 73. 1888.
Phlyctis andensis Nyl., Bull. Soc. Linn. Norm. II. 2:514. 1868. *Platygrapha phlyctella* Nyl.
Thallus thin, white, obscurely chinky; apothecia small, 0.3–0.6 mm. across, becoming sessile, round to angular or irregular, the disk flat, grayish pruinose to black, the exciple thin, brownish black, surrounded by a thin, whitish, thalloid one; hypothecium hyaline; spores 8, hyaline, fusiform, 5–7-septate, 35–45 × 5–7 μ.
On trees, Florida.

150. **Phlyctidia** Müll. Arg., Hedwigia 34:141. 1895.

Thallus crustose, smooth to rough, chinky, areolate or powdery, the upper cortex usually wanting, the algal layer indistinct, the medullary layer of loosely interwoven, thin-walled hyphae, attached to the substratum by hyphal rhizoids; apothecia minute to small or middle-sized, immersed to adnate, the disk concave to flat, the exciple colored like the thallus, thin to thick, irregular; hypothecium hyaline to yellowish or brownish; hymenium hyaline or brownish above; paraphyses irregularly and netlike interwoven; asci clavate; spores 1–8, hyaline, oblong to ellipsoid, several–many-septate, the cells lenticular.
The algal host is Pleurococcus.

1. **Phlyctidia ludoviciensis** Müll. Arg., Hedwigia 34:141. 1895.
Thallus thin, smooth to minutely warty, becoming wrinkled and areolate, ashy white; apothecia minute, 0.1–0.25 mm. across, round to somewhat irregular, sometimes clustered, immersed to adnate, the disk flat, flesh-colored to brown or grayish pruinose, the exciple colored like the thallus, thick, irregular; spores 1, hyaline, oblong-ellipsoid, 11–19-septate, the cells appearing irregularly pitted, 85–100 × 25–30 μ.
On trees, Louisiana.

151. **Candelariella** Müll. Arg., Bull. Herb. Boiss. 2:11. 1894.

Thallus crustose, smooth to rough, granulose, warty, areolate, sometimes lobed at the margins, scarcely differentiated or showing poorly developed upper cortex and medullary layer, attached to substratum by hyphal rhizoids; apothecia small to middle-sized, adnate to sessile, the disk concave to flat or slightly convex, the exciple colored like the thallus, more or less irregular; hypothecium hyaline; hymenium hyaline or brownish above; paraphyses unbranched, more or less jointed toward the apices; asci clavate; spores 8–many, hyaline, oblong to ellipsoid, non-septate or rarely 1-septate.

The algal host is Pleurococcus.

A. Spores not more than 20 μ in length
  B. Thallus granulose
    C. Thallus pale to lemon-yellow . . . . 4. C. crenulata
    C. Thallus not lemon-yellow
      D. Thallus greenish yellow to olive-green . . . . 3. C. cerinella
      D. Thallus greenish gray to blackish . . . . 2. C. aurella
  B. Thallus more or less squamulose, squamules forming
    areole-like clusters . . . . 1. C. vitellina
A. Spores large, 25–46 μ in length . . . . 5. C. Spraguei

1. **Candelariella vitellina** (Ehrh.) Müll. Arg., Bull. Herb. Boiss. 2: app. 47. 1894.
    Lichen vitellinus Ehrh., Pl. Crypt. Exsicc. 155. 1785. *Parmelia vitellina* (Ehrh.) Ach. *Placodium vitellinum* (Ehrh.) Hepp. *Pleochroma vitellina* (Ehrh.) Clements.
Thallus granulose or of small round to crenate-lobed squamules, scattered or continuous and forming areole-like clusters, bright greenish yellow; apothecia small to middle-sized, 0.3–1.3 mm. across, sessile, the disk flat, tawny-yellow to olive-green, the exciple of the same color as the thallus, granulose-crenate; spores commonly 12–32, rarely 8, non-septate or more commonly 1-septate, 8–16 × 4–7 μ.
On rocks and old wood, throughout the United States.

2. **Candelariella aurella** (Hoffm.) Zahlbr., Cat. Lich. Univ. 5:790. 1928.
    Verrucaria aurella Hoffm., Deutschl. Fl. 197. 1796. *Lecanora epixantha* (Ach.) Nyl. *Placodium vitellinum* var. *aurellum* (Hoffm.) Tuck.
Thallus thin and inconspicuous, greenish gray to blackish, smooth to rough, soon scattered and often granulose, sometimes disappearing; apothecia minute to small, 0.1–0.6 mm. across, adnate to sessile, the disk flat, tawny-yellow or orange to olive-green, the exciple entire, lemon-yellow to orange or olive-green; spores oblong-ellipsoid, frequently more than twenty in an ascus, often slightly curved, non-septate or sometimes 1-septate, 8–14 × 4–6 μ.
On rocks and old wood, from Ohio westward to California and Washington.

3. **Candelariella cerinella** (Vainio) Zahlbr., in E. & P., Nat. Pfl. 1¹:207. 1907.
    Lecanora cerinella Vainio, Term. Füz. 22:284. 1899.
Thallus thin, of more or less scattered round granules, greenish yellow to olive-green; apothecia minute to small, 0.1–0.8 mm. across, sessile, the disk flat to convex, greenish yellow, the exciple thin, greenish to bright yellow, entire to subcrenulate, soon disappearing; spores oblong-ellipsoid, some slightly curved, non-septate to obscurely 1-septate, 9–13 × 5–7 μ.
On rocks and soil, Nevada, California, and Washington.

4. **Candelariella crenulata** (Wahl.) Zahlbr., Cat. Lich. Univ. 5:812. 1928.
    Lichen murorum var. *crenulatus* Wahl., Flora Lapp. 416. 1812. *Placodium crenulatum* (Wahl.) Tuck.
Thallus moderately thick, round, minutely granulose, crenately lobed, pale to lemon-yellow; apothecia small to middle-sized, 0.4–0.8 mm. across, adnate to sessile, often crowded, the disk flat to convex, pale to tawny yellow, the exciple thin, colored like the thallus, becoming crenate; spores 8 to many, ellipsoid, non-septate to 1-septate, the cells polar, 9.5–15 × 4.5–7 μ.
On rocks, Massachusetts and Colorado.

5. **Candelariella Spraguei** (Tuck.) Zahlbr., Cat. Lich. Univ. 5:802. 1928.
    Placodium Spraguei Tuck., Syn. N. A. Lich. 1:179. 1882. *Lecanora Spraguei* Tuck.
Thallus composed of short branches crowded into a papillate greenish yellow crust, sometimes expanding into lobulate squamules toward the margin; apothecia

middle-sized, 0.8–1.5 mm. across, subsessile, the disk flat to slightly convex, dull brownish yellow, the exciple thick, colored like the thallus, becoming flexuous and crenate; spores 8, 1-septate, ellipsoid to acicular, irregularly broken within, 25–46 × 3–5 μ.

On soil over rocks, Colorado, Montana, and Washington.

OTHER SPECIES REPORTED

Candelariella rosulans (Müll. Arg.) Zahlbr.—Colorado.

39. PARMELIACEAE

Thallus foliose, or rarely fruticose, differentiated into cortical, algal, and medullary layers, attached to the substratum by rhizoids, or the under surface rarely bearing cyphellae or densely covered with a mass of darkened hyphae; apothecia round, sessile, or somewhat pedicellate, with well-developed thalloid exciple.

The algal hosts are Pleurococcus and Protococcus.

A. Upper cortex plectenchymatous
   B. Thallus yellow; spores many in each ascus . . . . . . 152. CANDELARIA
   B. Thallus rarely yellow; spores commonly 8 in each ascus
      C. Thallus more or less upright; apothecia marginal . . . . 155. CETRARIA
      C. Thallus flat; apothecia not marginal . . . . 154. PARMELIA
A. Upper cortex of interwoven hyphae . . . . 153. PARMELIOPSIS

152. Candelaria Mass., Flora 35:567. 1852.

Thallus foliose, more or less irregularly lobed, commonly yellow, differentiated into upper and lower plectenchymatous cortices, a thin algal layer, and a medullary layer of thin-walled, intertangled hyphae, attached to the substratum by short rhizoids; apothecia small to middle-sized, sessile, the disk concave to flat, commonly yellow or brownish, the exciple prominent, colored like the thallus, becoming somewhat irregular; hypothecium hyaline or brownish; hymenium hyaline to brownish above; paraphyses spongy, unbranched or rarely forked toward the somewhat enlarged apices; asci broadly clavate; spores many (16–32), hyaline, ellipsoid to ovoid-ellipsoid, non-septate or rarely becoming 1-septate.

The algal host is Pleurococcus.

A. Exciple not fibrillose below
   B. Thallus much lobed . . . . 1. C. concolor
   B. Thallus reduced to granulose squamules or passing
      into a powdery crust . . . . 1. C. concolor effusa
A. Exciple fibrillose below . . . . 2. C. fibrosa

1. **Candelaria concolor** (Dicks.) Arn., Flora 62:364. 1879.
   Lichen concolor Dicks. Pl., Crypt. Brit. 3:18. pl. 9, f. 8. 1793. *Parmelia parietina* var. *concolor* (Dicks.) E. Fries. *Physcia candelaris* Nyl. *Teloschistes concolor* (Dicks.) Tuck. *C. laciniosa* var. *effusa* (Tuck.) Riddle.

Thallus round to irregular, greenish yellow to yellow or ashy, composed of many, small, scattered or more or less imbricated lobes, these often passing into a continuous crust toward the center, and becoming narrow and much divided toward the circumference, with finely granulose, slightly ascending margins; ashy below, bearing minute, ashy rhizoids and marginal fibrils; apothecia small, 0.5–1.5 mm. across, subsessile, the disk concave to flat, yellow or becoming brownish, the exciple thin to rather thick, colored like the thallus, becoming crenulate; hypothecium hyaline; spores numerous, hyaline, oblong, becoming 1-septate, 6–11 × 3–5 μ.

On trees, throughout the United States.

var. **effusa** (Tuck.) Merrill & Burnh., Bryologist 25:73. 1922.

Teloschistes concolor var. *effusa* Tuck., Syn. N. A. Lich. 1:52. 1882.

Thallus reduced to granulose, more or less scattered squamules, or sometimes passing into a more or less continuous powdery crust.

On trees, throughout the United States.

2. **Candelaria fibrosa** (E. Fries) Müll. Arg., Flora 70:319. 1887.

Parmelia fibrosa E. Fries, Syst. Orb. Veg. 1:284. 1825. *Physcia candelaria* var. *stellata* Nyl. *C. stellata* (Nyl.) Müll. Arg.

Thallus round to irregular and stellate, more or less irregularly lobed, the lobes imbricated, smooth to rough, short and broad to more or less elongated, the margins repeatedly and deeply incised, yellow to rarely ashy; white below and bearing numerous, short, white rhizoids; apothecia minute to small, 0.2–1 mm. across, round, sessile, slightly constricted at the base, the disk flat, yellow, the exciple thin, prominent, colored like the thallus, entire to crênulate, bearing minute fibrils below; hypothecium hyaline; hymenium yellowish above and hyaline below; spores many, hyaline, ellipsoid or ovoid-ellipsoid, straight, non-septate to 1-septate, 9–12 × 4–6 μ.

On trees and rocks, from New England to South Carolina, and westward to Ohio and Texas (description compiled from Zahlbruckner, who studied the original specimen in Herbarium of Jean Müller of Argo).

153. **Parmeliopsis** Nyl., Syn. Lich. 2:53. 1863.

Thallus foliose, compressed, more or less irregularly lobed, differentiated into an upper and lower cortex of more or less vertically extending, somewhat interwoven hyphae, and irregular algal and medullary layers; apothecia small to middle-sized, sessile, the disk concave to more or less convex, usually brown, the exciple colored like the thallus, becoming irregular; hypothecium hyaline to brownish; hymenium hyaline or brownish above; paraphyses rarely branched; asci clavate; spores 8, hyaline, subspherical to ellipsoid or broadly ellipsoid, sometimes curved, non-septate.

The algal host is Pleurococcus.

A. Thallus bearing coralloid granules or soredia
  B. Thallus bearing coralloid granules
    C. Granules densely crowded over the thallus except
      toward the margins . . . . 2. P. aleurites
    C. Granules scattered over the thallus . . . . . . 2. P. aleurites diffusa
  B. Thallus bearing soredia
    C. Thallus straw-colored to ashy white or yellowish,
      bearing yellowish or sulphur-colored soredia
      D. Exciple crenulate . . . . 3. P. ambigua
      D. Exciple constantly powdery-sorediate . . . . . 3. P. ambigua Halei
    C. Thallus whitish to ashy or ashy brown, bearing whitish
      or dirty-ashy soredia . . . . 4. P. diffusa
A. Thallus without coralloid granules or soredia . . . . 1. P. placorodia

1. **Parmeliopsis placorodia** (Ach.) Nyl., Syn. Lich. 2:55. 1860.

Parmelia placorodia Ach., Syn. Meth. Lich. 196. 1814. *Cetraria placorodia* (Ach.) Tuck. *Cetraria aleurites* var. *placorodia* (Ach.) Tuck.

Thallus small, round, adnate throughout or marginally ascending, greenish gray to ashy, smooth to wrinkled toward the center, the lobes more or less regularly arranged, narrow, branched, the margins deeply wavy to pinnate-cleft; whitish below, with scattered brownish to brown rhizoids; apothecia small to middle-sized, 1.5–7 mm. across, sessile, the disk concave to convex, yellowish to chestnut-brown, the exciple thin, colored like the thallus, crenulate; spores subspherical to broadly ellipsoid, 4.5–9 × 3.5–6 μ.

On trees and old wood, from Massachusetts to North Carolina.

2. **Parmeliopsis aleurites** (Ach.) Nyl., Not. Sällsk. Faun. Flor. Fenn. 8:121. 1866.
   Lichen aleurites Ach., Lich. Prod. 117. 1798. *Cetraria aleurites* (Ach.) T. Fries. *P. pallescens* (Neck.) Zahlbr.

Thallus small, round, adnate, greenish gray to ashy or brownish, smooth toward the margin, elsewhere wrinkled and densely covered with whitish to brownish coralloid granules, the lobes short, narrow, with round to crenate margins; whitish and wrinkled below, with scattered brownish rhizoids; apothecia small, 1.5–3 mm. across, or reaching 5 mm., sessile, the disk concave, chestnut-brown, the exciple colored like the thallus, crenulate to lobulate; spores broadly ellipsoid, 4.5–9 × 3.5–5 μ. (PLATE 33.)

On trees and old wood, Connecticut, Pennsylvania, and Michigan.

var. **diffusa** (Ach.) Riddle, Bryologist 20:74. 1917.
Parmelia aleurites var. *diffusa* Ach., Lich. Univ. 485. 1810.

Thallus irregularly and somewhat imbricately lobed, the coralloid granules smaller, fewer, and scattered.

On trees and old wood, from New England to Georgia.

3. **Parmeliopsis ambigua** (Wulf.) Nyl., Syn. Lich. 2:54. pl. 9, f. 4. 1860.
   Lichen ambiguus Wulf., in Jacq., Coll. Bot. 4:239. pl. 4, f. 2. 1790. *Parmelia ambigua* (Wulf.) Ach. *Parmelia diffusa* (Schrad.) T. Fries.

Thallus small to middle-sized, round, adnate, smooth toward the circumference and chinky and broken toward the center, straw-colored to ashy white or yellow, more or less densely covered with yellowish or sulphur-colored soredia or soralia, the lobes elongated, dichotomously much-branched, often imbricated, the margins wavy to incised-crenate; chestnut-brown below, varying toward blackish, with scattered black rhizoids; apothecia small to middle-sized, 1–5 mm. across, sessile, the disk concave to convex, chestnut-brown to darker, the exciple colored like the thallus, becoming crenulate; spores oblong-ovoid, commonly curved, 8–13 × 2–3.5 μ.

On trees, old wood, and rocks, from New England to South Carolina, and westward to Wyoming and New Mexico.

var. **Halei** (Tuck.) Zahlbr., Cat. Lich. Univ. 6:13. 1929.
Parmelia ambigua var. *Halei* Tuck., Syn. N. A. Lich. 1:66. 1882.

Apothecia somewhat larger than in the species, with wax-colored disk and a constantly powdery-sorediate exciple.

On coniferous trees, Massachusetts, New Jersey, Virginia, South Carolina, and Louisiana.

4. **Parmeliopsis diffusa** (Weber) Riddle, Bryologist 20:75. 1917.
   Lichen diffusus Weber, Sp. Fl. Goett. 250. 1778. *Parmelia ambigua* var. *albescens* (Wahl.) Schaer. *Parmelia hyperopta* Ach.

Thallus round, small to middle-sized, adnate, whitish to ashy or ashy brown, smooth and shining toward the circumference to chinky toward the center, with more or less elevated, whitish to dirty-ashy, scattered or clustered soredia, in the latter condition forming soralia, the lobes more or less regularly radiate, dichotomously much-branched, the margins crenate; brownish black below, with scattered, black rhizoids; apothecia small to middle-sized, 2–6 mm. across, sessile, the disk flat to slightly convex, chestnut-brown to darker, the exciple colored like the thallus, crenulate; spores oblong-ovoid, commonly curved, 8–15 × 2–3.5 μ.

On trees, old wood, and rocks, Maine, New Hampshire, New York, and Washington.

154. **Parmelia** Ach., Meth. Lich. 153. pl. 4, f. 3–6. 1803.

Thallus foliose or rarely somewhat fruticose, more or less lobed, smooth or more or less covered by soredia or coralloid branchlets, sometimes ciliate along the margins, differentiated into well-developed, plectenchymatous upper and lower cortex, algal layer, and medullary layer of more or less loosely interwoven hyphae, usually attached to the substratum by heavy rhizoids; apothecia small to large, sessile or subpedicellate, the disk more or less concave to flat, usually brown, the exciple colored like the thallus, prominent; hypothecium hyaline to brownish; hymenium hyaline or brownish above; paraphyses rarely branched; asci clavate or broadly clavate; spores commonly 8, rarely 2–6 or many, hyaline, subspherical to oblong, ellipsoid or ovoid-ellipsoid, non-septate.

The algal host is Protococcus.

A. Thallus greenish gray to grayish black
  B. Thallus light-colored to darker below, but not black
    C. With coralloid branchlets or soredia above
      D. With coralloid branchlets above . . . . 1. P. rudecta
      D. With soredia above
        E. More or less covered by soredia . . . . 2. P. Borreri
        E. Marginally sorediate . . . . 5. P. hypotropa
    C. Without coralloid branchlets or soredia above
      D. Lobes broad; bearing light-colored rhizoids below . . . 4. P. cubensis
      D. Lobes narrow; without rhizoids below . . . . 3. P. lanata
  B. Thallus brownish black to black below
    C. Thallus inflated
      D. Thallus not perforated
        E. Thallus large, lobes dichotomously branched,
          margins becoming black . . . . 6. P. physodes
        E. Thallus smaller, lobes irregularly much-branched . . 7. P. encausta
      D. Thallus perforated by round or oblong holes . . . . . 8. P. pertusa
    C. Thallus not inflated
      D. Thallus with coralloid branchlets or soredia above
        E. Lobes broad
          F. With coralloid branchlets or rarely soredia above
            G. Thallus densely covered with coralloid branchlets
              H. Bearing few scattered rhizoids below . . 9. P. coralloidea
              H. Bearing many rhizoids below . . . . . . 11. P. crinita
            G. Thallus bearing few coralloid branchlets and
              sometimes sorediate
              H. Without soredia . . . . 10. P. latissima
              H. Margins sorediate . . . . . . 10. P. latissima sorediata
          F. With soredia above
            G. Bearing many, more or less scattered rhizoids
              H. Thallus becoming wrinkled above, bearing many
                soredia, especially toward the margins . . . 15. P. cetrata
              H. Thallus bearing few marginal soredia . . . 13. P. olivaria
            G. Bearing few or no rhizoids
              H. Margins bearing powdery soredia . . . . 14. P. perlata
              H. Margins bearing rather large, globose
                soredia . . . . 12. P. cristifera
        E. Lobes narrow
          F. With coralloid branchlets above
            G. Coralloid branchlets small, more or less
              spherical or cylindrical
              H. Lobes more or less branched
                I. Thallus small, with few scattered
                  rhizoids below . . . . 16. P. Finkii
                I. Thallus middle-sized to large, with
                  many rhizoids below . . . . 18. P. saxatilis
              H. Lobes rarely branched, sometimes bearing
                fibrils . . . . 17. P. caroliniana
            G. Coralloid branchlets larger, flat and often
              lobed . . . . 19. P. frondifera
          F. With soredia above, sometimes rarely so
            G. Without rhizoids below
              H. Papillate below . . . . 21. P. texana
              H. Reticulately pitted or finally perforate
                below . . . . 20. P. lophyrea

G. With numerous black rhizoids below . . . . 22. P. sulcata
D. Thallus without coralloid branchlets or soredia above
  E. Lobes broad
    F. Without rhizoids below
      G. Margins bearing numerous black cilia . . . 24. P. subrugata
      G. Margins sometimes bearing few black cilia . 23. P. submarginalis
    F. With rhizoids below
      G. Margins sometimes bearing short cilia;
      apothecia commonly perforate
        H. Lobes more or less branched and
        imbricated . . . . 25. P. perforata
        H. Lobes sometimes extending into narrow
        flat divisions . . . . 26. P. hypotrypodes
      G. Margins rarely bearing cilia; apothecia not
      perforate . . . . : . . . 27. P. proboscidea
  E. Lobes narrow
    F. Thallus bearing few to many rhizoids below;
    spores constantly 8 in each ascus
      G. Thallus whitish within
        H. Thallus greenish gray to whitish
          I. Lobes short to elongated
            J. Lobes subdichotomously branched . . 30. P. quercina
            J. Lobes subpinnately branched and
            elongated . . . . 29. P. sublaevigata
          I. Lobes shorter and narrower . . . 30. P. quercina minor
        H. Thallus black to greenish olivaceous or
        dark greenish gray . . . . 28. P. atrofusca
      G. Thallus sulphur-yellow within . . . . . 31. P. sulphurosa
    F. Thallus covered below with a dense, spongy nap;
    spores many in each ascus . . . . 32. P. colpodes
A. Thallus straw-colored or yellowish green or brown
  B. Light-colored to darker below, but not black
    C. Lobes broad . . . . 33. P. sphaerosporella
    C. Lobes narrow
      D. Without soredia above
        E. On trees; lobes flat, somewhat branched
        and imbricated . . . . 34. P. leucochlora
        E. On rocks; lobes convex, much branched . . . . 35. P. centrifuga
      D. With raised powdery soredia above . . . . . . 36. P. incurva
  B. Brownish black to black below
    C. Lobes broad
      D. Rhizoids scanty or absent
        E. Bearing few scattered rhizoids below
          F. With soredia above . . . . 37. P. flavicans
          F. Without soredia above . . . . 38. P. praesignis
        E. Bearing minute, black tubercles below . . . . . 39. P. arizonica
      D. Rhizoids usually present
        E. Rhizoids few, not at the margins
          F. Thallus bearing coralloid branchlets breaking
          up into soredia . . . . 40. P. caperata
          F. Thallus bearing powdery soredia . . . . . . 41. P. ulophylla
        E. Rhizoids few to many, to the margins
          F. Thallus sulphur-colored or yellowish within
            G. Bearing granules or coralloid branchlets . . 42. P. sulphurata
            G. Bearing soredia . . . . 43. P. aurulenta
          F. Thallus whitish within . . . . 44. P. soredica
    C. Lobes narrow
      D. Thallus closely adnate
        E. On trees; spores 8–10 $\times$ 4–5 μ . . . . 45. P. scortella
        E. On rocks and rarely on old wood; spores
        8–12 $\times$ 4.5–7 μ . . . . 46. P. conspersa
      D. Thallus loosely adnate or subfruticose
        E. Thallus loosely adnate . . . . 47. P. laevigata
        E. Thallus subfruticose . . . . 48. P. molliuscula

A. Thallus olivaceous, brown or darker
  B. With coralloid branchlets or soredia above
    C. Lobes broad
      D. Bearing scattered warts or coralloid branchlets
        on the thallus and exciple . . . . 49. P. aspidota
      D. Bearing powdery soredia on the thallus,
        especially toward the margins . . . . 50. P. conspurcata
    C. Lobes narrow
      D. Lobes variously branched and imbricated, sometimes
        bearing coralloid branchlets or soredia
        E. Lobes smooth and often shiny; spores $8–15 \times 7–9 \mu$. 52. P. omphalodes
        E. Lobes becoming wrinkled; spores $8–11 \times 5–7 \mu$ . . . 53. P. prolixa
      D. Lobes digitately much-branched, usually thickly
        covered with whitish or greenish gray soredia . . . . 51. P. sorediata
  B. Without coralloid branchlets or soredia above
    C. Lobes broad
      D. Spores constantly 8 in each ascus
        E. On rocks; lobes wavy and radiately folded . . . . 55. P. glabra
        E. On trees; lobes branched and sometimes imbricated . 56. P. olivacea
      D. Spores 16–24 or more in each ascus . . . . . . 54. P. multispora
    C. Lobes narrow, palmately much-branched . . . . 57. P. stygia

1. **Parmelia rudecta** Ach., Syn. Meth. Lich. 197. 1814.
  P. Borreri var. *rudecta* (Ach.) Tuck.
  Thallus middle-sized to large, rather closely adnate, greenish gray to ashy, commonly wrinkled, bearing many granules or coralloid branchlets, the lobes wide and short, somewhat branched, the margins entire to cut-crenate, and rarely white-powdery; ashy to pale brown below with white or darkening rhizoids; apothecia rare, small, 3–5 mm. across, subsessile, the disk deeply concave, chestnut-brown, the exciple entire, crenulate, or irregular; spores ellipsoid, $10–16 \times 6–8.5 \mu$.
  On trees and rarely on rocks, throughout the United States.

2. **Parmelia Borreri** Turn., in J. E. Smith & Sowerby, Engl. Bot. 25:1780. 1807.
  P. Borreri var. *hypomela* Tuck. *P. Bolliana* Müll. Arg.
  Thallus middle-sized or larger, usually wrinkled, rather closely adnate, greenish gray or varying toward ashy or brownish, sometimes covered more or less by round soredia, the lobes rather wide and short, more or less branched, with usually cut-crenate margins; ashy to pale brownish, or very rarely blackening below, with white or darkening rhizoids; apothecia middle-sized to large, 3–14 mm. across, subsessile, the disk concave to deeply concave, chestnut-brown, the exciple entire to crenate or irregular; spores ellipsoid, $9–18 \times 6–8 \mu$.
  On trees and rarely on rocks, widely distributed, eastern United States.

3. **Parmelia lanata** (L.) Wallr., in Bluff & Fing., Comp. Fl. Germ. 1:529. 1831.
  Lichen lanatus L., Sp. Pl. 1155. 1753. *P. pubescens* (L.) Vainio. *P. stygia* var. *lanata* (L.) E. Fries.
  Thallus small, usually subfruticose and procumbent, blackening, the lobes narrow and round, subdichotomously much-branched, the branches usually entangled; usually lighter colored below and without rhizoids; apothecia middle-sized, 2–6 mm. across, the disk flat to convex, chestnut-brown and darker, the exciple subgranulate; spores round to ellipsoid, $5–12 \times 3–7 \mu$.
  On rocks, California and Wyoming.

4. **Parmelia cubensis** Nyl., Flora 68:611. 1885.
  Thallus middle-sized, adnate, grayish white, smooth to more or less roughened, the lobes short and wide, or becoming somewhat elongated and obscurely branched, sometimes imbricated, the margins wavy to incised-crenate; dirty olivaceous below, with pale rhizoids; apothecia small, 1–2.5 mm. across, the disk concave, chestnut-brown, the exciple entire; spores ovoid-ellipsoid, $9–12 \times 7–8.5 \mu$.
  On trees, Louisiana and Florida. (Nylander states that this species is near *Parmelia texana* but not sorediate.)

5. **Parmelia hypotropa** Nyl., Syn. Lich. 1:403. 1860.

P. perforata var. *hypotropa* Nyl., Syn. Meth. 1:378, 379. 1858.

Thallus loosely adnate, middle-sized, light greenish gray to white, smooth or slightly wrinkled, sorediate particularly toward the margins, the lobes rather broad and not much elongated, somewhat imbricated, with undulate, crenulate, or irregular margins; pale to brownish below with scattered brownish to black rhizoids; apothecia middle-sized to large, 4–12 mm. across, subpedicellate, the disk deeply concave, chestnut-brown, commonly perforate at the center, the exciple entire to crenate; spores oblong-ellipsoid, 9–15 × 6–8 μ.

On trees and rocks, from South Carolina to Texas, and northward to Massachusetts and Minnesota, and in California.

6. **Parmelia physodes** (L.) Ach., Meth. Lich. 250. 1803.

Lichen physodes L., Sp. Pl. 1144. 1753. *P. physodes* var. *obscurata* Ach. *P. physodes* var. *enteromorpha* Tuck. *P. physodes* var. *vittata* Ach.

Thallus loosely adnate, usually smooth, greenish gray to ashy, or rarely becoming brown or brownish black at the margins and finally throughout, showing open spaces between the upper cortex and the medullary layer, the lobes usually narrow, becoming long and wavy, dichotomously branched and often imbricated, somewhat ascending toward the entire to wavy-crenate and sometimes sorediate margins; brownish black to black below, or brown, or white-sorediate toward the margins, wrinkled and without rhizoids; apothecia rare, middle-sized to large, 3–14 mm. across, sessile to subpedicellate, the disk concave, chestnut-brown or lighter, the exciple entire to somewhat irregular; spores subspherical to short-ellipsoid, 4–9 × 3.5–6 μ.

On trees and rocks, throughout northern United States, and sparingly southward (a variable plant).

7. **Parmelia encausta** (J. E. Smith) Ach., Meth. Lich. 202. 1803.

Lichen encaustus J. E. Smith, Trans. Linn. Soc. 1:83. pl. 4, f. 6. 1791.

Thallus middle-sized, loosely adnate, greenish gray to ashy, the crowded, wrinkled lobes finally narrowed, round, much branched, interwoven, slightly inflated, with round margins; brownish black below and without rhizoids; apothecia middle-sized to large, 3–12 mm. across, sessile, the disk flat to slightly convex, chestnut-brown, the exciple crenulate; spores ellipsoid to ovoid-ellipsoid, 7–10 × 5–7 μ.

On trees and rocks, Colorado and the White Mountains.

8. **Parmelia pertusa** (Schrank.) Schaer., Lich. Helv. Spic. 10:457. 1839.

Lichen pertusus Schrank., Baier. Fl. 2:519. 1789.

Thallus middle-sized or larger, usually shining, greenish gray to whitish, closely adnate, inflated, perforated by round to oblong holes, bearing scattered, round, white soredia, the lobes crowded, freely branching and often imbricated, their margins scarcely ascending; black below, or brownish toward the margins, wrinkled and without rhizoids; apothecia rare, small to middle-sized, 3–8 mm. across, the disk chestnut-brown, the exciple entire; spores 2–4, ellipsoid, 45–60 × 22–28 μ. (PLATE 34.)

On trees and rarely on rocks, New England, Ohio, Minnesota, and Washington.

9. **Parmelia coralloidea** (Meyen & Flot.) Vainio, Act. Soc. Faun. Flor. Fenn. 7:33, 34. 1890.

P. perlata var. *coralloidea* Meyen & Flot., Act. Acad. Caes. Leop. Car. Suppl. 19:219. 1843.

Thallus large, loosely adnate, greenish gray to ashy white, bearing short, slender coralloid branchlets toward the center, the lobes large, not much elongated, ascending toward the entire to wavy-crenate margins; black below with scattered, short, black rhizoids, light or darker brown toward the margins; apothecia middle-sized to large, 5–14 mm. across, perforate at the center, subpedicellate, the disk deeply concave, light to darker brown, the exciple subentire, finally bearing coralloid branchlets; spores ellipsoid, 10–14 × 5.5–9 μ.

On trees, Georgia, Florida, and Louisiana.

10. **Parmelia latissima** Fée, Suppl. Essai Crypt. 119. pl. 38, f. 4. 1837.

P. perlata var. *latissima* Mont.

Thallus middle-sized to large, adnate, whitish to greenish gray, naked or bearing coralloid branchlets, the lobes short, wide, sparingly branched, the margins round, entire to wavy; black below, brown toward the margins, rhizoids small and scattered, black; apothecia small to middle-sized, 3–8 mm. across, subsessile, the disk concave, chestnut-brown, the exciple with entire or irregular margin, sometimes bearing coralloid granules; spores ellipsoid, 22–34 × 11–20 μ.

On trees and fences, South Carolina, Georgia, Florida, Louisiana, and Texas.

var. **sorediata** Nyl.; Hue, Nouv. Arch. Mus. III. 2:282. 1890.

The margins of the lobes sorediate, and coralloid branchlets rarely if ever present.

On trees, Florida.

11. **Parmelia crinita** Ach., Syn. Meth. Lich. 196. 1814.

P. crinita var. *pilosella* (Hue) Merrill.

Thallus becoming large, rather loosely adnate, lighter to darker greenish gray, densely covered with granules or coralloid branchlets, the broad, wrinkled lobes often ascending slightly, with inconspicuously ciliate, irregular or crenate margins; black below and clothed with strong rhizoids of the same color, often brown toward the margins; apothecia rare, subpedicellate, small to middle-sized, 4–12 mm. across, the disk deeply concave, chestnut-brown, the exciple irregular or crenate, sometimes bearing cilia or coralloid branchlets; spores ellipsoid, 17–22 × 9–15 μ.

On trees and rarely on rocks, throughout the United States.

12. **Parmelia cristifera** Tayl., in Hook., Journ. Bot. 6:165. 1847.

Thallus middle-sized to large, adnate, greenish gray to whitish, the lobes short, broad, subimbricate toward the center, the margins raised and sometimes bearing globose soredia, or these fusing into soralia; black below and bearing few rhizoids toward the center, brownish and smooth toward the edges; apothecia small to middle-sized, 3–8 mm. across, subsessile, the disk concave, chestnut-brown, the exciple thin, colored like the thallus, becoming wavy; spores ellipsoid, 20–30 × 10–18 μ.

On trees, Florida.

13. **Parmelia olivaria** (Ach.) T. Fries, Lich. Scand. 1:112. 1871.

P. perlata var. *olivaria* Ach., Meth. Lich. 217. 1803.

Thallus middle-sized, loosely adnate, smooth, ashy to greenish gray or yellowish brown, the lobes wide and short, ascending and often bearing white soredia at least toward the entire to wavy-crenate margins; black below and bearing scattered black rhizoids; apothecia middle-sized, 3–7 mm. across, subsessile, the disk concave to flat, chestnut-brown, the exciple entire, sometimes sorediate; spores ellipsoid, 14–18 × 7–12 μ.

On trees, Rockland, Maine, sterile, and doubtfully admitted.

14. **Parmelia perlata** (L.) Ach., Meth. Lich. 216, 217. 1803.

Lichen perlatus L., Syst. Nat. ed. 12. 712. 1770. *P. perlata* var. *ciliata* (Lam. & DC.) Duby.

Thallus middle-sized to large, adnate, pale or darker greenish gray, the lobes rather large, not much elongated, often more or less branched, often imbricated, slightly ascending toward the often white-sorediate, rarely ciliate, wavy to crenate margins; black below, brown toward the margins, usually bearing scattered black rhizoids; apothecia middle-sized, 4–12 mm. across, the disk concave, chestnut-brown, the exciple entire; spores short-ellipsoid, 10–17 × 6–10 μ.

On rocks and rarely on trees, throughout northern United States, especially in the mountain areas.

15. **Parmelia cetrata** Ach., Syn. Meth. Lich. 198. 1814.

Thallus large, adnate, light or darker greenish gray, sometimes becoming wrinkled toward the center, the lobes short and wide or elongated and branched, wavy-incised, usually ascending toward the more or less sorediate or rarely ciliate margins; black below with rhizoids of the same color, usually brown toward the margins; apothecia middle-sized to large, 4–15 mm. across, subpedicellate, the disk chestnut-brown, more or less deeply concave, commonly perforate at the center, the exciple entire to crenate; spores oblong-ellipsoid, 10–16 × 6–8 μ.

On trees, old wood, and rocks, widely distributed throughout the United States, but usually sterile.

16. **Parmelia Finkii** Zahlbr.; Hedrick, Mycologia 26:162. 1934.

Thallus small, adnate, greenish gray to ashy, bearing small coralloid branchlets of the same colors, the lobes becoming moderately elongated and laterally branched, sometimes imbricated, the tips entire or rarely crenate, often narrowed; black and roughened below, with few and scattered obscure rhizoids; apothecia small, 2–3 mm. across, the disk concave, chestnut-brown, the exciple crenate to obscurely coralloid-lobed; spores oblong-ellipsoid, 8–11 × 4.5–6 μ.

On bark and on mosses over the bark, Wayne County, Missouri.

17. **Parmelia caroliniana** Nyl., Flora 68:614. 1885.

Thallus middle-sized, grayish white, more or less roughened and reticulated, becoming sparingly fibrillose and bearing coralloid branchlets, the lobes somewhat narrow, with wavy-incised margins; brownish black below, with scattered rhizoids; apothecia small, 2–3 mm. across, the disk concave, brick-red to chestnut-brown, the exciple entire, bearing obscure coralloid branchlets; spores ellipsoid, 12–14 × 6–7 μ.

On trees, South Carolina.

18. **Parmelia saxatilis** (L.) Ach., Meth. Lich. 204, 205. 1803.

Lichen saxatilis L., Sp. Pl. 1142. 1753. *P. saxatilis* var. *furfuracea* Schaer. *P. saxatilis* var. *laevis* Nyl. *P. saxatilis* f. *panniformis* (Ach.) Schaer.

Thallus middle-sized, rather closely adnate, smooth to obscurely wrinkled, greenish gray to ashy or rarely brown, often bearing coralloid granules or branchlets, the lobes commonly long, narrow, and subdichotomously branched, with wavy margins; black below, or brown toward the margins, covered with black rhizoids; apothecia rare, middle-sized to large, 4–12 mm. across, subsessile, the disk concave or deeply concave, chestnut-brown, the exciple irregular or crenulate; spores ellipsoid, 10–20 × 7–12 μ.

On trees, wood, and rocks, northern United States, but rare southward (the plants on rocks are usually smaller).

19. **Parmelia frondifera** Merrill, Bryologist 11:91. 1908.

Thallus small to middle-sized or rarely larger, round to expanded, more or less closely adnate, greenish gray to more commonly brownish, irregularly lobed, the lobes divided and often much imbricated, more or less covered with minute, finely divided lobules; white within; black below or brownish toward the margins, bearing short black or brownish rhizoids; apothecia rather large, short-pedicellate, the disk deeply concave, light chestnut-brown, the exciple radiately rugose and sometimes fissured; spores oblong-ellipsoid, 10 × 5–7 μ.

On old wood and trees, New York, North Carolina, and Florida (herbarium specimen sterile, the apothecial characters taken from Merrill).

20. **Parmelia lophyrea** Ach., Meth. Lich. 198. 1803.

P. cribellata Tayl.

Thallus small, loosely adnate, greenish gray to ashy, rarely sorediate, the lobes narrow, not much elongated, more or less branched, flat, sometimes lacunulose, the margins cut-crenate; black below and reticulately pitted or finally perforate, without rhizoids; apothecia small to middle-sized, 3–11 mm. across, subsessile, the disk concave to flat or possibly convex, chestnut-brown, the exciple entire to sub-crenate; spores spherical, 3.5–4.5 μ in diameter.

On trees, Washington, Oregon, and California.

21. **Parmelia texana** Tuck., Am. Journ. Sci. II. 25:424. 1858.

Thallus small to middle-sized, adnate, greenish gray, varying toward ashy, becoming reticulately cracked, bearing round, finally confluent soredia, the lobes narrow, becoming long and subdichotomously branched, expanded toward the torn-crenate to lobulate margins; black and papillate below, without rhizoids; apothecia middle-sized, 4–10 mm. across, the disk concave, chestnut-brown, the exciple entire; spores ellipsoid, 11–15 × 4.5–5.5 μ.

On old wood, Texas (near *P. quercina* and *P. Borreri*).

22. **Parmelia sulcata** Tayl., in Mack., Fl. Hibern. 2:145. 1856.

P. saxatilis var. *rosaeformis* Ach. *P. saxatilis* var. *sulcata* (Tayl.) Linds.

Thallus middle-sized to large, adnate, ashy or less often greenish gray, usually smooth, bearing round to oblong, whitish, finally confluent soredia, the lobes usually broad, oblong to linear, often imbricated, with round, angular, or wavy margins; black below, varying to brown toward the margins, bearing numerous black rhizoids; apothecia rare, middle-sized or larger, 4–12 mm. across, sessile to subsessile, the disk concave to deeply concave, chestnut-brown, the exciple entire to crenulate or irregular; spores short-ellipsoid, 9–15 × 6–9 μ.

On trees and rarely on rocks, throughout northern United States.

23. **Parmelia submarginalis** (Michx.) Nyl., Flora 68:607. 1885.

Lobaria submarginalis Michx., Flor. Am. Bor. 2:325. 1803.

Thallus middle-sized to large, greenish gray, adnate, smooth to rough, the lobes broad, becoming crenate and more or less ciliate; black and naked below; apothecia middle-sized to large, 10–20 mm. across, the disk concave, often perforate, chestnut-brown, the exciple colored like the thallus; spores ovoid-ellipsoid, 14–18 × 8–12 μ.

On trees, the Carolinas, and near New Bedford, Massachusetts.

24. **Parmelia subrugata** Nyl., Flora 52:291. 1869.

Thallus middle-sized to large, adnate, greenish gray varying toward brown, the lobes short and wide to longer and branched, ascending toward the wavy-incised margins, the margins bearing strong, dark rhizoids; black and naked below, pale toward the margins; apothecia middle-sized to large, 4–12 mm. across, sub-pedicellate, the disk deeply concave and becoming perforate at the center, chestnut-brown, the exciple torn-crenate to lobulate, pitted on the outside; spores oblong-ellipsoid, 30–40 × 18–27 μ.

On trees, near New Bedford, Massachusetts. It may be but a form of *Parmelia perforata* (Wulf.) Ach.

25. **Parmelia perforata** (Wulf.) Ach., Meth. Lich. 217. 1803.

Lichen perforatus Wulf., in Jacq., Coll. Bot. 1:116. 1786. *P. perforata* var.
corrugis E. Fries.

Thallus middle-sized to large, adnate, greenish gray to whitish, frequently wrinkled toward the center, the lobes wide, not much elongated, more or less branched and sometimes imbricated, with round, ciliate, subentire to crenate or irregular margins; brownish black to black below, usually brown toward the margins, and bearing strong, black rhizoids; apothecia middle-sized to very large, 5–24 mm. across, subsessile, the disk deeply concave and commonly perforate toward the center, chestnut-brown, the exciple entire to crenate; spores ellipsoid, 9–14 × 6–8 μ.

On trees and rarely on rocks, throughout the United States.

26. **Parmelia hypotrypodes** (Nyl.) Willey, Bot. Gaz. 21:204, 205. 1896.
    P. cetrata var. *hypotrypodes* Nyl. in Litt.
    Thallus large, greenish gray to brownish, wrinkled and folded, the lobes round, more or less crenate, or elongated into narrow, flat divisions, the margins ciliate; black below with black rhizoids; apothecia large, 4–12 mm. across, sessile, perforate, the disk concave to flat, chestnut-brown to darker, the exciple thin, colored like the thallus, slightly wavy; spores ellipsoid, 9–17 × 6–9 μ.
    On trees, near New Bedford, Massachusetts.

27. **Parmelia proboscidea** Tayl., in Mack., Fl. Hibern. 2:143. 1836.
    Thallus middle-sized to large, loosely adnate, round, irregularly lobed, greenish gray to whitish, lobes convex or flat, smooth, often imbricated, with ascending or recurved, crenate and scarcely ciliate margins; black to brownish below, and densely covered with rhizoids toward the center; apothecia small to middle-sized, 0.8–4 mm. across, sessile or subsessile, the disk deeply concave, chestnut-brown or lighter, the exciple colored like the thallus, becoming wavy; spores ellipsoid, 12–23 × 8–12 μ.
    On trees, Florida.

28. **Parmelia atrofusca** (Schaer.) Comb., Grevill. 7:99. 1879.
    P. ceratophylla var. *atrofusca* Schaer., Lich. Eur. 42. 1850. *P. alpicola* T. Fries.
    P. encausta var. *alpicola* (T. Fries) Nyl.
    Thallus middle-sized, loosely adnate, black, varying to greenish olivaceous or greenish gray, the lobes very narrow, irregular and crowded, convex, often more or less wrinkled and imbricated, not inflated; very black below with few fibrils; apothecia middle-sized, 3–7 mm. across, sessile, the disk concave, becoming black, the exciple entire; spores subspherical to ellipsoid, 7–12 × 5–9 μ.
    On alpine rocks, New Hampshire and Oregon.

29. **Parmelia sublaevigata** Nyl., Ann. Sci. Nat. Bot. V. 7:306. 1867.
    P. tiliacea var. *sublaevigata* Nyl., Syn. Meth. Lich. 1:383. 1858. *P. subquercifolia* Hue.
    Thallus middle-sized, adnate, greenish gray, the lobes elongated, narrow, subpinnately branched, the margins wavy-incised; black below, densely covered with black rhizoids; apothecia small to middle-sized, 3–10 mm. across, subsessile, the disk deeply to slightly concave, chestnut-brown, the exciple subentire to crenate; spores short-ellipsoid, 7–11 × 5–7 μ.
    On trees and rocks, Massachusetts, Louisiana, Florida, Nebraska, and Minnesota.

30. **Parmelia quercina** (Willd.) Vainio, Term. Füz. 22:279. 1899.
    Lichen quercinus Willd., Fl. Berol. Prod. 353. pl. 7, f. 13. 1787. *P. tiliacea* (Hoffm.) Ach. *P. vicinior* Hue.
    Thallus closely adnate, rather small, greenish gray, commonly wrinkled, especially toward the center, the lobes short and round or rarely elongated and subdichotomously branched, the margins irregular or crenate; black below and densely covered with black rhizoids; apothecia middle-sized, 4–12 mm. across, subsessile, the disk slightly to deeply concave, chestnut-brown, the exciple subentire to much more commonly crenate; spores short-ellipsoid, 5–11 × 4–7 μ.
    On trees, wood, and rocks, throughout the United States.

    f. **minor** (Kremphl.) Zahlbr., Cat. Lich. Univ. 6:190. 1929.
    P. tiliacea f. *minor* Kremphl., Reise Oest. Bot. 1:115. 1870.
    Thallus wrinkled toward the center and smooth toward the margins, the lobes much shorter and narrower than in the species and the branching dichotomous and finally pinnatifid.
    On trees, Louisiana and Texas.

31. **Parmelia sulphurosa** (Tuck.) Fink n. comb.
    P. tiliacea var. *sulphurosa* Tuck., Syn. N. A. Lich. 1:57. 1882. *P. quercina* var. *sulphurosa* (Tuck.) Zahlbr.

Thallus small to middle-sized, adnate, greenish gray, usually more or less wrinkled, sulphur-yellow within, the lobes short or more or less elongated and branched, the margins entire to crenate; black below and bearing black rhizoids; apothecia middle-sized, 3–10 mm. across, subsessile, the disk more or less concave, chestnut-brown, the exciple entire to crenate; spores short-ellipsoid, 6–10 × 4–6 μ.
On trees, Illinois.

32. **Parmelia colpodes** (Ach.) Nyl., Syn. Meth. Lich. 404. 1858.
Lichen colpodes Ach., Lich. Suec. 124. 1798. *P. cristulata* Ach. *Imbricaria convexiuscula* Michx. *Anzia colpodes* (Ach.) Stizenb.
Thallus thin and rather flat, grayish green, varying toward whitish or brownish, the lobes deeply much-branched, radiately clustered toward the margins; covered below by a dense, spongy, dark brown to black nap and scattered coarse rhizoids; apothecia small to middle-sized, 3–8 mm. across, sessile to subpedicellate, the disk concave, chestnut-brown and becoming darker, the exciple entire; spores many, oblong or club-shaped, often curved, 3–6 × 1.2–2 μ.
On trees, throughout eastern United States, west to Louisiana and Nebraska.

33. **Parmelia sphaerosporella** Müll. Arg., Flora 74:378. 1891.
Thallus small to middle-sized, adnate, greenish yellow, roughened and folded, the lobes wide, closely placed toward the center, but spreading and branched toward the obtuse, crenate margins; pale below and bearing pale rhizoids; apothecia small to middle-sized, 3–6 mm. across, the disk deeply concave to flat, flesh-colored to brown, the exciple entire, narrow, and externally rough; spores spherical, 5–7 μ in diameter.
On trees, Montana, Oregon, and California.

34. **Parmelia leucochlora** Tuck., Syn. N. A. Lich. 1:64. 1882.
P. conspersa var. *leucochlora* Tuck., in Nyl., Syn. Meth. Lich. 1:392. 1858.
Thallus small to middle-sized, adnate, roughened, greenish gray to yellowish straw-colored, the lobes flat, rather narrow, becoming elongated and branched, often imbricated, the margins wavy to crenate; light- to chestnut-brown below with darker rhizoids; apothecia small, 2–5 mm. across, sessile, the disk concave, chestnut-brown, the exciple entire to subentire; spores ovoid-ellipsoid, 7–10 × 5–7 μ.
Commonly on bald cypresses, from South Carolina to Florida, and westward to Missouri and Arkansas.

35. **Parmelia centrifuga** (L.) Ach., Meth. Lich. 206. 1803.
Lichen centrifugus L., Sp. Pl. 1142. 1753.
Thallus small, adnate, yellowish or greenish straw-colored, the central crust of convex, imbricated, wrinkled, frequently disappearing lobes, the marginal lobes more elongated, with sinuous, crenate, or incised margins; white below, with darker rhizoids; apothecia small to middle-sized, 3–8 mm. across, sessile, the disk concave, chestnut-brown, the exciple subcrenulate; spores ellipsoid, 7–10 × 4.5–5.5 μ.
On rocks, Maine, New Hampshire, Massachusetts, and Minnesota.

36. **Parmelia incurva** (Pers.) E. Fries, Sched. Crit. Lich. Exsicc. Suec. fasc. 9. 31. 1826.
Lichen incurvus Pers., Ann. Bot. Usteri 1:24. 1794. *P. recurva* Ach.
Thallus middle-sized, loosely adnate, varying from greenish to yellowish straw-colored, bearing raised whitish to sulphur-colored soredia, the lobes narrow, strongly convex, much branched, the branches crowded and often imbricated, the margins somewhat incurved; pale below with blackening rhizoids; apothecia small to middle-sized, 3–7 mm. across, the disk concave to flat, chestnut- to darker brown, the exciple subentire; spores ellipsoid, 7–13 × 5–6 μ.
On granitic rocks, New Hampshire and Maine.

37. **Parmelia flavicans** Tuck., Syn. N. A. Lich. 1:53. 1882.
   P. perlata var. *flavicans* Tuck., Lich. Calif. 13. 1866.
   Thallus middle-sized, loosely adnate, pale yellow, smooth, bearing pale soredia, the lobes wide, not much elongated, with round, wavy-crenate margins; black below and brown toward the margins, black rhizoids scattered or absent; apothecia small to middle-sized, 3–7 mm. across, sessile, the disk concave, chestnut-brown, the exciple entire; spores ellipsoid, 17–22 × 8–12 μ.
   On rocks, California.

38. **Parmelia praesignis** Nyl., Bull. Soc. Linn. Norm. II. 6:270. 1872.
   Thallus middle-sized to large, loosely adnate, smooth to wrinkled, greenish yellow to yellowish brown, the lobes irregular, broad, somewhat imbricated, the margins broadly crenate; black below, densely wrinkled and bearing few black rhizoids; apothecia small to middle-sized, 1–3 mm. across, sessile, the disk concave, chestnut-brown to dark brown, the exciple thin, colored like the thallus or slightly darker, becoming obscurely wavy; hypothecium hyaline; spores ovoid, 13–16 × 6–9 μ.
   On trees, Arizona. Material scanty and doubtfully admitted.

39. **Parmelia arizonica** (Tuck.) Nyl., Lich. Jap. 104. 1890.
   Omphalodium hottentottum var. *arizonicum* Tuck.; Willey, Bull. Torr. Club 8:140. 1881. *Omphalodium arizonicum* Tuck.
   Thallus small to middle-sized, irregularly lobed, minutely wrinkled, becoming ridged, greenish gray to yellowish or yellowish green, the lobes few, broad, with crenate margins; black and ridged below, and densely covered with minute black tubercles; apothecia small to middle-sized, 1.5–5 mm. across, sessile to subsessile, the disk concave to slightly convex, chestnut-brown to brownish black, the exciple thin, colored like the thallus, becoming flexuous and subcrenate, rarely blackening; asci becoming ventricose; spores ellipsoid, 8–14 × 6–8 μ.
   On rocks, Nevada, Arizona, and New Mexico.

40. **Parmelia caperata** (L.) Ach., Meth. Lich. 216. 1803.
   Lichen caperatus L., Sp. Pl. 1147. 1753. *P. cylisphora* (Ach.) Vainio.
   Thallus middle-sized to large, closely adnate, straw-colored to yellowish or whitish, commonly more or less wrinkled and often bearing soredia or coralloid branchlets, the lobes short and wide, more or less branched, with incised, crenate or subentire, ascending margins; black below with rhizoids of the same color, except toward the margins, where lighter colored, usually with lighter colored rhizoids; apothecia sessile, middle-sized, 4–12 mm. across, rarely present, the disk concave, chestnut-brown, the exciple subentire to crenulate, and frequently bearing soredia or coralloid branchlets; spores 13–20 × 7–10 μ. (PLATE 35.)
   On trees, old wood, and rocks, throughout the United States.

41. **Parmelia ulophylla** (Ach.) Merrill, Bryologist 11:91, 92. 1908.
   P. caperata var. *ulophylla* Ach., Lich. Univ. 458. 1810.
   Thallus middle-sized to large, almost round, greenish yellow to brownish, densely wrinkled and folded, granulose and often whitish sorediate or soraliate toward the center, the lobes marginal, convex or flat, with ascending, cut-crenate margins; black below, and brownish toward the margin, with few and scattered rhizoids; apothecia rare, small to middle-sized, 5–10 mm. across, subsessile, the disk concave, chestnut-brown, the exciple colored like the thallus, slightly crenate and sometimes externally sorediate; spores ellipsoid, 14–18 × 6–9 μ.
   On trees, North Carolina and New Mexico.

42. **Parmelia sulphurata** Nees & Flot., Linnaea 9:501. 1834.
   P. chrysantha Tuck.
   Thallus middle-sized to large, loosely adnate, greenish yellow, bearing granules or coralloid branchlets, sulphur-colored within, the lobes broad and wrinkled, becoming more or less branched, with crenate, ciliate margins; black below with black rhizoids, often brown toward the margins; apothecia rare, subsessile, small

to middle-sized, 3–10 mm. across, the disk deeply concave, chestnut-brown, the exciple entire to crenate; spores ellipsoid, 18–24 × 7–13 μ.

On trees, from Virginia to Florida and westward to Texas (possibly a color form of *Parmelia crinita* Ach.).

43. **Parmelia aurulenta** Tuck., Am. Journ. Sci. II. 25:424. 1858.

Thallus small to middle-sized, adnate, greenish to yellowish gray, wrinkled, sprinkled over more or less densely with whitish or yellowish, often confluent soredia, sulphur-yellow internally, the lobes short and wide, somewhat branched, with round, entire to irregular margins; brownish black to black below with blackening rhizoids; apothecia small to middle-sized, 5–10 mm. across, subsessile, the disk concave, chestnut-brown, the exciple entire to wavy-crenate; spores ellipsoid, 10–16 × 4–7 μ.

On trees and rocks, from the White Mountains westward to Minnesota, and southward to Alabama and Louisiana.

44. **Parmelia soredica** Nyl., Flora 68:605. 1885.

Thallus large, adnate, greenish gray to yellowish green, bearing white soredia and breaking away centrally, the lobes rather wide, more or less branched, the peripheral ascending lobes wavy-crenate, the other lobes ascending and confluently white-sorediate; black below, often brown and rarely bearing black rhizoids toward the margins; apothecia middle-sized, 4–10 mm. across, sessile, the disk concave, chestnut-brown, the exciple entire to lobulate, usually sorediate; spores short-ellipsoid, 11–14 × 6–8 μ.

On trees, old wood, and rocks, Santa Cruz Peninsula, California.

45. **Parmelia scortella** Nyl., Flora 68:615. 1885.

Thallus small to middle-sized or rarely larger, thin, closely adnate, greenish to yellowish gray, the lobes short to somewhat elongated, subdichotomously branched, more or less covered by minute coralloid branchlets; black below, with many black rhizoids; apothecia small, 2–6 mm. across, subsessile, the disk slightly concave to flat or slightly convex, chestnut-brown, the exciple entire to crenate and bearing minute coralloid branchlets; spores short-ellipsoid, 8–10 × 4–5 μ.

On trees, Texas (doubtfully admitted).

46. **Parmelia conspersa** (Ehrh.) Ach., Meth. Lich. 205. 1803.

Lichen conspersus Ehrh.; Ach., Lich. Suec. 118. 1798. *P. conspersa* var. *stenophylla* Ach. *P. subconspersa* Nyl. *P. conspersa* var. *imbricata* Mass. *P. conspersa* f. *isidiata* Anzi.

Thallus closely adnate, middle-sized or larger, straw-colored, varying toward greenish or yellowish, smooth or somewhat wrinkled, often sorediate or bearing coralloid branchlets toward the center, the lobes long and rather narrow, crowded and often imbricated, sometimes much branched, the margins wavy to crenate, the imbricated central lobes often forming a continuous crust; black below with brown margins, dark rhizoids usually present; apothecia subsessile, small to middle-sized, 3–12 mm. across, the disk concave, chestnut-brown, the exciple subentire to crenulate; spores ellipsoid, 8–12 × 4.5–7 μ.

On rocks and rarely on wood, throughout northern United States, and southward in the mountains.

47. **Parmelia laevigata** (J. E. Smith) Ach., Syn. Meth. Lich. 212. 1814.

Lichen laevigatus J. E. Smith, in Sowerby, Engl. Bot. 24: pl. 1852. 1808. *P. laevigata* var. *sinuosa* (Ach.) Nyl.

Thallus thin, smooth, middle-sized, loosely adnate, pale yellowish to light greenish gray, sometimes sorediate, the lobes narrow, often imbricated, with crenate margins; black below with middle-sized black rhizoids; apothecia small to middle-sized, 3–6 mm. across, the disk concave, chestnut-brown, the exciple entire to serrate; spores ellipsoid, 12–22 × 6–10 μ.

On trees and rocks, from Florida to Louisiana, and doubtfully northward to New England, and in Illinois.

48. **Parmelia molliuscula** Ach., Lich. Univ. 492. 1810.
    P. chlorochroa Tuck. *P. molliuscula* var. *vagans* Nyl.
    Thallus middle-sized, procumbent, subfruticose, straw-colored, the lobes narrow, substellate or loosely entangled, repeatedly dichotomously or irregularly branched, the branches convex, with recurved margins; brownish black to black below, channeled, and bearing rhizoids; apothecia extremely rare, middle-sized, 2–6 mm. across, subsessile, the disk concave to flat, chestnut-brown, the exciple entire to subcrenate; spores ellipsoid, 4–5.5 × 9.5–10.5 μ.
    On soil, from Nebraska to North Dakota, and westward into the Rocky Mountains.

49. **Parmelia aspidota** (Ach.) Röhling, Deutschl. Fl. 3²:100. 1813.
    P. olivacea var. *aspidota* Ach., Meth. Lich. 214. 1803. *P. olivacea* var. *exasperata* (Ach.) Nyl.
    Thallus small to middle-sized, closely adnate, pale to darker olivaceous, more or less wrinkled and covered with minute warts or coralloid branchlets, the lobes moderately wide, sometimes branched and imbricated, the margins entire to crenate; brownish black below with scattered brown to black rhizoids; apothecia small to middle-sized, 3–6 mm. across, subsessile, the disk concave to flat, chestnut-brown or darker, the exciple thin, becoming warty or covered with minute coralloid branchlets; spores ovoid-ellipsoid, 7–10 × 5–7 μ.
    On trees and wood, throughout the northern states, and southward, especially in the mountains.

50. **Parmelia conspurcata** (Schaer.) Vainio, Medd. Soc. Faun. Flor. Fenn. 14:22. 1888.
    P. olivacea var. *corticola* f. *conspurcata* Schaer., Lich. Helv. Spic. 10:466. 1840.
    P. verruculifera Nyl.
    Thallus middle-sized or larger, loosely adnate, olivaceous, more or less wrinkled, usually bearing whitening coralloid branchlets or soredia, the lobes rather broad and short or somewhat elongated, radiate and often branched, sometimes imbricated, the margins often ascending more or less, wavy or crenate, rarely white-powdery; black or blackish below, except the brown areas toward the margins, and bearing blackish rhizoids; apothecia middle-sized, 4–7 mm. across, subsessile, the disk concave, chestnut-brown, the exciple crenate and often wrinkled; spores oblong-ellipsoid, 9–15 × 6–8 μ.
    On trees and rarely on rocks, Massachusetts, Minnesota, Iowa, and California.

51. **Parmelia sorediata** (Ach.) Röhling, Deutschl. Fl. 3²:103. 1813.
    P. stygia var. *sorediata* Ach., Lich. Univ. 471. 1810. *P. prolixa* var. *sorediata* (Ach.) Nyl.
    Thallus small to middle-sized, closely adnate, olive-brown to brownish black, the central portions wrinkled and folded, covered usually thickly with whitish to greenish gray soredia, the lobes narrow and becoming long and digitately much-branched, with entire to obscurely crenate margins; black below with numerous fibrils of the same color; apothecia small to middle-sized, 3–7 mm. across, subsessile, the disk concave, of the same color as the thallus, the exciple entire; spores ellipsoid, 10–14 × 5–10 μ.
    On rocks, New England, New York, Ohio, Wyoming, New Mexico, and California.

52. **Parmelia omphalodes** (L.) Ach., Lich. Meth. 204. 1803.
    Lichen omphalodes L., Sp. Pl. 1143. 1753. *P. saxatilis* var. *omphalodes* E. Fries.
    Thallus small to middle-sized, loosely adnate, brown to brownish black, smooth and often shining, sometimes bearing coralloid branchlets, the lobes becoming long and narrow, branched and often imbricated; brownish black to black below and covered by black rhizoids; apothecia small to very large, 4–18 mm. across, sub-

sessile, becoming irregular, the disk concave, chestnut-brown and becoming darker, the exciple entire to crenulate or irregular; spores ellipsoid, 8–15 × 7–9 μ.
On rocks, White Mountains, New Hampshire.

53. **Parmelia prolixa** (Ach.) Röhling, Deutschl. Fl. 3:100. 1813.
    P. olivacea var. *prolixa* Ach., Meth. Lich. 214. 1803. *P. prolixa* var. *panniformis* Nyl.
    Thallus middle-sized, loosely adnate, olive-brown to brassy-chestnut, becoming wrinkled and bearing coralloid branchlets, the lobes short or becoming elongated, variously branched and often imbricated, sometimes ascending toward the wavy to crenate-cut margins; darker and blackening below, with black rhizoids; apothecia small to middle-sized, 3–6 mm. across, the disk concave, brown to brownish black, the exciple entire to subcrenate; spores short-ellipsoid, 8–11 × 5–7 μ.
    On rocks, New England, Illinois, South Dakota, Minnesota, Wyoming, and California.

54. **Parmelia multispora** Schneider, Guide Stud. Lich. 154, 155. 1904.
    P. olivacea var. *multispora* (Schneider) Merrill.
    Thallus small, possibly reaching middle-size, adnate, olive-brown, lobes wide and short, little branched, the margins round, entire to incised; black below with short, black rhizoids, brown and naked toward the margins; apothecia small to middle-sized, 2–6 mm. across, subsessile, the disk concave to flat, chestnut-brown, the exciple entire to crenulate; spores 16–24 or possibly even 100, ovoid, 8–9 × 5–8 μ, or spherical and 6–8 μ in diameter.
    On trees and shrubs, Utah, Idaho, Washington, and California.

55. **Parmelia glabra** (Schaer.) Nyl., Flora 55:548. 1872.
    P. olivacea var. *corticola* f. *glabra* Schaer., Lich. Helv. Spic. 466. 1840.
    Thallus various shades of brown, often bright and shining, minutely wrinkled, wavy or radiately folded, smooth toward the round lobes, the margins crenate to irregularly cleft, the central lobes of the thallus often ascending or erect; dark brown to black below, with brown margins, and bearing brown to black rhizoids; apothecia small to middle-sized, 0.8–3 mm. across, sessile, the disk strongly concave, chestnut-brown, the exciple colored like the thallus, becoming erect and coarsely crenate; hypothecium hyaline; spores ellipsoid, 12–18 × 6–9 μ.
    On rocks and mosses, Nevada, New Mexico, and California (may not be distinct from *Parmelia conspurcata*).

56. **Parmelia olivacea** (L.) Ach., Meth. Lich. 213. 1803.
    Lichen olivaceus L., Sp. Pl. 1143. 1753. *P. subolivacea* Nyl.
    Thallus small to middle-sized, closely adnate, pale to darker olivaceous, becoming wrinkled, the lobes moderately wide and not much elongated, often radiately branched and sometimes imbricated, the margins entire to wavy-crenate; olivaceous to more commonly black below, with scattered brown to black rhizoids; apothecia small to middle-sized, 3–7 mm. across, subsessile, the disk concave to flat, chestnut-brown or darker, the exciple entire to crenulate; spores ovoid-ellipsoid, 7–16 × 6–10 μ.
    On trees and wood, throughout northern United States, and southward, especially in the mountains.

57. **Parmelia stygia** (L.) Ach., Meth. Lich. 203. 1803.
    Lichen stygius L., Sp. Pl. 1143. 1753.
    Thallus small, loosely adnate, olivaceous brown and shining, finally blackening, the lobes becoming linear, convex, palmately much-branched, the branches round, often twisted and more or less imbricated, the tips usually recurved; of nearly the same color but duller below, and sparingly rhizoid-bearing; apothecia small to middle-sized, 2–8 mm. across, the disk slightly concave, chestnut-brown to black, the exciple subgranular; spores subspherical to short-ellipsoid, 5–12 × 5–7 μ.
    On rocks, mostly at high altitudes, from New England westward to Wyoming, and doubtfully to Washington.

OTHER SPECIES REPORTED

Parmelia cetrarioides Del.—Massachusetts.
Parmelia endoxantha Merrill—Florida.
Parmelia fuliginosa (Wibel) Nyl.—Washington.
Parmelia Halseyana Tuck.—New England.
Parmelia Herrei Zahlbr.—California.
Parmelia hypotropa var. sorediata Müll. Arg.—Texas.
Parmelia mesogens Nyl.—Washington.
Parmelia olivetorum (Ach.) Nyl.—Louisiana and southern California.
Parmelia oncodes Tuck.—Lake Superior region.
Parmelia phaea Tuck.—Pennsylvania.
Parmelia recipienda Nyl.—Louisiana.
Parmelia scortea Ach.—Louisiana.
Parmelia subcapitata Nyl.—Southern California.
Parmelia xanthomela Nyl.—Florida.

155. **Cetraria** Ach., Meth. Lich. 292. pl. 5, f. 3. 1803.

Thallus foliose or fruticose, foliose forms closely adnate or more or less ascendant, lobed, with well-developed cellular cortex above and below, the fruticose
forms cylindrico-compressed or more or less channeled, erect, branched; apothecia
small to large, round to irregular, sessile to subpedicellate, terminal or marginal,
the disk concave to convex, flesh-colored to brown, the exciple entire to more or
less irregular; hypothecium hyaline to brownish; hymenium hyaline below to more
commonly brownish above; paraphyses short, unbranched to branched; asci short,
clavate; spores 8, hyaline, non-septate, subellipsoid to subspherical.
    The algal host is Protococcus.

A. Thallus foliose to somewhat subfruticose
    B. Thallus greenish gray to yellowish or straw-colored, rarely darker
        C. Margins more or less sorediate or bearing spinules
            D. Margins more or less sorediate
                E. Soredia whitish or greenish gray
                    F. Thallus middle-sized to large, margins very irregular
                        G. Lobes broad to narrow, margins sometimes
                            extending into much-branched coralloid
                            branchlets . . . . 1. C. glauca
                        G. Lobes narrow to linear, the margins rarely
                            extending into short coralloid branchlets . . 2. C. Tuckermani
                    F. Thallus small, margins entire to crenulate . . . 3. C. Oakesiana
                E. Soredia yellowish . . . . 4. C. juniperina
            D. Margins beset with spinules . . . . 3. C. Oakesiana spinulosa
        C. Margins not sorediate or spinulose
            D. Lobes reticulately pitted
                E. Lobes broad . . . . 5. C. lacunosa
                E. Lobes narrow and elongated . . . . 7. C. stenophylla
            D. Lobes smooth to wrinkled . . . . 6. C. aurescens
    B. Thallus greenish gray to brownish or blackening
        C. Thallus small and often scanty
            D. Lobes short, margins undulate to crenate . . . . . 9. C. saepincola
            D. Lobes small, much divided, margins toothed . . . . . 8. C. Fendleri
        C. Thallus middle-sized to larger, abundant
            D. Margins not sorediate
                E. Lobes narrow and much branched
                    F. On trees; thallus greenish gray to brownish, margins
                        ascending, sometimes ciliate . . . . 12. C. ciliaris
                    F. On rocks; thallus dusky brown to blackening,
                        closely adnate . . . . 11. C. fahlunensis
                E. Lobes broad, not much branched . . . . . 13. C. platyphylla
            D. Margins usually sorediate . . . . 10. C. chlorophylla
A. Thallus subfruticose to fruticose
    B. Thallus straw-colored, yellowish or greenish to rarely brown
        C. Lobes narrow, smooth, rarely divided above . . . . . 14. C. cucullata

    C. Lobes somewhat broad to narrow, more or less channeled
        or pitted, repeatedly divided above . . . . 15. C. nivalis
  B. Thallus greenish gray to brownish or blackening
    C. Thallus without spinules
      D. Lobes round to compressed in section . . . . 20. C. tristis
      D. Lobes flat . . . . 16. C. californica
    C. Thallus with spinules
      D. Lobes round to compressed in section . . . . . . 19. C. aculeata
      D. Lobes expanded with inrolled margins
        E. Margins thickly spinulose, usually with soredia below . 17. C. islandica
        E. Margins spinulose above, entire below without soredia . 18. C. hiascens

1. **Cetraria glauca** (L.) Ach., Meth. Lich. 296, 297. 1803.
  Lichen glaucus L., Sp. Pl. 1148. 1753.
  Thallus middle-sized to large, foliose, wavy to laciniately lobed, greenish gray iately lobed, the lobes irregular, narrow to linear, elongated, often much branched, smooth to lacunose, the margins often ascending, entire to crenate, often jagged or curled, the edges sometimes prolonged into coralloid branchlets, frequently sorediate; pale to dusky brown, becoming black, more or less wrinkled, sometimes with rhizoids below; apothecia rare, middle-sized to large, 6–14 mm. across, adnate, marginal to submarginal, the disk chestnut-brown, the exciple irregular and disappearing; spores ellipsoid, 4.5–9 × 3.5–5 μ.
  On trees and old wood, across the northern portion of the United States.

2. **Cetraria Tuckermani** Herre, Proc. Wash. Acad. Sci. 7:340. 1906.
  C. glauca var. *stenophylla* Tuck. name preoccupied.
  Thallus middle-sized to large, foliose, greenish gray to pale yellowish, laciniately lobed, the lobes irregular, narrow to linear, elongated, often much branched, smooth to channeled or lacunose, the margins often ascending, entire to crenate, often jagged or curled, frequently sorediate; pale to dusky brown, becoming black, usually reticulate-lacunose below; sterile.
  On trees, Washington, Oregon, and California.

3. **Cetraria Oakesiana** Tuck., Bost. Journ. Nat. Hist. 3:445. 1841.
  Thallus small, foliose, greenish gray to straw-colored, irregularly lobed, the lobes loosely separated to compact, often long, branched, flat to curled, the margins often undulate, entire to somewhat crenulate, whitish sorediate; brownish with dark rhizoids below; apothecia marginal, small to middle-sized, 2–6 mm. across, sessile, the disk concave to irregular; spores round-ellipsoid to longer, 5–10 × 4.5–6 μ.
  On trees and rocks, New Hampshire, Massachusetts, New York, Maryland, the Carolinas, and Georgia (rarely fertile except in alpine areas).
  var. **spinulosa** Merrill, Bryologist 13:25. 1910.
  Thallus marginally beset with scattered or abundant, short to somewhat elongated, dentate spinules.
  On trees, West Virginia (description compiled).

4. **Cetraria juniperina** (L.) Ach., Meth. Lich. 298. 1803.
  Lichen juniperinus L., Sp. Pl. 1147. 1753. *C. juniperina* var. *pinastri* (Scop.)
  Ach. *C. juniperina* var. *terrestris* Schaer. *C. viridis* Schwein. *C. juniperina*
    var. *virescens* Tuck.
  Thallus small to middle-sized, foliose, greenish gray to straw-colored, the lobes small, narrow, irregularly divided, crowded, more or less lacunose, ascending, the margins curled, irregularly notched, crenate, often yellow-sorediate; paler to nearly the same color below; apothecia small to middle-sized, 2–6.5 mm. across, submarginal, sessile to subpedicellate, the disk concave to convex, chestnut-brown, exciple crenulate; spores subspherical to ellipsoid, 4.5–8 × 4–5.5 μ. (PLATE 36 a.)
  On rocks, soil, trees, and old wood, widely distributed throughout northern United States.

5. **Cetraria lacunosa** Ach., Meth. Lich. 295. pl. 5, f. 3. 1803.
Platysma lacunosum f. *atlanticum* (Tuck.) Nyl. *C. lacunosa* f. *cavernosa* (Menz.) Merrill.
Thallus foliose, middle-sized to large, greenish gray to straw-colored, the lobes crowded, wide, reticulately pitted, the margins ascending, torn-crenate; brownish to black below; apothecia middle-sized to large, 1–10 mm. across, numerous, sessile to subpedicellate, marginal to subterminal, frequently perforate in the center, the disk concave, chestnut-brown, the exciple thin, entire, sometimes disappearing; spores short-ellipsoid, 5–8 × 4–5 μ. (PLATE 36 b.)
On trees, throughout northern United States, and southward in the mountains.

6. **Cetraria aurescens** Tuck., Proc. Am. Acad. 1:208. 1848.
Thallus small to middle-sized, foliose, straw-colored to greenish gray, the lobes narrow, many-cleft, the margins ascending, laciniate, curled; pale below, with frequent pale to brownish rhizoids; apothecia middle-sized to large, 1–7 mm. across, marginal, subpedicellate, the disk concave to irregular, chestnut-brown, the exciple crenulate; spores subspherical to ellipsoid, 3–6 × 3–5 μ.
On conifers and old rails, from New England to Alabama, and westward to South Dakota and Minnesota.

7. **Cetraria stenophylla** (Tuck.) Merrill, Bryologist 13:27. 1910.
C. lacunosa var. *stenophylla* Tuck., Syn. N. A. Lich. 1:35. 1882.
Thallus foliose, middle-sized to large, greenish gray to straw-colored or brownish, much lobed, the lobes narrow, elongated, crowded, somewhat channeled, the margins ascending, irregularly torn-crenate; whitish to straw-colored or darker below; apothecia middle-sized to large, 1–10 mm. across, terminal, sessile to subpedicellate, the disk concave, irregular, chestnut-brown, the exciple thin, entire, sometimes disappearing; spores short-ellipsoid, 5–7 × 3.5–5 μ.
On trees, throughout northern United States, and in California.

8. **Cetraria Fendleri** (Nyl.) Tuck., Gen. Lich. 280. 1872.
Parmelia Fendleri Nyl., Syn. Meth. Lich. 1:309. 1860.
Thallus scanty to small, foliose, smooth, irregularly many-cleft, pale to brownish olive-green, the lobes irregular, very narrow, branched, becoming crowded and complicate, the margins toothed; pale and rough below with scattered pale rhizoids; apothecia numerous, small, 1–4 mm. across, marginal, the disk concave to convex, becoming irregular, chestnut-brown, usually shining, the exciple crenulate; spores subspherical to ellipsoid, 4.5–11 × 3.5–5 μ.
On trees and wood, from Massachusetts to Alabama, and westward to New Mexico and Colorado.

9. **Cetraria saepincola** (Ehrh.) Ach., Meth. Lich. 297. 1803.
Lichen saepincola Ehrh., Hanover Mag. 206. 1783.
Thallus small, foliose, pale to darker chestnut-brown, or olive-green, the lobes few and short, prostrate to ascending, smooth to somewhat wrinkled, the margins undulate and crenate; pale below without rhizoids; apothecia small, 0.7–4.5 mm. across, marginal, sessile, the disk concave to convex, of the same color as thallus to darker, the exciple entire to crenulate; spores ellipsoid, 6–9.5 × 3–6 μ.
On trees, from New England westward to Oregon and California.

10. **Cetraria chlorophylla** (Willd.) Vainio, Lich. Caucas. Term. Füz. 22:278. 1899.
Lichen chlorophyllus Willd., in Humb., Fl. Friberg 20. 1793. *C. saepincola* var. *chlorophylla* (Willd.) Schaer.
Thallus small to scarcely middle-sized, pale to darker chestnut-brown or olive-green, the lobes numerous, short, irregular, prostrate or ascending, the margins

undulate, curled, crenate, white-sorediate; pale below with occasional scattered rhizoids; apothecia rare, small, 1–2.5 mm. across, marginal, sessile, the disk concave to convex, of same color as thallus to darker, the exciple entire to crenulate; spores ellipsoid, 6–9 × 3–6 μ.

On fences and trees, New England, California, Oregon, and Washington.

11. **Cetraria fahlunensis** (L.) Schaer., Lich. Helv. Spic. 5:255–57. 1833.
Lichen fahlunensis L., Sp. Pl. 1143. 1753.

Thallus small to middle-sized, foliose, many-cleft, irregularly divided, dusky brown to blackening, the lobes laciniate, overlapping, the margins entire to crenate; smooth to wrinkled and blackening below with scattered rhizoids; apothecia small to middle-sized, 2–9 mm. across, marginal, the disk concave to convex, becoming irregular and dilated, chestnut-brown, the exciple wrinkled, crenulate; spores ellipsoid, 5–11 × 3.5–7 μ.

On alpine rocks, New England and New Jersey.

12. **Cetraria ciliaris** Ach., Lich. Univ. 508. 1810.
C. ciliaris var. *montana* Tuck. *Nephromopsis ciliaris* (Ach.) Hue.

Thallus middle-sized, foliose, greenish gray to brownish, wavy to laciniately lobed, the lobes often narrow and many-cleft, more or less lacunose, crowded, ascending, the margins crenate, bearing scattered cilia; of same color to paler below, pitted-lacunose, bearing scattered to frequent rhizoids; apothecia small to large, 1.5–12 mm. across, marginal, sessile, the disk concave to irregular, pale to chestnut-brown, the exciple crenulate; spores spherical to subspherical, 5–7 × 4–5 μ.

On trees and old wood, from New England westward to the Pacific Coast.

13. **Cetraria platyphylla** Tuck., Syn. N. A. Lich. 1:34, 35. 1882.
Platysma orbatum Nyl., Flora 52:442. 1869 with insufficient diagnosis. *Nephromopsis platyphylla* (Tuck.) Herre.

Thallus small to middle-sized, foliose, rigid, greenish brown, irregularly cleft, the lobes round to irregular, reticulate-lacunose, tuberculate, the margins entire to crenulate or jagged, sometimes crinkled; apothecia marginal, middle-sized, 1–9 mm. across, sessile, the disk concave to irregular, pale to dark chestnut-brown, shining, the exciple crenulate or tuberculate; spores subspherical to short-ellipsoid, 4.5–7 × 4–6 μ.

On trees and dead limbs, Montana, Washington, Oregon, and California.

14. **Cetraria cucullata** (Bell.) Ach., Meth. Lich. 293. 1803.
Lichen cucullatus Bell., Osserv. Bot. 154. 1788.

Thallus small to middle-sized, fruticose, erect, tufted, greenish gray to straw-colored or brownish, the lobes narrow, long, branched, smooth, more or less lacunose, flattened to rolled or tubular, the margins undulate, entire to crenate; apothecia middle-sized, 6–9 mm. across, adnate to the lower side of the lobes, the disk often dilated, chestnut-brown, the exciple thin, entire; spores ellipsoid, 7–10 × 3–4 μ.

On soil, in alpine areas, New England and the Rocky Mountains.

15. **Cetraria nivalis** (L.) Ach., Meth. Lich. 294, 295. 1803.
Lichen nivale L., Sp. Pl. 1145. 1753.

Thallus small to middle-sized, erect, rigid, tufted, straw-colored to yellowish white or yellowish toward the base, much and deeply lobed, the lobes narrow or rather broad, more or less widely channeled or reticulately pitted, many-cleft above, the margins irregularly dentate; apothecia small to middle-sized, 2–5 mm. across, adnate, subterminal, the disk flat, becoming irregular, yellowish flesh-colored to brownish, the exciple thin, irregular, crenulate; spores ellipsoid, 7–9 × 3–5 μ.

On soil, New England, Montana, Wyoming, and Colorado.

16. **Cetraria californica** Tuck., Am. Journ. Sci. II. 28:203. 1859.
   Alectoria cetrariza Nyl. *Coelocalon californicum* (Tuck.) Howe. *Alectoria californica* (Tuck.) Merrill.

Thallus small, fruticose, ascending, tufted, greenish brown to black, much branched, the branches spreading, smooth to canalled or lacunose, flat and narrow-linear to compressed-round, the tips much divided, the margins sometimes crenulate or jagged; paler below; apothecia small to middle-sized, 1.5–6 mm. across, terminal, sessile, the disk flat to convex or irregular, dark green to black, rarely shining, the exciple nearly entire to toothed or fringed; spores ellipsoid, 6–9 × 3–5 μ.

On fences and trees, California, Oregon, and Washington.

17. **Cetraria islandica** (L.) Ach., Meth. Lich. 293. 1803.
   Lichen islandicus L., Sp. Pl. 1145. 1753. *C. islandica* var. *crispa* Ach. *C. islandica* var. *platyna* Ach. *C. islandica* var. *arborialis* Merrill.

Thallus small to middle-sized, subfoliose or fruticose, tufted, rigid, shining, pale to dusky chestnut-brown or olive-green, sometimes reddish toward the base, many-lobed, the lobes very narrow and elongated to shorter and wide, subdichotomously to irregularly branched, smooth to lacunose, flattened to rolled, often into a closed tube, the margins entire to thickly spinulose; paler below, and often more or less covered with impressed white soredia; apothecia small to middle-sized, 1.5–14 mm. across, sessile at tips of lobes, the disk concave to convex or irregular, chestnut-brown to darker, the exciple thin, entire to crenulate; spores oblong-ellipsoid, 6–10 × 3.5–5 μ.

On soil and rarely on twigs, from New England to the Carolinas, and westward to the Pacific Coast (more common in alpine areas).

18. **Cetraria hiascens** (E. Fries) T. Fries, Lich. Scand. 98, 99. 1871.
   C. aculeata var. *hiascens* E. Fries, Lich. Eur. 36. 1831. *C. islandica* var. *Delisaei* Bory.

Thallus small to middle-sized, fruticose, erect, densely tufted, rigid, pale to dusky brown, many-lobed, the lobes narrow, elongated, subdichotomously much-branched, especially toward the apices, smooth, often lacunose, flattened to rolled, the margins entire toward the base, crenulate to spinulose toward the apices; apothecia rare, small to middle-sized, 1–7 mm. across, adnate, marginal or terminal, the disk concave, pale to chestnut-brown, the exciple entire to crenulate; spores ellipsoid, 6–11 × 3.5–6 μ.

On soil and rocks, New Hampshire, Delaware, the Carolinas, Rocky Mountains, Oregon, and Washington (usually in alpine areas).

19. **Cetraria aculeata** (Schreb.) E. Fries, Lich. Eur. 35, 36. 1831.
   Lichen aculeatus Schreb., Spic. Fl. Lips. 125. 1771. *C. aculeata* var. *alpina* Schaer.

Thallus small to middle-sized or larger, fruticose, erect, tufted, rigid, hollow, round to compressed, angulose and more or less contorted, often shining, pale to blackening chestnut-brown, much branched, the branches spreading and more or less beset with spicules especially toward the apices; apothecia small to middle-sized, 2–7 mm. across, subterminal, the disk concave to convex and irregular, chestnut-brown, the exciple toothed and spinous; spores ellipsoid, 6–9 × 3–4 μ.

On soil and over exposed rocks, in alpine areas, from New England westward to Wyoming and Washington.

20. **Cetraria tristis** (Web.) E. Fries, Lich. Eur. 34, 35. 1831.
   Lichen tristis Web., Spicil. 209. 1778.

Thallus small, fruticose, tufted, very rigid, brownish black, branched, the branches repeatedly divided especially toward the tips into subparallel branchlets, round to compressed; apothecia small to middle-sized, 1–5 mm. across, subterminal on deflexed tips, the disk flat to convex, dark chestnut-brown, the exciple entire to toothed; spores ellipsoid, 7–11 × 5–6 μ.

On rocks, in alpine regions, Oregon.

40. USNEACEAE

Thallus fruticose, erect or hanging, usually radial, rarely dorsiventral, differentiated into a cortical layer, surrounding a thin algal layer and the central hollow or solid medullary cylinder, attached to the substratum by rhizoids; apothecia round, sessile or somewhat pedicellate, with a thalloid exciple.

The algal host is Protococcus.

A. Spores non-septate
  B. Apothecia frequent
    C. Thallus dorsiventral . . . . 156. EVERNIA
    C. Thallus upright or hanging
      D. Thallus short . . . . 157. DUFOUREA
      D. Thallus much elongated
        E. Thallus greenish gray or straw-colored . . . . . . 160. USNEA
        E. Thallus brownish to brown . . . . 158. ALECTORIA
  B. Apothecia unknown
    C. Podetia with hollow centers . . . . 161. THAMNOLIA
    C. Podetia solid . . . . 162. SIPHULA
A. Spores 1–3-septate . . . . 159. RAMALINA

156. **Evernia** Ach., Lich. Univ. 84. pl. 10, f. 1–3. 1810.

Thallus fruticose, erect to prostrate, or hanging, much branched, often entangled, differentiated into a thin irregular pseudo-cortex, an algal layer of large cells, and the medullary layer composed of loosely interwoven hyphae usually surrounding a more or less complete hollow cylinder; apothecia large, terminal or marginal, the disk concave, differing in color from the thallus, the margin colored like the thallus, persistent; hypothecium hyaline; hymenium hyaline to brownish below, brownish above; paraphyses thick, unbranched; asci short; spores 8, hyaline, non-septate, commonly ellipsoid.

The algal host is Protococcus.

A. Thallus more or less sorediate . . . . 3. E. prunastri
A. Thallus not sorediate
  B. Thallus straw-colored or greenish to sulphur-colored
    C. Thallus straw-colored, branches beset with prickles . . . 2. E. divaricata
    C. Thallus sulphur-colored, obscurely pitted . . . . 1. E. vulpina
  B. Thallus greenish gray to ashy
    C. Thallus usually bearing scales or coralloid branchlets above . 4. E. furfuracea
    C. Thallus without scales or coralloid branchlets
      D. Branches smooth, very slender . . . . . . 5. E. ceratea Cladonia
      D. Branches wrinkled above . . . . 5. E. ceratea

1. **Evernia vulpina** (L.) Ach., Lich. Univ. 443. 1810.

Lichen vulpinus L., Sp. Pl. 1155. 1753. *Letharia vulpina* (L.) Hue. *E. vulpina* var. *californica* (Lév.) Müll. Arg.

Thallus tufted or rarely pendulous, rigid, greenish to sulphur-colored, subcylindrical to flattened, and angular, wrinkled, obscurely pitted, frequently expanded toward the base, dichotomously much-branched, the branches strongly diverging, the tips tapering; apothecia large, subterminal, the disk concave, the exciple wrinkled, sometimes radiately extended above into narrow branches and usually bearing one or more larger branches below; spores short-ellipsoid, 5–8.5 × 4.5–5.5 μ.

On trees and old wood, rarely on rocks, from Nebraska and South Dakota westward to the Pacific Coast.

2. **Evernia divaricata** (L.) Ach., Lich. Univ. 441. 1810.
   Lichen divaricatus L., Syst. Nat. ed. 12. 713. 1767.
   Thallus flaccid, pendulous, straw-colored, subcylindrical to flattened or angular, wrinkled, the cortex broken annularly, cottony and stringlike within, dichotomously branched, the branches strongly divergent, long, sometimes beset with prickles, the tips long-tapered, and filiform, darkening; apothecia small to middle-sized, 2–6 mm. across, infrequent, lateral, the disk concave to flat, the exciple finally much wrinkled; spores ellipsoid, 5–10 × 3.5–6 μ.
   On conifers, mountains of Montana, Colorado, and California.

3. **Evernia prunastri** (L.) Ach., Lich. Univ. 442. pl. 10, f. 1. 1810.
   Lichen prunastri L., Sp. Pl. 1147. 1753. *E. prunastri* var. *sorediifera* Ach. *E. prunastri* var. *thamnodes* Flot. *E. prunastri* var. *mollis* Merrill.
   Thallus tufted, subpendulous to pendulous, rather flaccid and soft, flattened, finally expanded, wrinkled or obscurely pitted, more or less sorediate, dichotomously much-branched, the branches strongly divergent, the tips forked, greenish to straw-colored; lighter colored and channeled below; apothecia middle-sized, 3–7 mm. across, lateral, the disk concave, the exciple absent; spores short-ellipsoid, 5–7 × 3.5–4.5 μ. (PLATE 37.)
   On trees and old wood, sometimes on rocks, from Washington to California.

4. **Evernia furfuracea** (L.) Mann., Lich. Bohem. 105. 1826.
   Lichen furfuraceus L., Sp. Pl. 1146. 1753. *E. furfuracea* var. *olivetorinc* (Zopf.) Elenk. *Parmelia furfuracea* (L.) Ach.
   Thallus tufted and ascending to prostrate, or sometimes pendulous, rather rigid, flattened, usually bearing soft scales or coralloid branchlets, dichotomously and subpinnately branched, much divided toward the usually forked tips, greenish gray to ashy; below channeled and obscurely pitted, white and darkening to black; apothecia large, 3–15 mm. across, marginal, the disk concave, the exciple usually persistent; spores short-ellipsoid, 5.5–8 × 3.5–5 μ.
   On trees, from New England to Florida, and westward to Texas and Arizona.

5. **Evernia ceratea** (Ach.) Zopf., Beih. Bot. Centralb. 14:107. 1903.
   Parmelia furfuracea var. *ceratea* Ach., Meth. Lich. 255. 1803. *E. furfuracea* var. *ceratea* (Ach.) Opiz. *E. furfuracea* var. *nuda* (Ach.) Nyl.
   Thallus tufted and ascending to prostrate or sometimes pendulous, rather rigid, wrinkled, dichotomously and subpinnately branched, sometimes considerably entangled, greenish gray to ashy; below channeled toward the base, brown to black and reticulated within the channels; apothecia large, 3–15 mm. across, marginal, the disk concave, the exciple persistent; spores short-ellipsoid, 5–7.5 × 3.5–5 μ.
   On trees, from New England to North Carolina, and westward to the Pacific coast (may be merely an old form of *Evernia furfuracea*).

   var. **Cladonia** (Tuck.) Fink n. comb.
   E. furfuracea var. *Cladonia* Tuck., Syn. Lich. N. E. 12. 1848. *Parmelia Cladonia* (Tuck.) DR. *Parmelia furfuracea* var. *Cladonia* (Tuck.) Merrill.
   Thallus branches smooth, very slender, round above but open and channeled toward the base, more or less interwoven; apothecia absent.
   On trees, from New England to West Virginia, usually at high elevations.

157. Dufourea Ach., Lich. Univ. 103. 1810.

Thallus fruticose, dichotomously branched, the cortex of closely packed, sparingly branched, longitudinally extending hyphae; medulla of loosely interwoven, branched hyphae, extending in various directions within the cortex, and leaving the center of the cylinder mostly hollow; apothecia with thalloid exciple; hypothecium hyaline; paraphyses becoming gelatinized and indistinct; asci broadly clavate; spores 6–8, hyaline, non-septate.
The algal host is Protococcus.

1. **Dufourea madreporiformis** (Wulf.) Ach., Lich. Univ. 525. 1810.
  Lichen madreporiformis Wulf., in Jacq., Coll. Bot. 3:105. 1789. *Cetraria madreporiformis* (Wulf.) Müll. Arg.
  Thallus of medium size, straw-colored, smooth, erect, usually tufted, swollen and hollow, roughly finger-shaped, passing into dichotomous, short, nodulose, bluntly tipped branches; apothecia lateral; spores ellipsoid, $7-8 \times 3-4 \mu$.
  On soil, mountains of Colorado and California. Apothecia were not seen and their presence is doubted for this species by some authors.

158. **Alectoria** Ach., Lich. Univ. 120. pl. 13, f. 1-4. 1810.

Thallus fruticose, cylindrical to flattened-cylindrical, erect, spreading or hanging, branching dichotomous or subdichotomous, cortex of a thick layer of densely packed, stout, parallel, longitudinal hyphae, center of the cylinder hollow, surrounded by the medulla of loosely interwoven hyphae; color from greenish gray or straw-color to blackish brown; apothecia usually rare, lateral or subterminal, immersed to more commonly sessile, the disk differing in color from the thallus, the exciple usually entire; the hypothecium and hymenium hyaline, or the latter somewhat colored, especially above; paraphyses unbranched or but slightly branched; spores non-septate, hyaline to brownish or brown.
  The algal host is Protococcus, and the algae lie in scattered clusters within the medulla just within the cortex.

A. Thallus erect to prostrate or rarely hanging
  B. Thallus usually dark brown throughout
    C. Apices furcate, without soredia . . . . 1. A. divergens
    C. Apices simple, sorediate . . . . 4. A. chalybeiformis
  B. Thallus straw-colored or greenish to dark brown
    C. Apices commonly grayish or yellowish . . . . 3. A. bicolor
    C. Apices commonly dark brown or blackening
      D. Thallus straw-colored or greenish . . . . 8. A. ochroleuca
      D. Thallus chestnut-brown or darker . . . . 7. A. nigricans
A. Thallus rarely prostrate to commonly hanging
  B. Thallus usually dark brown throughout
    C. Slender throughout . . . . 2. A. jubata implexa
    C. Stout with slender tips
      D. More or less white-sorediate
        E. Exciple entire . . . . 2. A. jubata
        E. Exciple ciliate . . . . 6. A. oregana
      D. Yellow-sorediate . . . . 5. A. Fremontii
  B. Thallus rarely dark brown
    C. Sulphur-green tinged with brown . . . . 10. A. virens
    C. Straw-colored to greenish, or sometimes blackening . . . 9. A. sarmentosa

1. **Alectoria divergens** (Ach.) Nyl., Mém. Soc. Imp. Sci. Nat. Cherb. 3:171. 1855.
  Cornicularia divergens Ach., Meth. Lich. 303. 1803.
  Thallus medium length, erect to prostrate, tufted, becoming rigid, smooth, often shining, pale chestnut-brown to blackish brown, dichotomously much-branched, branches widely divergent, slender, rough, subangular and cylindrical to flattened, flexuous, twisted, the tips long and slender with curved forks; apothecia middle-sized to large, 4-9 mm. across, lateral, the disk convex, chestnut-brown to darker, the exciple crenulate, becoming rough externally; spores ellipsoid, hyaline, $8-10 \times 4.5-5.5 \mu$.
  On soil and rocks, Oregon, confined to high altitudes and latitudes.

2. **Alectoria jubata** (L.) Ach., Lich. Univ. 592. pl. 13, f. 2. 1810.
  Lichen jubatus L., Sp. Pl. 1155. 1753. *A. jubata* var. *prolixa* Ach.
  Thallus prostrate to more commonly hanging, becoming much elongated, rarely white-sorediate, freely branching subdichotomously, greenish gray to more commonly brown or blackening, cylindrical, the branches sometimes entangled; apothecia rare, small, 2-3 mm. across, the disk flat to convex, chestnut-brown, the

exciple soon covered; spores hyaline, short-ellipsoid, 6–9 × 4–6 μ. (PLATE 38.)
On trees, old wood, and soil, throughout the United States.
var. **implexa** (Hoffm.) Ach., Lich. Univ. 593. 1810.
  Usnea implexa Hoffm., Deutschl. Fl. 2:134, 135. 1795.
Thallus shorter, slender, much branched, the branches intertangled, brown.
On trees, old wood, and soil, throughout northern United States, and south-
ward in the mountains.

3. **Alectoria bicolor** (Ehrh.) Nyl., Act. Soc. Linn. Bord. 21:291. 1856.
  Lichen bicolor Ehrh., Plant. Crypt. Linn. Exsicc. 40. 1785. *Evernia jubata* var.
    bicolor (Ehrh.) E. Fries. *A. jubata* var. *bicolor* (Ehrh.) Tuck.
Thallus rather short, prostrate to erect or rarely hanging, cylindrical, rigid,
rarely somewhat sorediate, dichotomously much-branched, the branches more or
less fibrillose, brownish black and commonly grayish to yellowish toward the apices;
apothecia small, 1.5–3 mm. across, rare, lateral, the disk flat to convex, brownish
to dark brown, the exciple disappearing; spores 8, hyaline, 5–9 × 4–6.5 μ.
On trees, old wood, and soil, Maine and New Hampshire.

4. **Alectoria chalybeiformis** (L.) Röhling, Deutschl. Fl. 3²:137. 1831.
  Lichen chalybeiformis L., Sp. Pl. 1155. 1753. *A. jubata* var. *chalybeiformis* (L.)
    Ach.
Thallus rather short, spreading to prostrate and rarely hanging, cylindrical to
flattened, light to darker brown, densely tufted, rigid, from greenish gray to brown,
rather remotely and divergently branched, flexuous, commonly more or less white-
sorediate, sparingly fibrillose, especially along the smaller branches, the fibrils
frequently several in a cluster; apothecia rare and doubtful, undefined.
On trees, old wood, and rocks, throughout northern United States, and southward in the mountains.

5. **Alectoria Fremontii** Tuck., Am. Journ. Sci. II. 25:422. 1858.
Thallus hanging, reddish brown to black, more or less flattened and lacunose
toward the base, sometimes bearing greenish or sulphur-colored soredia, irregularly
and remotely much-branched, the branches elongated, round to flattened, smooth,
flexuous, much entangled; apothecia small to middle-sized, 2–6 mm. across, the
disk flat to convex, yellow-pruinose, the exciple thin, entire, soon covered; spores
hyaline, ovoid-ellipsoid, 5–8 × 4–5 μ.
On branches, mainly of conifers, California, Oregon, Idaho, Wyoming, and
Montana.

6. **Alectoria oregana** Nyl., Lich. Jap. 104. 1890.
Thallus of medium length to long, erect to hanging, smooth and shining, greenish gray to reddish brown and blackening, often paler toward the base and darker
above, sparingly to frequently branched, the branches tufted, angulose and contorted to cylindrical and flattened, slender, tapering toward the round and pointed
tips; apothecia small to middle-sized, 2–7 mm. across, lateral and subterminal,
sessile, the disk concave to convex, circular to irregular, dark brown, the exciple
roughened to tuberculate, dark brown and shining, with short, pointed, spreading
or deflexed brown fibrils; spores hyaline, ovoid to subglobose, 5–8 × 3–5 μ.
On trees, especially conifers, and on old wood, Oregon, Montana, Washington,
and California.

7. **Alectoria nigricans** (Ach.) Nyl., Not. Sällsk. Faun. Flor. Fenn. 5:71, 72.
  1861.
  Cornicularia ochroleuca var. *nigricans* Ach., Lich. Univ. 615. 1810.
Thallus long, erect to spreading, chestnut-brown to black, darker above,
cylindrical to flattened, becoming rigid, subdichotomously much-branched; apothecia middle-sized, 2–4 mm. across, lateral or terminal, the disk concave to convex, chestnut-brown, the exciple becoming covered; spores 2–3, hyaline, ellipsoid,
20–34 × 13–18 μ.
On soil, Maine and Washington, usually occurring at high altitudes.

8. **Alectoria ochroleuca** (Ehrh.) Mass., Sched. Crit. 2:47. 1855.
   Lichen ochroleucus Ehrh., Beitr. Naturk. 3:82. 1788. *A. ochroleuca* var. *rigida*
   E. Fries.

Thallus long, erect, rigid, straw-colored or greenish, the reflexed tips blackening, often pitted or papillate, dichotomously much-branched, branches cylindrical to flattened, the tips often furcate; apothecia small to middle-sized, 3–8 mm. across, subterminal to lateral, sessile, the disk concave to convex, chestnut-brown or darker, the exciple becoming covered; spores 2–4, brown, ellipsoid, 18–48 × 9–24 μ.

On soil, rocks, mosses, and trees, Maine and California, usually at high altitudes.

9. **Alectoria sarmentosa** Ach., Lich. Univ. 595. 1810.
   Lichen sarmentosus Ach., Kongl. Vet. Acad. Nya Handl. 16:212. 1795. *A. ochroleuca* var. *cincinnata* (E. Fries) Nyl.

Thallus long, prostrate to hanging, straw-colored to greenish, or sometimes blackening, often pitted or papillate, sparingly branched dichotomously, or branched more frequently toward the tapering ends, the branches cylindrical to slightly flattened, dilated here and there; apothecia small to middle-sized, 3–7 mm. across, lateral, sessile, the disk concave to convex, pale yellow to dark brown, the exciple becoming covered; spores brown, ellipsoid, 20–48 × 12–24 μ.

On trees, especially conifers, mountains of Maine, New Hampshire, and Vermont, southward to New Jersey, and reappearing in California, Oregon, Washington, Montana, and Idaho.

10. **Alectoria virens** Tayl., Lond. Journ. Bot. 6:188. 1847.
    A. tortuosa Merrill.

Thallus pliant, long, hanging, sulphur-green tinged with brown, subdichotomously branched, the branches slender, elongated, cylindrical to flattened, bent and twisted, the tips tapering, flexuous, and black; apothecia rare and uncertain.

On trees and old wood, Oregon and Washington.

159. **Ramalina** Ach., Lich. Univ. 122. pl. 13, f. 5–11. 1810.

Thallus fruticose, erect or prostrate, the lobes flattened, usually tufted, more or less dichotomously branched, differentiated into a cortical layer of closely interwoven, longitudinally extending hyphae, an indistinct algal layer and the medullary tissue of loosely interwoven, longitudinally or variously extending hyphae; apothecia small to large, lateral to terminal, sessile to pedicellate, the disk concave to convex, flesh-colored to buff or greenish gray, the exciple colored like the thallus or rarely black; hypothecium hyaline; hymenium hyaline or brownish above; paraphyses rarely branched, adglutinate; asci clavate to cylindrico-clavate; spores 8, hyaline, oblong-ellipsoid or ellipsoid, 1-septate. The algal host is Protococcus.

A. Thallus black-ciliate . . . . 20. R. crinita
A. Thallus not black-ciliate
  B. Thallus fistulous
    C. Thallus over 10 mm. in height
      D. Apices multifid-dendroid . . . . 22. R. pollinariella
      D. Apices not multifid-dendroid . . . . 23. R. inflata
    C. Thallus not over 10 mm. in height . . . . 21. R. dilacerata
  B. Thallus not fistulous
    C. Thallus open-reticulate . . . . 16. R. reticulata
    C. Thallus not open-reticulate
      D. Thallus erect, caespitose
        E. Laciniae expanded
          F. Medulla with adglutinated hyphae . . . . . 2. R. testudinaria
          F. Medulla without adglutinated hyphae
            G. Coriaceous . . . . 13. R. fraxinea

G. Membranaceous
  H. Lobes reticulate . . . . 5. R. Duriaei
  H. Lobes never reticulate
    I. Laciniae lanceolate . . . . 14. R. yemensis
    I. Laciniae never lanceolate . . . . . 15. R. Menziesii
E. Laciniae never expanded
  F. Medulla with adglutinated hyphae
    G. Laciniae terete
      H. Apothecia terminal . . . . 4. R. combeoides
      H. Apothecia lateral . . . . 3. R. ceruchis
    G. Laciniae bifacial . . . . 1. R. homalea
  F. Medulla without adglutinated hyphae
    G. Sorediate or soraliate
      H. Sorediate
        I. Branches longitudinally rugose . . . 7. R. polymorpha
        I. Branches not longitudinally rugose . . 8. R. pollinaria
      H. Soraliate . . . . 9. R. farinacea
    G. Not sorediate or soraliate
      H. Branches canaliculate
        I. Laciniae open-canaliculate . . . . 12. R. canaliculata
        I. Laciniae connivo-canaliculate . . . . 17. R. linearis
      H. Branches not canaliculate
        I. Papillate
          J. Terete, torulose
            K. Spores ellipsoid . . . . . . 19. R. Willeyi
            K. Spores fusiform . . . . . 24. R. Montagnei
          J. Compressed . . . . 18. R. complanata
        I. Not papillate
          J. Calcareous . . . . 6. R. calicaris
          J. Coriaceous
            K. Spores ellipsoid
              L. Branches laciniate, apothecia
                scattered . . . . 10. R. fastigiata
              L. Branches wide, apothecia
                lateral . . . . 11. R. subamplicata
            K. Spores fusiform . . . . . 25. R. stenospora
D. Thallus pendulous . . . . 26. R. usneoides

1. **Ramalina homalea** Ach., Lich. Univ. 598. 1810.
Thallus rigid, greenish gray to straw-colored, becoming reddish when dried, the lobes flattened, two-edged, smooth, or chinky and wrinkled, moderately dichotomously branched, or digitate toward the ends, the tips cylindrical, tapering; apothecia small to large, 2–8 mm. across, lateral, the disk concave to flat, the exciple finally wavy to torn-lobate; spores oblong-ellipsoid, straight or rarely slightly curved, 11–18 × 3–5 μ.
On maritime rocks and possibly on trees, California.

2. **Ramalina testudinaria** Nyl., Bull. Soc. Linn. Norm. II. 4:108. 1870.
R. testudinaria var. *intermedia* Müll. Arg.
Thallus rigid, greenish to reddish, the lobes short, flattened, sometimes expanded, smooth to cracked or wrinkled, or sometimes obscurely pitted, rarely dichotomously branched, the tips blunt; apothecia middle-sized to large, 5–10 mm. across, commonly subterminal, often clustered, the disk concave to flat, flesh-colored to reddish, the exciple becoming torn; spores oblong-ellipsoid, straight to slightly curved, 10–20 × 3–5 μ.
On maritime rocks, southern California.

3. **Ramalina ceruchis** (Ach.) De Not., Giorn. Bot. Ital. 2:218. 1846.
Parmelia ceruchis Ach., Meth. Lich. 260. 1803. *R. ceruchis* var. *tumidula* (Tayl.) Nyl. *R. testudinaria* var. *humilis* Müll. Arg. *R. ceruchis* f. *cephalata* Tuck.
Thallus rather rigid, greenish gray to straw-colored or reddish, the lobes smooth to deeply pitted or wrinkled, sparsely black-spotted, subcylindrical, unbranched or sparingly branched dichotomously, sometimes bearing gray, capitate soredia;

apothecia small to middle-sized, 1–4 or rarely 7 mm. across, lateral or sublateral, the disk concave to convex, often pruinose, the exciple becoming crenulate; spores oblong-ellipsoid, straight or slightly curved, 12–19 × 3.5–5 μ.

On trees, Washington, Oregon, and California.

4. Ramalina combeoides Nyl., Bull. Soc. Linn. Norm. II. 4:107. 1870.

Thallus rigid, greenish gray or straw-colored to ashy, the lobes cylindrical to somewhat flattened and angular, bearing numerous shallow pits, slender and podetia-like, rarely branched; apothecia small to middle-sized, 1.5–5 mm. across, terminal, the disk concave to flat, the exciple becoming crenulate; spores straight or slightly curved, 10–20 × 3.5–5 μ.

On trees and maritime rocks, southern California.

5. Ramalina Duriaei (De Not.) Bagl., Giorn. Bot. Ital. 11:58. 1879.

R. pollinaria var. *Duriaei* De Not., Giorn. Bot. Ital. 2:216. 1846.

Thallus flaccid, greenish gray to straw-colored, the lobes flattened, expanded, netted-wrinkled, sorediate, variously wavy and torn-lobate; apothecia small to middle-sized, very rare, unknown in our territory, marginal, the disk concave, the exciple usually persistent; spores oblong-ellipsoid to ellipsoid, curved, 10–15 × 3.5–4.5 μ.

On trees and shrubs, southern California. (*R. evernoides* Nyl. according to some authors, but the two are not identical.)

6. Ramalina calicaris (L.) Röhling, Deutschl. Fl. 3²:139. 1813.

Lichen calicaris L., Sp. Pl. 1146. 1753.

Thallus rigid, greenish gray to gray, the lobes flattened, narrow, striate or obscurely pitted, considerably furrowed, branched usually dichotomously, numerous and crowded, the tips tapering; apothecia small to middle-sized, 1–6 mm. across, lateral or mostly subterminal, the disk concave to convex, often pruinose, the exciple finally disappearing; spores oblong-ellipsoid to ellipsoid, straight or slightly curved, 9–18 × 4–7 μ. (PLATE 39.)

On trees, old wood, and rarely on rocks, eastern United States, and westward to Oklahoma and Minnesota.

7. Ramalina polymorpha Ach., Lich. Univ. 600. 1810.

Lichen polymorphus Ach., Vet. Akad. Handl. 18:270. pl. 11, f. 3. 1797.

Thallus rigid, greenish gray to straw-colored, the lobes flattened, narrow, longi-tudinally wrinkled, granulose-sorediate, moderately branched, the tips blunt; apo-thecia small to middle-sized, 2–5 mm. across, marginal, the disk concave, the exciple usually persistent; spores oblong-ellipsoid to ellipsoid, straight or rarely slightly curved, 11–16 × 4–5 μ.

On maritime and alpine rocks, Washington and New Hampshire.

8. Ramalina pollinaria (Westr.) Ach., Lich. Univ. 608. 1810.

Lichen pollinarius Westr., Vet. Akad. Nya Handl. 1795:56. 1795.

Thallus flaccid, greenish gray to flesh-colored, the lobes flattened, sometimes wrinkled, narrow, torn-lobate, powdery-sorediate, especially at the vaulted or bursting tips; apothecia small, 0.8–3 mm. across, subterminal, the disk concave, the exciple rarely disappearing; spores oblong-ellipsoid to ellipsoid, straight or slightly curved, 10–14 × 4–6 μ.

On trees, rarely on rocks, New England, New York, Ohio, Minnesota, South Dakota, and California.

9. Ramalina farinacea (L.) Ach., Lich. Univ. 606. 1810.

Lichen farinaceus L., Sp. Pl. 1146. 1753. *R. calicaris* var. *farinacea* (L.) Rabh. *R. intermedia* Del. *R. farinacea* f. *lata* Merrill.

Thallus rather rigid, greenish gray to pale straw-colored, the lobes narrow, subcylindrical to flattened, rarely somewhat channeled, longitudinally wrinkled or pitted, dichotomously branched, sorediate, the tips usually tapering; apothecia small, 0.8–2.5 mm. across, rare, marginal, the disk concave to convex, the exciple finally disappearing; spores oblong-ellipsoid to ellipsoid, straight or rarely curved, 13–17 × 5–7 μ.

On trees, old wood, and rarely on rocks, throughout the United States, except the Gulf states.

10. **Ramalina fastigiata** (Pers.) Ach., Lich. Univ. 603. 1810.

Lichen fastigiatus Pers., Ann. Bot. Usteri 7:156. 1794. *R. calicaris* var. *fastigiata* (Pers.) E. Fries. *R. calicaris* var. *subfastigiata* Nyl.

Thallus rather rigid, greenish gray to pale straw-colored, the lobes flattened, narrow, longitudinally wrinkled or obscurely pitted, frequently somewhat channeled, dichotomously branched, the tips tapering; apothecia small to middle-sized, 1–5 mm. across, lateral, often subterminal, the disk concave to convex, the exciple finally disappearing; spores oblong-ellipsoid to ellipsoid, straight or slightly curved, 9–18 × 4–7 μ.

On trees, shrubs, old wood, and rarely on rocks, from Maine to Florida, and westward to Missouri and Minnesota.

11. **Ramalina subamplicata** (Nyl.) Fink n. comb.

R. calicaris var. *subamplicata* Nyl., Bull. Soc. Linn. Norm. II. 4:132. 1870. *R. calicaris* var. *fraxinea* (L.) E. Fries. *R. fastigiata* var. *subamplicata* (Nyl.) Howe.

Thallus rather rigid, pale to dark greenish gray, the lobes flattened, wrinkled or obscurely pitted, torn-lobate, sparsely branched, the tips blunt; apothecia small, 1.5–4 mm. across, lateral and marginal, the disk concave to convex, the exciple finally disappearing; spores oblong-ellipsoid to ellipsoid, straight, 9–17 × 4–7 μ. (PLATE 42 *b*.)

On trees and old wood, from New England to Florida, westward to Kansas, Iowa, and Michigan, and recurring in California.

12. **Ramalina canaliculata** (E. Fries) Herre, Proc. Wash. Acad. Sci. 12:220. 1910.

R. calicaris var. *canaliculata* E. Fries, Lich. Eur. 30. 1831.

Thallus rather rigid, greenish gray to gray, the lobes flattened, striate or obscurely pitted, distinctly channeled, narrow, numerous, often crowded, dichotomously branched, the tips deflexed; apothecia small to middle-sized, 1–4 mm. across, subterminal below the deflexed tips, the disk concave to convex, often pruinose, the exciple finally disappearing; spores oblong-ellipsoid to ellipsoid, straight to slightly curved, 9–18 × 4–7 μ.

On trees, widely distributed throughout the United States.

13. **Ramalina fraxinea** (L.) Ach., Lich. Univ. 602. 1810.

Lichen fraxineus L., Sp. Pl. 1146, 1147. 1753. *R. fraxinea* var. *ampliata* Ach.

Thallus rather rigid, greenish gray to straw-colored, the lobes flattened, wrinkled or veined, expanded, long-lobulate, the tips round; apothecia middle-sized to large, 3–12 mm. across, or larger, lateral and marginal, the disk concave to convex, the exciple wrinkled, finally torn-crenate; spores oblong-ellipsoid to ellipsoid, curved, 11–16 × 5–7 μ.

On trees, Connecticut, Maryland, Delaware, Louisiana, Ohio, Illinois, Iowa, Minnesota, Arizona, and California.

14. **Ramalina yemensis** (Ach.) Nyl., Bull. Soc. Linn. Norm. II. 4:144. 1870.

R. fraxinea var. *yemensis* Ach., Lich. Univ. 602, 603. 1810. *R. laevigata* E. Fries.

Thallus rather rigid, greenish gray to straw-colored, the lobes flattened, longitudinally wrinkled or veined, expanded, lanceolate, narrowing toward the pointed tips; apothecia small, 0.5–1.4 mm. across, lateral, the disk concave to convex, the exciple persistent; spores oblong-ellipsoid to ellipsoid, straight to slightly curved, 10–18 × 4.5–7 μ.

On trees, South Carolina, Alabama, Louisiana, Texas, New Mexico, Wyoming, and southern California.

15. **Ramalina Menziesii** Tuck., Syn. Lich. N. E. 12. 1848.

R. leptocarpha Tuck. *R. Menziesii* var. *sorediata* Tuck.

Thallus rather rigid, pale greenish to straw-colored, the lobes tufted or pendulous, flattened, wrinkled and obscurely pitted, channeled in ˙the younger states, later expanded above, sometimes sorediate, the tips tapering; apothecia small to large, 1.5–7 mm. across, lateral and marginal, the disk concave to convex, the exciple sometimes disappearing; spores oblong-ellipsoid to ellipsoid, curved, 10–17 × 3.5–6 μ.

On trees, shrubs, and old wood, rarely on soil, Washington, Oregon, and California.

16. **Ramalina reticulata** (Noedh.) Kremph., Gesch. Lich. 2:617. 1869.

Lichen reticulatus Noedh., in Schrad., Journ. Bot. 2:237, 238. 1800. *R. reti-formis* Menz.

Thallus pendulous, not tufted, rather rigid, greenish gray to ashy, the lobes flattened, rarely subcylindrical, longitudinally striate or furrowed, narrow or expanded, finally perforated and extensively netted, the tips tapering; apothecia small, 0.4–3 mm. across, marginal or lateral, the disk concave to convex, the exciple finally disappearing; spores oblong-ellipsoid to ellipsoid, striate or slightly curved, 12–19 × 4–7 μ. (PLATE 40.)

On trees and old wood, Washington, Oregon, and California.

17. **Ramalina linearis** (Swartz) Ach., Lich. Univ. 598. 1810.

Lichen linearis Swartz, Meth. Musc. 36. pl. 2, f. 3. 1781.

Thallus rather rigid, straw-colored, the lobes slender, flattened and sometimes channeled, the tips tapering; apothecia minute to small, 0.5–2 mm. across, marginal, the disk flat to convex, the exciple finally disappearing; spores ellipsoid, curved, 9–18 × 4–7 μ.

On trees, Florida and southern California.

18. **Ramalina complanata** (Swartz) Ach., Lich. Univ. 599. 1810.

Lichen complanatus Swartz, Fl. Ind. Occ. 3:1911. 1806. *R. denticulata* (Eschw.) Nyl.

Thallus rather rigid, greenish gray to straw-colored, the lobes flattened, narrow, smooth or striate, frequently furrowed, the margins papillate, sparingly branched below, becoming dichotomously much-branched above, the tips subcylindrical, tapering; apothecia small to middle-sized, 0.8–5 mm. across, lateral, the disk concave to convex, the exciple becoming crenulate; spores oblong-ellipsoid to ellipsoid, curved or rarely straight, 10–18 × 4–7 μ.

On trees, Florida and Texas.

19. **Ramalina Willeyi** Howe, Bryologist 17:36. 1914.

R. rigida (Pers.) Tuck.

Thallus rigid, pale greenish, the lobes subcylindrical, frequently flattened below, often twisted-angular, often bearing scattered wartlike elevations, dichotomously branched, the tips long-tapered; apothecia middle-sized, 2–6 mm. across, mostly subterminal, the disk concave to convex, the exciple becoming torn, finally disappearing; spores oblong-ellipsoid, straight, 9–16 × 6–8 μ.

On trees and rarely on old wood, New England, New York, New Jersey, and the Gulf states.

20. **Ramalina crinita** Tuck., Bull. Torr. Club 10:43. 1883.

Thallus rigid, pale greenish gray, the lobes flattened, much expanded, striate or obscurely pitted, sparingly dichotomously branched, the margins beset with stout, black, branching fibrils, the tips tapering; apothecia middle-sized to large, 3–10 mm. across, lateral or subterminal, the disk concave, the exciple black; spores oblong-ellipsoid to ellipsoid, straight, 10–20 × 5–6 μ.

On trees, southern California.

21. **Ramalina dilacerata** (Hoffm.) Vainio, Not. Syn. Lich. 21. 1886.

Lichen dilacerata Hoffm., Deutschl. Fl. 3:140. 1795. *R. pusilla* Duby. *R. cali-caris* var. *minuscula* (Nyl.) T. Fries.

Thallus small, rather rigid, greenish gray to straw-colored, the lobes hollow-inflated, frequently perforated, cylindrical to flattened, dichotomously branched, the tips forked, tapering, pointed; apothecia small, 1–3 mm. across, terminal, the disk concave to convex, the exciple finally disappearing; spores oblong-ellipsoid to ellipsoid, straight or rarely curved, 10–17 × 4–7 μ. (PLATE 41 b.)

On trees, Maine, New Hampshire, Massachusetts, Minnesota, South Dakota, New Mexico, Washington, and Oregon.

22. **Ramalina pollinariella** Nyl., Flora 67:218. 1884.

    R. minuscula var. *pollinariella* Nyl., Bull. Soc. Linn. Norm. II. 4:165. 1870. *R. pusilla* var. *geniculata* (Tayl. & Hook.) Tuck. *R. dilacerata* var. *pollinariella* Arn.

Thallus small, rather rigid, greenish gray to straw-colored, the lobes hollow-inflated, perforated, subcylindrical to flattened, much branched, the tips frequently digitate, cylindrical, frequently sorediate; apothecia rare, small, 0.8–2 mm. across, marginal, the disk concave, the exciple persistent; spores oblong-ellipsoid, straight or rarely slightly curved, 10–17 × 4–7 μ.

On trees, Maine, New Hampshire, Minnesota, South Dakota, Iowa, New Mexico, Idaho, and Washington.

23. **Ramalina inflata** Hook. & Tayl., Lond. Journ. Bot. 3:646. 1844.

Thallus rather rigid, pale greenish gray to straw-colored, the lobes subflattened, narrow, netted-veined to perforated and sievelike, dichotomously branched, the tips tapering, pointed; apothecia small, 1–4 mm. across, terminal or subterminal, the disk concave to convex, the exciple rarely disappearing; spores oblong-ellipsoid to ellipsoid, straight, 14–18 × 9–11 μ.

On trees, Washington, Oregon, California, and Idaho.

24. **Ramalina Montagnei** De Not., Giorn. Bot. Ital. 2:218. 1846.

    R. rigida var. *Montagnei* (De Not.) Tuck.

Thallus rigid, greenish gray to straw-colored, the lobes subcylindrical to flattened, smooth to striate, frequently bearing wartlike, sometimes sorediate elevations, dichotomously branched, the tips gradually tapering, pointed; apothecia small, 0.8–3 mm. across, marginal, the disk concave to convex, the exciple finally disappearing; spores fusiform, straight or slightly curved, 20–28 × 3–5.5 μ.

On trees, South Carolina, Florida, Louisiana, and Texas.

25. **Ramalina stenospora** Müll. Arg., Flora 60:477, 478. 1877.

Thallus rigid, greenish gray to straw-colored, the lobes narrow, more or less flattened, striate, dichotomously branched, the tips long-pointed; apothecia middle-sized, 3–4 mm. across, lateral, the disk concave to finally convex, the exciple becoming crenulate, sometimes disappearing; spores fusiform, straight, 18–32 × 3–6 μ.

On trees, from Massachusetts to Florida, and westward to Texas and California.

26. **Ramalina usneoides** (Ach.) E. Fries, Lich. Eur. 468. 1831.

    Parmelia usneoides Ach., Meth. Lich. 270. 1803. *R. Usnea* (L.) Howe. *R. Usnea* var. *usneoidella* (Nyl.) Howe.

Thallus pendulous, not tufted, pale greenish gray, the lobes flattened, often spirally twisted, two-edged, usually longitudinally striate, much branched, the tips tapering; apothecia small, 0.5–3 mm. across, marginal, the disk convex, the exciple absent; spores fusiform, straight or slightly curved, 18–27 × 3–6 μ.

On trees, Florida.

OTHER SPECIES REPORTED

Ramalina bistorta Nyl.—California.
Ramalina cuspidata (Ach.) Nyl.—North America.
Ramalina flaccescens Nyl.—Southern California.
Ramalina scopulorum (Retz.) Ach.—North America.
Ramalina subfraxinea Nyl.—Massachusetts.

160. **Usnea** (Dill.) Adans., Fam. Pl. 2:7. 1763.

Thallus fruticose, erect or pendulous, commonly branched, cylindrical or sometimes angular, smooth to more or less rough, differentiated into a cortical layer of closely interwoven, variously extending hyphae, a thin algal layer, and medullary tissue composed of a central cylinder of closely interwoven, longitudinally extending hyphae and a surrounding cylinder of loosely interwoven hyphae, uniting the inner portion of the medullary tissue and the cortex; apothecia small to large, lateral or terminal, sessile, the disk cyathiform to slightly concave, greenish to flesh-colored or buff, the exciple colored like the thallus, more or less irregular; hypothecium hyaline; hymenium hyaline; paraphyses agglutinate, more or less branched; asci clavate to cylindrico-clavate; spores 8, hyaline, ellipsoid or round-ellipsoid, nonseptate.

The algal host is Protococcus.

A. Thallus papillate
  B. Thallus rigid, erect
    C. Thallus very rigid, fibrilloid branchlets stiff . . . . . 1. U. florida strigosa
    C. Thallus not so rigid, fibrilloid branches flexible . . . . 1. U. florida
  B. Thallus flexible, pendant
    C. Branches slender, sparingly divided, fibrilloid
      branchlets rarely divided . . . . 3. U. barbata
    C. Branches coarser, much divided, fibrilloid branches
      frequently divided . . . . 2. U. plicata
A. Thallus not papillate
  B. Branches coarse, angulate . . . . 4. U. angulata
  B. Branches slender, not angulate
    C. Thallus scaly whitish-sorediate . . . . 6. U. longissima
    C. Thallus smooth
      D. Thallus usually pitted near the base . . . . 5. U. cavernosa
      D. Thallus not pitted . . . . 7. U. trichodea

1. **Usnea florida** (L.) Web., in Wigg., Prim. Fl. Hols. 91. 1780.
Lichen floridus L., Sp. Pl. 1156. 1753. *U. florida* f. *major* Michx. *U. mutabilis* Stirt. *U. barbata* var. *florida* f. *rubiginea* (Michx.) Tuck. *U. barbata* var. *hirta* (L.) E. Fries. *U. barbata* var. *comosa* (Ach.) Biroli.

Thallus small, erect, rigid, tufted, shrublike, greenish gray, rarely reddening or blackening, sometimes sorediate, soon rough and more or less papillate, the cortex frequently seamed or broken in partial or complete rings, sometimes exposing the whitish medulla within, the branches coarse, cylindrical, short, spreading, much divided, usually dichotomously, bearing numerous, short, rectangularly divergent, rarely divided, fibrilloid branchlets; apothecia small to large, 2–12 mm. across, or larger, terminal, the exciple frequently lobate or torn, radiately extending into fibrilloid branches; spores 6–10 × 4–8 μ. (PLATE 42 a.)

On trees, old wood, and rarely on rocks, throughout the United States.

var. **strigosa** Ach., Meth. Lich. 310. 1803.

Thallus very rigid, the branches short, bearing numerous short, stiff, sharp-pointed fibrilloid branchlets; apothecia large, the disk greenish.

On trees and old wood, from Maine to Iowa, and southward to New Mexico.

2. **Usnea plicata** (L.) Wigg., Prim. Fl. Hols. 91. 1780.
Lichen plicatus L., Sp. Pl. 1154. 1753. *U. barbata* var. *plicata* (L.) E. Fries. *U. linearis* Schneid. *U. plicata* var. *Huei* (Boist.) Howe. *U. barbata* var. *ceratina* (Ach.) Schaer. *U. californica* Herre.

Thallus pendulous, flexible, greenish gray to straw-colored, rarely reddening, sometimes sorediate, usually rough, thickly papillate, especially toward the base, the cortex often seamed or broken in partial or complete rings, sometimes exposing the whitish medulla within, the branches coarse, long, cylindrical, lax or frequently interwoven, rather spreading, much divided, usually dichotomously, frequently bearing scattered, rectangularly divergent, frequently branched, fibrilloid branchlets; apothecia middle-sized to large, 3–10 mm. across, lateral or subterminal, the exciple entire or radiately extending into fibrilloid branchlets; spores 6–10 × 4–8 μ.

On trees and sometimes on old wood, throughout northern United States, and southward to the Gulf of Mexico, and in California.

3. **Usnea barbata** (L.) Wigg., Prim. Fl. Hols. 91. 1780.

    Lichen barbatus L., Sp. Pl. 1155. 1753. *U. barbata* var. *dasypoga* Ach. *U. plicata* var. *barbata* (L.) E. Fries. *U. barbata* var. *pendula* (Schaer.) Krempl.

Thallus pendulous, flexible, greenish gray to straw-colored, rarely reddening, often blackening toward the base, sometimes bursting-sorediate, rough, more or less papillate, especially toward the base, the cortex sometimes seamed or broken in partial or complete rings, and rarely exposing the whitish medulla within, the branches rather slender, long, cylindrical, spreading, sparingly divided, usually dichotomously, rarely finally interwoven, bearing numerous, rather short, rectangularly divergent, rarely divided, fibrilloid branchlets; apothecia small, 1.5–6 mm. across, rare, lateral or subterminal, the exciple entire or radiately extending into fibrilloid branchlets; spores 6–10 × 4–8 μ.

On trees and sometimes on old wood, throughout the United States.

4. **Usnea angulata** Ach., Syn. Lich. 307. 1814.

Thallus pendulous, rigid, greenish gray to straw-colored, finally darkening, rough, frequently scaly, the branches coarse, angulate, often very long, sparingly divided dichotomously, bearing numerous, slender, sometimes branched, fibrilloid branchlets; apothecia middle-sized to large, 5–15 mm. across, lateral, terminal, or subterminal, the exciple smooth or netted-veined, usually extending into fibrilloid branchlets; spores 5–9 × 4–6 μ.

On trees, throughout northern United States.

5. **Usnea cavernosa** Tuck., in Agassiz, Lake Superior 171. 1850.

Thallus pendulous, flexible, greenish gray, the cortex sometimes seamed and ridged or broken in partial or complete rings, rarely exposing the whitish medulla within, the branches slender, cylindrical or subcylindrical, long, rough, especially toward the base, and pitted, much-divided dichotomously, bearing long, slender, twisting, more or less scattered, fibrilloid branchlets; apothecia small, 1–4.5 mm. across, lateral, the exciple usually extending into rather numerous fibrilloid branchlets; spores 6–9 × 4–6.5 μ.

On trees, Maine, New Hampshire, Michigan, Iowa, Minnesota, South Dakota, Colorado, Arizona, and Washington.

6. **Usnea longissima** Ach., Lich. Univ. 626. 1810.

Thallus pendulous, flexible, greenish gray to straw-colored, the branches slender, often very long, subcylindrical or flattened, sparingly divided, rough, scaly whitish-sorediate, especially toward the base, bearing numerous, rather straight, rectangularly divergent, often long, rarely divided, fibrilloid branchlets; apothecia small, 1–3 mm. across, very rare, terminal, the exciple usually extending into fibrilloid branchlets; spores 7–10 × 4–6 μ.

On trees and sometimes on old wood, throughout northern United States.

7. **Usnea trichodea** Ach., Meth. Lich. 312. 1803.

    U. trichodea var. *ciliata* Müll. Arg.

Thallus pendulous, flexible, greenish gray, sometimes bursting-sorediate, smooth, or rough toward the base, often seamed and ridged or broken in partial or complete rings, sometimes exposing the whitish medulla within, the branches slender, long, cylindrical, much divided, usually dichotomously, bearing long, slender, twisting, fibrilloid branchlets; apothecia small, 1.5–4 mm. across, lateral, the exciple entire or extending into scattered fibrilloid branchlets; spores 6–10 × 4–8 μ.

On trees, usually conifers, and old wood, from New England to Alabama, and westward to Texas and Minnesota.

OTHER SPECIES REPORTED

Usnea articulata (L.) Hoffm.—Minnesota and the Pacific Coast.

161. **Thamnolia** Ach., in Schaer., Enum. Lich. Eur. 243. 1850.

Thallus fruticose, composed of prostrate to erect, hollow, rarely branched, pointed podetia, differentiated into a plectenchymatous cortical layer of horizontally extending hyphae, an algal layer and a thin medullary layer of longitudinally extending hyphae around the hollow center; apothecia unknown.

The algal host is Pleurococcus.

1. **Thamnolia vermicularis** (Swartz) Schaer., Enum. Lich. Eur. 243. pl. 9, f. 7. 1850.

Lichen vermicularis Swartz, Meth. Musc. 37. 1781.

Podetia short to elongated, ascending or erect, hollow and cylindrical or slightly flattened, smooth to somewhat wrinkled and becoming furrowed, often densely clustered, sparingly branched, sometimes forked toward the pointed tips, chalky white to ashy; apothecia unknown.

On soil, New England, New York, Montana, and Washington.

162. **Siphula** E. Fries, Syst. Orb. Veg. 1:238. 1825.

Thallus fruticose, sparingly branched, the cortex of closely packed, branched, longitudinally extending hyphae, the medulla of loosely packed, branched hyphae, extending in various directions and filling the entire cylinder; apothecia unknown.

The algal host is Protococcus.

1. **Siphula simplex** (Tayl.) Nyl., Syn. Meth. Lich. 1:262. 1860.

Dufourea simplex Tayl., Lond. Journ. Bot. 6:185. 1847.

Thallus small to middle-sized, ashy white to rarely grayish, smooth to becoming minutely granulose, erect, solid, cylindrical, passing into short, nodulose, bluntly or pointedly tipped branches; apothecia unknown.

On old wood, southern California.

41. CALOPLACACEAE

Thallus crustose or rarely somewhat fruticose, showing little or no differentiation into layers, attached to the substratum by hyphal rhizoids; apothecia round, immersed to adnate or sessile, with well-developed proper or thalloid exciple.

The algal host is Protococcus.

A. Apothecia with proper exciple
  B. Spores non-septate . . . . 163. PROTOBLASTENIA
  B. Spores septate
    C. Spores 1-septate, cells polar . . . . 164. BLASTENIA
    C. Spores 3–several-septate . . . . 165. BOMBYLIOSPORA
A. Apothecia with thalloid exciple . . . . 166. CALOPLACA

163. **Protoblastenia** Steiner, Verh. Ges. Wien. 61:47. 1911.

Thallus crustose, smooth to rough, granulose, chinky or areolate, devoid of differentiation into layers, attached to the substratum by hyphal rhizoids; apothecia minute to small or middle-sized, immersed to adnate or sessile, the disk concave to flat or convex, the exciple colored like the disk, often disappearing; hypothecium hyaline; hymenium hyaline or brownish above; paraphyses unbranched; asci clavate; spores 8, hyaline, oblong to ellipsoid or oblong-ellipsoid, non-septate.

The algal host is Protococcus.

1. **Protoblastenia rupestris** (Scop.) Steiner, Verh. Ges. Wien. 61:47. 1911.

Lichen rupestris Scop., Fl. Carn. ed. 2. 1. 396. 1772. *Lecanora calva* (Dicks.) Nyl. *Placodium rupestre* (Scop.) Branth & Rostr. *Lecidea rupestris* (Scop.) Ach.

Thallus thin, ashy to dirty whitish, minutely granulose, sometimes crumbling and disappearing; apothecia small to middle-sized, 0.3–1 mm. across, adnate, the disk flat to convex, yellowish to reddish brown, the exciple thin, colored like the disk, soon disappearing; spores ellipsoid or short-ellipsoid, 8–14 × 5–7.5 μ.

On rocks, from Vermont to Georgia, and westward to West Virginia and Tennessee.

164. **Blastenia** Mass., Atti Ist. Veneto II. 3:101. 1852.

Thallus crustose, smooth to powdery, granulose, squamulose, chinky or rarely areolate, commonly devoid of differentiation into layers, attached to the substratum by hyphal rhizoids; apothecia immersed to adnate or sessile, minute to small or middle-sized, the disk more or less concave to flat or convex, the exciple colored like the disk, often disappearing; hypothecium hyaline; hymenium hyaline or brownish above; paraphyses unbranched, septate, enlarged at the apices; asci clavate; spores 4–16, commonly 8, hyaline, ellipsoid to oblong-ellipsoid, 1-septate or rarely non-septate, the cells usually polar.

The algal host is Protococcus.

A. On trees or old wood
  B. Thallus smooth to chinky or areolate
    C. Thallus bordered and often intersected by a black
      hypothallus. . . . . 3. B. floridana
    C. Thallus without a black hypothallus . . . . 2. B. diphasia
  B. Thallus more or less granulose . . . . 5. B. atrosanguinea
A. Not limited to trees or old wood
  B. On rocks and soil
    C. Spores constantly 8 in each ascus
      D. Thallus gray to ashy or whitish . . . . 1. B. fraudans
      D. Thallus greenish yellow to orange . . . . . . 6. B. novomexicana
    C. Spores 4–12 or more in each ascus . . . . 7. B. luteominia
  B. On soil and over moss . . . . 4. B. sinapisperma

1. **Blastenia fraudans** (T. Fries) B. de Lesd., Bull. Soc. Bot. Fr. 59:688. 1912.
    Caloplaca ferruginea var. *fraudans* T. Fries, Vet. Akad. Handl. Stockholm 7:27. 1867. *B. ferruginea* var. *fraudans* (T. Fries) Hazsl.

Thallus thin, ashy to whitish, minutely granulose to warty, widespread or disappearing; apothecia small to middle-sized, 0.4–1.2 mm. across, sessile, numerous and frequently crowded, the disk flat to convex, pale to yellowish orange, the proper exciple thin, yellowish, surrounded by a very thin, soon disappearing, whitish thalloid exciple; spores oblong-ellipsoid, 12–16 × 4–7.5 μ.

On shale, southern California.

2. **Blastenia diphasia** (Tuck.) Zahlbr., Cat. Lich. Univ. 7:28. 1930.
    Lecanora diphasia Tuck., Am. Journ. Sci. II. 25:426. 1858. *Placodium diphasium* Tuck.

Thallus thin, smooth to granulose-areolate, greenish gray to ashy white; apothecia minute to small, 0.2–0.8 mm. across, sessile, the disk flat to convex, reddish brown and blackening, sometimes greenish pruinose, the exciple sometimes raised, orange, entire to crenulate; spores ellipsoid, 10–16 × 8–11 μ.

On trees, Texas, Louisiana, and Florida.

3. **Blastenia floridana** (Tuck.) Zahlbr., Cat. Lich. Univ. 7:30. 1930.
    Lecanora floridana Tuck., Proc. Am. Acad. 5:402, 403. 1862.

Thallus thin, continuous, rough, becoming chinky, greenish gray to ashy, limited and often intersected more or less by the black hypothallus; apothecia minute, 0.15–0.45 mm. across, adnate, the disk flat, brownish black, the exciple thick, entire, and darkening to the color of the disk; spores ellipsoid, 10–16 × 5–7.5 μ.

On trees, from Florida to Texas.

4. **Blastenia sinapisperma** (Lam. & DC.) Mass., Flora 35:575. 1852.
    Patellaria sinapisperma Lam. & DC., Fl. Fr. ed. 3. 2:349, 350. 1805. *Placodium sinapispermum* (Lam. & DC.) Hepp.

Thallus thin, granulose, whitish, commonly running over mosses; apothecia

minute to small, 0.1–0.7 mm. across, adnate, the disk flat to strongly convex, yellowish to rusty brown or blackening, the exciple thin, colored like the disk, soon disappearing; spores oblong-ellipsoid, 21–34 × 13–18 μ.
On soil and over mosses, Colorado.

5. **Blastenia atrosanguinea** (Merrill) Fink n. comb.
Lecanora atrosanguinea Merrill, Ottawa Naturalist 117. 1913. *B. Herrei* Hasse.
Thallus thin, scattered, minutely granulose, becoming chinky, pale greenish gray to ashy; apothecia small to middle-sized, 0.5–1.25 mm. across, sessile, the disk flat, reddish brown to black, the exciple thin, colored like the disk, becoming irregular and wavy; hypothecium hyaline to tinged reddish; spores ovoid-ellipsoid to oblong-ellipsoid, cells becoming polar, 13–19 × 7.5–10 μ.
On trees, Washington.

6. **Blastenia novomexicana** Fink; Hedrick, Mycologia 26:163. 1934.
Thallus composed of minute to small, convex, greenish yellow to orange, granulose squamules, running together into a more or less continuous crust; apothecia small, 0.3–0.6 mm. across, subsessile, the disk flat to slightly convex, orange, the proper exciple thin, lighter or more rarely colored like the disk; spores oblong-ellipsoid, becoming 1-septate, the cells polar, 12–16 × 6–7.5 μ.
On rocks, near Las Vegas, New Mexico.

7. **Blastenia luteominia** (Tuck.) Hasse, Cont. U. S. Nat. Herb. 17:112. 1913.
Placodium luteominium Tuck., Lich. Calif. 18. 1866.
Thallus thin, dirty whitish, squamulose, with the squamules strongly convex, passing into granulose conditions and disappearing; apothecia small to middle-sized, 0.3–1 mm. across, subsessile, the disk flat to slightly convex, orange to vermilion, the proper exciple well developed, of same color, entire to radiately striate; spores 4–12 or more, 13–23 × 3.5–5 μ, the cells rarely polar.
On soil, California.

165. **Bombyliospora** De Not., in Mass., Ric. Lich. 114. 1852.

Thallus crustose, smooth to powdery, granulose, minutely warty, chinky, or areolate, commonly devoid of differentiation into layers, attached to the substratum by hyphal rhizoids; apothecia middle-sized to large, adnate to subsessile or sessile, the disk flat to more or less convex, the exciple colored like the disk, sometimes disappearing; hypothecium hyaline to brown; hymenium hyaline or brownish above; paraphyses unbranched, septate; asci broadly clavate; spores 1–8, hyaline, ellipsoid to oblong-ellipsoid, 3–11-septate, the cells lenticular.
The algal host is Protococcus.

A Spores 2–5-septate . . . . 3. B. porphyrites
A. Spores 5–many-septate
   B. Thallus rough, areolate to powdery; spores 40–80 × 15–24 μ . 2. B. pachycheila
   B. Thallus smooth to rough, areolate to warty;
     spores 75–110 × 20–30 μ . . . . 1. B. tuberculosa

1. **Bombyliospora tuberculosa** (Fée) Mass., Ric. Lich. 116. 1852.
Lecidea tuberculosa Fée, Essai Crypt. 107. pl. 27, f. 1. 1824. *Heterothecium tuberculosum* (Fée) Flot. *Heterothecium tuberculosum* var. *pachycarpum* (Del.) Tuck.
Thallus smooth to rough, wrinkled, chinky to areolate and finally warty, greenish gray, often surrounded wholly or in part by a blackening hypothallus, occasionally sulphur-colored within; apothecia middle-sized to large, 0.6–2.5 mm. or more across, subsessile, the disk flat to slightly convex, reddish brown to blackish, the exciple thick, paler to blackish; hypothecium reddish to brownish; spores oblong-ellipsoid, 5–11-septate, 75–110 × 20–30 μ.
On trees, from Massachusetts to Florida, and westward to Alabama and Louisiana.

2. **Bombyliospora pachycheila** (Tuck.) Zahlbr., Sitz. Kais. Acad. Wiss. 111[1]: 397. 1902.
Lecidea pachycheila Tuck.; Nyl., Ann. Sci. Nat. Bot. IV. 19:352. 1863. *Heterothecium tuberculosum* var. *pachycheilum* Tuck. *Heterothecium pachycheilum* Tuck.

Thallus rough, wrinkled, chinky to areolate, becoming powdery, greenish gray to ashy white; apothecia middle-sized to large, 1–2.5 mm. across, subsessile, the disk flat to slightly convex, reddish brown, the exciple thick, pale; hypothecium reddish brown; spores ellipsoid, curved, 5–7-septate, 40–80 × 15–24 μ.

On trees, from South Carolina and Florida throughout the Gulf states westward to Texas.

3. **Bombyliospora porphyrites** (Tuck.) Mass., Atti Ist. Veneto III. 5:262. 1860.
Biatora porphyrites Tuck., Lich. N. E. 61. 1848. *Heterothecium porphyrites* Tuck. *B. tuberculosa* var. *porphyrites* (Tuck.) Zahlbr.

Thallus smooth and chinky to wrinkled, greenish gray, becoming mealy; apothecia middle-sized to large, 1.4–5 mm. across, sessile, the disk flat to convex, reddish brown to black and usually whitish pruinose, the exciple thick, pale, becoming dark, finally disappearing; hypothecium hyaline; spores ellipsoid, 2–5-septate, 40–70 × 16–24 μ.

On trees, New England and New York, and southward to Florida.

166. **Caloplaca** T. Fries, Lich. Scand. 1:167. 1871.

Thallus crustose or rarely somewhat foliose, granulose, chinky, areolate, sometimes more or less lobed and ascending toward the circumference, rarely showing differentiation into poorly developed, more or less plectenchymatous upper and lower cortices of vertically extending, coherent hyphae, indistinct algal layer, and poorly developed medullary layer of entangled hyphae, commonly attached to the substratum by hyphal rhizoids; apothecia rarely immersed to adnate and sessile, minute to small or middle-sized, the disk concave to flat or convex, the exciple thin to thick, colored like the thallus; hypothecium hyaline; hymenium hyaline; paraphyses unbranched, septate, enlarged at the apices; asci clavate; spores 8 or rarely less, hyaline, ellipsoid to oblong-ellipsoid, 1-septate or rarely non-septate, the cells polar.

The algal host is Protococcus.

A. Thallus pale or darker yellow to yellowish brown or orange, rarely gray
  B. Thallus crustose to squamulose
    C. Thallus not lobed at the margins
      D. On rocks and soil
        E. Thallus crustose
          F. Thallus smooth to chinky or areolate
            G. Exciple moderately thick, becoming wavy or flexuous
              H. Spores 1-septate, 12–16 × 5.5–7.5 μ . . . 6. C. Schaereri
              H. Spores sometimes non-septate, 14–18 × 6.5–8 μ . . . . 5. C. flavovirescens
            G. Exciple raised, entire
              H. Spores 7–13 × 5–7 μ . . . . 1. C. cinnabarina
              H. Spores 12–20 × 6–8 μ . . . . . . 4. C. subpyracella
          F. Thallus minutely granulose . . . . 7. C. citrina
        E. Thallus squamulose . . . . 24. C. Spaldingi
      D. On trees, old wood, and rarely on rocks
        E. Thallus smooth to chinky or areolate
          F. Thallus yellow to gray or whitish . . . . . 2. C. aurantiaca
          F. Thallus yellow to orange or brownish . . . . . 3. C. erythrella
        E. Thallus granulose . . . . 8. C. discolor
    C. Thallus more or less distinctly lobed at the margins
      D. Lobes not branched or rarely so
        E. Thallus smooth to wrinkled or areolate

F. Spores rarely more than 12 μ in length
 G. Thallus orange to greenish gray
  H. Apothecia 0.1–0.6 mm. across, exciple
   entire . . . . 30. C. modesta
  H. Apothecia 0.2–1 mm. across, exciple
   entire to slightly wavy . . . . 32. C. lobulata
 G. Thallus pale yellow . . . . 27. C. fulgens
F. Spores 12–18 × 5–7 μ . . . . 28. C. bolacina
E. Thallus more or less granulose
 F. On rocks, soil, or moss
  G. Apothecia 0.2–0.35 mm. across . . . . . 33. C. cirrochroa
  G. Apothecia 0.2–1 mm. across . . . . . . 31. C. bracteata
 F. On trees . . . . 35. C. microphylina
D. Lobes more or less branched
 E. Lobes long and usually much-branched
  F. Bearing many granules . . . . . 34. C. elegans trachyphylla
  F. Smooth or obscurely coralloid-granulose . . . . 34. C. elegans
 E. Lobes short and somewhat branched . . . . . . 29. C. murorum
B. Thallus subfruticose
 C. Spores 10–16 × 5–7 μ . . . . 40. C. coralloides
 C. Spores 20–26 × 15–20 μ . . . . 41. C. cladodes
A. Thallus greenish gray to ashy or brownish, rarely darker
 B. Thallus not lobed at the margins
  C. Usually on rocks
   D. Thallus smooth to areolate or squamulose
    E. Thallus smooth to areolate
     F. Apothecia not more than 0.6 mm. across . . . . 12. C. festiva
     F. Apothecia reaching 1 or more mm. across
      G. Thallus warty to areolate
       H. Thallus thin; apothecia adnate to
        sessile . . . . 9. C. cerina
       H. Thallus thicker; apothecia immersed
        to adnate . . . . 10. C. sideritis
      G. Thallus distinctly areolate . . . . . 9. C. cerina areolata
    E. Thallus squamulose
     F. Apothecia 0.1–0.3 mm. across . . . . 22. C. amabilis
     F. Apothecia 0.2–1 mm. across . . . . 21. C. variabilis
   D. Thallus more or less granulose
    E. Thallus very thin, dark ashy to whitish . . . . . 15. C. pyracea
    E. Thallus thicker, dirty gray to darker . . . . . 19. C. oxfordensis
  C. Usually on trees, old wood, moss and soil
   D. Thallus smooth to wrinkled or areolate
    E. Spores 11–20 × 6–10 μ
     F. Disk rust-colored to black, often sub-
      pruinose . . . . 11. C. ferruginea
     F. Disk olive-green to black . . . . 13. C. Pollinii
    E. Spores 10–14 × 5–8 μ . . . . 14. C. camptidia
   D. Thallus more or less granulose
    E. Thallus crustose
     F. Apothecia 0.2–1 or more mm. across
      G. Disk dark red to reddish brown . . . . . 18. C. Wrightii
      G. Disk dull waxy-yellow . . . . 16. C. ulmorum
     F. Apothecia 0.2–0.6 mm. across . . . . 17. C. gilva
    E. Thallus more or less plainly squamulose
     F. Spores rarely more than 15 μ in length
      G. Thallus light gray . . . . 23. C. stillicidiora
      G. Thallus dark greenish to brownish . . . . 25. C. pelodella
     F. Spores 14–23 × 7–11 μ . . . . 20. C. jungermanniae
 B. Thallus more or less distinctly lobed at the margins
  C. Spores rarely more than 15 μ in length
   D. Thallus minutely granulose or powdery
    E. Spores 9–13 × 4–6.5 μ . . . . 36. C. eugyra
    E. Spores 12–16 × 7–9 μ . . . . 37. C. teicholyta
   D. Thallus smooth . . . . 39. C. galactophylla

C. Spores rarely less than 15 μ in length
   D. Apothecia large, 0.7–2 mm. across . . . . 38. C. peliophylla
   D. Apothecia smaller, 0.4–0.8 mm. across . . . . . . 26. C. atroalba

1. **Caloplaca cinnabarina** (Ach.) Zahlbr., in E. & P., Nat. Pfl. 1¹:228. 1907.
   Lecanora cinnabarina Ach., Lich. Univ. 402. 1810. *Placodium cinnabarinum* (Ach.) Nyl.

Thallus chinky to areolate, light or darker orange, the areoles becoming scaly and somewhat imbricated or scattered and more or less crenately lobed; apothecia minute to small, 0.2–0.7 mm. across, adnate, sometimes angular, numerous, often obscuring much of the thallus, the disk flat to slightly convex, dark orange to cinnabar, the exciple somewhat lighter or of the same color as the thallus, sometimes raised, entire; spores ellipsoid, 7–13 × 5–7 μ.
On rocks, throughout the United States.

2. **Caloplaca aurantiaca** (Lightf.) T. Fries, Nov. Act. Reg. Soc. Sci. Ups. III. 3:219. 1861.
   Lichen aurantiacus Lightf., Fl. Scot. 2:810. 1777. *Placodium aurantiacum* (Lightf.) Anzi.

Thallus well developed, pale to lemon- or darker-yellow, gray, or whitish, smooth and chinky or becoming verrucose, wrinkled, or even areolate, sometimes scattered; apothecia small to middle-sized, 0.2–1 mm. across, adnate to sessile, the disk flat to slightly convex, orange to chestnut-brown, the exciple sometimes raised, lemon-yellow to greenish gray, becoming wavy, rarely disappearing; spores ellipsoid, 11–18 × 6–9 μ.
On trees, old wood, and rocks, throughout the United States.

3. **Caloplaca erythrella** (Ach.) Kieffer, Bull. Soc. Hist. Nat. Metz. 67. 1895.
   Lichen erythrellus Ach., Lich. Suec. 43. 1798. *Placodium aurantiacum* var. *erythrellum* (Ach.) E. Fries.

Thallus thin to moderately thick, smooth to somewhat rough, chinky to areolate, yellow to yellowish orange or brownish; apothecia small to middle-sized, 0.4–0.8 mm. across, adnate, the disk flat to slightly convex, yellow to brownish orange or yellowish brown, the exciple thin, colored like the thallus, becoming crenulate; spores ellipsoid, 12–18 × 7–10 μ.
On old wood and stones, New England.

4. **Caloplaca subpyracella** (Nyl.) Zahlbr., Beih. Bot. Centralb. 13:149. 1902.
   Lecanora subpyracella Nyl.; Hasse, Bull. Torr. Club 24:446, 447. 1897. *Blastenia subpyracella* (Nyl.) Hasse.

Thallus thin and evanescent, when present subgranulose, yellowish to reddish yellow or brownish; apothecia small to middle-sized, 0.25–0.8 mm. across, subsessile, the disk concave to slightly convex, light orange to olive-green, the exciple yellow to light orange, raised; spores oblong-ellipsoid, 12–20 × 6–8 μ.
On soil and sandstone, southern California.

5. **Caloplaca flavovirescens** Arn.; Wulf., Verh. Zool. Bot. Ges. Vein. 32:151. 1882.

Thallus thin, granulose to chinky or areolate, yellow-ashy to brownish orange, often more or less scattered; apothecia minute to small, 0.1–0.5 mm. across, often crowded and angular, subimmersed to adnate, the disk flat to slightly convex, orange to rusty brown, the exciple thin or moderately thick, colored like the thallus, becoming wavy or disappearing and exposing a yellowish proper one; spores ellipsoid, often slightly curved, non-septate to 1-septate, the cells polar, 14–18 × 6.5–8 μ.
On rocks, Indiana and South Dakota.

6. **Caloplaca Schaereri** (Floerke) Zahlbr., Ann. Nat. Hofm. Wein. 5:29. 1890.
   Lecidea Schaereri Floerke; Arn., Flora 64:312. pl. 6, f. 5–7. 1881.

Thallus thin, becoming chinky to minutely areolate, yellowish orange, varying toward brown; apothecia minute to small, 0.25–0.6 mm. across, sessile, the disk flat to slightly convex, yellowish orange to chestnut-brown, the exciple moderately thick, colored like the thallus, becoming flexuous; spores oblong-ellipsoid, 12–16 × 5.5–7.5 μ.

On rocks, Alabama and Tennessee.

7. **Caloplaca citrina** (Hoffm.) T. Fries, Nov. Act. Reg. Soc. Sci. Ups. III. 3:218, 219. 1861.
   Verrucaria citrina Hoffm., Deutschl. Fl. 2:198. 1795. *Placodium citrinum* (Hoffm.) Hepp.

Thallus of minute granules, scattered or compacted into an irregular or widespread subareolate crust, lemon-yellow; apothecia minute to small, 0.2–0.5 mm. across, adnate, the disk flat, waxy-yellow to orange, the exciple pale yellow to orange, subgranulose and disappearing; spores ellipsoid to oblong-ellipsoid, 8–14 × 4.5–7 μ.

On rocks and mortar, throughout northern United States, and in South Carolina.

8. **Caloplaca discolor** (Willey) Fink n. comb.
   Placodium ferrugineum var. *discolor* Willey, in Tuck., Syn. N. A. Lich. 1:178. 1882. *C. ferruginea* var. *discolor* (Willey) Zahlbr.

Thallus thin, pale to bright yellow, granulose, more or less scattered; apothecia minute to small, 0.2–1 mm. across, adnate to sessile, the disk flat to convex, rusty red to reddish brown, the exciple evanescent, when present of the same color as the disk; spores ellipsoid, 11–18 × 7–11 μ.

On trees, New England and New York.

9. **Caloplaca cerina** (Ehrh.) T. Fries, Nov. Act. Reg. Soc. Sci. Ups. III. 3:218. 1861.
   Lichen cerinus Ehrh., in Hoffm., Pl. Lich. 2:62. pl. 21, f. *B*. 1789. *Placodium cerinum* (Ehrh.) Naeg.

Thallus thin, ashy to lead-gray, brownish or whitish, smooth and chinky to subareolate, often verrucose, becoming irregular and widespread, rarely disappearing; apothecia small to middle-sized, 0.2–1.3 mm. across, adnate to sessile, the disk slightly concave to convex, lemon-yellow to reddish or greenish brown, the exciple of the same color, whitish, or of the same color as the thallus, sometimes raised, entire or becoming wavy; spores ellipsoid, 8–18 × 5–10 μ. (PLATE 43 a.)

On rocks, trees, and rarely old wood, throughout the United States.

var. **areolata** Zahlbr., Oesterr. Bot. Zeitschrift 53:289. 1903.

Thallus thin, more or less widespread, lead-gray, distinctly areolate, the areoles usually flat; apothecia 1–4 in each areole, round to angular and crowded.

On rocks, Vermont.

10. **Caloplaca sideritis** (Tuck.) Zahlbr., Trav. Sous. Troit. Soc. Imp. Russe 12:92. 1911.
    Lecanora sideritis Tuck., Am. Journ. Sci. II. 25:426. 1858. *Placodium cerinum* var. *sideritis* Tuck. *Placodium sideritis* (Tuck.) Fink. *C. cerina* var. *sideritis* (Tuck.) Merrill.

Thallus moderately thick, iron to greenish gray, continuous, of somewhat scaly and often convex warts or areoles; apothecia small to middle-sized, 0.2–1 mm. across, immersed to adnate, the disk flat to convex, yellowish rust-colored to rusty-brown or black, the exciple of the same color as the thallus, entire, sometimes disappearing; spores ellipsoid, 8–15 × 5–8 μ.

On rocks, northeastern United States.

11. **Caloplaca ferruginea** (Huds.) T. Fries, Nov. Act. Reg. Soc. Sci. Ups. III. 3:223. 1861.
    Lichen ferrugineum Huds., Fl. Angl. ed. 2. 526. 1778. *Placodium ferrugineum* (Huds.) Rabh. *Placodium ferrugineum* var. *Bolanderi* Tuck. *Blastenia ferruginea* (Huds.) Mass.

Thallus commonly thin, ashy to whitish, smooth and chinky to wrinkled and verrucose, sometimes scattered and tending to disappear; apothecia small to middle-sized, 0.3–1.3 mm. across, adnate to sessile, the disk flat to convex, rust-colored to black, often subpruinose, the exciple evanescent; spores ellipsoid, 11–20 $\times$ 6–10 μ.

On trees, old wood, and rocks, throughout the United States.

12. **Caloplaca festiva** (Ach.) Zwackh., Flora 47:85. 1864.
> *Lecidea caesiorufa* var. *festiva* Ach., Syn. Lich. 44. 1814. *Placodium festivum* (Ach.) Hepp. *Blastenia festiva* (Ach.) Mass.

Thallus thin, gray to ashy, chinky to areolate, becoming more or less scattered or disappearing; apothecia minute to small, 0.2–0.6 mm. across, sessile, the disk flat to convex, bright orange to brownish red, the exciple thick, orange to brownish, becoming flexuous or crenulate, often disappearing; spores oblong-ellipsoid, 11–17 $\times$ 5–7 μ.

On rocks, Montana and California.

13. **Caloplaca Pollinii** (Mass.) Jatta, Syll. Lich. Ital. 244. 1900.
> *Blastenia Pollinii* Mass., Flora 35:575. 1852. *Placodium ferrugineum* var. *Pollinii* (Mass.) Hepp. *Placodium ferrugineum* var. *nigricans* (Nyl.) Tuck. in litt.

Thallus thin, whitish, smooth to slightly wrinkled, tending to disappear; apothecia small to middle-sized, 0.2–1.2 mm. across, adnate to sessile, the disk flat to convex, olive-green to black, the exciple evanescent, when present entire, of the same color as the disk; spores ellipsoid, 11–20 $\times$ 6–10 μ.

On living and dead conifers, from New England and Maryland westward to Nebraska and Minnesota.

14. **Caloplaca camptidia** (Tuck.) Zahlbr., Cat. Lich. Univ. 7:83. 1930.
> *Lecanora camptidium* Tuck., Proc. Am. Acad. 5:403. 1862. *Placodium camptidium* Tuck.

Thallus thin, smooth to chinky and wrinkled or verrucose, ashy to brownish gray; apothecia minute to small, 0.2–1 mm. across, sessile, the disk flat to convex, reddish brown to dark chestnut-brown, white-pruinose, the exciple of the same color as the thallus or slightly darker, entire; spores ellipsoid, 10–14 $\times$ 5–8 μ.

On trees and wood, throughout eastern United States westward to Illinois, and in Oregon and Texas.

15. **Caloplaca pyracea** (Ach.) T. Fries, Sven. Vet. Akad. Handl. 7:25. 1867.
> *Parmelia cerina* var. *pyracea* Ach., Meth. Lich. 176. 1803. *Placodium pyraceum* (Ach.) Anzi. *Placodium cerinum* var. *pyraceum* (Ach.) Branth & Rostr.

Thallus very thin, dark ashy to whitish, scurfy-granulose, often disappearing; apothecia minute to small, 0.2–0.6 mm. across, adnate to sessile, often numerous, clustered, and angular, obscuring the thallus, the disk flat to convex, yellowish- to dark-orange, the exciple thin, yellowish to whitish, usually disappearing early; spores ellipsoid to ovoid-ellipsoid, 10–16 $\times$ 5–9 μ.

On rocks and old wood, northern United States and California.

16. **Caloplaca ulmorum** Fink n. comb.
> *Placodium cerinum* var. *ulmorum* Fink, Proc. Iowa Acad. Sci. 11:143. 1904. *Placodium ulmorum* Fink. *C. cerina* var. *ulmorum* (Fink) Zahlbr.

Thallus moderately thick, greenish gray to ashy, granulose-verrucose, irregularly spread in small patches; apothecia small to middle-sized, 0.2–1.3 mm. across, sessile, the disk concave to flat, dull waxy-yellow, roughened, somewhat pruinose, the exciple ashy whitish, prominent, entire to subcrenulate or radiately striate; spores ellipsoid, 8–18 $\times$ 5–10 μ.

On elms, and rarely on oaks, cedars, and other trees, Ohio, Minnesota, Iowa, and Kansas.

17. **Caloplaca gilva** (Hoffm.) Zahlbr., in E. & P., Nat. Pfl. 1¹:228. 1907.
Verrucaria gilva Hoffm., Deutschl. Fl. 2:179. 1795. *Placodium gilvum* (Hoffm.)
   Vainio. *Placodium cerinum* var. *gilvum* (Hoffm.) Tuck.
   Thallus thin, ashy gray to yellowish, granulose or warty, often scattered, becoming inconspicuous or disappearing; apothecia minute to small, 0.2–0.6 mm. across, becoming sessile, the disk slightly concave to convex, orange to brownish orange, the proper exciple thin to moderately thick, yellow to light orange, surrounded by a thin, finally disappearing thalloid one; spores oblong-ellipsoid, 12–16 × 5–7 μ.
   On trees, Massachusetts, Illinois, North Dakota, Washington, and California.

18. **Caloplaca Wrightii** (Tuck.) Fink n. comb.
Placodium ferrugineum var. *Wrightii* Tuck., Syn. N. A. Lich. 1:178. 1882.
   Blastenia ferruginea var. *Wrightii* (Tuck.) Hasse. *C. ferruginea* var.
   Wrightii (Tuck.) Zahlbr.
   Thallus moderately thick, light greenish gray to whitish, densely sprinkled over with white granules or coralloid branchlets; apothecia small to middle-sized, 0.3–1 mm. across, adnate, the disk flat to convex, dark red to reddish brown, the exciple moderately thick, lighter or colored like the disk, becoming flexuous, sometimes bordered more or less by a thin thalloid one; spores ellipsoid, 12–19 × 6–9 μ.
   On trees, Texas and New Mexico.

19. **Caloplaca oxfordensis** Fink; Hedrick, Mycologia 26:162. 1934.
   Thallus thin to moderately thick, composed of minute, flat to convex, dirty gray and darkening granules, scattered or crowded into a continuous, areolate crust; apothecia minute to small, 0.1–0.4 mm. across, adnate to subsessile, often crowded and irregular, the disk slightly concave to flat or somewhat convex, orange to brown or dusky, the thalloid exciple rather thin, orange to darker, becoming flexuous; spores ellipsoid to oblong-ellipsoid, 13–16 × 5.5–8 μ.
   On exposed rocks, near Oxford, Ohio.

20. **Caloplaca jungermanniae** (Vahl.) T. Fries, Nov. Act. Reg. Soc. Sci. Ups.
   III. 3:221. 1861.
   Lichen jungermanniae Vahl., Nat. Selsk. Skr. II. 29. 1792. *Placodium jungermanniae* (Vahl.) Tuck. *Placodium fulvolutea* (Arn.) Tuck.
   Thallus thin, minutely granulose to subsquamulose, ashy or whitish; apothecia small to middle-sized, 0.4–1.2 mm. across, sessile, the disk flat to slightly convex, orange to brownish, the exciple thick, swollen, colored like the disk, becoming flexuous and finally disappearing; spores oblong-ellipsoid, 14–23 × 7–11 μ.
   Over mosses, Colorado, Montana, Idaho, and Washington.

21. **Caloplaca variabilis** (Pers.) Müll. Arg., Mém. Soc. Phys. Hist. Nat. Genève.
   16:387. 1862.
   Lichen variabilis Pers., Ann. Bot. Usteri 7:26. 1794. *Placodium variabile* (Pers.)
   Hepp.
   Thallus roughened and chinky, grayish brown and blackening, areolate, the margin sometimes squamulose; apothecia minute to small, 0.2–1 mm. across, adnate, the disk flat, of the same color as the thallus, the exciple whitish to light gray, entire to crenulate; spores oblong-ellipsoid, 13–20 × 5–9 μ.
   On rocks, from the Rocky Mountains westward to California.

22. **Caloplaca amabilis** Zahlbr., Bull. Torr. Club 35:298. 1908.
   Placodium amabile (Zahlbr.) Fink.
   Thallus thick, greenish gray to rusty green, squamulose to subareolate, becoming somewhat scattered; apothecia minute, 0.1–0.3 mm. across, adnate to sessile, sometimes angular when crowded, the disk flat to convex or wavy, yellow to tawny yellow or orange, waxy, the exciple of the same color as the thallus, entire, soon depressed; spores oblong-ellipsoid, 8–13 × 5–7 μ.
   On basaltic rocks, Arizona.

23. **Caloplaca stillicidiora** (Vahl.) Lynge, Vid. Skrift. Kl. 4. 1921.
    Lichen stillicidiorum Vahl., Fl. Dan. fasc. 18. pl. 1063, f. 2. 1792. *Placodium cerinum* var *stillicidiorum* (Vahl.) Willey.
    Thallus thin, light gray, scurfy-granulose to subsquamulose, becoming somewhat scattered; apothecia small to middle-sized, 0.3–1.5 mm. across, sessile, the disk flat to convex or somewhat wavy, yellowish green to dark olive, often white-pruinose, the exciple light gray, raised, entire to wavy, sometimes radiately striate; spores oblong-ellipsoid, 10–15 × 7–9 μ.
    On moss and soil, Massachusetts.

24. **Caloplaca Spaldingi** Zahlbr., Ann. Mycol. 7:476. 1909.
    Thallus squamulose, lemon-yellow to orange, the squamules becoming crenately lobed and more or less scattered; apothecia minute to small, 0.2–0.6 mm. across, adnate to sessile, the disk flat to convex, orange to rusty brown, the exciple yellow to orange, entire, sometimes raised; spores ellipsoid, 10–13 × 5–8 μ.
    On basaltic rocks, Arizona.

25. **Caloplaca pelodella** (Nyl.) Hasse, Cont. U. S. Nat. Herb. 17:115, 116. 1913.
    Lecanora pelodella Nyl., in Hasse, Lich. South. Calif. 10. 1898.
    Thallus thin, minutely squamulose, forming small, round to irregular, dark greenish to brownish patches; apothecia small to middle-sized, 0.4–1.4 mm. across, the disk flat to more or less convex, dark brown to dull black, the exciple moderately thick, colored like the thallus, becoming wavy; spores oblong-ellipsoid, 10–12 × 5–6 μ.
    On granite rocks, southern California.

26. **Caloplaca atroalba** (Tuck.) Zahlbr., Cat. Lich. Univ. 7:68. 1930.
    Placodium atroalbum Tuck., Proc. Am. Acad. 12:172. 1877.
    Thallus crustose, closely adnate, chinky-areolate, yellowish brown, the areoles sometimes obscurely lobed toward the margin; apothecia small to middle-sized, 0.4–0.8 mm. across, adnate, the disk flat to slightly convex, black, the exciple thin, whitish or colored like the thallus, rarely flexuous; spores infrequently and obscurely 1-septate, the cells polar, 14–24 × 5–8.5 μ.
    On rocks, Nebraska and Utah.

27. **Caloplaca fulgens** (Swartz) Koerb., Abh. Schl. Ges. 31. 1862.
    Lichen fulgens Swartz, Nov. Act. Soc. Ups. 4:246. 1784. *Placodium fulgens* (Swartz) Lam. & DC.
    Thallus thick, pale yellow, subfoliose, becoming wrinkled and areolate towards the center, the margin crenately lobed, somewhat imbricated; apothecia minute to small, 0.2–1 mm. across, sessile, occurring singly or in groups of two or more, the disk flat to convex, rusty orange to reddish brown, the exciple lemon-yellow to orange, wavy to crenate, finally disappearing; spores ellipsoid, 9–13 × 3–5 μ.
    On soil and rocks, from South Dakota and Nebraska northwestward to Montana, and in California.

28. **Caloplaca bolacina** (Tuck.) Herre, Proc. Wash. Acad. Sci. 12:233. 1910.
    Placodium bolacinum Tuck., Lich. Calif. 18. 1866.
    Thallus well developed, tawny yellow, areolate-squamulose toward the center, the margin subfoliosely lobed; apothecia minute to small, 0.2–1 mm. across, sessile, the disk concave to slightly convex, tawny yellow to orange, the exciple of the same color as the thallus, entire, disappearing; spores oblong-ellipsoid, 12–18 × 5–7 μ.
    On rocks and soil, California.

29. **Caloplaca murorum** (Hoffm.) T. Fries, Lich. Scand. 1:170. 1871.
    Lichen murorum Hoffm., Enum. Lich. Icon. 63. pl. 9, f. 2. 1784. *C. murorum*
    var. *miniatum* (Hoffm.) T. Fries. *C. murorum* var. *decipiens* (Arn.) Herre.
    Placodium murorum var. *miniatum* (Hoffm.) Duby. *Placodium murorum*
    (Hoffm.) DC.
    Thallus crustose to lobed and subfoliose, bright yellow to orange, sometimes
whitish subpruinose, somewhat verrucose toward the center, the margin lobed,
the lobes short and somewhat branched, or the whole thallus verrucose to squamulose without marginal lobing; apothecia small, 0.4–1 mm. across, sessile, concave
to flat, orange-red, the exciple of the same color as the thallus, commonly crenulate; spores ovoid-ellipsoid, 10–15 × 5–8 μ.
    On rocks, northern United States, also in Arizona.

30. **Caloplaca modesta** (Zahlbr.) Fink n. comb.
    Xanthoria modesta Zahlbr., Bull. Torr. Club 35:298, 299. 1908. *Teloschistes*
    modesta (Zahlbr.) Fink.
    Thallus well developed, dirty yellow to greenish gray, areolate, the margin
rarely of short crenate lobules; apothecia minute to small, 0.1–0.6 mm. across,
sessile, the disk flat to convex, rusty brown to orange, the exciple dirty yellow to
orange or of the same color as the thallus, entire, soon depressed; spores ellipsoid,
9–12 × 5–8 μ.
    On rocks, Maryland and Arizona.

31. **Caloplaca bracteata** (Hoffm.) Jatta, Syll. Lich. Ital. 236. 1900.
    Psora bracteata Hoffm., Deutschl. Fl. 2:169. 1795. *Placodium bracteatum*
    (Hoffm.) Nyl. *Placodium fulgens* var. *bracteatum* (Hoffm.) Ach.
    Thallus granulose to subareolate or verrucose-lobulate, pale to lemon-yellow;
apothecia minute to small, 0.2–1 mm. across, sessile, angular when crowded, the
disk flat, tawny red to brown, the exciple of the same color as the thallus, entire
to wavy, sometimes disappearing; spores ellipsoid, obscurely or rarely 1-septate,
the cells polar, 8–11 × 4–6 μ.
    On moss and soil, from Montana and South Dakota southward to Nebraska.

32. **Caloplaca lobulata** (Floerke) Hellb., Bih. Kgl. Sven. Vet. 21:67. 1896.
    Lecanora lobulata Floerke, in Spreng., Neue Entd. 1:219. 1820. *C. elegans* var.
    brachyloba (Fink) Zahlbr.
    Thallus well developed, orange-yellow to bright orange above, whitish or black-
ening below, verrucose or rarely areolate, the margin frequently of short crenate
lobules; apothecia minute to small, 0.2–1 mm. across, sessile, the disk flat, light
yellowish brown to dark orange, the exciple thick, raised, lemon-yellow to bright
orange, entire or slightly wavy; spores oblong-ellipsoid, 10–14 × 5–7 μ.
    On rocks, from Nebraska to Arizona, and in Washington.

33. **Caloplaca cirrochroa** (Ach.) T. Fries, Lich. Scand. 1:171, 172. 1871.
    Lecanora cirrochroa Ach., Syn. Meth. Lich. 181, 182. 1814. *Placodium cirro-*
    chroum (Ach.) Hepp.
    Thallus rather thin, closely adnate, radiately laciniate to minutely warty to-
wards the center, the warts sorediate or granulose-sorediate, yellowish to yellowish
brown; apothecia minute, 0.2–0.35 mm. across, adnate, the disk flat, yellowish to
reddish yellow, the exciple thin, colored like the thallus; spores oblong-ellipsoid,
11–18 × 4.5–6 μ.
    On rocks, Vermont, South Dakota, Iowa, Texas, and California.

34. **Caloplaca elegans** (Link) T. Fries, Lich. Scand. 1:168. 1871.
    Lichen elegans Link, Beitr. Naturgesch. 1:37. 1794. *Placodium elegans* (Link)
    DC.
    Thallus subfoliose, orange to yellowish or reddish above, white or darkening
below, obscurely coralloid-granulose toward the center, the margin usually stellately lobed, the lobes long, branched, sometimes subimbricated, often somewhat
lacunose; apothecia small to middle-sized, 0.5–2 mm. across, subsessile to sessile,

the disk concave to slightly convex, orange, the exciple of the same color as the thallus, entire to crenulate, sometimes becoming wavy; spores ovoid-ellipsoid, 9–18 × 5–8.5 μ. (PLATE 43 b.)

On rocks, throughout the United States, chiefly confined to the mountains in the South.

  var. trachyphylla (Tuck.) Fink n. comb.
  Placodium elegans var. *trachyphyllum* Tuck., Syn. N. A. Lich. 1:170. 1882. *C. trachyphylla* (Tuck.) Zahlbr.
  Thallus closely adnate, dark orange, roughened by minute or larger granules. On rocks, Montana, Wyoming, and Nevada.

35. **Caloplaca microphylina** (Tuck.) Hasse, Cont. U. S. Nat. Herb. 17:114. 1913.
  Placodium microphylinum Tuck., Syn. N. A. Lich. 1:174. 1882.
  Thallus of small, closely adnate squamules, sometimes forming an areolate crust towards the center, dirty greenish yellow to orange, the marginal squamules often crenately lobed, often obscured by minute yellow granules; apothecia minute to small, 0.3–0.5 mm. across, adnate, the disk flat, dark orange, the exciple greenish yellow to orange or grayish or darkening, usually crenulate; spores ellipsoid, 9–15 × 5–7 μ.
  On old wood, throughout northern United States, and in California and Texas.

36. **Caloplaca eugyra** (Tuck.) Zahlbr., Cat. Lich. Univ. 7:239. 1930.
  Placodium eugyrum Tuck., Am. Journ. Sci. II. 25:425. 1858.
  Thallus thin, round to irregular, dirty brownish green to brownish yellow, chinky-areolate, passing toward the margins into short, paler, white-powdery, crenate lobes; apothecia small to middle-sized, 0.4–0.8 mm. across, adnate, the disk flat, brownish yellow to reddish brown, the exciple thin, colored much like the thallus, crenulate; spores ovoid-ellipsoid, 9–13 × 4–6.5 μ.
  On rocks, Texas and Colorado.

37. **Caloplaca teicholyta** (Ach.) Stenr., Sitz. Kais. Acad. Wiss. 104¹:388. 1895.
  Lecanora teicholytum Ach., Lich. Univ. 425. 1810. *Placodium teicholytum* (Ach.) DC.
  Thallus thin, minutely granulose to powdery, rarely becoming radiately lobed toward the circumference, pale greenish gray to ashy; apothecia small, 0.3–0.6 mm. across, adnate to subsessile, the disk flat to slightly convex, orange to brownish red, the exciple thick, colored like the thallus, elevated, rarely becoming powdery; spores ellipsoid, 12–16 × 7–9 μ.
  On sandstone, southern California.

38. **Caloplaca peliophylla** (Tuck.) Zahlbr., Cat. Lich. Univ. 7:262. 1930.
  Placodium peliophyllum Tuck., Gen. Lich. 108. 1872.
  Thallus warty, greenish gray and blackening, the margins extended into many narrow, linear, unequal lobes; apothecia middle-sized to large, 0.7–2 mm. across, sessile, the disk flat, chestnut-brown, the exciple moderately thick, colored like the thallus, becoming flexuous; spores ellipsoid, 14–20 × 5–9 μ.
  On granite rocks, California.

39. **Caloplaca galactophylla** (Tuck.) Zahlbr., Cat. Lich. Univ. 7:239. 1930.
  Placodium galactophyllum Tuck., Proc. Am. Acad. 12:171. 1877.
  Thallus well developed, dirty whitish, yellowish brown when rubbed, squamulose to areolate, the areoles sometimes passing into crenate lobules at the margin; apothecia minute to small, 0.2–0.6 mm. across, immersed to adnate, the disk flat, cinnamon-brown, the exciple of the same color as the thallus, thick, entire to wavy; spores oblong-ellipsoid, 10–15 × 5–7 μ.
  On calcareous rocks, Kansas and Missouri.

40. **Caloplaca coralloides** (Tuck.) Hult., Hedwigia 35:187. 1896.
  Placodium coralloides Tuck., Proc. Am. Acad. 6:287. 1866.
  Thallus of linear, subdichotomously branching, nodulose, bright yellow to orange

lobes, loosely attached and sometimes rising from the substratum; apothecia small, 0.3–1 mm. across, lateral or terminal, subpedicellate, the disk concave to convex, dark orange, the exciple light orange, entire, raised; spores oblong-ellipsoid, 10–16 × 5–7 μ.

On frequently submerged rocks, California.

41. **Caloplaca cladodes** (Tuck.) Zahlbr., in E. & P., Nat. Pfl. 1¹:228. 1907.
Placodium cladodes Tuck., Proc. Am. Acad. 6:265. 1866.

Thallus composed of short, pale, round, slender, erect, clustered branches, crowded into a papillate orange-yellow crust; blackening below; apothecia small to middle-sized, 0.7–1.3 mm. across, sessile, the disk flat, powdery, dull brownish yellow, the exciple thick, crenulate, colored like the thallus; spores 1, oblong-ellipsoid, 20–26 × 15–20 μ.

On soil, Wyoming and Colorado.

OTHER SPECIES REPORTED

Caloplaca callopisma (Ach.) T. Fries—California.
Caloplaca discernenda (Nyl.) Zahlbr.—New Mexico.

42. TELOSCHISTACEAE

Thallus crustose to foliose, or rarely fruticose, showing more or less differentiation into cortical layers on one or both sides and algal and medullary layers, the cortex often plectenchymatous in the higher form, attached to the substratum by rhizoids or hyphal rhizoids; apothecia round, scattered, adnate to sessile, with a thalloid exciple; both thallus and apothecia commonly yellow to orange.

The algal host is Protococcus.

167. **Teloschistes** Norm., Nyt Mag. Naturv. 7:228. pl. 1, f. 4*a–g*.
1853.

Thallus foliose to fruticose, prostrate to ascending and erect, or rarely pendulant, more or less lobed or branched, smooth to rough, sometimes ciliate, attached to the substratum by rhizoids, differentiated into well-developed plectenchymatous upper and lower cortices, rather indistinct algal layer and loosely interwoven medullary layer, or in the fruticose forms an algal layer on both sides of the medullary tissue; apothecia minute to small or middle-sized, lateral, terminal or scattered, sessile to subsessile, the disk concave to flat, commonly yellow or orange, the exciple colored like the thallus, entire, crenulate, or ciliate; hypothecium hyaline or brownish; hymenium hyaline or brownish above; paraphyses unbranched, sometimes forked at the apices; asci clavate to cylindrico-clavate; spores 8, hyaline, oblong-ellipsoid or ellipsoid, 1–3-septate, the cells polar.

The algal host is Protococcus.

A. Thallus foliose
  B. Thallus closely adnate, margins rarely ascending
    C. Thallus bearing many rhizoids and fibrils below;
      apothecia numerous and crowded . . . . 3. T. polycarpus
    C. Thallus bearing few rhizoids and fibrils below;
      apothecia less numerous . . . . 1. T. parietinus
  B. Thallus more loosely adnate, margins commonly ascending
    C. Lobes sparingly branched
      D. Thallus small, lobes small . . . . 4. T. ramulosus
      D. Thallus larger, lobes wider . . . . 2. T. candelarius
    C. Lobes much branched
      D. Lobes more or less fibrillose . . . . 2. T. candelarius laciniosus
      D. Lobes marginally granulose . . . . 2. T. candelarius pygmaeus
A. Thallus subfruticose to fruticose
  B. Thallus small, branches short . . . . 8. T. euplocus

B. Thallus larger, branches more or less elongated
  C. Branches hispid or fibrillose
    D. Greenish gray to yellow, dichotomously
      branched . . . . 5. T. chrysophthalmus
    D. Ashy gray, much branched . . . . 7. T. villosus
  C. Branches minutely sorediate . . . . 6. T. flavicans

1. **Teloschistes parietinus** (L.) Norm., Nyt Mag. Naturv. 7:229. 1853.
    Lichen parietinus L., Sp. Pl. 1143. 1753. *Xanthoria parietina* (L.) Beltr.
    Thallus middle-sized to large, round or irregular, closely adnate, bright yellow to yellowish gray or orange, composed of more or less imbricated, smooth to minutely wrinkled and folded, sparingly divided, marginally crenate and dilated, radiately arranged lobes; ashy yellow below, bearing few ashy rhizoids and fibrils; apothecia small to middle-sized, 1–3.5 mm. across, subsessile, sometimes crowded, the disk concave to flat, orange, the exciple thin, colored like the thallus, becoming flexuous; hypothecium hyaline; spores ellipsoid, 13–18 × 7–10 μ.
    On trees and rarely on rocks, northern United States, and California.

2. **Teloschistes candelarius** (L.) Fink n. comb.
    Lichen candelarius L., Sp. Pl. 1141. 1753. *T. lychneus* (Ach.) Tuck. *Xanthoria lychnea* (Ach.) T. Fries. *Xanthoria candelaria* (L.) Kickx. *Physcia parietina* var. *finmarkica* (Ach.) Tuck.
    Thallus middle-sized, round to irregular, greenish yellow or orange, composed of rather broad, more or less imbricated, sparingly branched, somewhat ascending, marginally coralloid or granulose lobes; yellowish to ashy below, bearing many ashy yellow rhizoids and marginal fibrils; apothecia small to middle-sized, 1–4 mm. across, subsessile, rarely fibrillose below, the disk concave to flat, orange or reddish orange, the exciple thin, colored like the thallus, becoming crenulate, coralloid or granulose; hypothecium hyaline; spores ellipsoid, 12–17 × 5.5–9 μ.
    On trees and old wood, throughout the United States.

  var. **laciniosus** (Duf.) Fink n. comb.
    Parmelia parietina var. *laciniosa* Duf., in Schaer., Enum. Lich. Eur. 51. 1850. *T. lychneus* var. *laciniosus* (Duf.) Herre. *Xanthoria lychnea* var. *laciniosa* (Duf.) Herre. *Xanthoria candelaria* var. *laciniosa* (Duf.) Arn.
    Thallus composed of many, much-branched, marginally ascending and often more or less fibrillose lobes.
    On old wood, Louisiana, Nevada, and southern California.

  var. **pygmaeus** (Bory) Fink n. comb.
    Parmelia parietina var. *pygmaea* Bory, in E. Fries, Lich. Eur. 73. 1831. *T. lychneus* var. *pygmaeus* (Bory) Tuck. *T. parietinus* var. *pygmaeus* (Bory) E. Fries. *Xanthoria lychnea* var. *pygmaea* (Bory) T. Fries. *Xanthoria candelaria* var. *pygmaea* (Bory) Arn.
    Thallus small, composed of many, irregularly much-branched, ascending or erect, marginally granulose lobes.
    On rocks, Montana, Oregon, California, and Texas.

3. **Teloschistes polycarpus** (Ehrh.) Tuck., Syn. N. A. Lich. 1:50. 1882.
    Lichen polycarpus Ehrh., in Ach., Lich. Suec. 135. 1798. *Xanthoria lychnea* var. *polycarpa* (Ehrh.) T. Fries. *Xanthoria polycarpa* (Ehrh.) Oliv. *Parmelia parietina* var. *polycarpa* (Ehrh.) E. Fries.
    Thallus small to middle-sized, round to irregular, closely adnate, yellow to dark orange, composed of many, small, narrow, much divided, imbricated or rarely scattered, marginally crenate and rarely ascending lobes; ashy white below, bearing many ashy white or gray rhizoids and marginal fibrils; apothecia small to middle-sized, 1–4 mm. across, subsessile, numerous, crowded, the disk concave to flat, dark orange, the exciple thin, colored like the thallus, becoming crenulate; hypothecium hyaline; spores ellipsoid, 12–18 × 5–8 μ. (PLATE 41 *a*.)
    On trees and old wood, throughout the United States.

4. **Teloschistes ramulosus** Tuck., Syn. N. A. Lich. 1:51. 1882.

Physcia parietina var. *ramulosa* Tuck., Proc. Âm. Acad. 4:387. 1860. *Xanthoria ramulosa* (Tuck.) Herre.

Thallus yellow to yellowish gray, composed of minute, scattered, sparingly branched, semi-cylindrical, slightly ascending, finally imbricated lobules; ashy yellow below, bearing scattered rhizoids; apothecia minute, 0.3–0.8 mm. across, subsessile, the disk concave to flat, yellowish orange, the exciple thick, colored like the thallus, entire; hypothecium hyaline; spores ellipsoid, $12–17 \times 6–9 \mu$.

On trees and shrubs, along the coast of California.

5. **Teloschistes chrysophthalmus** (L.) Beltr., Lich. Bass. 109. 1858.

Lichen chrysophthalmus L., Mant. Pl. 2:311. 1771.

Thallus tufted, erect or spreading or more rarely pendulant, greenish gray to yellow, composed of rigid, compressed, more or less fibrillose, dichotomously branched lobes; yellowish or grayish below, sometimes reticulately veined; apothecia small to middle-sized, 1–5 mm. across, terminal or subterminal, the disk concave to flat, orange, the exciple thin, colored like the thallus, more or less ciliate; hypothecium hyaline; spores ellipsoid, $10–16 \times 5–8 \mu$. (PLATE 44.)

On trees and old wood, throughout the United States.

6. **Teloschistes flavicans** (Swartz) Norm., Nyt Mag. Naturv. 7:229. 1853.

Lichen flavicans Swartz, Fl. Ind. Occ. 147. 1788. *T. chrysophthalmus* var. *flavicans* (Swartz) Tuck. *T. exilis* (Michx.) Vainio.

Thallus tufted, erect and spreading or rarely pendulant, yellowish orange to yellow or ashy, composed of many elongated, entangled, somewhat compressed, more or less twisted, pitted or channeled, minutely whitish or yellowish sorediate branches; apothecia small to middle-sized, 1–2.5 mm. across, lateral, scattered, the disk concave to flat, dark orange, the exciple thin, colored like the thallus, becoming crenulate, sometimes disappearing; hypothecium hyaline; spores ellipsoid, $12–18 \times 6–10 \mu$.

On trees, from Massachusetts to Florida, and in Texas, California, Nevada, and Oregon.

7. **Teloschistes villosus** (Ach.) Norm., Nyt Mag. Naturv. 7:229. 1853.

Parmelia villosa Ach., Meth. Lich. 254. 1803. *Physcia villosa* (Ach.) Duby.

Thallus ashy gray, erect and spreading or pendulant, composed of many compressed, channeled, much-divided, more or less entangled, minutely hispid branches; apothecia small to middle-sized, 1–2.5 mm. across, subterminal, subsessile, the disk concave, yellowish red or orange, the exciple thin, colored like the thallus, more or less ciliate; hypothecium hyaline; spores oblong-ellipsoid, $11–15 \times 4.5–6 \mu$.

On trees, southern California.

8. **Teloschistes euplocus** (Tuck.) Zahlbr., in E. & P., Nat. Pfl. 1^1:230. 1907.

Physcia euploca Tuck., Am. Journ. Sci. II. 25:424. 1858. *Speerschneidera euploca* (Tuck.) Trev.

Thallus erect or suberect, dichotomously much-branched, pale brownish to whitish, the branches short, slender, interwoven, forked or pointed at the apices; apothecia small to middle-sized, 0.5–1.2 mm. across, sessile, the disk flat to convex, flesh-colored to brownish, the exciple thin, colored like the thallus, becoming wavy and sometimes disappearing; hypothecium hyaline to yellowish; paraphyses simple or little branched; asci clavate; spores ellipsoid to ovoid-ellipsoid, $10–15 \times 3.5–5 \mu$.

On rocks, Texas, Missouri, and Kansas.

43. BUELLIACEAE

Thallus crustose to scaly, or rarely squamulose, entire or lobed at the margin, showing little or no differentiation into layers, attached to the substratum by hyphal rhizoids; apothecia round, immersed to adnate or sessile, with a well-developed proper or thalloid exciple.

The algal host is Protococcus.

A. Parasitic on other lichens
  B. Spores 1-septate . . . . 169. BUELLIELLA
  B. Spores 3-septate . . . . 170. LECIOGRAPHA
A. Not parasitic on other lichens
  B. Apothecia with proper exciple
    C. Spores 1-septate . . . . 168. BUELLIA
    C. Spores 3-septate . . . . 171. BUELLIOPSIS
  B. Apothecia with thalloid exciple . . . . 172. RINODINA

168. Buellia De Not., Giorn. Bot. Ital. 2^1:195, 196. 1846.

Thallus crustose, granulose, warty, or more commonly areolate, mainly above the substratum, rudimentary and attached by hyphal rhizoids; apothecia hard, immersed to sessile, the disk flat to convex, commonly black, the exciple of the same color, soon disappearing; hypothecium brown to black or rarely tinged reddish; hymenium hyaline or brownish; paraphyses rarely branched, usually enlarged and brownish toward the apex; asci clavate, broadly clavate, or cylindrical; spores 8 to rarely many, brown or rarely almost hyaline, 1-septate, ellipsoid to oblong-ellipsoid.
The algal host is Protococcus.

A. On rocks and soil
  B. Thallus ashy to greenish or reddish brown or black
    C. Spores rarely more than 18 μ in length
      D. Thallus a more or less chinky-areolate crust
        E. Spores 8–13 $\times$ 4–6 μ . . . . 22. B. turgescentoides
        E. Spores 12–18 $\times$ 5.5–9 μ . . . . 24. B. pullata
      D. Thallus of more or less scattered areoles . . . . . 4. B. coracina
    C. Spores larger, usually more than 18 μ in length
      D. Spores 14–27 $\times$ 7–13 μ . . . . 18. B. colludens
      D. Spores 25–38 $\times$ 11–17 μ . . . . 19. B. badioatra
  B. Thallus greenish gray, whitish, ashy, or yellowish
    C. Thallus greenish gray to ashy
      D. Black hypothallus usually conspicuous
        E. Apothecia 0.4–0.8 mm. across, disk wrinkled or papillate . 16. B. spuria
        E. Apothecia 0.2–0.5 mm. across, disk smooth
          F. Spores 9–14 $\times$ 3.5–6 μ . . . . 5. B. stigmaea
          F. Spores 10–19 $\times$ 5.5–8 μ . . . . 25. B. lepidastra
      D. Black hypothallus not conspicuous
        E. Thallus minutely areolate or warty
          F. Thallus areolate, greenish gray to ashy . . . 8. B. retrovertens
          F. Thallus becoming rough and warty, milky white to
            greenish gray, sometimes subpruinose . . . . . 6. B. Blumeri
        E. Thallus granulose or subsquamulose . . . . . . 27. B. bolacina
    C. Thallus yellowish, gray, or whitish
      D. Black hypothallus usually conspicuous
        E. Apothecia 0.4–1 mm. across
          F. Thallus squamulose . . . . 29. B. pulchella
          F. Thallus chinky to areolate . . . . 3. B. halonia
        E. Apothecia smaller, 0.15–0.25 mm. across . . . . . 2. B. stellulata
      D. Black hypothallus not conspicuous
        E. Apothecia 0.6–1 mm. or more across
          F. Thallus sulphur-yellow, becoming pale; spores
            14–27 $\times$ 7–10 μ . . . . 7. B. semitensis
          F. Thallus whitish; spores 14–18 $\times$ 5.5–7.5 μ . . 23. B. tucsonensis
        E. Apothecia rarely more than 0.6 mm. across
          F. Thallus areolate to rarely granulose
            G. Thallus thin, ashy to whitish
              H. Spores 10–18 $\times$ 5–8.5 μ . . . . 10. B. aethalea
              H. Spores 9–12 $\times$ 3–4.5 μ . . . . 9. B. insidians
            G. Thallus coarser, chinky, white-powdery or
              dirty orange . . . . 20. B. rinodinoides
          F. Thallus lobed . . . . 26. B. epigaea

A. On trees, old wood, over moss, and rarely on rocks
  B. Thallus greenish gray to ashy
    C. Thallus more or less bordered by a black hypothallus
      D. Spores 1-septate . . . . 1. B. parasema
      D. Spores 2–3-septate . . . . 1. B. parasema triphragmia
    C. Thallus without a black hypothallus
      D. Thallus scurfy or chinky, often disappearing
        E. Spores 8 in each ascus . . . . 11. B. punctata
        E. Spores 12–24 in each ascus . . . . 11. B. punctata polyspora
      D. Thallus minutely granulose . . . . 13. B. Elizae
  B. Thallus not greenish gray
    C. Thallus whitish or ashy
      D. Spores 10–15 × 5–8 μ . . . . 12. B. conspirans
      D. Spores 19–30 × 7–11 μ . . . . 15. B. dialyta
    C. Thallus not whitish or ashy or rarely so
      D. Thallus chinky or minutely granulose
        E. Thallus ashy to brownish gray . . . . 14. B. Schaereri
        E. Thallus greenish straw-colored, granules more or
        less heaped . . . . 17. B. caloosensis
      D. Thallus squamulose or areolate
        E. Thallus squamulose, brownish to greenish brown . . . 28. B. badia
        E. Thallus areolate, brownish ashy to reddish or
        yellowish . . . . 21. B. turgescens

1. **Buellia parasema** (Ach.) De Not., Giorn. Bot. Ital. 2^1:198. 1846.
    Lichen parasema Ach., Lich. Suec. 64. 1798. *B. disciformis* (E. Fries) Mudd.
    B. parasema var. *microcarpa* (Ach.) Koerb. *B. subdisciformis* (Leight.)
    Jatta.
    Thallus continuous, smooth, becoming roughened, chinky and finally areolate, greenish gray to ashy, darkening or yellowish, bordered more or less by a black hypothallus; apothecia small to middle-sized, 0.3–0.8 mm. across, adnate to sessile, rarely even more or less immersed, the disk flat to convex, black, the exciple black, becoming flexuous, thin, and rarely disappearing; hypothecium dark brown; spores oblong-ellipsoid, 10–22 × 5–10 μ. (PLATE 45.)
    On trees, throughout the United States.

  var. **triphragmia** (Nyl.) T. Fries, Nov. Act. Reg. Soc. Sci. Ups. III. 3:327. 1861.
    Lecidea triphragmia Nyl., Mém. Soc. Sci. Nat. Cherb. 5:126. 1857. *B. lauricassiae* (Fée) Müll. Arg. *B. triphragmia* (Nyl.) Arn.
    Spores becoming 2–3-septate, and, on the whole, longer.
    On trees, from New England to Louisiana, and westward to California and Washington.

2. **Buellia stellulata** (Tayl.) Mudd, Man. Brit. Lich. 216. 1861.
    Lecidea stellulata Tayl., in Mack., Fl. Hibern. 2:118. 1836.
    Thallus thin, minutely areolate, gray to ashy white, the areoles flat or a little convex, smooth, scattered or crowded into a chinky crust upon the black hypothallus; apothecia minute, 0.15–0.25 mm. across, immersed to adnate, the disk flat to somewhat convex, black, the exciple black, thin, infrequently and tardily disappearing; hypothecium blackish brown; spores ellipsoid, 8–14 × 4–6.5 μ.
    On rocks, Massachusetts, New Jersey, Tennessee, Alabama, and California.

3. **Buellia halonia** (Ach.) Tuck., Lich. Calif. 26. 1866.
    Lecidea halonia Ach., Meth. Lich. 47. 1803.
    Thallus chinky to areolate, greenish yellow to grayish, areoles smooth, flat, irregular, upon a black hypothallus; apothecia small to middle-sized, 0.4–1 mm. across, adnate, the disk flat to strongly convex, black and more or less greenish white pruinose, the exciple black, raised, thin, and disappearing; hypothecium reddish-brown; spores ellipsoid, 11–16 × 6–8 μ.
    On rocks, California.

4. **Buellia coracina** (Hoffm.) T. Fries, Nov. Act. Soc. Sci. Ups. III. 3:331. 1861.
Verrucaria coracina Hoffm., Deutschl. Fl. 183. 1795. *Lecidea coracina* (Hoffm.)
Nyl. *B. moriopsis* (Mass.) T. Fries.

Thallus chinky to areolate, the areoles often convex and scattered, ashy black,
on a black hypothallus; apothecia small, 0.3–0.6 mm. across, immersed to adnate,
the disk flat to convex, black, more or less greenish pruinose, the exciple uneven,
black, soon disappearing; hypothecium brown to brownish black; spores ellipsoid,
8–18 × 5.5–9.5 μ.

On rocks, New Hampshire, Vermont, Tennessee, and South Dakota.

5. **Buellia stigmaea** Tuck., Syn. N. A. Lich. 2:90. 1888.

Thallus smooth, greenish gray to yellowish or ashy, soon becoming chinky and
areolate, intersected and bordered by the blackish hypothallus; apothecia minute to
small, 0.2–0.5 mm. across, adnate, the disk flat, black, the exciple thin, light-colored
to black; hypothecium dark brown; spores ellipsoid, 9–14 × 3.5–6 μ.

On rocks, Massachusetts, Pennsylvania, Alabama, and South Carolina.

6. **Buellia Blumeri** Zahlbr., Ann. Mycol. 7:477. 1909.

Thallus thin, becoming roughened and verrucose, milky white to greenish gray,
sometimes subpruinose; apothecia small, 0.3–0.5 mm. across, sessile, the disk concave to convex, black, the exciple prominent, brownish black; hypothecium dark
brown; spores ellipsoid, 13–16 × 5–6 μ.

On rocks, near Tucson, Arizona.

7. **Buellia semitensis** Tuck., Syn. N. A. Lich. 2:95, 96. 1888.

Thallus thin, rough, wrinkled-verrucose, sometimes crumbling, sulphur-yellow
becoming pale; apothecia middle-sized to large, 0.6–1.4 mm. across, the disk flat to
convex, black, the exciple black, often disappearing; hypothecium reddish to brownish black; spores ellipsoid, 14–27 × 7–10 μ.

On rocks, California.

8. **Buellia retrovertens** Tuck., Syn. N. A. Lich. 2:89, 90. 1888.

Thallus minutely areolate, greenish gray to ashy, the areoles smooth, separate,
often convex; apothecia minute to middle-sized, 0.2–0.8 mm. across, adnate, the disk
flat to convex, black, the exciple brown to black, thin, disappearing; hypothecium
brown to brownish black; spores ellipsoid, 10–17 × 6–8 μ.

On rocks, Colorado and California.

9. **Buellia insidians** (Nyl.) Zahlbr., Cat. Lich. Univ. 7:370. 1931.
Lecidea insidians Nyl., Lab. & Sing. 41, 42. 1891.

Thallus thin, smooth to rough, chinky to areolate, sometimes minutely granulose,
ashy to whitish; apothecia minute to small, 0.2–0.5 mm. across, partly immersed,
the disk flat to slightly convex, black, the exciple rather thick, black, prominent,
rarely disappearing; hypothecium dark brown to brownish black; spores oblong,
9–12 × 3–4.5 μ.

On rocks, Tennessee.

10. **Buellia aethalea** (Ach.) T. Fries, Lich. Scand. 1:604. 1874.
Gyalecta aethalea Ach., Lich. Univ. 669. 1810. *B. atroalbella* (Nyl.) Mong.
Lecidea atroalbella Nyl. *Lecidea cohibilis* Nyl.

Thallus thin, chinky to minutely areolate, ashy or becoming white; apothecia
small, 0.2–0.5 mm. across, partly immersed to adnate, the disk flat to somewhat
convex, black, the exciple prominent, dull black; hypothecium dark brown; spores
ovoid-ellipsoid, 10–18 × 5–8.5 μ.

On rocks, Tennessee.

11. **Buellia punctata** (Hoffm.) Mass., Ric. Lich. 81. f. 165. 1852.
Verrucaria punctata Hoffm., Deutschl. Fl. 192. 1796. *B. myriocarpa* (Lam. &
DC.) De Not. *B. myriocarpa* var. *punctiformis* (Hoffm.) Mudd.

Thallus thin, greenish gray to ashy, scurfy or compacted into a smoothish or chinky crust, becoming rough, often disappearing; apothecia minute to small, 0.15–0.6 mm. across, adnate, the disk flat to convex, black, the exciple black, thin, and disappearing; hypothecium dark brown; spores ellipsoid, 7–16 × 4–7.5 μ.

On wood and rocks, throughout the United States.

var. **polyspora** (Willey) Fink n. comb.

    B. myriocarpa var. *polyspora* Willey, in Tuck., Syn. N. A. Lich. 2:97. 1888.

    B. polyspora (Willey) Vainio.

Differing from the species in that there are 12–24 spores in each ascus.

On trees, from Massachusetts westward to Iowa and Minnesota.

12. **Buellia conspirans** (Nyl.) Vainio, Ann. Acad. Sci. Fenn. A. 6:88. 1915.

    Lecidea conspirans Nyl., Flora 51:345. 1868.

Thallus thin, minutely granulose, becoming chinky, white to ashy; apothecia minute to small, 0.2–0.6 mm. across, adnate, round, the disk flat, black, becoming irregular, the exciple thin, colored like the disk; hypothecium dark brown; spores 8, brown, oblong to ellipsoid, 1-septate, one cell slightly larger, 10–15 × 5–8 μ.

On old wood, Florida.

13. **Buellia Elizae** Tuck., Lich. Calif. 25. 1866.

    Lecidea Elizae Tuck., Am. Journ. Sci. 25:428. 1858.

Thallus of minute, round, greenish gray, scattered or crowded granules, on a white hypothallus; apothecia minute to small, 0.3–0.7 mm. across, immersed to adnate, the disk flat to convex, orange-red to black, the exciple prominent, black, thin, and finally disappearing; hypothecium brown; spores ellipsoid, 9–15 × 4–7 μ.

On trees, Vermont, Massachusetts, and Virginia.

14. **Buellia Schaereri** De Not., Giorn. Bot. Ital. 2:199. 1846.

    Lecidea nigritula Nyl.

Thallus thin, scurfy, becoming minutely granulose, brownish ashy, often disappearing; apothecia minute, 0.15–0.4 mm. across, adnate, the disk flat to convex, black, the exciple thin, brownish black, and disappearing; hypothecium brownish black; spores ellipsoid, 6–10 × 2.5–4.5 μ.

On old wood, from New England to New Jersey, and westward to Illinois and Minnesota.

15. **Buellia dialyta** (Nyl.) Tuck., Gen. Lich. 187. 1872.

    Lecidea dialyta Nyl., Flora 52:123. 1869.

Thallus thin, granulose, white to ashy, often compacted into a scurfy, widespread crust, resting on an obscure whitish hypothallus; apothecia minute to small, 0.2–0.6 mm. across, adnate to sessile, the disk flat to slightly convex, black, the exciple thin and disappearing; hypothecium dark brown; spores fusiform-ellipsoid, 19–30 × 7–11 μ.

On trees, from New England to North Carolina, westward to Minnesota, and in California.

16. **Buellia spuria** (Schaer.) Anzi, Cat. Lich. Sondr. 87. 1860.

    Lecidea spuria Schaer., Lich. Helv. Spic. 3:127. 1827. *B. lactea* (Mass.) Koerb.

Thallus areolate, the areoles greenish gray to ashy, many-sided, often black-edged, small and flat or becoming convex, scattered upon the black hypothallus or crowded into a continuous chinky crust; apothecia small to middle-sized, 0.4–0.8 mm. across, slightly immersed to adnate, the disk flat to convex, often wrinkled or papillate, black, the exciple black, prominent, finally flexuous, and rarely disappearing; hypothecium dark brown; spores ellipsoid, 9–17 × 4.5–8 μ.

On rocks, throughout the United States.

17. **Buellia caloosensis** Tuck., Syn. N. A. Lich. 2:99. 1888.

Thallus granulose, greenish straw-colored, the granules minute, globose, more or less heaped, finally confluent on a whitish or darkening hypothallus; apothecia minute to small, 0.25–0.55 mm. across, adnate, the disk flat to finally convex, becom-

ing black, the exciple thin and disappearing; hypothecium brown to blackish; spores ellipsoid, 7–12 × 3–5 μ.
On trees, from Florida to Texas.

18. **Buellia colludens** (Nyl.) Arn., Flora 53:479. 1870.
  Lecidea colludens Nyl., Flora 53:38. 1870. *Lecidea atroalba* var. *chlorospora*
     Nyl. *B. atroalba* Tuck.
Thallus somewhat rough, chinky to areolate, greenish gray to reddish or brownish, continuous or rarely scattered, surrounded by a black hypothallus; apothecia small to middle-sized, 0.5–1.2 mm. across, subsessile, the disk flat, black, the exciple black, raised, rarely crenulate; hypothecium dark brown; spores ellipsoid, 14–27 × 7–13 μ.
On rocks, from New England to Florida, and westward to Tennessee and Ohio.

19. **Buellia badioatra** (Floerke) Koerb., Syst. Lich. 223. 1855.
  Lecidea badioatra Floerke, in Spreng., Neu. Entd. 2:95. 1821. *Rhizocarpon
     badioatrum* (Floerke) T. Fries.
Thallus chinky-areolate, the areoles becoming strongly convex, scattered upon the blackish hypothallus or crowded into a crust, gray to brownish or reddish brown; apothecia small to middle-sized, 0.3–0.75 mm. across, slightly immersed to adnate, the disk flat to slightly convex, black, the exciple black, sometimes inconspicuous; hypothecium brown to blackish; spores oblong-ellipsoid, 25–38 × 11–17 μ, surrounded by a halo.
On rocks, Minnesota and New Hampshire.

20. **Buellia rinodinoides** Anzi, Atti Soc. Ital. Sci. Nat. 253. 1866.
Thallus coarsely chinky and areolate, the areoles flat to convex, angular, white-powdery, sometimes becoming dirty orange-colored; apothecia minute to small, 0.2–0.5 mm. across, immersed to superficial, often clustered, the disk flat to convex, black, the exciple black, thin, disappearing; hypothecium dark brown; spores ellipsoid, 9–15 × 5–8 μ.
On rocks, California.

21. **Buellia turgescens** (Nyl.) Tuck., Gen. Lich. 185. 1872.
  Lecidea turgescens Nyl., Mém. Soc. Sci. Nat. Cherb. 5:337. 1857.
Thallus chinky, warty, and commonly areolate, or the swollen warts often crowded into a more or less folded crust, brownish ashy varying to reddish or yellowish; apothecia minute to small, 0.2–0.6 mm. in diameter, partly immersed to adnate, the disk flat to convex, black, the exciple thin, black, and sometimes disappearing; hypothecium dark brown; spores ellipsoid, 9–15 × 4.5–7 μ.
On old wood and rocks, from New England to Illinois and Minnesota, and recurring in Washington.

22. **Buellia turgescentoides** Fink, Ohio Biol. Surv. 2:349. 1921.
Thallus thick, flat to warty, chinky to areolate, scattered or crowded into a crust, dull greenish brown and darkening, the marginal lobules sometimes lobulate; apothecia minute to small, 0.2–0.5 mm. across, immersed to adnate, scattered or clustered, the disk flat to convex, black, the exciple black, thin, and disappearing; hypothecium pale to darker brown; spores oblong-ellipsoid, 8–13 × 4–6 μ.
On rocks, Lake County, Ohio.

23. **Buellia tucsonensis** Zahlbr., Ann. Mycol. 7:477, 478. 1909.
Thallus thin, whitish, chinky to areolate, becoming warty and convoluted toward the center, often scattered with lobed areoles toward the margins; apothecia small to middle-sized, 0.6–1 mm. across, sessile, the disk flat to convex, brownish black, the exciple thin, brownish black, and disappearing; hypothecium brown; spores ellipsoid, 14–18 × 5.5–7.5 μ.
On rocks, near Tucson, Arizona.

24. **Buellia pullata** Tuck., Lich. Calif. 26. 1866.

Thallus chinky to minutely areolate, passing into a chinky, dark greenish brown crust; apothecia small, 0.2–0.6 mm. across, sessile, the disk flat to slightly convex, black, becoming irregular, the exciple thin, black, prominent, disappearing; hypothecium brownish black; spores ellipsoid, $12–18 \times 5.5–9 \mu$.

On rocks, Iowa, Minnesota, and California.

25. **Buellia lepidastra** Tuck., Syn. N. A. Lich. 2:90, 91. 1888.

Lecidea lepidastra Tuck., Am. Journ. Sci. II. 25:249. 1858.

Thallus squamulose-areolate, the greenish gray to ashy areoles becoming undulate to crenate, scattered or crowded into a broken, finally crumbling crust on a dark hypothallus; apothecia small, 0.3–0.5 mm. across, adnate, sometimes conglomerate, the disk flat, black, the exciple black, thick, but disappearing; hypothecium dark brown; spores ellipsoid, $10–19 \times 5.5–8 \mu$.

On rocks, from New England to Alabama, and westward to Texas and California.

26. **Buellia epigaea** (Hoffm.) Tuck., Gen. Lich. 185. 1872.

Lichen epigaeus Hoffm., Deutschl. Fl. 164. 1796. *Lecidea epigaea* (Hoffm.) Schaer.

Thallus lobed, white and powdery, the lobes crowded, often forming a rosette, or reduced and scattered; apothecia small to middle-sized, 0.3–0.8 mm. across, adnate to sessile, the disk flat and finally convex, dark brown to black, the exciple prominent, white-powdery, and disappearing; hypothecium brown; spores ellipsoid, $13–19 \times 6.5–9 \mu$.

On calcareous soil, Nebraska, Montana, and Wyoming.

27. **Buellia bolacina** Tuck., Syn. N. A. Lich. 2:88. 1888.

Thallus granulose or subsquamulose, greenish to greenish gray or white, the granules swollen, wavy, and plicate; apothecia small to middle-sized, 0.5–0.9 mm. across, adnate, the disk flat to convex, black, the exciple black, and soon disappearing; hypothecium brownish black; spores ellipsoid, $12–18 \times 6–9 \mu$.

On soil and rocks, California.

28. **Buellia badia** (E. Fries) Mass., Mem. Lich. 124. 1855.

Lecidea badia E. Fries, Syst. Orb. Veg. 287. 1825.

Thallus thin, of flat to hemispherical, brownish to greenish brown, crenately lobed squamules, or in part areolate; apothecia small to middle-sized, 0.2–0.8 mm. across, adnate, the disk flat to convex, black, the exciple thin, raised, black, becoming irregular, and disappearing; hypothecium brown; spores ellipsoid, $8–16 \times 5–9 \mu$.

On mosses over rocks, from South Carolina and Tennessee westward to California and Washington.

29. **Buellia pulchella** (Schrad.) Tuck., Gen. Lich. 185. 1872.

Lichen pulchellus Schrad., Journ. Bot. St. 1. pl. 74. 1799. *Lecidea Wahlenbergii* Ach.

Thallus squamulose, the swollen squamules crowded into a moderately thick, greenish yellow crust, becoming wavy-folded, upon a black hypothallus; apothecia small to middle-sized or larger, 0.4–1 mm. across, partly immersed to subsessile, sometimes clustered to confluent, the disk flat to convex, black, the exciple black, becoming flexuous, thin, and disappearing; hypothecium brownish black; spores ellipsoid, $10–17 \times 7–10 \mu$.

On rocks, New England.

OTHER SPECIES REPORTED

Buellia leptocline Koerb.—Oregon.

Buellia verruculosa (Borr.) Mudd.—Maine.

Buellia parasema var. vulgata T. Fries—Southern California.

169. Buelliella Fink.*

Parasitic on other lichens and the thallus invisible but probably parasitic on the algae within the lichen host; apothecia adnate to sessile, the disk flat to convex, commonly black, the exciple colored like the thallus, sometimes disappearing; hypothecium brown to black; hymenium hyaline to brownish above; paraphyses rarely branched, sometimes enlarged and brownish toward the apex; asci clavate or cylindrico-clavate; spores 8, brown, 1-septate, oblong-ovoid to ellipsoid or oblong. The algal host is Protococcus.

A. Exciple persistent or tardily disappearing
   B. Apothecia reaching 0.7 mm. across . . . . 2. B. inquilina
   B. Apothecia not more than 0.4 mm. across
      C. Spores 9–12 × 4.5–6.5 μ . . . . 1. B. saxatilis
      C. Spores 12–15 × 5–6 μ . . . . 6. B. Nuttallii
A. Exciple commonly disappearing
   B. Apothecia not more than 0.2 mm. across
      C. Spores 8–12 × 4–5 μ . . . . 7. B. Usneae
      C. Spores 14–16 × 5–7 μ . . . . 4. B. minimula
   B. Apothecia reaching 0.5 mm. across
      C. Spores 10–15 × 3.5–6 μ . . . . 5. B. Parmeliarum
      C. Spores 16–18 × 6.5–8.5 μ . . . . 3. B. Trypethelii

1. **Buelliella saxatilis** (Schaer.) Fink n. comb.
Calicium saxatile Schaer., Naturv. Anzeig. Schw. Ges. 5:35. 1821. *Buellia saxatilis* (Schaer.) Koerb.
Thallus immersed in that of the host and invisible; apothecia minute to small, 0.2–0.4 mm. across, subsessile, the disk flat to slightly convex, black, the exciple thick, brownish black; hypothecium dark brown; spores ellipsoid, 9–12 × 4.5–6.5 μ.
On *Baeomyces byssoides,* Vermont and Minnesota.

2. **Buelliella inquilina** (Tuck.) Fink n. comb.
Buellia inquilina Tuck., Lich. Calif. 32. 1866.
Thallus immersed in that of the host and invisible; apothecia minute to small, 0.2–0.7 mm. across, adnate to sessile, the disk flat to convex, brownish black to black, the exciple black, prominent, but finally disappearing; hypothecium brown; spores ellipsoid, 10–17 × 5.5–8 μ.
On species of Pertusaria and Lecanora, from Pennsylvania to South Carolina, and westward to Minnesota and Texas.

3. **Buelliella Trypethelii** (Tuck.) Fink n. comb.
Buellia Trypethelii Tuck., Syn. N. A. Lich. 2:106. 1888.
Thallus immersed in that of the host and invisible; apothecia minute to small, 0.2–0.4 mm. across, sessile, sometimes becoming oblong-difform, the disk flat to slightly convex, black, the exciple thin, black, and disappearing; hypothecium blackish brown; spores oblong-ovoid, 16–18 × 6.5–8.5 μ.
On *Trypethelium carolinianum,* Florida.

4. **Buelliella minimula** (Tuck.) Fink n. comb.
Buellia minimula Tuck., Syn. N. A. Lich. 2:106. 1888.
Thallus immersed in that of the host and invisible; apothecia very minute, 0.07–0.12 mm. across, adnate, the disk flat, brownish to black, the exciple thin, blackish, and disappearing; hypothecium brown; spores oblong-ovoid, hyaline to brownish, 14–16 × 5–7 μ.
On a species of Pertusaria, Florida.

5. **Buelliella Parmeliarum** (Sommerf.) Fink n. comb.
Lecidea Parmeliarum Sommerf., Suppl. Fl. Lapp. 176, 177. 1826. *Buellia Parmeliarum* (Sommerf.) Tuck.

---

* Buelliella Fink gen. nov. A Buellia De Not. thallo parasitico et inconspicuo, in hospitis thallo immerso differens.

Thallus immersed in that of the host and invisible, but deforming the hostal thallus; apothecia minute to small, 0.15–0.5 mm. across, adnate, the disk flat to convex, brown to black, the exciple prominent, black, and commonly disappearing; hypothecium brownish black; spores ellipsoid, 10–15 × 3.5–6 μ.

On *Parmelia saxatilis* and *Parmelia Borreri*, from New England to California, northward to Minnesota, and southward to Arkansas.

6. **Buelliella Nuttallii** (Calkins & Nyl.) Fink n. comb.

    Lecidea Nuttallii Calkins & Nyl., Bot. Gaz. 22:334. 1896.

Thallus immersed in that of the host and invisible; apothecia minute, 0.1–0.3 mm. across, subsessile, the disk flat, black, the exciple thick, black, prominent, rarely disappearing; hypothecium dark brown; asci clavate; spores oblong to oblong-ovoid, sometimes slightly constricted, 12–15 × 5–6 μ.

On the thallus of *Sticta erosa*, West Virginia.

7. **Buelliella Usneae** (Linds.) Fink n. comb.

    Abrothallus Usneae Linds., Trans. Roy. Soc. Edinb. 24:444. 1866,

Thallus immersed in that of the host and invisible; apothecia minute, 0.05–0.1 mm. across, adnate, the disk flat to slightly convex, black, the exciple thin, black, disappearing; hypothecium brown; spores oblong-ellipsoid, 8–12 × 4–5 μ.

On *Usnea barbata*, Colorado.

<h3 style="text-align:center">170. Leciographa Mass., Gen. Lich. 14. 1854.</h3>

Thallus imbedded in that of the lichen host and therefore invisible; apothecia adnate to sessile, hard, the disk and exciple brownish black to black; hypothecium brown to brownish black or tinged reddish; hymenium hyaline to brownish above; paraphyses rarely branched; asci broadly clavate; spores 8, brown, oblong-ellipsoid to fusiform, usually 3-septate.

The algal host is Protococcus.

A. Spores 1–3-septate . . . . 4. L. pertusaricola
A. Spores 3-septate
   B. Exciple thin . . . . 1. L. parasitica
   B. Exciple thick, somewhat wrinkled
      C. Spores 21–26 × 7.5–9 μ . . . . 2. L. glaucomaria
      C. Spores 11–16 × 4.5–7 μ . . . . 3. L. glaucomarioidea

1. **Leciographa parasitica** (Floerke) Mass., Gen. Lich. 14. 1854.

    Lecidea parasitica Floerke, Deutsch. Lich. no. 101. 1819. *Buellia parasitica*
        (Floerke) T. Fries.

Thallus imbedded and invisible; apothecia minute, 0.1–0.2 mm. across, sessile, the disk flat to slightly convex, black, the exciple thin, black; hypothecium dark brown; spores ellipsoid, 3-septate, 10–16 × 3–6 μ.

On the thalli of species of Lecanora and Pertusaria, Minnesota, Michigan, California, and Oregon.

2. **Leciographa glaucomaria** (Nyl.) A. L. Smith, Brit. Lich. 2:186. 1911.

    Lecidea glaucomaria Nyl., Bot. Not. 1852. 177. 1852. *Buellia glaucomaria*
        (Nyl.) Tuck.

Thallus imbedded and invisible; apothecia minute, 0.05–0.15 mm. across, adnate, sometimes heaped, the disk flat, black, the exciple thick and somewhat wrinkled; hypothecium brownish black; spores oblong-ovoid, 3-septate, hyaline to brown, 21–26 × 7.5–9 μ.

On thalli of species of Lecanora and Pertusaria, Massachusetts and Minnesota.

3. **Leciographa glaucomarioidea** (Willey) Fink n. comb.

    Buellia glaucomarioidea Willey, Enum. Lich. New Bedford, Mass. 27. 1892.

Thallus imbedded and invisible; apothecia minute, 0.05–0.15 mm. across, adnate, often clustered or heaped, the disk flat, black, the exciple thick, black, somewhat wrinkled; hypothecium brownish black; spores ellipsoid, 3-septate, 11–16 × 4.5 –7 μ. On the thallus of *Lecanora tartarea*, near New Bedford, Massachusetts.

4. **Leciographa pertusaricola** (Willey) Fink n. comb.

> *Buellia pertusaricola* Willey, in Tuck., Syn. N. A. Lich. 2:108. 1888.

Thallus imbedded in the host and invisible; apothecia minute to small, 0.2–0.5 mm. across, immersed to adnate, the disk concave, black, the exciple thick, black; hypothecium blackish brown; spores 30–50, ellipsoid, 1–3-septate, 5–8 × 2–2.5 μ. On the thallus of *Pertusaria communis* on rocks, Massachusetts and Nebraska.

171. Buelliopsis Schneid., Text. Gen. Lich. 136. 1897.

Thallus crustose, sometimes granulose and variously rugose, warty, chinky and verrucose, mainly above the substratum and attached by hyphal rhizoids; apothecia immersed to adnate, sometimes flexuous, the disk flat to convex, commonly brown to black, the exciple dark-colored and usually persistent; hypothecium brown to black; hymenium hyaline to brownish above; paraphyses rarely branched, usually enlarged and brownish toward the apex; asci clavate to cylindrico-clavate; spores 8, brown, ellipsoid, fusiform or dactyloid, 3-septate, sometimes tardily so. The algal host is Protococcus.

A. Thallus whitish; spores 18–30 × 7–13 μ . . . . 1. B. papillata
A. Thallus greenish to yellowish gray; spores 12–15 × 4–5.5 μ . . . 2. B. vernicoma

1. **Buelliopsis papillata** (Sommerf.) Fink n. comb.

> *Lecidea papillata* Sommerf., Suppl. Fl. Lapp. 154. 1826. *Buellia papillata* (Sommerf.) Tuck. *Buellia papillata* var. *albocincta* T. Fries.

Thallus minutely granulose, whitish to white, the granules forming thin to thicker crust, becoming chinky, wrinkled, warty and crumbling; apothecia small to middle-sized, 0.3–0.8 mm. across, adnate, often clustered and confluent, the disk flat to convex, black, the exciple black, thin, and disappearing; hypothecium brownish black; spores 1–3-septate, ellipsoid, 18–30 × 7–13 μ.
On mosses, Rocky Mountains and Washington.

2. **Buelliopsis vernicoma** (Tuck.) Schneid., Text. Gen. Lich. 136. pl. 15, f. 5. 1897.

> *Lecidea vernicoma* Tuck., Am. Journ. Sci. II. 25:429. 1858. *Buellia vernicoma* Tuck.

Thallus minutely granulose, greenish to yellowish gray, the granules round, scattered, or crowded into a thin, chinky crust, surrounded wholly or in part by the blackish hypothallus; apothecia minute to small, 0.15–0.45 mm. across, adnate, the disk flat to slightly convex, black, the exciple thin, black, at length flexuously irregular; hypothecium blackish brown; spores ellipsoid, 3-septate, 12–15 × 4–5.5 μ.
On trees and rocks, New England, New Jersey, Pennsylvania, South Carolina, and Alabama.

172. Rinodina Ach.; S. F. Gray, Nat. Arr. Brit. Pl. 1:448. 1821.

Thallus crustose, granulose, areolate, or rarely squamulose, sometimes lobed, closely adnate, attached to the substratum by hyphal rhizoids, differentiated into a poorly developed cortical layer of bent and branched hyphae or in the squamulose forms appearing to be more or less plectenchymatous, a thin algal layer and a more or less developed medullary layer of loosely interwoven hyphae; apothecia minute or small to middle-sized, more or less immersed to adnate or sessile, the disk slightly concave or flat to more or less convex, brown to black or pruinose, the exciple colored like the thallus, irregular, sometimes disappearing; hypothecium hyaline to brownish; hymenium hyaline or brownish above; paraphyses rarely branched; asci clavate to inflated-clavate; spores 8– rarely 16–24, brown, 1– rarely 3-septate.
The algal host is Protococcus.

A. Always on rocks
  B. Thallus areolate
    C. Thallus brownish to black
      D. Thallus black . . . . 16. R. nigra
      D. Thallus brownish green or reddish brown
        E. Apothecia 0.2–0.4 mm. across . . . . 17. R. californica
        E. Apothecia 0.5–0.9 mm. across . . . . 34. R. thysanota
    C. Thallus lighter colored
      D. Thallus greenish gray to ashy brown or grayish white to ashy
        E. Disk blackish brown to black
          F. Spores 1-septate
            G. Thallus very thin, soon disappearing . . . . 19. R. destitula
            G. Thallus moderately thick, rough, persistent
              H. Apothecia 0.3–0.8 mm. across, immersed
                1 or more in each areole . . . . 21. R. ocellata
              H. Apothecia 0.5–1.2 mm. across, adnate . . 18. R. tephraspis
          F. Spores 3-septate, and becoming 1-septate
            longitudinally . . . . 29. R. microbola
        E. Disk more or less densely whitish pruinose . . . . 35. R. radiata
      D. Thallus straw-colored to yellowish or brownish
        E. Thallus becoming lobed toward the circumference
          F. Thallus greenish yellow to ashy
            G. Disk black . . . . 31. R. novomexicana
            G. Disk whitish pruinose . . . . . 31. R. novomexicana caesia
          F. Thallus greenish straw-colored to yellowish . . . 30. R. oreina
        E. Thallus not lobed toward the circumference
          F. Spores 12–16 $\times$ 6–10 μ . . . . 20. R. euryspora
          F. Spores 20–25 $\times$ 9–11 μ . . . . 22. R. ochrocea
  B. Thallus squamulose, granulose, or rarely smooth to chinky
    C. Thallus granulose
      D. Spores 14–20 μ in length
        E. Thallus dark greenish black or dirty gray to black
          F. Thallus dark greenish black to black;
            apothecia 0.25–0.5 mm. across . . . . 12. R. aterrima
          F. Thallus dirty gray to dull black;
            apothecia 0.1–0.25 mm. across . . . . . 10. R. kentuckyensis
        E. Thallus ashy or whitish to brownish
          F. Granules scattered upon a thin, black hypothallus,
            or passing into an areolate crust . . . . . . 13. R. milvina
          F. Granules commonly passing into a chinky, scurfy crust
            G. Apothecia 0.3–0.8 mm. across, sessile . . . 14. R. Bischoffii
            G. Apothecia 0.2–0.5 mm. across, immersed 14. R. Bischoffii immersa
      D. Spores larger, 18–32 μ in length . . . . 28. R. Conradi
    C. Thallus not granulose
      D. Thallus smooth to chinky . . . . 7. R. Thomae
      D. Thallus squamulose
        E. Squamules yellow or yellowish to ashy
          F. Squamules minutely lobed; apothecia 0.3–0.8 mm.
           across . . . . 32. R. chrysomelaena
          F. Squamules broadly lobed; apothecia 1.5–3 mm.
           across . . . . 25. R. platyloba
        E. Squamules greenish gray to ashy . . . . 23. R. biatorina
A. Not always on rocks
  B. Always on trees or old wood
    C. Apothecia not more than 0.5 mm. across
      D. Spores 8 in each ascus . . . . 5. R. milliaria
      D. Spores 8 or more in each ascus
        E. Thallus sometimes disappearing . . . . 26. R. exigua
        E. Thallus bordered and sometimes intersected by a
          black hypothallus . . . . 27. R. polyspora
    C. Apothecia rarely less than 0.5 mm. across
      D. Thallus greenish yellow to lemon-colored . . . . . . 4. R. lepida
      D. Thallus grayish white to ashy brown or brown
        E. Spores 14–20 $\times$ 6–9 μ . . . . 3. R. roboris

E. Spores 18–30 × 8–14 μ . . . . 1. R. Hallii
B. Not always on trees or old wood
  C. On soil and rocks
    D. Thallus granulose
      E. Spores 14–20 × 6–8.5 μ . . . . 9. R. bolodes
      E. Spores 20–36 × 10–16 μ . . . . 11. R. orbata
    D. Thallus more or less squamulose or areolate
      E. Thallus pale yellowish to dull brown or
        grayish pruinose . . . . 33. R. phaeocarpa
      E. Thallus greenish gray to grayish flesh-colored . . . 24. R. angelica
  C. On trees and rocks
    D. Spores 14–22 μ in length
      E. Thallus of minute granules, ashy to greenish brown . . 6. R. sophodes
      E. Thallus areolate, greenish gray to ashy . . . . 15. R. atrocinerea
    D. Spores 20–35 μ in length
      E. Thallus smooth to more or less concentrically wrinkled 2. R. ascociscana
      E. Thallus coarsely granulose or warty . . . . . . 8. R. confragosa

1. **Rinodina Hallii** Tuck., Bull. Torr. Club 5:20. 1874.

Thallus thin to moderately thick, chinky to areolate, gray to ashy brown or brown, bordered by a black hypothallus; apothecia small to middle-sized, 0.8–1.2 mm. across, adnate, the disk flat to convex, reddish brown to black, the exciple thin, colored like the thallus, finally disappearing; hypothecium hyaline to brownish; spores ellipsoid to oblong-ellipsoid, 18–30 × 8–14 μ.

On trees, Washington, Oregon, and California.

2. **Rinodina ascociscana** Tuck., Gen. Lich. 124. 1872.

Psoroma ascociscana Tuck., Am. Journ. Sci. II. 25:424. 1858.

Thallus thin, round to irregular, smooth to more or less concentrically wrinkled, becoming chinky, areolate and scaly, greenish gray to pale cinnamon-brown; apothecia small to middle-sized, 0.6–1.5 mm. across, sessile, the disk flat to slightly convex, pale brown to black, sometimes wrinkled, the exciple thick, colored like the thallus, finally crenate; hypothecium hyaline to yellowish; spores oblong-ellipsoid, 20–35 × 10–16 μ.

On trees, New England, Ohio, Illinois, Minnesota, and California.

3. **Rinodina roboris** (Nyl.) Arn., Flora 64:197. 1881.

Lecanora roboris Nyl., Mém. Soc. Imp. Sci. Nat. Cherb. 2:326. 1854.

Thallus thin, grayish white, minutely granulose, becoming chinky, sometimes bordered by a black hypothallus; apothecia small to middle-sized, 0.3–1 mm. across, sessile, the disk flat to convex, dark brown to dull black, the exciple colored like the thallus, often crenate, finally disappearing; hypothecium hyaline; spores oblong-ellipsoid, 14–20 × 6–9 μ.

On trees and old wood, Louisiana and California.

4. **Rinodina lepida** (Nyl.) Müll. Arg., Flora 64:515. 1881.

Lecanora lepida Nyl., Mém. Soc. Imp. Sci. Nat. Cherb. 5:115. 1857. *R. flavoni-gella* Tuck.

Thallus thin, chinky to wrinkled, minutely granulose, greenish yellow to lemon-colored; apothecia small to middle-sized, 0.4–1 mm. across, closely adnate, the disk flat to slightly convex, brownish black to black, the margin thin, colored like the thallus, becoming crenulate; hypothecium yellowish; spores ellipsoid to oblong-ellipsoid, 20–31 × 9–14 μ.

On trees and old wood, Georgia, Florida, and Alabama.

5. **Rinodina milliaria** Tuck., Proc. Am. Acad. 12:175. 1877.

Thallus thin, chinky, minutely granulose, greenish gray to greenish brown or green; apothecia minute, 0.15–0.3 mm. across, adnate, numerous, the disk flat to convex, blackish brown to black, the exciple thin, colored like the thallus or becoming black; hypothecium dark brown; spores oblong-ellipsoid, slightly constricted at the septum, 9–15 × 5–8 μ.

On trees, New England, New York, and Pennsylvania.

6. **Rinodina sophodes** (Ach.) Mass., Ric. Lich. 14, 15. 1852.
   Lichen sophodes Ach., Lich. Suec. 67. 1798.
   Thallus thin, becoming areolate, composed of minute, rough, ashy to greenish brown, continuous or scattered granules, sometimes bordered by a thin black hypothallus; apothecia small, 0.3–0.8 mm. across, adnate, the disk flat to slightly convex, dark brown to dull black, the proper exciple thin, black, surrounded by a rather thick, crenulate, sometimes disappearing, thalloid one; hypothecium hyaline to brownish; spores oblong-ellipsoid, 14–22 × 6–12 μ.
   On trees and rocks, throughout the United States.

7. **Rinodina Thomae** Tuck., Syn. N. A. Lich. 209, 210. 1882.
   Thallus smooth to chinky, finally rough and crumbling, straw-colored to ashy, upon a thin black hypothallus; apothecia small, 0.4–0.8 mm. across, adnate, the disk flat to slightly convex, black, the exciple thick, colored like the thallus, but soon blackening; hypothecium dark brown; spores oblong-ellipsoid, 12–20 × 6–10 μ.
   On rocks, North Carolina and Louisiana.

8. **Rinodina confragosa** (Ach.) Koerb., Syst. Lich. 125. 1855.
   Parmelia confragosa Ach., Meth. Lich. Suppl. 33. 1803. *R. sophodes* var. *confragosa* (Ach.) Tuck.
   Thallus thin to moderately thick, coarsely granulose or warty, grayish to dirty white, the granules commonly scattered upon an inconspicuous black hypothallus; apothecia small to middle-sized, 0.4–1.2 mm. across, sessile, the disk flat, brownish black to black, the exciple thick, colored like the thallus, becoming crenulate; hypothecium yellowish; spores ovoid-ellipsoid, 20–33 × 10–16 μ.
   On rocks and rarely on trees, Massachusetts, New Jersey, Louisiana, Illinois, Minnesota, Oregon, and California.

9. **Rinodina bolodes** Tuck.; Hedrick, Mycologia 26:165. 1934.
   Thallus thick, composed of small, coarse, yellowish to gray, convex, crowded granules; apothecia small to middle-sized, 0.5–1.2 mm. across, sessile, the disk flat to convex, black or grayish pruinose, the exciple thick, colored like the thallus, becoming flexuous; hypothecium yellowish; spores ellipsoid to ovoid-ellipsoid, 14–20 × 6–8.5 μ.
   On soil, southern California.

10. **Rinodina kentuckyensis** Fink; Hedrick, Mycologia 26:164. 1934.
    Thallus thin, smooth to minutely granulose, continuous or scattered, dirty gray to dull black; apothecia minute, 0.1–0.25 mm. across, numerous, round to somewhat irregular when crowded, partly immersed to adnate, the disk concave to almost flat, dull black or slightly grayish pruinose, the exciple rather thick, entire, prominent, colored like the thallus; hypothecium and hymenium hyaline; spores oblong-ellipsoid, usually constricted at the septum, 15–18 × 7.5–8.5 μ, irregularly arranged.
    On sandstone rocks, Kentucky.

11. **Rinodina orbata** (Ach.) Vainio, Arkiv. Bot. 8:71. 1909.
    Lecanora sophodes var. *orbata* Ach., Lich. Univ. 678. 1810. *R. turfacea* (Wahl.) T. Fries. *R. turfacea* var. *mniaraea* (Nyl.) Arn.
    Thallus thin, granulose to minutely warty, pale greenish gray to brownish ashy; apothecia small to middle-sized, 0.5–1 mm. across, adnate, the disk slightly concave to convex, reddish brown to brownish black or rarely grayish pruinose, the thalloid exciple thin, elevated, wrinkled, rarely disappearing; spores ellipsoid or oblong-ellipsoid, 20–36 × 10–16 μ.
    On soil and rocks, New Hampshire, Montana, Wyoming, Colorado, Washington, and California.

12. **Rinodina aterrima** Krempelh., in Anzi, Comm. Soc. Ital. Critt. 2:11. 1864.
    Thallus thin, minutely granulose or scurfy, dark greenish black to black;

apothecia minute, 0.25–0.5 mm. across, partly immersed to adnate, the disk flat to slightly convex, black, the exciple thin, colored like the thallus; hypothecium yellowish to brownish; spores ellipsoid, slightly constricted at the septum, one cell sometimes larger, 14–20 × 5–9 μ.

On rocks, California.

13. **Rinodina milvina** (Wahl.) T. Fries, Nov. Act. Reg. Soc. Sci. Ups. III. 3:224. 1861.

Parmelia milvina Wahl., in Ach., Meth. Lich. Suppl. 34. 1803.

Thallus moderately thick, granulose, ashy to brownish or brown, the granules flat to convex, often passing into an areolate crust, or scattered upon a very thin, black hypothallus; apothecia small to middle-sized, 0.4–0.8 mm. across, partly immersed to adnate, commonly crowded and irregular, the disk flat, brownish black, the exciple thin, colored like the thallus; hypothecium brownish to brown; spores oblong to oblong-ellipsoid, 14–20 × 6–11 μ.

On rocks, Massachusetts and Ohio.

14. **Rinodina Bischoffii** (Hepp) Mass., Fram. Lich. 26. 1855.

Psora Bischoffii Hepp, Spor. Flecht. Eur. 81, 411. 1853. *R. Penardiana* Müll. Arg.

Thallus thin to moderately thick, minutely granulose, the granules whitish to greenish gray or brownish, scattered or more commonly running together into a more or less chinky, scurfy, or subareolate crust, sometimes disappearing; apothecia minute to small, 0.3–0.8 mm. across, sessile, the disk flat to slightly convex, dark brown to black, the exciple thin, colored like the thallus, rarely blackening; hypothecium hyaline to yellowish; spores ovoid-ellipsoid, 15–20 × 8–12 μ.

On rocks, from Minnesota to Texas, and westward to California.

var. **immersa** Koerb., Par. Lich. 75. 1865.

Thallus ashy to whitish; apothecia minute, 0.2–0.5 mm. across, immersed in minute pits of the substratum.

On limestone, southern California.

15. **Rinodina atrocinerea** (Dicks.) Koerb., Syst. Lich. 125. 1855.

Lichen atrocinereus Dicks., Pl. Crypt. Brit. 3:14. pl. 14, f. 9. 1793. *R. sophodes* var. *atrocinerea* (Dicks.) Tuck.

Thallus thin, composed of smooth, greenish gray to ashy, squamule-like areoles, more or less scattered upon a conspicuous black hypothallus; apothecia small to middle-sized, 0.5–1.2 mm. across, adnate to sessile, the disk flat to convex, dark brown to black, the exciple thin, colored like the thallus, becoming crenulate, often finally disappearing; hypothecium yellowish; spores ellipsoid to oblong-ellipsoid, 14–22 × 8–12 μ.

On rocks and rarely on trees, Massachusetts, Ohio, Minnesota, and California.

16. **Rinodina nigra** Fink, Minn. Bot. Stud. 2:695. 1901.

Thallus thin to moderately thick, minutely areolate, the areoles somewhat concave to flat, dark slate-colored, scattered or continuous, and forming irregular, chinky areas; apothecia minute, 0.15–0.4 mm. across, partly immersed, 1–3 in each areole, round to irregular, the disk slightly concave to flat, black, the exciple moderately thick, colored like the thallus; hypothecium hyaline; spores oblong-ellipsoid, sometimes slightly constricted at the septum, 9–15 × 5–8 μ.

On rocks, Minnesota.

17. **Rinodina californica** Magn., Meddel. Got. Bot. Trägdärg 3:16. 1927.

Thallus areolate, the areoles small, round to somewhat irregular, dark reddish brown to dark brown, or in part slightly grayish pruinose, forming a chinky crust, distinctly radiately lobed at the circumference, the lobes short and flat; apothecia minute to small, 0.2–0.4 mm. across, numerous, immersed, the disk flat, black, the exciple distinct, colored like the thallus; spores 8, dark greenish brown, 10–11 × 5–5.5 μ.

On rocks, Santa Monica Range, California (description compiled).

18. **Rinodina tephraspis** (Tuck.) Herre, Proc. Wash. Acad. 12:250. 1910.
   Lecanora tephraspis Tuck., Am. Journ. Sci. II. 25:425. 1858. *R. sophodes* var.
   tephraspis Tuck.
   Thallus moderately thick, rough, composed of crenulate or often warty, crowded,
brownish gray to ashy areoles; apothecia small to middle-sized, 0.5–1.2 mm. across,
adnate, irregular, the disk flat to convex, black, the exciple thin, colored like the
thallus, becoming crenulate; hypothecium hyaline to cloudy; spores ellipsoid to
oblong-ellipsoid, 16–22 × 7–10 μ.
   On rocks, South Carolina, Minnesota, Iowa, and California.

19. **Rinodina destitula** (Nyl.) Zahlbr., Cat. Lich. Univ. 7:510. 1931.
   Lecidea destitula Nyl., Lab. et Sing. 41. 1891.
   Thallus very thin, minutely areolate, grayish white, soon disappearing; apothecia
small, 0.3–0.6 mm. across, adnate, round to irregular and clustered, the disk flat,
black, the exciple prominent, colored like the thallus; hypothecium brownish; spores
ellipsoid, 20–23 × 8–11 μ.
   On rocks, Illinois.

20. **Rinodina euryspora** Zahlbr., Bryologist 18:23. 1915.
   Thallus thin to moderately thick, chinky to areolate, the areoles small, concave,
dirty yellowish or brownish; apothecia minute to small, 0.2–0.6 mm. across, adnate
to sessile, the disk flat, black or whitish pruinose, the exciple rather thick, colored
like the thallus, becoming crenulate; hypothecium hyaline to yellowish; spores
ovoid-ellipsoid, 12–16 × 6–10 μ.
   On rocks, southern California.

21. **Rinodina ocellata** (Hoffm.) Arn., Flora 67:318. 1884.
   Verrucaria ocellata Hoffm., Plant. Lich. 1:92. pl. 20, f. 2. 1790. *R. lecanorina*
   Mass. *R. iowensis* Zahlbr.
   Thallus rough, moderately thick, composed of flat to slightly convex, small
to middle-sized, greenish gray to green or ashy brown, scattered or continuous
areoles; apothecia minute to small, 0.3–0.8 mm. across, 1 or more immersed in
each areole or becoming superficial, round to more or less irregular, the disk flat
to slightly convex, blackish brown to black, the exciple thin, colored like the
thallus, rarely becoming wavy; hypothecium hyaline to cloudy; spores oblong
to oblong-ellipsoid, 15–21 × 8–10 μ.
   On rocks, Minnesota and Iowa.

22. **Rinodina ochrocea** Willey; Hedrick, Mycologia 26:165. 1934.
   Thallus thin, chinky-areolate, the areoles minute to small, irregular, continuous, yellowish gray to brownish; apothecia minute to small, 0.2–0.4 mm. across,
immersed to adnate, more or less crowded, round to irregular, the disk concave,
black, the exciple rather thick, colored like the thallus, more or less uneven;
hypothecium hyaline; spores oblong-ellipsoid, 20–25 × 9–11 μ.
   On rocks, South Carolina.

23. **Rinodina biatorina** Koerb., Par. Lich. 76. 1865.
   Thallus thin, composed of minute to small, flat to convex, greenish gray to
ashy squamules, continuous or scattered upon an inconspicuous black hypothallus;
apothecia minute, 0.1–0.3 mm. across, adnate, the disk flat to slightly convex,
black, the exciple thin, colored like the thallus, rarely disappearing; hypothecium
hyaline to yellowish; spores ovoid-ellipsoid, 14–20 × 7–9 μ.
   On rocks, Maryland.

24. **Rinodina angelica** Stizenb.; Hasse, Bull. Torr. Club 24:447. 1897.
   Thallus chinky to coarsely areolate or rarely squamulose, greenish gray to
grayish flesh-colored, sometimes becoming lobed toward the circumference; apothecia small to middle-sized, 0.35–1 mm. across, partly immersed to adnate, the
disk flat to slightly convex, dull black or rarely grayish pruinose, the exciple thin

to moderately thick, colored like the thallus, becoming crenulate; hypothecium
hyaline to cloudy; spores ellipsoid, 16–24 × 8–11 μ.
On soil, southern California.

25. **Rinodina platyloba** Willey, in Cummings, Williams and Seymour, Dec. N. A.
Lich. no. 204.
Thallus foliose, composed of thick, middle-sized to large, irregular, much folded,
broadly lobed, yellowish to ashy squamules; whitish within; apothecia middle-sized
to large, 1.5–3 mm. across, partly immersed, the disk concave to flat, black or
rarely grayish pruinose, becoming rough, the exciple thick, colored like the thallus,
wavy to crenate; hypothecium hyaline; spores oblong, constricted at the septum,
12–16 × 6–7.5 μ.
On rocks, southern California.

26. **Rinodina exigua** (Ach.) S. F. Gray, Nat. Arr. Brit. Pl. 1:450. 1821.
Lichen exiguus Ach., Lich. Suec. 69. 1798. *R. sophodes* var. *exigua* (Ach.) Tuck.
Thallus thin, minutely granulose, the granules whitish to ashy gray or gray,
more or less scattered, sometimes disappearing; apothecia minute to small, 0.15–
0.5 mm. across, adnate to sessile, sometimes crowded, the disk flat to convex,
blackish brown to black, the exciple thin, colored like the thallus, becoming
crenulate; hypothecium yellowish; spores 8– rarely 16 or more, ellipsoid to oblong-
ellipsoid, 11–20 × 6–10 μ.
On old wood and trees, throughout the United States.

27. **Rinodina polyspora** T. Fries, Arct. 126. 1860.
R. palustus Willey in litt.
Thallus very thin, smooth to minutely granulose or warty, sometimes becoming chinky, ashy or darker gray to whitish; bordered and sometimes intersected by
a black hypothallus; apothecia minute to small, 0.2–0.5 mm. across, adnate, the
disk flat to slightly convex, brownish black to black, the exciple thin, colored like
the thallus, becoming darker and sometimes disappearing; hypothecium hyaline;
spores 12–24, oblong or oblong-ellipsoid, some slightly curved, 13–16 × 6–8 μ.
On trees, Massachusetts.

28. **Rinodina Conradi** Koerb., Syst. Lich. 123. 1855.
Thallus minutely granulose, the granules greenish gray to ashy or brownish,
flat or slightly convex, scattered or continuous and forming a thin, chinky to
areolate crust; apothecia small, 0.4–0.8 mm. across, sessile, the disk flat to slightly
convex, blackish brown to black, the exciple thick, colored like the thallus, becoming crenulate; hypothecium yellowish; spores ellipsoid, 1–3-septate transversely and
the middle cells becoming 1-septate longitudinally, 18–32 × 9–14 μ.
On rocks, Colorado, Washington, and California.

29. **Rinodina microbola** Tuck.; Hedrick, Mycologia 26:164. 1934.
Thallus thin, coarsely areolate, ashy to whitish, the areoles scattered or continuous; apothecia minute to small, 0.15–0.4 mm. across, partly immersed to
adnate, the disk flat to convex, black, the exciple thin, colored like the thallus;
hypothecium yellowish to brownish; spores ovoid-ellipsoid, 3-septate transversely
and becoming 1-septate longitudinally, 13–22 × 7–11 μ.
On rocks, California.

30. **Rinodina oreina** (Ach.) Mass., Ric. Lich. 16. f. 24. 1852.
Lecanora straminea var. *oreina* Ach., Lich. Univ. 433. 1810.
Thallus thin to moderately thick, closely adnate, warty-areolate, the areoles
small, greenish straw-colored to yellowish, passing into somewhat elongated,
branched, densely crowded, black-edged squamules toward the circumference;
apothecia minute to small, 0.2–0.75 mm. across, immersed to adnate or sessile,
the disk flat to slightly convex, black, the exciple thin, colored like the thallus,

obtuse, rarely disappearing; hypothecium hyaline; spores short-ellipsoid, 9–12 × 4.5–7.5 μ.

On rocks, throughout the United States except in the extreme south.

31. **Rinodina novomexicana** B. de Lesd., Bull. Soc. Bot. de France 613, 614. 1930.

Thallus moderately thick, smooth to rough, composed of minute to small, irregular, crowded, flat to convex, greenish yellow to ashy areoles, becoming radiately lobed toward the circumference; apothecia small to middle-sized, 0.35–0.8 mm. across, partly immersed to adnate, irregular, sometimes crowded, the disk flat to slightly convex, black, the exciple thin, colored like the thallus, sometimes disappearing; hypothecium hyaline to brownish; hymenium hyaline; spores ovoid to ovoid-ellipsoid, 8–13 × 4–7 μ.

On rocks, New Mexico.

var. **caesia** B. de Lesd., Bull. Soc. Bot. de France 614. 1930.
Apothecia larger, reaching 1.2 mm. across, the disk grayish pruinose.
On rocks, New Mexico.

32. **Rinodina chrysomelaena** (Ach.) Tuck., Gen. Lich. 123. 1872.

Lecanora chrysomelaena Ach., Syn. Meth. Lich. 148. 1814.

Thallus squamulose, the squamules yellow, flat to slightly convex, minutely lobed, scattered upon a thin, blackish hypothallus; apothecia small, 0.3–0.8 mm. across, the disk slightly concave to flat, dark reddish brown to black, the exciple thick, colored like the thallus, becoming wrinkled and flexuous; hypothecium yellowish to brownish; spores ellipsoid, 18–30 × 10–14 μ.

On rocks, Massachusetts, North Carolina, Georgia, Pennsylvania, Tennessee, and Montana.

33. **Rinodina phaeocarpa** (Sommerf.) Vainio, Term. Füz. 22:302. 1899.

Lecidea phaeocarpa Sommerf., Suppl. Fl. Lapp. 159. 1826. *R. nimbosa* (E. Fries) T. Fries.

Thallus squamulose, pale yellowish to dull brown or grayish pruinose, the squamules more or less crowded and finally running together, the central ones sometimes reduced and round, the marginal ones lobed, the lobes often crenate and imbricate; apothecia small to middle-sized, 0.5–1.2 mm. across, partly immersed, the disk flat to slightly convex, brownish black or rarely grayish pruinose, the exciple thick, colored like the thallus; hypothecium hyaline; spores ellipsoid, sometimes slightly constricted at the septum, 14–20 × 7–10 μ.

On soil, Colorado.

34. **Rinodina thysanota** Tuck., Proc. Am. Acad. 12:174. 1877.

Lecanora thysanota (Tuck.) Hasse.

Thallus closely adnate, brownish green, warty-areolate, radiately lobed toward the circumference; apothecia small to middle-sized, 0.5–0.9 mm. across, sessile, the disk flat, blackish brown, the exciple thick, colored like the thallus; hypothecium hyaline to yellowish; spores oblong-ellipsoid, 9–13 × 5–7 μ.

On rocks, Nevada, Arizona, Oregon, and California.

35. **Rinodina radiata** Tuck., Proc. Am. Acad. 12:173. 1877.

Buellia radiata Tuck., Lich. Calif. 25, 26. 1866. *R. radiata* f. *fimbriata* Tuck. *R. radiata* f. *lactea* Hasse.

Thallus thin to moderately thick, closely adnate, somewhat chinky, composed of minute to small, greenish gray to ashy or whitish, flat to convex, continuous areoles, becoming radiately lobed toward the circumference, more or less bordered by a thin black hypothallus; apothecia small to middle-sized, 0.4–1 mm. across, partly immersed to adnate, crowded toward the center of the thallus, the disk flat to slightly convex, dull black or more or less densely whitish pruinose, the exciple thin, colored like the thallus; hypothecium dark brown; spores oblong-ellipsoid, sometimes slightly constricted at the septum, 9–14 × 5–7 μ.

On rocks, California.

OTHER SPECIES REPORTED

Rinodina dirinoides Zahlbr.—California.

Rinodina succedens Nyl.—Southern California.

44. PHYSCIACEAE

Thallus foliose to fruticose, dorsiventral or radial, differentiated into well-developed cortices of plectenchyma or interwoven hyphae, algal and medullary layers, in the fruticose forms the medulla forming the central cylinder, attached to the substratum by rhizoids; apothecia round, adnate to sessile, with well-developed proper or thalloid exciple.

The algal host is Protococcus.

A. Upper cortex plectenchymatous
  B. The exciple colored like the thallus . . . . 174. PHYSCIA
  B. The exciple becoming black . . . . 173. PYXINE
A. Upper cortex not plectenchymatous . . . . 175. ANAPTYCHIA

173. Pyxine E. Fries, Syst. Orb. Veg. 267. 1825.

Thallus foliose, more or less lobed and imbricated, commonly sorediate, closely adnate, differentiated into a more or less well-developed plectenchymatous upper cortex, algal and medullary layers, the lower surface more or less covered with black or brownish black rhizoids; apothecia small to rarely middle-sized, sessile, the disk flat to more or less convex, black or pruinose, the exciple thin, colored like the disk, covered by a more conspicuous thalloid one, soon becoming black; hypothecium dark brown to brownish black; hymenium brownish; paraphyses unbranched, thickened and brownish at the apex; asci clavate; spores 8, brown, oblong to ellipsoid, 1–3-septate.

The algal host is Protococcus.

A. Spores 1-septate
  B. Thallus small to middle-sized; spores not more than 23 μ in length
    C. On trees; apothecia rarely less than 0.8 mm. across
      D. Thallus smooth . . . . 3. P. cocoës
      D. Thallus smooth to wrinkled, or passing into a warty crust
        E. Thallus small, rarely bearing soredia . . . . . . 4. P. Meissneri
        E. Thallus larger, often bearing soredia . . . . 5. P. picta
    C. On rocks; apothecia 0.5–0.8 mm. across . . . . 6. P. Frostii
  B. Thallus middle-sized to large; spores 17–28 × 6–10 μ . . . . 1. P. sorediata
A. Spores 3-septate . . . . 2. P. Eschweileri

1. Pyxine sorediata (Ach.) E. Fries, in Sagra, Hist. Cuba 188. 1842.

Lecidea sorediata Ach., Syn. Meth. Lich. 54. 1814.

Thallus middle-sized to large, closely adnate, smooth or wrinkled, greenish gray to ashy or greenish, the lobes somewhat elongated, subdichotomously branched, more or less imbricated, the ends round or crenate, usually more or less covered with white or grayish soredia; black below, or brownish toward the margins, with black rhizoids; apothecia small, 0.75–1.5 mm. across, the disk flat to convex, black or rarely whitish pruinose, the exciple thin, colored like the disk; hypothecium brown to blackish brown; spores oblong to ellipsoid, 1-septate, 17–28 × 6–10 μ. (PLATE 46.)

On trees and rocks, throughout the United States.

2. **Pyxine Eschweileri** (Tuck.) Vainio, Lich. Bresil 1:156. 1890.
   P. cocoës var. *Eschweileri* Tuck., Obs. Lich. 4:167. 1877. *P. sorediata* var.
   Eschweileri Tuck.
   Thallus small to middle-sized, greenish gray to ashy, smooth to slightly wrinkled, bearing soredia or rarely coralloid branchlets, the lobes rather short, imbricated, the margins becoming crenate; brownish black below, bearing numerous brownish black rhizoids; apothecia middle-sized, 0.7–2 mm. across, sessile, round to slightly irregular, the disk flat to convex, black or obscurely grayish pruinose, the exciple thin to rather thick, becoming black; hypothecium dark brown; spores ellipsoid, 3-septate, 14–17 × 5–7 μ.
   On trees, Florida.

3. **Pyxine cocoës** (Swartz) Nyl., Mém. Soc. Sci. Nat. Cherb. 5:108. 1857.
   Lichen cocoës Swartz, Fl. Ind. Occ. 146. 1788. *P. cocoës* var. *caesiopruinosa* Tuck.
   Thallus small to middle-sized, smooth, greenish gray to ashy, bearing whitish soredia, the lobes elongated, subdichotomously branched, imbricated, the margins entire to slightly crenate; black below, bearing short, brownish black rhizoids; white within; apothecia small, 0.8–1.5 mm. across, the disk flat to slightly convex, black or grayish pruinose, the exciple thin to moderately thick, becoming black; hypothecium dark brown; spores ellipsoid, 1-septate, 15–22 × 6–9 μ.
   On trees, Florida and Louisiana.

4. **Pyxine Meissneri** Tuck., in Nyl., Syn. Meth. Lich. 2:1. 1860.
   Thallus small, smooth to slightly wrinkled, ashy to whitish, the lobes rarely elongated, commonly imbricated, rarely bearing whitish soredia, the margins crenate; black below, with minute black rhizoids; whitish to yellowish within; apothecia small, 0.8–1.5 mm. across, sometimes clustered, the disk flat to slightly convex, black, the exciple thin, wavy, becoming black; hypothecium dark brown; spores ellipsoid, 1-septate, 15–22 × 6–9 μ.
   On trees, Florida.

5. **Pyxine picta** (Swartz) Tuck., Proc. Am. Acad. 4:398. 1862.
   Lichen pictus Swartz, Fl. Ind. Occ. 146. 1788. *P. picta* var. *applanata* (Fée)
      Stizenb. *P. picta* var. *erythrocardia* Tuck.
   Thallus small to middle-sized, closely adnate, smooth to wrinkled, ashy or whitish, often passing into a warty crust toward the center, the lobes somewhat elongated, subdichotomously branched, commonly imbricated, sometimes bearing white soredia, the margins crenate; black below, with few black rhizoids; whitish to rarely yellowish orange within; apothecia small, 0.75–2 mm. across, sessile, the disk flat, brownish black to black or sometimes pruinose, the exciple thin, becoming black; hypothecium dark brown; spores ellipsoid, 1-septate, 15–23 × 7–9 μ.
   On trees, from South Carolina to Florida, and westward to Texas.

6. **Pyxine Frostii** Tuck., Syn. N. A. Lich. 1:79. 1882.
   Squamaria Frostii Tuck., Am. Journ. Sci. II. 25:425. 1858. *Lecanora Frostii*
      Tuck.
   Thallus small to middle-sized, closely adnate, smooth, greenish gray to cream-colored, usually bearing scattered white soredia, the lobes subpalmately divided, imbricated, the margins crenate; black below, bearing minute brownish black rhizoids; white within; apothecia small, 0.5–0.8 mm. across, sessile, the disk flat, black, the exciple thin, crenate; hypothecium dark brown; spores oblong-ellipsoid, 1-septate, 14–20 × 5–7 μ.
   On granite, New England and Virginia.

174. **Physcia** Ach., Kgl. Vet. Akad. Nya Handl. 15:252. 1794.

Thallus foliose, rarely becoming crustose, smooth to rough, more or less lobed, often sorediate, rarely bearing coralloid branchlets, differentiated into well-developed, plectenchymatous upper and lower cortices of vertical extending hyphae, the lower cortex often thinner and less well-developed, distinct algal and medullary layers, the margins sometimes ciliate; more or less covered with rhizoids below; apothecia minute to small and middle-sized or rarely large, adnate to sessile, the disk more or less concave to flat or rarely convex, brown to black or pruinose, the exciple colored like the thallus, thick, more or less irregular; hypothecium hyaline to yellowish or brownish; hymenium hyaline or brownish above; paraphyses unbranched; asci clavate; spores 8, brown, oblong to ellipsoid, 1-septate.

The algal host is Protococcus.

A. Thallus more or less adnate throughout
  B. Thallus closely adnate
    C. On rocks . . . . 2. P. teretiuscula
    C. On trees . . . . 1. P. adglutinata
  B. Thallus adnate but not closely so
    C. Thallus more or less sorediate, sometimes rarely so
      D. Exciple not hispid
        E. Thallus small, becoming granulose or bearing
          massed soredia toward the center . . . . 4. P. astroidea
        E. Thallus larger, bearing round soredia . . . . 3. P. caesia
      D. Exciple plainly hispid
        E. Thallus whitish within
          F. Rarely whitish sorediate . . . . 6. P. obscura
          F. Commonly greenish sorediate . . . . 5. P. virella
        E. Thallus saffron-colored within . . . . 7. P. endochrysea
    C. Thallus not sorediate
      D. Exciple hispid
        E. Spores $20-30 \times 10-15 \mu$ . . . . 9. P. setosa
        E. Spores $15-23 \times 6-10 \mu$ . . . . 8. P. lithotodes
      D. Exciple not hispid
        E. Whitish to darker below
          F. Thallus ashy to white; spores $12-20 \times 5-7.5 \mu$ . . 13. P. callosa
          F. Thallus greenish gray to darker; spores $14-24 \times 8-11 \mu$
            G. Margins ciliate . . . . 10. P. stellaris leptalea
            G. Margins not ciliate . . . . 10. P. stellaris
        E. Brown to black below
          F. Spores $26-32 \times 15-18 \mu$ . . . . 11. P. venusta
          F. Spores $15-20 \times 7.5-10 \mu$ . . . . 12. P. obsessa
A. Thallus ascending, at least toward the margins
  B. Thallus more or less pruinose
    C. Thallus pruinose, bearing coralloid branchlets or
    powdery granules or soredia
      D. Thallus bluish pruinose . . . . 14. P. isidiigera
      D. Thallus whitish pruinose, margins yellow-
      powdery or sorediate . . . . 15. P. muscigena
    C. Thallus white-pruinose . . . . 16. P. pulverulenta
  B. Thallus not pruinose
    C. Thallus smooth
      D. Lobes inflated and open at the ends . . . . 17. P. hispida
      D. Lobes not inflated and open . . . . 18. P. Leana
    C. Thallus granulose or sorediate
      D. Thallus small, margins granulose . . . . 20. P. tribacia
      D. Thallus larger, margins powdery . . . . 19. P. crispa

1. **Physcia adglutinata** (Floerke) Nyl., Mém. Soc. Sci. Nat. Cherb. 5:107. 1857. *Lecanora adglutinata* Floerke, Deutsch. Lich. 4:7. 1815.

Thallus small, foliose, closely adnate to adglutinate, greenish gray, varying toward ashy or brownish, the lobes usually long and branched with entire to crenulate margins, finally passing toward the center into a granular crust; whitish below or sometimes darker, rarely bearing scattered rhizoids; apothecia minute to small, 0.4-1.75 mm. across, sessile, the disk flat, blackish brown, the exciple entire to subcrenulate, scarcely ciliate; spores oblong to ellipsoid, $13-22 \times 7-10 \mu$.

On trees and shrubs, throughout the United States, but more common east of the Rocky Mountains and north of the Gulf states.

2. **Physcia teretiuscula** (Ach.) Lynge, Vid. Skrif. Math.-nat. Klasse. 96. 1916.
Parmelia caesia var. *teretiuscula* Ach., Lich. Univ. 479. 1810. *P. caesia* var.
teretiuscula (Ach.) Nyl.
Thallus small, closely adnate, light greenish gray, rarely sorediate, the lobes
somewhat round, elongated, much branched, sometimes imbricated, the margins
entire to crenate; pale below with pale to light brown rhizoids; apothecia small,
1–2 mm. across, sessile, the disk slightly concave to flat, dark brown to dull black,
the exciple entire to subentire; spores oblong-ellipsoid, 12–17 × 6–9 μ.
On rocks, Minnesota, Iowa, and North Dakota.
Often confused with *P. caesia* (Hoffm.) Hampe, though quite different.

3. **Physcia caesia** (Hoffm.) Hampe; Fürn., Nat. Top. Regen. 2:250. 1839.
Lichen caesius Hoffm., Enum. Lich. Icon. 65. pl. 12, f. 1. 1788. *Parmelia caesia*
var. *stellata* Tuck.   .
Thallus middle-sized, adnate, light greenish gray to ashy, bearing round gray
soredia, the lobes usually quite elongated and branched, sometimes imbricated, the
margins entire to crenate; whitish below or rarely blackening, with usually dark
rhizoids; apothecia infrequent, small, 1.5–4 mm. across, sessile, the disk slightly
concave to flat, dark brown to black or rarely gray-pruinose, the exciple inflexed,
entire to crenulate; spores oblong-ellipsoid, 15–22 × 8–12 μ.
On rocks and rarely on trees, northeastern United States, westward to the
Rocky Mountains.

4. **Physcia astroidea** (Clem.) Nyl., Act. Soc. Linn. Bord. 21:308. 1856.
Parmelia astroidea Clem., Essai Sob. Veg. And. 302. 1807.
Thallus thin, irregular to round, adnate, grayish white, the lobes narrow, flattened, much branched with crenate margins, becoming granulose toward the center
or passing into finally massed soredia; whitish below with short blackening rhizoids; apothecia small, 0.8–1.5 mm. across, closely sessile, the disk concave to flat,
black, sometimes pruinose, the exciple thin, colored like the thallus, becoming wavy
and curved inward; spores oblong-ellipsoid, 17–25 × 7–11 μ.
On trees and rocks, New England, and southward to Florida and Texas.

5. **Physcia virella** (Ach.) Flagey, Rev. Myc. 13:110. 1891.
Lichen virellus Ach., Lich. Suec. 108, 109. 1798. *P. obscura* var. *virella* (Ach.)
T. Fries.
Thallus small, closely attached to the substratum or ascending toward the
margins, grayish, greenish, or varying toward brown, the lobes short, closely packed
and often imbricate, plane or convex, crenately branched, with marginal and often
dorsal whitish to grayish green soredia; dark below, with short, black, usually
unbranched rhizoids; apothecia small, 1–1.5 mm. across, sessile, the disk flat, reddish
to dark brown, the exciple raised, of same color as the thallus and more or less
plainly hispid, at least below; spores oblong-ellipsoid, 15–25 × 7.5–12 μ.
On trees, Michigan (no doubt more widely distributed, but no other specimens
studied belong here).

6. **Physcia obscura** (Ehrh.) Hampe; Fürn., Nat. Top. Regen. 2:249. 1839.
Parmelia obscura Ehrh., Plant. Crypt. Exsicc. 177. 1785. *P. obscura* var.
ulothrix (Ach.) E. Fries. *P. obscura* var. *ulothricoides* Nyl. *P. obscura* var.
muscicola (Schaer.) T. Fries.
Thallus middle-sized, adnate, smooth or rarely rough, greenish gray to brown
or ashy, rarely sorediate, the lobes commonly long and subdichotomously branched,
often imbricated, the margins round to crenate, rarely ciliate, often passing toward
the center into a subcrustose condition; black or rarely lighter below with rhizoids of the same colors; apothecia middle-sized to large, 0.8–4 mm. across, sessile,
the disk concave to slightly convex, reddish brown to black, the exciple entire to
crenulate, more or less hispid, at least below; spores oblong to ellipsoid, 15–27 ×
8.5–12 μ.
On trees, wood, rocks, and mosses, throughout the United States.

7. **Physcia endochrysea** (Hampe) Nyl., Flora 58:442. 1875.
Parmelia endochrysea Hampe, in Nyl., Syn. Lich. 1:427. 1858. *P. obscura* var.
endochrysea (Hampe) Nyl. *P. obscura* f. *endococcinea* (Koerb.) T. Fries.

Thallus small to middle-sized, adnate, smooth to slightly rough, greenish gray to
brownish, sometimes sorediate, saffron-colored within, the lobes becoming elongated and branched, often imbricated, the margins round to crenate; black below
with black rhizoids; apothecia middle-sized to large, 0.5–3 mm. across, sessile, the
disk concave to flat, reddish brown to black, the exciple entire to crenulate, more
or less hispid, at least below; spores oblong-ellipsoid, 14–22 × 7–10 μ.

On trees and rocks, from New England to Alabama, and westward to Texas
and Minnesota.

8. **Physcia lithotodes** Nyl., Flora 58:360. 1875.
P.lithotea var. *lithotodes* (Nyl.) Lynge.

Thallus small, adnate, irregular, greenish gray to brownish, the lobes short,
much branched, imbricated, with ragged, digitate margins; blackish below and
densely covered with black rhizoids; apothecia minute to small, 0.5–2 mm. across,
sessile, the disk flat, black, the exciple thin to moderately thick, colored like the
thallus, becoming wavy and flexuous, with or without fibrils below; hypothecium
hyaline; spores ellipsoid, 15–23 × 6–10 μ.

On trees, Maine and New York.

9. **Physcia setosa** (Ach.) Nyl., Syn. Lich. 1:429. 1860.
Parmelia setosa Ach., Syn. Meth. Lich. 203. 1814.

Thallus middle-sized, adnate, greenish gray to ashy, the lobes elongated, much
branched, sometimes imbricated, with entire to wavy margins, sometimes passing
toward the center into a crust of closely packed and imbricated lobules; black
below, resting on and bordered by strong black rhizoids; apothecia small to middle-
sized, 2–5 mm. across, sessile, the disk more or less deeply concave, reddish brown,
the exciple entire or subentire, hispid; spores oblong-ellipsoid, 20–30 × 10–15 μ.

On soil, rocks, and trees, from New England to New York, thence westward
to Ohio and New Mexico.

10. **Physcia stellaris** (L.) Nyl., Syn. Lich. 1:424. 1858.
Lichen stellaris L., Sp. Pl. 1144. 1753. *P. stellaris* var. *aipolia* (Ehrh.) Hampe.

Thallus middle-sized, adnate, greenish gray to whitish or brownish, the lobes
rather narrow, frequently elongated, much branched, sometimes imbricated, the
margins entire to crenate, often passing centrally into a crust; white below with
white rhizoids, or sometimes becoming darker to black with rhizoids of the same
dark color; apothecia small, 2–4 mm. across, sessile, the disk slightly concave to
convex, whitish pruinose to dark brown or black, the exciple entire to crenate;
spores oblong-ellipsoid, 14–24 × 8–11 μ. (PLATE 47 *a*.)

On trees and rocks, throughout the United States (usually becoming dark below
when growing on rocks).

var. **leptalea** (Ach.) Nyl., Syn. Lich. 1:425. 1858.
Lichen leptaleus Ach., Lich. Prod. 108. 1798.

Thallus narrowly lobed and ciliate at the margins.
On trees, California.

11. **Physcia venusta** (Ach.) Nyl., Syn. Lich. 1:421. 1858.
Parmelia venusta Ach., Syn. Meth. Lich. 214. 1814. *P. pulverulenta* var. *subvenusta* Nyl.

Thallus small to middle-sized, closely adnate, greenish gray to tawny brown,
the lobes long, narrow, much branched with round to crenate, sometimes grayish
pruinose margins, the inner lobes often marked with small toothlike lobules; black
below or paler toward the margins, and densely covered with black rhizoids; apothecia minute to small, 0.5–1.5 mm. across, sessile, the disk flat, reddish black to
black, often gray or bluish pruinose, the exciple thick, colored like the thallus.

becoming wavy; hypothecium hyaline to brownish; spores short-ellipsoid, 26–32 × 15–18 μ.

On trees, Santa Cruz Peninsula, California.

12. **Physcia obsessa** (Mont.) Nyl., Mém. Soc. Imp. Sci. Nat. Cherb. 3:175. 1855.
Parmelia obsessa Mont., in Sagra, Hist. Nat. Cub. 227. 1842. *P. integrata* var. *obsessa* (Mont.) Vainio.

Thallus small, adnate, smooth, light greenish gray to whitish, the narrow lobes usually separated, moderately branched with entire to irregularly crenate margins; brown to black below or rarely light-colored, with dark-colored rhizoids; apothecia small, 1–3 mm. across, sessile, the disk flat, white-pruinose to brownish black, the exciple entire; spores oblong-ellipsoid, 15–20 × 7.5–10 μ, or larger in some foreign material.

On trees, near Sanford, Florida.

13. **Physcia callosa** Nyl., Flora 52:119. 1869.

Thallus thin to moderately thick, closely adnate, rough and wrinkled, ashy to white, the lobes short and narrow, with crenate margins, frequently passing into a continuous, coarsely wrinkled, warty crust; brownish below with short, blackening rhizoids; apothecia small, 1–3 mm. across, sessile, the disk concave to flat, black, usually grayish pruinose, the exciple moderately thick, colored like the thallus, irregular and wavy; spores oblong-ellipsoid, 12–20 × 5–7.5 μ.

On arenaceous rocks, near San Francisco, California (closely related to *P. stellaris*).

14. **Physcia isidiigera** (Zahlbr.) Fink n. comb.
P. pulverulenta var. *isidiigera* Zahlbr.; Herre, Wash. Acad. Sci. 7:362. 1906.

Thallus small, adnate, brownish black or often bluish pruinose, coralloid or powdery-granular, passing centrally into a crust, the lobes short, not much branched, often imbricated, the margins ascending and crenate; black below, pale toward the margins, with short black rhizoids; apothecia small, 1–2.5 mm. across, the disk concave, black or sometimes pruinose, the exciple thick, elevated, sorediate; spores oblong-ellipsoid, 32–38 × 14–20 μ.

On trees and wood, California.

15. **Physcia muscigena** (Ach.) Cromb., Brit. Lich. 1:309. 1894.
Parmelia muscigena Ach., Lich. Univ. 472. 1810. *P. pulverulenta* var. *muscigena* (Ach.) Nyl.

Thallus middle-sized, chestnut-brown or lighter colored, white-pruinose in part or throughout, the lobes short, narrow, ascending, more or less branched and often bearing coralloid branchlets, the margins yellow-powdery or sorediate; white below, or becoming dark, covered densely with black rhizoids; apothecia rare, small to middle-sized, 2–4 mm. across, sessile, the disk concave to flat, white-pruinose to dark brown, the exciple thick, entire to crenate, becoming sorediate; spores oblong-ellipsoid, 25–35 × 12–18 μ.

On mosses over rocks, soil, and trees, California and South Dakota.

16. **Physcia pulverulenta** (Schreb.) Nyl., Act. Soc. Linn. Bord. 21:308. 1856.
Lichen pulverulentus Schreb., Spic. Fl. Lips. 128. 1771. *P. pulverulenta* var. *leucoleiptes* Tuck. *P. pulverulenta* var. *pityrea* (Ach.) Nyl. *P. pulverulenta* var. *angustata* Nyl. *P. pulverulenta* var. *argyphaea* (Ach.) Nyl.

Thallus usually middle-sized to large, adnate, greenish gray to brown, usually completely or interruptedly white-pruinose, the lobes narrow, sometimes elongated, somewhat branched, the margins entire, crenate or rarely lobulate, sometimes ascending and powdery; brownish black to black below, lighter toward the margins, with numerous brown to black rhizoids; apothecia rare, small to middle-sized, 2.5–5 mm. across, sessile, the disk concave to flat, whitish pruinose to dark brown, the exciple entire, crenate, or irregularly lobed; spores oblong-ellipsoid, 23–40 × 12–20 μ.

On trees, old wood, rocks, and rarely on mosses, throughout the United States.

17. **Physcia hispida** (Schreb.) Frege, Deutsch. Bot. Tasch. 169. 1812.
  Lichen hispidus Schreb., Spic. Fl. Lips. 126. 1771. *P. tenella* (Scop.) DC.
  Thallus small, often growing in clusters covering large areas, loosely adnate to ascending, greenish gray, the lobes usually somewhat elongated, more or less branched and often imbricated, the margins entire to crenate, sometimes ciliate, usually swollen by a large air space often opening outward as a terminal cavity; white below, bearing light or darker rhizoids; apothecia small, 1–2.5 mm. across, sessile to subsessile, the disk slightly concave to flat, commonly whitish pruinose, but sometimes dark brown, the exciple entire to crenulate; spores oblong-ellipsoid, 12–18 × 6–9 μ.
  On trees and rarely on rocks, throughout northern United States.

18. **Physcia Leana** Tuck., Proc. Am. Acad. 4:394. 1860.
  Parmelia Leana Tuck., in Lea, Cat. Pl. Cincin. 45. 1849.
  Thallus thin, smooth, more or less ascending, greenish gray to ashy, the lobes narrow, elongated, and much branched, the branches often imbricated, the margins entire to crenate; pale below with few pale, marginal rhizoids; apothecia small to middle-sized, subpedicellate, 0.3–0.6 mm. across, the disk concave, brown, the exciple entire; spores 18–23 × 9–10 μ.
  On mosses, Ohio. (Material is doubtfully included.)

19. **Physcia crispa** (Pers.) Nyl., Syn. Lich. 1:423. 1858.
  Parmelia crispa Pers., in Gaud., Bot. Voy. Uran. Phys. 196. 1826. *P. crispa* f. *hypomela* Tuck.
  Thallus middle-sized, adnate, greenish gray to whitish or pinkish, the lobes rather wide, not much elongated, palmately branched, somewhat imbricated, powdery, and ascending at the wavy to crenate margins; pale below, with scattered pale rhizoids, or rarely darkening; apothecia small to middle-sized, 2–4 mm. across, sessile, the disk concave, chestnut-brown, the exciple incurved, crenate or granulate; spores oblong-ellipsoid, 15–24 × 8–11 μ.
  On trees and wood, from South Carolina to Georgia, and westward to Texas and California.

20. **Physcia tribacia** (Ach.) Nyl., Flora 57:48. 1874.
  Parmelia tribacia Ach., Lich. Univ. 415. 1810.
  Thallus small to middle-sized, loosely adnate, greenish gray to ashy, sometimes forming a crust toward the center, the flat lobes short, or becoming long and more branched, the branches sometimes imbricated, with usually strongly ascending, granulose, rarely crenate margins; whitish below, with rhizoids of the same color; apothecia small, 1.5–2.5 mm. across, sessile to subsessile, the disk slightly concave to flat, blackish brown to black, or obscurely whitish pruinose, the exciple entire to crenulate; spores oblong-ellipsoid, 16–23 × 7–10 μ.
  On trees and rocks, throughout the United States.

OTHER SPECIES REPORTED

Physcia adglutinata var. pyrithrocardia Müll. Arg.—Massachusetts.

175. **Anaptychia** Koerb., in Mass., Mem. Lich. 33. 1853.

Thallus foliose or fruticose, more or less lobed and branched, prostrate, ascending, or more or less upright, the branches short, flat or grooved, often ciliate, attached to the substratum by rhizoids, differentiated into a more or less well-developed upper cortex of interwoven hyphae, algal and medullary layers, and rarely a thin, poorly developed lower cortex of interwoven hyphae; apothecia small to large, sessile to pedicellate, the disk slightly concave to flat or convex, brown to black or pruinose, the exciple colored like the thallus, more or less irregular; hypothecium hyaline; hymenium hyaline or brownish above; paraphyses unbranched; asci clavate; spores 8, brown, oblong to ellipsoid, 1-septate.
The algal host is Protococcus.

A. Thallus foliose
  B. Lobes short and rather narrow
    C. Spores 14–21 × 7.5–10.5 μ . . . . 3. A. granulifera
    C. Spores more than 20 μ in length
      D. Margins minutely notched and sorediate . . . . 2. A. Ravenelii
      D. Margins crenate or crenately lobed . . . . 1. A. major
  B. Lobes more or less elongated and narrow
    C. Thallus often brownish, becoming coralloid or with
    minute wartlike lobules toward the center
      D. Rarely bearing coralloid branchlets, the central lobes
      becoming much crowded and imbricated . . . . 7. A. aquila
      D. Central lobes covered with minute, wartlike lobules . . . 5. A. Wrightii
    C. Thallus greenish gray to ashy, smooth toward the center or
    throughout
      D. Margins more or less densely sorediate . . . . . . 4. A. speciosa
      D. Margins rarely sorediate . . . . 6. A. hypoleuca
A. Thallus subfruticose to fruticose
  B. Thallus fruticose, small to middle-sized
    C. Margins bearing white or darker cilia
      D. Lobes much elongated, narrow, commonly channeled below 11. A. ciliaris
      D. Lobes not so elongated and broader . . . . 9. A. comosa
    C. Margins bearing strong, much-branched, blackening cilia . 10. A. leucomela
  B. Thallus subfruticose, small . . . . 8. A. erinacea

1. **Anaptychia major** (Nyl.) Fink n. comb.
Physcia major Nyl., Flora 41:379. 1858. *A. speciosa* var. *major* (Nyl.) Zahlbr.
Thallus middle-sized, adnate, whitish, often coralloid-granular, the lobes not much elongated and slightly branched, the margins crenate or crenately lobed, the lobes sometimes fusing toward the center to form a crust; black or blackish below with rhizoids of the same color; apothecia small to middle-sized, 0.5–4 mm. across, the disk slightly concave, whitish pruinose to brownish black, the exciple crenulate; spores oblong-ellipsoid, 22–26 × 11–14 μ.
On trees, Florida.

2. **Anaptychia Ravenelii** (Tuck.) Zahlbr., Cat. Lich. Univ. 7:737. 1931.
Physcia Ravenelii Tuck., Syn. N. A. Lich. 1:68, 69. 1882.
Thallus adnate, greenish gray, smooth, the lobes short, rather wide, more or less branched, the margins minutely notched and sorediate; apothecia middle-sized, 1.5–3 mm. across, the disk concave to flat, brownish black, the exciple crenate, soon powdery; spores 20–26 × 11–16 μ.
On trees, South Carolina, Louisiana, and Texas.

3. **Anaptychia granulifera** (Ach.) Mass., Mem. Lich. 41. 1853.
Parmelia granulifera Ach., Syn. Meth. Lich. 212. 1814. *Physcia granulifera* (Ach.) Tuck.
Thallus adnate, greenish gray to whitish, pruinose at least at the margins, bearing numerous white soredia, the lobes flat, usually wider than long, the margins toothed-crenate; pale below with black rhizoids; apothecia small to middle-sized, 2–4.5 mm. across, the disk concave, brown, the exciple inflexed and crenate; spores 14–21 × 7.5–10.5 μ, or surpassing these measurements.
On trees, Pennsylvania, Maryland, and Illinois.

4. **Anaptychia speciosa** (Wulf.) Mass., Mem. Lich. 36. f. 32. 1853.
Lichen speciosus Wulf., in Jacq., Coll. Bot. 3:119. 1789. *Physcia speciosa* var. *galactophylla* Tuck. *Physcia speciosa* (Wulf.) Nyl.
Thallus large, adnate, greenish gray to ashy, the lobes rather narrow, becoming elongated, much branched, the more or less ascending margins entire to crenulate, and usually more or less sorediate; whitish below with fibrils of the same color; apothecia small to middle-sized, 2–7 mm. across, subsessile, the disk usually deeply

concave, brown, the exciple subentire to crenulate; spores oblong-ellipsoid, 22–34 × 12–15 μ.

On trees and mossy rocks, throughout northeastern United States, westward to Minnesota, and southward in the mountains.

5 **Anaptychia Wrightii** (Tuck.) Zahlbr., Cat. Lich. Univ. 7:743. 1931.

Physcia Wrightii Tuck., Syn. N. A. Lich. 1:68. 1882.

Thallus middle-sized to large, adnate, greenish gray to brown, covered toward the center with minute, wartlike lobules, and smooth toward the margins, the lobes moderately long, more or less branched and imbricated with round to crenate margins; brown below with hyaline rhizoids; apothecia small to large, 1.5–5 mm. across, the disk flat, blackish brown, the exciple thick, colored like the thallus, crenate; spores ellipsoid, 21–25 × 11–15 μ.

On rocks, Texas and New Mexico.

6. **Anaptychia hypoleuca** (Mühlb.) Mass., Atti Ist. Veneto III. 5:249. 1860.

Parmelia hypoleuca Mühlb., Cat. Plant. Amer. Sept. 105. 1813. *Physcia hypo-leuca* (Mühlb.) Tuck. *Parmelia speciosa* var. *hypoleuca* (Mühlb.) Ach.

Thallus middle-sized to large, adnate, greenish gray, the lobes elongated, rather narrow, usually much branched, ascending at the entire margins; usually white and decorticate below with black rhizoids; apothecia middle-sized to large, 4–8 mm. across, subpedicellate, the disk deeply concave, brown to brownish black, the exciple crenate to lobulate; spores oblong to ellipsoid, 25–38 × 14–20 μ.

On trees, eastern United States, and westward to the Rocky Mountains.

7. **Anaptychia aquila** (Ach.) Mass., Mem. Lich. 36. f. 31. 1853.

Lichen aquilus Ach., Lich. Suec. 109. 1798. *Physcia aquila* (Ach.) Nyl. *Physcia aquila* var. *detonsa* (E. Fries) Tuck. *Parmelia detonsa* E. Fries. *Physcia fusca* var. *detonsa* (E. Fries) Burnh.

Thallus small to middle-sized, closely adnate, smooth, greenish gray to dark brown, rarely bearing coralloid branchlets, the subdichotomously much-branched lobes usually elongated and narrow, often imbricated, those of the center frequently more crowded and narrower, the margins entire to crenate or lobulate; pale below with scattered rhizoids of the same color, or rarely blackening; apothecia small to middle-sized, 1.5–5 mm. across, sessile, the disk concave to convex, brown to brownish black, the thalloid exciple subcrenate to lobulate; spores oblong to ellipsoid, 28–43 × 16–25 μ.

On trees and rarely on rocks, eastern United States.

8. **Anaptychia erinacea** (Ach.) Trevis., Flora 44:52. 1861.

Borrea erinacea Ach., Lich. Univ. 499. pl. 9, f. 6. 1810. *Physcia erinacea* (Ach.) Tuck.

Thallus small to middle-sized, subfruticose, light greenish gray to whitish, the lobes somewhat elongated, flat, ascending, with entire to torn-wavy margins; white and decorticate below, with long whitish cilia at the margins; apothecia small, 0.5–3 mm. across, pedicellate, the disk flat to finally convex, grayish pruinose to blackish brown, the exciple entire, finally covered; spores ellipsoid, 20–25 × 8–12 μ.

On shrubs, California.

9. **Anaptychia comosa** (Eschw.) Mass., Mem. Lich. 39. f. 41. 1853.

Parmelia comosa Eschw., in Mart., Fl. Bras. 199, 200. 1829. *Physcia comosa* (Eschw.) Nyl.

Thallus small, fruticose, ascending, light greenish gray to ashy, irregularly much-branched, the end lobes short and dilated upward, the margins and rarely the upper surface bearing light-colored cilia; decorticate and white below; apothecia small to middle-sized or large, 3–8 mm. across, pedicellate, the disk concave, grayish pruinose, the exciple crenate or irregular, usually ciliate; spores oblong-ovoid, 25–38 × 15–20 μ.

On trees, throughout eastern United States westward to Iowa and Arkansas.

10. **Anaptychia leucomela** (L.) Mass., Mem. Lich., 35. f. 28. 1853.
   Lichen leucomelas L., Sp. Pl. ed. 3. 1613. 1764. *Physcia leucomela* (L.) Michx.
   A. leucomelaena Vainio.

Thallus middle-sized, greenish gray to whitish, fruticose and ascending, long and much branched, the branches linear, entangled, the ends entire to crenate, sometimes recurved and white-sorediate, the margins bearing strong, branched, blackening cilia; white and decorticate below; apothecia middle-sized, 4–6 mm. across, pedicellate, the disk flat, white-pruinose, the exciple lobulate; spores ellipsoid, 35–55 × 16–25 μ.

On trees, from New York southward to North Carolina, westward to Louisiana and Ohio, and appearing again in California.

11. **Anaptychia ciliaris** (L.) Koerb., in Mass., Mem. Lich. 35. f. 27. 1853.
   Lichen ciliaris L., Sp. Pl. 1144. 1753. *Physcia ciliaris* (L.) Ach. *Physcia ciliaris*
   var. *crinalis* (Torss.) Schaer.

Thallus fruticose, tufted, ascending or pendant, whitish or brownish, bearing trichomatic hyphae, the lobes convex, elongated, narrow, frequently round, much branched and usually becoming entangled, bearing pale or darkening rhizoids, especially toward the ends; whitish and commonly channeled below; apothecia small to middle-sized, 2–4.5 mm. across, short-pedicellate, the disk more or less concave, the exciple subentire to crenate, or more or less toothed-ciliate; spores oblong-ellipsoid, 30–46 × 15–21 μ. (PLATE 47 b.)

On rocks and soil and rarely on trees, northeastern United States, westward to the Rocky Mountains.

45. THELEPHORACEAE

Thallus irregularly spread over the algal host and the substratum or becoming pileate, showing little or no differentiation, closely attached to the substratum at one side or throughout; hymenium on the under side of the thallus, composed of basidia and paraphyses.

The algal host is Scytonema.

A. Thallus kidney-shaped or circular . . . . 176. CORA
A. Thallus more or less irregularly spread over the substratum,
   rarely circular . . . . 177. DICTYONEMA

176. **Cora** E. Fries, Syst. Orb. Veg. 300. 1825.

Pileus thin, kidney-shaped or circular in outline, composed of loosely interwoven hyphae; ventral hymenium forming an irregular, chinky to subareolate layer, composed of cystidia and basidia, each of the latter bearing 4 short sterigmata; spores borne singly on the tips of the sterigmata, non-septate, hyaline to brownish, spheroidal or somewhat elongated.

The algal host is Scytonema contained in a definite zone about midway between the dorsal and ventral surfaces of the pileus.

1. **Cora pavonia** (Web.) E. Fries, Syst. Orb. Veg. 300. 1825.
   Thelophora pavonia Web., in Web. & Mohr, Beitr. Naturk. 1:236. 1805.

Pileus kidney-shaped to circular in outline, 10–100 or more mm. across, thin and membranaceous, often more or less overlapping, horizontal or ascending, the margin usually inward-rolled, smooth, concentrically striate, often obscurely wrinkled, grayish white above; pale yellowish, flesh-colored to pale brick-red below; spores 10–15 × 6–12 μ.

On mossy soil, old wood, and trees, Florida.

177. **Dictyonema** Agardh., Kunth. Syn. Pl. Aequin. Orb.
Nov. 1:1. 1822.

Thallus semicircular and attached at one side to the substratum or forming an uneven layer over the substratum, composed of loosely interwoven hyphae;

hymenium ventral and scattered over the thallus, forming an irregular, areolate layer, composed of cystidia and basidia, each of the latter bearing 4 short sterigmata; spores 1 on each sterigma, brownish, non-septate, spheroidal or somewhat oblong.

The algal host is Scytonema, found in a definite layer about midway of the thallus.

A. Thallus forming semicircular or half-kidney-shaped pilei .   .   .   . 1. D. irpicinum
A. Thallus forming an irregular layer over the substratum .   .   . 2. D. guadalupense

1. **Dictyonema irpicinum** Mont., Ann. Sci. Nat. Bot. III. 10:119. 1848.

Rhipidonema irpicinum Mont., Cent. 6:8. 1848. *D. sericeum* var. *irpicinum* (Mont.) Nyl.

Pileus semicircular or half-kidney-shaped, 8–25 or more mm. across, thin and membranaceous, rough and tufted or sometimes toothed, greenish gray and becoming pale yellowish toward the uneven, scarcely fringed margin; flesh-colored to pale yellow or greenish below; spores light brown, spheroidal or somewhat oblong, 8–12 × 6–8 μ.

On trees, Florida.

2. **Dictyonema guadalupense** (Rabenh.) Zahlbr., in E. & P., Nat. Pfl. 1:239. 1907.

D. membranaceum var. *guadalupense* Rabenh.; Alq., Hedwigia 13:7. 1874. *Laudatea caespitose* Johow.

Thallus forming a thin, rough and irregularly tufted, bright greenish layer over the substratum; hymenium in small, irregular, furrowed patches; spores light brown, spheroidal or somewhat oblong, 8–10 × 6–7 μ.

On trees, Florida.

46. LEPRARIACEAE

Thallus very rudimentary, devoid of any differentiation into layers, consisting of a tangled mass of hyphae; apothecia unknown.

The algal host is Protococcus.

178. **Amphiloma** E. Fries, in Koerb., Syst. Lich. 110. 1855.

Thallus a tangled mass of hyphae, with no differentiation into cortex and medulla, with the inclosed algal cells forming a soredioid, greenish gray to whitish, mealy, friable mass, confined to moist places; attached to the substratum by hyphal rhizoids; apothecia unknown.

The algal host is Protococcus, and algal cells with parasitic fungal hyphae forming differently appearing masses are often seen. Some of these may be early stages in development of well-known lichens, and others may be other imperfect lichens. Some of the masses are yellow, others greenish gray to whitish.

1. **Amphiloma lanuginosum** (Hoffm.) Nyl., Act. Soc. Linn. Bord. 21:315. 1856.

Lichen lanuginosum Hoffm., Enum. Lich. Icon. 182. 1784.

Thallus closely adnate, granulose, greenish gray to whitish, orbicular with plain lobation at the circumference, or widely spread over the substratum and irregular in form, often without the lobation; apothecia unknown.

On rocks, bases of trees, and rarely on soil in moist, shady places, throughout the United States east of the Rocky Mountains.

INDEX

abaphoides (Graphina) 117
abaphoides (Graphis) 117
abbreviatula (Cladonia) 253
abductans (Bacidia) 231
abductans (Lecidea) 231
abietina (Lecanactis) 128
abietina (Xylographa) 96
abietinum (Calicium) 70
abietinum (Hysterium) 96
abietinum (Schismatomma) 128
abietinus (Lichen) 128
abnorme (Arthothelium) 94
abnormis (Arthonia) 94
abnormis (Opegrapha) 94
absconsa f. (Gyalecta) 140
absconsa f. (Ramonia) 140
absolutus (Baeomyces) 242
Acarospora 283
ACAROSPORACEAE 277
acarosporoides (Dermatocarpon) ... 40
accline (Arthrosporum) 224
acclinis (Bacidia) 224
acclinis (Bilimbia) 224
Achariana (Glyphis) 120
Acharii (Graphina) 117
Acharii (Graphis) 117
achrista var. (Lecidea) elaeochroma 203
achrista var. (Lecidea) enteroleuca 203
achrista var. (Lecidea) parasema 203
acicularis var. (Pilophorus) 243
acrophaea (Graphina) 116
acrustacea f. (Catillaria) 220
actinostoma (Urceolaria) 137
actinostomus (Diploschistes) 137
aculeata (Cetraria) 338
aculeatus (Lichen) 338
acuminata var. (Cenomyce) 262
acuminata (Cladonia) 262
adglutinata (Lecanora) 384
adglutinata (Physcia) 384
admiscens (Lecidea) 212
adscribens (Graphina) 115
adscribens (Graphis) 115
adspersa var. (Arthonia) 83
adspersa (Ustalia) 83
adunca f. (Cladonia) 253
adveniens (Arthothelium) 95
aenea (Verrucaria) 61
aeneum (Trypethelium) 61
aequata var. (Lecidea) coniops 208
aequata var. (Lecidea) enteroleuca 208
aequata f. (Lecidea) latypea 208
aeruginosa (Acarospora) 286
aeruginosa (Icmadophila) 310
aeruginosus (Baeomyces) 310

aethalea (Buellia) 368
aethalea (Gyalecta) 368
aethiobola (Verrucaria) 31
aethioboloides var. (Polyblastia) 35
aethioboloides var. (Verrucaria) 35
affine var. (Heterothecium) 217
affinis var. (Megalospora) 217
Afzelii (Graphis) 107
agelaea (Opegrapha) 98
agelaea (Phlyctis) 315
agelaeus (Lichen) 315
aggregata (Melanotheca) 61
aggregata (Verrucaria) 61
aggregatum (Collema) 156
aggregatum var. (Collema) 156
aggregatus (Synechoblastus) 156
aglaea (Lecidea) 208
aipolia var. (Physcia) 386
aitema (Biatora) 197
aitema var. (Lecanora) 202
aitema (Lecidea) 202
akompsa (Bacidia) 229
akompsa (Biatora) 229
alba (Arthopyrenia) 48
alba (Verrucaria) 48
albariella (Lecania) 312
albariella (Lecanora) 312
albella (Lecanora) 303
albella (Parmelia) 303
albescens (Bacidia) 227
albescens var. (Parmelia) 320
albicans (Stereocaulon) 270
albidula (Biatora) 282
albidula (Biatorella) 282
albinea f. (Buellia) 240
albineum (Rhizocarpon) 240
albineum f. (Rhizocarpon) 240
albiseda f. (Porina) 54
albissima (Urceolaria) 136
albissima var. (Urceolaria) 136
albissimus (Diploschistes) 136
alboater (Lichen) 238
alboatrum (Rhizocarpon) 238
albocaerulescens (Lecidea) 210
albocaerulescens (Lichen) 210
albociliatum (Leptogium) 145
albociliatum (Polychidium) 145
albocincta var. (Buellia) 374
albofuscescens (Arthonia) 85
albomarginatum (Thelocarpon) 279
albonigrum (Calicium) 72
albonigrum var. (Calicium) 72
albonigrum (Mycocalicium) 72
albovirescens (Allarthothelium) 95
albovirescens (Arthonia) 95

albovirescens (Arthothelium) 95
alcicornis (Cladonia) 267
Alectoria 341
aleurites (Cetraria) 320
aleurites (Lichen) 320
aleurites (Parmeliopsis) 320
aleuromela (Arthonia) 88
allophana var. (Lecanora) 301
alpestris (Cladonia) 249
alpestris var. (Lichen) 249
alpicola (Buellia) 237
alpicola (Lecidea) 237
alpicola var. (Lecidea) atrovirens 237
alpicola var. (Lecidea) geographica 237
alpicola (Parmelia) 328
alpicola var. (Parmelia) 328
alpicolum (Rhizocarpon) 237
alpigena var. (Lecanora) polytropa .. 304
alpigena var. (Lecanora) varia 304
alpina var. (Cetraria) 338
alpina (Lecanora) 300
alpina var. (Lecidea) 217
alpina var. (Umbilicaria) 275
alpinum (Stereocaulon) 271
alpinum var. (Stereocaulon) 271
alpinus var. (Mycoblastus) 217
alumenensis (Heppia) 170
amabile (Placodium) 359
amabilis (Caloplaca) 359
amara (Pertusaria) 293
amaurocraea (Capitularia) 253
amaurocraea (Cladonia) 253
ambigens (Lecanora) 291
ambigens (Pertusaria) 291
ambigua (Biatora) 203
ambigua var. (Buellia) 238
ambigua var. (Lecidea) enteroleuca 203
ambigua var. (Lecidea) parasema ... 203
ambigua var. (Lecidea) petraea 239
ambigua (Parmelia) 320
ambigua (Parmeliopsis) 320
ambiguum (Rhizocarpon) 239
ambiguus (Lichen) 320
americana (Belonia) 56
americanum (Pyrenastrum) 64
americanus (Pyrgillus) 78
amicta (Graphis) 111
amota (Melaspilea) 105
Amphiloma 392
ampliata var. (Ramalina) 346
amplissima (Lobaria) 179
amplissima (Sticta) 179
amplissimus (Lichen) 179
amygdalina (Clathroporina) 56
amygdalina (Porina) 56
amylacea (Lecidea) 201
amylaceus (Lichen) 201
analepta (Arthopyrenia) 48
analeptella (Arthopyrenia) 50
analeptus (Lichen) 48
Anaptychia 388
anastomosans var. (Arthonia) 94
anastomosans (Arthothelium) 94
andensis (Phlyctella) 316

andensis (Phlyctis) 316
Andersoni (Cyphelium) 77
angelica (Rinodina) 379
anguilliformis (Graphis) 111
angulata (Gyrophora) 275
angulata (Umbilicaria) 275
angulata (Usnea) 350
angulosa (Lecanora) 303
angulosa var. (Lecanora) 303
angulosa (Melaspilea) 104
angulosus (Lichen) 303
angustata f. (Arthonia) 91
angustata var. (Physcia) 387
anthocephala f. (Cladonia) 262
anthracina (Gyrophora) 272
anthracina (Umbilicaria) 272
anthracinus (Lichen) 272
anthracophila var. (Lecidea) 214
anthracophila (Psora) 214
Anthracothecium 58
anthraspis (Sticta) 181
anthraspis (Stictina) 181
apalachense (Collema) 165
apalachense (Leptogium) 165
aphthosa (Peltigera) 186
aphthosus (Lichen) 186
apodocarpa (Cladonia) 260
apolepta f. (Cladonia) 266
applanata var. (Pyxine) 383
aquaticum (Dermatocarpon) 39
aquaticus (Lichen) 39
aquila (Anaptychia) 390
aquila (Physcia) 390
aquilella (Verrucaria) 32
aquilus (Lichen) 390
aractina var. (Verrucaria) 31
arboreum (Dermatocarpon) 41
arboreum (Endocarpon) 41
arborialis var. (Cetraria) 338
arceutina (Bacidia) 230
arceutina var. (Biatora) effusa 230
arceutina var. (Biatora) luteola 230
arceutina var. (Lecidea) 230
arctica (Gyrophora) 273
arctica (Lecidea) 205
arctica var. (Umbilicaria) 273
arcticum (Nephroma) 184
arcticus (Lichen) 184
arenaria (Caliciella) 72
arenarium (Cyphelium) 72
arenosa (Acarospora) 286
areolata var. (Caloplaca) 357
argena (Phlyctis) 315
argentata var. (Lecanora) 301
argenus (Lichen) 315
argyphaea var. (Physcia) 387
arizonica (Parmelia) 330
arizonicum (Leptogium) 165
arizonicum (Omphalodium) 330
arizonicum var. (Omphalodium) 330
armeniaca (Lecidea) 202
armeniacum (Rhizocarpon) 202
aromatica (Lecidea) 234
aromatica (Toninia) 234

aromaticus (Lichen) 234
articulata (Usnea) 350
Arthonia 79
ARTHONIACEAE 78
arthonioides (Lecidea) 105
arthonioides (Melaspilea) 105
Arthopyrenia 45
Arthothelium 93
artyta (Biatora) 225
artyta (Bilimbia) 225
artyta (Lecidea) 225
ascociscana (Psoroma) 376
ascociscana (Rinodina) 376
asotea var. (Cladonia) 251
asoteus var. (Baeomyces) 251
aspera var. (Capitularia) 263
aspera var. (Cladonia) 263
aspidota (Parmelia) 332
aspidota var. (Parmelia) 332
aspistea (Pyrenula) 57
aspistea (Verrucaria) 57
assimilata (Lecidea) 212
assimilis (Graphis) 109
asteriscus (Arthonia) 92
astraea (Opegrapha) 100
astroidea (Arthonia) 91
astroidea (Parmelia) 385
astroidea (Parmentaria) 64
astroidea (Physcia) 385
ASTROTHELIACEAE 63
ater (Lichen) 299
aterrima (Microthelia) 45
aterrima (Rinodina) Anzi 45
aterrima (Rinodina) Krempelh. 377
athalloides (Lecidea) 240
athalloides (Rhizocarpon) 240
athroocarpa (Lecanora) 311
atlantica (Arthonia) 92
atlantica var. (Biatora) 218
atlantica var. (Biatorina) 218
atlantica var. (Catillaria) 218
atlanticum f. (Platysma) 336
atra (Lecanora) 299
atra (Opegrapha) 98
atra (Parmelia) 299
atrata (Arthonia) 92
atriseda (Lecanora) 305
atriseda var. (Parmelia) 305
atroalba (Buellia) 370
atroalba (Caloplaca) 360
atroalbella (Buellia) 368
atroalbella (Lecidea) 368
atroalbum (Placodium) 360
atrobrunnea (Lecidea) 211
atrobrunneum (Rhizocarpon) 211
atrocinerea (Rinodina) 378
atrocinerea var. (Rinodina) 378
atrocinereus (Lichen) 378
atrofusca var. (Lecidea) 199
atrofusca (Parmelia) 328
atrofusca var. (Parmelia) 328
atrogrisea (Bacidia) 229
atrogrisea (Biatora) 229
atrolutescens (Lecidea) 202

atropurpurea (Biatorina) 220
atropurpurea (Catillaria) 220
atropurpurea var. (Lecidea) 220
atrorimalis (Opegrapha) 98
atrorubens (Graphis) 108
atrorubens (Lecidea) 195
atrorufa (Biatora) 212
atrorufa (Psora) 212
atrosanguinea (Bacidia) 230
atrosanguinea (Blastenia) 353
atrosanguinea (Lecanora) 353
atrynea (Lecanora) 301
atrynea var. (Lecanora) 301
Auberianum (Leptotrema) 133
Auberianum (Phaeotrema) 133
Auberianum (Thelotrema) 133
Augustini (Bacidia) 228
Augustini (Biatora) 228
Augustini (Heterothecium) 234
Augustini (Lopadium) 234
aurantiaca (Caloplaca) 356
aurantiaca (Pyrenula) 58
aurantiacum (Placodium) 356
aurantiacus (Lichen) 356
aurata (Sticta) 181
aurella (Candelariella) 317
aurella (Verrucaria) 317
aurellum var. (Placodium) 317
aurescens (Cetraria) 336
auriculata (Lecidea) 207
auriculatum (Collema) 160
aurulenta (Parmelia) 331
Austini (Arthonia) 88
azureum var. (Leptogium) 165
azureus (Lichen) 165

Bachmanianum (Collemodes) 160
Bacidia 226
bacillaris (Cenomyce) 250
bacillaris (Cladonia) 250
bacillifera (Bacidia) 229
bacillifera (Lecidea) 229
bacillosa (Hassea) 65
bacillosa (Verrucaria) 65
badia (Buellia) 371
badia (Lecanora) 304
badia (Lecidea) 371
badia (Lichen) 304
badia (Parmelia) 304
badioatra (Buellia) 370
badioatra (Lecidea) 370
badioatrum (Rhizocarpon) 370
Baeomyces 241
balbisina (Graphis) 111
Balfourii var. (Cladonia) 269
barbata (Usnea) 350
barbata var. (Usnea) 350
barbatus (Lichen) 350
Beaumontii (Cladonia) 261
Beaumontii var. (Cladonia) 261
Beaumontii (Graphis) 107
Beauvoisii f. (Cladonia) 252
bella (Acarospora) 285
bella (Lecanora) Ach. 285

bella (*Lecanora*) Nyl. 285
bellidiflora (Cladonia) 252
bellidiflora (*Lichen*) 252
Belonia 56
bermudiana (Collema) 160
betulina (Opegrapha) 98
Biatorella 279
biatorina (Rinodina) 379
bicincta var. (*Lecanora*) 306
bicolor (Alectoria) 342
bicolor var. (*Alectoria*) 342
bicolor var. (*Evernia*) 342
bicolor (*Lichen*) 342
biformis (*Arthonia*) 86
biformis (Arthopyrenia) 46
biformis (*Verrucaria*) 46
Bilimbia 221
bipruinosa (Lecanora) 308
Bischoffii (*Psora*) 378
Bischoffii (Rinodina) 378
bistorta (Ramalina) 348
Blakei (Cladonia) 269
Blastenia 352
blastenicola (Thelidiella) 35
Blumeri (Buellia) 368
Bockii (Lecanora) 305
bolacina (Buellia) 371
bolacina (Caloplaca) 360
bolacinum (*Placodium*) 360
Bolanderi (*Acolium*) 77
Bolanderi (*Buellia*) 238
Bolanderi (Cypheliopsis) 77
Bolanderi (*Endocarpiscum*) 169
Bolanderi (Heppia) 169
Bolanderi (Lecanora) 309
Bolanderi (*Pannaria*) 169
Bolanderi var. (*Placodium*) 357
Bolanderi (Rhizocarpon) 238
Bolliana (*Parmelia*) 323
bolodes (Rinodina) 377
Bombyliospora 353
Bonplandi (Opegrapha) 102
Borreri (Parmelia) 323
Boryi (*Cladonia*) 254
botryocarpa (Cladonia) 269
botryosa (Graphis) 107
botryosum (*Stereocaulon*) 271
botryosum var. (Stereocaulon)
    alpinum 271
botryosum var. (*Stereocaulon*)
    tomentosum 271
botrytes (Cladonia) 268
botrytes (*Lichen*) 268
brachyloba var. (*Caloplaca*) 361
bracteata (Caloplaca) 361
bracteata (*Psora*) 361
bracteatum (*Placodium*) 361
bracteatum var. (*Placodium*) 361
bractiata f. (*Cladonia*) 251
Brandegei (Lecidea) 200
Brandegei (Pyrenothamnia) 44
Brandegei (*Staurothele*) 44
Brujeriana var. (*Biatora*) 202
Brujeriana var. (*Lecanora*) 202

Brujeriana (Lecidea) 202
brunnea (*Pannaria*) 176
brunneola (Chaenotheca) 69
brunneolum (*Calicium*) 69
Brunonis (Lecania) 312
Brunonis (*Lecanora*) 312
bryophila var. (*Parmelia*) 136
bryophila (Polyblastia) 35
bryophila var. (Urceolaria) 136
bryophila (*Verrucaria*) 35
bryophilus (*Diploschistes*) 136
bryophilus (*Lichen*) 136
Buellia 366
BUELLIACEAE 365
Buelliella 372
Buelliopsis 374
bullatum (Leptogium) 166
bullatus (*Lichen*) 166
Burgessii (Leptogium) 164
Burgessii (*Lichen*) 164
byssacea (Arthonia) 86
byssacea f. (*Catillaria*) 219
byssacea (*Sphaeria*) 86
byssacea (*Stenocybe*) 74
byssina (*Pannaria*) 162
byssinum (Leptogium) 162
byssinus (*Lichen*) 162
byssoides (*Baeomyces*) 242
byssoides (*Biatora*) 242
byssoides (*Leptogidium*) 144

cadubriae (*Biatora*) 197
cadubriae (Lecidea) 197
caerulea (Verrucaria) 33
caeruleonigricans (*Lecidea*) 233
caeruleonigricans (*Lichen*) 233
caeruleonigricans (Toninia) 233
caesia var. (*Lecidea*) 172
caesia var. (*Pannaria*) 172
caesia (Physcia) 385
caesia var. (Rinodina) 381
caesiellum (Leptogium) 163
caesiocarpa var. (*Allarthonia*) 87
caesiocarpa var. (Arthonia) 87
caesiopruinosa (*Arthonia*) 118
caesiopruinosa (Phaeographina) 118
caesiopruinosa var. (*Pyxine*) 383
caesiorubella (*Lecanora*) 303
caesium var. (Placynthium) 172
caesius (*Lichen*) 385
caespiticia (Cladonia) 258
caespiticius (*Baeomyces*) 258
caespitose (*Laudatea*) 392
calcarea (Lecanora) 297
calcarea (Opegrapha) 99
calcarea (*Parmelia*) 297
calcarea (*Zahlbruckera*) 142
calcarea (Zahlbrucknerella) 142
calcareus (*Lichen*) 297
calciseda (Verrucaria) 33
calcivora (Lecidea) 198
calcivorus (*Lichen*) 198
calicaris (*Lichen*) 345
calicaris (Ramalina) 345

CALICIACEAE 67
Caliciella 72
Calicium 69
california (Acarospora) 286
california (Dirina) 124
california (Schismatomma) 124
californica (Alectoria) 338
californica (Cetraria) 338
californica var. (Evernia) 339
californica (Lecania) 312
californica var. (Lecania) 312
californica f. (Pannaria) 174
californica f. (Parmeliella) 174
californica (Rinodina) 378
californica (Schizopelte) 126
californica (Trachylia) 77
californica (Usnea) 349
californicum (Acolium) 77
californicum (Chiodecton) 123
californicum (Coelocalon) 338
californicum (Cyphelium) 77
californicum (Leptogium) 167
californicum (Mycoporellum) 67
californicum (Phaeotrema) 132
californicum (Sclerophyton) 123
californicum (Thelotrema) 132
callibotrys (Collema) 159
callopisma (Caloplaca) 363
callosa (Physcia) 387
caloosensis (Bacidia) 222
caloosensis (Biatora) 222
caloosensis (Bilimbia) 222
caloosensis (Buellia) 369
Caloplaca 354
CALOPLACACEAE 351
calva (Lecanora) 351
calycantha (Cladonia) 265
campestris (Biatora) 281
campestris (Biatorella) 281
campestris var. (Lecanora) rubina 308
campestris var. (Lecanora) subfusca 301
camptidia (Caloplaca) 358
camptidium (Lecanora) 358
camptidium (Placodium) 358
camptocarpa (Biatora) 282
camptocarpa (Biatorella) 282
canaliculata (Ramalina) 346
canaliculata var. (Ramalina) 346
cancriformis var. (Lecanora) albella 303
cancriformis var. (Lecanora) pallida 303
cancriformis (Verrucaria) 303
Candelaria 318
candelaria (Xanthoria) 364
Candelariella 316
candelaris (Physcia) 318
candelarius (Lichen) 364
candelarius (Teloschistes) 364
candicans (Lichen) 313
candicans (Placolecania) 313
candicans (Solenopsora) 313
candida (Diphloeis) 234
candida (Lecidea) 234
candida (Opegrapha) 99
candida (Toninia) 234

candidus (Lichen) 234
canella subsp. (Verrucaria) 33
canina (Peltigera) 188
caninus (Lichen) 188
caperata (Parmelia) 330
caperatus (Lichen) 330
caribaea (Arthonia) 84
caribaea (Graphis) 84
cariosa (Cladonia) 261
cariosus (Lichen) 261
carnea (Ocellularia) 132
carneum (Thelotrema) 132
Carnegiei (Acarospora) 287
carneoalbens (Lecidea) 195
carneola (Cenomyce) 268
carneola (Cladonia) 268
carneoluteola (Gyalecta) 139
carneoluteola (Secoliga) 139
carneopallida (Lecidea) 291
carneopallida (Pertusaria) 291
carneorufa (Arthonia) 81
carnosa (Massalongia) 171
carnosa (Pannaria) 171
carnosus (Lichen) 171
carnulenta (Biatora) 197
carnulenta (Lecidea) 197
caroliniana (Cenomyce) 254
caroliniana (Cladonia) 254
caroliniana var. (Cladonia) 254
caroliniana (Parmelia) 326
caroliniana (Umbilicaria) 276
carolinianum (Acolium) 76
carolinianum (Cyphelium) 76
carolinianum (Trypethelium) 62
Carpinea (Porina) 54
Carpinea (Verrucaria) 54
castanea (Lecanora) 309
catalinariae (Dirina) 124
catalinariae (Lecidea) 202
catawbensis (Buellia) 277
catawbensis (Dermatiscum) 277
catervaria (Verrucaria) 62
catervarium (Trypethelium) 62
Catillaria 217
caudata (Arthonia) 92
caudata (Bilimbia) 226
caudata (Lecidea) 226
caulescens (Lecidea) 233
caulescens var. (Lecidea) 233
caulescens (Toninia) 233
caulophylla (Biatora) 214
caulophylla (Lecidea) 214
caulophylla (Psora) 214
cavernosa f. (Cetraria) 336
cavernosa (Usnea) 350
Celtidis (Graphis) 110
cenisia (Lecanora) 300
cenisia var. (Lecanora) 300
cenotea (Cladonia) 259
cenoteus (Baeomyces) 259
centrifuga (Parmelia) 329
centrifugus (Lichen) 329
cephalata f. (Ramalina) 344
Cerasi (Arthopyrenia) 49

Cerasi (*Verrucaria*) 49
cerasphora (Cladonia) 263
ceratea (Evernia) 340
ceratea var. (*Evernia*)............... 340
ceratea var. (*Parmelia*) 340
ceratina (*Gyalecta*) 140
ceratina var. (*Usnea*) 349
ceratodes f. (*Cladonia*) *fimbriata* 266
ceratodes f. (*Cladonia*) *ochrochlora*..... 266
cereolus (*Lichen*) 243
cereolus (Pilophorus) 243
cerina (Caloplaca) 357
cerina (Pyrenula) 58
cerinella (Candelariella) 317
cerinella (*Lecanora*) 317
cerinum (*Placodium*) 357
cerinus (*Lichen*) 357
ceruchis (*Parmelia*) 344
ceruchis (Ramalina) 344
cervicornis var. (Cladonia) 265
cervicornis (*Lichen*) 265
cervina (Acarospora) 287
cervina (*Lecanora*) 287
cervina (*Parmelia*) 287
cestrensis (Porina) 55
cestrensis (*Sagedia*) 55
Cetraria 334
cetrarioides (Cladonia) 269
cetrarioides (Parmelia) 334
cetrariza (*Alectoria*) 338
cetrata (Parmelia) 326
ceuthocarpa (Verrucaria) 30
Chaenotheca 68
chalybeia (*Biatorina*) 220
chalybeia (Catillaria) 220
chalybeia (*Lecidea*) 220
chalybeiformis (Alectoria) 342
chalybeiformis var. (*Alectoria*) 342
chalybeiformis (*Lichen*) 342
cheileum (Collema) 158
cheileus (*Lichen*) 158
cheiroloba (Parmeliella) 174
chevallieri (*Opegrapha*) 99
chiodectella (Arthonia) 85
Chiodecton 121
CHIODECTONACEAE 119
chiodectonoides var. (*Arthonia*) 85
chlarona (*Lecanora*) 301
chlarona var. (*Lecanora*) 301
chlorantha (Bacidia) 229
chlorantha (*Biatora*) 229
chlorellum (Stereocaulon) 271
chlorochroa (*Parmelia*) 332
chloroconia (*Lecanactis*) 127
chloroconia var. (Lecanactis)....... 127
chloroconium (*Acolium*) 76
chloroconium (Cyphelium) 76
chloromelum (Leptogium) 164
chloromelus (*Lichen*) 164
chlorophaea var. (*Cladonia*) 264
chlorophylla (Cetraria) 336
chlorophylla var. (*Cetraria*) 336
chlorophyllus (*Lichen*) 336
chloroplana (*Acarospora*) 285

chlorospora var. (*Lecidea*) 370
chlorosticta (Bacidia) 231
chlorosticta (*Biatora*) 231
chlorosticta (*Lecidea*) 231
chlorotica (Porina) 54
chlorotica (*Sagedia*) 54
chlorotica (*Verrucaria*) 54
chordalis var. (*Capitularia*) 262
chordalis var. (Cladonia) 262
chrysantha (*Parmelia*) 330
chrysocephala (Chaenotheca) 68
chrysocephalum (*Calicium*) 68
chrysocephalus (*Lichen*) 68
chrysomelaena (*Lecanora*) 381
chrysomelaena (Rinodina) 381
chrysophthalmus (*Lichen*) 365
chrysophthalmus (Teloschistes) 365
chrysops (*Lecanora*) 285
cicatricosa (Glyphis) 120
ciliaris (Anaptychia) 391
ciliaris (Cetraria) 337
ciliaris (*Lichen*) 391
ciliaris (*Nephromopsis*) 337
ciliaris (*Physcia*) 391
ciliata var. (*Parmelia*) 325
ciliata var. (*Usnea*) 350
Cinchonae (Arthopyrenia) 49
Cinchonae (*Pyrenula*) 49
Cinchonae (*Verrucaria*) 49
cincinnata var. (*Alectoria*) 343
cineracea (Acarospora) 286
cineracea (*Lecanora*) 286
cineracea f. (*Lecanora*) 286
cinerascens (Melaspilea) 104
cinerascens (*Opegrapha*) 104
cinerata (Lecidea) 205
cinerea var. (*Chaenotheca*) 69
cinerea (Graphis) 111
cinerea (Lecanora) 298
cinerea (Opegrapha) 100
cinerea (*Parmelia*) 298
cinerea (Porina) 53
cinerea (*Verrucaria*) 53
cinerella (*Pyrenula*) 45
cinereoalba var. (*Acarospora*) 287
cinereoatra (Lecidea) 207
cinereopruinosa (Arthonia) 86
cinereopruinosa (Arthopyrenia) 47
cinereopruinosa (*Verrucaria*) 47
cinereorufescens (Lecanora) 298
cinereorufescens (*Urceolaria*) 298
cinereovirens (*Patellaria*) 237
cinereovirens (Rhizocarpon) 237
cinereum (Dermatocarpon) 40
cinereum (*Endocarpon*) 40
cinereus (*Lichen*) 298
cinnabarina (*Arthonia*) 83
cinnabarina (*Biatora*) 195
cinnabarina (Caloplaca) 356
cinnabarina (*Lecanora*) 356
cinnabarina (Lecidea) 195
cinnabarinum (*Placodium*) 356
circinata (Lecanora) 306
circinata (Staurothele) 36

circinatus (Lichen) 306
cirrochroa (Caloplaca) 361
cirrochroa (Lecanora) 361
cirrochroum (Placodium) 361
cismonicum (Haematomma) 315
citrina (Acarospora) 285
citrina (Caloplaca) 357
citrina (Urceolaria) 285
citrina (Verrucaria) 357
citrinum (Calicium) 72
citrinum (Placodium) 357
cladodes (Caloplaca) 363
cladodes (Collema) 152
cladodes (Lempholemma) 152
cladodes (Placodium) 363
cladodes (Physma) 152
cladomorpha f. (Cladonia) degenerans.. 263
cladomorpha f. (Cladonia) pityrea 266
Cladonia 243
Cladonia var. (Evernia) ceratea 340
Cladonia var. (Evernia) furfuracea 340
Cladonia (Parmelia) 340
Cladonia var. (Parmelia) 340
CLADONIACEAE 241
cladonioides (Lecidea) 214
cladoniscum (Biatora) 217
cladoniscum (Nesolechia) 217
Clathroporina 55
claudestina (Pyrenula) 58
clavata f. (Cladonia) bacillaris 250
clavata f. (Cladonia) fimbriata 266
clavulifera (Cladonia) 260
clavus (Biatorella) 281
clavus (Patellaria) 281
Clementis (Bacidia) 230
clopima (Staurothele) 36
clopima var. (Staurothele) 36
clopima (Verrucaria) 36
coarctata (Biatora) 198
coarctata (Lecanora) 198
coarctata (Lecidea) 198
coarctatus (Lichen) 198
coccifera (Cladonia) 251
cocciferus (Lichen) 251
coccineum (Haematomma) 315
coccineus (Lichen) 315
Coccocarpia 178
coccophorum (Collema) 154
coccophorus (Synechoblastus) 154
cocoës var. (Coccocarpia) 178
cocoës (Lichen) 383
cocoës (Pyxine) 383
COENOGONIACEAE 140
Coenogonium 140
cohibilis (Lecidea) 368
coilocarpa (Lecanora) 301
coilocarpa var. (Lecanora) 301
Collema 157
COLLEMACEAE 152
Collemodes 160
colludens (Buellia) 370
colludens (Lecidea) 370
colpodes (Anzia) 329
colpodes (Lichen) 329

colpodes (Parmelia) 329
columbiana (Graphis) 119
columbiana (Phaeographina) 119
combeoides (Ramalina) 345
cometia (Graphis) 118
comma (Graphis) 109
communis (Pertusaria) 292
comosa (Anaptychia) 390
comosa (Parmelia) 390
comosa (Physcia) 390
comosa var. (Usnea)............... 349
compacta var. (Biatora) 231
compacta (Pyrenopsis) 146
complanata (Arthonia) 90
complanata (Ramalina) 347
complanata (Strigula) 65
complanatus (Lichen) 347
complicatum var. (Dermatocarpon) . 39
complicatus var. (Lichen) 39
compunctum (Thelotrema) 133
concatervans (Melanotheca) 61
concatervans (Verrucaria) 61
concentricum (Rhizocarpon) 240
concentricum var. (Rhizocarpon) 240
concentricus (Lichen) 240
conchatum var. (Leptogium) 165
conchiloba (Heppia) 170
concolor (Candelaria) 318
concolor (Lichen) 318
concolor var. (Parmelia) 318
concolor (Teloschistes) 318
concreta (Buellia) 237
condensatum (Stereocaulon) 270
confervoides (Rhizocarpon) 239
confervoides var. (Rhizocarpon) 239
confinis (Lichen) 151
confinis (Lichina) 151
confluens (Glyphis) 120
confluens var. (Glyphis) cicatricosa .. 120
confluens var. (Glyphis) favulosa 120
conformis (Arthopyrenia) 49
conformis (Verrucaria) 49
confragosa (Parmelia) 377
confragosa (Rinodina) 377
confragosa var. (Rinodina) 377
congesta (Lecidea) 196
conglomeratum var. (Stereocaulon) .. 270
conglomeratus (Synechoblastus) 155
congruella (Lecidea) 140
coniocraea (Cenomyce) 266
coniocraea var. (Cladonia) 266
Coniocybe 73
conizaea (Lecanora) 309
conoidea (Arthopyrenia) 48
conoidea (Verrucaria) 48
conoplea (Pannaria) 177
conoplea var. (Pannaria) 177
conoplea (Parmelia) 177
Conotrema 135
Conradi (Rinodina) 380
consequella (Arthopyrenia) 47
consequella (Verrucaria) 47
consequens (Verrucaria) 47
conspersa (Biatorella) 280

conspersa *(Lecidea)* 280
conspersa (Parmelia) 331
conspersus (Lichen) 331
conspicua var. *(Cladonia)* 259
conspirans (Buellia) 369
conspirans (Lecidea) 369
conspurcata (Parmelia) 332
conspurcata f. *(Parmelia)* 332
constans (Lecanora) 283
constans (Maronea) 283
constans (Rinodina) 283
constipans (Lecanora) 309
constrictella (Melaspilea) 104
constrictella (Opegrapha) 104
contigua (Lecidea) 208
contigua var. *(Lecidea)* 241
contiguum f. *(Rhizocarpon)* 241
contorta (Lecanora) 297
contorta var. *(Lecanora)* 297
contorta (Verrucaria) 297
convexella (Arthonia) 87
convexella var. *(Lecidea)* 208
convexiuscula (Imbricaria) 329
Cora 391
coracina (Buellia) 368
coracina (Lecidea) 368
coracina var. *(Lecidea)* 281
coracina (Verrucaria) 368
corallina var. *(Biatora)* 200
corallina (Pyrenopsis) 145
corallinoides var. *(Parmelia)* 174
corallinoides (Parmeliella) 174
corallinoides (Stereocaulon) 174
coralloidea (Parmelia) 324
coralloidea var. *(Parmelia)* 324
coralloides (Caloplaca) 362
coralloides (Placodium) 362
coralloides (Sphaerophorus) 78
coralloides (Stereocaulon) 270
corallophora var. *(Pannaria)* 174
corallophora var. (Parmeliella) 174
cornucopioides (Cladonia) 251
cornuta (Cladonia) 263
cornutoradiata var. *(Cladonia)* 266
cornutus (Lichen) 263
corrugis var. *(Parmelia)* 327
corticola (Gyalecta) 140
corymbosa var. *(Cladonia)* 254
corymbosula (Cladonia) 260
costata f. *(Cladonia)* 264
crenata (Biatora) 214
crenata (Lecidea) 214
crenata (Placolecania) 313
crenata (Psora) 214
crenata (Solenopsora) 313
crenatellum (Leptogium) 166
crenatum (Endocarpon) 214
crenulata (Candelariella) 317
crenulatum (Placodium) 317
crenulatus var. *(Lichen)* 317
cribellata (Parmelia) 326
cribrosa f. (Cladonia) 261
cribrosa f. *(Patellaria)* 261
crinalis var. *(Physcia)* 391

crinita (Parmelia) 325
crinita (Ramalina) 347
crispa var. *(Cetraria)* 338
crispa (Parmelia) 388
crispa (Physcia) 388
crispata var. *(Baeomyces)* 256
crispata (Cladonia) 256
crispata var. *(Cladonia)* 256
crispum (Collema) 158
crispus (Lichen) 158
cristatella (Cladonia) 252
cristatellum (Collema) 159
cristifera (Parmelia) 325
cristulata (Parmelia) 329
crocata (Sticta) 181
crocata (Stictina) 181
crocatus (Lichen) 181
crocea (Solorina) 184
croceus (Lichen) 184
cronia (Coccocarpia) 178
crossophylla (Pannaria) 173
crossophylla (Parmeliella) 173
crossota var. *(Cenomyce)* 259
crossota var. (Cladonia) 259
cruciaria (Lecidea) 204
cruenta (Melanotheca) 60
cruentum (Trypethelium) 60
crustulata (Lecidea) 208
cubensis (Parmelia) 323
cucullata (Cetraria) 337
cucullatus (Lichen) 337
cumulata (Biatora) 233
cumulata (Lecidea) 233
cumulata (Toninia) 233
cupreorosella (Biatora) 222
cupreorosella (Bilimbia) 222
cupreorosella (Lecidea) 222
cupressi (Lecanora) 303
cupressina (Arthonia) 85
cupularis (Gyalecta) 138
cupularis (Melaspilea) 105
cupularis (Secoliga) 138
Curtisii (Calicium) 70
Curtisii (Gyrostomum) 135
curtum (Calicium) 70
cuspidata (Ramalina) 348
cyanea (Lecidea) 201
cyanea var. *(Lecidea)* 201
cyanescens var. *(Collema)* 165
cyanipes (Cenomyce) 268
cyanipes (Cladonia) 268
cyanipes var. *(Cladonia)* 268
cyanolepra (Pannaria) 174
cyanolepra var. *(Pannaria)* 174
cyanolepra (Parmeliella) 174
cylindrica (Gyrophora) 274
cylindrica (Umbilicaria) 274
cylindricus (Lichen) 274
cylisphora (Parmelia) 330
cyphalea (Biatora) 282
cyphalea (Biatorella) 282
CYPHELIACEAE 75
Cypheliopsis 77
Cyphelium 75

Cypressi (Graphina) 114
Cypressi var. (Graphina) 114
cyrtaspis (Collema) 155
cyrtaspis (Synechoblastus) 155
cyrtella (Lecania) 311
cyrtella (Lecidea) 311
cyrtidia (Lecidea) 210
Cytisi (Arthonia) 88

dacryodes (Verrucaria) 33
dactylina (Pertusaria) 291
dactylinum (Leptogium) 163
dactylinus (Lichen) 291
dasypoga var. (Usnea) 350
daytoniana (Cladonia) 256
dealbata f. (Biatora) decipiens ... 215
dealbata f. (Biatora) Russellii ... 213
dealbata f. (Lecanora) 285
dealbata f. (Lecidea) 214
dealbata f. (Psora) 215
dealbens (Polyblastiopsis) 51
decipiens (Biatora) 215
decipiens var. (Caloplaca) 361
decipiens (Lecidea) 215
decipiens (Lichen) 215
decipiens (Psora) 215
declinis (Bacidia) 223
declinis (Biatora) 223
declinis (Bilimbia) 223
declinis (Lecidea) 223
decolorans (Lecidea) 198
decorticata (Capitularia) 261
decorticata (Cladonia) 261
decussata (Gyrophora) 272
decussatus (Lichen) 272
deformis (Cladonia) 252
deformis (Lichen) 252
deformis (Melaspilea) 104
deformis var. (Opegrapha) 104
degenerans (Baeomyces) 263
degenerans (Cladonia) 263
delicata (Cladonia) 258
delicatus (Lichen) 258
Delisaei var. (Cetraria) 338
Demangeonii (Collema) 150
Demangeonii (Phylliscum) 150
Demangeonii (Thyrea) 150
demissa (Hazslinszkya) 104
demissa (Lecidea) 212
demissa (Melaspilea) 104
demissa (Opegrapha) 104
demissa (Psora) 212
demissus (Lichen) 212
dendriscum (Leptogidium) 144
dendriscum (Leptogium) 144
dendritica (Opegrapha) 112
dendritica (Phaeographis) 112
dendriticella (Phaeographis) 112
Dendrographa 125
densissima var. (Cladonia) 252
denticollis (Cladonia) 257
denticollis var. (Cladonia) 257
denticulata (Ramalina) 347
denudatum (Stereocaulon) 271

depauperata f. (Acarospora)
  glaucocarpa 288
depauperata f. (Acarospora) cervina ... 288
deplanans (Lecanora) 298
Dermatiscum 277
DERMATOCARPACEAE 37
Dermatocarpon 38
deserticola (Heppia) 169
Despreauxii (Cladonia) 268
Despreauxii (Heppia) 170
Despreauxii (Solorina) 170
Despreauxii (Solorinaria) 170
destitula (Lecidea) 379
destitula (Rinodina) 379
detonsa (Parmelia) 390
detonsa var. (Physcia) aquila 390
detonsa var. (Physcia) fusca 390
deusta (Gyrophora) Ach. 273
deusta (Gyrophora) Turn. & Borr. 274
deustus (Lichen) 273
develata f. (Arthonia) 86
diabolica (Gyrophora) 275
dialyta (Buellia) 369
dialyta (Lecidea) 369
diapensiae (Biatora) 206
diapensiae (Lecidea) 206
diaphora (Opegrapha) 100
diaphoroides (Opegrapha) 98
diaphoroides f. (Opegrapha) 98
diaphorus (Lichen) 100
dicraea f. (Cladonia) 253
dictyiza (Umbilicaria) 277
Dictyonema 391
diducens (Lecidea) 207
didyma (Arthonia) 92
didyma (Cladonia) 250
didymus (Scyphophorus) 250
difficilis (Roccella) 126
difforme (Mycoporum) 67
difforme (Mycoporellum) 67
diformis (Biatora) 280
diformis (Dermatina) 67
diffracta (Lecanora) 307
difracta var. (Lecanora) muralis .. 307
difracta var. (Lecanora) saxicola .. 307
diffractella (Phalostauris) 36
diffractella (Staurothele) 36
difractella (Verrucaria) 36
difractus (Lichen) 307
diffusa (Arthonia) 89
diffusa (Parmelia) 320
diffusa var. (Parmelia) 320
diffusa (Parmeliopsis) 320
diffusa var. (Parmeliopsis) 320
diffusella (Arthonia) 89
diffusus (Lichen) 320
digitata (Cladonia) 251
dilacerata var. (Cladonia) 262
dilacerata (Lichen) 347
dilacerata (Ramalina) 347
dilatata var. (Cladonia) 262
Dillenii (Gyrophora) 276
Dillenii (Umbilicaria) 276
diluta (Microphiale) 138

diluta (Peziza) 138
dimera (Lecania) 311
dimera var. (Lecania) 311
dimera (Lecanora) 311
dimidiata (Arthopyrenia) 49
diphasia (Blastenia) 352
diphasia (Lecanora) 352
diphasium (Placodium) 352
DIPLOSCHISTACEAE 135
Dirina 124
DIRINACEAE 123
dirinoides (Rinodina) 382
discernenda (Caloplaca) 363
disciformis (Buellia) 367
discolor (Caloplaca) 357
discolor var. (Caloplaca) 357
discolor var. (Lecanora) 301
discolor var. (Placodium) 357
discolor (Pyrenula) 52
discordans (Thrombium) 37
disjunctum (Coenogonium) 141
dispersa (Arthonia) 88
dispersa (Lecanora) 302
dispersa (Opegrapha) 88
dispersula (Arthonia) 88
dispersus (Lichen) 302
dispora (Lecidea) 238
dispora (Polyblastiopsis) 52
disporum (Rhizocarpon) 238
dissectula f. (Cladonia) 269
disseminata (Chaenotheca) 72
disseminata (Xylographa) 96
disseminatum (Cyphelium) 72
disseminatum (Mycocalicium) 72
distans var. (Acarospora) 288
distans (Arthopyrenia) 49
distans var. (Lecanora) 301
distans (Thelidium) 49
distans (Verrucaria) 49
distendens (Arthonia) 93
distendens (Arthothelium) 93
distinctum (Rhizocarpon) 239
divaricata (Evernia) 340
divaricatus (Lichen) 340
divergens (Alectoria) 341
divergens (Cornicularia) 341
diversa (Graphis) 111
divulsa (Cenomyce) 257
divulsa var. (Cladonia) 257
dolodes (Lecidea) 209
dolosum (Schismatomma) 129
domingense (Ascidium) 131
domingense (Heterothecium) 235
domingense (Lopadium) 235
domingense (Patellaria) 235
domingense (Thelotrema) 131
domingensis (Ocellularia) 131
dryina (Bacidia) 232
dryina (Biatora) 232
dryina (Lecidea) 232
dubium (Placynthium) 173
Dudleyi (Lecania) 312
Dufourea 340
Dumastii (Fissurina) 107

Dumastii (Graphis) 107
duplicata (Graphis) 110
Duriaei (Ramalina) 345
Duriaei var. (Ramalina) 345

Eckfeldtii (Arthonia) 86
ecmocyna var. (Cladonia) 262
ECTOLECHIACEAE 137
effusa (Bacidia) 229
effusa (Biatora) 229
effusa var. (Candelaria) 319
effusa var. (Candelaria) 318
effusa (Lecanora) 303
effusa var. (Teloschistes) 319
effusus (Lichen) Pers. 303
effusus (Lichen) J. E. Smith 229
egenuloidea (Bacidia) 228
elabens (Lecidea) 200
elaeochroa (Verrucaria) 32
elatina (Lecanora) 314
elatinum (Haematomma) 314
elegans (Caloplaca) 361
elegans (Enterographa) 122
elegans (Graphis) 110
elegans (Lichen) 361
elegans (Opegrapha) 110
elegans (Placodium) 361
elegans (Strigula) 65
Elizae (Buellia) 369
Elizae (Lecidea) 369
elongata var. (Cladonia) 263
elongatus (Lichen) 263
eluteriae (Trypethelium) 63
encausta (Parmelia) 324
encaustus (Lichen) 324
endiviaefolia (Cladonia) 267
Endocarpon 42
endochlora (Lecidea) 214
endochroma (Biatora) 219
endochroma (Catillaria) 219
endochroma (Lecanora) 219
endochromum (Heterothecium) ... 219
endochrysea (Parmelia) 386
endochrysea (Physcia) 386
endochrysea var. (Physcia) 386
endococcinea f. (Physcia) 386
endococcoidea (Pyrenulella) 58
endococcoidea (Verrucaria) 58
endocyanea (Bacidia) 231
endocyanea (Biatora) 231
endoleuca (Bacidia) 229
endoxantha (Cladonia) 269
endoxantha (Parmelia) 334
enteroleuca (Lecidea) 203
enteromorpha var. (Parmelia) 324
Enterostigma 123
EPHEBACEAE 142
Ephebe 143
epidermidis (Arthopyrenia) 47
epidermidis (Leptorhaphis) 50
epidermidis (Lichen) 50
epidermidis (Verrucaria) 47
epigaea (Buellia) 371
epigaea (Lecidea) 371

epigaea (*Sphaeria*) 37
epigaea (*Verrucaria*) 37
epigaeum (Thrombium) 37
epigaeus (*Lichen*) 371
epilithellum (Thelocarpon) 279
epilutescens (Acarospora) 286
epipasta var. (*Arthonia*) 88
epipastoides (Arthonia) 90
epipastoides var. (*Arthonia*) *astroidea* .. 91
epipastoides var. (Arthonia) radiata. 91
epiphylla f. (Cladonia) 252
epiphylla var. (*Cladonia*) 260
epipolia var. (*Lecidea*) 238
epixantha (*Lecanora*) 317
epulotica (*Gyalecta*) 299
epulotica (Lecanora) 299
ericetorum (Icmadophila) 310
ericetorum (*Lichen*) 310
erinacea (Anaptychia) 390
erinacea (*Borrea*) 390
erinacea (*Physcia*) 390
erosa (Gyrophora) 274
erosa (*Lobaria*) 180
erosa (*Parmelia*) 180
erosa (Sticta) 180
erosa (*Umbilicaria*) 274
erosus (*Lichen*) 274
erubescens (Arthonia) 84
erumpens (*Graphis*) 113
erumpens (Phaeographis) 113
erupta (Arthonia) 92
erysibe (Lecania) 312
erysibe (*Lecanora*) 312
erysibe (*Lichen*) 312
erythrantha (Lecanora) 309
erythrella (Caloplaca) 356
erythrellum var. (*Placodium*) 356
erythrellus (*Lichen*) 356
erythrocardia var. (*Pyxine*) 383
Eschweileri (Mycoporum) 67
Eschweileri (Pyxine) 383
Eschweileri var. (*Pyxine*) *cocoës* 383
Eschweileri var. (*Pyxine*) *sorediata* 383
eugyra (Caloplaca) 362
eugyrum (*Placodium*) 362
eulectra (Graphis) 109
eulectra (*Phaeographis*) 109
eupetraeum (*Rhizocarpon*) 238
euphorea f. (*Cladonia*) 263
euphorea (Lecidea) 206
euphorea var. (*Lecidea*) 206
euploca (*Physcia*) 365
euploca (Speerschneidera) 365
euplocus (Teloschistes) 365
euryspora (Rinodina) 379
euspora (*Stenocybe*) 74
Evansiana (Peltigera) 189
Evernia 339
evoluta var. (*Cladonia*) 264
exalbescens var. (*Cladonia*) 249
exaltata f. (Cladonia) 259
exasperata var. (*Parmelia*) 332
exasperatula (Cladonia) 256
excedens (Arthonia) 90

excipienda (*Arthonia*) 88
exigua (*Lecidea*) 195
exigua (Rinodina) 380
exigua var. (*Rinodina*) 380
exiguus (*Lichen*) 380
exilis (*Allarthonia*) 87
exilis (Arthonia) 87
exilis var. (*Lecidea*) 87
exilis (*Teloschistes*) 365
exocanthum (Trypethelium) 62
expallens (*Lecanora*) 303
explicans var. (*Graphis*) 119
explicans (Phaeographina) 119

fagicola (*Bacidia*) 140
fagicola (*Gyalecta*) 140
fagicola (Pachyphiale) 140
fagicola (*Secoliga*) 140
faginea (*Pertusaria*) 290
faginea (Porina) 55
fahlunensis (Cetraria) 337
fahlunensis (*Lichen*) 337
fallaciosa (Polyblastiopsis) 52
fallaciosa (*Pyrenula*) 52
fallaciosum (*Sporodictyon*) 52
fallax (*Arthopyrenia*) 52
fallax var. (*Arthopyrenia*) 52
fallax (*Didymella*) 52
fallax (Polyblastiopsis) 52
fallax (*Porina*) 292
fallax var. (*Pyrenula*) 52
fallax var. (*Verrucaria*) 52
farinacea (Ramalina) 345
farinacea var. (*Ramalina*) 345
farinaceus (*Lichen*) 345
Farlowii (Acolium) 76
Farlowii (Cyphelium) 76
farrea (Pyrenula) 57
farrea (*Verrucaria*) 57
fasciculare (*Collema*) 155
fascicularis (*Lichen*) 155
fascicularis (Synechoblastus) 155
fastigiata (Ramalina) 346
fastigiata var. (*Ramalina*) 346
fastigiatus (*Lichen*) 346
favulosa (*Glyphis*) 120
favulosum (Trypethelium) 63
fayettensis (Collema) 159
Féei (*Strigula*) 65
Fendleri (Cetraria) 336
Fendleri (*Parmelia*) 336
ferruginea (*Blastenia*) 357
ferruginea (Caloplaca) 357
ferrugineum (*Lichen*) 357
ferrugineum (*Placodium*) 357
festiva (*Blastenia*) 358
festiva (Caloplaca) 358
festiva var. (*Lecidea*) 358
festivum (*Placodium*) 358
fibrosa (Candelaria) 319
fibrosa (*Parmelia*) 319
fibula f. (*Cladonia*) 266
Fibula (Pilophorus) 243
Fibula var. (*Pilophorus*) 243

Fibula (*Stereocaulon*) 243
filaris f. (*Chaenotheca*) 68
filicina (*Fouragea*) 99
filicina (Opegrapha) 99
filicina (*Opegraphella*) 99
fimbriata (Cladonia) 265
fimbriata f. (*Rinodina*) 381
fimbriatus (*Lichen*) 265
fimicola (Thelocarpon) 278
Finkii (Arthopyrenia) 47
Finkii var. (Cladonia) 255
Finkii (Parmelia) 326
Finkii (Pertusaria) 292
finmarkica var. (*Physcia*) 364
fissa f. (*Cladonia*) 254
fissurina (Arthonia) 83
flabelliformis (*Capitularia*) 250
flabelliformis (Cladonia) 250
flabellosa (*Pannaria*) 172
flabellosum (Placynthium) 172
flaccescens (Ramalina) 348
flaccidum (*Collema*) 154
flaccidus (*Synechoblastus*) 154
flava (Acarospora) 285
flavens (*Bacidia*) 218
flavens (*Biatora*) 218
flavens (Catillaria) 218
flavens var. (Lecidea) 203
flavicans (*Lichen*) 365
flavicans (Parmelia) 330
flavicans var. (*Parmelia*) 330
flavicans (Teloschistes) 365
flavicans var. (*Teloschistes*) 365
flavicunda (Pertusaria) 290
flavida var. (*Cladonia*) 249
flavida var. (*Lecidea*) 203
flavidolivens (*Biatora*) 199
flavidolivens (Lecidea) 199
flavocaerulescens var. (*Lecidea*) 210
flavonigella (*Rinodina*) 376
flavovirescens (Bacidia) 232
flavovirescens (Caloplaca) 356
flavovirescens (*Lecidea*) 232
flavovirescens (*Lichen*) 232
flavus (*Lichen*) 285
flexuosa (*Biatora*) 209
flexuosa (Lecidea) 209
flocculosa (*Gyrophora*) 273
flocculosa (*Umbilicaria*) 273
Floerkeana (*Cenomyce*) 249
Floerkeana (Cladonia) 249
florida (Usnea) 349
floridana (Arthonia) 82
floridana (*Arthopyrenia*) 49
floridana (*Bacidia*) 222
floridana (*Biatora*) 222
floridana (Bilimbia) 222
floridana (Blastenia) 352
floridana (Cladonia) 256
floridana (Graphis) 108
floridana (*Lecanora*) 352
floridana (Lopadiopsis) 137
floridana (Polyblastiopsis) 51
floridensis (Lecidea) 202

floridensis (Ocellularia) 131
floridus (*Lichen*) 349
Flotowii (Gyalecta) 139
fluviatile (*Dermatocarpon*) 39
foliacea (Cladonia) 267
foliaceus (*Lichen*) 267
Forssellia 149
fossarum (*Biatora*) 281
fossarum (Biatorella) 281
fossarum (*Lecidea*) 281
fragile (Leptogium) 168
fragilis (*Lichen*) 78
fragilis (Sphaerophorus) 78
franciscana (*Biatora*) 219
franciscana (Catillaria) 219
franciscana (Dirina) 124
fraudans (Blastenia) 352
fraudans var. (*Blastenia*) 352
fraudans var. (*Caloplaca*) 352
fraxinea (Ramalina) 346
fraxinea var. (*Ramalina*) 346
fraxineus (*Lichen*) 346
Fremontii (Alectoria) 342
Friesii (*Biatora*) 214
Friesii (*Lecidea*) 214
Friesii (Psora) 214
frondifera (Parmelia) 326
frondosa f. (*Cenomyce*) 258
frondosa f. (Cladonia) 258
Frostii (*Lecanora*) 383
Frostii (Pyxine) 383
Frostii (*Squamaria*) 383
fructigena (Lecania) 313
frustulosa (Lecanora) 305
frustulosa (*Lichen*) 305
fuciformis (*Lichen*) 126
fuciformis (Roccella) 126
fucoides (*Lichen*) 126
fucoides (*Roccella*) 126
fulgens (Caloplaca) 360
fulgens (*Lichen*) 360
fulgens (*Placodium*) 360
fuliginea var. (*Lecidea*) 199
fuliginosa (Lecidea) 211
fuliginosa (Parmelia) 334
fuliginosa (Sticta) 182
fuliginosa (*Stictina*) 182
fuliginosus (*Lichen*) 182
fulva (Lecanora) 309
fulvescens var. (Graphina) 117
fulvescens var. (*Graphis*) 117
fulvofuscum (Dermatocarpon) . 39
fulvofuscum var. (*Endocarpon*)
    fluviatile 39
fulvofuscum var. (*Endocarpon*)
    miniatum 39
fulvolutea (*Placodium*) 359
fumosa (*Lecidea*) 211
fungoides (Baeomyces) 242
fungoides var. (*Baeomyces*) 242
fungoides (*Lichen*) 242
furcata (Cladonia) 254
furcatus (*Lichen*) 254
furcellata var. (*Cladonia*) 259

furcellata f. (*Cladonia*) 266
furfuracea (Coniocybe) 73
furfuracea (Evernia) 340
furfuracea (Lecidea) 197
furfuracea (*Parmelia*) 340
furfuracea var. (*Parmelia*) 326
furfuraceus (*Lichen*) 340
furfuraceus (*Mucor*) 73
furfurellum (*Collema*) 145
furfurellus (Porocyphus) 145
furfurosa (*Biatora*) 198
furfurosa (Lecidea) 198
furvonigrans (*Biatora*) 196
furvonigrans (Lecidea) 196
furvum (Collema) 159
furvus (*Lichen*) 159
fusca (Lecidea) 208
fusca var. (*Lecidea*) 208
fuscata (Acarospora) 287
fuscata var. (*Acarospora*) 287
fuscata (*Lecanora*) 287
fuscatoatra (Lecidea) 211
fuscatus (*Lichen*) 287
fuscella (*Lecania*) 311
fuscella (Verrucaria) 32
fuscellus (*Lichen*) 32
fuscescens (*Biatora*) 200
fuscescens (Lecidea) 200
fuscipes (*Calicium*) 72
fuscipes (Mycocalicium) 72
fuscoatra (Lecidea) 211
fuscoatra (*Lichen*) 211
fuscoatra (Pyrenopsis) 147
fuscocinerea (Lecidea) 209
fuscolutea (*Biatora*) 235
fuscoluteum (*Heterothecium*) 235
fuscoluteum (Lopadium) 235
fuscoluteus (*Lichen*) 235
fusconigricans (Verrucaria) 33
fuscorubella (Bacidia) 230
fuscorubella (*Verrucaria*) 230
fuscorubens (*Biatora*) 206
fuscorubens (Lecidea) 206
fuscospora f. (Verrucaria) 33

galactina (Lecanora) 309
galactitella (Arthonia) 92
galactophylla (Caloplaca) 362
galactophylla var. (*Physcia*) 389
galactophyllum (*Placodium*) 362
Garovaglii var. (*Endocarpon*) 42
Garovaglii (*Lecanora*) 307
Garovaglii var. (Lecanora) 307
Garovaglii (*Placodium*) 307
gelasinata (Sphinctrina) 74
gelasinatus (*Lichen*) 74
gelatinosa (Lecidea) 205
gelatinosa var. (*Biatora*) 205
gelatinosa (Polyblastia) 35
gelida (Lecanora) 308
gelidus (*Lichen*) 308
gemella var. (Opegrapha) 102
geminatum (*Rhizocarpon*) 238
gemmata (*Arthopyrenia*) 48

gemmata (*Pyrenula*) 48
gemmeum (*Pyrenastrum*) 64
geniculata var. (*Ramalina*) 348
genuina var. (*Megalospora*) 221
geographica (*Buellia*) 241
geographica (*Lecidea*) 241
geographica var. (Lecidea) elaeochroma 209
geographica var. (*Lecidea*) *olivacea*.... 209
geographicum (Rhizocarpon) 241
geographicus (*Lichen*) 241
geoica (*Gyalecta*) 139
geoica (Secoliga) 139
geoicus (*Lichen*) 139
geophana (*Biatora*) 280
geophana (Biatorella) 280
geophana (*Lecidea*) 280
gibbosa (Lecanora) 297
gibbosa var. (*Lecanora*) 297
gibbosus (*Lichen*) 297
gilva (Caloplaca) 359
gilva (*Verrucaria*) 359
gilvum (*Placodium*) 359
gilvum var. (*Placodium*) 359
Girardi (*Collema*) 150
Girardi (*Omphalaria*) 150
Girardi (Thyrea) 150
glabra (Parmelia) 333
glabra f. (*Parmelia*) 333
glabrata (*Pyrenula*) 57
glauca (Cetraria) 335
glauca (Cladonia) 259
glaucescens (Arthonia) 86
glaucescens (Collema) 160
glaucescens (Leptotrema) 134
glaucescens (*Stereocaulon*) 271
glaucescens (*Thelotrema*) 134
glaucescens var. (*Thelotrema*) 134
glaucocarpa (Acarospora) 288
glaucocarpa (*Lecanora*) 288
glaucocarpa (*Parmelia*) 288
glaucoderma (Graphina) 114
glaucoderma (*Graphis*) 114
glaucoma (*Lecanora*) 306
glaucomaria (*Buellia*) 373
glaucomaria (*Lecidea*) 373
glaucomaria (Leciographa) 373
glaucomarioidea (*Buellia*) 373
glaucomarioidea (Leciographa) 373
glaucomela (Lecanora) 299
glauconigrans (*Biatora*) 220
glauconigrans (Catillaria) 220
glaucopholis (Lecidea) 212
glaucophana (Lecanora) 309
glaucophthalmum (*Collema*) 156
glaucophthalmum var. (*Collema*) 156
glaucopsina (Lecanora) 306
glaucus (*Lichen*) 335
glebosa (Acarospora) 288
glebosa (Arthonia) 86
glebosa var. (*Zeora*) 288
glebulosa (*Biatora*) 195
glebulosa (Lecidea) 195
globifera (*Biatora*) 215
globifera (*Lecidea*) 215

globifera (Psora) 215
globiferus (Sphaerophorus) 78
globosus (Lichen) 78
globosus (Sphaerophorus) 78
globularis (Pertusaria) 293
globularis (Porina) 293
globulifera (Pertusaria) 293
globulosa (Biatora) 219
globulosa (Catillaria) 219
globulosa (Lecidea) 219
glomerata (Pertusaria) 292
glomerata (Porina) 292
glomulifera (Sticta) 179
Glyphis 120
gonatodes var. (Lecanora) 310
goniophila (Lecidea) 207
goniophila var. (Lecidea) 207
gracilescens (Capitularia) 264
gracilescens (Cladonia) 264
gracilescens var. (Cladonia) crispata 257
gracilescens var. (Cladonia) rangiferina 257
gracilescens (Coniocybe) 73
gracilis (Cladonia) 262
gracilis (Lichen) 262
granatina (Lecanora) 176
granatina (Pannaria) 176
grande (Rhizocarpon) 238
grande var. (Rhizocarpon) 238
grandis var. (Buellia) 238
grandis f. (Lecidea) 238
granosa (Bilimbia) 225
granosa (Lecidea) 225
granosa (Toninia) 225
granosum (Collema) 160
granosus (Lichen) 160
granulifera (Anaptychia) 389
granulifera (Lecanora) 300
granulifera (Parmelia) pro parte...... 300
granulifera (Parmelia) 389
granulifera (Physcia) 389
granulosa (Biatora) 198
granulosa f. (Cladonia) 258
granulosa (Lecidea) 198
granulosa (Ocellularia) 131
granulosa (Verrucaria) 198
granulosum (Thelotrema) 131
GRAPHIDACEAE 95
Graphina 113
Graphis 106
gregaria (Arthonia) 83
gregaria (Sphaeria) 83
griffithii (Biatorina) 218
grisea (Gyrophora) 275
grisea var. (Gyrophora) 275
grisella (Lecidea) 208
griseoatra (Lecidea) 212
griseus (Lichen) 275
grossa (Catillaria) 220
grossa (Lecidea) 220
grossum (Heterothecium) 220
grypea var. (Cladonia) 259
guadalupense ·(Dictyonema) 392
guadalupense var. (Dictyonema) 392
Guepini (Endocarpiscum) 168

Guepini (Endocarpon) 168
Guepini (Heppia) 168
Gyalecta 138
GYALECTACEAE 137
gyalectiformis (Bacidia) 223
gyalectiformis (Bilimbia) 223
gyalectoides (Arthonia) 82
gyalizella (Bacidia) 223
gyalizella (Biatora) 223
gyalizella (Bilimbia) 223
gyalizella (Lecidea) 223
gypsacea (Urceolaria) 136
gypsacea var. (Urceolaria) 136
gypsaceus (Diploschistes) 136
Gyrophora 271
GYROPHORACEAE 271
gyrophoroides (Lecidea) 212
Gyrostomum 135

haemaleella (Euopsis) 147
haemaleella (Pyrenopsis) 147
haematites (Graphis) 113
haematites (Phaeographis) 113
Haematomma 314
haematomma (Lecanora) 315
Hageni (Lecanora) 302
Hageni (Lichen) 302
Halei (Pannaria) 177
Halei var. (Parmelia) 320
Halei var. (Parmeliopsis) 320
Halei (Thelotrema) 133
Hallii (Arthonia) 95
Hallii (Arthothelium) 95
Hallii (Lobaria) 181
Hallii (Pilophorus) 243
Hallii f. (Pilophorus) 243
Hallii (Rinodina) 376
Hallii (Sticta) 181
Hallii (Stictina) 181
halodytes (Arthopyrenia) 47
halodytes (Verrucaria) 47
halonia (Buellia) 367
halonia (Lecidea) 367
Halseyana (Parmelia) 334
Hamamelidis (Arthonia) 91
hapalea var. (Opegrapha) 98
Hassea 65
Hassei (Acarospora) 287
Hassei (Dirina) 124
Hassei (Heppia) 169
Hassei (Lecidea) 202
Hassei (Microglaena) 37
Hassei (Mycoporellum) 66
Hassei (Opegrapha) 101
Hassei (Placolecania) 313
Hassei (Psorotichia) 149
Hassei (Solenopsora) 313
Haydenii (Lecanora) 308
hebescens (Lecidea) 210
Helminthocarpon 119
helveticum (Nephroma) 184
helveticum f. (Nephroma) 184
Henscheliana (Polyblastia) 35
hepaticum (Dermatocarpon) 39

hepaticum (*Endocarpon*) 39
Heppia 168
HEPPIACEAE 168
Heppii (Acarospora) 286
Heppioides (Dermatocarpon) 41
herbacea (Sticta) 180
herbaceus (*Lichen*) 180
Herrei (Bacidia) 228
Herrei (*Blastenia*) 353
Herrei (Cladonia) 255
Herrei (Parmelia) 334
Herrei (Pyrenula) 58
Herrii (*Biatora*) 219
Herrii (*Biatorina*) 219
Herrii (Catillaria) 219
Heterocarpon 41
heterochroa (*Verrucaria*) 61
heteromorpha (Cladonia) 269
heteromorpha var. (Lecanora) 308
heterospora var. (Porina) 55
heterosporum var. (Collema) 158
heterosporum (Leptotrema) 134
heterosporum (*Thelotrema*) 134
hians (Xylographa) 96
hiascens (Cetraria) 338
hiascens var. (*Cetraria*) 338
hibernica (*Arthonia*) 88
Hildenbrandii (*Collema*) 164
Hildenbrandii (Leptogium) 164
hirsuta (Gyrophora) 276
hirta var. (*Usnea*) 349
hirtella f. (*Strigula*) 65
hispida (Physcia) 388
hispidus (*Lichen*) 388
holophaea (Lecanora) 309
holopolia (*Biatora*) 196
holopolia (Lecidea) 196
homalea (Ramalina) 344
horizontalis (*Lichen*) 187
horizontalis (Peltigera) 187
Huei var. (*Usnea*) 349
humicola (*Lecidea*) 210
humilis var. (*Ramalina*) 344
humosa (Lecidea) 210
humosa var. (*Lecidea*) 210
humosus (*Lichen*) 210
hyalospora (Arthopyrenia) 50
hyalospora (*Pyrenula*) 50
hyalospora (*Verrucaria*) 50
hybrida f. (*Cladonia*) 262
hydrela (Verrucaria) 31
hydrela var. (*Verrucaria*) 31
hydrophila var. (*Lecidea*) 208
Hydrothyria 171
hyperborea (Gyrophora) 273
hyperborea (*Umbilicaria*) 273
hyperboreus (*Lichen*) 273
hyperellum (Calicium) 70
hyperellus (*Lichen*) 70
hyperopta (*Parmelia*) 320
hypnophila (*Biatora*) 226
hypnophila (*Bilimbia*) 226
hypnophila (*Lecidea*) 226
hypnorum var. (Lecanora) 301

hypnorum (*Lichen*) Vahl. 177
hypnorum (*Lichen*) Wulf. 301
hypnorum (*Pannaria*) 177
hypnorum (*Parmelia*) 177
hypnorum (Psoroma) 177
hypoleuca (Anaptychia) 390
hypoleuca (*Parmelia*) 390
hypoleuca var. (*Parmelia*) 390
hypoleuca (*Physcia*) 390
hypomela (*Biatora*) 199
hypomela (Lecidea) 199
hypomela var. (*Parmelia*) 323
hypomela f. (*Physcia*) 388
hypomela var. (*Sticta*) 180
hypophaea (Biatorella) 282
hypophaea (*Lecanora*) 282
hypophylla f. (*Cladonia*) 263
hypoptoides (Lecanora) 300
hypoptoides (*Lecidea*) 300
hypothallina (*Platygrapha*) 129
hypothallinum (Schismatomma) 129
hypotropa (Parmelia) 324
hypotropa var. (*Parmelia*) 324
hypotrypodes (Parmelia) 328
hypotrypodes var. (*Parmelia*) 328
hypoxantha (Cladonia) 269

Icmadophila 310
icmadophila (*Lecidea*) 310
icterica (*Biatora*) 214
icterica (*Lecidea*) 214
icterica (Psora) 214
ignobile (*Rhizocarpon*) 237
illusoria f. (Lecanora) 304
illusoria var. (*Lecanora*) 304
imbricata var. (*Parmelia*) 331
imbricatula f. (*Cladonia*) 260
immersa (Acarospora) 286
immersa var. (*Lecidea*) 281
immersa var. (Rinodina) 378
impallens (Arthonia) 82
implexa var. (Alectoria) 342
implexa (*Usnea*) 342
impolita (Arthonia) 85
impolitus (*Lichen*) 85
incarnata (Arthonia) 82
incisa (Coccocarpia) 178
incisa var. (*Coccocarpia*) *molybdaea*... 178
incisa var. (*Coccocarpia*) *pellita*...... 178
incisa var. (*Pannaria*) 178
incompta (Bacidia) 231
incompta (*Biatora*) 231
incompta var. (*Biatora*) 231
incompta (*Lecidea*) 231
incrustans (*Fissurina*) 114
incrustans (Graphina) 114
incurva (Parmelia) 329
incurvus (*Lichen*) 329
inductula (Polyblastia) 51
inductula (Polyblastiopsis) 51
inductula (*Verrucaria*) 51
inflata (Ramalina) 348
infundibulifera var. (*Cladonia*) 256
inquilina (*Buellia*) 372

inquilina (Buelliella) 372
inquinans (Cyphelium) 76
inquinans (Lichen) 76
inscriptum (Chiodecton) 122
inscriptum (Sclerophyton) 122
inscriptum (Stigmatidium) 122
insidians (Buellia) 368
insidians (Lecidea) 368
insularis (Lecidea) 211
integrella (Verrucaria) 32
intercedens (Polyblastia) 35
intercedens (Verrucaria) 35
intermedia var. (Cladonia) 269
intermedia (Ramalina) 345
intermedia var. (Ramalina) 344
intermediellum (Thelocarpon) 278
interponens (Lecidea) 239
interponens (Rhizocarpon) 239
interpositum (Ascidium) 133
interpositum (Coenogonium) 141
interpositum (Thelotrema) 133
interrupta (Graphis) 130
interrupta (Platygraphopsis) 130
intertexta (Graphis) 110
interveniens (Arthonia) 95
interveniens (Arthothelium) 95
intestiniforme (Dermatocarpon) 39
intricans (Graphis) 112
intricans (Phaeographis) 112
intricata (Graphis) 109
intricata (Lecanora) 306
intricata var. (Lecanora) 306
intricatulum (Leptogium) 168
intropallida (Lecidea) 198
intrusa (Polyblastiopsis) 51
intrusa (Verrucaria) 51
intumescens (Lecidea) 211
intumescens var. (Lecidea) 211
inundata (Bacidia) 229
inundata (Biatora) 229
inusta (Graphis) 113
inusta var. (Graphis) 113
inusta (Opegrapha) 113
inusta (Phaeographis) 113
ioëssa (Bacidia) 232
iowensis (Lecanora) 297
iowensis (Rinodina) 379
irpicinum (Dictyonema) 392
irpicinum var. (Dictyonema) 392
irpicinum (Rhipidonema) 392
isidiata f. (Parmelia) 331
isidiigera (Physcia) 387
isidiigera var. (Physcia) 387
islandica (Cetraria) 338
islandicus (Lichen) 338

Jacobi (Bacidia) 231
Jacobi (Biatora) 231
javanicum (Calicium) 78
javanicus (Pyrgillus) 78
jenensis (Gyalecta) 138
jenensis (Peziza) 138
jubata (Alectoria) 341
jubatus (Lichen) 341

jungermanniae (Caloplaca) 359
jungermanniae (Lichen) 359
jungermanniae (Normandina) 38
jungermanniae (Placodium) 359
juniperina (Cetraria) 335
juniperinum (Leptogium) 165
juniperinum var. (Leptogium) 165
juniperinus (Lichen) 335

kansana (Omphalaria) 150
kansana (Peccania) 150
kansana (Pleoconis) 150
kentuckyensis (Rinodina) 377
Kingmani (Bacidia) 232
Kunzei (Trypethelium) 61

labyrinthica (Glyphis) 121
labyrinthica (Sarcographa) 121
lacerum (Leptogium) 167
lachneum (Dermatocarpon) 39
laciniatum (Collema) 154
laciniatus (Synechoblastus) 154
laciniosa var. (Parmelia) 364
laciniosa var. (Xanthoria) candelaria .. 364
laciniosa var. (Xanthoria) lychnea 364
laciniosus var. (Teloschistes)
    candelarius 364
laciniosus var. (Teloschistes) lychneus .. 364
lactea (Blastodesmia) 51
lactea (Buellia) 369
lactea (Graphis) 111
lactea (Lecidea) 205
lactea (Polyblastiopsis) 51
lactea (Pyrenula) 51
lactea f. (Rinodina) 381
lactevirens (Normandina) 38
lacunosa (Cetraria) 336
lacunosa var. (Cladonia) 254
lacustris (Lecanora) 299
lacustris (Lichen) 299
laetevirens (Lobaria) 180
laevata (Lecanora) 298
laevata var. (Lecanora) 298
laevata (Sagedia) 298
laevigata (Parmelia) 331
laevigata var. (Pertusaria) 290
laevigata (Pyrenula) 57
laevigata (Ramalina) 346
laevigata (Verrucaria) 57
laevigatum (Nephroma) 185
laevigatus (Lichen) 331
laevis var. (Parmelia) 326
laeviusculum (Leptotrema) 134
laeviusculum (Thelotrema) 134
lanata (Ephebe) 143
lanata (Parmelia) 323
lanata var. (Parmelia) 323
lanatus (Lichen) pro parte 143
lanatus (Lichen) 323
lanuginosa var. (Pannaria) 177
lanuginosum (Amphiloma) 392
lanuginosum (Lichen) 392
lanuginosus (Lichen) 177
laontera f. (Cladonia) 263

lapicida (Lecidea) 207
lapicida (*Lichen*) 207
lapidicola (Arthonia) 87
lapidicola (*Lecidea*) 87
lata f. (*Ramalina*) 345
lathraea (Ocellularia) 131
lathraeum (*Thelotrema*) 131
latissima (Parmelia) 325
latissima var. (*Parmelia*) 325
latypea (Lecidea) 208
Laurera 63
Laureri (*Biatora*) 220
Laureri (Catillaria) 220
Laureri (*Sphaeropsis*) 278
Laureri (Thelocarpon) 278
lauri-cassiae (*Buellia*) 367
lavata (*Jonaspis*) 299
lavata (Lecanora) 299
laxiuscula var. (*Cenomyce*) 249
Leana (*Parmelia*) 388
Leana (Physcia) 388
LECANACTIDACEAE 127
lecanactidea (Arthonia) 82
Lecanactis 127
Lecania 310
lecanina (Pertusaria) 290
Lecanora 293
lecanora f. (*Rhizocarpon*) 240
LECANORACEAE 293
lecanorina var. (*Buellia*) 240
lecanorina (*Rinodina*) 379
Lecidea 190
LECIDEACEAE 189
lecideella (Arthonia) 85
lecideella (Pyrenopsis) 147
lecideoides (Dermatocarpon) 41
lecideoides (*Thrombium*) 41
Leciographa 373
lectissima (Porina) 54
lectissima (*Segestria*) 54
Leeprevostii (Helminthocarpon) ... 119
leioplaca (Pertusaria) 292
leioplaca (*Porina*) 292
leioplacoides (*Pertusaria*) 291
Lempholemma 152
lenticulare (Calicium) 70
lenticularis (*Biatorina*) 220
lenticularis (Catillaria) 220
lenticularis (*Lecidea*) 220
lenticularis (*Trichia*) 70
lentigera (Lecanora) 307
lentigerus (*Lichen*) 307
lentiginosula (Melaspilea) 105
lentiginosula (*Opegrapha*) 105
lepadinum (Thelotrema) 132
lepadinus (*Lichen*) 132
lepadodes (Thelotrema) 133
lepida (*Lecanora*) 376
lepida (Rinodina) 376
lepidallum (Endocarpon) 42
lepidastra (Buellia) 371
lepidastra (*Lecidea*) 371

lepidifera f. (*Cladonia*) 268
lepidiota var. (*Lecidea*) 173
lepidiota (*Pannaria*) 173
lepidiota (Parmeliella) 173
lepidophora f. (*Cladonia*) 264
lepidota (*Cladonia*) 268
leporina (Cladonia) 253
LEPRARIACEAE 392
Lepricurii var. (*Coenogonium*) 141
leprocarpa (Graphina) 116
leprocarpa (*Graphis*) 116
leprocarpum (*Thelotrema*) 116
leptalea var. (Physcia) 386
leptaleum (*Collema*) 156
leptaleus (*Lichen*) 386
leptaleus (Synechoblastus) 156
leptocarpha (*Ramalina*) 347
leptocheila (Catillaria) 219
leptocheila (*Lecidea*) 219
leptocheilum (*Heterothecium*) 219
leptocline (Buellia) 371
leptoderma (*Peltigera*) 189
Leptogidium 144
Leptogium 161
leptopholis (Heppia) 169
Leptorhaphis 50
leptothallina (Cladonia) 261
Leptotrema 133
Lesquereauxii (*Ephebe*) 143
leucastraea (Arthonia) 86
leucoblephara (*Biatora*) 225
leucocarpum (*Collema*) 156
leucocarpus (Synechoblastus) 156
leucocephala (*Pyrenothea*) 128
leucochlora (Arthopyrenia) 48
leucochlora (Parmelia) 329
leucochlora var. (*Parmelia*) 329
leucochlorum (Calicium) 70
leucoleiptes var. (*Physcia*) 387
leucomela (Anaptychia) 391
leucomela (*Physcia*) 391
leucomelaena (*Anaptychia*) 391
leucomelas (*Lichen*) 391
leuconephela (*Fissurina*) 115
leuconephela (Graphina) 115
leuconephela (*Graphis*) 115
leucopepla var. (*Collema*) 153
leucopepla (Graphis) 110
leucopeplus var. (*Synechoblastus*) 153
leucophaea (*Biatora*) 205
leucophaea (Dendrographa) 125
leucophaea (*Lecidea*) 205
leucophaea (*Roccella*) 125
leucophaeoides (Lecidea) 195
leucophyllina (Bacidia) 227
leucophyllina (*Biatora*) 227
leucophyllina (*Lecidea*) 227
leucophyllina (*Psorella*) 227
leucoplaca (Opegrapha) 100
leucoplaca (*Pyrenula*) 57
leucopoda (Sphinctrina) 75
leucorrhiza (Peltidea) 188
leucorrhiza f. (Peltigera) 188
leucosticta (Pannaria) 176

leucoxanthum (*Heterothecium*) 235
leucoxanthum (*Lecidea*) 235
leucoxanthum (Lopadium) 235
levidensis (Opegrapha) 102
libricola (Anthracothecium) 59
libricola (*Pyrenula*) 59
lichenoides (Leptogium) 167
lichenoides (Opegrapha) 100
lichenoides (*Opegrapha*) *atra*, ... 100
lichenoides (*Tremella*) 167
Lichina 151
LICHINACEAE 151
lignaria (*Bacidia*) 225
lignaria f. (*Bacidia*) 225
lignaria (Bilimbia) 225
lignaria (*Lecidea*) 225
limbata (Sticta) 183
limbata (*Stictina*) 183
limitata var. (Graphis) 109
limitata (*Opegrapha*) 109
limosa (Lecidea) 208
limosum (*Collema*) 160
linearis (*Lichen*) 347
linearis (Ramalina) 347
linearis (*Usnea*) 349
lineola (Graphis) 109
Linkii (Coenogonium) 141
linita (*Lobaria*) 180
linita (Sticta) 180
linita var. (*Sticta*) 180
lithina (*Staurothele*) 36
lithophila (*Lecidea*) Ach. in Fink 203
lithophila (Lecidea) 204
lithophila var. (*Lecidea*) 204
lithotodes (Physcia) 386
lithotodes var. (*Physcia*) 386
lithyrga (Opegrapha) 100
lithyrga var. (*Opegrapha*) 100
litoralis (Arthopyrenia) 47
litoralis (*Verrucaria*) 47
lobata (Phaeographis) 113
lobatum (*Leiogramma*) 113
lobulata (Caloplaca) 361
lobulata (*Lecanora*) 361
longissima (Opegrapha) 101
longissima (Usnea) 350
Lopadiopsis 137
Lopadium 234
lophaeum var. (*Leptogium*) 167
lophotum var. (*Leptogium*) 167
lophyrea (Parmelia) 326
lucida (*Biatora*) 197
lucida (Lecidea) 197
lucida (*Trachylia*) 76
lucidum (*Acolium*) 76
lucidum (Cyphelium) 76
lucidus (*Lichen*) 197
ludoviciensis (Phlyctidia) 316
lugubris (*Bacidia*) 226
lugubris (Lecidea) 205
lulensis (*Lecidea*) 195
lurida (Arthonia) 82
lurida (*Biatora*) 215
lurida (*Lecidea*) 215

lurida (Pannaria) 177
lurida (Psora) 215
luridella (*Biatora*) 213
luridella (*Lecidea*) 213
luridella (Psora) 213
luridoalba (Arthonia) 89
luridum (*Collema*) 177
luridum (*Physma*) 177
luridus (*Lichen*) 215
lusitanicum (Nephroma) 185
lusitanicum (*Nephromium*) 185
lutea (*Gyalecta*) 138
lutea (Microphiale) 138
luteola (Bacidia) 230
luteola (*Biatora*) 230
luteolus (*Lichen*) 230
luteominia (Blastenia) 353
luteominium (*Placodium*) 353
lutescens (*Lepra*) 291
lutescens (Pertusaria) 291
luteus (*Lichen*) 138
lychnea (*Xanthoria*) 364
lychneus (*Teloschistes*) 364

macilenta (Cladonia) 250
Macounii var. (*Lecanora*) 311
macrocarpa (Arthopyrenia) 50
macrocarpa (*Lecidea*) 206
macroceras f. (*Cladonia*) 263
macrospora (*Arthopyrenia*) Fink 47
macrospora (*Arthopyrenia*) Stiz. 47
macrotheca (*Arthonia*) 95
macrothecum (Arthothelium) 95
macularis var. (*Opegrapha*) 91
maculosa (*Glyphis*) 104
maculosa (Melaspilea) 104
madreporiforme (*Trypethelium*) 63
madreporiformis (*Cetraria*) 341
madreporiformis (Dufourea) 341
madreporiformis (Laurera) 63
madreporiformis (*Lichen*) 341
major (Anaptychia) 389
major var. (*Anaptychia*) 389
major (*Physcia*) 389
major (Stenocybe) 74
major f. (*Usnea*) 349
majusculum (Thelocarpon) 278
malacea (*Peltidea*) 187
malacea (Peltigera) 187
mamillana (Lecidea) 209
mamillana (Pyrenula) 57
mamillana (*Verrucaria*) 57
mammulata (*Umbilicaria*) 276
mammillosum (Ephebe) 143
manitense (*Dermatocarpon*) 39
Manni (Lecidea) 209
margacea (Verrucaria) 31
margaceum (*Thelotrema*) 31
marginalis (Lecanora) 306
marginata (Pertusaria) .,........ 292
marginellum (Leptogium) 166
marginellus (*Lichen*) 166
mariana (Pannaria) 176
mariana (*Parmelia*) 176

marmorea (Verrucaria) 33
marmoreus (Lichen) 33
Maronea 282
Massalongia 171
massata (Lecidea) 233
massata (Toninia) 233
mastoidea (Porina) 55
mastoidea (Pyrenula) 55
mastoideum (Bathelium) 62
mastoideum (Leptotrema) 134
mastoideum (Trypethelium) 62
mateocyatha (Cladonia) 264
maura (Verrucaria) 31
Meadii (Biatora) 226
Meadii (Bilimbia) 226
medusula var. (Phaeographis) 112
Medusulina 121
medusulina (Glyphis) 121
medusulina (Sarcographa) 121
Megalospora 221
megaspora var. (Lecanactis) amylacea .. 128
megaspora var. (Lecanactis)
    illecebrosa 128
megasperma (Laurera) 63
megaspermum (Trypethelium) 63
Meissneri (Pyxine) 383
melaena (Bacidia) 225
melaena (Biatora) 225
melaena (Bilimbia) 225
melaena (Lecanora) 299
melaena var. (Lecanora) 299
melaena (Lecidea) 225
melambola (Pyrenopsis) 147
melambola (Synalissa) 147
melamphylla (Pannaria) 177
melanaspis (Lecanora) 306
melanaspis var. (Lecanora) 306
melanaspis (Parmelia) 306
melancheima (Lecidea) 200
melanophaea (Chaenotheca) 69
melanophacum (Calicium) 69
melanophthalma (Lecanora) 305
melanophthalma (Squamaria) 305
Melanotheca 60
melas (Verrucaria) 33
Melaspilea 103
melaspora (Arthonia) 89
membranacea var. (Peltidea) 188
membranacea f. (Peltigera) 188
mendax (Graphina) 117
mendax (Graphis) 117
Menziesii (Ramalina) 347
mesogens (Parmelia) 334
mesophlaebia (Opegrapha) 102
metabolica (Lecanora) 311
Metzleri (Microthelia) 45
Michenerii (Lecidea) 212
microbola (Rinodina) 380
microbola (Verrucaria) 34
microbolum (Thelidium) 34
microcarpa (Bacidia) 225
microcarpa (Bilimbia) 225
microcarpa var. (Bilimbia) 225
microcarpa var. (Buellia) 367

microcephala (Sphinctrina) 75
microcephalum (Calicium) 72
microcephalum (Mycocalicium) 72
microcephalus (Lichen) pro parte...... 72
microcephalus (Lichen) 75
micrococca (Biatora) 218
micrococca (Catillaria) 218
microcyclia (Opegrapha) 99
microcyclos var. (Acarospora) 288
microcyclos var. (Lecanora) 288
microdium (Leptogium) 168
Microglaena 37
Microphiale 138
microphylina (Caloplaca) 362
microphylinum (Placodium) 362
microphylla (Pannaria) 174
microphylla (Parmelia) 174
microphylla (Parmeliella) 174
microphyllina (Bacidia) 228
microphyllina (Biatora) 228
microphyllina (Lecidea) 228
microphylliza (Cladonia) 267
microphylliza (Pannularia) 172
microphyllizum (Placynthium) 172
microphyllum (Collema) 157
microphyllum var. (Leptogium) 165
microphyllus (Lichen) 174
micropora (Ocellularia) 131
microporum (Thelotrema) 131
microps (Lecidea) 212
microptychium (Collema) 155
microptychius (Synechoblastus) 155
microspermella (Arthonia) 89
microspora var. (Lecanora) 298
microspora var. (Porina) 54
Microthelia 44
micula (Microthelia) 45
miculata (Lecanora) 300
micytho (Lecidea) 206
milliaria (Bacidia) 225
milliaria (Biatora) 225
milliaria (Rinodina) 376
milvina (Parmelia) 378
milvina (Rinodina) 378
miniatum var. (Caloplaca) 361
miniatum (Dermatocarpon) 39
miniatum var. (Placodium) 361
miniatus (Lichen) 39
minimula (Buellia) 372
minimula (Buelliella) 372
minnesotensis (Forssellia) 149
minnesotensis var. (Lecanora) 302
minnesotensis (Omphalaria) 149
minnesotensis (Thyrea) 149
minor f. (Cladonia) fimbriata........ 265
minor f. (Cladonia) rangiferina....... 249
minor (Dendrographa) 125
minor var. (Heppia) 169
minor var. (Lecanora) 315
minor var. Opegrapha 101
minor f. (Parmelia) quercina....... 328
minor f. (Parmelia) tiliacea.......... 328
minor var. (Peltigera) aphthosa....... 186
minuscula var. (Ramalina) 347

minuta f. (Cladonia) 252
minutella (Lecanora) 300
minutissimum (Collema) 163
minutissimum (Leptogium) 163
misella (Lecidea) 194
misella var. (Lecidea) 194
mitis (Cladonia) 249
mitrula (Cladonia) 260
mixta (Biatora) 218
mniaraea var. (Rinodina) 377
modesta (Caloplaca) 361
modesta (Teloschistes) 361
modesta (Xanthoria) 361
molariformis f. (Cladonia) 249
mollis var. (Evernia) 340
mollis (Lecidea) 196
mollis var. (Lecidea) 196
molliuscula (Parmelia) 332
molybdaea (Pannaria) 178
molybdina (Acarospora) 288
molybdina (Lecanora) 288
molybdina (Parmelia) 288
molybditis (Bacidia) 222
molybditis (Biatora) 222
molybditis (Bilimbia) 222
Monicae (Endocarpon) 43
moniliforme (Coenogonium) 141
monocarpon var. (Collema) 158
monosporum (Leptotrema) 134
monosporum (Thelotrema) 134
monstrosa var. (Lecanora) 297
monstrosa var. (Cladonia) 269
Montagnaei (Chiodecton) 123
Montagnaei (Enterostigma) 123
Montagnaei (Roccella) 126
Montagnei (Buellia) 238
Montagnei var. (Buellia) 238
Montagnei (Ramalina) 348
Montagnei var. (Ramalina) 348
Montagnei var. (Rhizocarpon) disporum 238
Montagnei var. (Rhizocarpon) petraeum 238
montana var. (Cetraria) 337
morbida var. (Cenomyce) 249
moriformis (Arthonia) 280
moriformis (Biatorella) 280
morio (Lecidea) 281
moriopsis (Buellia) 368
mosquitensis (Graphis) 108
Moulinsii (Dermatocarpon) 40
Moulinsii (Endocarpon) 40
mucosa (Bottaria) 60
mucosa (Verrucaria) 31
mucosa var. (Verrucaria) 31
mucosum (Anthracothecium) 60
Mühlenbergii (Dermatocarpon) 39
Mühlenbergii var. (Endocarpon) 39
Mühlenbergii (Gyrophora) 274
Mühlenbergii (Umbilicaria) 274
multibrachiata var. (Cladonia) 257
multibrachiata f. (Cladonia) 257
multiformis (Cladonia) 255
multipuncta (Pertusaria) 290
multipuncta (Variolaria) 290
multispora (Parmelia) 333

multispora var. (Parmelia) 333
mundula (Lecidea) 212
muralis (Lecanora) 307
muralis (Lichen) 307
muralis (Verrucaria) 33
muricella var. (Cenomyce) 257
muricella var. (Cladonia) 257
murina f. (Cladonia) 269
murorum (Caloplaca) 361
murorum (Lichen) 361
murorum (Placodium) 361
muscicola (Leptogium) 144
muscicola (Lichen) 144
muscicola var. (Physcia) 385
muscicola (Polychidium) 144
muscigena var. (Cladonia) 250
muscigena (Parmelia) 387
muscigena (Physcia) 387
muscigena var. (Physcia) 387
muscorum (Bacidia) 230
muscorum (Biatora) 230
muscorum var. (Lecidea) enteroleuca... 203
muscorum var. (Lecidea) parasema 203
muscorum (Lichen) Swartz 230
muscorum (Lichen) Wulf. 203
mutabilis (Biatora) 196
mutabilis (Lecanora) 298
mutabilis f. (Lecanora) 298
mutabilis (Lecidea) 196
mutabilis (Urceolaria) 298
mutabilis (Usnea) 349
Mycoblastus 217
Mycocalicium 71
MYCOPORACEAE 66
Mycoporellum 66
Mycoporum 67
myochroum (Leptogium) 164
myrina (Lecanora) 309
myriocarpa (Buellia) 368
myriocarpa (Opegrapha) 99
myriocarpella (Biatora) 200
myriocarpella (Lecidea) 200
myriocarpoides (Biatora) 210
myriocarpoides (Lecidea) 210
myriococcum (Collema) 152
myriococcum (Lempholemma) 152
myriococcum (Physma) 152
myriococcus (Lichen) 152

Naegelii (Bacidia) 223
Naegelii (Biatora) 223
Naegelii (Bilimbia) 223
nannaria (Biatorella) 280
nannarium (Heterothecium) 280
nanodes (Stereocaulon) 270
nanum (Stereocaulon) 270
neglecta var. (Cladonia) 264
neglecta (Lecidea) 207
nemoxyna var. (Baeomyces) 266
nemoxyna var. (Cladonia) 266
Nephroma 184
Nesolechia 216
niger (Lichen) 172
nigra (Pannaria) 172

nigra var. (Pertusaria) 290
nigra (Pyrenothrix) 66
nigra (Rinodina) 378
nigrescens (Collema) 153
nigrescens (Lichen) 153
nigrescens (Synechoblastus) 153
nigrescens (Verrucaria) 32
nigrescentoidea (Verrucaria) 32
nigricans (Alectoria) 342
nigricans var. (Cornicularia) 342
nigricans var. (Placodium) 358
nigritula (Lecidea) 369
nigrum (Placynthium) 172
nimbosa (Rinodina) 381
nitida (Graphis) 107
nitida (Pyrenula) 58
nitida (Sphaeria) 58
nitida (Verrucaria) 58
nitidella (Pyrenula) 58
nitidella var. (Pyrenula) 58
nitidescens (Graphis) 114
nitidum (Diorygna) 107
nivale (Lichen) 337
nivalis (Cetraria) 337
nolens (Pertusaria) 291
Normandina 38
Norrlini (Cladonia) 262
notha var. (Opegrapha) 100
novomexicana (Blastenia) 353
novomexicana (Rinodina) 381
nucula (Porina) 55
nucula (Porophora) 55
nuda var. (Evernia) 340
Nuttallii (Buelliella) 373
Nuttallii (Lecidea) 373
Nylanderi (Biatora) 195
Nylanderi (Lecidea) 195
Nylanderiana (Lecania) 312
Nylanderianum (Collema) 154

Oakesiana (Cetraria) 335
oblongata (Microthelia) 45
oblongata (Pyrenula) 45
obpallens (Acarospora) 287
obpallens (Lecanora) 287
obscura var. (Arthonia) 83
obscura (Parmelia) 385
obscura (Physcia) 385
obscurata (Bacidia) 226
obscurata var. (Lecanora) 309
obscurata var. (Lecidea) panaeola..... 239
obscurata var. (Lecidea) petraea....... 239
obscurata var. (Parmelia) 324
obscuratum (Rhizocarpon) 239
obscuratum var. (Rhizocarpon) 239
obsessa (Parmelia) 387
obsessa (Physcia) 387
obsessa var. (Physcia) 387
obtusata (Cenomyce) 254
obtusata f. (Cladonia) 254
ocellata (Platygrapha) 128
ocellata (Rinodina) 379
ocellata (Verrucaria) 379
ocellatum (Schismatomma) 128

Ocellularia 130
ochraceoflava (Verrucaria) 59
ochraceoflavum (Anthracothecium). 59
ochrocarpia var. (Cladonia) coccifera.. 251
ochrocarpia var. (Cladonia) cristatella .. 252
ochrocea (Rinodina) 379
ochrochlora (Cladonia) 266
ochrochlora var. (Cladonia) 266
ochrocincta (Arthonia) Nyl. 83
ochrocincta (Arthonia) Willey 83
ochrodiscodes (Arthonia) 82
Ochrolechia 309
ochroleuca (Alectoria) 343
ochroleuca (Urceolaria) 136
ochroleucum (Chiodecton) 122
ochroleucum (Endocarpon) 41
ochroleucum (Heterocarpon) 41
ochroleucus (Lichen) 343
ochrolutea (Arthonia) 82
ochrophaea (Biatora) 315
ochrophaeum var. (Haematomma).. 315
octomera (Melaspilea) 104
odora (Gyalecta) 298
odora (Lecanora) 298
Oederi (Buellia) 237
Oederi (Lichen) 237
Oederi (Rhizocarpon) 237
ohiense (Mycoporum) 67
ohiense var. (Mycoporum) 67
ohioense (Collema) 154
ohioensis (Synechoblastus) 154
oidalea (Lecidea) 241
oidaleum (Rhizocarpon) 241
oligospora var. (Lecanora) 288
olivacea (Lecanora) 309
olivacea (Lecidea) 209
olivacea (Parmelia) 333
olivacea f. (Sagedia)............... 55
olivacea (Verrucaria) 209
olivaceus (Lichen) 333
olivaria (Parmelia) 325
olivaria var. (Parmelia) 325
olivetorina var. (Evernia) 340
olivetorum (Parmelia) 334
omphalodes (Lichen) 332
omphalodes (Parmelia) 332
omphalodes var. (Parmelia) 332
oncodes (Parmelia) 334
opaca var. (Parmelia) 305
Opegrapha 97
opegraphella (Xylographa) 96
Opegraphoidea 102
ophthalmiza var. (Pertusaria) 290
orbata var. (Lecanora) 377
orbata (Rinodina) 377
orbatum (Platysma) 337
orbillifera (Arthonia) 94
orbilliferum (Arthothelium) 94
oregana (Alectoria) 342
oregana (Lecanora) 304
oregana (Lobaria) 180
oregana (Sticta) 180
oreina var. (Lecanora) 380
oreina (Rinodina) 380

ornata var. (*Lecidea*) 198
orosthea (Lecanora) 303
orosthea (*Lichen*) 303
ostreata (*Biatora*) 215
ostreata (*Lecidea*) 215
ostreata (Psora) 215
oulocheila (Opegrapha) 102
oxfordensis (Caloplaca) 359
oxydata f. (*Lecidea*) 207
oxyspora (*Biatora*) 216
oxyspora (*Lecidea*) 216
oxyspora (*Leptorhaphis*) 50
oxyspora (Nesolechia) 216
oxyspora (*Sagedia*) 50
oxysporella (*Lecidea*) 216
oxysporella (Nesolechia) 216
oxysporus (*Abrothallus*) 216
oxytera (Arthonia) 92

pachycarpum var. (*Heterothecium*) 353
pachycheila (Bombyliospora) 354
pachycheila (*Lecidea*) 354
pachycheila (*Pyrenula*) 59
pachycheilum (*Anthracothecium*) 59
pachycheilum (*Heterothecium*) 354
pachycheilum var. (*Heterothecium*).... 354
pachycladodes (Cladonia) 269
Pachyphiale 140
pacifica (Lecanora) 301
pacifica (Lecidea) 204
paddensis (*Biatora*) 194
paddensis (Lecidea) 194
palamaea (Cladonia) 255
palamaea var. (*Cladonia*) 255
palamaeus var. (*Baeomyces*) 255
pallescens (*Lecanora*) 310
pallescens (*Lichen*) 310
pallescens (Ochrolechia) 310
pallescens (*Parmeliopsis*) 320
pallescens (Trypethelium) 62
pallescens var. (*Trypethelium*) 62
pallida (Coniocybe) 73
pallida (Lecanora) 303
pallida var. (*Lecidea*) 205
pallidella (Caliciella) 73
pallidellum (*Calicium*) 73
pallidiuscula var. (*Arthonia*) 87
pallidum (*Calicium*) 73
pallidum (Endocarpon) 43
pallidus (*Lichen*) 303
palmatum (Leptogium) 167
palmatus (*Lichen*) ....; 167
paludicola (*Cladonia*) 252
paludicola var. (Cladonia) 252
palustus (*Rinodina*) 380
Pammellii (Bilimbia) 224
panaeola (Lecidea) 205
Pannaria 175
PANNARIACEAE 170
panniformis var. (*Parmelia*) 333
panniformis f. (*Parmelia*) 326
pannosa (*Pannaria*) 176
pantherina (Lecidea) 205
pantherina (*Verrucaria*) 205

papillaria (Cladonia) 249
papillaria (*Lichen*) 249
Papillariae (*Biatora*) 216
Papillariae (Nesolechia) 216
papillata (*Buellia*) 374
papillata (Buelliopsis) 374
papillata (*Lecidea*) 374
papillosa (Verrucaria) 31
papillosa var. (*Verrucaria*) 31
papulosa var. (*Umbilicaria*) 277
paradoxa f. (*Cladonia*) 255
paradoxum (Spilonema) 143
paralia (*Arthonia*) 92
parallela (*Xylographa*) 96
parasema (Buellia) 367
parasema (Lecidea) 203
parasema (*Lichen*) 367
parasemus (*Lichen*) 203
parasitica (*Buellia*) 373
parasitica var. (*Lecanora*) 136
parasitica (*Lecidea*) 373
parasitica (Leciographa) 373
parasitica var. (Urceolaria) 136
parasiticus var. (*Diploschistes*) 136
parietina (Xanthoria) 364
parietinum (*Calicium*) 71
parietinum (Mycocalicium) 71
parietinus (*Lichen*) 364
parietinus (Teloschistes) 364
parile (Nephroma) 185
parile f. (*Nephroma*) 185
parilis (*Lichen*) 185
parisensis (Lecanora) 303
parisensis f. (*Lecanora*)............. 303
Parmelia 320
PARMELIACEAE 318
Parmeliarum (*Buellia*) 372
Parmeliarum (Buelliella) 372
Parmeliarum (*Lecidea*) 372
Parmeliella 173
Parmeliopsis 319
Parmentaria 64
parvifolia (*Biatora*) 200
parvifolia (Lecidea) 200
parvula (Arthopyrenia) 46
paschale (*Lichen*) 270
paschale (Stereocaulon) 270
patellula (Phaeographis) 113
patellulata (*Allarthonia*) 87
patellulata (Arthonia) 87
paupera f. (*Lecidea*) 207
pavonia (Cora) 391
pavonia (*Thelophora*) 391
Pavoniana (Graphis) 108
Peccania 150
peliaspis (*Biatora*) 198
peliaspsis (Lecidea) 198
peliophylla (Caloplaca) 362
peliophyllum (*Placodium*) 362
pelioscypha (Acarospora) 288
pellita (Coccocarpia) 178
pellita (*Parmelia*) 178
pelodella (Caloplaca) 360
pelodella (*Lecanora*) 360

peltasticta (Acarospora) 284
peltatum (Dermatocarpon) 41
Peltigera 185
PELTIGERACEAE 183
Penardiana (Rinodina) 378
pendula var. (Usnea) 350
penichra (Buellia) 239
penichra var. (Buellia) 239
penichrum (Rhizocarpon) 239
pennsylvanica (Umbilicaria) 277
perforata (Parmelia) 327
perforatus (Lichen) 327
periclea (Platygrapha) 129
pericleum (Schismatomma) 129
pericleus (Lichen) 129
perlata (Parmelia) 325
perlatus (Lichen) 325
perminuta (Arthonia) 84
perminutum (Leptogium) 163
perplexum (Chiodecton) 122
perproxima (Lecania) 311
perproxima (Lecanora) 311
perpusilla (Verrucaria) 33
persimilans f. (Toninia) 233
pertusa (Parmelia) 324
pertusa (Pertusaria) 292
pertusa (Porina) 292
Pertusaria 289
PERTUSARIACEAE 289
pertusaricola (Buellia) 374
pertusaricola (Leciographa) 374
pertusus (Lichen) L. 292
pertusus (Lichen) Schrank. 324
Petersii (Pannaria) 151
Petersii (Placynthium) 151
Petersii (Pterygium) 151
petersii (Staurothele) 36
petraea (Buellia) 238
petraeum (Rhizocarpon) 238
petraeus (Lichen) 238
Petri (Biatora) 213
Petri (Lecidea) 213
Petri (Psora) 213
petrolepideum (Endocarpon) 43
pezizoidea (Lecidea) 235
pezizoides (Lichen) 176
pezizoides (Pannaria) 176
pezizoideum (Heterothecium) 235
pezizoideum (Lopadium) 235
phaea (Biatora) 206
phaea (Gyrophora) 273
phaea (Parmelia) 334
phaea (Umbilicaria) 273
phaeobaea (Arthonia) 92
phaeobaea (Segestrella) 92
phaeobola (Lecanora) 305
phaeocarpa (Lecidea) 381
phaeocarpa (Rinodina) 381
phaeocephala (Chaenotheca) 68
phaeocephalum (Calicium) 68
phaeocephalus (Lichen) 68
phaeococca (Psorotichia) 147
phaeococca (Pyrenopsis) 147
phaeococca (Synalissa) 147

phaeophora (Biatora) 194
phaeophora (Lecidea) 194
Phaeographina 118
Phaeographis 111
Phaeotrema 132
Phlyctella 316
phlyctella (Platygrapha) 316
Phlyctidia 316
Phlyctis 315
phryganitis (Lecanora) 309
phycopsis (Roccella) 126
phyllisca (Omphalaria) 150
phylliscina (Pyrenopsis) 146
phylliscina (Synalissa) 146
phyllizans var. (Lecidea) 198
phyllocarpum (Collema) 166
phyllocarpum (Leptogium) 166
phyllocarpum var. (Leptogium) 166
phyllocephala f. (Cladonia) 264
phyllocharis (Biatora) 236
phyllocharis (Heterothecium) 236
phyllocharis (Lopadium) 236
phyllocharis (Sporopodium) 236
phyllocoma f. (Cladonia) coccifera ... 251
phyllocoma var. (Cladonia) 258
phyllocoma f. (Cladonia) squamosa 258
phyllopoda f. (Cladonia) 257
phyllophora var. (Cladonia) 267
phyllophora f. (Cladonia) 267
Physcia 383
PHYSCIACEAE 382
physodes (Lichen) 324
physodes (Parmelia) 324
picta (Pyxine) 383
pictus (Lichen) 383
piedmontensis (Cladonia) 268
pileatum (Stereocaulon) 270
pileolata (Cladonia) 260
pilosella var. (Parmelia) 325
pilularis var. (Lecidea) elaechroma 207
pilularis var. (Lecidea) enteroleuca 207
Pilophorus 243
pinastri (Arthonia) 90
pinastri var. (Cetraria) 335
Pineti (Gyalecta) 138
pinguicula (Verrucaria) 32
pinguis (Lecanora) 308
pinguis (Platygrapha) 129
pinguis (Pyrenula) 58
piniperda (Lecanora) 302
pinnata var. (Cenomyce) 254
pinnata var. (Cladonia) 254
pityrea (Capitularia) 266
pityrea (Cladonia) 266
pityrea f. (Cladonia) 257
pityrea var. (Physcia) 387
placodizans (Endocarpiscum) 170
placodizans (Heppia) 170
placophyllus (Baeomyces) 242
placorodia (Cetraria) 319
placorodia var. (Cetraria) 319
placorodia (Parmelia) 319
placorodia (Parmeliopsis) 319
Placynthium 171

plana (Lecidea) 200
plana (Lecidella) 200
planescens (Heppia) 170
planetica (Lecidea) 208
platycarpa (Graphina) 116
platycarpa (Graphis) 116
platycarpa (Lecidea) 206
platygraphidea (Arthonia) 92
Platygraphopsis 130
platyloba (Rinodina) 380
platyna var. (Cetraria) 338
platynum (Leptogium) 167
platynum var. (Leptogium) californicum 167
platynum var. (Leptogium) scotinum .. 167
platyphylla (Cetraria) 337
platyphylla (Nephromopsis) 337
platyspilea (Arthonia) 85
platyspora var. (Porina) 55
plectenchymum (Leptogium) 162
pleiospora (Acarospora) 285
pleistospora (Acarospora) 285
pleistospora (Lecanora) 285
pleurota (Capitularia) 251
pleurota var. (Cladonia) coccifera .. 251
pleurota var. (Cladonia) cornucopioides 251
plicata (Usnea) 349
plicata var. (Usnea) 349
plicatile (Collema) 159
plicatile (Leptogium) 159
plicatilis (Lichen) 159
plicatus (Lichen) 349
plumbaria (Porina) 53
plumbaria (Verrucaria) 53
plumbaria (Verrucaria) carpinea, ... 53
plumbea (Pannaria) 175
plumbea (Parmeliella) 175
plumbeus (Lichen) 175
plumosa f. (Cladonia) 269
plurifera var. (Graphis) 118
plurifera (Phaeographina) 118
pluriloculare (Schismatomma) 129
plurilocularis (Platygrapha) 129
pluriloculata var. (Pyrenula) farrea . 57
pluriloculata var. (Pyrenula) leucoplaca. . 57
pocillum (Baeomyces) 264
pocillum var. (Cladonia) 264
Poitaeoides (Graphis) 110
pollinaria (Ramalina) 345
pollinariella (Ramalina) 348
pollinariella var. (Ramalina) dilacerata 348
pollinariella var. (Ramalina) minuscula . 348
pollinarius (Lichen) 345
Pollinii (Blastenia) 358
Pollinii (Caloplaca) 358
Pollinii var. (Placodium) 358
Polyblastia 35
Polyblastiopsis 50
polycarpa (Lecidea) 203
polycarpa var. (Parmelia) 364
polycarpa (Xanthoria) 364
polycarpa var. (Xanthoria) 364
polycarpon var. (Collema) 155
polycarpum (Collema) 155
polycarpus (Lichen) 364

polycarpus (Synechoblastus) 155
polycarpus (Teloschistes) 364
Polychidium 144
polycocca (Pyrenopsis) 146
polycocca (Synalissa) 146
polydactyla (Peltigera) 187
polydactylon (Lichen) 187
polygramma (Arthonia) 84
polymorpha (Arthonia) 90
polymorpha (Ramalina) 345
polymorphus (Lichen) 345
polyphylla (Gyrophora) 273
polyphylla (Umbilicaria) 273
polyphyllum (Dermatocarpon) 39
polyphyllus (Lichen) L. 273
polyphyllus (Lichen) Wulf. 39
polyporeum (Calicium) 71
polyrrhiza (Gyrophora) 275
polyrrhizus (Lichen) 275
polyspora (Buellia) 369
polyspora var. (Buellia) myriocarpa 369
polyspora var. (Buellia) punctata ... 369
polyspora (Endocarpiscum) 169
polyspora (Heppia) 169
polyspora (Rinodina) 380
polytropa (Lecanora) 304
polytropa var. (Lecanora) 304
polytropa var. (Parmelia) 304
polytropa (Verrucaria) 304
populneum (Calicium) 71
porcellaneum (Dermatiscum) 277
Porina 52
Porocyphus 145
porosum (Trypethelium) 63
porphyrites (Biatora) 354
porphyrites (Bombyliospora) 354
porphyrites var. (Bombyliospora) 354
porphyrites (Heterothecium) 354
porriginosa var. (Biatora) 230
postuma (Lecidea) 237
postumum (Rhizocarpon) 237
praecrenata (Lecanora) 302
praesignis (Parmelia) 330
praetextata (Peltigera) 188
praetextata var. (Peltidea) 188
praetextata var. (Peltigera) 188
prasina (Biatorina) 219
prasina (Catillaria) 219
prasina (Micorea) 219
prasinellum (Thelocarpon) 279
prasiniza f. (Catillaria) 219
premnea (Lecanactis) 127
premnea (Lecidea) 127
Pringlei (Lecidea) 201
privigna (Lecanora) 281
proboscidea (Gyrophora) 274
proboscidea (Parmelia) 328
proboscidea (Umbilicaria) 274
proboscideus (Lichen) 274
prolifer var. (Lichen) 266
prolifera f. (Cladonia) 269
prolifera var. (Cladonia) 266
prolifera var. (Lecanora) 303
prolixa var. (Alectoria) 341

prolixa (Parmelia) 333
prolixa var. (Parmelia) 333
promiscens (Lecidea) 206
propinqua (Pertusaria) 292
prosodea (Opegrapha) 102
prospersella (Arthopyrenia) ... 48
prospersella (Verrucaria) 48
prostans (Verrucaria) 49
prostrata f. (Cladonia) 269
protabacina (Lecidea) 211
Protoblastenia 351
proximella (Arthonia) 105
proximella (Melaspilea) 105
pruinascens (Arthothelium) 94
pruinosa var. (Acarospora) 287
pruinosa (Arthonia) 85
pruinosa (Biatorella) 281
pruinosa var. (Biatorella) 281
pruinosa var. (Lecanora) 281
pruinosa (Lecidea) 203
pruinosella (Arthonia) 88
pruinosula (Arthonia) 90
pruinosus (Lichen) 281
prunastri (Evernia) 340
prunastri (Lichen) 340
psammophila (Heppia) 170
Pseudopyrenula 52
Psora 212
Psoroma 177
Psorotichia 148
Pterygium 151
pubescens (Ephebe) 143
pubescens (Parmelia) 323
pulchella (Buellia) 371
pulchella (Cladonia) 250
pulchella (Normandina) 38
pulchella (Verrucaria) 38
pulchellum (Collema) 166
pulchellum (Leptogium) 166
pulchellus (Lichen) 371
pulicaris (Opegrapha) 101
pulicaris var. (Opegrapha) 101
pulicina (Pyrenula) 58
pullata (Biatora) 196
pullata (Buellia) 371
pullatula (Stenocybe) 74
pullatulum (Calicium) 74
pulmonaria (Lobaria) 180
pulmonaria (Sticta) 180
pulmonarius (Lichen) 180
pulposum (Collema) 159
pulposus (Lichen) 159
pulverulenta var. (Graphis) 109
pulverulenta (Opegrapha) 109
pulverulenta (Peltidea) 189
pulverulenta (Peltigera) 189
pulverulenta (Physcia) 387
pulverulentus (Lichen) 387
pulvillus (Leptogium) 168
pulvinata (Omphalaria) 149
pulvinata (Opegrapha) 103
pulvinata (Opegraphoidea) 103
pulvinata var. (Parmelia) 149
pulvinata (Thyrea) 149

pulvinatum (Collema) 168
pulvinatum (Endocarpon) 43
pulvinatum var. (Leptogium) lacerum .. 168
pulvinatum var. (Leptogium)
  lichenoides 168
punctata (Buellia) 368
punctata (Verrucaria) 368
punctella (Biatora) 194
punctella (Lecidea) 194
punctiforme (Leiogramma) 112
punctiformis (Arthonia) 90
punctiformis (Arthopyrenia) 49
punctiformis var. (Buellia) 368
punctiformis (Lichen) 49
punctiformis (Phaeographis) 112
punctiformis (Pyrenula) 49
punctiformis (Verrucaria) 49
punctum (Nesolechia) 216
pungens var. (Cladonia) furcata 256
pungens var. (Cladonia) rangiformis 256
pungens (Lecidea) 207
pungens (Lichen) 256
punicea (Lecanora) 314
puniceum (Haematomma) 314
Pupula (Pseudopyrenula) 52
Pupula (Pyrenula) 52
purpurascens (Verrucaria) 33
purpurascens var. (Verrucaria) 33
pusilla (Ramalina) 347
pusillum (Calicium) 71
pusillum (Endocarpon) 42
pustulata (Pertusaria) 291
pustulata (Porina) 291
pustulata (Umbilicaria) 277
pustulatum (Collema) 158
pustulatus (Lichen) 277
pycnocarpum (Collema) 155
pycnocarpum (Dicollema) 155
pycnocarpum (Mycoporum) 67
pycnocarpus (Synechoblastus) 155
pycnoclada (Cenomyce) 249
pycnoclada (Cladonia) 249
pygmaea var. (Parmelia) parietina 364
pygmaea var. (Xanthoria) candelaria ... 364
pygmaea var. (Xanthoria) lychnea 364
pygmaeus var. (Teloschistes)
  candelarius 364
pygmaeus var. (Teloschistes) lychneus .. 364
pygmaeus var. (Teloschistes) parietinus 364
pyracea (Caloplaca) 358
pyracea var. (Parmelia) 358
pyraceum (Placodium) 358
pyraceum var. (Placodium) 358
pyrenastraeum (Pyrenastrum) 64
Pyrenastrum 64
pyrenastrum (Astrothelium) 64
PYRENIDIACEAE 65
pyrenocarpa (Dermatina) 67
pyrenocarpum (Mycoporum) 67
pyrenoides (Omphalaria) 150
pyrenoides (Thyrea) 150
pyrenophora (Verrucaria) 34
pyrenophorum (Thelidium) 34
PYRENOPSIDACEAE 145

Pyrenopsis 145
Pyrenothamnia 43
PYRENOTHAMNIACEAE 43
PYRENOTRICHACEAE 65
Pyrenothrix 65
Pyrenula 56
PYRENULACEAE 44
Pyrenulella 58
pyrenuloides (Anthracothecium) ... 59
pyrenuloides (*Trypethelium*) 59
Pyrgillus 77
pyrithrocardia var. (Physcia) 388
pyrrhula (Arthonia) 83
pyrrhuliza (Arthonia) 85
pyxidata (Cladonia) 264
pyxidatus (*Lichen*) 264
Pyxine 382

quadriloculata var. (*Pyrenula*) 45
quadriloculata var. (Microthelia) ... 45
quaternella (*Opegrapha*) 102
quaternella (Opegraphoidea) 102
quercina (Parmelia) 328
quercinum (*Calicium*) 70
quercinus (*Lichen*) 328
quercizans (*Lobaria*) 182
quercizans (*Parmelia*) 182
quercizans (Sticta) 182
querina f. (*Cladonia*) 258
quernea (*Biatora*) 197
quernea (Lecidea) 197
querneus (*Lichen*) 197
quinqueseptata (Arthopyrenia) 50
quinqueseptata (*Pyrenula*) 50
quinqueseptata (*Verrucaria*) 50
quintaria (Arthonia) 91

racemosa (*Cladonia*) 254
racemosa var. (Cladonia) 254
Racodium 141
radiata (Arthonia) 91
radiata (*Buellia*) ....:..... 381
radiata var. (Cladonia) 266
radiata (Graphis) 111
radiata (*Opegrapha*) 91
radiata (Rinodina) 381
radiatilis (Gyalecta) 139
radiatus (*Lichen*) 266
Ramalina 343
rameum (Nephroma) 185
rameum f. (*Nephroma*) 185
rameum var. (*Nephromium*) 185
ramificans (Graphis) 111
Ramonia 139
ramosa var. (*Cladonia*) 252
ramulosa var. (*Physcia*) 365
ramulosa (*Xanthoria*) 365
ramulosum (Stereocaulon) 271
ramulosus (Teloschistes) 365
rangiferina (Cladonia) 248
rangiferinus (*Lichen*) 248
rangiformis (Cladonia) 255
Rappii (Biatorella) 280
Rappii (Haematomma) 315

Ravenelii (Anaptychia) 389
Ravenelii (Arthonia) 83
Ravenelii (*Bacidia*) 224
Ravenelii (*Biatora*) 224
Ravenelii (Bilimbia) 224
Ravenelii (*Calicium*) 72
Ravenelii (Cladonia) 251
Ravenelii (Leptotrema) 133
Ravenelii (Mycocalicium) 72
Ravenelii (Parmentaria) 64
Ravenelii (*Physcia*) 389
Ravenelii (*Platygrapha*) 129
Ravenelii (*Pyrenastrum*) 64
Ravenelii (Schismatomma) 129
Ravenelii (*Sticta*) 180
Ravenelii (*Thelotrema*) 133
reagens (Acarospora) 284
recedens (Lecidea) 212
recipienda (Parmelia) 334
recta var. (*Graphis*) 109
recurva f. (*Cladonia*) 255
recurva (*Parmelia*) 329
rediunta (Dirina) 124
rediunta (*Lecanora*) 124
reniformis (Arthonia) 90
reniformis (*Opegrapha*) 90
resinae (Biatorella) 280
resinae (*Peziza*) 280
resupinatum (Nephroma) 185
resupinatus (*Lichen*) 185
reticulata (Cladonia) 254
reticulata var. (*Cladonia*) 254
reticulata (*Gyrophora*) 272
reticulata (Ramalina) 347
reticulata var. (*Umbilicaria*) 272
reticulatus (*Lichen*) 347
retiformis (*Ramalina*) 347
retrovertens (Buellia) 368
revertens (Biatorella) 282
revertens var. (*Lecanora*) 282
rhabarbarina (Acarospora) 285
rhagadiosa (*Acarospora*) 285
rhaphidosperma (Porina) 55
rhexostoma (Pertusaria) 293
Rhizocarpon 236
rhodostroma (*Ocellularia*) 131
rhodostroma var. (*Thelotrema*) 131
Rhoidis (Arthonia) 88
rhyparodes (Leptogium) 163
rhyponta (Arthopyrenia) 48
rhyponta (*Pyrenula*) 48
rhyponta (*Verrucaria*) 48
rigida var. (*Alectoria*) 343
rigida f. (*Cenomyce*) 257
rigida f. (Cladonia) 257
rigida (*Graphis*) 117
rigida (*Ramalina*) 347
rimulosa (Graphis) 111
rimulosa (*Opegrapha*) 111
Rinodina 374
rinodinoides (Buellia) 370
rivale (*Leptogium*) 144
rivale (Polychidium) 144
rivulosa (*Biatora*) 196

rivulosa (Lecidea) 196
roboris (Lecanora) 376
roboris (Rinodina) 376
Roccella 125
ROCCELLACEAE 125
rosaeformis var. (Parmelia) 327
roscidum (Calicium) 71
rosea (Dibaeis) 242
rosella (Bacidia) 228
rosella var. (Lecanora) 310
rosella var. (Ochrolechia) 310
rosellus (Lichen) 228
roseus (Baeomyces) 242
rosulans (Candelariella) 318
rubella (Arthonia) 84
rubella (Bacidia) 230
rubella (Biatora) 230
rubella (Graphis) 84
rubidofusca (Bacidia) 224
rubidofusca (Biatora) 224
rubidofusca (Bilimbia) 224
rubiformis (Baeomyces) 215
rubiformis var. (Biatora) 215
rubiformis (Lecidea) 215
rubiformis (Psora) 215
rubiginea f. (Usnea) 349
rubiginosa (Pannaria) 177
rubiginosus (Lichen) 177
rubina (Lecanora) 308
rubinus (Lichen) 308
rubricosa (Bacidia) 224
rubricosa (Bilimbia) 224
rubricosa (Patellaria) 224
rubrocinctum (Chiodecton) 122
rudecta (Parmelia) 323
rudecta var. (Parmelia) 323
ruderatula (Pannularia) 175
ruderatula (Parmeliella) 175
ruderella (Verrucaria) 33
rufescens (Dermatocarpon) 40
rufescens (Endocarpon) 40
rufescens var. (Lecanora) 287
rufescens (Lichen) caninus, ... 188
rufescens (Peltigera) 188
rufofusca (Biatora) 197
rufofusca (Lecidea) 197
rufonigra (Biatora) 213
rufonigra (Lecidea) 213
rufonigra (Psora) 213
rufula (Graphis) 107
rufula (Opegrapha) 107
rufus (Baeomyces) 242
rufus (Lichen) 242
rugifera (Gyrophora) 274
rugifera (Umbilicaria) 274
ruginosa (Lecidea) 233
ruginosa (Toninia) 233
rugosa (Lecanora) 300
rugosa var. (Lecanora) 300
rugosus (Lichen) 300
rupestre (Collema) 154
rupestre (Placodium) 351
rupestre (Racodium) 141
rupestris (Lecidea) 351

rupestris (Lichen) Scop. 351
rupestris (Lichen) Swartz 154
rupestris (Pertusaria) 292
rupestris (Protoblastenia) 351
rupestris (Synechoblastus) 154
rupestris (Verrucaria) 33
rupicola (Arthonia) 87
rupicola (Lecanora) 306
rupicola (Lichen) 306
Russellii (Biatora) 213
Russellii (Lecidea) 213
Russellii (Parmelia) 177
Russellii (Psora) 213
russula (Biatora) 199
russula (Lecidea) 199
ryssoleum (Collema) 156
ryssoleum (Collema) nigrescens, ... 156
ryssoleus (Synechoblastus) 156

sabuletorum (Bacidia) 226
sabuletorum (Bilimbia) 226
sabuletorum (Lichen) 226
saccata (Solorina) 183
saccatus (Lichen) 183
saepincola (Cetraria) 336
saepincola var. (Lecanora) symmicta ... 304
saepincola var. (Lecanora) varia 304
saepincola (Lichen) 336
salicina (Lecanactis) 127
salicina (Porina) 54
salicinum (Calicium) 70
Sambuci (Lecanora) 302
Sambuci var. (Lecanora) 302
Sambuci (Lichen) 302
Sancti Jacobi (Acolium) 77
Sancti Jacobi (Cyphelium) 77
sanguinaria (Lecidea) 217
sanguinaria (Megalospora) 217
sanguinarium (Heterothecium) 217
sanguinarium (Lichen) 217
sanguinarius (Mycoblastus) 217
sanguinea (Arthonia) 93
sanguineoatra (Biatora) 199
sanguineoatra (Lecidea) 199
sanguineoatra (Lichen) 199
sanguineum (Arthothelium) 93
sanguineum (Byssus) 122
sanguineum (Chiodecton) 122
santense (Leptotrema) 134
santense (Thelotrema) 134
santensis (Cladonia) 256
santensis (Lecidea) 200
santensis (Pyrenula) 57
santensis var. (Pyrenula) 57
Sarcographa 120
sarmentosa (Alectoria) 343
sarmentosus (Lichen) 343
saturninum (Collema) 164
saturninum (Leptogium) 164
saturninus (Lichen) 164
saxatile (Calicium) 372
saxatilis (Buellia) 372
saxatilis (Buelliella) 372
saxatilis (Lichen) 326

saxatilis (Parmelia) 326
saxicola (Acarospora) 284
saxicola (*Lecanora*) 307
saxicola var. (Lecanora) 307
saxicola (*Lichen*) 307
saxicola (Opegrapha) 99
saxicola (*Parmelia*) 307
saxicola f. (*Rhizocarpon*) 238
scabra (Acarospora) 285
scabra (*Glypholecia*) 285
scabra (*Urceolaria*) 285
scabriuscula (*Cenomyce*) 255
scabriuscula var. (Cladonia) 255
scalpturata (*Graphis*) 118
scalpturata (Phaeographina) 118
Schaereri (Buellia) 369
Schaereri (Caloplaca) 356
Schaereri (*Endocarpon*) 42
Schaereri (*Lecidea*) 356
Schaereri (*Pannaria*) 148
Schaereri (Psorotichia) 148
Schaereri (*Pyrenopsis*) 148
Schaereri (*Synalissa*) 148
Schismatomma 128
Schizopelte 126
Schleicheri (Acarospora) 284
Schleicheri (*Lecanora*) 284
Schleicheri (*Urceolaria*) 284
Schraderi (*Collemodium*) 163
Schraderi (Leptogium) 163
Schraderi (*Lichen*) 163
Schweinitzii (Bacidia) 230
Schweinitzii (*Biatora*) 230
Sclerophyton 123
Scolecitis (Graphina) 115
Scolecitis (*Graphis*) 115
scopulorum (Ramalina) 348
scoria (*Trypethelium*) 62
scorites (Trypethelium) 62
scortea (Parmelia) 334
scortella (Parmelia) 331
scotinum (Leptogium) 167
scotinus (*Lichen*) 167
scotopholis (*Biatora*) 213
scotopholis (*Lecidea*) 213
scotopholis (Psora) 213
scripta (Graphis) 109
scriptus (*Lichen*) 109
scrobiculata (*Lobaria*) 181
scrobiculata (*Sticta*) 181
scrobiculata (*Stictina*) 181
scruposa (*Parmelia*) 136
scruposa (Urceolaria) 136
scruposus (*Diploschistes*) 136
scruposus (*Lichen*) 136
scutata (Peltigera) 187
scutata var. (*Peltigera*) 187
scutatus (*Lichen*) 187
scutellaris (Pertusaria) 293
scyphulifera (*Lecidea*) 135
scyphuliferum (Gyrostomum) 135
Secoliga 139
segregata (*Collemopsis*) 148
segregata (Psorotichia) 148

semitensis (Buellia) 368
semitensis (Lecanora) 308
semitensis var. (*Lecanora*) *muralis* 308
semitensis var. (*Lecanora*) *saxicola* 308
semitensis (Umbilicaria) 276
semitensis var. (*Umbilicaria*) 276
septiseptella (Arthonia) 92
serpentina var. (*Graphis*) 109
sessile (*Calicium*) 77
sessile (Cyphelium) 77
sessilis f. (*Baeomyces*) 242
setosa (*Parmelia*) 386
setosa (Physcia) 386
shastensis (Lecania) 313
sideritis (Caloplaca) 357
sideritis var. (*Caloplaca*) 357
sideritis (*Lecanora*) 357
sideritis (*Placodium*) 357
sideritis var. (*Placodium*) 357
silacea (*Lecidea*) 207
silicicola (Verrucaria) 31
silicola (*Verrucaria*) 31
simplex (Biatorella) 281
simplex var. (Cladonia) 265
simplex f. (*Cladonia*) 251
simplex (*Dufourea*) 351
simplex (*Lichen*) 281
simplex var. (*Lichen*) 265
simplex (Siphula) 351
simplex var. (Stereocaulon) 271
sinapisperma (Blastenia) 352
sinapisperma (*Patellaria*) 352
sinapispermum (*Placodium*) 352
sinopica f. (*Lecanora*) 287
sinuatum var. (*Leptogium*) 167
sinuosa var. (*Parmelia*) 331
Siphula 351
smaragdula (*Acarospora*) 287
sobolescens (*Cladonia*) 261
sobolifera (*Cladonia*) 267
Solenopsora 313
solida (Ephebe) 143
Solorina 183
Solorinaria 170
sonomense (*Placynthium*) 176
sonomensis (Pannaria) 176
sonomensis (*Parmeliella*) 176
sophistica (*Graphina*) 116
sophistica (*Graphis*) 116
sophistica var. (*Graphis*) 116
sophisticascens (Graphina) 115
sophisticascens (*Graphis*) 115
sophodes (*Lichen*) 377
sophodes (Rinodina) 377
soraligera f. (*Cladonia*) 253
sordida (*Lecanora*) 306
sordida (Verrucaria) 32
sorediata (*Lecidea*) 382
sorediata (Parmelia) 332
sorediata var. (Parmelia) hypotropa 334
sorediata var. (Parmelia) latissima .. 325
sorediata var. (*Parmelia*) *prolixa* 332
sorediata var. (*Parmelia*) *stygia* 332
sorediata (Peltigera) 189

sorediata var. (*Peltigera*) 189
sorediata f. (*Peltigera*) 189
sorediata var. (*Pertusaria*) 290
sorediata (Pyxine) 382
sorediata var. (*Ramalina*) 347
soredica (Parmelia) 331
sorediifera var. (*Evernia*) 340
sorediifera var. (*Lecanora*) 301
Spaldingi (Caloplaca) 360
sparsellum (Mycoporellum) 66
sparsellum (*Mycoporum*) 66
speciosa (Anaptychia) 389
speciosa (*Physcia*) 389
speciosus (*Lichen*) 389
spectabile (Arthothelium) 94
spectabilis (*Arthonia*) 94
speirea (Lecidea) 206
speireus (*Lichen*) 206
sphaerale (Chiodecton) 122
sphaeroides (Arthopyrenia) 50
sphaeroides (*Bacidia*) 223
sphaeroides (*Biatora*) 223
sphaeroides (Bilimbia) 223
sphaeroides (*Lichen*) 223
SPHAEROPHORACEAE 78
Sphaerophorus 78
sphaerospora (*Synalissa*) 148
sphaerosporella (Parmelia) 329
Sphinctrina 74
spilota (*Lecidea*) 201
Spilonema 142
spinulosa var. (Cetraria) 335
splendidula var. (*Calicium*) 70
spodophaeiza (Lecanora) 309
spongiosa f. (Peltigera) 188
spongiosa (Solorina) 183
spongiosa var. (*Solorina*) 183
spongiosus (*Lichen*) 183
Spraguei (Candelariella) 317
Spraguei (*Lecanora*) 317
Spraguei (*Placodium*) 317
Spraguei (Pyrenothamnia) 43
Sprengelii var. (*Trypethelium*) 63
Sprucei (Verrucaria) 33
spuria (Buellia) 369
spuria (*Lecidea*) 369
spuria (Peltigera) 189
spuria var. (*Peltigera*) 189
spurius (*Lichen*) 189
squalida (*Lecidea*) 233
squalida (*Toninia*) 233
squamella (*Verrucaria*) 40
squamellum (Dermatocarpon) 40
squamosa (Cladonia) 257
squamosus (*Lichen*) 257
squamulosa (Acarospora) 287
squamulosa f. (Cladonia) cariosa ... 261
squamulosa f. (*Cladonia*) *symphycarpa*.. 261
squamulosa var. (*Lecanora*) 287
squamulosa var. (*Parmelia*) 287
squamulosa (Psorotichia) 148
squamulosus (*Lichen*) 287
squarrosa (*Cladonia*) 249
squarrosa var. (*Lecidea*) 233

squarrosa (Toninia) 233
Stanfordi (Verrucaria) 33
staurospora (*Pyrenula*) 59
staurosporum (Anthracothecium) .. 59
Staurothele 35
staurothelicola (Opegraphoidea) ... 103
stellans var. (Leptogium) 165
stellaris (*Lichen*) 386
stellaris (Physcia) 386
stellata (*Candelaria*) 319
stellata (*Coccocarpia*) 175
stellata (*Pannaria*) 175
stellata var. (*Parmelia*) 385
stellata (Parmeliopsis) 175
stellata var. (*Physcia*) 319
stellulata (Buellia) 367
stellulata (*Lecidea*) 367
stemmatina var. (*Cladonia*) 251
stemonea var. (*Chaenotheca*) 69
Stenocybe 74
stenophylla (Cetraria) 336
stenophylla var. (*Cetraria*) glauca 335
stenophylla var. (*Cetraria*) lacunosa .. 336
stenophylla (*Pannaria*) 172
stenophylla var. (*Parmelia*) 331
stenophylla (*Parmeliella*) 172
stenophylla (Placynthium) 172
stenophyllia (*Cladonia*) 261
stenophylliza (*Cladonia*) 261
stenophyllodes (Cladonia) 269
stenophyllum (Collema) 160
stenospora (Ramalina) 348
Stereocaulon 269
steriza var. (*Lecidea*) 206
Sticta 178
STICTACEAE 178
stictarum (Celidium) 92
stictella (Arthonia) 92
stigmaea (Buellia) 368
stigmatella (Bacidia) 228
stigmatella (*Biatora*) 228
stigonella (*Trachylia*) 77
stillicidiora (Caloplaca) 360
stillicidiorum (*Lichen*) 360
stillicidiorum var. (*Placodium*) 360
stipata var. (Cladonia) 269
strepsilis (*Baeomyces*) 267
strepsilis (Cladonia) 267
striatula (Graphis) 110
striatula (*Opegrapha*) 110
striatula (Verrucaria) 30
strigosa var. (Usnea) 349
Strigula 65
STRIGULACEAE 64
stygia (Parmelia) 333
stygius (*Lichen*) 333
subacuta var. (Cladonia) 267
subamplicata (Ramalina) 346
subamplicata var. (*Ramalina*) calicaris . 346
subamplicata var. (*Ramalina*) fastigiata 346
subareolata (Pyrenopsis) 147
subastroidella (Arthonia) 91
subattingens (*Platygrapha*) 129
subattingens (Schismatomma) 129

subcapitata (Parmelia) 334
subcariosa (Cladonia) 260
subcervicornis var. (Cladonia) 265
subcinerascens var. (Arthothelium) 95
subcinerea (Porina) 53
subcinerea (Pyrenula) 53
subcinerea (Verrucaria) 53
subcinereum (Calicium) 70
subcircinata (Lecanora) 306
subconcentricum (Rhizocarpon) 240
subconspersa (Parmelia) 331
subcorallina (Microglaena) 37
subcyrtodes (Arthonia) 93
subcyrtodes (Arthothelium) 93
subdiffusa (Arthonia) 89
subdisciformis (Buellia) 367
subdispersa (Lecania) 312
subdispersa (Lecanora) 312
subdispuncta (Arthonia) 87
subdiversa (Graphis) 111
subepulotica (Lecanora) 299
subfastigiata var. (Ramalina) 346
subfraxinea (Ramalina) 348
subfulgurata (Graphis) 112
subfulgurata (Phaeographis) 112
subfuliginea (Pyrenopsis) 146
subfusca (Lecanora) 301
subfusca (Parmelia) 301
subfuscus (Lichen) 301
subgranulosa (Bacidia) 228
subgranulosa var. (Biatora) 200
subgranulosa var. (Lecidea) 228
subincruenta (Melanotheca) 60
subincruentum (Trypethelium) 60
sublaevigata (Parmelia) 328
sublaevigata var. (Parmelia) 328
sublecideina var. (Maronea) 283
sublugens (Lecidea) 124
submarginalis (Lobaria) 327
submarginalis (Parmelia) 327
subminutissima (Arthonia) 89
subminutula (Arthonia) 92
submuralis (Verrucaria) 32
submuralis var. (Verrucaria) 32
subnigrata (Catillaria) 221
subnitescens (Endocarpon) 42
subnitescens (Verrucaria) 42
subnitida (Fissurina) 116
subnitida (Graphina) 116
subnitida (Graphis) 116
subnitidula (Graphina) 116
subnitidula (Graphis) 116
subocellata var. (Opegrapha) 99
subochroleucum (Chiodecton) 123
subolivacea (Parmelia) 333
subpapillosum var. (Dermatocarpon) 40
subparilis (Graphis) 108
subplebeia (Lecidea) 201
subporinella (Dithelopsis) 56
subporinella (Thelopsis) 56
subprostans (Arthopyrenia) 47
subprostans (Pyrenula) 47
subprostans (Verrucaria) 47
subpunctiformis (Pyrenula) 49

subpyracella (Blastenia) 356
subpyracella (Caloplaca) 356
subpyracella (Lecanora) 356
subquercifolia (Parmelia) 328
subrubella (Arthonia) 84
subrugata (Parmelia) 327
subsiderella var. (Opegrapha) 101
subsquamosa (Cladonia) 258
subsquamosa var. (Cladonia) 258
substipitata (Biatora) 231
substraminea (Cladonia) pro parte 252
substraminea (Cladonia) pro parte 268
substriatula (Graphina) 116
substriatula (Graphis) 116
substriatula var. (Graphis) 116
subsuperficialis (Verrucaria) 30
subtile (Calicium) 71
subtilis (Ocellularia) 131
subtilis (Thelotrema) 131
subulata var. (Cenomyce) 255
subulata var. (Cladonia) 266
subulatus (Lichen) 266
subvenusta var. (Physcia) 386
subvirginalis (Graphina) 117
subvirginalis (Graphis) 117
succedens (Rinodina) 382
suffusa (Bacidia) 232
suffusa var. (Bacidia) 232
suffusa (Biatora) 232
sulcata (Parmelia) 327
sulcata var. (Parmelia) 327
sulphurata (Parmelia) 330
sulphurius (Scyphophorus) 252
sulphurosa var. (Buellia) 238
sulphurosa (Parmelia) 328
sulphurosa var. (Parmelia) quercina ... 328
sulphurosa var. (Parmelia) tiliacea ... 328
sulphurosa var. (Rhizocarpon) 238
superellum (Thelocarpon) 279
superflua (Catillaria) 221
Swartziana var. (Arthonia) astroidea ... 91
Swartziana var. (Arthonia) radiata 91
sychnogonoides (Microglaena) 37
sylvatica (Cladonia) 248
sylvatica (Sticta) 182
sylvatica (Stictina) 182
sylvaticus (Lichen) 182
sylvaticus var. (Lichen) 248
sylvestris var. (Cladonia) 249
sylvestris var. (Lichen) 249
sylvicola (Lecidea) 210
symmicta (Lecanora) 304
symmicta var. (Lecanora) 304
symphocarpea var. (Cladonia) 260
symphorea (Omphalaria) 148
symphorea (Synalissa) 148
symphoreus (Lichen) 148
symphycarpa (Cladonia) 260
symphycarpus (Lichen) 260
Synalissa 147
Synechoblastus 153
syringea (Lecania) 311
syringea var. (Parmelia) 311

taedescens (Arthonia) 89
taediosa (Arthonia) 94
taediosum (Arthothelium) 94
tartarea (Lecanora) 310
tartarea (Ochrolechia) 310
tartareus (Lichen) 310
teicholyta (Caloplaca) 362
teicholytum (Lecanora) 362
teicholytum (Placodium) 362
TELOSCHISTACEAE 363
Teloschistes 363
tenax (Collema) 158
tenax (Lichen) 158
tenebrosa (Lecidea) 201
tenella (Graphis) 108
tenella var. (Graphis) 108
tenella (Physcia) 388
tenellum (Stereocaulon) 270
tennessensis (Lecidea) 201
tenuior var. (Cladonia) 248
tenuis (Cladonia) 249
tenuissimum (Leptogium) 162
tenuissimus (Lichen) 162
tephraspis (Lecanora) 379
tephraspis (Rinodina) 379
tephraspis var. (Rinodina) 379
tephroides (Endocarpon) 40
terebrata (Verrucaria) 33
teretiuscula var. (Parmelia) 385
teretiuscula (Physcia) 385
teretiuscula var. (Physcia) 385
terrena (Biatora) 218
terrena (Catillaria) 218
terrena (Heppia) 169
terrestris var. (Cetraria) 335
terrestris subsp. (Verrucaria) 31
terrigena (Arthonia) 87
tessellata (Lecidea) 201
tessellina (Lecidea) 201
testudinaria (Ramalina) 344
testudinea (Biatorella) 281
testudinea var. (Lecidea) 281
tetramera (Arthonia) 92
tetrathalamia (Pertusaria) 291
tetrathalamia (Trypethelium) 291
texana (Medusulina) 121
texana (Parmelia) 327
texana (Pertusaria) 293
texana (Synalissa) 148
texanum (Collema) 154
texanus (Synechoblastus) 154
thamnina (Acarospora) 288
thamnina var. (Lecanora) 288
thamnitis (Lecanora) 309
thamnodes var. (Evernia) 340
Thamnolia 351
thamnoplaca (Lecanora) 305
theioplaca var. (Lecidea) enteroleuca... 204
theioplaca var. (Lecidea) parasema.. 204
thelena (Microthelia) 45
thelena (Pyrenula) 45
thelena (Verrucaria) 45
THELEPHORACEAE 391
Thelidiella 34

Thelidium 34
Thelocarpon .... :. 278
thelococcoides (Acarospora) 285
thelococcoides (Lecanora) 285
thelomorpha (Pyrenula) 59
thelomorphum (Anthracothecium) .. 59
Thelopsis 56
Thelotrema 132
THELOTREMACEAE 130
thermophila (Acarospora) 286
Thermutis 142
Thomae (Rinodina) 377
Thrombium 36
Thyrea 149
thysanota (Lecanora) 381
thysanota (Rinodina) 381
tigillare (Acolium) 75
tigillare (Cyphelium) 75
tigillaris (Lichen) 75
tiliacea (Parmelia) 328
tinctoria (Roccella) 126
tomentosum var. (Leptogium) 164
tomentosum (Nephroma) 185
tomentosum (Stereocaulon) 270
Toninia 232
toninioides (Lecania) 313
topographica var. (Graphis) 109
topographica (Verrucaria) 109
tornoensis (Biatora) 196
tornoensis (Lecidea) 196
torquata (Pertusaria) 292
torquens (Lecidea) 204
torrefacta (Gyrophora) 275
torrefacta var. (Gyrophora) 275
torrefactus (Lichen) 275
tortuosa (Alectoria) 343
tortuosa (Graphis) 111
tortuosa (Phaeographis) 111
tortuosum (Endocarpon) 43
torulosa (Arthonia) 91
trabinella var. (Chaenotheca) 68
trabinellum (Calicium) 71
trabinellum var. (Calicium) roscidum 71
trabinellum var. (Calicium) xylonellum. 71
trachelinum (Calicium) 70
trachelinum var. (Calicium) 70
trachona (Bacidia) 226
trachona (Biatora) 226
trachona (Bilimbia) 226
trachona (Verrucaria) 226
trachyphylla (Caloplaca) 362
trachyphylla var. (Caloplaca) 362
trachyphyllum var. (Placodium) ... 362
tremelloides (Leptogium) 165
tremelloides (Lichen) 165
tremulicola (Stenocybe) 74
tremulicola f. (Stenocybe) 74
tribacia (Parmelia) 388
tribacia (Physcia) 388
tribuloides (Melaspilea) 105
tribuloides (Opegrapha) 105
trichiale (Calicium) 69
trichialis (Chaenotheca) 69
trichodea (Usnea) 350

tricholoma (*Biatora*) 225
tricholoma (Bilimbia) 225
tricolor (*Biatorina*) 218
tricolor (Catillaria) 218
tricolor (*Lichen*) 218
tricosa (*Graphis*) 121
tricosa (Sarcographa) 121
Trimmatothele 34
triphragmia (*Buellia*) 367
triphragmia var. (Buellia) 367
triphragmia (*Lecidea*) 367
triptophylla (*Pannaria*) 174
triptophylla (*Parmelia*) 174
trisepta (*Bacidia*) 224
trisepta (*Biatora*) 224
trisepta (Bilimbia) 224
trisepta (*Lecidea*) 224
tristis (Cetraria) 338
tristis (*Lichen*) 338
trivialis f. (*Gyalecta*) 139
tropica (*Pyrenula*) 62
tropica (*Verrucaria*) 62
tropicum (Trypethelium) 62
TRYPETHELIACEAE 60
Trypethelii (*Buellia*) 372
Trypethelii (Buelliella) 372
Trypethelium 61
tubaeformis f. (*Cladonia*) 266
tubaeformis (*Sphinctrina*) 75
tuberculosa (Bombyliospora) 353
tuberculosa (*Lecidea*) 353
tuberculosum (*Heterothecium*) 353
Tuckeii (Lecidea) 212
Tuckermani (Cetraria) 335
Tuckermani (*Dermatocarpon*) 39
Tuckermaniana (Arthonia) 86
tucsonensis (Buellia) 370
tumidula var. (*Ramalina*) 344
turbinata (*Sphinctrina*) 74
turbinatum (*Calicium*) 74
turbulenta (Graphis) 107
turfacea (*Rinodina*) 377
turgescens (Buellia) 370
turgescens f. (Cladonia) 269
turgescens (*Lecidea*) 370
turgescentoides (Buellia) 370
turgida (Cladonia) 259
turgidula (*Biatora*) 199
turgidula (Lecidea) 199
turgidus (*Lichen*) 259
tympanellum (*Acolium*) 76

uliginosa (*Biatora*) 199
uliginosa (Lecidea) 199
uliginosus (*Lichen*) 199
ulmorum (Caloplaca) 358
ulmorum var. (*Caloplaca*) 358
ulmorum (*Placodium*) 358
ulmorum var. (*Placodium*) 358
ulophylla (Parmelia) 330
ulophylla var. (*Parmelia*) 330
ulothricoides var. (*Physcia*) 385
ulothrix var. (*Physcia*) 385
umbella (*Collema*) 152

umbella (Lempholemma) 152
umbella (*Omphalaria*) 152
Umbellulariae (Opegrapha) 98
Umbellulariae (Trimmatothele) 34
Umbilicaria 276
umbrina (Bacidia) 231
umbrina (*Biatora*) 231
umbrina var. (*Lecanora*) 302
umbrina (*Lecidea*) 231
umbrina (Staurothele) 36
umbrinula (Verrucaria) 33
umbrinus (*Lichen*) 36
uncialis (Cladonia) 253
uncialis (*Lichen*) 253
upsaliensis var. (*Lecanora*) 310
upsaliensis (*Ochrolechia*) 310
Urceolaria 136
urceolata (*Lecidea*) 135
urceolatum (Conotrema) 135
Usnea 349
Usnea (*Ramalina*) 348
USNEACEAE 339
Usneae (*Abrothallus*) 373
Usneae (Buelliella) 373
usneoidella var. (*Ramalina*) 348
usneoides (*Parmelia*) 348
usneoides (Ramalina) .... 348 .

vagans var. (*Parmelia*) 332
Valenzueliana (*Gyalecta*) 140
Valenzueliana (*Parmelia*) 140
Valenzueliana (Ramonia) 140
varia (Arthonia) 84
varia var. (Graphis) 111
varia (Lecanora) 304
varia (Opegrapha) 101
varia var. (*Opegrapha*) 84
varia (*Parmelia*) 304
varia (*Patellaria*) 304
variabile (*Placodium*) 359
variabilis (Caloplaca) 359
variabilis (*Lichen*) 359
varians (Arthonia) 92
varians (*Biatora*) 195
varians (Lecidea) 195
variatum (Trypethelium) 63
variegata (*Lecidea*) 205
variolascens (*Lecanora*) 301
variolosa var. (Lecanora) 301
velata (*Parmelia*) 290
velata (Pertusaria) 290
vellea (Gyrophora) 275
vellea (*Umbilicaria*) 275
velleus (*Lichen*) 275
velutina (Thermutis) 142
velutinus (*Lichen*) 142
venosa (Hydrothyria) 171
venosa (Peltigera) 186
venosus (*Lichen*) 186
ventosa (*Lecanora*) 314
ventosum (Haematomma) 314
ventosus (*Lichen*) 314
ventricosulum (*Acolium*) 76
ventricosulum (Cyphelium) 76

venusta (Parmelia) 386
venusta (Physcia) 386
vermicularis (Lichen) 351
vermicularis (Thamnolia) 351
vernalis (Biatora) 194
vernalis (Lecidea) 194
vernalis (Lichen) 194
vernans (Arthonia) 92
vernans (Platygrapha) 129
vernans (Schismatomma) 129
vernicoma (Buellia) 374
vernicoma (Buelliopsis) 374
vernicoma (Lecidea) 374
vernicomoideum (Rhizocarpon) 237
Verrucaria 29
VERRUCARIACEAE 29
verruciforme (Collema) 157
verruciforme var. (Collema) 157
verrucosa (Acarospora) 288
verrucosa (Lecanora) 297
verrucosa var. (Lecanora) 288
verrucosa (Parmelia) 297
verrucosa (Sticta) 181
verrucosa (Urceolaria) 297
verrucosus (Lichen) 181
verruculifera (Parmelia) 332
verruculosa (Buellia) 371
versicolor (Heterothecium) 221
versicolor (Lecanora) Ach. 307
versicolor (Lecanora) Fée 221
versicolor var. (Lecanora) 307
versicolor (Lichen) 307
versicolor (Megalospora) 221
verticillata (Cladonia) 264
vesicularis (Psora) 233
vesicularis (Toninia) 233
vespertilio (Synechoblastus) 153
vestita var. (Cladonia) 252
vicinior (Parmelia) 328
villosa (Parmelia) 365
villosa (Physcia) 365
villosus (Teloschistes) 365
virella (Physcia) 385
virella var. (Physcia) 385
virellus (Lichen) 385
virens (Alectoria) 343
virens (Trypethelium) 62
virens (Verrucaria) 32
virescens var. (Cetraria) 335
virescens (Heppia) 170
virgata (Cladonia) 256
virginalis (Graphina) 115
virginalis (Graphis) 115
virginea (Graphina) 118
virgineum (Leiogramma) 118
virginiensis (Lecidea) 204
viride (Calicium) 70
viride (Thelidium) 34
viridescens (Biatora) 204
viridescens (Lecidea) 204
viridescens (Lichen) 204
viridiater (Lichen) 240
viridiatrum (Rhizocarpon) 240
viridicans (Arthonia) 83

viridirufa (Pyrenopsis) 146
viridirufa (Synalissa) 146
viridis (Cetraria) 335
viridis (Opegrapha) 102
viridiseda (Porina) 54
viridiseda (Verrucaria) 54
viridula (Verrucaria) 33
viridula var. (Verrucaria) 33
viridulum (Calicium) 76
viridulum (Endocarpon) 33
vitellina (Candelariella) 317
vitellina (Parmelia) 317
vitellina (Pleochroma) 317
vitellinaria (Lecidea) 216
vitellinaria (Nesolechia) 216
vitellinum (Placodium) 317
vitellinus (Lichen) 317
vittata var. (Parmelia) 324
vorticosa (Lecidea) 207
vorticosa var. (Lecidea) 207
vulgaris var. (Buellia) 238
vulgaris var. (Lecanora) 288
vulgata var. (Buellia) 371
vulgata (Opegrapha) 101
vulpina (Evernia) 339
vulpina (Lecidea) 235
vulpina (Letharia) 339
vulpinum (Heterothecium) 235
vulpinum (Lopadium) 235
vulpinus (Lichen) 339

Wahlenbergii (Lecidea) 371
Weigelii (Sticta) 182
Weigelii var. (Sticta) 182
Weigelii (Stictina) 182
Wightii (Endocarpon) 134
Wightii (Leptotrema) 134
Wightii (Thelotrema) 134
Willeyana (Microthelia) 45
Willeyana (Pyrenula) 45
Willeyi (Arthonia) 88
Willeyi (Lecanora) 302
Willeyi f. (Lichina) 151
Willeyi (Phlyctis) 316
Willeyi (Ramalina) 347
Willeyi (Thamnidium) 151
Wilmsoides (Endocarpon) 42
Wrightii (Anaptychia) 390
Wrightii (Biatora) 214
Wrightii var. (Blastenia) 359
Wrightii (Caloplaca) 359
Wrightii var. (Caloplaca) 359
Wrightii (Lecanora) 214
Wrightii (Physcia) 390
Wrightii var. (Placodium) 359
Wulfenii var. (Lecidea) 203
Wulfenii (Pertusaria) 292
wyomingensis (Synechoblastus) 156

xanthococcoides (Lecidea) 210
xanthodes (Pertusaria) 293
xanthomela (Parmelia) 334
xanthoplana (Acarospora) 285
xanthoplana (Lecanora) 285

Xylographa 96
xylographica (Arthonia) 91

yemensis (Ramalina) 346
yemensis var. (Ramalina) 346

Zahlbrucknerella 142
Zahlbruckneri (Dermatocarpon) 41
Zahlbruckneri (Heppia) 170
Zahlbruckneri (Lecanactis) 127
Zopfii (Peltigera) 187

PLATE 1

A. VERRUCARIA VIRIDULA (SCHRAD.) ACH.

Plant on rock, showing the perithecia in raised spots of the thallus. Enlarged 3¼ diameters.

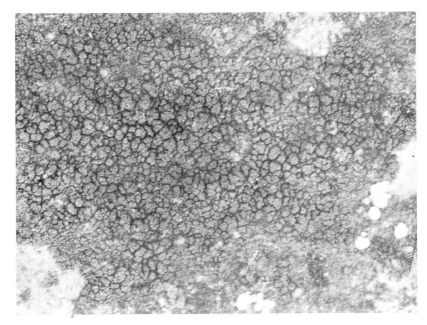

B. STAUROTHELE CLOPIMA (WAHL.) T. FRIES

Plant on rocks, showing the areolate thallus and a few perithecia. Enlarged 3 diameters.

PLATE 2

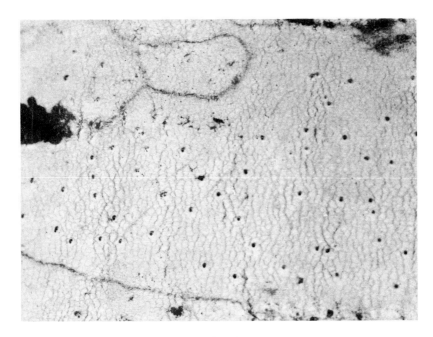

A. PYRENULA FARREA (ACH.) BRANTH & ROSTR.

Plant on tree trunk, showing the thin film of thallus and the imbedded perithecia. Enlarged 3¾ diameters.

B. CONIOCYBE PALLIDA (PERS.) E. FRIES

Plants on old wood, showing the tiny stipes bearing the apothecia. Enlarged 3 or more diameters.

PLATE 3

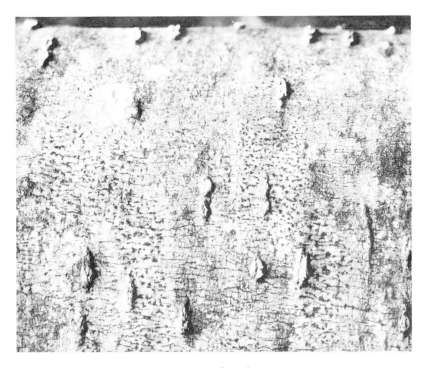

A. ARTHONIA RADIATA (PERS.) ACH.

Plants on tree trunk, showing the irregular apothecia and the whitish coloration caused by the thallus. Enlarged 1⅞ diameters.

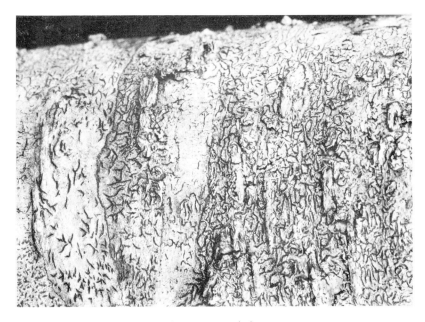

B. GRAPHIS SCRIPTA (L.) ACH.

Plants on tree trunk, showing the elongated and variously curved apothecia, and the whitish coloration caused by the thallus. Enlarged 1¾ diameters.

PLATE 4

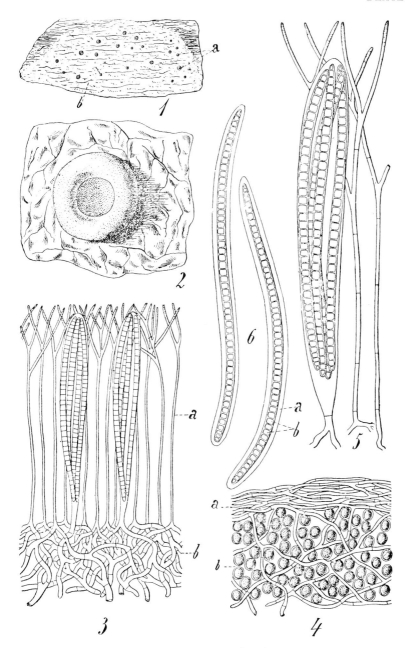

CONOTREMA URCEOLATUM (ACH.) TUCK.

Fig. 1, *a*, an apothecium; *b*, the thallus. Fig. 2, an apothecium and a portion of the thallus. Fig. 3, a section of an apothecium; *a*, the hymenium; *b*, the hypothecium. Fig. 4, a section of the thallus; *a*, the pseudocortex of entangled hyphae; *b*, the layer of algal cells and hyphae below. Fig. 5, paraphyses and an ascus. Fig. 6, free spores transversely septate; *a*, the exosporium; *b*, the cell lumina. Fig. 1, natural size; fig. 2, enlarged about 20 diameters; figs. 3, 4, enlarged about 400 diameters; figs. 5, 6, enlarged 650 diameters. From Schneider.

PLATE 5

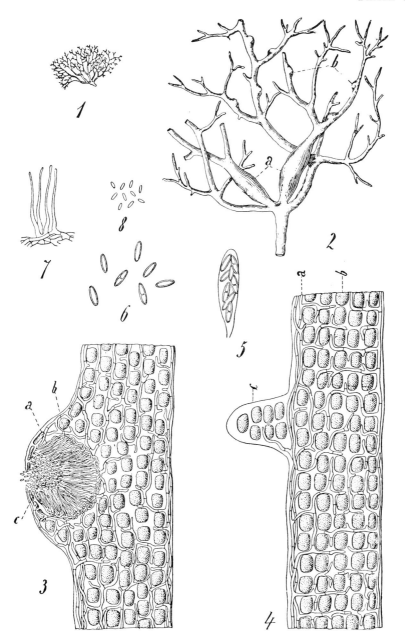

EPHEBE LANATA (L.) VAINIO

Fig. 1, the plant. Fig. 2, *a*, position of apothecia; *b*, the spermagonia. Fig. 3, a section of a branch and spermagonium; *a*, sterigmata; *b*, the inclosing hyphae; *c*, the spermatia. Fig. 4, a section of the thallus; *a*, hyphae; *b*, algal cells; *c*, a young branch. Fig. 5, an ascus. Fig. 6, free spores. Fig. 7, sterigmata. Fig. 8, spermatia. Fig. 1, natural size; fig. 2, enlarged about 4 diameters; figs. 3, 4, 7, enlarged 400 diameters; figs. 5, 6, 8, enlarged 650 diameters. From Schneider except 5 and 6, which are from Crombie.

PLATE 6

A. EPHEBE LANATA (L.) VAINIO
Plant on rocks, showing the fruticose thalloid body. Enlarged 2¾ diameters.

B. SYNECHOBLASTUS NIGRESCENS (HUDS.) TREV.
Plant on tree trunk, showing the foliose thalloid body and the rather inconspicuous apothecia. Enlarged 2¾ diameters.

PLATE 7

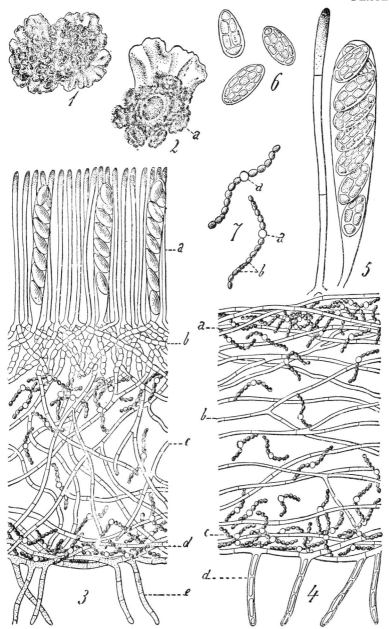

COLLEMA PULPOSUM (BERNH.) ACH.

Fig. 1, a plant showing the thalloid body and the apothecia. Fig. 2, a lobe of the thalloid body with apothecia. Fig. 3, a section of an apothecium; *a*, the hymenium; *b*, the hypothecium; *c*, the inner thalloid body with hyphae and algal filaments; *d*, the ventral horizontal hyphae; *e*, the rhizoids. Fig. 4, a section of the thalloid body; *a*, the algal filaments; *b*, the hyphae; *c*, algal filaments; *d*, the rhizoids. Fig. 5, a paraphysis and an ascus. Fig. 6, free spores, transversely and longitudinally septate. Fig. 7, algal filaments. Fig. 1, natural size; fig. 2, enlarged about 4 diameters; figs. 3, 4, enlarged 400 diameters; figs. 5–7, enlarged 650 diameters. From Schneider.

PLATE 8

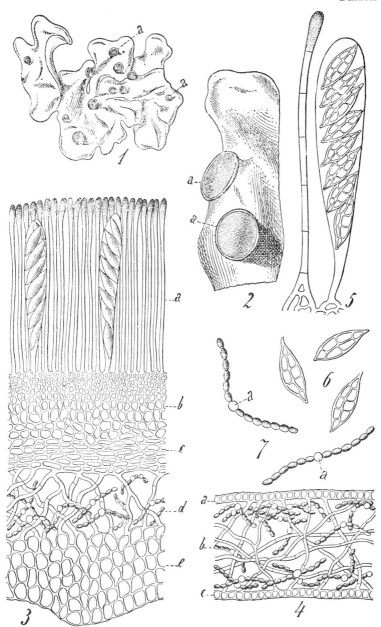

LEPTOGIUM TREMELLOIDES (L.) S. F. GRAY

Fig. 1, a plant showing the thalloid body and the apothecia. Fig. 2, a portion of a thalloid lobe with two apothecia. Fig. 3, a section of an apothecium and the thalloid body below; *a*, the hymenium; *b* and *c*, the hypothecium; *d*, the inner thalloid body showing hyphae and algal cells; *e*, the lower cortex, thickened below the apothecium. Fig. 4, a section of the thalloid body; *a*, the upper cortex; *b*, the hyphae and algal cells; *c*, the lower cortex. Fig. 5, a paraphysis and an ascus. Fig. 6, free spores. Fig. 7, algal filaments. Fig. 1, natural size; fig. 2, enlarged about 5 diameters; figs. 3, 4, enlarged 400 diameters; figs. 5, 6, 7, enlarged 650 diameters. From Schneider.

PLATE 9

PANNARIA LEUCOSTICTA TUCK.
Plants on tree trunk, showing the apothecia and the squamulose thallus. Enlarged 1¼ diameters.

PLATE 10

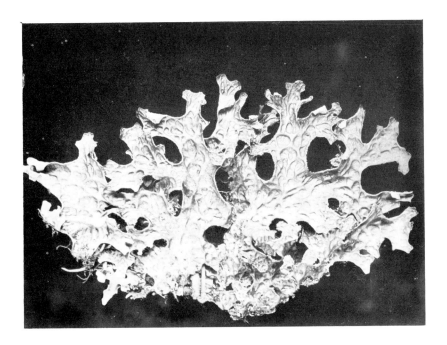

STICTA PULMONARIA (L.) BIR.
Plant showing the foliose thallus, with much branched lobes and reticulated surface.
Natural size.

PLATE 11

STICTA VERRUCOSA (HUDS.) FINK

Plant on mossy tree trunk, showing the lobed and pitted thallus. Natural size.

PLATE 12

A. SOLORINA SACCATA (L.) ACH.
Plant on rock, showing the foliose thallus and the immersed apothecia. Enlarged 2½ diameters.

B. PELTIGERA VENOSA (L.) BAUMG.
Plants showing the small, fan-shaped thalli, with the marginal position of the apothecia. Also shows the veined under surface. Enlarged 1½ diameters.

PLATE 13

PELTIGERA APHTHOSA (L.) WILLD.

Plant on earth, showing the ascending thallus lobes and the cephalodia dotted over the lobes. Natural size.

PLATE 14

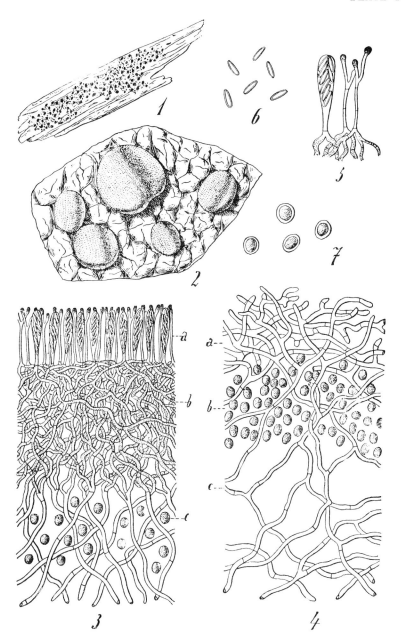

LECIDEA MELANCHEIMA TUCK.

Fig. 1, plant. Fig. 2, apothecia and a portion of the thallus. Fig. 3, a section of an apothecium and part of the thallus; *a*, the hymenium; *b*, the hypothecium; *c*, the algal layer. Fig. 4, a section of the thallus; *a*, the pseudocortex of entangled hyphae; *b*, the algal layers; *c*, the medullary layer. Fig. 5, paraphyses and an ascus. Fig. 6, free spores. Fig. 7, algal cells. Fig. 1, natural size; fig. 2, enlarged about 10 diameters; figs. 3, 4, enlarged 425 diameters; figs. 5, 6, 7, enlarged 650 diameters. From Schneider.

PLATE 15

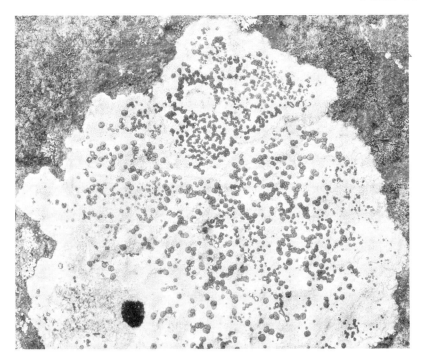

A. LECIDEA PANTHERINA (HOFFM.) ACH.

Plant on rock, showing the areolate thallus and the scattered or somewhat clustered and irregular apothecia. Three-fourths natural size.

B. LECIDEA GRANULOSA (HOFFM.) ACH.

Plants on soil, showing the granulose thallus and the conspicuous apothecia. Enlarged 1⅞ diameters.

PLATE 16

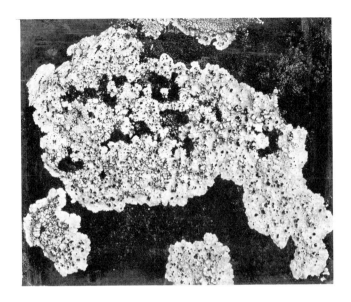

A. LECIDEA SPEIREA ACH.

Plants on rock, showing the crustose thallus and the apothecia. Enlarged 1½ diameters.

B. LECIDEA ALBOCAERULESCENS (WULF.) ACH.

Plants on rock, showing the crustose thallus and the apothecia. Natural size.

PLATE 17

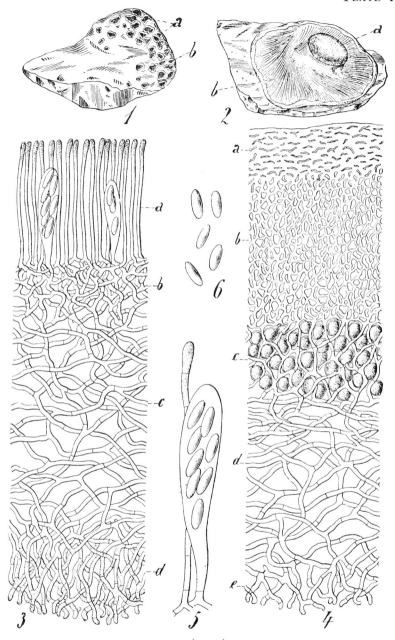

PSORA RUSSELLII (TUCK.) SCHNEID.

Fig. 1, *a*, a portion of the thallus; *b*, an apothecium. Fig. 2, *a*, an apothecium; *b*, a portion of the thallus. Fig. 3, a section through an apothecium and the underlying thallus; *a*, the hymenium; *b*, the hypothecium; *c*, the medullary layer; *d*, the hyphal rhizoids. Fig. 4, a section of the thallus; *a*, the dermis; *b*, the upper cortex; *c*, the algal layer; *d*, the medullary layer; *e*, the hyphal rhizoids. Fig. 5, a paraphysis and an ascus. Fig. 6, free simple spores. Fig. 1, natural size; fig. 2, enlarged about 8 diameters; fig. 3, enlarged 300 diameters; fig. 4, enlarged about 425 diameters; figs. 5, 6, enlarged 650 diameters. From Schneider.

PLATE 18

MYCOBLASTUS SANGUINARIUS (L.) NORM.
Plants on wood, showing the crustose thallus and the apothecia. Enlarged 1¼ diameters.

PLATE 19

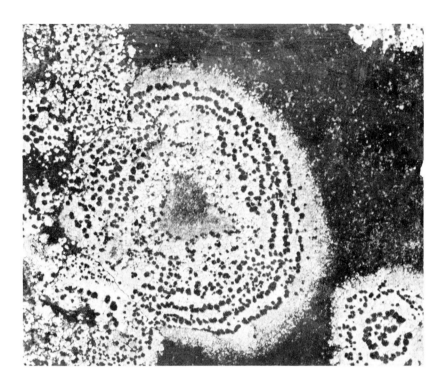

A. RHIZOCARPON CONCENTRICUM (DAV.) VAINIO

Plant on rock, showing the orbicular crustose thallus and the concentrically arranged apothecia. Enlarged 2½ diameters.

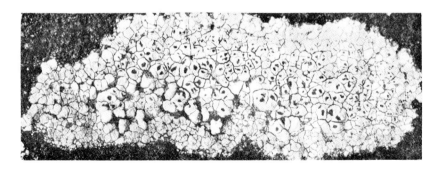

B. RHIZOCARPON GEOGRAPHICUM (L.) LAM. & DC.

Plant on rock, showing the areolate crustose thallus and the immersed apothecia. Enlarged 3 diameters.

PLATE 20

A. BAEOMYCES RUFUS (HUDS.) REBENT.
Plant on rocks, showing the thallus and the stipes surmounted by the apothecia. Enlarged nearly 2½ diameters.

B. CLADONIA FIMBRIATA CONIOCRAEA (FLOERKE) VAINIO
Plant on soil, showing the pointed, cupless podetia. Enlarged 2 diameters.

PLATE 21

CLADONIA PYXIDATA CHLOROPHAEA (SPRENG.) FLOERKE
Plants on old wood, showing the primary thallus and the cupped podetia. Natural size.

PLATE 22

A. CLADONIA DEFORMIS (L.) HOFFM.

Several plants in part, showing few squamules of the primary thallus, and the irregular podetia, some with cups and others more or less pointed. Enlarged 2 diameters.

B. CLADONIA BELLIDIFLORA (ACH.) SCHAER.

Plants on old wood, showing the squamules and the podetia more or less covered with squamules and bearing apothecia. Enlarged 2 diameters.

PLATE 23

CLADONIA VERTICILLATA HOFFM.

Plants on soil, showing the squamules of the primary thallus, and the podetia in three or four tiers. Enlarged 1½ diameters.

PLATE 24

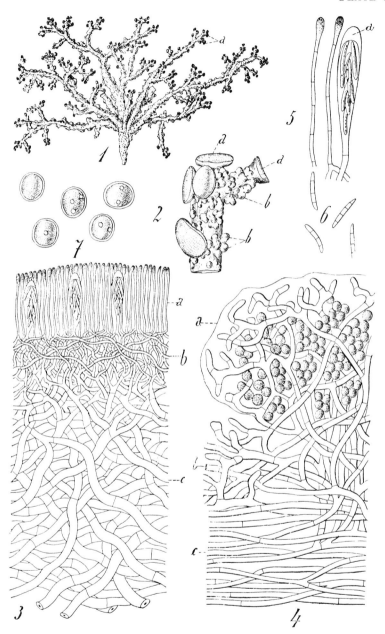

STEREOCAULON CORALLOIDES E. FRIES

Fig. 1, part of a plant. Fig. 2, *a*, the apothecia; *b*, the phyllocladia. Fig. 3, a section of the apothecium and a portion of the thallus; *a*, the hymenium; *b*, the hypothecium; *c*, the medullary layer. Fig. 4, a longitudinal radial section of a podetium; *a*, a phyllocladium; *b*, the external loose network of hyphae; *c*, the internal mechanical tissue of longitudinal hyphae. Fig. 5, paraphyses and (*a*) an ascus. Fig. 6, free single spores. Fig. 7, algal cells. Fig. 1, natural size; fig. 2, enlarged about 10 diameters; figs. 3, 4, enlarged 300 diameters; figs. 5–7, enlarged 650 diameters. From Schneider.

PLATE 25

GYROPHORA HYPERBOREA (HOFFM.) MUDD
Plants on rock, showing the irregularly lobed and jagged thallus. Natural size.

PLATE 26

GYROPHORA DILLENII (TUCK.) MÜLL. ARG.
Plant on rocks, showing the large, irregularly lobed thallus. Two-thirds natural size.

PLATE 27

A. UMBILICARIA PUSTULATA (L.) HOFFM.
Many plants on rock, showing the habit of growth and the round to irregular, pustulate thalli. Natural size.

B. PERTUSARIA VELATA (TURN.) NYL.
Plant on the branch of a tree, showing the crustose thallus and the apothecia. Enlarged 1¾ diameters.

PLATE 28

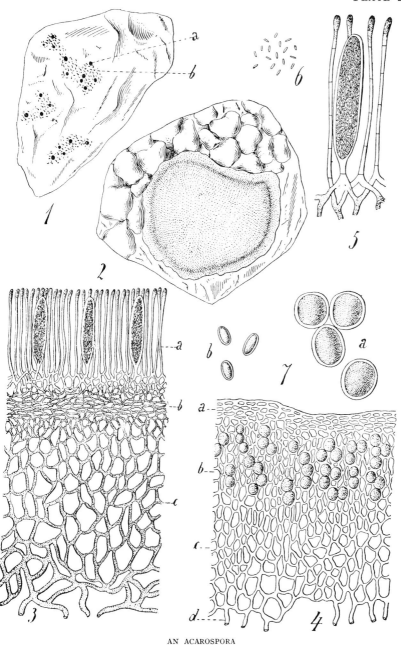

AN ACAROSPORA

Fig. 1, *a,* the apothecia; *b,* the thallus on the substratum. Fig. 2, a single apothecium and a small portion of the thallus. Fig. 3, a section of an apothecium and part of the thallus; *a,* the hymenium; *b,* the hypothecium; *c,* the plectenchymatous medullary layer. Fig. 4, a section of the thallus; *a,* the upper cortex; *b,* the algal layer; *c,* the plectenchymatous medullary layer; *d,* the hyphal rhizoids. Fig. 5, paraphyses and an ascus. Fig. 6, free, non-septate spores. Fig. 7, algal cells; *a,* as they occur in the thallus; *b,* normal size. Fig 1, natural size; fig. 2, enlarged about 35 diameters; fig. 3, enlarged 400 diameters; fig. 4, enlarged 300 diameters; figs. 5 and 6, enlarged 650 diameters; fig. 7, enlarged *a,* 650 diameters; *b,* 500 diameters. From Schneider.

PLATE 29

A. LECANORA VARIA (HOFFM.) ACH.
Plant on old wood, showing the thin, somewhat areolate thallus, and the numerous round
to irregular apothecia. Enlarged 1¼ diameters.

B. LECANORA FRUSTULOSA (DICKS.) ACH.
Plant showing the warty irregular thallus and the large, irregular apothecia. Enlarged
1½ diameters.

PLATE 30

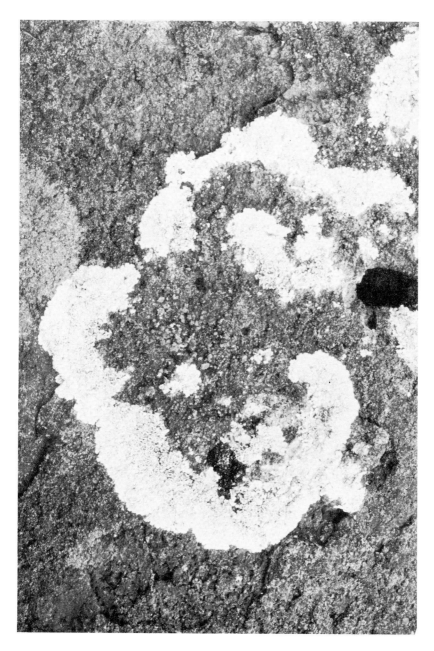

LECANORA VERSICOLOR (PERS.) ACH.

Plant on rock, showing the characteristic fairy ring formation of the thallus. Natural size.

PLATE 31

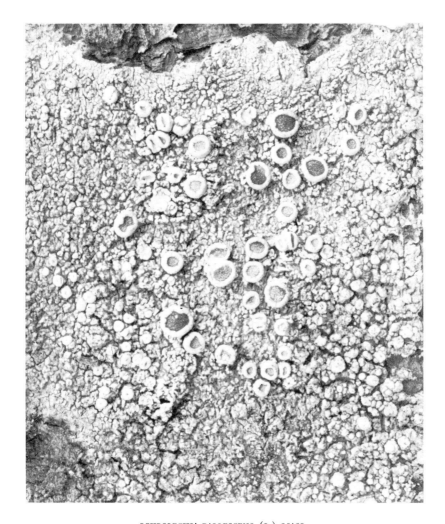

OCHROLECHIA PALLESCENS (L.) MASS.
Plant on tree trunk, showing the thick, rough crustose thallus and the large apothecia with the heavy exciple. Enlarged 3⅓ diameters.

PLATE 32

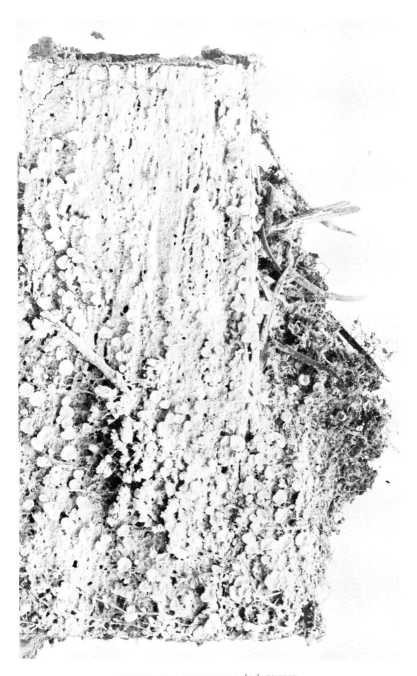

ICMADOPHILA ERICETORUM (L.) ZAHLBR.
Plant on old wood, showing the thallus and the apothecia. Enlarged 1½ diameters.

PLATE 33

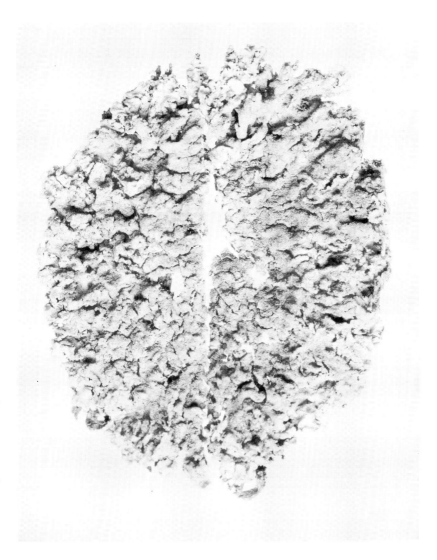

PARMELIOPSIS ALEURITES (ACH.) NYL.
Plant showing the finely sorediate thallus. Enlarged 2 diameters.

PLATE 34

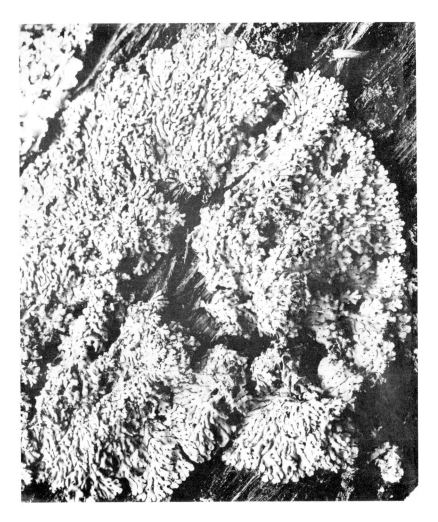

PARMELIA PERTUSA (SCHRANK.) SCHAER.
Plant on a tree trunk, showing the pertuse, foliose thallus. Natural size.

PLATE 35

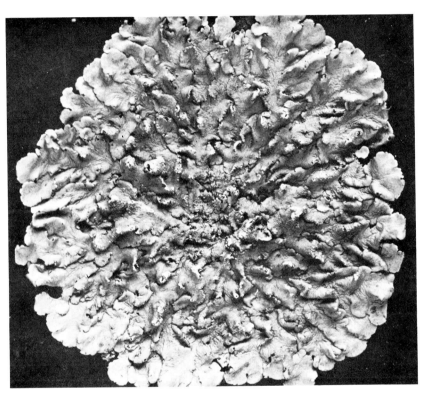

PARMELIA CAPERATA (L.) ACH.
Plant showing the foliose, lobed, more or less irregular thallus. Natural size.

PLATE 36

A. CETRARIA JUNIPERINA PINASTRI (SCOP.) ACH.

Plant on tree trunk, showing the crisped ascendant thallus lobes. Enlarged 1¾ diameters.

B. CETRARIA LACUNOSA ACH.

A plant on a tree trunk, showing the much lobed, irregular thallus. Natural size.

PLATE 37

EVERNIA PRUNASTRI (L.) ACH.
Plant on the limb of a tree, showing the fruticose thallus and the rare apothecia.
Natural size.

PLATE 38

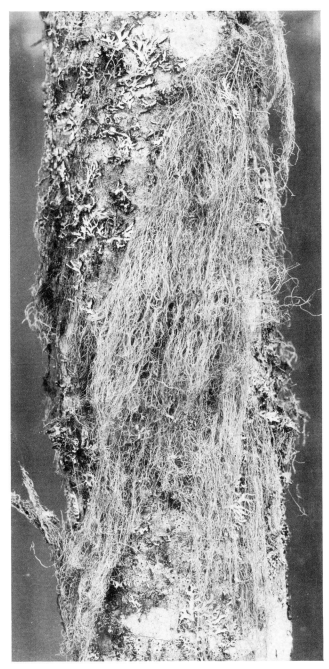

ALECTORIA JUBATA (L.) ACH.
Plant on trunk of tree, showing the pendulous fruticose thallus. Natural size.

PLATE 39

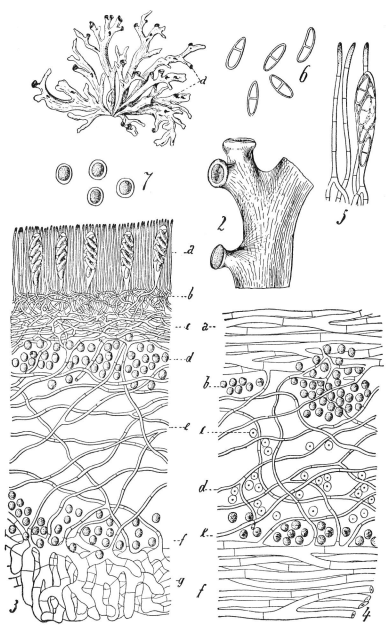

RAMALINA CALICARIS (L.) E. FRIES

Fig. 1, the plant, showing the lobed thallus and the apothecia. Fig. 2, a portion of the thallus and three apothecia. Fig. 3, a section through an apothecium and the thallus below; *a*, the hymenium; *b* and *c*, the hypothecium; *d*, the algal layer; *e*, the medullary layer; *f*, the algal layer; *g*, the pseudocortex of entangled hyphae. Fig. 4, a longitudinal section of the thallus; *a* and *f*, the pseudocortex; *b* and *e*, the algal layer; *c* and *d*, the medullary layer. Fig. 5, paraphyses and an ascus. Fig. 6, 1-septate spores. Fig. 7, algal cells. Fig. 1, natural size; fig. 2, enlarged about 10 diameters; figs. 3, 4, enlarged 400 diameters; figs. 5–7, enlarged 650 diameters. From Schneider.

PLATE 40

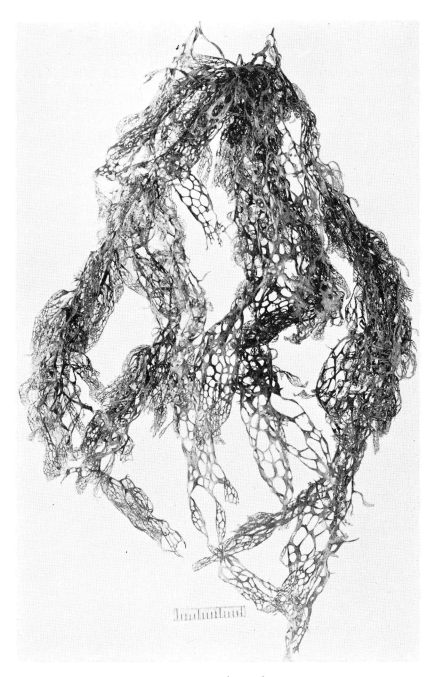

RAMALINA RETICULATA (NOEDH.) KREMPH.
Plant showing the fruticose thallus, much branched and giving the lacy appearance
often seen. Natural size.

Plate 41

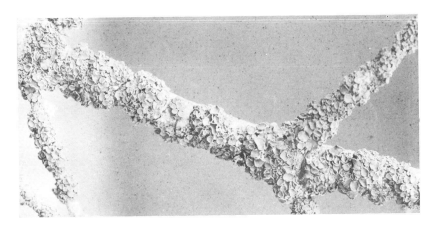

A. TELOSCHISTES POLYCARPUS (HOFFM.) TUCK.
Plant on limb of tree, showing the numerous crowded apothecia characteristic of the species. Enlarged 1⅝ diameters.

B. RAMALINA DILACERATA (EHRH.) VAINIO
Plants on a limb of balsam fir, showing the fruticose thallus and the apothecia Enlarged 2 diameters.

PLATE 42

A. RAMALINA SUBAMPLICATA (NYL.) FINK
Two plants showing the irregularly lobed, more or less reticulated thallus and the apothecia. Enlarged 1⅜ diameters.

B. USNEA FLORIDA (L.) WEB.
Plant showing the fruticose, much branched thallus, with the branches bearing many tiny fibrils. Natural size.

PLATE 43

A. CALOPLACA CERINA (EHRH.) T. FRIES
Plant on tree trunk, showing the small apothecia. Enlarged 2 diameters.

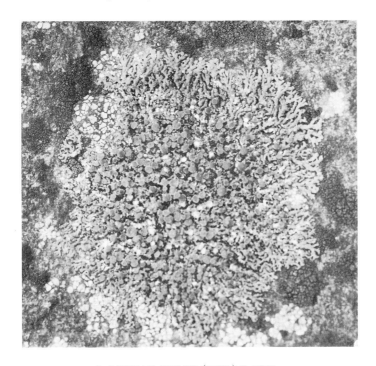

B. CALOPLACA ELEGANS (LINK.) T. FRIES
Plant on rock, showing the marginally lobed thallus and the apothecia. Enlarged 1¼ diameters.

PLATE 44

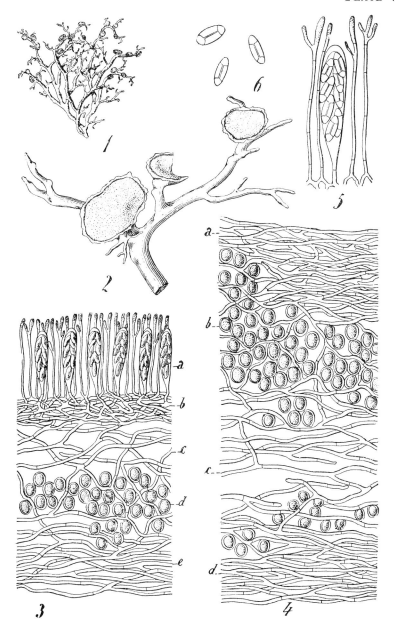

TELOSCHISTES CHRYSOPHTHALMUS (L.) BELTR.

Fig. 1, the plant, showing the branching fruticose thallus and the apothecia. Fig. 2, a portion of thallus and three apothecia. Fig. 3, a section of an apothecium and the thallus below; *a*, the hymenium; *b*, the hypothecium; *c*, the fungal hyphae; *d*, the algal cells; *e*, the pseudo-cortex of entangled hyphae. Fig. 4, a longitudinal section of the thallus; *a* and *d*, the pseudocor-tex of hyphae; *b*, the better devloped algal layer of the upper side of the ascending branch; *c*, the medullary layer. Fig. 5, paraphyses and an ascus. Fig. 6, free, 1-septate spores with polar cells. Fig. 1, natural size; fig. 2, enlarged about 8 diameters; figs. 3, 4, enlarged 400 diameters; figs. 5, 6, enlarged 650 diameters. From Schneider.

PLATE 45

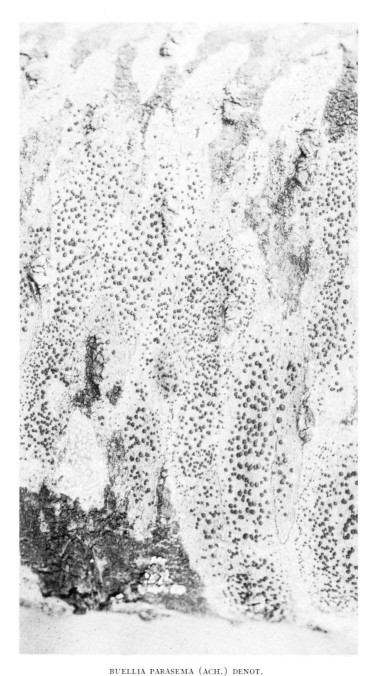

BUELLIA PARASEMA (ACH.) DENOT.

Plant on bark, showing many apothecia and the black margin which more or less commonly bounds the thallus. Enlarged 2½ diameters.

PLATE 46

PYXINE SOREDIATA (ACH.) E. FRIES
Plant on tree trunk, showing the sorediate thallus. Natural size.

PLATE 47

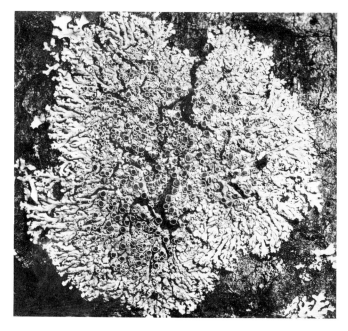

A. PHYSCIA STELLARIS (L.) NYL.
A plant on tree trunk, showing the apothecia and the lobed, closely adnate, foliose thallus.
Enlarged 1⅖ diameters.

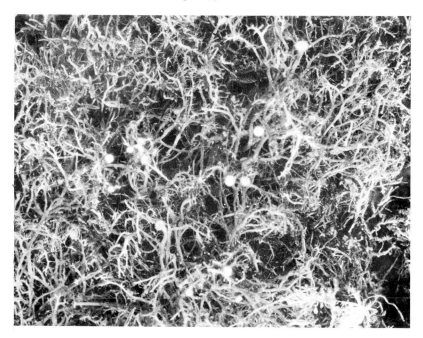

B. ANAPTYCHIA CILIARIS (L.) KOERB.
Plant on rock, showing the fruticose thallus and the apothecia. Enlarged 1¾ diameters.